CI
AIRC
MARKINGS
2002

Alan J. Wright

Contents

This fifty third edition published 2002

ISBN 0 7110 2845 1

© Ian Allan Publishing Ltd 2002

Published by Ian Allan Publishing

an imprint of Ian Allan Publishing Ltd,
Hersham, Surrey KT12 4RG.
Printed by Ian Allan Printing Ltd, Hersham, Surrey KT12 4RG.

Code: 0203/J

Front cover: 5X-JOE Douglas DC-10-30 of DAS Air Cargo. *Richard Cooper*

All photographs by Alan J. Wright unless otherwise indicated.

Introduction

The 'G' prefixed four letter registration system was adopted in 1919 after a short-lived spell of about three months with serial numbers beginning at K-100. Until July 1928 the UK allocations were in the G-Exxx range, but as a result of further International agreements, this series was ended at G-EBZZ, the replacement being G-Axxx. From this point the registrations were issued in a reasonably orderly manner through to G-AZZZ, reached in July 1972. There were two exceptions. To avoid possible confusion with signal codes, the G-AQxx sequence was omitted, while G-AUxx was reserved for Australian use originally. In recent years however, an individual request for a mark in the latter range has been granted by the Authorities.

Although the next logical sequence was started at G-Bxxx, it was not long before the strictly applied rules relating to aircraft registration began to be relaxed. Permission was readily given for personalised marks to be issued incorporating virtually any four-letter combination, while re-registration has also become a common feature, a practice almost unheard of in the past. In this book, where this has taken place at some time, all previous UK civil identities appear in parenthesis after the owner's/operator's name. An example of this is the Airbus A.320-231 G-JOEM which originally carried G-OUZO.

Some aircraft have also been allowed to wear military markings without displaying their civil identity. In this case the serial number actually carried is shown in parenthesis after the type's name. For example EE Canberra TT.18 G-BURM flies in RAF colours as WJ680. As an aid to the identification of these machines, a military conversion list is provided.

Other factors caused a sudden acceleration in the number of registrations allocated by the Civil Aviation Authority in the early 1980s. The first surge came with the discovery that it was possible to register plastic bags and other items even less likely to fly, on payment of the standard fee. This erosion of the main register was checked in early 1982 by the issue of a special sequence for such devices commencing at G-FYAA. Powered hang-gliders provided the second glut of allocations as a result of the decision that these types should be officially registered. Although a few of the early examples penetrated the current in-sequence register, in due course all new applicants were given marks in special ranges, this time G-MBxx, G-MGxx, G-MJxx, G-MMxx, G-MNxx, G-MTxx, G-MVxx, G-MWxx, G-MYxx and G-MZxx. It took some time before all microlights displayed an official mark but gradually the registration was carried, the size and position depending on the dimensions of the component to which it was applied.

There was news of a further change in mid-1998 when the CAA announced that with immediate effect microlights would be issued with registrations in the normal sequence alongside aircraft in other classes. In addition, it meant that owners could also apply for an out-of-sequence mark upon payment of the current fee of £170 from April 1999, a low price for those wishing to display their status symbol. These various changes played their part in exhausting the current G-Bxxx range after some 26 years, with G-BZxx coming into use before the end of 1999. As this batch approached completion the next series to be used surprisingly began at G-CBxx instead of the anticipated and more logical G-CAxx. The reason for this step was to avoid the re-use of marks issued in Canada during the 1920s, although a few have appeared more recently as out-of-sequence UK registrations.

Throughout this section of the book, there are many instances when the probable base of the aircraft has been included. This is positioned at the end of the owner/operator details preceded by an oblique stroke. It must of course be borne in mind that changes do take place and that no attempt has been made to record the residents at the many private strips. The base of airline equipment has been given as the company's headquarter's airport, although frequently aircraft are outstationed for long periods.

Non-airworthy and preserved aircraft are shown with a star ★ after the type.

The three-letter codes used by airlines to prefix flight numbers are included for those carriers appearing in the book. Radio frequencies for the larger airfields/airports are also listed.

The air transport scene has changed considerably through the years and has seen many airlines exercising a preference for leasing equipment when considering expansion. During 2001 the worldwide economic situation was responsible for the marked decline in the demand for air transport. This factor resulted in the demise of a number of well known carriers, while others have struggled to survive by placing aircraft in store as a temporary expedient. A series of restructuring, take-overs and mergers have also added to the turbulent times which will hopefully have settled down by the start of the next summer season in 2002.

In addition to these problems the industry suffered serious effects from the terrorist attacks in New York on 11 September 2001, followed a few weeks later by the A300 crash in the same city at a time when confidence was slowly beginning to return. However, suffice to say that as always every effort has been made to record the many changes during the past year in order to produce an accurate source of reference. Nevertheless it must be borne in mind that it is inevitable that discrepancies may occur.

Acknowledgements

Once again thanks are extended to the Registration Department of the Civil Aviation Authority for its assistance and allowing access to its files. As always the comments and amendments flowing from the indefatigable Wal Gandy have proved of considerable value, while George Pennick and Bob Elliot have also contributed much useful material and help. Both A. S. Wright and C. P. Wright provided valuable assistance during the update of this edition which enabled the multitude of assorted facts and figures to be assembled to meet the press deadline. AJW

International Civil Aircraft Markings

A2-	Botswana
A3-	Tonga
A4O-	Oman
A5-	Bhutan
A6-	United Arab Emirates
A7-	Qatar
A9C-	Bahrain
AP-	Pakistan
B-	China/Taiwan/Hong Kong
C-/CF-	Canada
C2-	Nauru
C3	Andora
C5-	Gambia
C6-	Bahamas
C9-	Mozambique
CC-	Chile
CN-	Morocco
CP-	Bolivia
CS-	Portugal
CU-	Cuba
CX-	Uruguay
D-	Germany
D2-	Angola
D4-	Cape Verde Islands
D6-	Comores Islands
DQ-	Fiji
E3-	Eritrea
EC-	Spain
EI-	Republic of Ireland
EK-	Armenia
EL-	Liberia
EP-	Iran
ER-	Moldova
ES-	Estonia
ET-	Ethiopia
EW-	Belarus
EX-	Kyrgyzstan
EY-	Tajikistan
EZ-	Turkmenistan
F-	France, Colonies and Protectorates
G-	United Kingdom
H4-	Solomon Islands
HA-	Hungary
HB-	Switzerland and Liechtenstein
HC-	Ecuador
HH-	Haiti
HI-	Dominican Republic
HK-	Colombia
HL-	Korea (South)
HP-	Panama
HR-	Honduras
HS-	Thailand
HV-	The Vatican
HZ-	Saudi Arabia
I-	Italy
J2-	Djibouti
J3-	Grenada
J5-	Guinea Bissau
J6-	St Lucia
J7-	Dominica
J8-	St Vincent
JA-	Japan
JU	Mongolia
JY-	Jordan
LN-	Norway
LV-	Argentina
LX-	Luxembourg
LY-	Lithuania
LZ-	Bulgaria
N-	United States of America

OB-	Peru
OD-	Lebanon
OE-	Austria
OH-	Finland
OK-	Czech Republic
OM-	Slovakia
OO-	Belgium
OY-	Denmark
P-	Korea (North)
P2-	Papua New Guinea
P4-	Aruba
PH-	Netherlands
PJ-	Netherlands Antilles
PK-	Indonesia and West Irian
PP-,PT-	Brazil
PZ-	Surinam
RA-	Russia
RDPL-	Laos
RP-	Philippines
S2-	Bangladesh
S5-	Slovenia
S7-	Seychelles
S9-	São Tomé
SE-	Sweden
SP-	Poland
ST-	Sudan
SU-	Egypt
SU-Y	Palestine
SX-	Greece
T2-	Tuvalu
T3-	Kiribati
T7-	San Marino
T8A	Palau
T9-	Bosnia-Herzegovina
TC-	Turkey
TF-	Iceland
TG-	Guatemala
TI-	Costa Rica
TJ-	United Republic of Cameroon
TL-	Central African Republic
TN-	Republic of Congo (Brazzaville)
TR-	Gabon
TS-	Tunisia
TT-	Tchad
TU-	Ivory Coast
TY-	Benin
TZ-	Mali
UK-	Uzbekistan
UN-	Kazakhstan
UR-	Ukraine
V2-	Antigua
V3-	Belize
V4	St Kitts & Nevis
V5-	Namibia
V6	Micronesia
V7-	Marshall Islands
V8-	Brunei
VH-	Australia
VN-	Vietnam
VP-B	Bermuda
VP-C	Cayman Islands
VP-F	Falkland Islands
VP-G	Gibraltar
VP-LA	Anguilla
VP-LM	Montserrat
VP-LV	Virgin Islands
VQ-T	Turks & Caicos Islands
VT-	India
XA-,XB-,XC-	Mexico
XT-	Burkina Faso

XU-	Cambodia	5R-	Malagasy Republic (Madagascar)
XY-	Myanmar	5T-	Mauritania
YA-	Afghanistan	5U-	Niger
YI-	Iraq	5V-	Togo
YJ-	Vanuatu	5W-	Western Samoa (Polynesia)
YK-	Syria	5X-	Uganda
YL-	Latvia	5Y-	Kenya
YN-	Nicaragua	6O-	Somalia
YR-	Romania	6V-	Senegal
YS-	El Salvador	6Y-	Jamaica
YU-	Yugoslavia	7O-	Yemen
YV-	Venezuela	7P-	Lesotho
Z-	Zimbabwe	7Q-	Malawi
Z3-	Macedonia	7T-	Algeria
ZA-	Albania	8P-	Barbados
ZK-	New Zealand	8Q-	Maldives
ZP-	Paraguay	8R-	Guyana
ZS-	South Africa	9A-	Croatia
3A-	Monaco	9G-	Ghana
3B-	Mauritius	9H-	Malta
3C-	Equatorial Guinea	9J-	Zambia
3D-	Swaziland	9K-	Kuwait
3X-	Guinea	9L-	Sierra Leone
4K-	Azerbaijan	9M-	Malaysia
4L-	Georgia	9N-	Nepal
4R-	Sri Lanka	9Q-	Congo Kinshasa
4X-	Israel	9U-	Burundi
5A-	Libya	9V-	Singapore
5B-	Cyprus	9XR-	Rwanda
5H-	Tanzania	9Y-	Trinidad and Tobago
5N-	Nigeria		

Aircraft Type Designations & Abbreviations

(eg PA-28 Piper Type 28)

A.	Beagle, Auster, Airbus
AA-	American Aviation, Grumman American
AB	Agusta-Bell
AG	American General
ANEC	Air Navigation & Engineering Co.
AS	Aérospatiale
A.S.	Airspeed
A.W.	Armstrong Whitworth
B.	Blackburn, Bristol, Boeing, Beagle
BA	British Airways
BAC	British Aircraft Corporation
BAe	British Aerospace
BAPC	British Aviation Preservation Council
BAT	British Aerial Transport
B.K.	British Klemm
BN	Britten-Norman
Bo	Bolkow
Bu	Bücker
CAARP	Co-operative des Ateliers Aer de la Région Parisienne
CAC	Commonwealth Aircraft Corporation
CAF	Canadian Air Force
C.A.S.A.	Construcciones Aeronautics SA
CCF	Canadian Car & Foundry Co
CEA	Centre-Est Aeronautique
C.H.	Chrislea
CHABA	Cambridge Hot-Air Ballooning Association
CLA	Comper

CP.	Piel
CUAS	Cambridge University Air Squadron
Cycl	Cyclone
D.	Druine
DC-	Douglas Commercial
D.H.	de Havilland
D.H.A.	de Havilland Australia
D.H.C.	de Havilland Canada
DR.	Jodel (Robin-built)
EE	English Electric
EAA	Experimental Aircraft Association
EMB	Embraer
EoN	Elliotts of Newbury
EP	Edgar Percival
F.	Fairchild, Fokker
F.A.A.	Fleet Air Arm
FFA	Flug und Fahrzeugwerke AG
FH	Fairchild-Hiller
FrAF	French Air Force
FRED	Flying Runabout Experimental Design
Fw	Focke-Wulf
G.	Grumman
GA	Gulfstream American
G.A.L.	General Aircraft
G.C.	Globe
GECAS	General Electric Capital Aviation Services
GY	Gardan
H	Helio
HM.	Henri Mignet

HP.	Handley Page	RAFGSA	Royal Air Force Gliding & Soaring Association
HPR	Handley Page Reading	RCAF	Royal Canadian Air Force
HR.	Robin	RF	Fournier
H.S.	Hawker Siddeley	R.N.	Royal Navy
ICA	Intreprinderea de Constructii	S.	Short, Sikorsky
IHM	International Helicopter Museum	SA, SE, SO	Sud-Aviation, Aérospatiale, Scottish Aviation
I.I.I.	Iniziative Industriali Italiane	SAAB	Svenska Aeroplan Aktieboleg
IL	Ilyushin	SC	Short
ILFC	International Lease Finance Corporation	SCD	Side Cargo Door
IMCO	Intermountain Manufacturing Co	SNCAN	Societe Nationale de Constructions Aeronautiques du Nord
J.	Auster	SOCATA	Societe de Construction d'Avions de Tourisme et d'Affaires
JT	John Taylor		
KR	Rand-Robinson	Soc	Society
L.	Lockheed	SPP	Strojirny Prvni Petilesky
L.A.	Luton, Lake	S.R.	Saunders-Roe, Stinson
L.V.G.	Luft-Verkehrs Gesellschaft	SS	Special Shape
M.	Miles, Mooney	ST	SOCATA
MBA	Micro Biplane Aviation	SW	Solar Wings
MBB	Messerschmitt-Bölkow-Blohm	T.	Tipsy
McD	McDonnell	TB	SOCATA
MDH	McDonnell Douglas Helicopters	Tu	Tupolev
MH	Max Holste	UH.	United Helicopters (Hiller)
MHCA	Manhole Cover	UK	United Kingdom
MJ	Jurca	USAF	United States Air Force
M.S.	Morane-Saulnier	USAAC	United States Army Air Corps
NA	North American	USN	United States Navy
NC	Nord	V.	Vickers-Armstrongs
NE	North East	V.L.M.	Vlaamse Luchttransportmaatschappij
P.	Hunting (formerly Percival), Piaggio	V.S.	Vickers-Supermarine
PA-	Piper	WA	Wassmer
PC.	Pilatus	WAR	War Aircraft Replicas
PZL	Panstwowe Zaklady Lotnicze	WHE	W.H.Ekin
QAC	Quickie Aircraft Co	W.S.	Westland
R.	Rockwell	Z.	Zlin
RAF	Rotary Air Force		
RAAF	Royal Australian Air Force		

British Civil Aircraft Registrations

Reg.	Type (†False registration)	Owner or Operator	Notes
G-EAGA	Sopwith Dove (replica)	A. Wood/O. Warden	
G-EAOU†	Vickers Vimy (replica)(NX71MY)	Greenco (UK) Ltd	
G-EASD	Avro 504L	AJD Engineering Ltd	
G-EASQ†	Bristol Babe (replica) (BAPC87)★	Bristol Aero Collection *(stored)*/Kemble	
G-EAVX	Sopwith Pup (B1807)	K. A. M. Baker	
G-EBED†	Vickers 60 Viking (replica) (BAPC114)	Brooklands Museum of Aviation/ Weybridge	
G-EBHX	D.H.53 Humming Bird	The Shuttleworth Collection/O. Warden	
G-EBIA	RAF SE-5A (F904)	The Shuttleworth Collection/O. Warden	
G-EBIB	RAF SE-5A ★	Science Museum/S. Kensington	
G-EBIC	RAF SE-5A (F938) ★	RAF Museum	
G-EBIR	D.H.51	The Shuttleworth Collection/O. Warden	
G-EBJE	Avro 504K (E449) ★	RAF Museum	
G-EBJG	Parnall Pixie III ★	Midland Aircraft Preservation Soc	
G-EBJO	ANEC II ★	The Shuttleworth Collection/O. Warden	
G-EBKY	Sopwith Pup (N6181)	The Shuttleworth Collection/O. Warden	
G-EBLV	D.H.60 Cirrus Moth	British Aerospace PLC/Woodford	
G-EBMB	Hawker Cygnet I ★	RAF Museum	
G-EBNV	English Electric Wren	The Shuttleworth Collection/O. Warden	
G-EBQP	D.H.53 Humming Bird (J7326) ★	Russavia Collection	
G-EBWD	D.H.60X Hermes Moth	The Shuttleworth Collection/O. Warden	
G-EBXU	D.H.60X Moth Seaplane	D. E. Cooper-Maguire	
G-EBZM	Avro 594 Avian IIIA ★	Manchester Museum of Science & Industry	
G-EBZN	D.H.60X Moth	J. Hodgkinson (G-UAAP)	

Other G-E registrations are listed in the Out-of-Sequence section

G-AAAH†	D.H.60G Moth (replica) (BAPC 168) ★	Yorkshire Air Museum/Elvington	
G-AAAH	D.H.60G Moth ★	Science Museum *Jason*/S. Kensington	
G-AACA†	Avro 504K (BAPC 177) ★	Brooklands Museum of Aviation/ Weybridge	
G-AACN	H.P.39 Gugnunc ★	Science Museum/Wroughton	
G-AADR	D.H.60GM Moth	H. F. Moffatt	
G-AAEG	D.H.60G Moth	J. Dixon	
G-AAHI	D.H.60G Moth	N. J. W. Reid	
G-AAHY	D.H.60M Moth	D. J. Elliott	
G-AAIN	Parnall Elf II	The Shuttleworth Collection/O. Warden	
G-AALY	D.H.60G Moth	K. M. Fresson	
G-AAMX	D.H.60GM Moth ★	Aerospace Museum/Cosford	
G-AAMY	D.H.60GMW Moth	Totalsure Ltd	
G-AANG	Blériot XI	The Shuttleworth Collection/O. Warden	
G-AANH	Deperdussin Monoplane	The Shuttleworth Collection/O. Warden	
G-AANI	Blackburn Monoplane	The Shuttleworth Collection/O. Warden	
G-AANJ	L.V.G.-C VI (7198/18)	The Shuttleworth Collection/O. Warden	
G-AANL	D.H.60M Moth	P. L. Allwork	
G-AANM	Bristol 96A F.2B (D7889) (BAPC166)	Aero Vintage Ltd	
G-AANO	D.H.60GMW Moth	A. W. & M. E. Jenkins	
G-AANV	D.H.60G Moth	R. A. Seeley	
G-AAOK	Curtiss Wright Travel Air 12Q	Shipping & Airlines Ltd/Biggin Hill	
G-AAOR	D.H.60G Moth	V. S. E. Norman/Rendcomb	
G-AAPZ	Desoutter I (mod.)	The Shuttleworth Collection/O. Warden	
G-AAUP	Klemm L.25-1A	J. I. Cooper	
G-AAWO	D.H.60G Moth	N. J. W. Reid & L. A. Fenwick	
G-AAXK	Klemm L.25-1A ★	C. C. Russell-Vick *(stored)*	
G-AAYX	Southern Martlet	The Shuttleworth Collection/O. Warden	
G-AAZG	D.H.60G Moth	J. A. Pothecary	
G-AAZP	D.H.80A Puss Moth	R. P. Williams	
G-ABAA	Avro 504K ★	Manchester Museum of Science & Industry	
G-ABAG	D.H.60G Moth	The Shuttleworth Collection/O. Warden	
G-ABBB	B.105A Bulldog IIA (K2227) ★	RAF Museum/Hendon	
G-ABDW	D.H.80A Puss Moth (VH-UQB) ★	Museum of Flight/E. Fortune	
G-ABDX	D.H.60G Moth	M. D. Souch	
G-ABEV	D.H.60G Moth	S. L. G. Darch	

Notes	Reg.	Type	Owner or Operator
	G-ABLM	Cierva C.24 ★	De Havilland Heritage Museum
	G-ABLS	D.H.80A Puss Moth	R. C. F. Bailey
	G-ABMR	Hart 2 (J9941) ★	RAF Museum
	G-ABNT	Civilian C.A.C.1 Coupe	Shipping & Airlines Ltd/Biggin Hill
	G-ABNX	Redwing 2	J. A. Pothecary *(stored)*/Shoreham
	G-ABOI	Wheeler Slymph ★	Midland Air Museum/Coventry
	G-ABOX	Sopwith Pup (N5195)	C. M. D. & A. P. St. Cyrien/Middle Wallop
	G-ABSD	D.H.A.60G Moth	M. E. Vaisey
	G-ABTC	CLA.7 Swift	P. Channon *(stored)*
	G-ABUL†	D.H.82A Tiger Moth ★	F.A.A. Museum (G-AOXG)/Yeovilton
	G-ABUS	CLA.7 Swift	R. C. F. Bailey
	G-ABVE	Arrow Active 2	J. D. Penrose
	G-ABWP	Spartan Arrow	R. E. Blain/Barton
	G-ABXL	Granger Archaeopteryx ★	The Shuttleworth Collection/O. Warden
	G-ABYA	D.H.60G Gipsy Moth	J. F. Moore
	G-ABZB	D.H.60G-III Moth Major	R. Earl & B. Morris
	G-ACAA	Bristol 96A F.2B (D8084†)	Patina Ltd/Duxford
	G-ACBH	Blackburn B.2 ★	–/West Hanningfield, Essex
	G-ACCB	D.H.83 Fox Moth	E. A. Gautrey
	G-ACDA	D.H.82A Tiger Moth	B. D. Hughes
	G-ACDC	D.H.82A Tiger Moth	Tiger Club Ltd/Headcorn
	G-ACDI	D.H.82A Tiger Moth	J. A. Pothecary/Shoreham
	G-ACDJ	D.H.82A Tiger Moth	de Havilland School of Flying Ltd
	G-ACEJ	D.H.83 Fox Moth	Newbury Aeroplane Co
	G-ACET	D.H.84 Dragon	M. D. Souch
	G-ACGT	Avro 594 Avian IIIA ★	Yorkshire Light Aircraft Ltd/Leeds
	G-ACGZ	D.H.60G-III Moth Major	N. H. Lemon
	G-ACIT	D.H.84 Dragon ★	Science Museum/Wroughton
	G-ACLL	D.H.85 Leopard Moth	D. C. M. & V. M. Stiles
	G-ACMA	D.H.85 Leopard Moth	S. J. Filhol/Sherburn
	G-ACMD	D.H.82A Tiger Moth	M. J. Bonnick
	G-ACMN	D.H.85 Leopard Moth	C. S. Grace
	G-ACNS	D.H.60G-III Moth Major	R. I. & D. Souch
	G-ACOJ	D.H.85 Leopard Moth	Norman Aeroplane Trust/Rendcomb
	G-ACSP	D.H.88 Comet ★	K. Fern & T. M. Jones
	G-ACSS	D.H.88 Comet ★	The Shuttleworth Collection *Grosvenor House*/O. Warden
	G-ACSS†	D.H.88 Comet (replica) (BAPC216) ★	G. Gayward
	G-ACSS†	D.H.88 Comet (replica) (BAPC257) ★	The Galleria/Hatfield
	G-ACTF	CLA.7 Swift ★	The Shuttleworth Collection/O. Warden
	G-ACUS	D.H.85 Leopard Moth	R. A. & V. A. Gammons
	G-ACUU	Cierva C.30A (HM580) ★	G. S. Baker/Duxford
	G-ACUX	S.16 Scion (VH-UUP) ★	Ulster Folk & Transport Museum
	G-ACVA	Kay Gyroplane ★	Glasgow Museum of Transport
	G-ACWM	Cierva C.30A (AP506) ★	IHM/Weston-s-Mare
	G-ACWP	Cierva C.30A (AP507) ★	Science Museum/S. Kensington
	G-ACXB	D.H.60G-III Moth Major	D. F. Hodgkinson
	G-ACXE	B.K. L-25C Swallow	J. G. Wakeford
	G-ACYK	Spartan Cruiser III ★	Museum of Flight *(front fuselage)*/ E. Fortune
	G-ACZE	D.H.89A Dragon Rapide	Wessex Aviation & Transport Ltd (G-AJGS)/Henstridge
	G-ADAH	D.H.89A Dragon Rapide ★	Manchester Museum of Science & Industry Pioneer
	G-ADEV	Avro 504K (H5199)	The Shuttleworth Collection (G-ACNB)/ O. Warden
	G-ADFV	Blackburn B-2 ★	Lincolnshire Aviation Heritage Centre
	G-ADGP	M.2L Hawk Speed Six	R. A. Mills
	G-ADGT	D.H.82A Tiger Moth	D. R. & Mrs M. Wood
	G-ADGV	D.H.82A Tiger Moth	K. J. Whitehead
	G-ADHD	D.H.60G-III Moth Major	M. E. Vaisey
	G-ADIA	D.H.82A Tiger Moth	S. J. Beaty
	G-ADJJ	D.H.82A Tiger Moth	J. M. Preston
	G-ADKC	D.H.87B Hornet Moth	A. J. Davy/Carlisle
	G-ADKK	D.H.87B Hornet Moth	R. M. Lee
	G-ADKL	D.H.87B Hornet Moth	P. R. & M. J. F. Gould
	G-ADKM	D.H.87B Hornet Moth	L. V. Mayhead
	G-ADLY	D.H.87B Hornet Moth	Totalsure Ltd
	G-ADMT	D.H.87B Hornet Moth	P. A. de Courcy Swoffer

Reg.	Type	Owner or Operator	Notes
G-ADMW	M.2H Hawk Major (DG590) ★	Museum of Army Flying/Middle Wallop	
G-ADND	D.H.87B Hornet Moth (W9385)	The Shuttleworth Collection/O. Warden	
G-ADNE	D.H.87B Hornet Moth	G-ADNE Ltd	
G-ADNL	M.5 Sparrowhawk ★	A. G. Dunkerley	
G-ADNZ	D.H.82A Tiger Moth (DE673)	D. C. Wall	
G-ADOT	D.H.87B Hornet Moth ★	De Havilland Heritage Museum	
G-ADPC	D.H.82A Tiger Moth	D. J. Marshall	
G-ADPJ	B.A.C. Drone ★	N. H. Ponsford/Breighton	
G-ADPS	B.A. Swallow 2	J. F. Hopkins	
G-ADRA	Pietenpol Air Camper	A. J. Mason	
G-ADRG†	Mignet HM.14 (replica) (BAPC77) ★	Lower Stondon Transport Museum	
G-ADRH	D.H.87B Hornet Moth	R. G. Grocott/Switzerland	
G-ADRR	Aeronca C.3	S. J. Rudkin	
G-ADRX†	Mignet HM.14 (replica) (BAPC231) ★	S. Copeland Aviation Group	
G-ADRY†	Mignet HM.14 (replica) (BAPC29) ★	Brooklands Museum of Aviation/ Weybridge	
G-ADSK	D.H.87B Hornet Moth	R. G. Grocott	
G-ADUR	D.H.87B Hornet Moth	R. A. Seeley	
G-ADVU†	Mignet HM.14 (replica) (BAPC211) ★	N.E. Aircraft Museum/Usworth	
G-ADWJ	D.H.82A Tiger Moth	C. Adams	
G-ADWO	D.H.82A Tiger Moth (BB807) ★	Southampton Hall of Aviation	
G-ADWT	M.2W Hawk Trainer	R. Earl & B. Morris	
G-ADXS	Mignet HM.14 ★	Thameside Aviation Museum/Shoreham	
G-ADYS	Aeronca C.3	J. I. Cooper/Rendcomb	
G-ADYV†	Mignet HM.14 (replica) (BAPC243) ★	P. Ward	
G-ADZW†	Mignet HM.14 (replica) (BAPC253) ★	H. Shore/Sandown	
G-AEAJ†	D.H.89A Dragon Rapide (replica)★	Marriott Liverpool South Hotel	
G-AEBB	Mignet HM.14 ★	The Shuttleworth Collection/O. Warden	
G-AEBJ	Blackburn B-2	BAE Systems (Operations) Ltd/Warton	
G-AEDB	B.A.C. Drone 2	R. E. Nerou & P. L. Kirk	
G-AEDU	D.H.90 Dragonfly	Norman Aeroplane Trust/Rendcomb	
G-AEEG	M.3A Falcon Skysport	P. R. Holloway/O.Warden	
G-AEEH	Mignet HM.14 ★	Aerospace Museum/Cosford	
G-AEFG	Mignet HM.14 (BAPC75) ★	N. H. Ponsford/Breighton	
G-AEFT	Aeronca C.3	N. S. Chittenden	
G-AEGV	Mignet HM.14 ★	Midland Air Museum/Coventry	
G-AEHM	Mignet HM.14 ★	Science Museum/Wroughton	
G-AEJZ	Mignet HM.14 (BAPC120) ★	Bomber County Museum/Hemswell	
G-AEKR	Mignet HM.14 (BAPC121) ★	S. Yorks Aviation Soc	
G-AEKV	Kronfeld Drone ★	Brooklands Museum of Aviation/ Weybridge	
G-AEKW	M.12 Mohawk ★	RAF Museum	
G-AELO	D.H.87B Hornet Moth	M. J. Miller	
G-AEML	D.H.89 Dragon Rapide	Amanda Investments Ltd	
G-AENP	Hawker Hind (K5414) (BAPC78)	The Shuttleworth Collection/O. Warden	
G-AEOA	D.H.80A Puss Moth	P. & A. Wood/O. Warden	
G-AEOF†	Mignet HM.14 (BAPC22) ★	Aviodome/Schiphol, Netherlands	
G-AEOF	Rearwin 8500	Shipping & Airlines Ltd/Biggin Hill	
G-AEOH	Mignet HM.14 ★	Midland Air Museum	
G-AEPH	Bristol F.2B (D8096)	The Shuttleworth Collection/O. Warden	
G-AERV	M.11A Whitney Straight ★	Ulster Folk & Transport Museum	
G-AESB	Aeronca C.3	R. J. M. Turnbull	
G-AESE	D.H.87B Hornet Moth	J. G. Green/Redhill	
G-AESZ	Chilton D.W.1	R. E. Nerou	
G-AETA	Caudron G.3 (3066) ★	RAF Museum/Hendon	
G-AEUJ	M.11A Whitney Straight	R. E. Mitchell	
G-AEVS	Aeronca 100	A. M. Lindsay & N. H. Ponsford/Breighton	
G-AEXD	Aeronca 100	Mrs M. A. & R. W. Mills	
G-AEXF	P.6 Mew Gull	J. D. Penrose/Old Warden	
G-AEXT	Dart Kitten II	A. J. Hartfield	
G-AEXZ	Piper J-2 Cub	Mrs M. & J. R. Dowson/Leicester	
G-AEZF	S.16 Scion 2 ★	Acebell Aviation/Redhill	
G-AEZJ	P.10 Vega Gull	R. A. J. Spurrell/White Waltham	
G-AEZX	Bücker Bü133C Jungmeister (LG+03)	A. J. E. Ditheridge	
G-AFAP†	C.A.S.A. C.352L ★	Aerospace Museum/Cosford	

Notes	Reg.	Type	Owner or Operator
	G-AFAX	B. A. Eagle 2	J. G. Green
	G-AFBS	M.14A Hawk Trainer 3 ★	G. D. Durbridge-Freeman (G-AKKU)/ Duxford
	G-AFCL	B. A. Swallow 2	C. P. Bloxham
	G-AFDO	Piper J-3F-60 Cub	R. Wald
	G-AFDX	Hanriot HD.1 (HD-75) ★	RAF Museum/Hendon
	G-AFEL	Monocoupe 90A	M. Rieser
	G-AFFD	Percival Q-6 ★	B. D. Greenwood
	G-AFFH	Piper J-2 Cub	M. J. Honeychurch
	G-AFFI†	Mignet HM.14 (replica) (BAPC76) ★	Yorkshire Air Museum/Elvington
	G-AFGC	B. A. Swallow 2	G. E. Arden
	G-AFGD	B. A. Swallow 2	A. T. Williams & ptnrs/Shobdon
	G-AFGE	B. A. Swallow 2	G. R. French
	G-AFGH	Chilton D.W.1.	M. L. & G. L. Joseph
	G-AFGI	Chilton D.W.1.	J. E. & K. A. A. McDonald
	G-AFGM	Piper J-4A Cub Coupé	P. H. Wilkinson/Carlisle
	G-AFGZ	D.H.82A Tiger Moth	M. R. Paul & P. A. Shaw (G-AMHI)
	G-AFHA	Mosscraft MA.1. ★	C. V. Butler
	G-AFIN	Chrislea LC.1 Airguard (BAPC203) ★	N. Wright
	G-AFIR	Luton LA-4 Minor	A. J. Mason
	G-AFJA	Watkinson Dingbat ★	K. Woolley
	G-AFJB	Foster-Wikner G.M.1. Wicko (DR613) ★	J. Dibble
	G-AFJR	Tipsy Trainer 1	M. E. Vaisey *(stored)*
	G-AFJU	M.17 Monarch ★	Museum of Flight/E. Fortune
	G-AFJV	Mosscraft MA.2 ★	C. V. Butler
	G-AFNG	D.H.94 Moth Minor	The Gullwing Trust
	G-AFNI	D.H.94 Moth Minor	J. Jennings
	G-AFOB	D.H.94 Moth Minor	Wessex Aviation & Transport Ltd
	G-AFOJ	D.H.94 Moth Minor ★	De Havilland Heritage Museum
	G-AFPN	D.H.94 Moth Minor	J. W. & A. R. Davy/Carlisle
	G-AFRZ	M.17 Monarch	R. E. Mitchell (G-AIDE)
	G-AFSC	Tipsy Trainer 1	D. M. Forshaw
	G-AFSV	Chilton D.W.1A	R. E. Nerou
	G-AFSW	Chilton D.W.2 ★	R. I. Souch
	G-AFTA	Hawker Tomtit (K1786)	The Shuttleworth Collection/O. Warden
	G-AFTN	Taylorcraft Plus C2 ★	Leicestershire County Council Museums
	G-AFUP	Luscombe 8A Silvaire	R. Dispain
	G-AFVE	D.H.82A Tiger Moth (T7230)	Tigerfly/Booker
	G-AFVN	Tipsy Trainer 1	D. F. Lingard
	G-AFWH	Piper J-4A Cub Coupé	C. W. Stearn & R. D. W. Norton
	G-AFWI	D.H.82A Tiger Moth	E. Newbigin
	G-AFWT	Tipsy Trainer 1	C. C. & J. M. Lovell
	G-AFYD	Luscombe 8F Silvaire	J. D. Iliffe
	G-AFYO	Stinson H.W.75	R. N. Wright
	G-AFZA	Piper J-4A Cub Coupe	G-AFZA Group
	G-AFZK	Luscombe 8A Silvaire	M. G. Byrnes
	G-AFZL	Porterfield CP.50	P. G. Lucas & S. H. Sharpe/ White Waltham
	G-AFZN	Luscombe 8A Silvaire	A. L. Young/Henstridge
	G-AGAT	Piper J-3F-50 Cub	O. T. Taylor & C. J. Marshall
	G-AGBN	G.A.L.42 Cygnet 2 ★	Museum of Flight/E. Fortune
	G-AGEG	D.H.82A Tiger Moth	Norman Aeroplane Trust/Rendcomb
	G-AGFT	Avia FL.3 (W7)	K. Joynson & K. Cracknell
	G-AGHY	D.H.82A Tiger Moth	P. Groves
	G-AGIV	Piper J-3C-65 Cub	P. C. & F. M. Gill
	G-AGJG	D.H.89A Dragon Rapide	M. J. & D. J. T. Miller/Duxford
	G-AGLK	Auster 5D	C. R. Harris/Biggin Hill
	G-AGMI	Luscombe 8A Silvaire	P. R. Bush
	G-AGNJ	D.H.82A Tiger Moth	B. P. Borsberry & ptnrs
	G-AGNV	Avro 685 York 1 (TS798) ★	Aerospace Museum/Cosford
	G-AGOH	J/1 Autocrat ★	Newark Air Museum
	G-AGOS	R.S.4 Desford Trainer (VZ728) ★	Museum of Flight/E. Fortune
	G-AGOY	M.48 Messenger 3 (U-0247)	P. A. Brook
	G-AGPG	Avro 19 Srs 2 ★	Avro Heritage Soc/Woodford
	G-AGPK	D.H.82A Tiger Moth	Delta Aviation Ltd
	G-AGRU	V.498 Viking 1A ★	Brooklands Museum of Aviation/Weybridge
	G-AGSH	D.H.89A Dragon Rapide 6	Venom Jet Promotions Ltd/Bournemouth
	G-AGTM	D.H.89A Dragon Rapide 6	Air Atlantique Ltd/Coventry

Reg.	Type	Owner or Operator	Notes
G-AGTO	J/1 Autocrat	M. J. Barnett & D. J. T. Miller/Duxford	
G-AGTT	J/1 Autocrat	R. Farrer	
G-AGVG	J/1 Autocrat (modified)	S. J. Riddington/Leicester	
G-AGVN	J/1 Autocrat	G. H. Farrar	
G-AGVV	Piper J-3C-65 Cub	M. Molina-Ruano/Spain	
G-AGXN	J/1N Alpha	Gentleman's Aerial Touring Carriage Syndicate Ltd	
G-AGXT	J/1N Alpha ★	Nene Valley Aircraft Museum	
G-AGXU	J/1N Alpha	B. H. Austen	
G-AGXV	J/1 Autocrat	B. S. Dowsett	
G-AGYD	J/1N Alpha	P. D. Hodson	
G-AGYH	J/1N Alpha	W. R. V. Marklew	
G-AGYK	J/1 Autocrat	Autocrat Syndicate	
G-AGYL	J/1 Autocrat ★	Military Vehicle Conservation Group	
G-AGYT	J/1N Alpha	P. J. Barrett	
G-AGYU	D.H.82A Tiger Moth (DE208)	P. L. Jones	
G-AGYY	Ryan ST.3KR (27)	Nostalgic Flying/Netherlands	
G-AGZZ	D.H.82A Tiger Moth	G. C. P. Shea-Simonds/Netheravon	
G-AHAG	D.H.89A Rapide	Pelham Ltd/Membury	
G-AHAL	J/1N Alpha	Wickenby Flying Club Ltd	
G-AHAM	J/1 Autocrat	C. P. L. Jenkin	
G-AHAN	D.H.82A Tiger Moth	Tiger Associates Ltd	
G-AHAP	J/1 Autocrat	F.J. Bellamy	
G-AHAT	J/1N Alpha ★	Dumfries & Galloway Aviation Museum	
G-AHAU	J/1 Autocrat	Andreas Auster Group	
G-AHBL	D.H.87B Hornet Moth	H. D. Labouchere	
G-AHBM	D.H.87B Hornet Moth	P. A. & E. P. Gliddon	
G-AHCK	J/1N Alpha	Skegness Air Taxi Service Ltd	
G-AHCL	J/1N Alpha	Electronic Precision Ltd (G-OJVC)	
G-AHCR	Gould-Taylorcraft Plus D Special	D. E. H. Balmford & D. R. Shepherd/ Dunkeswell	
G-AHEC	Luscombe 8A Silvaire	P. G. Baxter	
G-AHED	D.H.89A Dragon Rapide (RL962) ★	RAF Museum Storage & Restoration Centre/RAF Wyton	
G-AHGD	D.H.89A Dragon Rapide	R. Jones	
G-AHGW	Taylorcraft Plus D (LB375)	C. V. Butler/Coventry	
G-AHGZ	Taylorcraft Plus D (LB367)	M. Pocock	
G-AHHH	J/1 Autocrat	H. A. Jones/Norwich	
G-AHHT	J/1N Alpha	A. C. Barber & N. J. Hudson	
G-AHHU	J/1N Alpha ★	L. A. Groves & I. R. F. Hammond	
G-AHIP	Piper J-3C-65 Cub	A. R. Mangham	
G-AHIZ	D.H.82A Tiger Moth	C.F.G. Flying Ltd/Cambridge	
G-AHKX	Avro 19 Srs 2	BAe PLC/Avro Heritage Soc/Woodford	
G-AHKY	Miles M.18 Series 2 ★	Museum of Flight/E. Fortune	
G-AHLK	Auster 3	E. T. Brackenbury/Leicester	
G-AHLT	D.H.82A Tiger Moth	K. J. Jarvis	
G-AHMM	D.H.82A Tiger Moth	M. D. Souch	
G-AHMN	D.H.82A Tiger Moth (N6985)	Museum of Army Flying/Middle Wallop	
G-AHNR	Taylorcraft BC-12D	P. E. Hinkley/Redhill	
G-AHOO	D.H.82A Tiger Moth	J. T. & A. D. Milsom	
G-AHPZ	D.H.82A Tiger Moth	N. J. Wareing	
G-AHRI	D.H.104 Dove 1 ★	Newark Air Museum	
G-AHRO	Cessna 140	R. H. Screen/Kidlington	
G-AHSA	Avro 621 Tutor (K3215)	The Shuttleworth Collection/O. Warden	
G-AHSD	Taylorcraft Plus D	A. L. Hall-Carpenter	
G-AHSO	J/1N Alpha	W. P. Miller	
G-AHSP	J/1 Autocrat	R. M. Weeks	
G-AHSS	J/1N Alpha	A. M. Roche	
G-AHST	J/1N Alpha	A. C. Frost	
G-AHTE	P.44 Proctor V	D. K. Tregilgas	
G-AHTW	A.S.40 Oxford (V3388) ★	Skyfame Collection/Duxford	
G-AHUF	D.H.82A Tiger Moth (T7997)	First County Finance (UK) Ltd	
G-AHUG	Taylorcraft Plus D	D. Nieman	
G-AHUI	M.38 Messenger 2A ★	Museum of Berkshire Aviation/Woodley	
G-AHUJ	M.14A Hawk Trainer 3 (R1914) ★	Strathallan Aircraft Collection	
G-AHUN	Globe GC-1B Swift	R. J. Hamlett	
G-AHUV	D.H.82A Tiger Moth	J. D. Gordon	
G-AHVU	D.H.82A Tiger Moth (T6313)	Foley Farm Flying Group	
G-AHVV	D.H.82A Tiger Moth	B. M. Pullen	
G-AHWJ	Taylorcraft Plus D (LB294)	M. D. Pitcher	
G-AHXE	Taylorcraft Plus D (LB312)	J. M. C. Pothecary/Shoreham	

Notes	Reg.	Type	Owner or Operator
	G-AIBE	Fulmar II (N1854) ★	F.A.A. Museum/Yeovilton
	G-AIBH	J/1N Alpha	M. J. Bonnick
	G-AIBM	J/1 Autocrat	D. G. Greatrex
	G-AIBR	J/1 Autocrat	R. H. & J. A. Cooper
	G-AIBW	J/1N Alpha	W. E. Bateson/Blackpool
	G-AIBX	J/1 Autocrat	Wasp Flying Group
	G-AIBY	J/1 Autocrat	D. Morris/Sherburn
	G-AICX	Luscombe 8A Silvaire	R. V. Smith/Henstridge
	G-AIDL	D.H.89A Dragon Rapide 6	Atlantic Air Transport Ltd/Coventry
	G-AIDS	D.H.82A Tiger Moth	K. D. Pogmore & T. Dann
	G-AIEK	M.38 Messenger 2A (RG333)	J. Buckingham
	G-AIFZ	J/1N Alpha	M. D. Ansley
	G-AIGD	J/1 Autocrat	R. B. Webber
	G-AIGF	J/1N Alpha	A. R. C. Mathie
	G-AIGU	J/1N Alpha	N. K. Geddes
	G-AIIH	Piper J-3C-65 Cub	J. A. de Salis
	G-AIJI	J/1N Alpha ★	C. J. Baker
	G-AIJM	Auster J/4	N. Huxtable
	G-AIJS	Auster J/4 ★	(stored)
	G-AIJT	Auster J/4 Srs 100	Aberdeen Auster Flying Group
	G-AIJZ	J/1 Autocrat	A. A. Marshall (stored)
	G-AIKE	Auster 5	C. J. Baker
	G-AIPR	Auster J/4	MPM Flying Group/Booker
	G-AIPV	J/1 Autocrat	W. P. Miller
	G-AIRC	J/1 Autocrat	R. C. Tebbett/Shobdon
	G-AIRI	D.H.82A Tiger Moth	E. R. Goodwin (stored)
	G-AIRK	D.H.82A Tiger Moth	R. C. Teverson & ptnrs
	G-AISA	Tipsy B Srs 1	A. A. M. Huke
	G-AISC	Tipsy B Srs 1	Wagtail Flying Group
	G-AISS	Piper J-3C-65 Cub	K. W. Wood & F. Watson/Insch
	G-AIST	V.S.300 Spitfire 1A (K9853/AR213)	Sheringham Aviation UK Ltd
	G-AISX	Piper J-3C-65 Cub	Cubfly
	G-AITB	A.S.10 Oxford (MP425) ★	RAF Museum Store/Cardington
	G-AIUA	M.14A Hawk Trainer 3 ★	R. Trickett
	G-AIUL	D.H.89A Dragon Rapide 6	I. Jones/Chirk
	G-AIXA	Taylorcraft Plus D	G. L. Brown
	G-AIXJ	D.H.82A Tiger Moth	D. Green/Goodwood
	G-AIXN	Benes-Mraz M.1C Sokol	A. J. Wood
	G-AIYG	SNCAN Stampe SV-4B	L. Casteleyn/Belgium
	G-AIYR	D.H.89A Dragon Rapide	Fairmont Investments Ltd/Duxford
	G-AIYS	D.H.85 Leopard Moth	Wessex Aviation & Transport Ltd
	G-AIZE	F.24W Argus 2 ★	Aerospace Museum/Cosford
	G-AIZF	D.H.82A Tiger Moth ★	(stored)
	G-AIZG	V.S. Walrus 1 (L2301) ★	F.A.A. Museum/Yeovilton
	G-AIZU	J/1 Autocrat	C. J. & J. G. B. Morley
	G-AJAD	Piper J-3C-65 Cub	N. A. Rooney
	G-AJAE	J/1N Alpha	A. C. Ladd
	G-AJAJ	J/1N Alpha	R. B. Lawrence
	G-AJAM	J/2 Arrow	D. A. Porter
	G-AJAP	Luscombe 8A Silvaire	R. J. Thomas
	G-AJAS	J/1N Alpha	C. J. Baker
	G-AJCP	D.31 Turbulent	B. R. Pearson
	G-AJDW	J/1 Autocrat	D. R. Hunt
	G-AJEB	J/1N Alpha ★	Manchester Museum of Science & Industry
	G-AJEH	J/1N Alpha	J. T. Powell-Tuck
	G-AJEI	J/1N Alpha	W. P. Miller
	G-AJES	Piper J-3C-65 Cub (330485)	P. A. Crawford
	G-AJGJ	Auster 5 (RT486)	British Classic Aircraft Restoration Flying Group
	G-AJHJ	Auster 5 ★	(stored)
	G-AJHS	D.H.82A Tiger Moth	Vliegend Museum/Netherlands
	G-AJHU	D.H.82A Tiger Moth (T7471)	G. Valentini/Italy
	G-AJIH	J/1 Autocrat	A. H. Diver
	G-AJIS	J/1N Alpha	Husthwaite Auster Group
	G-AJIT	J/1 Kingsland Autocrat	A. J. Kay
	G-AJIU	J/1 Autocrat	M. D. Greenhalgh/Netherthorpe
	G-AJIW	J/1N Alpha	Truman Aviation Ltd/Tollerton
	G-AJJP	Jet Gyrodyne (XJ389) ★	Museum of Berkshire Aviation/Woodley
	G-AJJS	Cessna 120	Robhurst Flying Group
	G-AJJT	Cessna 120	J. S. Robson

Reg.	Type	Owner or Operator	Notes
G-AJJU	Luscombe 8E Silvaire	L. C. Moon	
G-AJKB	Luscombe 8E Silvaire	A. F. Hall & S. P. Collins/Tibenham	
G-AJOA	D.H.82A Tiger Moth (T5424)	F. P. Le Coyte	
G-AJOC	M.38 Messenger 2A ★	Ulster Folk & Transport Museum	
G-AJOE	M.38 Messenger 2A	P. W. Bishop	
G-AJON	Aeronca 7AC Champion	A. Biggs & J. L. Broad/Booker	
G-AJOV†	Sikorsky S-51 ★	Aerospace Museum/Cosford	
G-AJOZ	F.24W Argus 2 ★	Thorpe Camp Preservation Group/ Woodhall Spa	
G-AJPI	F.24R-41a Argus 3 (314887)	T. H. Bishop	
G-AJPZ	J/1 Autocrat ★	Wessex Aviation Soc	
G-AJRB	J/1 Autocrat	G-AJRB Group	
G-AJRC	J/1 Autocrat	M. Baker	
G-AJRE	J/1 Autocrat (Lycoming)	R. R. Harris	
G-AJRH	J/1N Alpha ★	Charnwood Museum/Loughborough	
G-AJRS	M.14A Hawk Trainer 3 (P6382)	The Shuttleworth Collection/O. Warden	
G-AJTW	D.H.82A Tiger Moth (N6965)	J. A. Barker/Tibenham	
G-AJUE	J/1 Autocrat	P. H. B. Cole	
G-AJUL	J/1N Alpha	M. J. Crees	
G-AJVE	D.H.82A Tiger Moth	R. A. Gammons	
G-AJWB	M.38 Messenger 2A	G. E. J. Spooner	
G-AJXC	Auster 5	J. E. Graves	
G-AJXV	Auster 4 (NJ695)	B. A. Farries/Leicester	
G-AJXY	Auster 4	D. A. Hall	
G-AJYB	J/1N Alpha	P. J. Shotbolt	
G-AKAT	M.14A Hawk Trainer 3 (T9738)	J. D. Haslam/Breighton	
G-AKAZ	Piper J-3C-65 Cub (57-H)	Frazerblades Ltd/Duxford	
G-AKBM	M.38 Messenger 2A ★	Bristol Plane Preservation Unit	
G-AKBO	M.38 Messenger 2A	Bravo Oscar Syndicate	
G-AKDN	D.H.C. 1A Chipmunk 10	P. S. Derry	
G-AKDW	D.H.89A Dragon Rapide ★	De Havilland Heritage Museum	
G-AKEL	M.65 Gemini 1A ★	Ulster Folk & Transport Museum	
G-AKER	M.65 Gemini 1A ★	Berkshire Aviation Group/Woodley	
G-AKEZ	M.38 Messenger 2A (RG333)	P. G. Lee	
G-AKGD	M.65 Gemini 1A ★	Berkshire Aviation Group/Woodley	
G-AKGE	M.65 Gemini 3C ★	Ulster Folk & Transport Museum	
G-AKHP	M.65 Gemini 1A	P. A. Brook/Shoreham	
G-AKHZ	M.65 Gemini 7 ★	Museum of Berkshire Aviation/Woodley	
G-AKIB	Piper J-3C-90 Cub (480015)	M. C. Bennett	
G-AKIF	D.H.89A Dragon Rapide	Airborne Taxi Services Ltd/Booker	
G-AKIN	M.38 Messenger 2A	R. Spiller & Sons/Sywell	
G-AKIU	P.44 Proctor V	Air Atlantique Ltd/Coventry	
G-AKKB	M.65 Gemini 1A	J. Buckingham	
G-AKKH	M.65 Gemini 1A	J. S. Allison	
G-AKKR	M.14A Magister (T9707) ★	Manchester Museum of Science & Industry	
G-AKKY	M.14A Hawk Trainer 3 (L6906) ★ (BAPC44) ★	Museum of Berkshire Aviation/Woodley	
G-AKLW	SA.6 Sealand 1 ★	Ulster Folk & Transport Museum	
G-AKOE	D.H.89A Dragon Rapide 4	H. J. E. Pierce/Chirk	
G-AKOT	Auster 5 ★	C. J. Baker	
G-AKOW	Auster 5 (TJ569) ★	Museum of Army Flying/Middle Wallop	
G-AKPF	M.14A Hawk Trainer 3 (V1075)	P. R. Holloway	
G-AKRA	Piper J-3C-65 Cub	W. R. Savin	
G-AKRP	D.H.89A Dragon Rapide 4	Fordaire Aviation Ltd/Sywell	
G-AKSY	Auster 5	A, Brier	
G-AKSZ	Auster 5	A. R. C. Mathie	
G-AKTH	Piper J-3C-65 Cub	G. H. Harry & Viscount Goschen	
G-AKTI	Luscombe 8A Silvaire	M. W. Olliver	
G-AKTK	Aeronca 11AC Chief	R. W. Marshall & ptnrs	
G-AKTN	Luscombe 8A Silvaire	M. G. Rummey	
G-AKTO	Aeronca 7BCM Champion	D. C. Murray	
G-AKTP	PA-17 Vagabond	G-AKTP Flying Group	
G-AKTR	Aeronca 7AC Champion	C. Fielder	
G-AKTS	Cessna 120	W. Fairney/Kemble	
G-AKTT	Luscombe 8A Silvaire	S. J. Charters	
G-AKUE	D.H.82A Tiger Moth	D. F. Hodgkinson	
G-AKUF	Luscombe 8F Silvaire	E. J. Lloyd	
G-AKUG	Luscombe 8A Silvaire	G-AKUG Group	
G-AKUH	Luscombe 8E Silvaire	I. M. Bower	
G-AKUI	Luscombe 8E Silvaire	D. A. Sims	
G-AKUJ	Luscombe 8E Silvaire	R. C. Green	

Notes	Reg.	Type	Owner or Operator
	G-AKUK	Luscombe 8A Silvaire	Leckhampstead Flying Group
	G-AKUL	Luscombe 8A Silvaire	E. A. Taylor
	G-AKUM	Luscombe 8F Silvaire	D. A. Young
	G-AKUN	Piper J-3F-65 Cub	W. R. Savin
	G-AKUO	Aeronca 11AC Chief	L. W. Richardson
	G-AKUP	Luscombe 8E Silvaire	D. A. Young
	G-AKUR	Cessna 140	J. Greenaway & C. A. Davies/Popham
	G-AKUW	Chrislea C.H.3 Super Ace 2	J. & S. Rickett
	G-AKVF	Chrislea C.H.3 Super Ace 2	B. Metters
	G-AKVM	Cessna 120	N. Wise & S. Walker
	G-AKVN	Aeronca 11AC Chief	Breckland Aeronca Group
	G-AKVO	Taylorcraft BC-12D	Albion Flyers
	G-AKVP	Luscombe 8A Silvaire	J. M. Edis
	G-AKVR	Chrislea C.H.3 Skyjeep 4	N. D. Needham
	G-AKVZ	M.38 Messenger 4B	Shipping & Airlines Ltd/Biggin Hill
	G-AKWS	Auster 5A-160 (RT610)	Fast Aerospace Ltd
	G-AKWT	Auster 5 ★	C. Baker
	G-AKXP	Auster 5	M. Pocock
	G-AKXS	D.H.82A Tiger Moth	P. A. Colman
	G-AKZN	P.34A Proctor 3 (Z7197) ★	RAF Museum/Hendon
	G-ALAH	M.38 Messenger 4A (RH377) ★	RAF Museum/Henlow
	G-ALAX	D.H.89A Dragon Rapide ★	Durney Aeronautical Collection/Andover
	G-ALBJ	Auster 5	P. N. Elkington
	G-ALBK	Auster 5	S. J. Wright & Co (Farmers) Ltd
	G-ALBN	Bristol 173 (XF785) ★	RAF Museum Storage & Restoration Centre/Cardington
	G-ALCK	P.34A Proctor 3 (LZ766) ★	Skyfame Collection/Duxford
	G-ALCS	M.65 Gemini 3C ★	(stored)
	G-ALCU	D.H.104 Dove 2 ★	Midland Air Museum/Coventry
	G-ALDG	HP.81 Hermes 4 ★	Duxford Aviation Soc (fuselage only)
	G-ALEH	PA-17 Vagabond	A. D. Pearce/White Waltham
	G-ALFA	Auster 5	S. P. Barrett
	G-ALFT	D.H.104 Dove 6 ★	Caernarfon Air World
	G-ALFU	D.H.104 Dove 6 ★	Duxford Aviation Soc
	G-ALGA	PA-15 Vagabond	G. A. Brady
	G-ALIJ	PA-17 Vagabond	Popham Flying Group/Popham
	G-ALIW	D.H.82A Tiger Moth	D. I. M. Geddes & F. Curry/Booker
	G-ALJF	P.34A Proctor 3	J. F. Moore/Biggin Hill
	G-ALJL	D.H.82A Tiger Moth	R. I. & D. Souch
	G-ALLF	Slingsby T.30A Prefect (ARK)	J. F. Hopkins & K. M. Fresson/Parham Park
	G-ALNA	D.H.82A Tiger Moth	R. J. Doughton
	G-ALND	D.H.82A Tiger Moth (N9191)	J. T. Powell-Tuck
	G-ALNV	Auster 5 ★	C. J. Baker (stored)
	G-ALOD	Cessna 140	J. R. Stainer
	G-ALRI	D.H.82A Tiger Moth (T5672)	Wessex Aviation & Transport Ltd
	G-ALSP	Bristol 171 Sycamore (WV783)★	R.N. Fleetlands Museum
	G-ALSS	Bristol 171 Sycamore (WA576)★	Dumfries & Galloway Aviation Museum
	G-ALST	Bristol 171 Sycamore (WA577)★	N.E. Aircraft Museum/Usworth
	G-ALSW	Bristol 171 Sycamore (WT933)★	Newark Air Museum
	G-ALSX	Bristol 171 Sycamore (G-48-1)★	IHM/Weston-s-Mare
	G-ALTO	Cessna 140	J. M. Edis
	G-ALTW	D.H.82A Tiger Moth ★	A. Mangham
	G-ALUC	D.H.82A Tiger Moth	D. R. & M. Wood
	G-ALVP	D.H.82A Tiger Moth ★	V. & R. Wheele (stored)
	G-ALWB	D.H.C.1 Chipmunk 22A	D. M. Neville
	G-ALWF	V.701 Viscount ★	Viscount Preservation Trust RMA Sir John Franklin/Duxford
	G-ALWS	D.H.82A Tiger Moth	A. P. Benyon/Welshpool
	G-ALWW	D.H.82A Tiger Moth	D. E. Findon
	G-ALXT	D.H.89A Dragon Rapide ★	Science Museum/Wroughton
	G-ALXZ	Auster 5-150	M. F. Cuming
	G-ALYB	Auster 5 (RT520) ★	S. Yorks Aircraft Preservation Soc
	G-ALYG	Auster 5D	A. L. Young/Henstridge
	G-ALYW	D.H.106 Comet 1 ★	RAF Exhibition Flight (fuselage converted to Nimrod)
	G-ALZE	BN-1F ★	M. R. Short/Southampton Hall of Aviation
	G-ALZO	A.S.57 Ambassador ★	Duxford Aviation Soc
	G-AMAW	Luton LA-4 Minor	R. H. Coates
	G-AMBB	D.H.82A Tiger Moth	J. Eagles
	G-AMCA	Douglas C-47B	Air Atlantique Ltd/Coventry

Reg.	Type	Owner or Operator	Notes
G-AMCK	D.H.82A Tiger Moth	Avia Special Ltd	
G-AMCM	D.H.82A Tiger Moth	A. K. & J. I. Cooper	
G-AMDA	Avro 652A Anson 1 (N4877) ★	Skyfame Collection/Duxford	
G-AMEN	PA-18 Super Cub 95	A. Lovejoy & W. Cook	
G-AMHF	D.H.82A Tiger Moth	Wavendon Social Housing Ltd	
G-AMHJ	Douglas C-47A	Air Atlantique Ltd/Coventry	
G-AMIU	D.H.82A Tiger Moth	M. D. Souch	
G-AMKU	J/1B Aiglet	P. G. Lipman	
G-AMLZ	P.50 Prince 6E ★	Caernarfon Air World Museum	
G-AMMS	J/5K Aiglet Trainer	A. J. Large	
G-AMNN	D.H.82A Tiger Moth	M. Thrower Spirit of Pashley/Shoreham	
G-AMOG	V.701 Viscount ★	Aerospace Museum/Cosford	
G-AMPG	PA-12 Super Cruiser	R. Simpson	
G-AMPI	SNCAN Stampe SV-4C	T. W. Harris	
G-AMPO	Douglas C-47B (KN556)	Gate Guardian/RAF Lyneham	
G-AMPY	Douglas C-47B	Atlantic Air Ltd/Thales/Coventry	
G-AMPZ	Douglas C-47B	Air Service Berlin GmbH/Templehof	
G-AMRA	Douglas C-47B	Atlantic Air Transport Ltd/Coventry	
G-AMRF	J/5F Aiglet Trainer	A. I. Topps/E. Midlands	
G-AMRK	G.37 Gladiator I (427)	The Shuttleworth Collection/O. Warden	
G-AMSG	SIPA 903	S. W. Markham	
G-AMSN	Douglas C-47B ★	Aces High Ltd/North Weald	
G-AMSV	Douglas C-47B	Atlantic Air Transport Ltd/Coventry	
G-AMTA	J/5F Aiglet Trainer	N. H. T. Cottrell	
G-AMTF	D.H.82A Tiger Moth (T7842)	M. Lageirse & P. Winters/Belgium	
G-AMTK	D.H.82A Tiger Moth	S. W. McKay & M. E. Vaisey	
G-AMTM	J/1 Autocrat	R. J. Stobo (G-AJUJ)	
G-AMTV	D.H.82A Tiger Moth	Medalbest Ltd	
G-AMUF	D.H.C.1 Chipmunk 21	Redhill Tailwheel Flying Club Ltd	
G-AMUI	J/5F Aiglet Trainer	D. Hatelie	
G-AMVD	Auster 5	M.Hammond	
G-AMVP	Tipsy Junior	A. R. Wershat	
G-AMVS	D.H.82A Tiger Moth	J. T. Powell-Tuck	
G-AMXA	D.H.106 Comet 2 (nose only) ★	Spectators' Terrace/Gatwick	
G-AMYA	Zlin Z.381	D. M. Fenton	
G-AMYD	J/5L Aiglet Trainer	G. H. Maskell	
G-AMYJ	Douglas C-47B ★	Yorkshire Air Museum/Elvington	
G-AMYL	PA-17 Vagabond	P. J. Penn-Sayers/Shoreham	
G-AMZI	J/5F Aiglet Trainer	J. F. Moore/Biggin Hill	
G-AMZT	J/5F Aiglet Trainer	D. Hyde & ptnrs/Cranfield	
G-AMZU	J/5F Aiglet Trainer	J. A. Longworth & ptnrs	
G-ANAF	Douglas C-47B	Air Atlantique Ltd/Thales/Coventry	
G-ANAP	D.H.104 Dove 6 ★	Brunel Technical College/Lulsgate	
G-ANCF	B.175 Britannia 308 ★	Bristol Aero Collection (stored)/Kemble	
G-ANCS	D.H.82A Tiger Moth	C. E. Edwards & E. A. Higgins	
G-ANCX	D.H.82A Tiger Moth	D. R. Wood/Biggin Hill	
G-ANDE	D.H.82A Tiger Moth	Montrose Aviation Ltd/Duxford	
G-ANDM	D.H.82A Tiger Moth	N. J. Stagg	
G-ANDP	D.H.82A Tiger Moth	A. H. Diver	
G-ANEC	D.H.82A Tiger Moth ★	(stored)	
G-ANEH	D.H.82A Tiger Moth (N6797)	G. J. Wells/Goodwood	
G-ANEL	D.H.82A Tiger Moth	Chauffair Ltd	
G-ANEM	D.H.82A Tiger Moth	P. J. Benest	
G-ANEN	D.H.82A Tiger Moth	A. J. D. Douglas-Hamilton	
G-ANEW	D.H.82A Tiger Moth	A. L. Young	
G-ANEZ	D.H.82A Tiger Moth	C. D. J. Bland/Sandown	
G-ANFC	D.H.82A Tiger Moth	H. J. E. Pierce/Chirk	
G-ANFH	Westland S-55 ★	IHM/Weston-s-Mare	
G-ANFI	D.H.82A Tiger Moth (DE623)	G. P. Graham	
G-ANFL	D.H.82A Tiger Moth	IDA Flying Group	
G-ANFM	D.H.82A Tiger Moth	Reading Flying Group/White Waltham	
G-ANFP	D.H.82A Tiger Moth	G. D. Horn	
G-ANFU	Auster 5 (NJ719) ★	N.E. Aircraft Museum/Usworth	
G-ANFV	D.H.82A Tiger Moth (DF155)	R. A. L. Falconer	
G-ANGK	Cessna 140A	G. A. Copeland	
G-ANHK	D.H.82A Tiger Moth	J. D. Iliffe	
G-ANHR	Auster 5	C. G. Winch	
G-ANHS	Auster 4	Tango Uniform Group	
G-ANHU	Auster 4	D. J. Baker (stored)	
G-ANHX	Auster 5D	D. J. Baker	
G-ANIE	Auster 5 (TW467)	S. J. Partridge	
G-ANIJ	Auster 5D (TJ672)	M. Pocock	

Notes	Reg.	Type	Owner or Operator
	G-ANIS	Auster 5	J. Clarke-Cockburn
	G-ANJA	D.H.82A Tiger Moth (N9389)	P. Auckland
	G-ANJD	D.H.82A Tiger Moth	A. C. Ladd
	G-ANKK	D.H.82A Tiger Moth (T5854)	Halfpenny Green Tiger Group
	G-ANKT	D.H.82A Tiger Moth (T6818)	The Shuttleworth Collection/O. Warden
	G-ANKV	D.H.82A Tiger Moth (T7793) ★	Westmead Business Group/Croydon Airport
	G-ANKZ	D.H.82A Tiger Moth (N6466)	D. W. Graham
	G-ANLD	D.H.82A Tiger Moth	K. Peters
	G-ANLH	D.H.82A Tiger Moth	T. R. Green
	G-ANLS	D.H.82A Tiger Moth	P. A. Gliddon
	G-ANLU	Auster 5	B. H. Hargrave
	G-ANLW	W.B.1. Widgeon (MD497) ★	Sloane Helicopters Ltd/Sywell
	G-ANMO	D.H.82A Tiger Moth (K4259)	E. & K. M. Lay
	G-ANMV	D.H.82A Tiger Moth (T7404)	J. W. Davy/Cardiff
	G-ANMY	D.H.82A Tiger Moth (DE470)	R. Earl & B. Morris
	G-ANNB	D.H.82A Tiger Moth	G. M. Bradley
	G-ANNE	D.H.82A Tiger Moth	C. R. Hardiman
	G-ANNG	D.H.82A Tiger Moth	P. F. Walter
	G-ANNI	D.H.82A Tiger Moth	A. R. Brett
	G-ANNK	D.H.82A Tiger Moth	P. J. Wilcox/Cranfield
	G-ANOA	Hiller UH-12A ★	Redhill Technical College
	G-ANOD	D.H.82A Tiger Moth	P. G. Grafton
	G-ANOH	D.H.82A Tiger Moth	N. Parkhouse/White Waltham
	G-ANOK	SAAB S.91C Safir ★	A. F. Galt & Co (stored)
	G-ANOM	D.H.82A Tiger Moth	A. L. Creer
	G-ANON	D.H.82A Tiger Moth (T7909)	Hields Aviation/Sherburn
	G-ANOO	D.H.82A Tiger Moth	R. K. Packman/Shoreham
	G-ANOR	D.H.82A Tiger Moth (T6991)	R. Clifford
	G-ANOV	D.H.104 Dove 6 ★	Museum of Flight/E. Fortune
	G-ANPE	D.H.82A Tiger Moth	I. E. S. Huddleston (G-IESH)/Clacton
	G-ANPK	D.H.82A Tiger Moth	A. D. Hodgkinson
	G-ANPP	P.34A Proctor 3	C. P. A. & J. Jeffrey
	G-ANRF	D.H.82A Tiger Moth	C. D. Cyster
	G-ANRM	D.H.82A Tiger Moth (DF112)	Fairmont Investments Ltd/Clacton
	G-ANRN	D.H.82A Tiger Moth	J. J. V. Elwes/Rush Green
	G-ANRP	Auster 5 (TW439)	I. C. Naylor
	G-ANRX	D.H.82A Tiger Moth ★	De Havilland Heritage Museum
	G-ANSM	D.H.82A Tiger Moth	R. M. Kimbell
	G-ANTE	D.H.82A Tiger Moth (T6562)	P. Reading
	G-ANTK	Avro 685 York ★	Duxford Aviation Soc
	G-ANTS	D.H.82A Tiger Moth (N6532)	J. G. Green
	G-ANUO	D.H.114 Heron 2D (G-AOXL) ★	Westmead Business Group/ Croydon Airport
	G-ANUW	D.H.104 Dove 6 ★	Jet Aviation Preservation Group
	G-ANWB	D.H.C.1 Chipmunk 21	G. Briggs/Blackpool
	G-ANWO	M.14A Hawk Trainer 3 ★	A. G. Dunkerley
	G-ANXB	D.H.114 Heron 1B ★	Newark Air Museum
	G-ANXC	J/5R Alpine	Alpine Group
	G-ANXR	P.31C Proctor 4 (RM221)	L. H. Oakins/Biggin Hill
	G-ANZJ	P.31C Proctor 4 (NP303) ★	A. Hillyard
	G-ANZT	Thruxton Jackaroo	D. J. Neville & P. A. Dear
	G-ANZU	D.H.82A Tiger Moth	P. A. Jackson
	G-ANZZ	D.H.82A Tiger Moth	J. I. B. Bennett & P. P. Amershi
	G-AOAA	D.H.82A Tiger Moth	R. C. P. Brookhouse
	G-AOBG	Somers-Kendall SK.1 ★	(stored)/Brabham
	G-AOBH	D.H.82A Tiger Moth (NL750)	P. Nutley/Thruxton
	G-AOBO	D.H.82A Tiger Moth	J. S. & S. V. Shaw
	G-AOBU	P.84 Jet Provost T.1 (XD693)	T. J. Manna/Cranfield
	G-AOBV	J/5P Autocar	P. E. Champney (stored)
	G-AOBX	D.H.82A Tiger Moth	David Ross Flying Group
	G-AOCP	Auster 5 ★	C. J. Baker (stored)
	G-AOCR	Auster 5D (NJ673)	G. J. McDill
	G-AOCU	Auster 5	S. J. Ball/Leicester
	G-AODA	Westland S-55 Srs 3 ★	IHM/Weston-s-Mare
	G-AODT	D.H.82A Tiger Moth (R5250)	R. A. Harrowven
	G-AOEH	Aeronca 7AC Champion	R. A & S. P. Smith
	G-AOEI	D.H.82A Tiger Moth	C.F.G. Flying Ltd/Cambridge
	G-AOEL	D.H.82A Tiger Moth ★	Museum of Flight/E. Fortune
	G-AOES	D.H.82A Tiger Moth	K. A. & A. J. Broomfield
	G-AOET	D.H.82A Tiger Moth	Venom Jet Promotions Ltd/Bournemouth
	G-AOEX	Thruxton Jackaroo	A. T. Christian

Reg.	Type	Owner or Operator	Notes
G-AOFE	D.H.C.1 Chipmunk 22A (WB702)	W. J. Quinn	
G-AOFJ	Auster 5 ★	R. Drew/Perth	
G-AOFM	J/5P Autocar	W. H. Dyozinski	
G-AOFS	J/5L Aiglet Trainer	P. N. A. Whitehead	
G-AOGA	M.75 Aries ★	Irish Aviation Museum *(stored)*	
G-AOGE	P.34A Proctor 3 ★	N. I. Dalziel *(stored)*/Biggin Hill	
G-AOGI	D.H.82A Tiger Moth	W. J. Taylor	
G-AOGR	D.H.82A Tiger Moth (XL714)	M. I. Edwards	
G-AOGV	J/5R Alpine	R. E. Heading	
G-AOHY	D.H.82A Tiger Moth (N6537)	Historic Aircraft Flight/Middle Wallop	
G-AOHZ	J/5P Autocar	A. D. Hodgkinson	
G-AOIL	D.H.82A Tiger Moth (XL716)	J. W. Lawless	
G-AOIM	D.H.82A Tiger Moth	D. A. Hardiman/Shobdon	
G-AOIR	Thruxton Jackaroo	L. H. Smith & I. M. Oliver	
G-AOIS	D.H.82A Tiger Moth	J. K. Ellwood	
G-AOIY	J/5G Autocar	J. B. Nicholson	
G-AOJD	V.802 Viscount ★	Jersey Airport Fire Service	
G-AOJH	D.H.83C Fox Moth	Norman Aeroplane Trust/Rendcomb	
G-AOJJ	D.H.82A Tiger Moth (DF128)	E. & K. M. Lay	
G-AOJK	D.H.82A Tiger Moth	D. E. Guck & P. W. Crispe	
G-AOJR	D.H.C.1 Chipmunk 22	G. J-H. Caubergs & N. Marien/Belgium	
G-AOJT	D.H.106 Comet 1 (F-BGNX) ★	De Havilland Heritage Museum *(fuselage only)*	
G-AOKH	P.40 Prentice 1	J. F. Moore/Biggin Hill	
G-AOKL	P.40 Prentice 1 (VS610)	The Shuttleworth Collection/O. Warden	
G-AOKO	P.40 Prentice 1 ★	Airport Fire Section/Coventry	
G-AOKZ	P.40 Prentice 1 (VS623) ★	Midland Air Museum/Coventry	
G-AOLK	P.40 Prentice 1	Hilton Aviation Ltd/Southend	
G-AOLU	P.40 Prentice 1 (VS356)	N. J. Butler	
G-AORB	Cessna 170B	Eaglescott Parachute Centre	
G-AORG	D.H.114 Heron 2	Duchess of Brittany (Jersey) Ltd	
G-AORW	D.H.C.1 Chipmunk 22A	P. M. Cottrell	
G-AOSF	D.H.C.1 Chipmunk 22 (WB571)	D. Mercer/Germany	
G-AOSK	D.H.C.1 Chipmunk 22 (WB726)	E. J. Leigh/Audley End	
G-AOSO	D.H.C.1 Chipmunk 22 (WD288)	Earl of Suffolk & Berkshire & J. Hoerner	
G-AOSU	D.H.C.1 Chipmunk 22 (Lycoming)	RAFGSA/Kinloss	
G-AOSY	D.H.C.1 Chipmunk 22 (WB585)	WFG Chipmunk Group	
G-AOTD	D.H.C.1 Chipmunk 22 (WB588)	S. Piech	
G-AOTF	D.H.C.1 Chipmunk 23 (Lycoming)	RAFGSA/Dishforth	
G-AOTI	D.H.114 Heron 2D ★	De Havilland Heritage Museum	
G-AOTK	D.53 Turbi	T. J. Adams	
G-AOTR	D.H.C.1 Chipmunk 22	M. R. Woodgate/Aldergrove	
G-AOTY	D.H.C.1 Chipmunk 22A (WG472)	A. A. Hodgson	
G-AOUJ	Fairey Ultra-Light ★	IHM/Weston-s-Mare	
G-AOUO	D.H.C.1 Chipmunk 22 (Lycoming)	RAFGSA/Bicester	
G-AOUP	D.H.C.1 Chipmunk 22	A. R. Harding	
G-AOUR	D.H.82A Tiger Moth ★	Ulster Folk & Transport Museum	
G-AOVF	B.175 Britannia 312F ★	Aerospace Museum/Cosford	
G-AOVS	B.175 Britannia 312F ★	Airport Fire Section/Luton	
G-AOVT	B.175 Britannia 312F ★	Duxford Aviation Soc	
G-AOVW	Auster 5	B. Marriott/Cranwell	
G-AOXL†	See G-ANUO		
G-AOXN	D.H.82A Tiger Moth	S. L. G. Darch	
G-AOZH	D.H.82A Tiger Moth (K2572)	M. H. Blois-Brooke	
G-AOZL	J/5Q Alpine	R. M. Weeks/Stapleford	
G-AOZP	D.H.C.1 Chipmunk 22	H. Darlington	
G-APAA	J/5R Alpine ★	L. A. Groves *(stored)*	
G-APAF	Auster 5 (TW511)	J. J. J. Mostyn (G-CMAL)	
G-APAH	Auster 5 (TJ324)	T. J. Goodwin	
G-APAL	D.H.82A Tiger Moth (N6847)	Avia Special Ltd	
G-APAM	D.H.82A Tiger Moth	R. P. Williams	
G-APAO	D.H.82A Tiger Moth	Fairmont Investments Ltd/Clacton	
G-APAP	D.H.82A Tiger Moth	J. Romain/Duxford	
G-APAS	D.H.106 Comet 1XB ★	Aerospace Museum/Cosford	
G-APBE	Auster 5	J. McCullough	
G-APBI	D.H.82A Tiger Moth	A. Wood	
G-APBO	D.53 Turbi	R. C. Hibberd	
G-APBW	Auster 5	N. Huxtable	
G-APCB	J/5Q Alpine	A. A. Beswick & I. A. Freeman	
G-APCC	D.H.82A Tiger Moth	L. J. Rice/Henstridge	
G-APDB	D.H.106 Comet 4 ★	Duxford Aviation Soc	

Notes	Reg.	Type	Owner or Operator
	G-APEP	V.953C Merchantman ★	Brooklands Museum of Aviation/ Weybridge
	G-APFA	D.54 Turbi	F. J. Keitch
	G-APFG	Boeing 707-436 ★	*Cabin water spray tests*/Cardington
	G-APFJ	Boeing 707-436 ★	Aerospace Museum/Cosford
	G-APFU	D.H.82A Tiger Moth	Mithril Racing Ltd/Goodwood
	G-APGL	D.H.82A Tiger Moth	K. A. Broomfield
	G-APHV	Avro 19 Srs 2 (VM360) ★	Museum of Flight/E. Fortune
	G-APIE	Tipsy Belfair B	D. Beale
	G-APIH	D.H.82A Tiger Moth	K. Stewering
	G-APIK	J/1N Alpha	G-APIK Flying Group
	G-APIM	V.806 Viscount ★	Brooklands Museum of Aviation/ Weybridge
	G-APIT	P.40 Prentice 1 (VR192) ★	WWII Aircraft Preservation Soc/Lasham
	G-APIY	P.40 Prentice 1 (VR249) ★	Newark Air Museum
	G-APIZ	D.31 Turbulent	E. J. I. Musty/White Waltham
	G-APJB	P.40 Prentice 1 (VR259)	Atlantic Air Transport Ltd/Coventry
	G-APJJ	Fairey Ultra-light ★	Midland Aircraft Preservation Soc
	G-APJO	D.H.82A Tiger Moth	D. R. & M. Wood
	G-APJZ	J/1N Alpha	P. G. Lipman
	G-APKH	D.H.85 Leopard Moth	A. R. Tarleton (G-ACGS)
	G-APKM	J/1N Alpha	D. E. A. Huggins *(stored)*
	G-APKN	J/1N Alpha	P. R. Hodson Ltd
	G-APKY	Hiller UH-12B	D. A. George *(stored)*
	G-APLG	J/5L Aiglet Trainer ★	Solway Aviation Soc
	G-APLO	D.H.C.1 Chipmunk 22A (WD379)	Lindholme Aircraft Ltd/Jersey
	G-APLU	D.H.82A Tiger Moth	R. A. Bishop & M. E. Vaisey
	G-APMB	D.H.106 Comet 4B ★	Gatwick Handling Ltd *(ground trainer)*
	G-APMH	J/1U Workmaster	J. L. Thorogood
	G-APMX	D.H.82A Tiger Moth	M. A. Boughton
	G-APMY	PA-23 Apache 160 ★	South Yorkshire Aviation Museum
	G-APNJ	Cessna 310 ★	Chelsea College/Shoreham
	G-APNS	Garland-Bianchi Linnet	P. M. Busaidy
	G-APNT	Currie Wot	B. J. Dunford
	G-APNZ	D.31 Turbulent	J. Knight
	G-APOI	Saro Skeeter Srs 8	B. Chamberlain
	G-APPA	D.H.C.1 Chipmunk 22	D. M. Squires
	G-APPL	P.40 Prentice 1	S. J. Saggers/Biggin Hill
	G-APPM	D.H.C.1 Chipmunk 22 (WB711)	Freston Aviation Ltd
	G-APPN	D.H.82A Tiger Moth	E. C. Waite-Roberts
	G-APRF	Auster 5	W. B. Bateson/Blackpool
	G-APRJ	Avro 694 Lincoln B.2 ★	D. Copley/Sandtoft
	G-APRL	AW.650 Argosy 101 ★	Midland Air Museum/Coventry
	G-APRR	Super Aero 45	R. H. Jowett
	G-APRS	SA Twin Pioneer Srs 3	Atlantic Air Transport Ltd (G-BCWF)/ Coventry
	G-APRT	Taylor JT.1 Monoplane	D. A. Slater
	G-APSA	Douglas DC-6A	Atlantic Air Transport Ltd/Coventry
	G-APSO	D.H.104 Dove 5 ★	Cormack (Aircraft Services) Ltd/Cumbernauld
	G-APSR	J/1U Workmaster	D. & K. Aero Services Ltd/Shobdon
	G-APTP	PA-22 Tri-Pacer 150 (tailwheel)	Contest (Ralph & Susan Chesters) Ltd
	G-APTR	J/1N Alpha	C. J. & D. J. Baker
	G-APTU	Auster 5	G-APTU Flying Group
	G-APTW	W.B.1 Widgeon ★	N.E. Aircraft Museum/Usworth
	G-APTY	Beech G.35 Bonanza	G. E. Brennand
	G-APTZ	D.31 Turbulent	The Tiger Club (1990) Ltd/Headcorn
	G-APUD	Bensen B.7M (modified) ★	Manchester Museum of Science & Industry
	G-APUE	L.40 Meta Sokol	S. E. & M. J. Aherne
	G-APUP	Sopwith Pup (replica) (N5182) ★	RAF Museum/Hendon
	G-APUR	PA-22 Tri-Pacer 160	L. F. Miller
	G-APUW	J/5V-160 Autocar	E. A. J. Hibbard
	G-APUY	D.31 Turbulent	C. Jones/Barton
	G-APUZ	PA-24 Comanche 250	Tatenhill Aviation
	G-APVF	Putzer Elster B (97+04)	A. & E. A. Wiseman
	G-APVG	J/5L Aiglet Trainer	R. Farrer/Cranfield
	G-APVN	D.31 Turbulent	R. Sherwin/Shoreham
	G-APVS	Cessna 170B	N. Simpson *Stormin' Norman*
	G-APVU	L.40 Meta Sokol	S. E. & M. J. Aherne
	G-APVZ	D.31 Turbulent	I. D. Daniels
	G-APWA	HPR-7 Herald 101 ★	Museum of Berkshire Aviation/Woodley
	G-APWJ	HPR-7 Herald 201 ★	Duxford Aviation Soc

Reg.	Type	Owner or Operator	Notes
G-APWN	WS-55 Whirlwind 3 ★	Midland Air Museum/Coventry	
G-APWY	Piaggio P.166 ★	Science Museum/Wroughton	
G-APXJ	PA-24 Comanche 250	T. Wildsmith/Netherthorpe	
G-APXR	PA-22 Tri-Pacer 160	A. Troughton	
G-APXT	PA-22 Tri-Pacer 150 (modified)	J. W. & I. Daniels	
G-APXU	PA-22 Tri-Pacer 125 (modified)	The Scottish Aero Club Ltd/Perth	
G-APXW	EP.9 Prospector (XM819) ★	Museum of Army Flying/Middle Wallop	
G-APXX	D.H.A.3 Drover 2 (VH-FDT) ★	WWII Aircraft Preservation Soc/Lasham	
G-APXY	Cessna 150	Merlin Flying Club Ltd/Hucknall	
G-APYB	Tipsy T.66 Nipper 3	B. O. Smith	
G-APYD	D.H.106 Comet 4B ★	Science Museum/Wroughton	
G-APYG	D.H.C.1 Chipmunk 22	E. J. I. Musty & P. A. Colman	
G-APYI	PA-22 Tri-Pacer 135	B. T. & J. Cullen	
G-APYN	PA-22 Tri-Pacer 160	S. J. Raw	
G-APYT	Champion 7FC Tri-Traveller	B. J. Anning	
G-APZJ	PA-18 Super Cub 150	Southern Sailplanes Ltd/Membury	
G-APZL	PA-22 Tri-Pacer 160	B. Robins	
G-APZR	Cessna 150 ★	Engine test-bed/Biggin Hill	
G-APZX	PA-22 Tri-Pacer 150	Applied Signs Ltd	
G-ARAD	Luton LA-5A Major	D. J. Bone & P. L. Jobes	
G-ARAI	PA-22 Tri-Pacer 160	J. Mann	
G-ARAM	PA-18 Super Cub 150	Fairmont Investments Ltd/Clacton	
G-ARAN	PA-18 Super Cub 150	A. P. Docherty/Redhill	
G-ARAO	PA-18 Super Cub 95 (607327)	R. G. Manton	
G-ARAS	Champion 7FC Tri-Traveller	Alpha Sierra Flying Group	
G-ARAT	Cessna 180C	C. Buck	
G-ARAW	Cessna 182C Skylane	Ximango UK/Rufforth	
G-ARAX	PA-22 Tri-Pacer 150	J. J. Bywater	
G-ARAZ	D.H.82A Tiger Moth	D. A. Porter	
G-ARBE	D.H.104 Dove 8	M. Whale & M. W. A. Lunn/Old Sarum	
G-ARBG	Tipsy T.66 Nipper 2	J. Horovitz & J. McLeod	
G-ARBM	J/1B Aiglet	A. D. Hodgkinson	
G-ARBO	PA-24 Comanche 250	Arrow Aviation Services Ltd	
G-ARBP	Tipsy T.66 Nipper 2	F. W. Kirk	
G-ARBS	PA-22 Tri-Pacer 160 (tailwheel)	S. D. Rowell	
G-ARBV	PA-22 Tri-Pacer 160	Oaksey Pacers	
G-ARBZ	D.31 Turbulent	G. Richards & R. Bishop	
G-ARCC	PA-22 Tri-Pacer 150	Popham Flying Group/Popham	
G-ARCF	PA-22 Tri-Pacer 150	M. J. Speakman	
G-ARCI	Cessna 310D ★	(stored)/Blackpool	
G-ARCS	Auster D6/180	E. A. Matty/Shobdon	
G-ARCT	PA-18 Super Cub 95	C. F. O'Neill	
G-ARCV	Cessna 175A	R. Francis & C. Campbell	
G-ARCW	PA-23 Apache 160	F. W. Ellis	
G-ARCX	A.W. Meteor 14 ★	Museum of Flight/E. Fortune	
G-ARDB	PA-24 Comanche 250	P. Crook	
G-ARDD	CP.301C1 Emeraude	G. E. Livings/Halton	
G-ARDE	D.H.104 Dove 6	T. E. Evans	
G-ARDJ	Auster D.6/180	RN Aviation (Leicester Airport) Ltd	
G-ARDO	Jodel D.112	W. R. Prescott	
G-ARDP	PA-22 Tri-Pacer 150	G. M. Jones	
G-ARDS	PA-22 Caribbean 150	A. C. Donaldson & C. I. Lavery	
G-ARDT	PA-22 Tri-Pacer 160	M. Henderson	
G-ARDV	PA-22 Tri-Pacer 160	R. W. Christie	
G-ARDY	Tipsy T.66 Nipper 2	D. Best	
G-ARDZ	Jodel D.140A	M. J. Wright	
G-AREA	D.H.104 Dove 8 ★	De Havilland Heritage Museum	
G-AREF	PA-23 Aztec 250 ★	Southall College of Technology	
G-AREH	D.H.82A Tiger Moth	N. K. Geddes	
G-AREI	Auster 3 (MT438)	P. J. Stock	
G-AREL	PA-22 Caribbean 150	H. H. Cousins/Fenland	
G-AREO	PA-18 Super Cub 150	Crown Service Gliding Club Ltd	
G-ARET	PA-22 Tri-Pacer 160	I. S. Runnalls	
G-AREV	PA-22 Tri-Pacer 160	D. J. Ash	
G-AREX	Aeronca 15AC Sedan	R. J. Middleton-Turnbull & P. Lowndes	
G-AREZ	D.31 Turbulent	J. St. Clair-Quentin/Shobdon	
G-ARFB	PA-22 Caribbean 150	R. Burgun	
G-ARFD	PA-22 Tri-Pacer 160	J. R. Dunnett	
G-ARFG	Cessna 175A Skylark	Foxtrot Golf Group	
G-ARFH	PA-24 Comanche 250	A. B. W. Taylor	
G-ARFI	Cessna 150A	J. H. Fisher	
G-ARFL	Cessna 175B Skylark	D. J. Mason	

Notes	Reg.	Type	Owner or Operator
	G-ARFO	Cessna 150A	Breakthrough Aviation Ltd
	G-ARFT	Jodel DR. 1050	R. Shaw
	G-ARFV	Tipsy T.66 Nipper 2	C. J. Pidler
	G-ARGB	Auster 6A ★	C. J. Baker (stored)
	G-ARGG	D.H.C.1 Chipmunk 22 (WD305)	B. Hook
	G-ARGO	PA-22 Colt 108	M. J. Speakman
	G-ARGV	PA-18 Super Cub 180	Wolds Gliding Club Ltd
	G-ARGY	PA-22 Tri-Pacer 160	G. K. Hare (G-JEST)
	G-ARGZ	D.31 Turbulent	The Tiger Club (1990) Ltd/Headcorn
	G-ARHB	Forney F-1A Aircoupe	A. V. Rash & D. R. Wickes
	G-ARHC	Forney F-1A Aircoupe	A. P. Gardner/Elstree
	G-ARHI	PA-24 Comanche 180	D. D. Smith
	G-ARHL	PA-23 Aztec 250	C. J. Freeman/Headcorn
	G-ARHM	Auster 6A	D. F. Hodgkinson
	G-ARHN	PA-22 Caribbean 150	J. R. Lawrence
	G-ARHP	PA-22 Tri-Pacer 160	R. N. Morgan
	G-ARHR	PA-22 Caribbean 150	A. R. Wyatt
	G-ARHT	PA-22 Caribbean 150 ★	Moston Technical College
	G-ARHW	D.H.104 Dove 8	Pacelink Ltd
	G-ARHX	D.H.104 Dove 8 ★	N.E. Aircraft Museum/Usworth
	G-ARHZ	D.62 Condor	T. J. Goodwin/Andrewsfield
	G-ARID	Cessna 172B	L. M. Edwards
	G-ARIF	Ord-Hume O-H.7 Minor Coupé ★	N. H. Ponsford (stored)
	G-ARIH	Auster 6A (TW591)	India Hotel Group
	G-ARIK	PA-22 Caribbean 150	C. J. Berry
	G-ARIL	PA-22 Caribbean 150	T. I. Carlin
	G-ARIM	D.31 Turbulent	R. M. White
	G-ARJB	D.H.104 Dove 8	M. Whale & M. W. A. Lunn
	G-ARJE	PA-22 Colt 108	C. I. Fray
	G-ARJF	PA-22 Colt 108	A. M. Noble
	G-ARJH	PA-22 Colt 108	A. Vine
	G-ARJR	PA-23 Apache 160G ★	Instructional airframe/Kidlington
	G-ARJS	PA-23 Apache 160G	Bencray Ltd/Blackpool
	G-ARJT	PA-23 Apache 160G	J. A. Cole
	G-ARJU	PA-23 Apache 160G	G. R. Manley
	G-ARJV	PA-23 Apache 160G	Metham Aviation Ltd/Blackbushe
	G-ARJW	PA-23 Apache 160G	(stored)/Bristol
	G-ARKG	J/5G Autocar	C. M. Milborrow
	G-ARKJ	Beech N35 Bonanza	P. A. Brook
	G-ARKK	PA-22 Colt 108	Rochford Hundred Flying Group/ Southend
	G-ARKM	PA-22 Colt 108	D. Dytch & J. Moffat
	G-ARKN	PA-22 Colt 108	T. D. Fuller
	G-ARKP	PA-22 Colt 108	J. P. A. Freeman/Headcorn
	G-ARKR	PA-22 Colt 108	B. J. M. Montegut
	G-ARKS	PA-22 Colt 108	R. A. Nesbitt-Dufort
	G-ARLG	Auster D.4/108	Auster D4 Group
	G-ARLK	PA-24 Comanche 250	Gibad Aviation Ltd
	G-ARLO	A.61 Terrier 1 ★	(stored)
	G-ARLP	A.61 Terrier 1	Gemini Flying Group
	G-ARLR	A.61 Terrier 2	M. Palfreman
	G-ARLU	Cessna 172B Skyhawk ★	Instructional airframe/Irish AC
	G-ARLW	Cessna 172B Skyhawk ★	(spares source)/Barton
	G-ARLX	Jodel D.140B	Shipping & Airlines Ltd/Biggin Hill
	G-ARLZ	D.31A Turbulent	Little Bear Ltd
	G-ARMA	PA-23 Apache 160G	C. J. Hopewell
	G-ARMB	D.H.C.1 Chipmunk 22A (WB660)	G. E. J. Spooner
	G-ARMC	D.H.C.1 Chipmunk 22A (WB703)	John Henderson Children's Trust
	G-ARMD	D.H.C.1 Chipmunk 22A (WD297)	D. M. Squires/Wellesbourne
	G-ARMF	D.H.C.1 Chipmunk 22A (WZ868)	D. M. Squires
	G-ARMG	D.H.C.1 Chipmunk 22A	MG Group/Bidford
	G-ARML	Cessna 175B Skylark	R. W. Boote
	G-ARMN	Cessna 175B Skylark	G. A. Nash
	G-ARMO	Cessna 172B Skyhawk	G. M. Jones
	G-ARMR	Cessna 172B Skyhawk	Sunsaver Ltd/Barton
	G-ARMZ	D.31 Turbulent	J. Mickleburgh & D. Clark
	G-ARNB	J/5G Autocar	R. F. Tolhurst
	G-ARND	PA-22 Colt 108	E. J. Clarke
	G-ARNE	PA-22 Colt 108	T. D. L. Bowden/Shipdham
	G-ARNG	PA-22 Colt 108	F. B. Rothera
	G-ARNH	PA-22 Colt 108 ★	Fenland Aircraft Preservation Soc
	G-ARNI	PA-22 Colt 108	B. A. Drury
	G-ARNJ	PA-22 Colt 108	R. A. Keech

Reg.	Type	Owner or Operator	Notes
G-ARNK	PA-22 Colt 108 (tailwheel)	N. G. & A-L. N. M. McDonald	
G-ARNL	PA-22 Colt 108	J. A. Dodsworth/White Waltham	
G-ARNO	A.61 Terrier 1 ★	–/Sywell	
G-ARNP	A.109 Airedale	S. W. & M. Isbister	
G-ARNY	Jodel D.117	D. P. Jenkins	
G-ARNZ	D.31 Turbulent	The Tiger Club (1990) Ltd/Headcorn	
G-AROA	Cessna 172B Skyhawk	D. E. Partridge	
G-AROC	Cessna 175B	A. J. Symes (G-OTOW)	
G-AROJ	A.109 Airedale ★	D. J. Shaw *(stored)*	
G-ARON	PA-22 Colt 108	R. W. Curtis	
G-AROO	Forney F-1A Aircoupe	W. J. McMeekan/Newtownards	
G-AROW	Jodel D.140B	Cubair Ltd/Redhill	
G-AROY	Boeing Stearman A.75N.1	W. A. Jordan	
G-ARPH	H.S.121 Trident 1C ★	Aerospace Museum/Cosford	
G-ARPK	H.S.121 Trident 1C ★	Manchester Airport Authority	
G-ARPO	H.S.121 Trident 1C ★	CAA Fire School/Teesside	
G-ARPP	H.S.121 Trident 1C ★	BAA Airport Fire Service/Glasgow	
G-ARPZ	H.S.121 Trident 1C ★	RFD Ltd/Dunsfold	
G-ARRD	Jodel DR.1050	C. M. Fitton	
G-ARRE	Jodel DR.1050	Romeo Echo Group/Barton	
G-ARRI	Cessna 175B	R. D. Fowden	
G-ARRL	J/1N Alpha	G. N. Smith & C. Webb	
G-ARRM	Beagle B.206-X ★	Bristol Aero Collection *(stored)*	
G-ARRO	A.109 Airedale	M. & S. W. Isbister	
G-ARRS	CP.301A Emeraude	Arssy Aviation	
G-ARRT	Wallis WA-116-1	K. H. Wallis	
G-ARRU	D.31 Turbulent	N. A. Morgan & J. Paget	
G-ARRX	Auster 6A (VF512)	J. E. D. Mackie	
G-ARRY	Jodel D.140B	Fictionview Ltd	
G-ARRZ	D.31 Turbulent	C. I. Jefferson	
G-ARSG	Roe Triplane Type IV (replica)	The Shuttleworth Collection/O. Warden	
G-ARSL	A.61 Terrier 1	D. J. Colclough	
G-ARSU	PA-22 Colt 108	D. P. Owen	
G-ARSW	PA-22 Colt 108	A. Barrow	
G-ARTH	PA-12 Super Cruiser	R. I. Souch & B. J. Dunford	
G-ARTJ	Bensen B.8M ★	Museum of Flight/E. Fortune	
G-ARTL	D.H.82A Tiger Moth (T7281)	F. G. Clacherty	
G-ARTT	MS.880B Rallye Club	R. N. Scott	
G-ARTZ	McCandless M.4 gyroplane	W. R. Partridge	
G-ARUG	J/5G Autocar	D. P. H. Hulme/Biggin Hill	
G-ARUH	Jodel DR.1050	PFA Group/Denham	
G-ARUI	A.61 Terrier	T. W. J. Dann	
G-ARUL	LeVier Cosmic Wind	P. G. Kynsey/Headcorn	
G-ARUV	CP.301A Emeraude	P. O'Fee	
G-ARUY	J/1N Alpha	D. Burnham	
G-ARUZ	Cessna 175C	Cardiff Skylark Group	
G-ARVM	V.1101 VC10 ★	Aerospace Museum/Cosford	
G-ARVO	PA-18 Super Cub 95	Northamptonshire School of Flying Ltd/ Sywell	
G-ARVT	PA-28 Cherokee 160	Red Rose Aviation Ltd/Liverpool	
G-ARVU	PA-28 Cherokee 160	Barton Mudwing Ltd	
G-ARVV	PA-28 Cherokee 160	G. E. Hopkins/Shobdon	
G-ARVZ	D.62B Condor	R. N. Wilkinson	
G-ARWB	D.H.C.1 Chipmunk 22 (WK611)	Thruxton Chipmunk Flying Club	
G-ARWH	Cessna 172C ★	*(stored)*	
G-ARWO	Cessna 172C	J. J. Sheeran	
G-ARWR	Cessna 172C	Devanha Flying Group/Insch	
G-ARWS	Cessna 175C	B. A. I. Torrington	
G-ARXB	A.109 Airedale	S. W. & M. Isbister	
G-ARXD	A.109 Airedale	D. Howden	
G-ARXG	PA-24 Comanche 250	Fairoaks Comanche	
G-ARXH	Bell 47G	A. B. Searle	
G-ARXP	Luton LA-4 Minor	E. Evans	
G-ARXT	Jodel DR.1050	CJM Flying Group	
G-ARXU	Auster AOP.6A (VF526)	E. C. Tait & M. Pocock	
G-ARXW	M.S.885 Super Rallye	A. F. Danton & A. Kennedy	
G-ARYB	H.S.125 Srs 1 ★	Midland Air Museum/Coventry	
G-ARYC	H.S.125 Srs 1 ★	De Havilland Heritage Museum	
G-ARYD	Auster AOP.6 (WJ358) ★	Museum of Army Flying/Middle Wallop	
G-ARYF	PA-23 Aztec 250B	I. J. T. Branson/Biggin Hill	
G-ARYH	PA-22 Tri-Pacer 160	C. Watt	
G-ARYI	Cessna 172C	J. Rhodes	
G-ARYK	Cessna 172C	G. W. Goodban	

Notes	Reg.	Type	Owner or Operator
	G-ARYR	PA-28 Cherokee 180	G-ARYR Flying Group
	G-ARYS	Cessna 172C	D. J. Squires & ptnrs
	G-ARYV	PA-24 Comanche 250	A. G. Wintle & D. C. Hanss
	G-ARZB	Wallis WA-116 Srs 1	K. H. Wallis
	G-ARZE	Cessna 172C ★	Parachute jump trainer/Cockerham
	G-ARZM	D.31 Turbulent ★	The Tiger Club (1990) Ltd/Headcorn
	G-ARZN	Beech N35 Bonanza	D. W. Mickleburgh/Leicester
	G-ARZS	A.109 Airedale	M. & S. W. Isbister
	G-ARZW	Currie Wot	B. R. Pearson/Eaglescott
	G-ASAA	Luton LA-4 Minor	M. J. Aubrey (stored)/Netherthorpe
	G-ASAI	A.109 Airedale	K. R. Howden
	G-ASAJ	A.61 Terrier 2 (WE569)	G-ASAJ Flying Group
	G-ASAK	A.61 Terrier 2	J. H. Oakins/Biggin Hill
	G-ASAL	SA Bulldog Srs 120/124	Pioneer Flying Co. Ltd/Prestwick
	G-ASAM	D.31 Turbulent ★	The Tiger Club (1990) Ltd/Headcorn
	G-ASAT	M.S.880B Rallye Club	M. Cutovic
	G-ASAU	M.S.880B Rallye Club	D. M. Dawson
	G-ASAX	A.61 Terrier 2	P. G. Morris
	G-ASAZ	Hiller UH-12E4 (XS165)	Hields Aviation
	G-ASBA	Phoenix Currie Wot	C. C. & J. M. Lovell
	G-ASBB	Beech 23 Musketeer	D. G. Sheppard
	G-ASBH	A.109 Airedale	D. T. Smollett
	G-ASBY	A.109 Airedale	R. K. Wilson
	G-ASCC	Beagle E3 Mk 11 (XP254)	K. R. Harris
	G-ASCD	A.61 Terrier 2 (TJ704) ★	Yorkshire Air Museum/Elvington
	G-ASCM	Isaacs Fury II (K2050)	E. C. & P. King
	G-ASCU	PA-18A Super Cub 150	Farm Aviation Services Ltd
	G-ASCZ	CP.301A Emeraude	I. Denham-Brown
	G-ASDF	Edwards Gyrocopter ★	B. King
	G-ASDK	A.61 Terrier 2	S. C. M. Jackson (G-ARLM)
	G-ASDL	A.61 Terrier 2	C. E. Mason (G-ARLN)
	G-ASDY	Wallis WA-116/F	K. H. Wallis
	G-ASEA	Luton LA-4A Minor	J. Bradstock
	G-ASEB	Luton LA-4A Minor	S. R. P. Harper
	G-ASEG	A.61 Terrier (VF548)	M. J. Kirk
	G-ASEO	PA-24 Comanche 250	M. Scott
	G-ASEP	PA-23 Apache 235	Arrowstate Ltd/Denham
	G-ASEU	D.62A Condor	W. M. Grant
	G-ASFA	Cessna 172D	D. Halfpenny
	G-ASFK	J/5G Autocar	T. D. G. Lancaster
	G-ASFL	PA-28 Cherokee 180	J. Simpson & D. Kennedy
	G-ASFR	Bo 208A1 Junior	S. T. Dauncey
	G-ASFX	D.31 Turbulent	E. F. Clapham & W. B. S. Dobie
	G-ASGC	V.1151 Super VC10 ★	Duxford Aviation Soc
	G-ASHD	Brantly B-2A ★	IHM/Weston-s-Mare
	G-ASHH	PA-23 Aztec 250	C. Fordham & L. Barr
	G-ASHS	SNCAN Stampe SV-4C	M & B Tools Ltd
	G-ASHT	D.31 Turbulent	C. W. N. Huke
	G-ASHU	PA-15 Vagabond	G. J. Romanes & T. J. Ventham/ Henstridge
	G-ASHV	PA-23 Aztec 250B	R. J. Ashley & G. O'Gorman
	G-ASHX	PA-28 Cherokee 180	Powertheme Ltd/Barton
	G-ASIB	Cessna F.172D	G-ASIB Flying Group
	G-ASII	PA-28 Cherokee 180	T. R. Hart & R. W. S. Matthews
	G-ASIJ	PA-28 Cherokee 180	G-ASIJ Group
	G-ASIL	PA-28 Cherokee 180	J. Dickenson & C. D. Powell
	G-ASIT	Cessna 180	A. & P. A. Wood
	G-ASIY	PA-25 Pawnee 235	RAFGSA/Bicester
	G-ASJL	Beech H.35 Bonanza	D. G. Lewendon
	G-ASJM	PA-30 Twin Comanche 160 ★	Via Nova Ltd (stored)
	G-ASJO	Beech B.23 Musketeer	R. M. Wilson/Sandown
	G-ASJV	V.S.361 Spitfire IX (MH434)	Merlin Aviation Ltd/Duxford
	G-ASJY	GY-80 Horizon 160	P. D. Bradbury & S. M. Derbyshire
	G-ASJZ	Jodel D.117A	W. J. Siertsema
	G-ASKC	D.H.98 Mosquito 35 (TA719) ★	Skyfame Collection/Duxford
	G-ASKK	HPR-7 Herald 211 ★	Norwich Aviation Museum
	G-ASKL	Jodel 150	J. M. Graty
	G-ASKP	D.H.82A Tiger Moth	Tiger Club (1990) Ltd/Headcorn
	G-ASKT	PA-28 Cherokee 180	A. A. Mattacks
	G-ASKV	PA-25 Pawnee 235	Southdown Gliding Club Ltd/Parham Park
	G-ASLH	Cessna 182F	J. M. Powell & J. A. Horton
	G-ASLK	PA-25 Pawnee 235	Bristol Gliding Club (Pty) Ltd/Nympsfield

Reg.	Type	Owner or Operator	Notes
G-ASLL	Cessna 336 ★	(stored)/Bournemouth	
G-ASLR	Agusta-Bell 47J-2	N. M. G. Pearson	
G-ASLV	PA-28 Cherokee 235	Sackville Flying Group/Riseley	
G-ASLX	CP.301A Emeraude	D. Wallace	
G-ASMA	PA-30 Twin Comanche 160 C/R	Mike Alpha Group	
G-ASME	Bensen B.8M	R. M. Harris & R. T. Bennett	
G-ASMF	Beech D.95A Travel Air	M. J. A. Hornblower	
G-ASMJ	Cessna F.172E	A. J. G. Crawshaw	
G-ASML	Luton LA-4A Minor	West Kesteven Flyers/Fenland	
G-ASMM	D.31 Tubulent	W. J. Browning	
G-ASMO	PA-23 Apache 160G ★	Aviation Enterprises/Fairoaks	
G-ASMS	Cessna 150A	P. P. Conner/Barton	
G-ASMT	Fairtravel Linnet 2	A. F. Cashin	
G-ASMW	Cessna 150D	Aviation Business Centres Ltd	
G-ASMZ	A.61 Terrier 2 (VF516)	B. Andrews	
G-ASNB	Auster 6A (VX118)	S. Alexander	
G-ASNC	Beagle D.5/180 Husky	Peterborough & Spalding Gliding Club Ltd/Crowland	
G-ASND	PA-23 Aztec 250	J. R. Grange/Shoreham	
G-ASNI	CP.1310-C3 Super Emeraude	D. Chapman	
G-ASNK	Cessna 205	Justgold Ltd	
G-ASNN	Cessna 182F ★	Parachute jump trainer/Tilstock	
G-ASNW	Cessna F.172E	G-ASNW Group	
G-ASNY	Campbell-Bensen B.8M gyroplane ★	R. Light & T. Smith	
G-ASOC	Auster 6A	Auster 6 Group	
G-ASOH	Beech 95-B55A Baron	GMD Group	
G-ASOI	A.61 Terrier 2	N. K. & C. M. Geddes	
G-ASOK	Cessna F.172E	D. W. Disney	
G-ASOM	A.61 Terrier 2	D. Humphries (G-JETS)	
G-ASPF	Jodel D.120	T. J. Bates	
G-ASPI	Cessna F.172E	J. Henderson	
G-ASPK	PA-28 Cherokee 140	Westward Airways (Lands End) Ltd/ St Just	
G-ASPP	Bristol Boxkite (replica)	The Shuttleworth Collection/O. Warden	
G-ASPS	Piper J-3C-90 Cub	A. J. Chalkley/Blackbushe	
G-ASPU	D.31 Turbulent	M. W. Bodger	
G-ASPV	D.H.82A Tiger Moth	B. S. Charters	
G-ASRB	D.62B Condor	T. J. McRae & H. C. Palmer/Shoreham	
G-ASRC	D.62C Condor	C. R. Isbell	
G-ASRI	PA-23 Aztec 250B ★	Graham Collins Associates Ltd	
G-ASRK	A.109 Airedale	Bio Pathica Ltd/Lydd	
G-ASRO	PA-30 Twin Comanche 160	D. W. Blake	
G-ASRR	Cessna 182G	P. Ragg/Austria	
G-ASRT	Jodel 150	P. Turton	
G-ASRW	PA-28 Cherokee 180	Alliance Aerolink Ltd	
G-ASSF	Cessna 182G Skylane	B. W. Wells	
G-ASSM	H.S.125 Srs 1/522 ★	Science Museum/S. Kensington	
G-ASSP	PA-30 Twin Comanche 160	P. H. Tavener	
G-ASSS	Cessna 172E	D. H. N. Squires & P. R. March/Filton	
G-ASST	Cessna 150D	F. R. H. Parker	
G-ASSU	CP.301A Emeraude	R. W. Millward (stored)/Redhill	
G-ASSV	Kensinger KF	C. I. Jefferson	
G-ASSW	PA-28 Cherokee 140	W. G. R. Wunderlich/Biggin Hill	
G-ASSY	D.31 Turbulent	D. Silsbury	
G-ASTA	D.31 Turbulent	P. A. Cooke	
G-ASTH	Mooney M.20C ★	E. L. Martin (stored)/Guernsey	
G-ASTI	Auster 6A	C. J. Harrison	
G-ASTL	Fairey Firefly I (Z2033) ★	F.A. A. Museum/Yeovilton	
G-ASTP	Hiller UH-12C ★	IHM/Weston-s-Mare	
G-ASTV	Cessna 150D (tailwheel) ★	(stored)	
G-ASUB	Mooney M.20E Super 21	S. C. Coulbeck	
G-ASUD	PA-28 Cherokee 180	S. J. Rogers & M. N. Petchey	
G-ASUE	Cessna 150D	D. Huckle	
G-ASUG	Beech E18S ★	Museum of Flight/E. Fortune	
G-ASUI	A.61 Terrier 2	K. W. Chigwell & D. R. Lee	
G-ASUP	Cessna F.172E	GASUP Air/Cardiff	
G-ASUR	Dornier Do 28A-1	Sheffair Ltd	
G-ASUS	Jurca MJ.2B Tempete	D. G. Jones/Coventry	
G-ASVG	CP.301B Emeraude	K. S. Woodard	
G-ASVM	Cessna F.172E	Golf Victor Mike Flying Group	
G-ASVN	Cessna U.206 Super Skywagon	D. & L. Johnston/USA	

Notes	Reg.	Type	Owner or Operator
	G-ASVO	HPR-7 Herald 214 (cockpit section) ★	Archive Visitor Centre/Shoreham
	G-ASVP	PA-25 Pawnee 235	Aquila Gliding Club Ltd/ Hinton-in-the-Hedges
	G-ASVZ	PA-28 Cherokee 140	J. S. Garvey
	G-ASWH	Luton LA-5A Major	J. T. Powell-Tuck
	G-ASWJ	Beagle 206 Srs 1 (8449M) ★	Brunel Technical College/Bristol
	G-ASWL	Cessna F.172F	J. A. Clegg
	G-ASWN	Bensen B.8M	D. R. Shepherd
	G-ASWW	PA-30 Twin Comanche 160	R. J. Motors
	G-ASWX	PA-28 Cherokee 180	A. F. Dadds
	G-ASXC	SIPA 901	M. K. Dartford & M. Cookson
	G-ASXD	Brantly B.2B	Lousada PLC
	G-ASXI	Tipsy T.66 Nipper 3	B. Dixon
	G-ASXJ	Luton LA-4A Minor	M. R. Sallows
	G-ASXR	Cessna 210	A. Schofield
	G-ASXS	Jodel DR.1050	R. A. Hunter
	G-ASXU	Jodel D.120A	The Jodel Group/Defford
	G-ASXX	Avro 683 Lancaster 7 (NX611) ★	Lincolnshire Aviation Heritage Centre/ E. Kirkby
	G-ASXY	Jodel D.117A	P. A. Davies & ptnrs/Cardiff
	G-ASXZ	Cessna 182G Skylane	Last Refuge Ltd
	G-ASYD	BAC One-Eleven 475 ★	Brooklands Museum of Aviation/ Weybridge
	G-ASYG	A.61 Terrier 2	G. Rea
	G-ASYJ	Beech D.95A Travel Air	Crosby Aviation (Jersey) Ltd
	G-ASYP	Cessna 150E	Henlow Flying Group
	G-ASYZ	Victa Airtourer 100	N. C. Grayson
	G-ASZB	Cessna 150E	R. J. Scott
	G-ASZD	Bo 208A2 Junior	M. J. Ayers
	G-ASZE	A.61 Terrier 2	P. J. Moore
	G-ASZR	Fairtravel Linnet 2	K. H. Bunt & R. Palmer
	G-ASZS	GY.80 Horizon 160	ZS Group
	G-ASZU	Cessna 150E	T. H. Milburn
	G-ASZV	Tipsy T.66 Nipper 2	J. M. Gough
	G-ASZX	A.61 Terrier 1	R. B. Webber
	G-ATAF	Cessna F.172F	P. J. Thirtle
	G-ATAG	Jodel DR. 1050	T. M. Dawes-Gamble
	G-ATAS	PA-28 Cherokee 180	ATAS Group
	G-ATAT	Cessna 150E	The Derek Pointon Group (stored)
	G-ATAU	D.62B Condor	M. A. Peare/Redhill
	G-ATAV	D.62C Condor	R. W. H. Watson
	G-ATBG	Nord 1002 (NJ+C11)	T. W. Harris/Little Snoring
	G-ATBH	Aero 145	P. D. Aberbach
	G-ATBI	Beech A.23 Musketeer	Three Musketeers Flying Group
	G-ATBJ	Sikorsky S-61N	CHC Scotia Ltd
	G-ATBL	D.H.60G Moth	J. M. Greenland
	G-ATBP	Fournier RF-3	D. McNicholl
	G-ATBS	D.31 Turbulent	D. R. Keene & J. A. Lear
	G-ATBU	A.61 Terrier 2	K9 Flying Group
	G-ATBW	Tipsy T.66 Nipper 2	Stapleford Nipper Group
	G-ATBX	PA-20 Pacer 135	G. D. & P. M. Thomson
	G-ATBZ	W.S.58 Wessex 60 ★	IHM/Weston-s-Mare
	G-ATCC	A.109 Airedale	J. R. Bowden
	G-ATCD	Beagle D.5/180 Husky	T. C. O'Gorman
	G-ATCE	Cessna U.206	British Parachute Schools/Langar
	G-ATCJ	Luton LA-4A Minor	P. R. Diffey
	G-ATCL	Victa Airtourer 100	A. D. Goodall/Cardiff
	G-ATCR	Cessna 310 ★	ITD Aviation Ltd/Denham
	G-ATCU	Cessna 337	University of Cambridge
	G-ATCX	Cessna 182H	K. J. Fisher/Bodmin
	G-ATDA	PA-28 Cherokee 160	Portway Aviation
	G-ATDB	Nord 1101 Noralpha	J. W. Hardie
	G-ATDN	A.61 Terrier 2 (TW641)	S. J. Saggers/Biggin Hill
	G-ATDO	Bo 208C1 Junior	P. Thompson/Crosland Moor
	G-ATEF	Cessna 150E	Swans Aviation/Blackbushe
	G-ATEM	PA-28 Cherokee 180	Chiltern Valley Aviation Ltd
	G-ATEP	EAA Biplane ★	E. L. Martin (stored)/Guernsey
	G-ATES	PA-32 Cherokee Six 260 ★	Parachute jump trainer/Stirling
	G-ATEV	Jodel DR. 1050	J. C. Carter & J. L. Altrip
	G-ATEW	PA-30 Twin Comanche 160	Air Northumbria (Woolsington) Ltd
	G-ATEX	Victa Airtourer 100	Medway Victa Group

Reg.	Type	Owner or Operator	Notes
G-ATEZ	PA-28 Cherokee 140	EFI Aviation Ltd	
G-ATFD	Jodel DR. 1050	V. Usher	
G-ATFF	PA-23 Aztec 250C	Neatspin Ltd/Tatenhill	
G-ATFG	Brantly B.2B ★	Museum of Flight/E. Fortune	
G-ATFK	PA-30 Twin Comanche 160	D. J. Crinnon/White Waltham	
G-ATFM	Sikorsky S-61N	Veritair Ltd	
G-ATFR	PA-25 Pawnee 150	Borders (Milfield) Gliding Club Ltd	
G-ATFV	Agusta-Bell 47J-2A ★	Caernarfon Air World	
G-ATFW	Luton LA-4A Minor	P. A. Rose	
G-ATFY	Cessna F.172G	H. Cowan	
G-ATGE	Jodel DR.1050	L. S. & K. L. Johnson	
G-ATGN	Thorn Coal Gas balloon	British Balloon Museum/Newbury	
G-ATGO	Cessna F.172G	JP Aviation Ltd	
G-ATGP	Jodel DR.1050	Madley Flying Group/Shobdon	
G-ATGY	GY.80 Horizon	P. W. Gibberson/Birmingham	
G-ATGZ	Griffiths GH-4 Gyroplane	R. W. J. Cripps	
G-ATHA	PA-23 Apache 235 ★	Brunel Technical College/Bristol	
G-ATHD	D.H.C.1 Chipmunk 22 (WP971)	Spartan Flying Group Ltd/Denham	
G-ATHF	Cessna 150F ★	Lincolnshire Aviation Heritage Centre/ E. Kirkby	
G-ATHK	Aeronca 7AC Champion	T. P. McDonald & ptnrs/Liverpool	
G-ATHM	Wallis WA-116 Srs 1	Wallis Autogyros Ltd	
G-ATHN	Nord 1101 Noralpha ★	E. L. Martin *(stored)*/Guernsey	
G-ATHR	PA-28 Cherokee 180	Britannia Airways Ltd/Luton	
G-ATHT	Victa Airtourer 115	D. A. Breeze	
G-ATHU	A.61 Terrier 1	J. A. L. Irwin	
G-ATHV	Cessna 150F	Cessna Hotel Victor Group	
G-ATIA	PA-24 Comanche 260	L. A. Brown	
G-ATIC	Jodel DR.1050	R. J. Major	
G-ATIE	Cessna 150F ★	*Parachute jump trainer*/Chetwynd	
G-ATIN	Jodel D.117	G. G. Simpson	
G-ATIR	AIA Stampe SV-4C	N. M. Bloom	
G-ATIS	PA-28 Cherokee 160	R. M. Jenner & J. H. Peploe	
G-ATIZ	Jodel D.117	D. K. Shipton/Leicester	
G-ATJA	Jodel DR.1050	Bicester Flying Group	
G-ATJC	Victa Airtourer 100	Aviation West Ltd/Cumbernauld	
G-ATJG	PA-28 Cherokee 140	C. A. McGee/North Weald	
G-ATJL	PA-24 Comanche 260	M. J. Berry & T. R. Quinn/Blackbushe	
G-ATJM	Fokker Dr.1 (replica) (152/17)	R. Lamplough/North Weald	
G-ATJN	Jodel D.119	Advanced Power Systems Ltd	
G-ATJT	GY.80 Horizon 160	N. Huxtable	
G-ATJV	PA-32 Cherokee Six 260	Wingglider Ltd/Hibaldstow	
G-ATKF	Cessna 150F	J. P. A.. Freeman/Headcorn	
G-ATKH	Luton LA-4A Minor	H. E. Jenner	
G-ATKI	Piper J-3C-65 Cub	J. P. Conlan	
G-ATKT	Cessna F.172G	P. J. Megson	
G-ATKX	Jodel D.140C	A. J. White & G. A. Piper/Biggin Hill	
G-ATKZ	Tipsy T.66 Nipper 2	J. W. Macleod	
G-ATLA	Cessna 182J Skylane	J. W. & J. T. Whicher	
G-ATLB	Jodel DR.1050/M1	Le Syndicate du Petit Oiseau/Brighton	
G-ATLC	PA-23 Aztec 250C ★	Alderney Air Charter Ltd *(stored)*	
G-ATLG	Hiller UH-12B	Bristow Helicopters Ltd	
G-ATLM	Cessna F.172G	Air Fotos Aviation Ltd/Newcastle	
G-ATLP	Bensen B.8M	R. F. G. Moyle	
G-ATLT	Cessna U.206A	A. I. M. & A. J. Guest	
G-ATLV	Jodel D.120	L. S. Thorne	
G-ATMC	Cessna F.150F	G. H. Farrah & D. Cunnane	
G-ATMH	Beagle D.5/180 Husky	Dorset Gliding Club Ltd	
G-ATMJ	H.S.748 Srs 2A	Emerald Airways Ltd/Liverpool	
G-ATML	Cessna F.150F	G. I. Smith	
G-ATMM	Cessna F.150F	Skytrax Aviation Ltd	
G-ATMT	PA-30 Twin Comanche 160	Montagu-Smith & Co Ltd	
G-ATMU	PA-23 Apache 160G	P. K. Martin & R. W. Harris	
G-ATMW	PA-28 Cherokee 140	Bencray Ltd/Blackpool	
G-ATMY	Cessna 150F	A. Dobson	
G-ATNB	PA-28 Cherokee 180	G. Taylor/Woodford	
G-ATNE	Cessna F.150F	A. D. Revill	
G-ATNK	Cessna F.150F	Pegasus Aviation Ltd	
G-ATNL	Cessna F.150F	G. A. Lauf	
G-ATNV	PA-24 Comanche 260	B. S. Reynolds/Bourn	
G-ATOA	PA-23 Apache 160G	Oscar Alpha Ltd/Stapleford	
G-ATOD	Cessna F.150F	E. Watson & ptnrs/St Just	
G-ATOE	Cessna F.150F	J. A. Richardson	

Notes	Reg.	Type	Owner or Operator
	G-ATOH	D.62B Condor	Three Spires Flying Group
	G-ATOI	PA-28 Cherokee 140	R. W. Nash
	G-ATOJ	PA-28 Cherokee 140	A Flight Aviation Ltd
	G-ATOK	PA-28 Cherokee 140	ILC Flying Group
	G-ATOL	PA-28 Cherokee 140	L. J. Nation & G. Alford
	G-ATOM	PA-28 Cherokee 140	A. Flight Aviation Ltd
	G-ATON	PA-28 Cherokee 140	R. G. Walters/Shobdon
	G-ATOO	PA-28 Cherokee 140	Wayauto Ltd/Carlisle
	G-ATOP	PA-28 Cherokee 140	P. R. Coombs/Blackbushe
	G-ATOR	PA-28 Cherokee 140	Aligator Group
	G-ATOT	PA-28 Cherokee 180	Totair Ltd
	G-ATOU	Mooney M.20E Super 21	M20 Flying Group/Sherburn
	G-ATOY	PA-24 Comanche 260 ★	Museum of Flight/E. Fortune
	G-ATOZ	Bensen B.8M	N. C. White & W. Stark
	G-ATPD	H.S.125 Srs 1B	Wessex Air (Holdings) Ltd
	G-ATPN	PA-28 Cherokee 140	M. F. Hatt & ptnrs/Southend
	G-ATPT	Cessna 182J Skylane	G. B. Scholes
	G-ATPV	JB.01 Minicab	C. F. O'Neill
	G-ATRA	LET L.13 Blanik (BXV)	Blanik Syndicate/Husbands Bosworth
	G-ATRB	LET L.13 Blanik (BXW)	Avon Soaring Centre/Bickmarsh
	G-ATRG	PA-18 Super Cub 150	Lasham Gliding Soc Ltd
	G-ATRI	Bo 208C1 Junior	Interesting Aircraft Co/Wolverhampton
	G-ATRK	Cessna F.150F	Armstrong Aviation
	G-ATRL	Cessna F.150F	A. A. W. Stevens
	G-ATRM	Cessna F.150F	J. Redfearn
	G-ATRO	PA-28 Cherokee 140	J. S. Jewell & H. A. Aldous
	G-ATRR	PA-28 Cherokee 140	Marnham Investments Ltd
	G-ATRW	PA-32 Cherokee Six 260	Pringle Brandon Architects
	G-ATRX	PA-32 Cherokee Six 260	Central Aviation Ltd
	G-ATSI	Bo 208C1 Junior	G-ATSI Group
	G-ATSL	Cessna F.172G	L. McMullin
	G-ATSM	Cessna 337A	Landscape & Ground Maintenance
	G-ATSR	Beech M.35 Bonanza	D. G. Lewendon
	G-ATSX	Bo 208C1 Junior	M. H. Jeffries
	G-ATSY	Wassmer WA41 Super Baladou IV	McLean Aviation
	G-ATSZ	PA-30 Twin Comanche 160B	Sierra Zulu Aviation Ltd
	G-ATTB	Wallis WA-116-1 (XR944)	D. A. Wallis
	G-ATTD	Cessna 182J Skylane	K. M. Brennan & ptnrs
	G-ATTF	PA-28 Cherokee 140	D. H. Fear/Tatenhill
	G-ATTI	PA-28 Cherokee 140	G-ATTI Flying Group/Lulsgate
	G-ATTK	PA-28 Cherokee 140	G-ATTK Flying Group/Southend
	G-ATTM	Jodel DR.250-160	R. W. Tomkinson
	G-ATTN	Piccard balloon ★	Science Museum/S. Kensington
	G-ATTR	Bo 208C1 Junior	S. Luck
	G-ATTV	PA-28 Cherokee 140	D. B. & M. E. Meeks
	G-ATTX	PA-28 Cherokee 180	IPAC Aviation Ltd
	G-ATUB	PA-28 Cherokee 140	R. H. Partington & M. J. Porter
	G-ATUD	PA-28 Cherokee 140	J. J. Ferguson
	G-ATUF	Cessna F.150F	D. P. Williams
	G-ATUG	D.62B Condor	R. Crosby
	G-ATUH	Tipsy T.66 Nipper 1	M. D. Barnard & C. Voelger
	G-ATUI	Bo 208C1 Junior	M. J. Grundy
	G-ATUL	PA-28 Cherokee 180	Kirkland Ltd
	G-ATVF	D.H.C.1 Chipmunk 22 (Lycoming)	RAFGSA/Syerston
	G-ATVK	PA-28 Cherokee 140	J. K. Beauchamp
	G-ATVO	PA-28 Cherokee 140	G. R. Bright
	G-ATVP	F.B.5 Gunbus (2345) ★	RAF Museum/Hendon
	G-ATVS	PA-28 Cherokee 180	S. M. Patterson
	G-ATVW	D.62B Condor	J. P. Coulter & J. Chidley/Panshanger
	G-ATVX	Bo 208C1 Junior	D. & G. Aviation
	G-ATWA	Jodel DR.1050	Jodel Syndicate
	G-ATWB	Jodel D.117	Andrewsfield Whiskey Bravo Group
	G-ATWJ	Cessna F.172F	J. P. A. Freeman/Headcorn
	G-ATWR	PA-30 Twin Comanche 160B	Lubair (Transport Services) Ltd/ E. Midlands
	G-ATXA	PA-22 Tri-Pacer 150	S. Hildrop
	G-ATXD	PA-30 Twin Comanche 160B	LGH Aviation Ltd
	G-ATXJ	H.P.137 Jetstream 300 ★	Fire Service Training Airframe/Cardiff
	G-ATXM	PA-28 Cherokee 180	G-ATXM Flying Group
	G-ATXN	Mitchell-Proctor Kittiwake 1	R. G. Day/Biggin Hill
	G-ATXO	SIPA 903	S. A. & D. C. Whitehead

Reg.	Type	Owner or Operator	Notes
G-ATXZ	Bolkow Bo 208C1 Junior	G-ATXZ Group	
G-ATYM	Cessna F.150G	J. F. Perry & Co	
G-ATYN	Cessna F.150G	J. S. Grant	
G-ATYS	PA-28 Cherokee 180	G-ATYS Flying Group	
G-ATZG	AFB2 gas balloon	S. Cameron	
G-ATZK	PA-28 Cherokee 180	Zulu Kilo Group	
G-ATZM	Piper J-3C-90 Cub	R. W. Davison	
G-ATZS	Wassmer WA41 Super Baladou IV	Temporal Songs Ltd & Anti Climb Guards/ Biggin Hill	
G-ATZY	Cessna F.150G	Fraggle Leasing Ltd/Edinburgh	
G-AVAK	M.S.893A Rallye Commodore 180	W. K. Anderson *(stored)*/Perth	
G-AVAR	Cessna F.150G	J. A. Rees	
G-AVAU	PA-30 Twin Comanche 160B	Enrico Ermano Ltd	
G-AVAW	D.62B Condor	Condor Aircraft Group	
G-AVAX	PA-28 Cherokee 180	J. J. Parkes	
G-AVBG	PA-28 Cherokee 180	G-AVBG Flying Group/White Waltham	
G-AVBH	PA-28 Cherokee 180	T. R. Smith (Agricultural Machinery) Ltd	
G-AVBS	PA-28 Cherokee 180	A. G. Arthur	
G-AVBT	PA-28 Cherokee 180	J. F. Mitchell	
G-AVCM	PA-24 Comanche 260	F. Smith & Sons Ltd/Stapleford	
G-AVCN	BN-2A-8 Islander	Airstream International Group Ltd	
G-AVCV	Cessna 182J Skylane	University of Manchester Institute of Science & Technology/Woodford	
G-AVCX	PA-30 Twin Comanche 160B	J. H. West	
G-AVDA	Cessna 182K Skylane	F. W. Ellis & M. C. Burnett	
G-AVDF	Beagle Pup 100 ★	Beagle Owners Club	
G-AVDG	Wallis WA-116 Srs 1	K. H. Wallis	
G-AVDS	Beech 65-B80 Queen Air ★	Airport Fire Service/Filton	
G-AVDT	Aeronca 7AC Champion	D. Cheney & G. Moore	
G-AVDV	PA-22 Tri-Pacer 150 (tailwheel)	S. C. Brooks/Slinfold	
G-AVDY	Luton LA-4A Minor	M. Stoney	
G-AVEC	Cessna F.172H	W. H. Ekin (Engineering) Co Ltd	
G-AVEF	Jodel 150	Heavy Install Ltd	
G-AVEH	SIAI-Marchetti S.205	EH Aviation	
G-AVEM	Cessna F.150G	T. D. & J. A. Warren	
G-AVEN	Cessna F.150G	150 Flying Group	
G-AVER	Cessna F.150G	E. Atherden	
G-AVEU	Wassmer WA.41 Baladou IV	S. Roberts	
G-AVEX	D.62B Condor	J. Riley & M. Mordue	
G-AVEY	Currie Super Wot	B. J. Anning	
G-AVEZ	HPR-7 Herald 210 ★	*Rescue trainer*/Norwich	
G-AVFB	H.S.121 Trident 2E ★	Duxford Aviation Soc	
G-AVFE	H.S.121 Trident 2E ★	Belfast Airport Authority	
G-AVFH	H.S.121 Trident 2E ★	De Havilland Heritage Museum *(fuselage only)*/London Colney	
G-AVFM	H.S.121 Trident 2E ★	Brunel Technical College/Bristol	
G-AVFP	PA-28 Cherokee 140	R. L. Howells/Barton	
G-AVFR	PA-28 Cherokee 140	VFR Flying Group/Newtownards	
G-AVFU	PA-32 Cherokee Six 300	Trixstar Farms Ltd	
G-AVFX	PA-28 Cherokee 140	J. Watson	
G-AVFZ	PA-28 Cherokee 140	G-AVFZ Flying Group	
G-AVGA	PA-24 Comanche 260	Conram Aviation/Biggin Hill	
G-AVGC	PA-28 Cherokee 140	A. P. H. Hay	
G-AVGD	PA-28 Cherokee 140	M. Tyler-Bennett	
G-AVGE	PA-28 Cherokee 140	A. J. Cutler	
G-AVGI	PA-28 Cherokee 140	D. G. Smith & C. D. Barden	
G-AVGK	PA-28 Cherokee 180	Golf Kilo Flying Group	
G-AVGU	Cessna F.150G	Coulson Flying Services Ltd	
G-AVGY	Cessna 182K Skylane	R. M. C. Sears & R. N. Howgego	
G-AVGZ	Jodel DR.1050	D. C. Webb	
G-AVHH	Cessna F.172H	The Bristol & Wessex Aeroplane Club	
G-AVHL	Jodel DR.105A	J. R. Tonkin	
G-AVHM	Cessna F.150G	M & N Flying Group	
G-AVHT	Auster AOP.9 (WZ711)	M. Somerton-Rayner/Middle Wallop	
G-AVHY	Fournier RF.4D	I. G. K. Mitchell	
G-AVIA	Cessna F.150G	Cheshire Air Training Services Ltd/ Liverpool	
G-AVIB	Cessna F.150G	Edinburgh Air Centre Ltd	
G-AVIC	Cessna F.172H	Leeside Flying Ltd	
G-AVID	Cessna 182K	Jaguar Aviation Ltd	
G-AVII	AB-206A JetRanger	Bristow Helicopters Ltd	
G-AVIL	Alon A.2 Aircoupe (VX147)	D. J. Hulks	

Notes	Reg.	Type	Owner or Operator
	G-AVIN	M.S.880B Rallye Club	P. Bradley
	G-AVIP	Brantly B.2B	N. J. R. Minchin
	G-AVIS	Cessna F.172H	J. P. A. Freeman
	G-AVIT	Cessna F.150G	Invicta Flyers
	G-AVIZ	Scheibe SF.25A Motorfalke	Spilsby Gliding Trust
	G-AVJE	Cessna F.150G	G-AVJE Syndicate
	G-AVJF	Cessna F.172H	J. A. & G. M. Rees
	G-AVJI	Cessna F.172H ★	Northbrook College/Shoreham
	G-AVJJ	PA-30 Twin Comanche 160B	A. H. Manser
	G-AVJK	Jodel DR.1050/M1	M. H. Wylde
	G-AVJO	Fokker E.III (replica) (422-15)	Bianchi Aviation Film Services Ltd/Booker
	G-AVJV	Wallis WA-117 Srs 1	K. H. Wallis (G-ATCV)
	G-AVJW	Wallis WA-118 Srs 2	K. H. Wallis (G-ATPW)
	G-AVKB	MB.50 Pipistrelle	W. B. Cooper
	G-AVKD	Fournier RF-4D	Lasham RF4 Group
	G-AVKE	Gadfly HDW.1 ★	IHM/Weston-s-Mare
	G-AVKG	Cessna F.172H	P. E. P. Sheppard/Breighton
	G-AVKI	Slingsby T.66 Nipper 3	J. M. Greenway
	G-AVKK	Slingsby T.66 Nipper 3	C. Watson
	G-AVKL	PA-30 Twin Comanche 160B	Bravo Aviation Ltd/Jersey
	G-AVKN	Cessna 401	Law Leasing Ltd
	G-AVKP	A.109 Airedale	D. R. Williams
	G-AVKR	Bolkow Bo 208C1 Junior	A. C. Dufton & S. F. Jeffery
	G-AVLB	PA-28 Cherokee 140	M. Wilson
	G-AVLC	PA-28 Cherokee 140	NE Wales Institute of Higher Education/Welshpool
	G-AVLD	PA-28 Cherokee 140	WLS Flying Group/Elstree
	G-AVLE	PA-28 Cherokee 140	Video Security Services/Tollerton
	G-AVLF	PA-28 Cherokee 140	G. H. Hughesdon
	G-AVLG	PA-28 Cherokee 140	R. Friedlander & D. C. Raymond
	G-AVLH	PA-28 Cherokee 140	M. B. Rothschild
	G-AVLI	PA-28 Cherokee 140	Lima India Aviation Group
	G-AVLJ	PA-28 Cherokee 140	Cherokee Aviation Holdings Jersey Ltd
	G-AVLM	B.121 Pup 3	T. M. & D. A. Jones/Egginton
	G-AVLN	B.121 Pup 2	A. P. Marks
	G-AVLO	Bo 208C1 Junior	P. J. Swain
	G-AVLR	PA-28 Cherokee 140	Group 140/Panshanger
	G-AVLT	PA-28 Cherokee 140	L. I. Bailey (G-KELC)
	G-AVLW	Fournier RF-4D	J. C. A. C. da Silva
	G-AVLY	Jodel D.120A	N. V. de Candole
	G-AVMA	GY-80 Horizon 180	B. R. Hildick
	G-AVMB	D.62B Condor	L. J. Dray
	G-AVMD	Cessna 150G	Bagby Aviation Flying Group
	G-AVMF	Cessna F. 150G	J. F. Marsh
	G-AVMI	BAC One-Eleven 510ED	European Aircharter Ltd
	G-AVMJ	BAC One-Eleven 510ED ★	European Aviation Ltd (cabin trainer)
	G-AVMN	BAC One-Eleven 510ED	European Aviation Ltd
	G-AVMO	BAC One-Eleven 510ED ★	Aerospace Museum/Cosford
	G-AVMP	BAC One-Eleven 510ED	European Aviation Ltd
	G-AVMS	BAC One-Eleven 510ED	European Aviation Ltd
	G-AVMU	BAC One-Eleven 510ED ★	Duxford Aviation Soc
	G-AVMW	BAC One-Eleven 510ED	European Aviation Ltd
	G-AVMY	BAC One-Eleven 510ED	European Aviation Ltd
	G-AVMZ	BAC One-Eleven 510ED	European Aviation Ltd
	G-AVNC	Cessna F.150G	J. Turner
	G-AVNE	W.S.58 Wessex Mk 60 Srs 1 ★	IHM/Weston-s-Mare
	G-AVNN	PA-28 Cherokee 180	G-AVNN Flying Group
	G-AVNO	PA-28 Cherokee 180	Allister Flight Ltd
	G-AVNR	PA-28 Cherokee 180	R. R. Livingstone
	G-AVNS	PA-28 Cherokee 180	E. Alexander/Earls Colne
	G-AVNU	PA-28 Cherokee 180	D. Durrant
	G-AVNW	PA-28 Cherokee 180	Len Smith's School of Sports Ltd
	G-AVNX	Fournier RF-4D	W. G. Woollard
	G-AVNZ	Fournier RF-4D	V. S. E. Norman/Rendcomb
	G-AVOA	Jodel DR.1050	D. A. Willies/Cranwell
	G-AVOC	CEA Jodel DR.221	T. Q. Loveday
	G-AVOH	D.62B Condor	Halegreen Associates Ltd
	G-AVOM	CEA Jodel DR.221	M. A. Mountford/Headcorn
	G-AVOO	PA-18 Super Cub 150	London Gliding Club (Pty) Ltd/Dunstable
	G-AVOZ	PA-28 Cherokee 180	Oscar Zulu Flying Group
	G-AVPC	D.31 Turbulent	S. A. Sharp
	G-AVPD	Jodel D.9 Bebe ★	S. W. McKay (stored)
	G-AVPH	Cessna F.150G	Zero 9 Flight Academy/Norwich

Reg.	Type	Owner or Operator	Notes
G-AVPI	Cessna F.172H	R. W. Cope	
G-AVPJ	D.H.82A Tiger Moth	C. C. Silk	
G-AVPM	Jodel D.117	J. C. Haynes/Breighton	
G-AVPN	HPR-7 Herald 213 ★	Yorkshire Air Museum/Elvington	
G-AVPO	Hindustan HAL-26 Pushpak	J. A. Coutts & W. G. Mitchell-Hudson	
G-AVPS	PA-30 Twin Comanche 160B	J. M. Bisco/Staverton	
G-AVPV	PA-18 Cherokee 180	K. A. Passmore	
G-AVRK	PA-28 Cherokee 180	J. Gama	
G-AVRP	PA-28 Cherokee 140	Trent-199	
G-AVRS	GY-80 Horizon 180	Air Venturas Ltd	
G-AVRU	PA-28 Cherokee 180	G-AVRU Partnership/Clacton	
G-AVRW	GY-20 Minicab	Kestrel Flying Group/Tollerton	
G-AVRY	PA-28 Cherokee 180	Brigfast Ltd/Blackbushe	
G-AVRZ	PA-28 Cherokee 180	Mantavia Group Ltd	
G-AVSA	PA-28 Cherokee 180	G-AVSA Flying Group	
G-AVSB	PA-28 Cherokee 180	D. L. Macdonald	
G-AVSC	PA-28 Cherokee 180	MCS019 Ltd	
G-AVSD	PA-28 Cherokee 180	Landmate Ltd	
G-AVSF	PA-28 Cherokee 180	Monday Club/Blackbushe	
G-AVSI	PA-28 Cherokee 140	G-AVSI Flying Group	
G-AVSP	PA-28 Cherokee 180	Airways Flight Training (Exeter) Ltd	
G-AVSR	Beagle D.5/180 Husky	A. L. Young	
G-AVSZ	AB-206B JetRanger	Burman Aviation Ltd/Cranfield	
G-AVTP	Cessna F.172H	Tango Papa Group/White Waltham	
G-AVTT	Ercoupe 415D	Wright's Farm Eggs Ltd/Andrewsfield	
G-AVTV	M.S.893A Rallye Commodore	D. B. & M. E. Meeks	
G-AVUD	PA-30 Twin Comanche 160B	F.M.Aviation/Biggin Hill	
G-AVUG	Cessna F.150H	Skyways Flying Group	
G-AVUH	Cessna F.150H	C. M. Chinn	
G-AVUS	PA-28 Cherokee 140	D. J. Hunter	
G-AVUT	PA-28 Cherokee 140	Bencray Ltd/Blackpool	
G-AVUU	PA-28 Cherokee 140	A. Jahanfar & ptnrs/Southend	
G-AVUZ	PA-32 Cherokee Six 300	Ceesix Ltd/Jersey	
G-AVVC	Cessna F.172H	A. Turnbull	
G-AVVE	Cessna F.150H ★	R. Windley *(stored)*	
G-AVVF	D.H.104 Dove ★	Airport Fire Service/Staverton	
G-AVVJ	M.S.893A Rallye Commodore	M. Powell	
G-AVVL	Cessna F.150H	N. E. Sams/Cranfield	
G-AVVO	Avro 652A Anson 19 (VL348) ★	Newark Air Museum	
G-AVWA	PA-28 Cherokee 140	SFG Ltd	
G-AVWD	PA-28 Cherokee 140	Evelyn Air	
G-AVWI	PA-28 Cherokee 140	L. M. Veitch	
G-AVWJ	PA-28 Cherokee 140	A. M. Harrhy	
G-AVWL	PA-28 Cherokee 140	Bobev Aviation	
G-AVWM	PA-28 Cherokee 140	P. E. Preston & ptnrs/Southend	
G-AVWN	PA-28R Cherokee Arrow 180	Vawn Air Ltd/Jersey	
G-AVWO	PA-28R Cherokee Arrow 180	R. G. Tweddle	
G-AVWR	PA-28R Cherokee Arrow 180	S. J. French & ptnrs/Exeter	
G-AVWT	PA-28R Cherokee Arrow 180	Cloudbase Aviation Ltd	
G-AVWU	PA-28R Cherokee Arrow 180	Arrow Flyers Ltd	
G-AVWV	PA-28R Cherokee Arrow 180	Strathtay Flying Group	
G-AVWY	Fournier RF-4D	P. Turner	
G-AVXA	PA-25 Pawnee 235	S. Wales Gliding Club Ltd/Usk	
G-AVXC	Slingsby T.66 Nipper 3	P. A. & D. N. Gibbs	
G-AVXD	Slingsby T.66 Nipper 3	Tayside Nipper Group	
G-AVXF	PA-28R Cherokee Arrow 180	JDR Arrow Group	
G-AVXJ	H.S.748 Srs 2A	Emerald Airways Ltd/Liverpool	
G-AVXW	D.62B Condor	A. J. Cooper/Rochester	
G-AVXY	Auster AOP.9 (XK417)	Auster Nine Group	
G-AVXZ	PA-28 Cherokee 140 ★	ATC Hayle *(instructional airframe)*	
G-AVYB	H.S.121 Trident 1E-140 ★	*SAS training airframe*/Hereford	
G-AVYE	H.S.121 Trident 1E-140 ★	–	
G-AVYK	A.61 Terrier 3	J. P. Roland/Aboyne	
G-AVYL	PA-28 Cherokee 180	N. E. Binner	
G-AVYM	PA-28 Cherokee 180	Carlisle Aviation (1985) Ltd/Crosby	
G-AVYP	PA-28 Cherokee 140	Aldergrove Flight Training Centre	
G-AVYR	PA-28 Cherokee 140	D.R. Flying Club Ltd/Staverton	
G-AVYS	PA-28R Cherokee Arrow 180	A. M. Playford	
G-AVYT	PA-28R Cherokee Arrow 180	J. R. Tindale	
G-AVYV	Jodel D.120	A. J. Sephton	
G-AVZB	Aero Z-37 Cmelak ★	Science Museum/Wroughton	
G-AVZI	Bo 208C1 Junior	C. F. Rogers	
G-AVZM	B.121 Pup 1	ARAZ Group/Elstree	

Notes	Reg.	Type	Owner or Operator
	G-AVZN	B.121 Pup 1	Shipdham Aviators Flying Club
	G-AVZO	B.121 Pup 1 ★	Thamesside Aviation Museum/E. Tilbury
	G-AVZP	B.121 Pup 1	T. A. White
	G-AVZR	PA-28 Cherokee 180	Lincoln Aero Club Ltd/Sturgate
	G-AVZU	Cessna F.150H	R. D. & E. Forster/Swanton Morley
	G-AVZV	Cessna F.172H	E. M. & D. S. Lightbown/Crosland Moor
	G-AVZW	EAA Biplane Model P	R. G. Maidment & G. R. Edmundson/ Goodwood
	G-AVZX	M.S.880B Rallye Club	J. Nugent
	G-AWAA	M.S.880B Rallye Club ★	P. A. Cairns (stored)/St Just
	G-AWAC	GY-80 Horizon 180	Gardan Party Ltd
	G-AWAH	Beech 95-D55 Baron	B. J. S. Grey/Duxford
	G-AWAJ	Beech 95-D55 Baron	Standard Hose Ltd/Leeds
	G-AWAT	D.62B Condor	Tarwood Ltd/Redhill
	G-AWAU	Vickers F.B.27A Vimy (replica) (F8614) ★	Bomber Command Museum/Hendon
	G-AWAW	Cessna F.150F ★	Science Museum/S. Kensington
	G-AWAX	Cessna 150D	H. H. Cousins
	G-AWAZ	PA-28R Cherokee Arrow 180	R. Staniszewski
	G-AWBA	PA-28R Cherokee Arrow 180	March Flying Group/Stapleford
	G-AWBB	PA-28R Cherokee Arrow 180	M. D. Parker & J. Lowe
	G-AWBC	PA-28R Cherokee Arrow 180	Anglo Aviation (UK) Ltd
	G-AWBE	PA-28 Cherokee 140	B. E. Boyle
	G-AWBH	PA-28 Cherokee 140	Mainstreet Aviation
	G-AWBJ	Fournier RF-4D	J. M. Adams
	G-AWBM	D.31 Turbulent	A. D. Pratt
	G-AWBN	PA-30 Twin Comanche 160B	Stourfield Investments Ltd/Jersey
	G-AWBS	PA-28 Cherokee 140	M. A. English & T. M. Brown
	G-AWBT	PA-30 Twin Comanche 160B ★	Instructional airframe/Cranfield
	G-AWBU	Morane-Saulnier N (replica) (MS.824)	Bianchi Aviation Film Services Ltd
	G-AWBW	Cessna F.172H ★	Brunel Technical College/Bristol
	G-AWBX	Cessna F.150H	J. Meddings/Tatenhill
	G-AWCM	Cessna F.150H	R. Garbett
	G-AWCN	Cessna FR.172E	Y. F. Herdman
	G-AWCP	Cessna F.150H (tailwheel)	C. E. Mason/Shobdon
	G-AWDA	Slingsby T.66 Nipper 3	J. A. Cheesebrough
	G-AWDI	PA-23 Aztec 250C ★	Queens Head/Willington, Beds
	G-AWDO	D.31 Turbulent	R. N. Crosland
	G-AWDP	PA-28 Cherokee 180	B. H. & P. M. Illston/Shipdham
	G-AWDR	Cessna FR.172E	B. A. Wallace
	G-AWDU	Brantly B.2B	B. M. Freeman
	G-AWEF	SNCAN Stampe SV-4B	The Tiger Club (1990) Ltd/Headcorn
	G-AWEI	D.62B Condor	J. M. C. Coyle
	G-AWEK	Fournier RF-4D	P. Barrett
	G-AWEL	Fournier RF-4D	A. B. Clymo/Halfpenny Green
	G-AWEM	Fournier RF-4D	B. J. Griffin/Wickenby
	G-AWEP	Barritault JB-01 Minicab	A. Louth
	G-AWES	Cessna 150H	P. Montgomery-Stuart
	G-AWET	PA-28 Cherokee 180D	Broadland Flying Group Ltd/Shipdham
	G-AWEV	PA-28 Cherokee 140	Norflight Ltd
	G-AWEX	PA-28 Cherokee 140	Sir W. G. Armstrong Whitworth Flying Group/Coventry
	G-AWEZ	PA-28R Cherokee Arrow 180	T. R. Leighton & ptnrs
	G-AWFB	PA-28R Cherokee Arrow 180	J. C. Luke/Filton
	G-AWFC	PA-28R Cherokee Arrow 180	B. J. Hines
	G-AWFD	PA-28R Cherokee Arrow 180	D. J. Hill
	G-AWFF	Cessna F.150H	J. A. Hardiman/Shobdon
	G-AWFJ	PA-28R Cherokee Arrow 180	Parplon Ltd
	G-AWFN	D.62B Condor	R. James
	G-AWFO	D.62B Condor	T. A. Major
	G-AWFP	D.62B Condor	Blackbushe Flying Club
	G-AWFR	D.31 Turbulent	J. R. Froud
	G-AWFT	Jodel D.9 Bebe	W. H. Cole
	G-AWFW	Jodel D.117	C. J. Rodwell
	G-AWFZ	Beech A23 Musketeer	K. A. W. Ashcroft
	G-AWGA	A.109 Airedale ★	(stored)/Sevenoaks
	G-AWGD	Cessna F.172H	R. P. Vincent
	G-AWGJ	Cessna F.172H	J. & C. J. Freeman/Headcorn
	G-AWGK	Cessna F.150H	G. E. Allen
	G-AWGN	Fournier RF-4D	R. H. Ashforth/Staverton
	G-AWGR	Cessna F.172H	P. A. Hallam

Reg.	Type	Owner or Operator	Notes
G-AWGZ	Taylor JT.1 Monoplane	R. L. Sambell	
G-AWHB	C.A.S.A. 2-111D (6J+PR) ★	Aces High Ltd/North Weald	
G-AWHX	Rollason Beta B.2	S. G. Jones	
G-AWHY	Falconar F.11-3	B. E. Smith (G-BDPB)	
G-AWIF	Brookland Mosquito 2	–/Husbands Bosworth	
G-AWII	V.S.349 Spitfire VC (AR501)	The Shuttleworth Collection/O. Warden	
G-AWIP	Luton LA-4A Minor	J. Houghton	
G-AWIR	Midget Mustang	K. E. Sword/Leicester	
G-AWIT	PA-28 Cherokee 180	Cherry Orchard Aparthotel Ltd	
G-AWIV	Airmark TSR.3	F. R. Hutchings	
G-AWIW	SNCAN Stampe SV-4B	R. E. Mitchell	
G-AWJE	Slingsby T.66 Nipper 3	T. Mosedale	
G-AWJV	D.H.98 Mosquito TT Mk 35 (TA634) ★	De Havilland Heritage Museum	
G-AWJX	Zlin Z.526 Trener Master	Aerobatics International Ltd	
G-AWJY	Zlin Z.526 Trener Master	M. Gainza	
G-AWKD	PA-17 Vagabond	A. T. & M. R. Dowie/ White Waltham	
G-AWKM	B.121 Pup 1	D. M. G. Jenkins/Swansea	
G-AWKO	B.121 Pup 1	P. G. Heward	
G-AWKP	Jodel DR.253	G-AWKP Group	
G-AWKT	M.S.880B Rallye Club	A. Ringland & P. Keating	
G-AWKX	Beech A65 Queen Air ★	(Instructional airframe)/Shoreham	
G-AWLA	Cessna F.150H	Bagby Aviation	
G-AWLF	Cessna F.172H	Gannet Aviation Ltd/Aldergrove	
G-AWLG	SIPA 903	S. W. Markham	
G-AWLI	PA-22 Tri-Pacer 150	J. S. Lewery/Shoreham	
G-AWLO	Boeing Stearman E.75	N. D. Pickard/Shoreham	
G-AWLP	Mooney M.20F	I. C. Lomax	
G-AWLR	Slingsby T.66 Nipper 3	T. D. Reid	
G-AWLS	Slingsby T.66 Nipper 3	G. A. Dunster & B. Gallagher	
G-AWLZ	Fournier RF-4D	Nympsfield RF-4 Group	
G-AWMD	Jodel D.11	D. A. Barr-Hamilton/Shobdon	
G-AWMF	PA-18 Super Cub 150 (modified)	Booker Gliding Club Ltd	
G-AWMI	Glos-Airtourer 115	M. Furse/Cardiff/Wales	
G-AWMM	M.S.893A Rallye Commodore 180	D. P. & S. White	
G-AWMN	Luton LA-4A Minor	B. J. Douglas	
G-AWMP	Cessna F.172H	R. J. D. Blois	
G-AWMR	D.31 Turbulent	M. J. Bond	
G-AWMT	Cessna F.150H	M. Paisley	
G-AWMZ	Cessna F.172H ★	Parachute jump trainer/Cark	
G-AWNT	BN-2A Islander	Sterling Helicopters Ltd/Norwich	
G-AWOA	M.S.880B Rallye Club	J. A. Rimmer	
G-AWOE	Aero Commander 680E	J. M. Houlder/Elstree	
G-AWOF	PA-15 Vagabond	C. M. Hicks	
G-AWOH	PA-17 Vagabond	The High Flatts Flying Group	
G-AWOT	Cessna F.150H	A. J. Hurran	
G-AWOU	Cessna 170B	S. Billington/Denham	
G-AWOX	W.S.58 Wessex 60 (150225) ★	IHM/Weston-s-Mare	
G-AWPH	P.56 Provost T.1	J. A. D. Bradshaw	
G-AWPJ	Cessna F.150H	W. J. Greenfield	
G-AWPN	Shield Xyla	K. R. Snell	
G-AWPP	Cessna F.150H	Coulson Flying Services Ltd	
G-AWPS	PA-28 Cherokee 140	A. R. Matthews	
G-AWPU	Cessna F.150J	LAC (Enterprises) Ltd/Barton	
G-AWPW	PA-12 Super Cruiser	AK Leasing (Jersey) Ltd	
G-AWPY	Bensen B.8M	J. Jordan	
G-AWPZ	Andreasson BA-4B	J. M. Vening	
G-AWRK	Cessna F.150J	Systemroute Ltd/Shoreham	
G-AWRP	Cierva Rotorcraft ★	IHM/Weston-s-Mare	
G-AWRS	Avro 19 Srs. 2 ★	N. E. Aircraft Museum/Usworth	
G-AWRY	P.56 Provost T.1 (XF836)	Slymar Aviation & Services Ltd	
G-AWSA	Avro 652A Anson 19 (VL349) ★	Norfolk & Suffolk Aviation Museum	
G-AWSH	Zlin Z.526 Trener Master	Aerobatics International Ltd	
G-AWSL	PA-28 Cherokee 180D	Fascia Services Ltd/Southend	
G-AWSM	PA-28 Cherokee 235	Aviation Projects	
G-AWSN	D.62B Condor	M. K. A. Blyth	
G-AWSP	D.62B Condor	R. Q. & A. S. Bond/Wellesbourne	
G-AWSS	D.62A Condor	N. J. & D. Butler	
G-AWST	D.62B Condor	P. L. Clements	
G-AWSV	Skeeter 12 (XM553)	Maj. M. Somerton-Rayner/Middle Wallop	
G-AWSW	D.5/180 Husky (XW635)	Windmill Aviation/Spanhoe	
G-AWTJ	Cessna F.150J	D. G. Williams	
G-AWTL	PA-28 Cherokee 180D	E. Alexander	

Notes	Reg.	Type	Owner or Operator
	G-AWTS	Beech A.23 Musketeer	J. Holden & G. Benet
	G-AWTV	Beech 19A Musketeer Sport	J. Whittaker
	G-AWUB	GY-201 Minicab	R. A. Hand
	G-AWUE	Jodel DR.1050	K. W. Wood & F. M. Watson
	G-AWUG	Cessna F.150H	Fraggle Leasing Ltd/Edinburgh
	G-AWUJ	Cessna F.150H	S. R. Hughes
	G-AWUL	Cessna F.150H	C. A. & L. P. Green
	G-AWUN	Cessna F.150H	D. Dean
	G-AWUO	Cessna F.150H	SAS Flying Group
	G-AWUT	Cessna F.150J	S. J. Black/Leeds
	G-AWUU	Cessna F.150J	A. L. Grey
	G-AWUX	Cessna F.172H	G-AWUX Group/St.Just
	G-AWUZ	Cessna F.172H	I. R. Judge
	G-AWVA	Cessna F.172H	Barton Air Ltd
	G-AWVB	Jodel D.117	H. Davies
	G-AWVC	B.121 Pup 1	J. H. Marshall & J. J. West
	G-AWVE	Jodel DR.1050/M1	E. A. Taylor/Southend
	G-AWVF	P.56 Provost T.1 (XF877)	Hunter Wing Ltd/Bournemouth
	G-AWVG	AESL Airtourer T.2	C. J. Schofield
	G-AWVN	Aeronca 7AC Champion	Champ Flying Group
	G-AWVZ	Jodel D.112	D. C. Stokes
	G-AWWE	B.121 Pup 2	J. M. Randle/Coventry
	G-AWWI	Jodel D.117	W. J. Evans
	G-AWWM	GY-201 Minicab	P. J. Brayshaw
	G-AWWN	Jodel DR.1051	R. A. J. Hurst
	G-AWWO	Jodel DR.1050	Whiskey Oscar Group/Barton
	G-AWWP	Aerosport Woody Pusher III	M. S. Bird & R. D. Bird
	G-AWWT	D.31 Turbulent	E. L. Phillips
	G-AWWU	Cessna FR.172F	Westward Airways (Lands End) Ltd
	G-AWWW	Cessna 401	Treble Whisky Aviation Ltd
	G-AWXR	PA-28 Cherokee 180D	Aero Club de Portugal
	G-AWXS	PA-28 Cherokee 180D	J. A. Hardiman/Shobdon
	G-AWXY	M.S.885 Super Rallye	K. Henderson/Hibaldstow
	G-AWXZ	SNCAN Stampe SV-4C	Bianchi Aviation Film Services Ltd
	G-AWYB	Cessna FR.172F	C. W. Larkin/Southend
	G-AWYJ	B.121 Pup 2	H. C. Taylor
	G-AWYL	Jodel DR.253B	K. Gillham
	G-AWYO	B.121 Pup 1	B. R. C. Wild/Popham
	G-AWYV	BAC One-Eleven 501EX	European Aviation Ltd
	G-AWYX	M.S.880B Rallye Club	M. J. Edwards/Henstridge
	G-AWYY	T.57 Camel replica (B6401) ★	F.A.A. Museum/Yeovilton
	G-AWZI	H.S.121 Trident 3B ★	Surrey Fire Brigade (instructional airframe)/Reigate
	G-AWZJ	H.S.121 Trident 3B ★	Prestwick Fire Department
	G-AWZK	H.S.121 Trident 3B ★	Trident Preservation Soc./Heathrow
	G-AWZM	H.S.121 Trident 3B ★	Science Museum/Wroughton
	G-AWZO	H.S.121 Trident 3B ★	De Havilland Heritage Museum/Hatfield
	G-AWZP	H.S.121 Trident 3B ★	Manchester Museum of Science & Industry (nose only)
	G-AWZU	H.S.121 Trident 3B ★	BAA Airport Fire Service/Stansted
	G-AWZX	H.S.121 Trident 3B ★	BAA Airport Fire Services/Gatwick
	G-AWZZ	H.S.121 Trident 3B ★	Airport Fire Services/Birmingham
	G-AXAB	PA-28 Cherokee 140	D. M. Loughlin
	G-AXAN	D.H.82A Tiger Moth (EM720)	M. E. Carrell
	G-AXAS	Wallis WA-116T	K. H. Wallis (G-AVDH)
	G-AXAT	Jodel D.117A	P. S. Wilkinson
	G-AXAU	PA-30 Twin Comanche 160C	Bartcourt Ltd/Bournemouth
	G-AXBF	Beagle D.5/180 Husky	C. H. Barnes
	G-AXBH	Cessna F.172H	D. F. Ranger
	G-AXBJ	Cessna F.172H	BJ Flying Group/Leicester
	G-AXBW	D.H.82A Tiger Moth (T5879)	Hunter Wing Ltd/Bournemouth
	G-AXBZ	D.H.82A Tiger Moth	D. H. McWhir
	G-AXCA	PA-28R Cherokee Arrow 200	R. A. Symmonds
	G-AXCG	Jodel D.117	Charlie Golf Group/Andrewsfield
	G-AXCI	Bensen B.8M	N. Martin (stored)
	G-AXCL	M.S.880B Rallye Club	P. P. Loucas/Andrewsfield
	G-AXCM	M.S.880B Rallye Club	D. C. Manifold
	G-AXCX	B.121 Pup 2	L. A. Pink
	G-AXCY	Jodel D.117	R. D. P. Cadle
	G-AXCZ	SNCAN Stampe SV-4C	J. Price
	G-AXDC	PA-23 Aztec 250D	N. J. Lilley/Bodmin

Reg.	Type	Owner or Operator	Notes
G-AXDI	Cessna F.172H	M. F. & J. R. Leusby/Conington	
G-AXDK	Jodel DR.315	Delta Kilo Flying Group/Sywell	
G-AXDM	H.S.125 Srs 400B	GEC Ferranti Defence Systems Ltd/ Edinburgh	
G-AXDN	BAC-Sud Concorde 01 ★	Duxford Aviation Soc	
G-AXDV	B.121 Pup 1	T. A. White	
G-AXDW	B.121 Pup 1	Cranfield Delta Whiskey Group	
G-AXDY	Falconar F-11	J. Nunn	
G-AXDZ	Cassutt Racer IIIM	A. Chadwick/Little Staughton	
G-AXEB	Cassutt Racer IIIM	G. E. Horder/Redhill	
G-AXED	PA-25 Pawnee 235	Wolds Gliding Club Ltd/Pocklington	
G-AXEH	B.125 Bulldog 1 ★	Museum of Flight/E. Fortune	
G-AXEI	Ward Gnome ★	Real Aeroplane Club/Breighton	
G-AXEO	Scheibe SF.25B Falke	The Borders (Milfield) Gliding Club Ltd	
G-AXEV	B.121 Pup 2	D. S. Russell & J. Powell-Tuck	
G-AXFG	Cessna 337D	County Garage (Cheltenham) Ltd	
G-AXFN	Jodel D.119	Fox November Group	
G-AXGE	M.S.880B Rallye Club	R. P. Loxton	
G-AXGG	Cessna F.150J	U. Schluter	
G-AXGP	Piper J-3C-65 Cub	W. K. Butler	
G-AXGR	Luton LA-4A Minor	B. A. Schlussler	
G-AXGS	D.62B Condor	G-AXGS Condor Group	
G-AXGV	D.62B Condor	R. J. Wrixon	
G-AXGZ	D.62B Condor	M. L. Jackson	
G-AXHA	Cessna 337A	G. Evans	
G-AXHC	SNCAN Stampe SV-4C	D. L. Webley	
G-AXHE	BN-2A Islander ★	*(parachute trainer)*/Strathallan	
G-AXHO	B.121 Pup 2	L. W. Grundy/Stapleford	
G-AXHP	Piper J-3C-65 Cub (480636)	Witham (Specialist) Vehicles Ltd	
G-AXHR	Piper J-3C-65 Cub (329601)	G-AXHR Cub Group	
G-AXHS	M.S.880B Rallye Club	B. & A. Swales	
G-AXHT	M.S.880B Rallye Club	J. M. Hedges	
G-AXHV	Jodel D.117A	Derwent Flying Group/Hucknall	
G-AXIA	B.121 Pup 1	N. J. Mines & K. Fernandez/Kemble	
G-AXIE	B.121 Pup 2	G. McD. Moir	
G-AXIF	B.121 Pup 2	J. A. Holmes & S. A. Self	
G-AXIG	B.125 Bulldog 104	A. A. A. Hamilton	
G-AXIO	PA-28 Cherokee 140B	White Waltham Airfield Ltd	
G-AXIR	PA-28 Cherokee 140B	A. G. Birch	
G-AXIW	Scheibe SF.25B Falke	M. B. Hill	
G-AXIX	Glos-Airtourer 150	J. C. Wood	
G-AXJB	Omega 84 balloon	Southern Balloon Group	
G-AXJH	B.121 Pup 2	The Henry Flying Group	
G-AXJI	B.121 Pup 2	D. R. Vale/Egginton	
G-AXJJ	B.121 Pup 2	M. L. Jones & ptnrs/Egginton	
G-AXJO	B.121 Pup 2	J. A. D. Bradshaw	
G-AXJR	Scheibe SF.25B Falke	Falke Syndicate	
G-AXJV	PA-28 Cherokee 140B	ATC (Lasham) Ltd	
G-AXJX	PA-28 Cherokee 140B	Patrolwatch Ltd/Sleap	
G-AXKH	Luton LA-4A Minor	M. E. Vaisey	
G-AXKJ	Jodel D.9 Bebe	C. C. Gordon & N. Mowbray	
G-AXKO	Westland-Bell 47G-4A	G. P. Hinkley	
G-AXKS	Westland Bell 47G-4A ★	Museum of Army Flying/Middle Wallop	
G-AXKW	Westland-Bell 47G-4A	Eyre Spier Associates Ltd	
G-AXKX	Westland Bell 47G-4A	Copley Farms Ltd	
G-AXKY	Westland Bell 47G-4A	G. A. Knight & G. M. Vowles	
G-AXLG	Cessna 310K	Smiths (Outdrives) Ltd	
G-AXLI	Slingsby T.66 Nipper 3	K. R. H. Wingate	
G-AXLS	Jodel DR.105A	Axle Flying Club	
G-AXLZ	PA-18 Super Cub 95	R. J. Quantrell	
G-AXMA	PA-24 Comanche 180	J. D. Bingham	
G-AXMD	Omega O-56 balloon ★	British Balloon Museum/Newbury	
G-AXMN	J/5B Autocar	C. D. Wilkinson	
G-AXMT	Bücker Bü133 Jungmeister	R. A. Fleming/Breighton	
G-AXMW	B.121 Pup 1	DJP Engineering (Knebworth) Ltd	
G-AXMX	B.121 Pup 2	Susan A. Jones/Cannes	
G-AXNJ	Wassmer Jodel D.120	Clive Flying Group/Sleap	
G-AXNL	B.121 Pup 1	Appleton Aviation Ltd	
G-AXNM	B.121 Pup 1	F. E. Green	
G-AXNN	B.121 Pup 2	Gabrielle Aviation Ltd/Shoreham	
G-AXNP	B.121 Pup 2	J. W. Ellis	
G-AXNR	B.121 Pup 2	The November Romeo Group	
G-AXNS	B.121 Pup 2	Derwent Aero Group/Gamston	

Notes	Reg.	Type	Owner or Operator
	G-AXNW	SNCAN Stampe SV-4C	C. S. Grace
	G-AXNX	Cessna 182M	D. B. Harper
	G-AXNZ	Pitts S.1C Special	W. A. Jordan
	G-AXOG	PA-E23 Aztec 250D	G. H. Nolan
	G-AXOH	M.S.894 Rallye Minerva	Bristol Cars Ltd/White Waltham
	G-AXOJ	B.121 Pup 0	Pup Flying Group
	G-AXOR	PA-28 Cherokee 180D	Oscar Romeo Aviation Ltd
	G-AXOS	M.S.894A Rallye Minerva	Henlow Thunderbolts
	G-AXOT	M.S.893 Rallye Commodore 180	P. Evans & J. C. Graves
	G-AXOZ	B.121 Pup 1	R. J. Ogborn/Liverpool
	G-AXPA	B.121 Pup 1	D. G. Lewendon
	G-AXPB	B.121 Pup 1	M. J. K. Seary & R. T. Austin
	G-AXPC	B.121 Pup 2	T. A. White/Bagby
	G-AXPF	Cessna F.150K	D. R. Marks/Denham
	G-AXPG	Mignet HM-293	W. H. Cole *(stored)*
	G-AXPM	B.121 Pup 1	R. G. Hayes/Elstree
	G-AXPN	B.121 Pup 2	The Pup Club
	G-AXPZ	Campbell Cricket	W. R. Partridge
	G-AXRC	Campbell Cricket	R. T. Jakeway
	G-AXRK	Practavia Pilot Sprite 115 ★	M. Oliver
	G-AXRP	SNCAN Stampe SV-4A	Skysport Engineering (G-BLOL) *(stored)*/ Hatch
	G-AXRR	Auster AOP.9 (XR241)	R. J. Burgess
	G-AXRT	Cessna FA.150K (tailwheel)	C. C. Walley
	G-AXSC	B.121 Pup 1	R. J. MacCarthy/Swansea
	G-AXSD	B.121 Pup 1	Bagby Aviation
	G-AXSF	Nash Petrel	Nash Aircraft Ltd/Lasham
	G-AXSG	PA-28 Cherokee 180	Admiral Property Ltd
	G-AXSI	Cessna F.172H	St. Mary's Flying Club (G-SNIP)
	G-AXSM	Jodel DR.1051	T. R. G. Barnby & M. S. Regendanz
	G-AXSR	Brantly B.2B	A. Murzyn (G-ROOF)
	G-AXSW	Cessna FA.150K	R. Mitchell
	G-AXSZ	PA-28 Cherokee 140B	The White Wings Flying Group/ White Waltham
	G-AXTA	PA-28 Cherokee 140B	G-AXTA Aircraft Group
	G-AXTC	PA-28 Cherokee 140B	G-AXTC Group
	G-AXTJ	PA-28 Cherokee 140B	K. Patel/Elstree
	G-AXTL	PA-28 Cherokee 140B	Pegasus Aviation (Midlands) Ltd
	G-AXTO	PA-24 Comanche 260	J. L. Wright
	G-AXTP	PA-28 Cherokee 180	C. W. R. Moore/Elstree
	G-AXTX	Jodel D.112	C. Sawford
	G-AXUA	B.121 Pup 1	P. Wood
	G-AXUB	BN-2A Islander	Headcorn Parachute Club Ltd
	G-AXUC	PA-12 Super Cruiser	J. J. Bunton
	G-AXUF	Cessna FA.150K	W. B. Bateson/Blackpool
	G-AXUK	Jodel DR.1050	Downland Flying Group
	G-AXUM	H.P.137 Jetstream 1 ★	Sodeteg Formation/France
	G-AXUW	Cessna FA.150K	Coventry Air Training School
	G-AXVB	Cessna F.172H	R. & J. Turner
	G-AXVK	Campbell Cricket	P. C. Lovegrove
	G-AXVM	Campbell Cricket	D. M. Organ
	G-AXVN	McCandless M.4	W. R. Partridge
	G-AXWA	Auster AOP.9 (XN437)	M. L. & C. M. Edwards/Biggin Hill
	G-AXWT	Jodel D.11	R. C. Owen
	G-AXWV	Jodel DR.253	J. R. D. Bygraves/O. Warden
	G-AXWZ	PA-28R Cherokee Arrow 200	P. Walkley
	G-AXXC	CP.301B Emeraude	L. F. Clayton
	G-AXXV	D.H.82A Tiger Moth (DE992)	C. N. Wookey
	G-AXXW	Jodel D.117	J. M. Walsh
	G-AXYK	Taylor JT.1 Monoplane	D. J. Hulks & R. W. Davies
	G-AXYU	Jodel D.9 Bebe	P. Turton & H. C. Peake-Jones
	G-AXYZ	WHE Airbuggy	B. Gunn
	G-AXZD	PA-28 Cherokee 180E	G. M. Whitmore
	G-AXZF	PA-28 Cherokee 180E	E. P. C. & W. R. Rabson/Southampton
	G-AXZK	BN-2A-26 Islander	P. Johnson
	G-AXZM	Slingsby T.66 Nipper 3	G. R. Harlow
	G-AXZO	Cessna 180	Bourne Park Flyers
	G-AXZP	PA-E23 Aztec 250D	Aztec Flying Group
	G-AXZT	Jodel D.117	N. Batty
	G-AXZU	Cessna 182N	C. D. Williams
	G-AYAB	PA-28 Cherokee 180E	Films Ltd
	G-AYAC	PA-28R Cherokee Arrow 200	Fersfield Flying Group

Reg.	Type	Owner or Operator	Notes
G-AYAJ	Cameron O-84 balloon	E. T. Hall	
G-AYAL	Omega 56 balloon ★	British Balloon Museum/Newbury	
G-AYAN	Slingsby Motor Cadet III	D. C. Pattison	
G-AYAR	PA-28 Cherokee 180E	A. Jahanfar & Seawing Flying Club Ltd	
G-AYAT	PA-28 Cherokee 180E	AYAT Flying Group	
G-AYAW	PA-28 Cherokee 180E	R. C. Pendle & M. J. Rose/Blackbushe	
G-AYBD	Cessna F.150K	Premiair Engineering Ltd/Shoreham	
G-AYBG	Scheibe SF.25B Falke	H. H. T. Wolf	
G-AYBO	PA-23 Aztec 250D	Twinguard Aviation Ltd/Elstree	
G-AYBP	Jodel D.112	G. J. Langston	
G-AYBR	Jodel D.112	R. T. Mosforth	
G-AYCC	Campbell Cricket	D. J. M. Charity	
G-AYCE	CP.301C Emeraude	S. D. Glover	
G-AYCF	Cessna FA.150K	E. J. Atkins/Popham	
G-AYCG	SNCAN Stampe SV-4C	N. Bignall/Booker	
G-AYCJ	Cessna TP.206D	White Knuckle Airways Ltd	
G-AYCK	AIA Stampe SV-4C	J. F. Graham (G-BUNT)	
G-AYCN	Piper J-3C-65 Cub	W. R. & B. M. Young	
G-AYCO	CEA DR.360	Charlie Oscar Club	
G-AYCP	Jodel D.112	D. J. Nunn	
G-AYCT	Cessna F.172H	Haimoss Ltd & D. C. Scouller	
G-AYDG	M.S.894A Rallye Minerva	Hunt & Ptnrs Ltd	
G-AYDI	D.H.82A Tiger Moth	R. B. Woods & ptnrs	
G-AYDR	SNCAN Stampe SV-4C	A. J. McLuskie	
G-AYDV	Coates SA.II-1 Swalesong	J. R. Coates	
G-AYDW	A.61 Terrier 2	A. S. Topen	
G-AYDX	A.61 Terrier 2	R. A. Kirby/Barton	
G-AYDY	Luton LA-4A Minor	T. Littlefair	
G-AYDZ	Jodel DR.200	Zero One Group	
G-AYEB	Jodel D.112	C. H. G. Baulf	
G-AYEC	CP.301A Emeraude	Redwing Flying Group	
G-AYED	PA-24 Comanche 260	J. V. Hutchinson	
G-AYEE	PA-28 Cherokee 180E	Halegreen Associates	
G-AYEF	PA-28 Cherokee 180E	G-AYEF Group	
G-AYEG	Falconar F-9	A. L. Smith	
G-AYEH	Jodel DR.1050	John Scott Jodel Group	
G-AYEJ	Jodel DR.1050	J. M. Newbold	
G-AYEN	Piper J-3C-65 Cub	P. Warde & C. F. Morris	
G-AYET	M.S.892A Rallye Commodore 150	A. T. R. Bingley	
G-AYEV	Jodel DR.1050	L. G. Evans/Headcorn	
G-AYEW	Jodel DR.1051	J. M. Gale & J. R. Hope	
G-AYFA	SA Twin Pioneer Srs 3 ★	Solway Aviation Soc/Carlisle	
G-AYFC	D.62B Condor	A. R. Chadwick/Breighton	
G-AYFD	D.62B Condor	B. G. Manning	
G-AYFE	D.62C Condor	D. I. H. Johnstone & W. T. Barnard	
G-AYFF	D.62B Condor	Condor Syndicate	
G-AYFG	D.62C Condor	W. A. Braim	
G-AYFJ	M.S.880B Rallye Club	Rallye FJ Group	
G-AYFP	Jodel D.140	A. R. Wood	
G-AYFV	Crosby BA-4B	A. R. C. Mathie/Norwich	
G-AYGA	Jodel D.117	M. F. Sedgwick	
G-AYGB	Cessna 310Q ★	Instructional airframe/Perth	
G-AYGC	Cessna F.150K	Alpha Aviation Group/Barton	
G-AYGD	Jodel DR.1050	G-AYGD Flying Group	
G-AYGE	SNCAN Stampe SV-4C	L. J. Proudfoot & ptnrs/Booker	
G-AYGG	Jodel D.120	J. M. Dean	
G-AYGX	Cessna FR.172G	Reims Rocket Group/Barton	
G-AYHA	AA-1 Yankee	E. C. Felix	
G-AYHX	Jodel D.117A	L. J. E. Goldfinch	
G-AYHY	Fournier RF-4D	P. M. & S. M. Wells	
G-AYIA	Hughes 369HS ★	G. D. E. Bilton/Sywell	
G-AYIG	PA-28 Cherokee 140C	Biggles Ltd	
G-AYII	PA-28R Cherokee Arrow 200	P. W. J. & P. A. S. Gove/Exeter	
G-AYIJ	SNCAN Stampe SV-4B	T. C. Beadle/Headcorn	
G-AYIM	H.S.748 Srs 2A	Emerald Airways Ltd/Liverpool	
G-AYIT	D.H.82A Tiger Moth	Ulster Tiger Group/Newtownards	
G-AYJA	Jodel DR.1050	G. Connell	
G-AYJB	SNCAN Stampe SV-4C	F. J. M. & J. P. Esson/Middle Wallop	
G-AYJD	Alpavia-Fournier RF-3	E. Shouler	
G-AYJP	PA-28 Cherokee 140C	RAF Brize Norton Flying Club Ltd	
G-AYJR	PA-28 Cherokee 140C	RAF Brize Norton Flying Club Ltd	
G-AYJW	Cessna FR.172G	Sir W. G. Armstrong-Whitworth Flying Group	

Notes	Reg.	Type	Owner or Operator
	G-AYJY	Isaacs Fury II	M. F. Newman
	G-AYKA	Beech 95-B55A Baron	Walsh Bros (Tunnelling) Ltd/Elstree
	G-AYKD	Jodel DR.1050	S. D. Morris
	G-AYKJ	Jodel D.117A	J. M. Alexander
	G-AYKK	Jodel D.117	D. M. Whitham
	G-AYKL	Cessna F.150L	M. A. Judge
	G-AYKS	Leopoldoff L-7	W. B. Cooper
	G-AYKT	Jodel D.117	D. I. Walker & S. A. Chambers
	G-AYKW	PA-28 Cherokee 140C	B. A. Mills
	G-AYKX	PA-28 Cherokee 140C	Robin Flying Group/Woodford
	G-AYKZ	SAI KZ-8	R. E. Mitchell/Cosford
	G-AYLA	Glos-Airtourer 115	D. S. P. Disney
	G-AYLC	Jodel DR.1051	E. W. B. Trollope
	G-AYLF	Jodel DR.1051	Sicile Flying Group
	G-AYLL	Jodel DR.1050	C. Joly
	G-AYLP	AA-1 Yankee	D. Nairn & E. Y. Hawkins
	G-AYLV	Jodel D.120	M. R. Henham
	G-AYLZ	SPP Super Aero 45 Srs 04	M. J. Cobb
	G-AYME	Fournier RF-5	R. D. Goodger/Biggin Hill
	G-AYMK	PA-28 Cherokee 140C	The Piper Flying Group/Newcastle
	G-AYMO	PA-23 Aztec 250C	R. Stephenson
	G-AYMR	Lederlin 380L	P. J. Brayshaw
	G-AYMU	Jodel D.112	M. R. Baker
	G-AYMV	Western 20 balloon	G. F. Turnbull
	G-AYMW	Bell 206A JetRanger 2	PLM Dollar Group Ltd
	G-AYNA	Phoenix Currie Wot	D. Silsbury
	G-AYND	Cessna 310Q	Source Group Ltd/Bournemouth
	G-AYNF	PA-28 Cherokee 140C	BW Aviation
	G-AYNJ	PA-28 Cherokee 140C	R. H. Ribbons
	G-AYNN	Cessna 185B Skywagon	Bencray Ltd/Blackpool
	G-AYNP	W.S.55 Whirlwind Srs 3 ★	IHM/Weston-s-Mare
	G-AYOW	Cessna 182N Skylane	D. W. Parfrey
	G-AYOY	Sikorsky S-61N Mk 2	CHC Scotia Ltd
	G-AYOZ	Cessna FA.150L	S. A. Hughes
	G-AYPE	MBB Bo 209 Monsun	Papa Echo Ltd/Biggin Hill
	G-AYPG	Cessna F.177RG	D. P. McDermott
	G-AYPH	Cessna F.177RG	M. R. & K. E. Slack
	G-AYPI	Cessna F.177RG	Cardinal Aviation Ltd/Guernsey
	G-AYPJ	PA-28 Cherokee 180	Mona Aviation Ltd
	G-AYPM	PA-18 Super Cub 95	R. Horner
	G-AYPO	PA-18 Super Cub 95	A. W. Knowles
	G-AYPR	PA-18 Super Cub 95	D. G. Holman & J. E. Burrell
	G-AYPS	PA-18 Super Cub 95	R. J. Hamlett & ptnrs
	G-AYPT	PA-18 Super Cub 95	B. L. Proctor & T. F. Lyddon
	G-AYPU	PA-28R Cherokee Arrow 200	Monalto Investments Ltd
	G-AYPV	PA-28 Cherokee 140D	Ashley Gardner Flying Club Ltd
	G-AYPZ	Campbell Cricket	A. Melody
	G-AYRF	Cessna F.150L	D. T. A. Rees
	G-AYRG	Cessna F.172K	Comed Aviation Ltd/Blackpool
	G-AYRH	M.S.892A Rallye Commodore 150	J. D. Watt
	G-AYRI	PA-28R Cherokee Arrow 200	A. E. Thompson & Delta Motor Co (Windsor) Sales Ltd/White Waltham
	G-AYRM	PA-28 Cherokee 140D	M. J. Saggers/Biggin Hill
	G-AYRO	Cessna FA.150L Aerobat	Fat Boys Flying Club
	G-AYRS	Jodel D.120A	L. R. H. D'Eath
	G-AYRT	Cessna F.172K	P. E. Crees
	G-AYRU	BN-2A-6 Islander	Army Parachute Association/ Netheravon
	G-AYSA	PA-23 Aztec 250C	R. F. Kuester-Johansson
	G-AYSB	PA-30 Twin Comanche 160C	C. P. Heptonstall
	G-AYSD	Slingsby T.61A Falke	P. W. Hextall
	G-AYSH	Taylor JT.1 Monoplane	C. J. Lodge
	G-AYSJ	Bücker Bü133C Jungmeister (LG+01)	Patina Ltd/Duxford
	G-AYSK	Luton LA-4A Minor	Luton Minor Group
	G-AYSX	Cessna F.177RG	A. P. R. Dean
	G-AYSY	Cessna F.177RG	Horizon Flyers Ltd/Denham
	G-AYTA	SOCATA M.S.880B Rallye Club ★	Manchester Museum of Science & Industry
	G-AYTR	CP.301A Emeraude	G. N. Hopcraft
	G-AYTT	Phoenix PM-3 Duet	H. E. Jenner
	G-AYTV	MJ.2A Tempete	Shoestring Flying Group
	G-AYUA	Auster AOP.9 (XK416)	De Havilland Aviation Ltd/Swansea

Reg.	Type	Owner or Operator	Notes
G-AYUB	CEA DR.253B	D. J. Clark	
G-AYUH	PA-28 Cherokee 180F	C. S. Sidle	
G-AYUJ	Evans VP-1	T. N. Howard	
G-AYUM	Slingsby T.61A Falke	M. H. Simms	
G-AYUN	Slingsby T.61A Falke	C. W. Vigar & R. J. Watts	
G-AYUP	Slingsby T.61A Falke	P. R. Williams	
G-AYUR	Slingsby T.61A Falke	R. Hanningan & R. Lingard	
G-AYUS	Taylor JT.1 Monoplane	R. R. McKinnon	
G-AYUT	Jodel DR.1050	D. M. Whitham	
G-AYUV	Cessna F.172H	Justgold Ltd	
G-AYVO	Wallis WA-120 Srs 1	K. H. Wallis	
G-AYVP	Woody Pusher	J. R. Wraight	
G-AYVT	Brochet MB.84 ★	Dunelm Flying Group (stored)	
G-AYWA	Avro 19 Srs 2 ★	N. K. Geddes	
G-AYWD	Cessna 182N	Wild Dreams Group	
G-AYWE	PA-28 Cherokee 140	Intelcomm (UK) Ltd	
G-AYWH	Jodel D.117A	D. Kynaston & J. Deakin	
G-AYWM	Glos-Airtourer Super 150	The Star Flying Group/Staverton	
G-AYWT	AIA Stampe SV-4C	Dawn Patrol Flight Training Ltd/Thruxton	
G-AYXP	Jodel D.117A	G. N. Davies	
G-AYXS	SIAI-Marchetti S205-18R	T. Montague-Moore/Denham	
G-AYXT	W.S. 55 Whirlwind Srs 2 (XK940) ★	IHM/Weston-s-Mare	
G-AYXU	Champion 7KCAB Citabria	E. T. & P. A. Wild	
G-AYXW	Evans VP-1	J. S. Penny	
G-AYYK	Slingsby T.61A Falke	Cornish Gliding & Flying Club Ltd/ Perranporth	
G-AYYL	Slingsby T.61A Falke	C. Wood	
G-AYYO	Jodel DR.1050/M1	Bustard Flying Club Ltd	
G-AYYT	Jodel DR.1050/M1	Echo November Flight	
G-AYYU	Beech C23 Musketeer	The Beech Group/Sturgate	
G-AYYW	BN-2A-21 Islander	Secretary of State for Foreign & Commonwealth Affairs	
G-AYYX	M.S.880B Ralle Club	J. G. MacDonald	
G-AYZE	PA-39 Twin Comanche 160 C/R	J. E. Palmer/Staverton	
G-AYZI	SNCAN Stampe SV-4C	W. H. Smout	
G-AYZJ	W.S.55 Whirlwind HAS.7 (XM685)★	Newark Air Museum	
G-AYZK	Jodel DR.1050/M1	D. G. Hesketh & R. L. Sambell	
G-AYZS	D.62B Condor	M. N. Thrush	
G-AYZU	Slingsby T.61A Falke	The Falcon Gliding Group/Elstree	
G-AYZW	Slingsby T.61A Falke	Portmoak Falke Syndicate	
G-AZAB	PA-30 Twin Comanche 160B	Bickertons Aerodromes Ltd	
G-AZAJ	PA-28R Cherokee Arrow 200B	J. McHugh & P. Woulfe/Stapleford	
G-AZAW	GY-80 Horizon 160	T. Brown	
G-AZAZ	Bensen B.8M ★	F.A.A. Museum/Yeovilton	
G-AZBA	T.66 Nipper 3	L. A. Brown	
G-AZBB	MBB Bo 209 Monsun 160FV	G. N. Richardson/Staverton	
G-AZBE	Glos-Airtourer Super 150	BE Flying Group/Staverton	
G-AZBI	Jodel 150	F. M. Ward	
G-AZBL	Jodel D.9 Bebe	J. Hill	
G-AZBN	AT-16 Harvard IIB (FT391)	Swaygate Ltd/Shoreham	
G-AZBU	Auster AOP.9 (XR246)	Auster Nine Group	
G-AZBY	W.S.58 Wessex 60 Srs 1 ★	IHM/Weston-s-Mare	
G-AZBZ	W.S.58 Wessex 60 Srs 1 ★	IHM/Weston-s-Mare	
G-AZCB	SNCAN Stampe SV-4C	M. L. Martin	
G-AZCK	B.121 Pup 2	D. R. Newell	
G-AZCL	B.121 Pup 2	J. J. Watts & D. Fletcher	
G-AZCN	B.121 Pup 2	D. M. Callaghan & I. C. Haywood	
G-AZCP	B.121 Pup 1	T. J. Watson/Elstree	
G-AZCT	B.121 Pup 1	J. Coleman	
G-AZCU	B.121 Pup 1	A. A. Harris/Shobdon	
G-AZCV	B.121 Pup 2	N. R. W. Long/Elstree	
G-AZCY	B.121 Pup 2	D. J. Deas	
G-AZCZ	B.121 Pup 2	L. & J. M. Northover/Cardiff-Wales	
G-AZDA	B.121 Pup 1	B. D. Deubelbeiss	
G-AZDD	MBB Bo 209 Monsun 150FF	Double Delta Flying Group/Elstree	
G-AZDE	PA-28R Cherokee Arrow 200B	C. Wilson	
G-AZDG	B.121 Pup 2	D. J. Sage & J. R. Heaps	
G-AZDJ	PA-32 Cherokee Six 300	K. J. Mansbridge & D. C. Gibbs/Cardiff	
G-AZDK	Beech 95-B55 Baron	C. C. Forrester	
G-AZDX	PA-28 Cherokee 180F	M. Cowan	

Notes	Reg.	Type	Owner or Operator
	G-AZDY	D.H.82A Tiger Moth	J. B. Mills
	G-AZEE	M.S.880B Rallye Club	J. Shelton
	G-AZEF	Jodel D.120	D. A. Palmer
	G-AZEG	PA-28 Cherokee 140D	Ashley Gardner Flying Club Ltd
	G-AZEU	B.121 Pup 2	G. M. Moir/Egginton
	G-AZEV	B.121 Pup 2	C. J. Partridge
	G-AZEW	B.121 Pup 2	K. Cameron
	G-AZEY	B.121 Pup 2	M. E. Reynolds
	G-AZFA	B.121 Pup 2	J. Smith/Sandown
	G-AZFC	PA-28 Cherokee 140D	M. L. Hannah/Blackbushe
	G-AZFF	Jodel D.112	D. J. Laughlin
	G-AZFI	PA-28R Cherokee Arrow 200B	G-AZFI Ltd/Sherburn
	G-AZFM	PA-28R Cherokee Arrow 200B	P. J. Jenness
	G-AZFR	Cessna 401B	Westair Flying Services Ltd/Blackpool
	G-AZGA	Jodel D.120	A. F. Vizoso
	G-AZGE	SNCAN Stampe SV-4A	M. R. L. Astor/Booker
	G-AZGF	B.121 Pup 2	K. Singh
	G-AZGI	M.S.880B Rallye Club	B. McIntyre
	G-AZGJ	M.S.880B Rallye Club	P. Rose
	G-AZGL	M.S.894A Rallye Minerva	The Cambridge Aero Club Ltd
	G-AZGY	CP.301B Emeraude	C. J. R. Gray
	G-AZGZ	D.H.82A Tiger Moth (NM181)	R. J. King
	G-AZHB	Robin HR.100-200	C. & P. P. Scarlett/Sywell
	G-AZHC	Jodel D.112	Aerodel Flying Group
	G-AZHD	Slingsby T.61A Falke	N. J. Orchard-Armitage
	G-AZHE	Slingsby T.61B Falke	M. R. Shelton/Tatenhill
	G-AZHH	SA 102.5 Cavalier	D. W. Buckle
	G-AZHI	Glos-Airtourer Super 150	Flying Grasshoppers Ltd
	G-AZHJ	SA Twin Pioneer Srs 3 ★	Air Atlantique Ltd/Coventry
	G-AZHK	Robin HR.100/200B	D. J. Sage (G-ILEG)
	G-AZHR	Piccard Ax6 balloon	C. Fisher
	G-AZHT	Glos-Airtourer T.3	Aviation West Ltd/Glasgow
	G-AZHU	Luton LA-4A Minor	W. Cawrey/Netherthorpe
	G-AZIB	ST-10 Diplomate	W. B. Bateson/Blackpool
	G-AZID	Cessna FA.150L	Aerobat Ltd
	G-AZII	Jodel D.117A	J. S. Brayshaw
	G-AZIJ	Jodel DR.360	K. J. Fleming/Liverpool
	G-AZIK	PA-34-200 Seneca II	Walkbury Aviation Ltd
	G-AZIL	Slingsby T.61A Falke	D. W. Savage/Portmoak
	G-AZIO	SNCAN Stampe SV-4C (Lycoming) ★	–/Booker
	G-AZIP	Cameron O-65 balloon	Dante Balloon Group Dante
	G-AZJC	Fournier RF-5	W. St. G. V. Stoney/Italy
	G-AZJE	Ord-Hume JB-01 Minicab	J. B. Evans/Sandown
	G-AZJN	Robin DR.300/140	Wright Farm Eggs Ltd
	G-AZJV	Cessna F.172L	R. P. Smith
	G-AZJY	Cessna FRA.150L	G. Firbank/Manchester
	G-AZKC	M.S.880B Rallye Club	L. J. Martin/Redhill
	G-AZKE	M.S.880B Rallye Club	D. A. Thompson & S. H. Little
	G-AZKK	Cameron O-56 balloon	Gemini Balloon Group Gemini
	G-AZKO	Cessna F.337F	P. W. Crispe
	G-AZKP	Jodel D.117	B. N. Stevens
	G-AZKR	PA-24 Comanche 180	J. Van Der Kwast
	G-AZKS	AA-1A Trainer	M. D. Henson
	G-AZKW	Cessna F.172L	J. C. C. Wright
	G-AZKZ	Cessna F.172L	R. D. & E. Forster/Swanton Morley
	G-AZLE	Boeing N2S-5 Kaydet (2)	Air Farm Flyers
	G-AZLF	Jodel D.120	M. S. C. Ball
	G-AZLH	Cessna F.150L	Coulson Flying Services Ltd
	G-AZLJ	BN-2A Mk.III-1 Trislander	Hebridean Air Services Ltd (G-OREG/G-OAVW)/Cumbernauld
	G-AZLN	PA-28 Cherokee 180F	Liteflite Ltd/Kidlington
	G-AZLV	Cessna 172K	B. L. F. Karthaus/Newcastle
	G-AZLY	Cessna F.150L	Cleveland Flying School Ltd/Teesside
	G-AZLZ	Cessna F.150L	A. G. Martlew
	G-AZMC	Slingsby T.61A Falke	Essex Gliding Club Ltd
	G-AZMD	Slingsby T.61C Falke	R. A. Rice/Wellesbourne
	G-AZMF	BAC One-Eleven 530FX	European Aircharter Ltd
	G-AZMJ	AA-5 Traveler	R. T. Love/Bodmin
	G-AZMN	Glos-Airtourer T.5	W. Crozier & I. Young
	G-AZMX	PA-28 Cherokee 140 ★	NE Wales Institute of Higher Education (Instructional airframe)/Flintshire
	G-AZMZ	M.S.893A Rallye Commodore 150	P. J. Wilcox/Cranfield

Reg.	Type	Owner or Operator	Notes
G-AZNK	SNCAN Stampe SV-4A	P. D. Jackson & R. A. G. Lucas	
G-AZNL	PA-28R Cherokee Arrow 200D	B. P. Liversidge	
G-AZNO	Cessna 182P	T. & K. Andrews	
G-AZOA	MBB Bo 209 Monsun 150FF	M. W. Hurst	
G-AZOB	MBB Bo 209 Monsun 150FF	G. N. Richardson/Staverton	
G-AZOE	Glos-Airtourer 115	G-AZOE 607 Group/Newcastle	
G-AZOF	Glos-Airtourer Super 150	Cirrus Flying Group/Denham	
G-AZOG	PA-28R Cherokee Arrow 200D	Southend Flying Club	
G-AZOL	PA-34-200 Seneca II	D. I. Barnes	
G-AZOR	MBB Bo 105D	Bond Air Services/Aberdeen	
G-AZOS	Jurca MJ.5-H1 Sirocco	N. M. Robbins	
G-AZOT	PA-34-200 Seneca II	Alliance Aerolink Ltd	
G-AZOU	Jodel DR.1050	Horsham Flying Group/Slinfold	
G-AZOZ	Cessna FRA.150L	Seawing Flying Club Ltd/Southend	
G-AZPA	PA-25 Pawnee 235	Black Mountains Gliding Club Ltd/Talgarth	
G-AZPC	Slingsby T.61C Falke	The Surrey Hills Gliding Club Ltd/Kenley	
G-AZPF	Fournier RF-5	R. Pye/Blackpool	
G-AZPH	Craft-Pitts S-1S Special ★	Science Museum/S. Kensington	
G-AZPV	Luton LA-4A Minor	J. R. Faulkner	
G-AZRA	MBB Bo 209 Monsun 150FF	Alpha Flying Ltd/Denham	
G-AZRD	Cessna 401B	Romeo Delta Group	
G-AZRH	PA-28 Cherokee 140D	Trust Flying Group	
G-AZRK	Fournier RF-5	A. B. Clymo & J. F. Rogers	
G-AZRL	PA-18 Super Cub 95	B. J. Stead	
G-AZRM	Fournier RF-5	A. R. Dearden & R. Speer/Ringmer	
G-AZRN	Cameron O-84 balloon	C. J. Desmet/Belgium	
G-AZRP	Glos-Airtourer 115	B. F. Strawford/Shobdon	
G-AZRR	Cessna 310Q	Routarrow Ltd/Norwich	
G-AZRS	PA-22 Tri-Pacer 150	R. H. Hulls	
G-AZRZ	Cessna U.206F	Hinton Skydiving Centre	
G-AZSA	Stampe et Renard SV-4B	J. K. Faulkner/Biggin Hill	
G-AZSC	AT-16 Harvard IIB (43)	Machine Music Ltd/Duxford	
G-AZSD	Slingsby T.29B Motor Tutor	Essex Aviation	
G-AZSF	PA-28R Cherokee Arrow 200D	Flight Simulation/Coventry	
G-AZSW	B.121 Pup 1	J. R. Parry	
G-AZSZ	PA-23 Aztec 250D	International Cladding Systems Ltd	
G-AZTA	MBB Bo 209 Monsun 150FF	Just Plane	
G-AZTF	Cessna F.177RG	D. A. Wiggins	
G-AZTK	Cessna F.172F	S. O'Ceallaigh	
G-AZTS	Cessna F.172L	C. E. Stringer	
G-AZTV	Stolp SA.500 Starlet	G. R. Rowland	
G-AZTW	Cessna F.177RG	I. M. Richmond	
G-AZUM	Cessna F.172L	Fowlmere Fliers	
G-AZUP	Cameron O-65 balloon	R. S. Bailey & A. B. Simpson	
G-AZUT	M.S.893A Rallye Commodore 180	J. Palethorpe	
G-AZUV	Cameron O-65 balloon ★	British Balloon Museum/Newbury	
G-AZUY	Cessna E.310L	W. B. Bateson/Blackpool	
G-AZUZ	Cessna FRA.150L	D. J. Parker/Netherthorpe	
G-AZVA	MBB Bo 209 Monsun 150FF	J. Nivison	
G-AZVB	MBB Bo 209 Monsun 150FF	M. H. James & D, Shrimpton	
G-AZVF	M.S.894A Rallye Minerva	Minerva Flying Group	
G-AZVG	AA-5 Traveler	Whelan Building & Development Ltd	
G-AZVH	M.S.894A Rallye Minerva	P. L. Jubb	
G-AZVI	M.S.892A Rallye Commodore	Shobdon Flying Group	
G-AZVJ	PA-34-200 Seneca II	Andrews Professional Colour Laboratories Ltd/Lydd	
G-AZVL	Jodel D.119	Forest Flying Group/Stapleford	
G-AZVM	Hughes 369HS	GTS Engineering (Coventry) Ltd	
G-AZVP	Cessna F.177RG	Cardinal Flyers Ltd	
G-AZWB	PA-28 Cherokee 140	B. N. Rides & L. Connor	
G-AZWD	PA-28 Cherokee 140	BM Aviation (Winchester)	
G-AZWE	PA-28 Cherokee 140	G-AZWE Flying Group	
G-AZWF	SAN Jodel DR.1050	Cawdor Flying Group	
G-AZWS	PA-28R Cherokee Arrow 180	Arrow 88 Flying Group/Newcastle	
G-AZWT	Westland Lysander IIIA (V9367)	The Shuttleworth Collection/O. Warden	
G-AZWY	PA-24 Comanche 260	Keymer Son & Co Ltd/Biggin Hill	
G-AZXA	Beech 95-C55 Baron	F.R. Aviation Ltd/Bournemouth	
G-AZXB	Cameron O-65 balloon	R. J. Mitchener & P. F. Smart	
G-AZXC	Cessna F.150L	D. C. Bonsall	
G-AZXD	Cessna F.172L	Birdlake Ltd/Wellesbourne	
G-AZXG	PA-23 Aztec 250D ★	*Instructional airframe*/Cranfield	
G-AZYA	GY-80 Horizon 160	P. J. Fahie	
G-AZYB	Bell 47H-1 ★	IHM/Weston-s-Mare	

Notes	Reg.	Type	Owner or Operator
	G-AZYD	M.S.893A Rallye Commodore	Storey Aviation Services
	G-AZYM	Cessna 310Q	Offshore Marine Consultants
	G-AZYS	CP.301C-1 Emeraude	C. G. Ferguson & D. Drew
	G-AZYU	PA-23 Aztec 250E	L. J. Martin/Biggin Hill
	G-AZYY	Slingsby T.61A Falke	J. A. Towers
	G-AZYZ	WA.51A Pacific	C. R. Buxton/France
	G-AZZH	Practavia Pilot Sprite 115	A. Moore
	G-AZZO	PA-28 Cherokee 140	R. J. Hind/Elstree
	G-AZZR	Cessna F.150L	G-AZZR Flying Group
	G-AZZS	PA-34-200 Seneca II	Robin Cook Aviation/Shoreham
	G-AZZT	PA-28 Cherokee 180 ★	Ground instruction airframe/Cranfield
	G-AZZV	Cessna F.172L	Cristal Air Ltd
	G-AZZZ	D.H.82A Tiger Moth	S. W. McKay
	G-BAAD	Evans Super VP-1	Breighton VP-1 Group
	G-BAAF	Manning-Flanders MF1 (replica)	Aviation Film Services Ltd/Booker
	G-BAAI	M.S.893A Rallye Commodore	R. D. Taylor/Thruxton
	G-BAAL	Cessna 172A	M. J. McRobert
	G-BAAT	Cessna 182P	Melrose Pigs Ltd
	G-BAAU	Enstrom F-28A-UK	G. Firbank
	G-BAAW	Jodel D.119	Alpha Whiskey Flying Group
	G-BABB	Cessna F.150L	Seawing Flying Club Ltd/Southend
	G-BABC	Cessna F.150L	Fordaire Ltd/Sywell
	G-BABD	Cessna FRA.150L (modified)	Anglia Flight
	G-BABE	Taylor JT.2 Titch	M. Bonsall/Netherthorpe
	G-BABG	PA-28 Cherokee 180	Mendip Flying Group/Bristol
	G-BABH	Cessna F.150L	Tindon Ltd/Little Snoring
	G-BABK	PA-34-200 Seneca II	D. F. J. Flashman/Biggin Hill
	G-BACB	PA-34-200 Seneca II	Halegreen Associates Ltd & G-BACB Ltd
	G-BACC	Cessna FRA.150L	C. M. & J. H. Cooper/Cranfield
	G-BACE	Fournier RF-5	R. W. K. Stead/Perranporth
	G-BACJ	Jodel D.120	Wearside Flying Association/Newcastle
	G-BACL	Jodel 150	M. L. Sargeant/Biggin Hill
	G-BACN	Cessna FRA.150L	Cornwall Flying Club Ltd/Bodmin
	G-BACO	Cessna FRA.150L	M. M. Pepper/Sibson
	G-BACP	Cessna FRA.150L	Vectair Aviation 1995 Ltd
	G-BADC	Rollason Beta B.2A	D. H. Greenwood
	G-BADH	Slingsby T.61A Falke	Falke Flying Group
	G-BADI	PA-23 Aztec 250D ★	Aces High Ltd/North Weald
	G-BADJ	PA-E23 Aztec 250E	C. Papadakis/Kidlington
	G-BADM	D.62B Condor	M. Harris & J. St. J. Mehta
	G-BADW	Pitts S-2A Special	R. E. Mitchell/Cosford
	G-BADZ	Pitts S-2A Special	A. F. D. Kingdon
	G-BAEB	Robin DR.400/160	P. D. W. King
	G-BAEC	Robin HR.100/210	Datacorp Enterprises Pty Ltd
	G-BAEE	Jodel DR.1050/M1	R. Little
	G-BAEM	Robin DR.400/125	M. A. Webb/Booker
	G-BAEN	Robin DR.400/180	European Soaring Club Ltd
	G-BAEO	Cessna F.172M	L. W. Scattergood
	G-BAEP	Cessna FRA.150L (modified)	A. M. Lynn
	G-BAER	Cosmic Wind	R. S. Voice/Redhill
	G-BAET	Piper J-3C-65 Cub	C. J. Rees
	G-BAEU	Cessna F.150L	L. W. Scattergood
	G-BAEV	Cessna FRA.L150L	Richard Technology Ltd
	G-BAEW	Cessna F.172M ★	Westley Aircraft/Cranfield
	G-BAEY	Cessna F.172M	Skytrax Aviation Ltd
	G-BAEZ	Cessna FRA.150L	Donair Flying Club Ltd/E. Midlands
	G-BAFA	AA-5 Traveler	C. F. Mackley/Stapleford
	G-BAFG	D.H.82A Tiger Moth	J. E. & P. J. Shaw
	G-BAFL	Cessna 182P	M. A. Pruden
	G-BAFP	Robin DR.400/160	A. S. Langdale & J. Bevis-Lawson
	G-BAFT	PA-18 Super Cub 150	T. J. Wilkinson/Riseley
	G-BAFU	PA-28 Cherokee 140	D. Matthews
	G-BAFV	PA-18 Super Cub 95	T. F. & S. J. Thorpe
	G-BAFW	PA-28 Cherokee 140	S. S. Delwarte
	G-BAFX	Robin DR.400/140	K. R. Gough
	G-BAGB	SIAI-Marchetti SF.260	British Midland Airways Ltd/E. Midlands
	G-BAGC	Robin DR.400/140	W. P. Nutt
	G-BAGE	Cessna T.210L ★	Aeroplane Collection Ltd
	G-BAGF	Jodel D.92 Bebe	E. Evans
	G-BAGG	PA-32 Cherokee Six 300E	G-BAGG Group
	G-BAGL	SA.341G Gazelle Srs 1	Foremans Aviation Ltd
	G-BAGN	Cessna F.177RG	R. W. J. Andrews

Reg.	Type	Owner or Operator	Notes
G-BAGO	Cessna 421B	Golden Aviation Ltd	
G-BAGR	Robin DR.400/140	F. C. Aris & J. D. Last/Mona	
G-BAGS	Robin DR.400/180 2+2	M. Whale & M. W. A. Lunn	
G-BAGT	Helio H.295 Courier	B. J. C. Woodall Ltd	
G-BAGV	Cessna U.206F	Scottish Parachute Club/Strathallan	
G-BAGX	PA-28 Cherokee 140	Golf X-Ray Group	
G-BAGY	Cameron O-84 balloon	P. G. Dunnington	
G-BAHD	Cessna 182P Skylane	G. G. Ferriman	
G-BAHE	PA-28 Cherokee 140	M. W. Kilvert & A. O. Jones	
G-BAHF	PA-28 Cherokee 140	BJ Services (Midlands) Ltd	
G-BAHG	PA-24 Comanche 260	D. G. Sheppard/Earls Colne	
G-BAHH	Wallis WA-121	K. H. Wallis	
G-BAHI	Cessna F.150H	I. S. McLeod	
G-BAHJ	PA-24 Comanche 250	K. Cooper	
G-BAHL	Robin DR.400/160	M. D. Hinge & L. A. Maynard	
G-BAHO	Beech C.23 Sundowner	P. H. White & J. A. L. Staig	
G-BAHP	Volmer VJ.22 Sportsman	Seaplane Group	
G-BAHS	PA-28R Cherokee Arrow 200-II	A. R. N. Morris	
G-BAHX	Cessna 182P	Dupost Group	
G-BAIG	PA-34-200-2 Seneca	Mid-Anglia School of Flying	
G-BAIH	PA-28R Cherokee Arrow 200-II	M. G. West	
G-BAII	Cessna FRA.150L	Cornwall Flying Club Ltd/Bodmin	
G-BAIK	Cessna F.150L	Wickenby Aviation Ltd	
G-BAIN	Cessna FRA.150L	S. J. Windle/Bodmin	
G-BAIP	Cessna F.150L	G. & S. A. Jones	
G-BAIS	Cessna F.177RG	Cardinal Syndicate	
G-BAIW	Cessna F.172M	W. J. Greenfield/Humberside	
G-BAIX	Cessna F.172M	R. A. Nichols/Elstree	
G-BAIZ	Slingsby T.61A Falke	Falke Syndicate/Hinton-in-the-Hedges	
G-BAJA	Cessna F.177RG	Don Ward Productions Ltd/Biggin Hill	
G-BAJB	Cessna F.177RG	C. M. Bain	
G-BAJC	Evans VP-1	S. J. Greer	
G-BAJE	Cessna 177	T. Barge	
G-BAJN	AA-5 Traveler	H. Snelson	
G-BAJO	AA-5 Traveler	G-BAJO Group	
G-BAJR	PA-28 Cherokee 180	Chosen Few Flying Group/Newtownards	
G-BAJY	Robin DR.400/180	Rolines Aviation	
G-BAJZ	Robin DR.400/125	Rochester Aviation Ltd	
G-BAKD	PA-34-200 Seneca II	Andrews Professional Colour Laboratories/Elstree	
G-BAKH	PA-28 Cherokee 140	Marnham Investments Ltd	
G-BAKJ	PA-30 Twin Comanche 160B	G. D. Colover & ptnrs	
G-BAKK	Cessna F.172H ★	*Parachute jump trainer*/Hinton-in-the-Hedges	
G-BAKM	Robin DR.400/140	D. V. Pieri	
G-BAKN	SNCAN Stampe SV-4C	M. Holloway	
G-BAKR	Jodel D.117	R. W. Brown	
G-BAKV	PA-18 Super Cub 150	A. J. B. Shaw & ptnrs/Thruxton	
G-BAKW	B.121 Pup 2	H. Beavan	
G-BAKY	Slingsby T.61C Falke	Buckminster Gliding Club Ltd/Saltby	
G-BALF	Robin DR.400/140	G. & D. A. Wasey	
G-BALG	Robin DR.400/180	R. Jones	
G-BALH	Robin DR.400/140B	G-BALH Flying Group	
G-BALI	Robin DR.400 2+2	A. Brinkley	
G-BALJ	Robin DR.400/180	D. A. Bett & D. de Lacey-Rowe	
G-BALN	Cessna T.310Q	O'Brien Properties Ltd/Shoreham	
G-BALZ	Bell 212	Bristow Helicopters Ltd	
G-BAMB	Slingsby T.61C Falke	G-BAMB Syndicate	
G-BAMC	Cessna F.150L	Systems & Research Ltd	
G-BAMF	MBB Bo 105D	Bond Air Services/Aberdeen	
G-BAMJ	Cessna 182P	A. E. Kedros	
G-BAMK	Cameron D-96 airship ★	British Balloon Museum	
G-BAML	Bell 206B JetRanger 2	Heliscott Ltd	
G-BAMM	PA-28 Cherokee 235	T. A. Astell	
G-BAMR	PA-16 Clipper	H. Royce	
G-BAMS	Robin DR.400/160	G-BAMS Ltd/Headcorn	
G-BAMU	Robin DR.400/160	The Alternative Flying Group	
G-BAMV	Robin DR.400/180	K. Jones & E. A. Anderson/Booker	
G-BAMY	PA-28R Cherokee Arrow 200-II	G-BAMY Group/Birmingham	
G-BANA	Robin DR.221	G. T. Pryor	
G-BANB	Robin DR.400/180	D. R. L. Jones	
G-BANC	GY-201 Minicab	J. T. S. Lewis & J. E. Williams	
G-BANU	Wassmer Jodel D.120	W. M. & C. H. Kilner	

Notes	Reg.	Type	Owner or Operator
	G-BANV	Phoenix Currie Wot	K. Knight
	G-BANW	CP.1330 Super Emeraude	P. S. Milner
	G-BANX	Cessna F.172M	Oakfleet 2000 Ltd
	G-BAOB	Cessna F.172M	M. Nicholl & ptnrs/Earls Colne
	G-BAOG	M.S.880B Rallye Club	J. Luck
	G-BAOH	M.S.880B Rallye Club	A. P. Swain
	G-BAOJ	M.S.880B Rallye Club	R. E. Jones
	G-BAOM	M.S.880B Rallye Club	P. J. D. Feehan
	G-BAOP	Cessna FRA.150L	S. A. Boyall
	G-BAOS	Cessna F.172M	Wingtask 1995 Ltd
	G-BAOU	AA-5 Traveler	R. C. Mark
	G-BAPB	D.H.C.1 Chipmunk 22	G. V. Bunyan
	G-BAPI	Cessna FRA.150L	Industrial Supplies (Peterborough) Ltd/ Sibson
	G-BAPJ	Cessna FRA.150L	M. D. Page/Manston
	G-BAPL	PA-23 Turbo Aztec 250E	Donington Aviation Ltd/E. Midlands
	G-BAPR	Jodel D.11	J. B. Liber & J. F. M. Bartlett
	G-BAPS	Campbell Cougar ★	IHM/Weston-s-Mare
	G-BAPV	Robin DR.400/160	J. D. & M. Millne/Newcastle
	G-BAPW	PA-28R Cherokee Arrow 180	I. W. Lindsey & P. S. Ferren/Elstree
	G-BAPX	Robin DR.400/160	G-BAPX Group
	G-BAPY	Robin HR.100/210	D. M. Hansell
	G-BARC	Cessna FR.172J	Severn Valley Aviation Group
	G-BARF	Jodel D.112 Club	J. J. Penney
	G-BARG	Cessna E.310Q	Tibus Aviation Ltd
	G-BARH	Beech C.23 Sundowner	J. R. Pybus
	G-BARN	Taylor JT.2 Titch	R. G. W. Newton
	G-BARP	Bell 206B JetRanger 2	S.W. Electricity Board/Bristol
	G-BARS	D.H.C.1 Chipmunk 22 (1377)	J. Beattie/Yeovilton
	G-BARV	Cessna 310Q	Old England Watches Ltd/Elstree
	G-BARZ	Scheibe SF.28A Tandem Falke	K. Kiely
	G-BASH	AA-5 Traveler	BASH Flying Group
	G-BASJ	PA-28 Cherokee 180	Challenger Flying Group
	G-BASL	PA-28 Cherokee 140	Justgold Ltd
	G-BASM	PA-34-200 Seneca II	M. Gipps & J. R. Whetlor
	G-BASN	Beech C.23 Sundowner	M. F. Fisher
	G-BASO	Lake LA-4 Amphibian	C. J. A. Macauley
	G-BASP	B.121 Pup 1	B. J. Coutts/Sywell
	G-BASX	PA-34-200 Seneca II	Air Consul SL/Spain
	G-BATC	MBB Bo 105D	Bond Air Services/Aberdeen
	G-BATJ	Jodel D.119	D. J. & K. S. Thomas
	G-BATN	PA-23 Aztec 250E	Marshall of Cambridge Ltd
	G-BATR	PA-34-200 Seneca II	Falcon Flying Services/Biggin Hill
	G-BATV	PA-28 Cherokee 180D	J. N. Rudsdale
	G-BATW	PA-28 Cherokee 140	Tango Whiskey Flying Partnership
	G-BAUC	PA-25 Pawnee 235	Southdown Gliding Club Ltd/Parham Park
	G-BAUH	Jodel D.112	G. A. & D. Shepherd
	G-BAUJ	PA-23 Aztec 250E ★	S. Bramwell/Cranfield
	G-BAUW	PA-23 Aztec 250E	R. E. Myson
	G-BAUZ	SNCAN NC.854S	W. A. Ashley & D. Horne
	G-BAVB	Cessna F.172M	C. P. Course
	G-BAVH	D.H.C.1 Chipmunk 22	Portsmouth Naval Gliding Club/ Lee-on-Solent
	G-BAVL	PA-23 Aztec 250E	S. P. & A. V. Chillott
	G-BAVO	Boeing Stearman N2S (26)	M. Shaw
	G-BAVR	AA-5 Traveler	G. E. Murray
	G-BAVZ	PA-23 Aztec 250E	Ravenair/Liverpool
	G-BAWG	PA-28R Cherokee Arrow 200-II	Solent Air Ltd
	G-BAWK	PA-28 Cherokee 140	Newcastle-upon-Tyne Aero Club Ltd
	G-BAWR	Robin HR.100/210	T. Taylor
	G-BAXE	Hughes 269A	Reethorpe Engineering Ltd
	G-BAXJ	PA-32 Cherokee Six 300B	UK Parachute Services/Stirling
	G-BAXK	Thunder Ax7-77 balloon ★	A. R. Snook
	G-BAXS	Bell 47G-5	RK Helicopters
	G-BAXU	Cessna F.150L	M. A. Wilson/Liverpool
	G-BAXV	Cessna F.150L	G. & S. A. Jones
	G-BAXY	Cessna F.172M	Eaglesoar Ltd
	G-BAXZ	PA-28 Cherokee 140	H. Martin & D. Norris/Halton
	G-BAYL	SNCAN Nord 1101 Norecrin ★	(stored)/Chirk
	G-BAYO	Cessna 150L	Messrs Rees of Poyston West
	G-BAYP	Cessna 150L	Yankee Papa Flying Group
	G-BAYR	Robin HR.100/210	L. A. Christie/Stapleford

Reg.	Type	Owner or Operator	Notes
G-BAYV	SNCAN 1101 Noralpha (3+) ★	Macclesfield Historical Aviation Soc/Barton	
G-BAZC	Robin DR.400/160	Southern Sailplanes Ltd/Membury	
G-BAZJ	HPR-7 Herald 209 ★	Guernsey Airport Fire Services	
G-BAZM	Jodel D.11	A. F. Simpson	
G-BAZS	Cessna F.150L	L. W. Scattergood	
G-BAZT	Cessna F.172M	Exeter Flying Club Ltd	
G-BAZU	PA-28R Cherokee Arrow 200	S. C. Simmons/White Waltham	
G-BBAK	M.S.894A Rallye Minerva	J. E. Selman	
G-BBAW	Robin HR.100/210	J. R. Williams	
G-BBAX	Robin DR.400/140	G. J. Bissex & P. H. Garbutt	
G-BBAY	Robin DR.400/140	Rothwell Group	
G-BBBC	Cessna F.150L	W. J. Greenfield	
G-BBBI	AA-5 Traveler	J. C. McCaig	
G-BBBK	PA-28 Cherokee 140	Bencray Ltd/Blackpool	
G-BBBN	PA-28 Cherokee 180	Estuary Aviation Ltd	
G-BBBO	SIPA 903	Mersey SIPA Group/Liverpool	
G-BBBW	FRED Srs 2	M. Palfreman	
G-BBBX	Cessna 310L	Atlantic Air Transport Ltd/Coventry	
G-BBBY	PA-28 Cherokee 140	G-BBBY Syndicate	
G-BBCA	Bell 206B JetRanger 2	Heliflight (UK) Ltd/Wolverhampton	
G-BBCC	PA-23 Aztec 250D	County Garage (Cheltenham) Ltd	
G-BBCH	Robin DR.400/2+2	A. J. & S. P. Smith	
G-BBCI	Cessna 150H	A. M. Alam	
G-BBCK	Cameron O-77 balloon	W. R. Teasdale	
G-BBCN	Robin HR.100/210	Gloucestershire Flying Club	
G-BBCS	Robin DR.400/140	Westfield Flying Group	
G-BBCW	PA-23 Aztec 250E	JDT Holdings Ltd/Sturgate	
G-BBCY	Luton LA-4A Minor	G. I. Ciupka	
G-BBCZ	AA-5 Traveler	Southern Flight Centre Ltd/Shoreham	
G-BBDC	PA-28 Cherokee 140	G-BBDC Group	
G-BBDE	PA-28R Cherokee Arrow 200-II	R. L. Coleman & A. E. Stevens/ Panshanger	
G-BBDG	Concorde 100 ★	British Aerospace PLC/Filton	
G-BBDH	Cessna F.172M	J. C. Holland	
G-BBDL	AA-5 Traveler	Delta Lima Flying Group	
G-BBDM	AA-5 Traveler	P. J. Marchant	
G-BBDO	PA-23 Turbo Aztec 250E	J. W. Anstee/Bristol	
G-BBDP	Robin DR.400/160	Robin Lance Aviation Associates Ltd	
G-BBDT	Cessna 150H	Delta Tango Group	
G-BBDV	SIPA S.903	W. McAndrew	
G-BBEA	Luton LA-4 Minor	Luton Group	
G-BBEB	PA-28R Cherokee Arrow 200-II	R. D. Rippingale/Thruxton	
G-BBEC	PA-28 Cherokee 180	A. A. Gardner	
G-BBED	M.S.894A Rallye Minerva 220	Vista Products	
G-BBEF	PA-28 Cherokee 140	Comed Aviation Ltd/Blackpool	
G-BBEL	PA-28R Cherokee Arrow 180	S. J. Weaving & K. S. Kalsi	
G-BBEN	Bellanca 7GCBC Citabria	C. A. G. Schofield	
G-BBEO	Cessna FRA.150L	Airx Ltd	
G-BBEV	PA-28 Cherokee 140	Comed Aviation Ltd/Blackpool	
G-BBEX	Cessna 185A	V. M. McCarthy	
G-BBEY	PA-23 Aztec 250E	M. Hall	
G-BBFD	PA-28R Cherokee Arrow 200-II	CR Aviation Ltd	
G-BBFL	GY-201 Minicab	D. Silsbury	
G-BBFV	PA-32 Cherokee Six 260	Airlaunch	
G-BBGB	PA-E23 Aztec 250E	Ravenair/Liverpool	
G-BBGC	M.S.893E Rallye 180GT	Seahawk Glding Club/Culdrose	
G-BBGI	Fuji FA.200-160	M. S. Bird	
G-BBGL	Baby Great Lakes	F. Ball	
G-BBGR	Cameron O-65 balloon	M. L. & L. P. Willoughby	
G-BBGX	Cessna 182P Skylane	GX Group	
G-BBHE	Enstrom F-28A	Clarke Aviation Ltd	
G-BBHF	PA-23 Aztec 250E	G. J. Williams/Sherburn	
G-BBHI	Cessna 177RG	T. G. W. Bunce	
G-BBHJ	Piper J-3C-65 Cub	R. V. Miller & J. Stanbridge	
G-BBHK	AT-16 Harvard IIB (FH153)	Bob Warner Aviation/Exeter	
G-BBHL	Sikorsky S-61N Mk II	Bristow Helicopters Ltd Glamis	
G-BBHM	Sikorsky S-61N	Bristow Helicopters Ltd	
G-BBHY	PA-28 Cherokee 180	Air Operations Ltd/Guernsey	
G-BBIA	PA-28R Cherokee Arrow 200-II	G. H. Kilby/Stapleford	
G-BBIF	PA-23 Aztec 250E	Home Doors (GB) Ltd	

Notes	Reg.	Type	Owner or Operator
	G-BBIH	Enstrom F-28A-UK	Stephenson Marine Co Ltd
	G-BBII	Fiat G-46-3B (14+)	Godshill Aviation/Sandown
	G-BBIL	PA-28 Cherokee 140	India Lima Flying Group
	G-BBIO	Robin HR.100/210	R. A. King/Headcorn
	G-BBIX	PA-28 Cherokee 140	Sterling Aviation Ltd
	G-BBJB	Thunder Ax7-77 balloon	St Crispin Balloon Group
	G-BBJI	Isaacs Spitfire (RN218)	T. E. W. Terrell
	G-BBJU	Robin DR.400/140	J. C. Lister
	G-BBJV	Cessna F.177RG	3grcomm Ltd
	G-BBJX	Cessna F.150L	L. W. Scattergood
	G-BBJY	Cessna F.172M	J. Lucketti/Barton
	G-BBJZ	Cessna F.172M	Burks, Green & ptnrs
	G-BBKA	Cessna F.150L	W. M. Wilson & R. Campbell
	G-BBKB	Cessna F.150L	Justgold Ltd/Blackpool
	G-BBKE	Cessna F.150L	J. D. Woodward
	G-BBKF	Cessna FRA.150L	D. W. Mickleburgh
	G-BBKG	Cessna FR.172J	R. Wright
	G-BBKI	Cessna F.172M	C. W. & S. A. Burman
	G-BBKL	CP.301A Emeraude	Piel G-BBKL
	G-BBKR	Scheibe SF.24A Motorspatz	P. I. Morgans
	G-BBKU	Cessna FRA.150L	Penguin Group
	G-BBKX	PA-28 Cherokee 180	DRA Flying Club Ltd/Farnborough
	G-BBKY	Cessna F.150L	Telesonic Ltd/Barton
	G-BBKZ	Cessna 172M	KZ Flying Group/Exeter
	G-BBLH	Piper J-3C-65 Cub (31145)	Shipping & Airlines Ltd/Biggin Hill
	G-BBLL	Cameron O-84 balloon ★	British Balloon Museum/Newbury
	G-BBLM	SOCATA Rallye 100S	Oakmast Systems Ltd
	G-BBLS	AA-5 Traveler	A. D. Grant
	G-BBLU	PA-34-200 Seneca II	Falcon Flying Services/Biggin Hill
	G-BBMB	Robin DR.400/180	Regent Flying Group
	G-BBMH	EAA. Sports Biplane Model P.1	I. S. Parker
	G-BBMJ	PA-23 Aztec 250E	Tindon Ltd/Little Snoring
	G-BBMN	D.H.C.1 Chipmunk 22	R. Steiner/Rush Green
	G-BBMO	D.H.C.1 Chipmunk 22	D. M. Squires/Wellesbourn
	G-BBMR	D.H.C.1 Chipmunk 22 (WB763)	A. J. Parkhouse
	G-BBMT	D.H.C.1 Chipmunk 22	J. Evans & D. Withers
	G-BBMV	D.H.C.1 Chipmunk 22 (WG348)	P. J. Morgan (Aviation) Ltd
	G-BBMW	D.H.C.1 Chipmunk 22 (WK628)	Mike Whisky Group/Shoreham
	G-BBMX	D.H.C.1 Chipmunk 22	K. A. Doornbos/Netherlands
	G-BBMZ	D.H.C.1 Chipmunk 22	Wycombe Gliding School Syndicate/ Booker
	G-BBNA	D.H.C.1 Chipmunk 22 (Lycoming)	Coventry Gliding Club Ltd/ Husbands Bosworth
	G-BBNC	D.H.C.1 Chipmunk T.10 (WP790) ★	De Havilland Heritage Museum
	G-BBND	D.H.C.1 Chipmunk 22 (WD286)	Bernoulli Syndicate
	G-BBNG	Bell 206B JetRanger 2	Helicopter Crop Spraying Ltd
	G-BBNH	PA-34-200 Seneca II	M. G. D. Baverstock/Bournemouth
	G-BBNI	PA-34-200 Seneca II	Noisy Moose Ltd
	G-BBNJ	Cessna F.150L	Sherburn Aero Club Ltd
	G-BBNO	PA-23 Aztec 250E ★	(stored)/Biggin Hill
	G-BBNV	Fuji FA.200-160	Caseright Ltd
	G-BBNX	Cessna FRA.150L	General Airline Ltd/Blackbushe
	G-BBNZ	Cessna F.172M	R. J. Nunn
	G-BBOA	Cessna F.172M	J. D & A. M. Black
	G-BBOC	Cameron O-77 balloon	J. A. B. Gray
	G-BBOD	Thunder O-45 balloon	B. R. & M. Boyle
	G-BBOH	Pitts S-1S Special	Venom Jet Promotions Ltd/Bournemouth
	G-BBOJ	PA-23 Aztec 250E ★	Instructional airframe/Cranfield
	G-BBOL	PA-18 Super Cub 150	Lakes Gliding Club Ltd/Walney Island
	G-BBOO	Thunder Ax6-56 balloon	K. Meehan Tigerjack
	G-BBOR	Bell 206B JetRanger 2	M. J. Easey
	G-BBOX	Thunder Ax7-77 balloon	R. C. Weyda
	G-BBPN	Enstrom F-28A-UK	Smarta Systems Ltd
	G-BBPO	Enstrom F-28A-UK	Wilco (Helicopters) Ltd/Shoreham
	G-BBPS	Jodel D.117	A. Appleby/Redhill
	G-BBPW	Robin HR.100/210	S. D. Cole
	G-BBPX	PA-34-200 Seneca II	Richel Investments Ltd/Guernsey
	G-BBPY	PA-28 Cherokee 180	Sunsaver Ltd
	G-BBRA	PA-23 Aztec 250D	R. C. Lough/Elstree
	G-BBRB	D.H.82A Tiger Moth (DF198)	R. Barham/Biggin Hill
	G-BBRC	Fuji FA.200-180	BBRC Ltd/Blackbushe
	G-BBRI	Bell 47G-5A	Alan Mann Helicopters Ltd/Fairoaks

Reg.	Type	Owner or Operator	Notes
G-BBRN	Procter Kittiwake 1 (XW784)	R. de H. Dobree-Carey	
G-BBRV	D.H.C.1 Chipmunk 22 (WD347)	J. A. Keen & H. M. Farrelly/Liverpool	
G-BBRX	SIAI-Marchetti S.205-18F	R. C. & A. K. West	
G-BBRZ	AA-5 Traveler	C. P. Osbourne	
G-BBSA	AA-5 Traveler	Usworth 84 Flying Associates Ltd	
G-BBSB	Beech C23 Sundowner	Sundowner Group/Woodford	
G-BBSM	PA-32 Cherokee Six 300E	MT Management Ltd	
G-BBSS	D.H.C.1A Chipmunk 22	Coventry Gliding Club Ltd/ Husbands Bosworth	
G-BBSW	Pietenpol Air Camper	J. K. S. Wills	
G-BBTB	Cessna FRA.150L	BBC Air Ltd/Compton Abbas	
G-BBTG	Cessna F.172M	R. W. & V. P. J. Simpson/Redhill	
G-BBTH	Cessna F.172M	K. Kwok-Kin Lee	
G-BBTJ	PA-23 Aztec 250E	Cooper Aerial Surveys Ltd/Sandtoft	
G-BBTK	Cessna FRA.150L	Cleveland Flying School Ltd/Teesside	
G-BBTL	PA-23 Aztec 250C	Air Navigation & Trading Co Ltd/Blackpool	
G-BBTS	Beech V35B Bonanza	Eastern Air	
G-BBTU	ST-10 Diplomate	D. Hayden-Wright	
G-BBTX	Beech C23 Sundowner	K. Harding/Blackbushe	
G-BBTY	Beech C23 Sundowner	A. W. Roderick & W. Price/Cardiff-Wales	
G-BBTZ	Cessna F.150L	Marnham Investments Ltd	
G-BBUE	AA-5 Traveler	Hebog (Mon) Cyfyngedig/Mona	
G-BBUF	AA-5 Traveler	W. McLaren	
G-BBUG	PA-16 Clipper	J. Dolan	
G-BBUJ	Cessna 421B	Coolflourish Ltd	
G-BBUT	Western O-65 balloon	G. F. Turnbull	
G-BBUU	Piper J-3C-65 Cub	O. J. J. Rogers	
G-BBUW	SA.102.5 Cavalier ★	Aeroplane Collection Ltd	
G-BBVA	Sikorsky S-61N Mk II	Bristow Helicopters Ltd Vega	
G-BBVF	SA Twin Pioneer Srs 3 ★	Museum of Flight/E. Fortune	
G-BBVG	PA-23 Aztec 250C ★	(stored)/Little Staughton	
G-BBVJ	Beech B24R Sierra	T. Keely	
G-BBVO	Isaacs Fury II (S1579)	J. Moore	
G-BBWZ	AA-1B Trainer	Telco Trading Ltd	
G-BBXB	Cessna FRA.150L	D. M. Fenton	
G-BBXH	Cessna FR.172F	D. Ridley	
G-BBXK	PA-34-200 Seneca	Poyston Aviation	
G-BBXL	Cessna 310Q	Appleton Aviation Ltd	
G-BBXO	Enstrom F-28A	Stephenson Marine Ltd	
G-BBXS	Piper J-3C-65 Cub	M. J. Butler (G-ALMA)/Langham	
G-BBXY	Bellanca 7GCBC Citabria	R. R. L. Windus	
G-BBXZ	Evans VP-1	R. W. Burrows	
G-BBYB	PA-18 Super Cub 95	Tiger Club (1990) Ltd/Headcorn	
G-BBYH	Cessna 182P	Croftmarsh Ltd	
G-BBYM	H.P.137 Jetstream 200 ★	Aerospace Museum (G-AYWR)/Cosford	
G-BBYP	PA-28 Cherokee 140	Jersey Aircraft Maintenance Ltd	
G-BBYS	Cessna 182P Skylane	I. M. Jones	
G-BBYU	Cameron 0-56 balloon	British Balloon Museum	
G-BBZF	PA-28 Cherokee 140	J. T. Mirley	
G-BBZH	PA-28R Cherokee Arrow 200-II	Zulu Hotel Club	
G-BBZJ	PA-34-200 Seneca II	European Flyers	
G-BBZN	Fuji FA.200-180	J. Westwood & P. D. Wedd	
G-BBZO	Fuji FA.200-160	G-BBZO Group	
G-BBZV	PA-28R Cherokee Arrow 200-II	P. B. Mellor/Kidlington	
G-BCAH	D.H.C.1 Chipmunk 22 (WG316)	Southern Flight Centre Ltd	
G-BCAP	Cameron O-56 balloon ★	Balloon Preservation Group/Lancing	
G-BCAR	Thunder Ax7-77 balloon ★	British Balloon Museum/Newbury	
G-BCAZ	PA-12 Super Cruiser	A. D. Williams	
G-BCBG	PA-23 Aztec 250E	M. J. L. Batt	
G-BCBH	Fairchild 24R-46A Argus III	Dreamticket Promotions Ltd	
G-BCBJ	PA-25 Pawnee 235	Deeside Gliding Club (Aberdeenshire) Ltd/Aboyne	
G-BCBL	Fairchild 24R-46A Argus III (HB751)	F. J. Cox	
G-BCBM	PA-23 Aztec 250C	Hatton & Westerman Trawlers	
G-BCBR	AJEP/Wittman W.8 Tailwind	D. P. Jones	
G-BCBX	Cessna F.150L	J. Kelly/Newtownards	
G-BCBZ	Cessna 337C	J. J. Zwetsloot	
G-BCCC	Cessna F.150L	Billins Air Services Ltd	
G-BCCD	Cessna F.172M	Austin Aviation Ltd	
G-BCCE	PA-23 Aztec 250E	Golf Charlie Echo Ltd/Shoreham	
G-BCCF	PA-28 Cherokee 180	Topcat Aviation Ltd	

Notes	Reg.	Type	Owner or Operator
	G-BCCG	Thunder Ax7-65 balloon	N. H. Ponsford
	G-BCCJ	AA-5 Traveler	T. Needham/Woodford
	G-BCCK	AA-5 Traveler	Prospect Air Ltd/Barton
	G-BCCR	CP.301A Emeraude (modified)	J. H. & C. J. Waterman
	G-BCCX	D.H.C.1 Chipmunk 22 (Lycoming)	RAFGSA/Dishforth
	G-BCCY	Robin HR.200/100	Charlie Yankee Ltd/Filton
	G-BCDJ	PA-28 Cherokee 140	Bristol Aero Club/Filton
	G-BCDK	Partenavia P.68B	Flyteam Aviation Ltd/Elstree
	G-BCDL	Cameron O-42 balloon	D. P. & Mrs B. O. Turner *Chums*
	G-BCDN	F.27 Friendship Mk 200 ★	*Instructional airframe*/Norwich
	G-BCDY	Cessna FRA.150L	W. Bayman & C. Draycott
	G-BCEA	Sikorsky S-61N Mk II	Veritair Ltd
	G-BCEB	Sikorsky S-61N Mk II	Veritair Ltd
	G-BCEC	Cessna F.172M	Trim Flying Club Ltd
	G-BCEE	AA-5 Traveler	N. F. Harrison
	G-BCEF	AA-5 Traveler	J. Fitzpatrick/France
	G-BCEN	BN-2A-26 Islander	Atlantic Air Transport Ltd/Coventry
	G-BCEO	AA-5 Traveler	Echo Oscar Flying Group
	G-BCEP	AA-5 Traveler	G. Edelmann
	G-BCER	GY-201 Minicab	D. Beaumont/Sherburn
	G-BCEX	PA-23 Aztec 250E	Western Air (Thruxton) Ltd
	G-BCEY	D.H.C.1 Chipmunk 22 (WG465)	Gopher Flying Group
	G-BCEZ	Cameron O-84 balloon	Balloon Collection
	G-BCFD	West balloon ★	British Balloon Museum *Hellfire*/Newbury
	G-BCFF	Fuji FA-200-160	G. W. Brown & M. R. Gibbons
	G-BCFO	PA-18 Super Cub 150	Portsmouth Naval Gliding Club/ Lee-on-Solent
	G-BCFR	Cessna FRA.150L	Bulldog Aviation Ltd & Motorhoods Colchester Ltd/Earls Colne
	G-BCFU	Thuner Ax6-56 balloon	British Balloon Museum/Newbury
	G-BCFW	SAAB 91D Safir	D. R. Williams
	G-BCFY	Luton LA-4A Minor	G. Capes
	G-BCGB	Bensen B.8	J. W. Birkett
	G-BCGC	D.H.C.1 Chipmunk 22 (WP903)	L. D. Chapman
	G-BCGH	SNCAN NC.854S	Nord Flying Group
	G-BCGI	PA-28 Cherokee 140	J. C. Dodd & ptnrs/Panshanger
	G-BCGJ	PA-28 Cherokee 140	BCT Aircraft Leasing Ltd
	G-BCGL	Jodel D.112	T. J. Maynard
	G-BCGM	Jodel D.120	M. H. D. Soltau
	G-BCGN	PA-28 Cherokee 140	Golf November Ltd/Kidlington
	G-BCGS	PA-28R Cherokee Arrow 200	Arrow Aviation Group
	G-BCGT	PA-28 Cherokee 140	L. Maikowski/Shoreham
	G-BCGW	Jodel D.11	G. H. & M. D. Chittenden
	G-BCHK	Cessna F.172H	E. C. & A. K. Shimmin
	G-BCHL	D.H.C.1 Chipmunk 22A (WP788)	Shropshire Soaring Ltd/Sleap
	G-BCHM	SA.341G Gazelle 1	Stratton Motor Co (Norfolk) Ltd
	G-BCHP	CP.1310-C3 Super Emeraude	G. Hughes & A. G. Just (G-JOSI)
	G-BCHT	Schleicher ASK.16	Dunstable K16 Group
	G-BCHX	SF.23A Sperling	*(stored)*/Rufforth
	G-BCID	PA-34-200 Seneca II	Shenley Farms (Aviation) Ltd
	G-BCIH	D.H.C.1 Chipmunk 22 (WD363)	J. M. Hosey/Stansted
	G-BCIJ	AA-5 Traveler	Arrow Association/Elstree
	G-BCIK	AA-5 Traveler	Trent Aviation Ltd
	G-BCIN	Thunder Ax7-77 balloon	R. A. Vale & ptnrs
	G-BCIR	PA-28-151 Warrior	P. J. Brennan
	G-BCJM	PA-28 Cherokee 140	Topcat Aviation Ltd
	G-BCJN	PA-28 Cherokee 140	Topcat Aviation Ltd
	G-BCJO	PA-28R Cherokee Arrow 200	R. Ross
	G-BCJP	PA-28 Cherokee 140	Omletair Flying Group
	G-BCKN	D.H.C.1A Chipmunk 22 (Lycoming)	RAFGSA/Cranwell
	G-BCKS	Fuji FA.200-180	Kestrel Aviation Ltd
	G-BCKT	Fuji FA.200-180	Kilo Tango Group
	G-BCKU	Cessna FRA.150L	Stapleford Flying Club Ltd
	G-BCKV	Cessna FRA.150L	Cleveland Flying School Ltd/Teesside
	G-BCLC	Sikorsky S-61N	Bristow Helicopters/HM Coastguard
	G-BCLD	Sikorsky S-61N	Bristow Helicopters Ltd
	G-BCLI	AA-5 Traveler	Pioneer Aviation Ltd/Cranfield
	G-BCLL	PA-28 Cherokee 180	G-BCLL Group/Blackbushe
	G-BCLS	Cessna 170B	N. Simpson
	G-BCLT	M.S.894A Rallye Minerva 220	Rallye Group
	G-BCLU	Jodel D.117	N. A. Wallace
	G-BCLW	AA-1B Trainer	J. R. Faulkner

Reg.	Type	Owner or Operator	Notes
G-BCMD	PA-18 Super Cub 95	P. Stephenson/Clacton	
G-BCMT	Isaacs Fury II	M. H. Turner	
G-BCNC	GY-201 Minicab	J. R. Wraight	
G-BCNP	Cameron O-77 balloon	P. Spellward	
G-BCNX	Piper J-3C-65 Cub (540)	K. J. Lord	
G-BCNZ	Fuji FA.200-160	BCNZ Fuji Group/Barton	
G-BCOB	Piper J-3C-65 Cub (329405)	R. W. & Mrs J. W. Marjoram	
G-BCOI	D.H.C.1 Chipmunk 22	D. S. McGregor	
G-BCOJ	Cameron O-56 balloon	T. J. Knott & M. J. Webber	
G-BCOL	Cessna F.172M	A. H. Creaser	
G-BCOM	Piper J-3C-65 Cub	Dougal Flying Group/Shoreham	
G-BCOO	D.H.C.1 Chipmunk 22	T. G. Fielding & M. S. Morton/Blackpool	
G-BCOR	SOCATA Rallye 100ST	P. R. W. Goslin & ptnrs	
G-BCOU	D.H.C.1 Chipmunk 22 (WK522)	P. J. Loweth	
G-BCOX	Bede BD-5A	H. J. Cox & B. L. Robinson	
G-BCOY	D.H.C.1 Chipmunk 22 (Lycoming)	Coventry Gliding Club Ltd/Husbands Bosworth	
G-BCPD	GY-201 Minicab	P. R. Cozens	
G-BCPG	PA-28R Cherokee Arrow 200-II	Roses Flying Group/Liverpool	
G-BCPH	Piper J-3C-65 Cub (329934)	M. J. Janaway	
G-BCPJ	Piper J-3C-65 Cub	Piper Cub Group	
G-BCPK	Cessna F.172M	D. C. C. Handley/Cranfield	
G-BCPN	AA-5 Traveler	G. K. Todd	
G-BCPU	D.H.C.1 Chipmunk 22	P. Waller/Booker	
G-BCRB	Cessna F.172M	D. E. Lamb	
G-BCRE	Cameron O-77 balloon ★	Balloon Preservation Group/Lancing	
G-BCRH	Alaparma Baldo B.75 ★	A. L. Scadding (stored)	
G-BCRI	Cameron O-65 balloon	V. J. Thorne	
G-BCRK	SA.102.5 Cavalier	P. G. R. Brown	
G-BCRL	PA-28-151 Warrior	BCRL Ltd	
G-BCRP	PA-E23 Aztec 250E	Airlong Charter Ltd	
G-BCRR	AA-5B Tiger	Capulet Flying Group/Elstree	
G-BCRT	Cessna F.150M	Blue Max Flying Group	
G-BCRX	D.H.C.1 Chipmunk 22 (WD292)	Tuplin Ltd/Denham	
G-BCSA	D.H.C.1 Chipmunk 22 (Lycoming)	RAFGSA/Bicester	
G-BCSL	D.H.C.1 Chipmunk 22	Jalawain Ltd/Barton	
G-BCSM	Bellanca 8GCBC Scout	York Gliding Centre/Rufforth	
G-BCST	M.S.893A Rallye Commodore 180	P. J. Wilcox/Cranfield	
G-BCSX	Thunder Ax7-77 balloon	C. Wolstenholm	
G-BCSY	Taylor JT.2 Titch	I. L. Harding	
G-BCTF	PA-28-151 Warrior	The St. George Flying Club/Teesside	
G-BCTI	Schleicher ASK.16	Tango India Syndicate/Cranfield	
G-BCTJ	Cessna 310Q	TJ Flying Group	
G-BCTK	Cessna FR.172J	R. T. Love	
G-BCTT	Evans VP-1	M. J. Watson	
G-BCUB	Piper J-3C-65 Cub	A. L. Brown & G. Attwell/Bourn	
G-BCUF	Cessna F.172M	John L. R. James & Co Ltd	
G-BCUH	Cessna F.150M	M. G. Montgomerie	
G-BCUJ	Cessna F.150M	BCT Aircraft Leasing Ltd	
G-BCUL	SOCATA Rallye 100ST	C. A. Ussher & Fountain Estates Ltd	
G-BCUO	SA Bulldog Srs 120/122	Cranfield University	
G-BCUS	SA Bulldog Srs 120/122	S. J. & J. J. Oliver	
G-BCUV	SA Bulldog Srs 120/122	Dolphin Property (Management) Ltd	
G-BCUW	Cessna F.177RG	S. J. Westley	
G-BCUY	Cessna FRA.150M	J. C. Carpenter	
G-BCVB	PA-17 Vagabond	A. T. Nowak/Popham	
G-BCVC	SOCATA Rallye 100ST	N. R. Vine	
G-BCVE	Evans VP-2	D. Masterson & D. B. Winstanley/Barton	
G-BCVF	Practavia Pilot Sprite	D. G. Hammersley	
G-BCVG	Cessna FRA.150L	G-BCVG Flying Group	
G-BCVH	Cessna FRA.150L	Multiflight Ltd	
G-BCVJ	Cessna F.172M	Rothland Ltd	
G-BCVY	PA-34-200T Seneca II	Oxford Aviation Services Ltd/Kidlington	
G-BCWB	Cessna 182P	Whisky Bravo Ltd	
G-BCWH	Practavia Pilot Sprite	R. Tasker/Blackpool	
G-BCWK	Alpavia Fournier RF-3	T. J. Hartwell & D. R. Wilkinson	
G-BCXB	SOCATA Rallye 100ST	A. Smails	
G-BCXE	Robin DR.400/2+2	Weald Air Services Ltd/Headcorn	
G-BCXJ	Piper L-4J Cub (480752)	Old Sarum Piper Cub Syndicate	
G-BCXN	D.H.C.1 Chipmunk 22 (WP800)	G. M. Turner/Halton	
G-BCYH	DAW Privateer Mk. 3	D. B. Limbert/Crosland Moor	
G-BCYJ	D.H.C.1 Chipmunk 22 (WG307)	R. A. L. Falconer	

Notes	Reg.	Type	Owner or Operator
	G-BCYK	Avro CF.100 Mk 4 Canuck (18393) ★	Imperial War Museum/Duxford
	G-BCYM	D.H.C.1 Chipmunk 22	G-BCYM Group
	G-BCYR	Cessna F.172M	Donne Enterprise/Edinburgh
	G-BCZH	D.H.C.1 Chipmunk 22 (WK622)	A. C. Byrne/Norwich
	G-BCZI	Thunder Ax7-77 balloon	R. G. Griffin & R. Blackwell
	G-BCZM	Cessna F.172M	Cornwall Flying Club Ltd/Bodmin
	G-BCZN	Cessna F.150M	Mona Aviation Ltd
	G-BCZO	Cameron O-77 balloon	W. O. T. Holmes Leo
	G-BDAD	Taylor JT.1 Monoplane	G-BDAD Group
	G-BDAG	Taylor JT.1 Monoplane	T. K. Gough
	G-BDAH	Evans VP-1	G. H. J. Geurts
	G-BDAI	Cessna FRA.150M	A. Sharma
	G-BDAK	R. Commander 112A	R. A. Denton
	G-BDAL	R. 500S Shrike Commander	X Jet Ltd
	G-BDAM	AT-16 Harvard IIB (FE992)	Silver Victory BVBA/Belgium
	G-BDAO	SIPA S.91	J. E. Mead
	G-BDAP	AJEP Tailwind	J. Whiting
	G-BDAR	Evans VP-1	R. B. Valler
	G-BDAY	Thunder Ax5-42A balloon	T. M. Donnelly Meconium
	G-BDBD	Wittman W.8 Tailwind	Tailwind Taildragger Group
	G-BDBF	FRED Srs 2	J. M. Brightwell & A. J. Wright
	G-BDBH	Bellanca 7GCBC Citabria	C. J. Gray
	G-BDBI	Cameron O-77 balloon	C. A. Butter & J. J. Cook
	G-BDBJ	Cessna 182P	H. C. Wilson
	G-BDBS	Short SD3-30 ★	Ulster Aviation Soc
	G-BDBU	Cessna F.150M	R. Edgar
	G-BDBV	Jodel D.11A	Seething Jodel Group
	G-BDBZ	W.S.55 Whirlwind Srs 2 ★	*Ground instruction airframe*/Kidlington
	G-BDCC	D.H.C.1 Chipmunk 22 (Lycoming)	Coventry Gliding Club Ltd/ Husbands Bosworth
	G-BDCD	Piper J-3C-85 Cub (480133)	Suzanne C. Brooks/Slinfold
	G-BDCE	Cessna F.172H	Copperplane Ltd
	G-BDCI	CP.301A Emeraude	D. L. Sentance
	G-BDCL	AA-5 Traveler	J. Crowe
	G-BDCO	B.121 Pup 1	R. J. Page & M. N. Simms
	G-BDDD	D.H.C.1 Chipmunk 22	DRA Aero Club Ltd
	G-BDDF	Jodel D.120	A. J. Hobbs
	G-BDDG	Jodel D.112	J. Pool & D. G. Palmer
	G-BDDS	PA-25 Pawnee 235	Vale of Neath Gliding Club/Rhigos
	G-BDDT	PA-25 Pawnee 235	Pawnee Aviation
	G-BDDX	Whittaker MW.2B Excalibur ★	Cornwall Aero Park/Helston
	G-BDDZ	CP.301A Emeraude	E. C. Mort
	G-BDEC	SOCATA Rallye 100ST	M. Mulhall
	G-BDEF	PA-34-200T Seneca II	L. R. Chiswell
	G-BDEH	Jodel D.120A	EH Flying Group
	G-BDEI	Jodel D.9 Bebe	The Noddy Group/Booker
	G-BDEU	D.H.C.1 Chipmunk 22 (WP808)	A. Taylor
	G-BDEX	Cessna FRA.150M	R. A. Powell
	G-BDEY	Piper J-3C-65 Cub	Ducksworth Flying Club
	G-BDEZ	Piper J-3C-65 Cub	R. J. M. Turnbull
	G-BDFB	Currie Wot	J. Jennings
	G-BDFH	Auster AOP.9 (XR240)	R. O. Holden/Booker
	G-BDFJ	Cessna F.150M	C. J. Hopewell
	G-BDFR	Fuji FA.200-160	A. Houghton/Blackpool
	G-BDFS	Fuji FA.200-160	B. Lawrence
	G-BDFU	Dragonfly MPA Mk 1 ★	Museum of Flight/E. Fortune
	G-BDFW	R. Commander 112A	M. E. & E. G. Reynolds/Blackbushe
	G-BDFX	Auster 5 (TW517)	J. Eagles
	G-BDFY	AA-5 Traveler	Grumman Group
	G-BDFZ	Cessna F.150M	L. W. Scattergood
	G-BDGB	GY-20 Minicab	D. G. Burden
	G-BDGH	Thunder Ax7-77 balloon	R. J. Mitchener & P. F. Smart
	G-BDGM	PA-28-151 Warrior	Comed Aviation Ltd/Blackpool
	G-BDGO	Thunder Ax7-77 balloon	Justerini & Brooks Ltd
	G-BDGY	PA-28 Cherokee 140	S. J. Willcox
	G-BDHK	Piper J-3C-65 Cub (329417)	A. Liddiard
	G-BDIE	R. Commander 112A	R. J. Adams
	G-BDIG	Cessna 182P	Air Group 6/Sturgate
	G-BDIH	Jodel D.117	N. D. H. Stokes
	G-BDIJ	Sikorsky S-61N	Bristow Helicopters Ltd
	G-BDIX	D.H.106 Comet 4C ★	Museum of Flight/E. Fortune

Reg.	Type	Owner or Operator	Notes
G-BDJC	AJEP W.8 Tailwind	M. A. Hales	
G-BDJD	Jodel D.112	J. E. Preston	
G-BDJF	Bensen B.8MV	R. P. White	
G-BDJG	Luton LA-4A Minor	Very Slow Flying Club	
G-BDJP	Piper J-3C-90 Cub	Holdcroft Aviation Services Ltd	
G-BDJR	SNCAN Nord NC.858	R. F. M. Marson	
G-BDKC	Cessna A185F	Bridge of Tilt Co Ltd	
G-BDKD	Enstrom F-28A	M. A. Crook & A. E. Wright	
G-BDKH	CP.301A Emeraude	P. N. Marshall	
G-BDKJ	K. & S. SA.102.5 Cavalier	D. A. Garner	
G-BDKM	SIPA 903	S. W. Markham	
G-BDKU	Taylor JT.1 Monoplane	B. N. Stevens & A. J. L. Eves	
G-BDKW	R. Commander 112A	Orwell Flying Ltd	
G-BDLO	AA-5A Cheetah	S. & J. Dolan/Denham	
G-BDLS	AA-1B Trainer	C. R. Tilley/Shobdon	
G-BDLT	R. Commander 112A	D. L. Churchward	
G-BDLY	SA.102.5 Cavalier	P. R. Stevens/Southampton	
G-BDMM	Jodel D.11	P. N. Marshall	
G-BDMS	Piper J-3C-65 Cub (FR886)	A. T. H. Martin	
G-BDMW	Jodel DR.100A	R. O. F. Harper	
G-BDNC	Taylor JT.1 Monoplane	D. W. Mathie	
G-BDNG	Taylor JT.1 Monoplane	S. B. Churchill	
G-BDNO	Taylor JT.1 Monoplane	S. D. Glover	
G-BDNP	BN-2A Islander ★	*Ground parachute trainer*/Headcorn	
G-BDNT	Jodel D.92 Bebe	R. F. Morton	
G-BDNU	Cessna F.172M	J. & K. G. McVicar	
G-BDNW	AA-1B Trainer	P. Mitchell	
G-BDNX	AA-1B Trainer	R. M. North	
G-BDOC	Sikorsky S-61N Mk II	Bristow Helicopters Ltd	
G-BDOD	Cessna F.150M	D. M. Moreau	
G-BDOE	Cessna FR.172J	P. E. Ward & ptnrs	
G-BDOG	SA Bulldog Srs 200	D. C. Bonsall/Netherthorpe	
G-BDOL	Piper J-3C-65 Cub	L. R. Balthazor	
G-BDON	Thunder Ax7-77A balloon	M. J. Smith	
G-BDOT	BN-2A Mk.III-2 Trislander	Lyddair	
G-BDOW	Cessna FRA.150	Boldlake Ltd	
G-BDPA	PA-28-151 Warrior	G-BDPA Flying Group/Staverton	
G-BDPJ	PA-25 Pawnee 235B	RAFGSA/Bicester	
G-BDPK	Cameron O-56 balloon	Rango Balloon & Kite Co	
G-BDRD	Cessna FRA.150M	I. P. Diment/Edinburgh	
G-BDRG	Taylor JT.2 Titch	D. R. Gray	
G-BDRJ	D.H.C.1 Chipmunk 22 (WP857)	J. C. Schooling	
G-BDRK	Cameron O-65 balloon	D. L. Smith Smirk	
G-BDSB	PA-28-181 Archer II	Testair Ltd/Blackbushe	
G-BDSE	Cameron O-77 balloon	British Airways Concorde	
G-BDSF	Cameron O-56 balloon	J. H. Greensides	
G-BDSH	PA-28 Cherokee 140 (modified)	The Wright Brothers Flying Group	
G-BDSK	Cameron O-65 balloon	Southern Balloon Group *Carousel II*	
G-BDSL	Cessna F.150M	D, C, Bonsall	
G-BDSM	Slingsby T.31B Cadet III	N. F. James	
G-BDTB	Evans VP-1	J. A. Hanslip	
G-BDTL	Evans VP-1	A. K. Lang	
G-BDTN	BN-2A Mk III-2 Trislander	Aurigny Air Services Ltd	
G-BDTO	BN-2A Mk III-2 Trislander	Aurigny Air Services Ltd (G-RBSI/G-OTSB)	
G-BDTU	Omega III gas balloon	R. G. Turnbull	
G-BDTV	Mooney M.20F	S. Redfearn	
G-BDTX	Cessna F.150M	S. L. Lefley & F. W. Ellis	
G-BDUI	Cameron V-56 balloon	D. C. Johnson	
G-BDUL	Evans VP-1	C. K. Brown	
G-BDUM	Cessna F.150M	B. P. Thorogood/Earls Colne	
G-BDUN	PA-34-200T Seneca II	Air Medical Ltd	
G-BDUO	Cessna F.150M	BM Aviation	
G-BDUX	Slingsby T.31B Cadet III	J. C. Anderson/Cranfield	
G-BDUY	Robin DR.400/140B	J. G. Anderson	
G-BDUZ	Cameron V-56 balloon	Zebedee Balloon Service	
G-BDVA	PA-17 Vagabond	I. M. Callier	
G-BDVB	PA-15 (PA-17) Vagabond	B. P. Gardner	
G-BDVC	PA-17 Vagabond	A. R. Caveen	
G-BDWA	SOCATA Rallye 150ST	J. Thompson-Wilson	
G-BDWE	Flaglor Scooter	Fenland Strut Flying Group	
G-BDWH	SOCATA Rallye 150ST	M. A. Jones	
G-BDWJ	SE-5A (replica) (F8010)	D. W. Linney	

Notes	Reg.	Type	Owner or Operator
	G-BDWL	PA-25 Pawnee 235	Peterborough & Spalding Gliding Club/Crowland
	G-BDWM	Mustang scale replica (FB226)	D. C. Bonsall
	G-BDWO	Howes Ax6 balloon	R. B. & C. Howes
	G-BDWP	PA-32R Cherokee Lance 300	W. M. Brown & B. J. Wood/Birmingham
	G-BDWX	Jodel D.120A	R. P. Rochester
	G-BDWY	PA-28 Cherokee 140	Comed Aviation Ltd/Blackpool
	G-BDXX	SNCAN NC.858S	M. Gaffney & K. Davis
	G-BDYD	R. Commander 114	M. B. Durkin
	G-BDYF	Cessna 421C	Hawkair
	G-BDYG	P.56 Provost T.1 (WV493) ★	Museum of Flight/E. Fortune
	G-BDYH	Cameron V-56 balloon	B. J. Godding
	G-BDZA	Scheibe SF.25E Super Falke	Hereward Flying Group/Crowland
	G-BDZC	Cessna F.150M	A. M. Lynn/Sibson
	G-BDZD	Cessna F.172M	JNJ Aviation Ltd
	G-BDZU	Cessna 421C	Eagle Flying Group/E. Midlands
	G-BEAB	Jodel DR.1051	R. C. Hibberd
	G-BEAC	PA-28 Cherokee 140	Clipwing Flying Group/Humberside
	G-BEAD	WG.13 Lynx ★	*Instructional airframe*/Middle Wallop
	G-BEAG	PA-34-200T Seneca II	Oxford Aviation Services Ltd/Kidlington
	G-BEAH	J/2 Arrow	Bedwell Hey Flying Group
	G-BEBC	W.S.55 Whirlwind 3 (XP355) ★	Norwich Aviation Museum
	G-BEBE	AA-5A Cheetah	Bills Aviation Ltd
	G-BEBG	WSK-PZL SDZ-45A Ogar	The Ogar Syndicate
	G-BEBI	Cessna F.172M	Hatfield Flying Club/Elstree
	G-BEBN	Cessna 177B	E. J. Lamb/Earls Colne
	G-BEBO	Turner TSW-2 Wot	E. Newsham/Breighton
	G-BEBS	Andreasson BA-4B	N. J. W. Reid
	G-BEBT	Andreasson BA-4B	M. Swanborough
	G-BEBU	R. Commander 112A	Cardiff-Wales Aviation Services Ltd
	G-BEBZ	PA-28-151 Warrior	Goodwood Terrena Ltd/Goodwood
	G-BECA	SOCATA Rallye 100ST	Bredon Flying Group/Defford
	G-BECB	SOCATA Rallye 100ST	A. J. Trible
	G-BECC	SOCATA Rallye 150ST	D. T. Price/Cardiff-Wales
	G-BECF	Scheibe SF.25A Falke	North County Ltd
	G-BECK	Cameron V-56 balloon	H. & D. J. Farrar
	G-BECN	Piper J-3C-65 Cub (80480)	G. Denney/Earls Colne
	G-BECS	Thunder Ax6-56A balloon	A. Sieger/Germany
	G-BECT	C.A.S.A.1.131E Jungmann 2000 (A-57)	Alpha 57 Group
	G-BECW	C.A.S.A.1.131E Jungmann 2000 (A-10)	R. A. Seeley
	G-BECZ	CAARP CAP.10B	Aerobatic Associates Ltd
	G-BEDB	Nord 1203 Norecrin ★	B. F. G. Lister *(stored)*/Chirk
	G-BEDD	Jodel D.117A	P. B. Duhig
	G-BEDF	Boeing B-17G-105-VE (124485)	B-17 Preservation Ltd/Duxford
	G-BEDG	R. Commander 112A	P. J. Lawton
	G-BEDJ	Piper J-3C-65 Cub (44-80594)	R. Earl
	G-BEDP	BN-2A Mk.III-2 Trislander	Lyddair
	G-BEDV	V.668 Varsity T.1 (WJ945) ★	Duxford Aviation Soc
	G-BEEE	Thunder Ax6-56A balloon ★	British Balloon Museum Avie/Newbury
	G-BEEG	BN-2A-26 Islander	NW Parachute Centre Ltd/Cark
	G-BEEH	Cameron V-56 balloon	Sade Balloons Ltd
	G-BEEP	Thunder Ax5-42 balloon	B. C. Faithfull/Netherlands
	G-BEER	Isaacs Fury II (K2075)	D. Crowhurst/Sywell
	G-BEEU	PA-28 Cherokee 140F	E. & H. Merkado
	G-BEFA	PA-28-151 Warrior	Verran Freight
	G-BEFF	PA-28 Cherokee 140F	J. JH. Howard
	G-BEFO	BN-2A Mk.III-2 Trislander	Keen Leasing Ltd (G-SARN)/Belfast
	G-BEGG	Scheibe SF.25E Super Falke	G-BEGG Flying Group
	G-BEHH	PA-32R Cherokee Lance 300	SMK Engineering Ltd/Leeds
	G-BEHU	PA-34-200T Seneca II	Pirin Aeronautical Ltd/Stapleford
	G-BEHV	Cessna F.172N	Fraggle Leasing Ltd/Edinburgh
	G-BEIA	Cessna FRA.150M	Halegreen Associates
	G-BEIF	Cameron O-65 balloon	C. Vening
	G-BEIG	Cessna F.150M	T. J. Chapman
	G-BEII	PA-25 Pawnee 235D	Burn Gliding Club Ltd
	G-BEIL	SOCATA Rallye 150T	The Rallye Flying Group
	G-BEIP	PA-28-181 Archer II	S. Pope
	G-BEIS	Evans VP-1	P. J. Hunt
	G-BEJB	Thunder Ax6-56A balloon	Justerini & Brooks Ltd
	G-BEJD	Avro 748 Srs 1	Emerald Airways Ltd *John Case*/Liverpool

Reg.	Type	Owner or Operator	Notes
G-BEJK	Cameron S-31 balloon	Rango Balloon & Kite Co	
G-BEJL	Sikorsky S-61N	CHC Scotiia Ltd	
G-BEJV	PA-34-200T Seneca II	Oxford Aviation Services Ltd/Kidlington	
G-BEKL	Bede BD-4E-150	A. J. Harpley	
G-BEKM	Evans VP-1	G. J. McDill/Glenrothes	
G-BEKN	Cessna FRA.150M ★	RFC (Bourn) Ltd/Sibson	
G-BEKO	Cessna F.182Q	G. J. & F. J. Leese	
G-BEKR	Rand-Robinson KR-2	A. N. Purchase	
G-BELF	BN-2A-26 Islander	The Black Knights Parachute Centre Ltd	
G-BELP	PA-28-151 Warrior	Aerohire Ltd	
G-BELT	Cessna F.150J	Multiflight Ltd (G-AWUV)/Leeds-Bradford	
G-BEMB	Cessna F.172M	Stocklaunch Ltd	
G-BEMM	Slingsby T.31B Motor Cadet III	B. J. Douglas	
G-BEMU	Thunder Ax5-42 balloon	M. A. Hall	
G-BEMW	PA-28-181 Archer II	Touch and Go Ltd	
G-BEMY	Cessna FRA.150M	A. J. Roper & P. A. L. Baker	
G-BEND	Cameron V-56 balloon	Dante Balloon Group Le Billet	
G-BENJ	R. Commander 112B	E. J. Percival/Blackbushe	
G-BENK	Cessna F.172M	Graham Churchill Plant Ltd	
G-BENN	Cameron V-56 balloon	S. J. Hollingsworth & M. K. Bellamy	
G-BEOD	Cessna 180 ★	Avionics Research Ltd/Cranfield	
G-BEOE	Cessna FRA.150M	W. J. Henderson	
G-BEOH	PA-28R-201T Turbo Arrow III	G-BEOH Group/Blackbushe	
G-BEOI	PA-18 Super Cub 150	Southdown Gliding Club Ltd/Parham Park	
G-BEOK	Cessna F.150M	D. C. Bonsall	
G-BEOL	SC.7 Skyvan 3 variant 100	Real Aviation Ltd	
G-BEOX	L-414 Hudson IV (A16-199) ★	RAF Museum/Hendon	
G-BEOY	Cessna FRA.150L	R. W. Denny	
G-BEOZ	A.W.650 Argosy 101 ★	Aeropark/E. Midlands	
G-BEPC	SNCAN Stampe SV-4C	Dawn Patrol Flight Training Ltd	
G-BEPF	SNCAN Stampe SV-4A	L. J. Rice	
G-BEPS	SC.5 Belfast	HeavyLift Cargo Airlines Ltd (stored)/ Southend	
G-BEPV	Fokker S.11-1 Instructor	L. C. MacKnight	
G-BEPY	R. Commander 112B	G-BEPY Group/Blackbushe	
G-BERA	SOCATA Rallye 150ST	P. J. Bloore & J. M. Biles	
G-BERC	SOCATA Rallye 150ST	Severn Valley Aero Group/Welshpool	
G-BERD	Thunder Ax6-56A balloon	P. M. Gaines	
G-BERI	R. Commander 114	K. B. Harper/Blackbushe	
G-BERN	Saffrey S-330 balloon	B. Martin Beeze	
G-BERT	Cameron V-56 balloon	Southern Balloon Group Bert	
G-BERW	R. Commander 114	Romeo Whisky Ltd	
G-BERY	AA-1B Trainer	R. H. J. Levi	
G-BETD	Robin HR.200/100	W. A. Stewart	
G-BETE	Rollason B.2A Beta	T. M. Jones/Tatenhill	
G-BETF	Cameron 'Champion' SS balloon ★	British Balloon Museum/Newbury	
G-BETG	Cessna 180K Skywagon	Norman Aeroplane Trust/Rendcomb	
G-BETI	Pitts S-1D Special	P. Metcalfe/Teesside	
G-BETL	PA-25 Pawnee 235D	Cambridge University Gliding Trust Ltd/ Gransden Lodge	
G-BETM	PA-25 Pawnee 235D	Yorkshire Gliding Club (Pty) Ltd/ Sutton Bank	
G-BETO	MS.885 Super Rallye	G-BETO Group	
G-BETT	PA-34-200 Seneca II	D. F. J. Flashman	
G-BETW	Rand KR-2	S. C. Solley	
G-BEUA	PA-18 Super Cub 150	London Gliding Club (Pty) Ltd/Dunstable	
G-BEUD	Robin HR.100/285R	E. A. & L. M. C. Payton/Cranfield	
G-BEUI	Piper J-3C-65 Cub	G-BEUI Group	
G-BEUK	Fuji FA.200-160	BM Aviation	
G-BEUM	Taylor JT.1 Monoplane	J. M. Burgess	
G-BEUN	Cassutt Racer IIIM	R. McNulty	
G-BEUP	Robin DR.400/180	A. V. Pound & Co Ltd	
G-BEUU	PA-18 Super Cub 95	F. Sharples/Sandown	
G-BEUX	Cessna F.172N	Multiflight Ltd/Leeds-Bradford	
G-BEUY	Cameron N-31 balloon	M. L. & L. P. Willoughby	
G-BEVA	SOCATA Rallye 150ST	The Rallye Group	
G-BEVB	SOCATA Rallye 150ST	N. R. Haines	
G-BEVC	SOCATA Rallye 150ST	B. W. Walpole	
G-BEVG	PA-34-200T-2 Seneca	C. Deith	
G-BEVO	Sportavia-Pützer RF-5 ★	T. Barlow/Barton	
G-BEVP	Evans VP-2	G. Moscrop & R. C. Crowley	

Notes	Reg.	Type	Owner or Operator
	G-BEVR	BN-2A Mk III-2 Trislander	Cormack (Aircraft Services) Ltd/ Cumbernauld
	G-BEVS	Taylor JT.1 Monoplane	D. Hunter
	G-BEVT	BN-2A Mk III-2 Trislander	Aurigny Air Services Ltd/Guernsey
	G-BEVV	BN-2A Mk III-2 Trislander	Cormack (Aircraft Services) Ltd (G-BNZD)/Cumbernauld
	G-BEVW	SOCATA Rallye 150ST	P. G. A. Sumner
	G-BEWM	Sikorsky S-61N Mk II	Brintel Helicopters
	G-BEWN	D.H.82A Tiger Moth	H. D. Labouchere
	G-BEWO	Zlin Z.326 Trener Master	P. A. Colman
	G-BEWR	Cessna F.172N	Cheshire Air Training Services Ltd/ Liverpool
	G-BEWX	PA-28R-201 Arrow III	A. Vickers
	G-BEWY	Bell 206B JetRanger 3	Polo Aviation Ltd (G-CULL)
	G-BEXN	AA-1C Lynx	D. M. Lockley
	G-BEXO	PA-23 Apache 160	G. R. Moore & A. A. K. Hulme
	G-BEXW	PA-28-181 Archer II	T. R. Kingsley
	G-BEXZ	Cameron N-56 balloon	D. C. Eager & G. C. Clark
	G-BEYA	Enstrom 280C	Hovercam Ltd
	G-BEYB	Fairey Flycatcher (replica) (S1287) ★	F.A.A. Museum/Yeovilton
	G-BEYF	HPR-7 Herald 401 ★	Jet Heritage Museum/Bournemouth
	G-BEYL	PA-28 Cherokee 180	Yankee Lima Group
	G-BEYO	PA-28 Cherokee 140	W. B. Bateson/Blackpool
	G-BEYT	PA-28 Cherokee 140	B. A. Mills
	G-BEYV	Cessna T.210M	Austen Aviation/Edinburgh
	G-BEYW	Taylor JT.1 Monoplane	R. A. Abrahams/Barton
	G-BEYZ	Jodel DR.1051/M1	M. L. Balding
	G-BEZA	Zlin Z.226T Trener	L. Bezak
	G-BEZC	AA-5 Traveler	T. V. Montgomery/Elstree
	G-BEZE	Rutan Vari-Eze	H. C. Mackinnon
	G-BEZF	AA-5 Traveler	RAF College Flying Club Ltd/Cranwell
	G-BEZG	AA-5 Traveler	M. D. R. Harling
	G-BEZH	AA-5 Traveler	L. & S. M. Sims
	G-BEZI	AA-5 Traveler	G-BEZI Flying Group/Elstree
	G-BEZK	Cessna F.172H	C. F. Strowger
	G-BEZL	PA-31-310 Turbo Navajo C	A. Jahanfar/Southend
	G-BEZO	Cessna F.172M	Staverton Flying Services Ltd
	G-BEZP	PA-32 Cherokee Six 300D	Falcon Styles Ltd/Booker
	G-BEZR	Cessna F.172M	Kirmington Aviation Ltd
	G-BEZV	Cessna F.172M	Insch Flying Group
	G-BEZY	Rutan Vari-Eze	I. J. Pountney
	G-BEZZ	Jodel D.112	G-BEZZ Jodel Group
	G-BFAA	GY-80 Horizon 160	Mary Poppins Ltd
	G-BFAF	Aeronca 7BCM (7797)	D. C. W. Harper/Finmere
	G-BFAH	Phoenix Currie Wot	R. W. Clarke
	G-BFAI	R. Commander 114	Alpha Flying Group
	G-BFAK	M.S.892A Rallye Commodore 150	J. R. Hammett
	G-BFAP	SIAI-Marchetti S.205-20R	A. O. Broin
	G-BFAS	Evans VP-1	A. I. Sutherland
	G-BFAW	D.H.C.1 Chipmunk 22	R. V. Bowles/Husbands Bosworth
	G-BFAX	D.H.C.1 Chipmunk 22 (WG422)	A. C. Kerr
	G-BFBA	Jodel DR.100A	W. H. Sherlock
	G-BFBB	PA-23 Aztec 250E	Air Training Services Ltd/Booker
	G-BFBC	Taylor JT.1 Monoplane	R. Trickett
	G-BFBE	Robin HR.200/100	A. C. Pearson
	G-BFBF	PA-28 Cherokee 140	Marnham Investments Ltd
	G-BFBM	Saffery S.330 balloon	B. Martin Beeze II
	G-BFBR	PA-28-161 Warrior II	Lowery Holdings Ltd/Fairoaks
	G-BFBU	Partenavia P.68B	Premiair Charter Ltd
	G-BFBY	Piper J-3C-65 Cub	U. Schuhmacher
	G-BFCT	Cessna TU.206F	Cecil Aviation Ltd/Cambridge
	G-BFCZ	Sopwith Camel (B7270) ★	Brooklands Museum Trust Ltd/Weybridge
	G-BFDC	D.H.C.1 Chipmunk 22	N. F. O'Neill/Newtownards
	G-BFDE	Sopwith Tabloid (replica) (168) ★	RAF Museum Storage & Restoration Centre/Cardington
	G-BFDF	SOCATA Rallye 235E	M. A. Wratten
	G-BFDI	PA-28-181 Archer II	Truman Aviation Ltd/Tollerton
	G-BFDK	PA-28-161 Warrior II	Priory Garage
	G-BFDL	Piper J-3C-65 Cub (454537)	S. Beresford & G. S. Claybourn/Sandtoft
	G-BFDO	PA-28R-201T Turbo Arrow III	A. J. Gow
	G-BFDZ	Taylor JT.1 Monoplane	G. J. Clare

Reg.	Type	Owner or Operator	Notes
G-BFEB	Jodel 150	Jodel Syndicate	
G-BFEF	Agusta-Bell 47G-3B1	R. C. Hields	
G-BFEH	Jodel D.117A	J. A. Crabb	
G-BFEK	Cessna F.152	Staverton Flying Services Ltd	
G-BFER	Bell 212	Bristow Helicopters Ltd	
G-BFEV	PA-25 Pawnee 235	Trent Valley Aerotowing Club Ltd/ Kirton-in-Lindsey	
G-BFEW	PA-25 Pawnee 235	Cornish Gliding & Flying Club Ltd/ Perranporth	
G-BFFB	Evans VP-2 ★	(stored)/Eaton Bray	
G-BFFC	Cessna F.152-II	Multiflight Ltd	
G-BFFE	Cessna F.152-II	A. J. Hastings/Edinburgh	
G-BFFJ	Sikorsky S-61N Mk II	Veritair Ltd/Penzance	
G-BFFK	Sikorsky S-61N Mk II	British International Helicopters	
G-BFFP	PA-18 Super Cub 150 (modified)	Booker Gliding Club Ltd	
G-BFFT	Cameron V-56 balloon	R. I. M. Kerr & D. C. Boxall	
G-BFFW	Cessna F.152	Tayside Aviation Ltd/Dundee	
G-BFFY	Cessna F.150M	G. D. Rodmell	
G-BFFZ	Cessna FR.172 Hawk XP	E. Francis	
G-BFGD	Cessna F.172N-II	J. T. Armstrong	
G-BFGG	Cessna FRA.150M	Cornwall Flying Club Ltd/Bodmin	
G-BFGH	Cessna F.337G	T. Perkins/Sherburn	
G-BFGK	Jodel D.117	B. F. J. Hope	
G-BFGL	Cessna FA.152	Multiflight Ltd	
G-BFGO	Fuji FA.200-160	R. J. Everett	
G-BFGS	M.S.893E Rallye 180GT	Chiltern Flyers Ltd	
G-BFGW	Cessna F.150H	C. E. Stringer	
G-BFGX	Cessna FRA.150M	Active Services Ltd	
G-BFGZ	Cessna FRA.150M	C. M. Barnes	
G-BFHH	D.H.82A Tiger Moth	P. Harrison & M. J. Gambrell/Redhill	
G-BFHI	Piper J-3C-65 Cub	N. Glass & A. J. Richardson	
G-BFHP	Champion 7GCAA Citabria	A. M. Read	
G-BFHR	Jodel DR.220/2+2	J. E. Sweetman	
G-BFHT	Cessna F.152-II	Westward Airways (Lands End) Ltd	
G-BFHU	Cessna F.152-II	D. J. Cooke	
G-BFHV	Cessna F.152-II	Falcon Flying Services/Biggin Hill	
G-BFHX	Evans VP-1	A. D. Bohanna & D. I. Trussler	
G-BFIB	PA-31 Turbo Navajo	Richard Hannon Ltd	
G-BFID	Taylor JT.2 Titch Mk III	N. A. Scully	
G-BFIE	Cessna FRA.150M	G-BFIE Ltd	
G-BFIG	Cessna FR.172K XPII	Tenair Ltd	
G-BFIJ	AA-5A Cheetah	T. H. & M. G. Weetman	
G-BFIN	AA-5A Cheetah	G-BFIN Group	
G-BFIP	Wallbro Monoplane 1909 (replica) ★	Norfolk & Suffolk Aviation Museum/ Flixton, Suffolk	
G-BFIU	Cessna FR.172K XP	B. M. Jobling	
G-BFIV	Cessna F.177RG	Kingfishair Ltd/Blackbushe	
G-BFIX	Thunder Ax7-77A balloon	R. Owen	
G-BFIY	Cessna F.150M	R. J. Scott	
G-BFJJ	Evans VP-1	M. J. Collins	
G-BFJR	Cessna F.337G	Mannix Aviation Ltd/E. Midlands	
G-BFJZ	Robin DR.400/140B	Weald Air Services Ltd/Headcorn	
G-BFKB	Cessna F.172N	Shropshire Flying Group	
G-BFKC	Rand-Robinson KR-2	L. H. S. Stephens & I. S. Hewitt	
G-BFKF	Cessna FA.152	Aerolease Ltd/Conington	
G-BFKH	Cessna F.152	TG Aviation Ltd/Manston	
G-BFKL	Cameron N-56 balloon	Merrythought Toys Ltd Merrythought	
G-BFKY	PA-34-200 Seneca II	S.L.H. Construction Ltd/Biggin Hill	
G-BFLH	PA-34-200T Seneca II	Air Medical Ltd	
G-BFLI	PA-28R-201T Turbo Arrow III	J. K. Chudzicki	
G-BFLU	Cessna F.152	Bravo Aviation Ltd	
G-BFLX	AA-5A Cheetah	G Force Two Ltd/Blackbushe	
G-BFLZ	Beech 95-A55 Baron	Caterite Food Service	
G-BFMG	PA-28-161 Warrior II	Stardial Ltd	
G-BFMH	Cessna 177B	Span Aviation Ltd/Newcastle	
G-BFMK	Cessna FA.152	RAF Halton Aeroplane Club Ltd	
G-BFMM	PA-28-181 Archer II	Aldergrove Flight Training Centre	
G-BFMR	PA-20 Pacer 125	J. Knight	
G-BFMX	Cessna F.172N	Broomco (406) Ltd	
G-BFMZ	Payne Ax6 balloon	E. G. Woolnough	
G-BFNG	Jodel D.112	M. T. Taylor	
G-BFNI	PA-28-161 Warrior II	P. Elliott/Biggin Hill	
G-BFNJ	PA-28-161 Warrior II	Fleetlands Flying Association Ltd	

Notes	Reg.	Type	Owner or Operator
	G-BFNK	PA-28-161 Warrior II	Oxford Aviation Services Ltd/Kidlington
	G-BFOD	Cessna F.182Q	G. N. Clarke
	G-BFOE	Cessna F.152	Redhill Air Services Ltd
	G-BFOF	Cessna F.152	Staverton Flying School Ltd
	G-BFOG	Cessna 150M	BBC Air Ltd/Compton Abbas
	G-BFOJ	AA-1 Yankee	A. J. Morton/Bournemouth
	G-BFOM	PA-31 Turbo Navajo C	Deer Hill Aviation Ltd
	G-BFOP	Jodel D.120	R. J. Wesley & G. D. Western/Ipswich
	G-BFOS	Thunder Ax6-56A balloon	N. T. Petty
	G-BFOU	Taylor JT.1 Monoplane	G. Bee
	G-BFOV	Cessna F.172N	D. J. Walker
	G-BFPA	Scheibe SF.25B Falke	N. Meiklejohn & J. Steel
	G-BFPB	AA-5B Tiger	Stesco Ltd/Guernsey
	G-BFPH	Cessna F.172K	Linc-Air Flying Group
	G-BFPM	Cessna F.172M	Sigma Corporation Ltd
	G-BFPO	R. Commander 112B	J. G. Hale Ltd
	G-BFPP	Bell 47J-2	M. R. Masters
	G-BFPS	PA-25 Pawnee 235D	Kent Gliding Club Ltd/Challock
	G-BFRD	Bowers Fly-Baby 1A	R. A. Phillips
	G-BFRF	Taylor JT.1 Monoplane	E. R. Bailey
	G-BFRI	Sikorsky S-61N	Bristow Helicopters Ltd Braerich
	G-BFRR	Cessna FRA.150M	Romeo Romeo Flying Group/Tatenhill
	G-BFRS	Cessna F.172N	Poplar Toys Ltd
	G-BFRV	Cessna FA.152	Solo Services Ltd
	G-BFRY	PA-25 Pawnee 260	Yorkshire Gliding Club (Pty) Ltd/ Sutton Bank
	G-BFSA	Cessna F.182Q	Clark Masts Ltd/Sandown
	G-BFSB	Cessna F.152	Tatenhill Aviation
	G-BFSC	PA-25 Pawnee 235D	M. A. Pruden
	G-BFSD	PA-25 Pawnee 235D	Deeside Gliding Club (Aberdeenshire) Ltd/Aboyne
	G-BFSK	PA-23 Apache 160 ★	*Sub-aqua instructional airframe/ Croughton*
	G-BFSR	Cessna F.150J	S. Bourne
	G-BFSS	Cessna FR.172G	Minerva Services
	G-BFSY	PA-28-181 Archer II	Downland Aviation
	G-BFTC	PA-28R-201T Turbo Arrow III	M. J. Milns/Sherburn
	G-BFTF	AA-5B Tiger	F. C. Burrow Ltd/Leeds
	G-BFTG	AA-5B Tiger	D. Hepburn & G. R. Montgomery
	G-BFTH	Cessna F.172N	J. Birkett
	G-BFTT	Cessna 421C	P&B Metal Components Ltd/Manston
	G-BFTX	Cessna F.172N	G-BFTX Group/Manston
	G-BFUB	PA-32RT-300 Lance II	Jolida Holdings Ltd
	G-BFUD	Scheibe SF.25E Super Falke	Lakes Libelle Syndicate/Walney Island
	G-BFUG	Cameron N-77 balloon	Headland Services Ltd
	G-BFVF	PA-38-112 Tomahawk	Truman Aviation Ltd/Tollerton
	G-BFVG	PA-28-181 Archer II	G-BFVG Flying Group/Blackpool
	G-BFVH	D.H.2 (replica) (5964)	M. J. Kirk
	G-BFVP	PA-23 Aztec 250F	Sub Marine Services Ltd
	G-BFVS	AA-5B Tiger	S. W. Biroth & T. Chapman/Denham
	G-BFVU	Cessna 150L	Deer Hill Aviation Ltd/Exeter
	G-BFWB	PA-28-161 Warrior II	Mid-Anglia School of Flying
	G-BFWD	Currie Wot	F. R. Donaldson
	G-BFWE	PA-23 Aztec 250E	Air Navigation & Trading Co Ltd/ Blackpool
	G-BFXF	Andreasson BA.4B	A. Brown/Sherburn
	G-BFXG	D.31 Turbulent	E. J. I. Musty & M. J. Whatley
	G-BFXK	PA-28 Cherokee 140	I. Simpson
	G-BFXL	Albatross D.5A (D5397/17) ★	F.A.A. Museum/Yeovilton
	G-BFXR	Jodel D.112	J. M. Pearson & S. J. Haigh
	G-BFXS	R. Commander 114	G. L. Owens
	G-BFXW	AA-5B Tiger	Campsol Ltd
	G-BFXX	AA-5B Tiger	W. R. Gibson
	G-BFYA	MBB Bo 105DB	Sterling Helicopters Ltd/Norwich
	G-BFYC	PA-32RT-300 Lance II	A. A. Barnes
	G-BFYE	Robin HR.100/285 ★	*(stored)*/Sywell
	G-BFYI	Westland-Bell 47G-3B1	B. Walker & Co (Dursley) Ltd
	G-BFYK	Cameron V-77 balloon	L. E. Jones
	G-BFYL	Evans VP-2	W. C. Brown
	G-BFYO	SPAD XIII (replica) (1/4513) ★	American Air Museum/Duxford
	G-BFZB	Piper J-3C-85 Cub	N. Rawlinson
	G-BFZD	Cessna FR.182RG	R. B. Lewis & Co/Sleap
	G-BFZH	PA-28R Cherokee Arrow 200	W. E. Lowe/Shobdon

Reg.	Type	Owner or Operator	Notes
G-BFZM	R. Commander 112TC	J. A. Hart & R. J. Lamplough	
G-BFZN	Cessna FA.152	Falcon Flying Services/Biggin Hill	
G-BFZO	AA-5A Cheetah	J. McCloskey	
G-BFZT	Cessna FA.152	Pooler-LMT Ltd	
G-BFZU	Cessna FA.152	Redhill Aviation Services Ltd	
G-BFZV	Cessna F.172M	R. Thomas	
G-BGAA	Cessna 152 II	PJC Leasing Ltd	
G-BGAB	Cessna F.152 II	TG Aviation Ltd/Manston	
G-BGAE	Cessna F.152 II	Aerolease Ltd/Conington	
G-BGAF	Cessna FA.152	M. F. Hatt & ptnrs/Southend	
G-BGAG	Cessna F.172N	Falcon Flying Services/Biggin Hill	
G-BGAJ	Cessna F.182Q II	Ground Airport Services Ltd/Guernsey	
G-BGAX	PA-28 Cherokee 140	C. D. Brack/Breighton	
G-BGAZ	Cameron V-77 balloon	C. J. Madigan & D. H. McGibbon	
G-BGBA	Robin R.2100A	D. Faulkner/Redhill	
G-BGBE	Jodel DR.1050	J. A. & B. Mawby	
G-BGBF	D.31A Turbulent	R. S. Jordan/Little Snoring	
G-BGBG	PA-28-181 Archer II	Harlow Printing Ltd/Newcastle	
G-BGBI	Cessna F.150L	Falcon Flying Services/Biggin Hill	
G-BGBK	PA-38-112 Tomahawk	F. Marshall & R. C. Priest/Netherthorpe	
G-BGBN	PA-38-112 Tomahawk	Bonus Aviation Ltd/Cranfield	
G-BGBR	Cessna F.172N	Falcon Flying Services/Biggin Hill	
G-BGBU	Auster AOP.9 (XN435)	P. Neilson	
G-BGBW	PA-38-112 Tomahawk	Truman Aviation Ltd/Tollerton	
G-BGBY	PA-38-112 Tomahawk	Ravenair/Liverpool	
G-BGBZ	R. Commander 114	R. S. Fenwick/Biggin Hill	
G-BGCG	Douglas C-47A ★	Datran Holdings Ltd *(stored)*	
G-BGCM	AA-5A Cheetah	G. & S. A. Jones	
G-BGCO	PA-44-180 Seminole	J. R. Henderson	
G-BGCY	Taylor JT.1 Monoplane	J. C. Metcalf	
G-BGEA	Cessna F.150M	C. J. Hopewell/Sibson	
G-BGED	Cessna U.206F	Chapman Aviation Ltd	
G-BGEE	Evans VP-1	R. E. Holmes	
G-BGEH	Monnett Sonerai II	D. & V. T. Hubbard	
G-BGEI	Baby Great Lakes	A. R. Robinson	
G-BGEK	PA-38-112 Tomahawk	Ravenair/Liverpool	
G-BGEW	SNCAN NC.854S	Tavair Ltd	
G-BGFC	Evans VP-2	S. W. C. Hollins	
G-BGFF	FRED Srs 2	I. Daniels	
G-BGFG	AA-5A Cheetah	Plane Talking Ltd/Elstree	
G-BGFH	Cessna F.182Q	Rayviation Ltd	
G-BGFI	AA-5A Cheetah	I. J. Hay & A. Nayyar/Biggin Hill	
G-BGFJ	Jodel D.9 Bebe	M. D. Mold	
G-BGFT	PA-34-200T Seneca II	Oxford Aviation Services Ltd/Kidlington	
G-BGFX	Cessna F.152	Falcon Flying Services/Biggin Hill	
G-BGGA	Bellanca 7GCBC Citabria	L. A. King	
G-BGGB	Bellanca 7GCBC Citabria	G. H. N. Chamberlain	
G-BGGC	Bellanca 7GCBC Citabria	R. P. Ashfield & J. P. Stone	
G-BGGD	Bellanca 8GCBC Scout	Bristol & Gloucestershire Gliding Club/ Nympsfield	
G-BGGE	PA-38-112 Tomahawk	Truman Aviation Ltd/Tollerton	
G-BGGF	PA-38-112 Tomahawk	Truman Aviation Ltd/Tollerton	
G-BGGG	PA-38-112 Tomahawk	Teesside Flight Centre Ltd	
G-BGGI	PA-38-112 Tomahawk	Truman Aviation Ltd/Tollerton	
G-BGGL	PA-38-112 Tomahawk	Grunwick Processing Laboratories Ltd/ Elstree	
G-BGGM	PA-38-112 Tomahawk	Grunwick Processing Laboratories Ltd/ Elstree	
G-BGGN	PA-38-112 Tomahawk	Domeastral Ltd/Elstree	
G-BGGO	Cessna F.152	E. Midlands Flying School Ltd	
G-BGGP	Cessna F.152	E. Midlands Flying School Ltd	
G-BGGU	Wallis WA-116/RR	K. H. Wallis	
G-BGGW	Wallis WA-112	K. H. Wallis	
G-BGGY	AB-206B Jet Ranger ★	*Instructional airframe*/Cranfield	
G-BGHE	Convair L-13A	J. M. Davis/Wichita	
G-BGHF	Westland WG.30 ★	IHM/Weston-s-Mare	
G-BGHI	Cessna F.152	V. R. McCready	
G-BGHJ	Cessna F.172N	F & H (Aircraft) & Castle Aviation Ltd	
G-BGHM	Robin R.1180T	H. Price	
G-BGHP	Beech 76 Duchess	Magneta Ltd	
G-BGHS	Cameron N-31 balloon	W. R. Teasdale	
G-BGHT	Falconar F-12	C. R. Coates	

Notes	Reg.	Type	Owner or Operator
	G-BGHU	NA T-6G Texan (115042)	C. E. Bellhouse
	G-BGHV	Cameron V-77 balloon	E. Davies
	G-BGHY	Taylor JT.1 Monoplane	R. A. Hand
	G-BGHZ	FRED Srs 2	A. Smith
	G-BGIB	Cessna 152 II	Redhill Air Services Ltd
	G-BGID	Westland-Bell 47G-3B1	A. Tasker
	G-BGIG	PA-38-112 Tomahawk	Air Claire Ltd
	G-BGIO	Montgomerie-Bensen B.8MR	R. M. Savage
	G-BGIP	Colt 56A balloon	R. D. Allen & M. Walker
	G-BGIU	Cessna F.172H	Skyhawk Flying Group
	G-BGIX	H.295 Super Courier	C. M. Lee
	G-BGIY	Cessna F.172N	Air Claire Ltd
	G-BGJB	PA-44-180 Seminole	Magenta Ltd (G-ISFT)
	G-BGJU	Cameron V-65 Balloon	J. A. Folkes
	G-BGKC	SOCATA Rallye 110ST	J. H. Cranmer & T. A. Timms
	G-BGKJ	MBB Bo 105D ★	Instructional airframe/Bourn
	G-BGKO	GY-20 Minicab	R. B. Webber
	G-BGKS	PA-28-161 Warrior II	Marnham Investments Ltd
	G-BGKT	Auster AOP.9 (XN441)	Auster Nine Group
	G-BGKU	PA-28R-201 Arrow III	Aerolease Ltd
	G-BGKV	PA-28R-201 Arrow III	R. Haverson & R. G. Watson
	G-BGKY	PA-38-112 Tomahawk	Top Cat Aviation Ltd
	G-BGKZ	J/5F Aiglet Trainer	D. Hatelie
	G-BGLA	PA-38-112 Tomahawk	Norwich School of Flying
	G-BGLB	Bede BD-5B ★	Science Museum/Wroughton
	G-BGLF	Evans VP-1 Srs 2	J. B. McNab
	G-BGLG	Cessna 152	L. W. Scattergood
	G-BGLI	Cessna 152	Luton Flying Club (stored)
	G-BGLN	Cessna FA.152	Bflying Ltd
	G-BGLO	Cessna F.172N	A. H. Slaughter/Southend
	G-BGLS	Oldfield Super Baby Lakes	J. F. Dowe
	G-BGLW	PA-34-200 Seneca II	London Executive Aviation Ltd
	G-BGLZ	Stits SA-3A Playboy	Stitts Playboy Flying Group
	G-BGMJ	GY-201 Minicab	S. L. Wakefield & ptnrs
	G-BGMN	H.S.748 Srs 2A	Emerald Airways Ltd/Liverpool
	G-BGMO	H.S.748 Srs 2A	Emerald Airways Ltd/Liverpool
	G-BGMP	Cessna F.172G	R. W. Collings
	G-BGMR	GY-201 Minicab	Mike Romeo Flying Group
	G-BGMS	Taylor JT.2 Titch	M. A. J. Spice
	G-BGMT	SOCATA Rallye 235E	C. G. Wheeler
	G-BGMU	Westland-Bell 47G-3B1	V. L. J. & V. English
	G-BGMV	Scheibe SF.25B Falke	C. A. Bloom & A. P. Twort/Shoreham
	G-BGND	Cessna F.172N	A. J. M. Freeman
	G-BGNT	Cessna F.152	Aerolease Ltd/Conington
	G-BGNV	GA-7 Cougar	G. J. Bissex
	G-BGOD	Colt 77A balloon	C. Allen & M. D. Steuer
	G-BGOG	PA-28-161 Warrior II	W. D. Moore
	G-BGOI	Cameron O-56 balloon	S. Ellis
	G-BGOL	PA-28R-201T Turbo Arrow III	Valley Flying Co Ltd
	G-BGON	GA-7 Cougar	Walsh Aviation
	G-BGOR	AT-6D Harvard III (14863)	M. L. Sargeant
	G-BGPA	Cessna 182Q	Papa Alpha Group
	G-BGPB	CCF T-6J Texan (1747)	J. Romain/Duxford
	G-BGPD	Piper J-3C-65 Cub (479744)	P. D. Whiteman
	G-BGPH	AA-5B Tiger	Shipping & Airlines Ltd/Biggin Hill
	G-BGPI	Plumb BGP-1	B. G. Plumb
	G-BGPJ	PA-28-161 Warrior II	W. Lancs Warrior Co Ltd/Woodvale
	G-BGPL	PA-28-161 Warrior II	TG Aviation Ltd/Manston
	G-BGPN	PA-18 Super Cub 150	D. McHugh
	G-BGPU	PA-28 Cherokee 140	Air Navigation & Trading Ltd/Blackpool
	G-BGPZ	M.S.890A Rallye Commodore	Popham Flying Group
	G-BGRC	PA-28 Cherokee 140	Tecair Aviation Ltd & G. F. Haigh
	G-BGRE	Beech A200 Super King Air	Martin-Baker (Engineering) Ltd/Chalgrove
	G-BGRG	Beech 76 Duchess	Aviation Rentals/Bournemouth
	G-BGRH	Robin DR.400/22	C. R. Beard
	G-BGRI	Jodel DR.1051	R. T. Gunn & J. R. Redhead
	G-BGRL	PA-38-112 Tomahawk	G. G. Mepham/Goodwood
	G-BGRM	PA-38-112 Tomahawk	D. E. Bamber
	G-BGRO	Cessna F.172M	Cammo Aviation
	G-BGRR	PA-38-112 Tomahawk	Goodair Leasing Ltd/Cardiff
	G-BGRS	Thunder Ax7-77Z balloon	P. M. Gaines
	G-BGRT	Steen Skybolt	J. H. Kimber & O. Meier
	G-BGRX	PA-38-112 Tomahawk	Bonus Aviation Ltd

Reg.	Type	Owner or Operator	Notes
G-BGSA	M.S.892E Rallye 150GT	D. H. Tonkin	
G-BGSG	PA-44-180 Seminole	Shemburn Ltd	
G-BGSH	PA-38-112 Tomahawk	Scotia Safari Ltd/Prestwick	
G-BGSI	PA-38-112 Tomahawk	Ravenair/Liverpool	
G-BGSJ	Piper J-3C-65 Cub	A. J. Higgins	
G-BGSN	Enstrom F-28C	Tindon Ltd (G-OIGS)	
G-BGSV	Cessna F.172N	Southwell Air Services Ltd	
G-BGSW	Beech F33 Debonair	C. Wood/Wellesbourne	
G-BGSY	GA-7 Cougar	Plane Talking Ltd/Elstree	
G-BGTB	SOCATA TB.10 Tobago ★	D. Pope (stored)	
G-BGTC	Auster AOP.9 (XP282)	P. T. Bolton	
G-BGTF	PA-44-180 Seminole	NG Trustees & Nominees Ltd	
G-BGTG	PA-23 Aztec 250F	Keen Leasing (IOM) Ltd	
G-BGTI	Piper J-3C-65 Cub	A. P. Broad	
G-BGTJ	PA-28 Cherokee 180	Serendipity Aviation/Staverton	
G-BGTT	Cessna 310R	Aviation Beauport Ltd/Jersey	
G-BGTX	Jodel D.117	Madley Flying Group/Shobdon	
G-BGUB	PA-32 Cherokee Six 300E	A. P. Diplock	
G-BGUY	Cameron V-56 balloon	J. L. Guy	
G-BGVB	Robin DR.315	P. J. Leggo	
G-BGVE	CP.1310-C3 Super Emeraude	Victor Echo Group	
G-BGVH	Beech 76 Duchess	Velco Marketing	
G-BGVK	PA-28-161 Warrior II	K. R. Holland	
G-BGVN	PA-28RT-201 Arrow IV	C. Smith & S. Carrington	
G-BGVS	Cessna F.172M	Kirkwall Flying Club	
G-BGVV	AA-5A Cheetah	A. H. McVicar/Prestwick	
G-BGVW	AA-5A Cheetah	Computech Aviation Ltd	
G-BGVY	AA-5B Tiger	R. J. C. Neal-Smith	
G-BGVZ	PA-28-181 Archer II	W. Walsh & S. R. Mitchell/Woodvale	
G-BGWC	Robin DR.400/180	P. R. Deacon	
G-BGWJ	Sikorsky S-61N	Bristow Helicopters Ltd	
G-BGWK	Sikorsky S-61N	Bristow Helicopters Ltd	
G-BGWM	PA-28-181 Archer II	Thames Valley Flying Club Ltd	
G-BGWN	PA-38-112 Tomahawk	Teesside Flight Centre Ltd	
G-BGWO	Jodel D.112	G-BGWO Group/Sandtoft	
G-BGWR	Cessna U.206A	The Parachute Centre Ltd (G-DISC)/ Tilstock	
G-BGWS	Enstrom 280C Shark	Whisky Sierra Helicopters	
G-BGWU	PA-38-112 Tomahawk	J. S. & L. M. Markey	
G-BGWV	Aeronca 7AC Champion	RFC Flying Group/Popham	
G-BGWW	PA-23 Turbo Aztec 250E	Aldergrove Flight Training Centre	
G-BGWY	Thunder Ax6-56Z balloon	P. J. Eley	
G-BGWZ	Eclipse Super Eagle ★	F.A.A. Museum/Yeovilton	
G-BGXA	Piper J-3C-65 Cub (329471)	E. C. & P. King/Kemble	
G-BGXB	PA-38-112 Tomahawk	Signtest Ltd/Cardiff-Wales	
G-BGXC	SOCATA TB.10 Tobago	D. H. Courtley	
G-BGXD	SOCATA TB.10 Tobago	D. F. P. Finan	
G-BGXJ	Partenavia P.68B	Cecil Aviation Ltd/Cambridge	
G-BGXL	Bensen B.8MV	B. P. Triefus	
G-BGXN	PA-38-112 Tomahawk	Panshanger School of Flying Ltd	
G-BGXO	PA-38-112 Tomahawk	Goodwood Terrena Ltd	
G-BGXR	Robin HR.200/100	Exray Group	
G-BGXS	PA-28-236 Dakota	Bawtry Road Service Station Ltd	
G-BGXT	SOCATA TB.10 Tobago	D. A. H. Morris	
G-BGYN	PA-18 Super Cub 150	B. J. Dunford	
G-BGYR	H.S.125 Srs 600B	BAE Systems (Operations) Ltd/Filton	
G-BGYT	EMB-110P1 Bandeirante	Keenair Charter Ltd/Liverpool	
G-BGZF	PA-38-112 Tomahawk	Metropolitan Services Ltd/Egginton	
G-BGZL	Eiri PIK-20E	F. Casolari/Italy	
G-BGZW	PA-38-112 Tomahawk	Ravenair/Liverpool	
G-BGZY	Jodel D.120	M. Hale	
G-BGZZ	Thunder Ax6-56 balloon	J. M. Robinson	
G-BHAA	Cessna 152 II	Herefordshire Aero Club Ltd/Shobdon	
G-BHAC	Cessna A.152	Herefordshire Aero Club Ltd/Shobdon	
G-BHAD	Cessna A.152	Shropshire Aero Club Ltd/Sleap	
G-BHAI	Cessna F.152	Fraggle Leasing Ltd/Edinburgh	
G-BHAJ	Robin DR.400/160	Rowantask Ltd	
G-BHAR	Westland-Bell 47G-3B1	E. A. L. Sturmer	
G-BHAV	Cessna F.152	T. M. & M. L. Jones/Egginton	
G-BHAW	Cessna F.172N	E. Alexander	
G-BHAX	Enstrom F-28C-UK-2	PVS (Barnsley) Ltd	
G-BHAY	PA-28RT-201 Arrow IV	Alpha Yankee Ltd	

Notes	Reg.	Type	Owner or Operator
	G-BHBA	Campbell Cricket	G. J. Layzell
	G-BHBE	Westland-Bell 47G-3B1 (Soloy)	T. R. Smith (Agricultural Machinery) Ltd
	G-BHBF	Sikorsky S-76A	Bristow Helicopters Ltd
	G-BHBG	PA-32R Cherokee Lance 300	L. T. Halpin
	G-BHBI	Mooney M.20J	G-BHBI Group
	G-BHBT	Marquart MA.5 Charger	R. G. & C. J. Maidment/Shoreham
	G-BHBZ	Partenavia P.68B	Philip Hamer & Co
	G-BHCC	Cessna 172M	Langtry Flying Group Ltd
	G-BHCE	Jodel D.112	D. M. Parsons
	G-BHCM	Cessna F.172H	J. Dominic
	G-BHCP	Cessna F.152	D. Copley
	G-BHCZ	PA-38-112 Tomahawk	J. E. Abbott
	G-BHDD	V.668 Varsity T.1 (WL626) ★	Aeropark/E. Midlands
	G-BHDE	SOCATA TB.10 Tobago	Alpha-Alpha Ltd
	G-BHDK	Boeing B-29A-BN (461748) ★	Imperial War Museum/Duxford
	G-BHDM	Cessna F.152 II	Tayside Aviation Ltd/Dundee
	G-BHDP	Cessna F.182Q II	Zone Travel Ltd/White Waltham
	G-BHDR	Cessna F.152 II	Tayside Aviation Ltd/Dundee
	G-BHDS	Cessna F.152 II	Tayside Aviation Ltd/Dundee
	G-BHDU	Cessna F.152 II	Falcon Flying Services/Biggin Hill
	G-BHDV	Cameron V-77 balloon	P. Glydon
	G-BHDW	Cessna F.152 II	Tayside Aviation Ltd/Dundee
	G-BHDX	Cessna F.172N	Skyhawk Group
	G-BHDZ	Cessna F.172N	Arrow Flying Ltd
	G-BHEC	Cessna F.152 II	Stapleford Flying Club Ltd
	G-BHED	Cessna FA.152	TG Aviation Ltd/Manston
	G-BHEG	Jodel 150	D. M. Griffiths
	G-BHEK	CP.1315-C3 Super Emeraude	D. B. Winstanley/Barton
	G-BHEL	Jodel D.117	N. Wright & C. M. Kettlewell
	G-BHEM	Bensen B.8M	G. C. Kerr
	G-BHEN	Cessna FA.152	Leicestershire Aero Club Ltd
	G-BHER	SOCATA TB.10 Tobago	Air Touring Ltd/Biggin Hill
	G-BHEU	Thunder Ax7-65 balloon	D. G. Such
	G-BHEV	PA-28R Cherokee Arrow 200	7-Up Group
	G-BHEX	Colt 56A balloon	A. S. Dear & ptnrs Super Wasp
	G-BHEZ	Jodel 150	Air Yorkshire Group
	G-BHFC	Cessna F.152	TG Aviation Ltd/Manston
	G-BHFE	PA-44-180 Seminole	Grunwick Ltd/Elstree
	G-BHFF	Jodel D.112	P. A. Dowell
	G-BHFG	SNCAN Stampe SV-4C	Stormswift Ltd
	G-BHFH	PA-34-200T Seneca II	G-WATS Aviation Ltd
	G-BHFI	Cessna F.152	BAe (Warton) Flying Group/Blackpool
	G-BHFJ	PA-28RT-201T Turbo Arrow IV	J. K. Beauchamp
	G-BHFK	PA-28-151 Warrior	Ilkeston Car Sales Ltd
	G-BHFR	Eiri PIK-20E-1	J. T. Morgan
	G-BHFS	Robin DR.400/180	C. J. Moss
	G-BHGC	PA-18 Super Cub 150	Vectis Gliding Club Ltd
	G-BHGF	Cameron V-56 balloon	P. Smallward
	G-BHGJ	Jodel D.120	Q. M. B. Oswell
	G-BHGK	Sikorsky S-76A	CHC Scotia Ltd
	G-BHGO	PA-32 Cherokee Six 260	DOCS Ltd/Newcastle
	G-BHGP	SOCATA TB.10 Tobago	D. Suleyman
	G-BHGY	PA-28R Cherokee Arrow 200	V. Humphries/Gamston
	G-BHHB	Cameron V-77 balloon	R. Powell
	G-BHHE	Jodel DR.1051/M1	P. Bridges
	G-BHHG	Cessna F.152 II	TG Aviation Ltd/Manston
	G-BHHH	Thunder Ax7-65 balloon	C. A. Hendley (Essex) Ltd
	G-BHHK	Cameron N-77 balloon	I. S. Bridge
	G-BHHN	Cameron V-77 balloon	Itchen Valley Balloon Group
	G-BHHX	Jodel D.112	Hotel X-Ray Flying Group
	G-BHHZ	Rotorway Scorpion 133	L. W. & O. Usherwood
	G-BHIB	Cessna F.182Q	S. N. Chater & B. Payne
	G-BHIC	Cessna F.182Q	W. F. Alton & Son
	G-BHIG	Colt 31A Arm Chair SS balloon	P. A. Lindstrand/Sweden
	G-BHIH	Cessna F.172N	M. A. Wilkinson
	G-BHII	Cameron V-77 balloon	R. V. Brown
	G-BHIJ	Eiri PIK-20E-1 (898)	I. W. Paterson/Portmoak
	G-BHIK	Adam RA-14 Loisirs	L. Lewis
	G-BHIR	PA-28R Cherokee Arrow 200	Factorcore Ltd/Barton
	G-BHIS	Thunder Ax7-65 balloon	Hedgehoppers Balloon Group
	G-BHIT	SOCATA TB.9 Tampico	C. J. P. Webster/Biggin Hill
	G-BHIY	Cessna F.150K	G. J. Ball
	G-BHJA	Cessna A.152	Cornwall Flying Club Ltd/Bodmin

Reg.	Type	Owner or Operator	Notes
G-BHJB	Cessna A.152	Flight Ltd	
G-BHJF	SOCATA TB.10 Tobago	Flying Fox Group/Blackbushe	
G-BHJI	Mooney M.20J	G. Harding	
G-BHJK	Maule M5-235C Lunar Rocket	T. P. Spurge	
G-BHJN	Fournier RF-4D	RF-4 Flying Group	
G-BHJO	PA-28-161 Warrior II	The Brackla Flying Group/Inverness	
G-BHJS	Partenavia P.68B	J. J. Watts & D. Fletcher	
G-BHJU	Robin DR.400/2+2	J. Barlow & P. Crow	
G-BHKE	Bensen B.8MS	N. B. Gray	
G-BHKH	Cameron O-65 balloon	D. G. Body	
G-BHKJ	Cessna 421C	Totaljet Ltd	
G-BHKR	Colt 12A balloon ★	British Balloon Museum/Newbury	
G-BHKT	Jodel D.112	The Evans Flying Group	
G-BHLE	Robin DR.400/180	B. D. Greenwood	
G-BHLH	Robin DR.400/180	P. E. Davis	
G-BHLJ	Saffery-Rigg S.200 balloon	I. A. Rigg	
G-BHLT	D.H.82A Tiger Moth	P. J. & A. J. Borsberry	
G-BHLU	Fournier RF-3	Skyview Systems Ltd	
G-BHLW	Cessna 120	L. W. Scattergood	
G-BHLX	AA-5B Tiger	M. D. McPherson	
G-BHMA	SIPA 903	H. J. Taggart	
G-BHMG	Cessna FA.152	R. D. Smith	
G-BHMI	Cessna F.172N	GMI Aviation Ltd (G-WADE)	
G-BHMJ	Avenger T.200-2112 balloon	R. Light *Lord Anthony 1*	
G-BHMK	Avenger T.200-2112 balloon	P. Kinder *Lord Anthony 2*	
G-BHMR	Stinson 108-3	D. G. French/Sandown	
G-BHMT	Evans VP-1	P. E. J. Sturgeon	
G-BHMY	F.27 Friendship Mk.200 ★	Norwich Aviation Museum	
G-BHNA	Cessna F.152	Sheffield Aero Club Ltd/Netherthorpe	
G-BHNC	Cameron O-65 balloon	D. & C. Bareford	
G-BHND	Cameron N-65 balloon	S. M. Wellband	
G-BHNK	Jodel D.120A	G-BHNK Flying Group	
G-BHNL	Jodel D.112	J. C. Mansell	
G-BHNO	PA-28-181 Archer II	Airfluid Hydraulics & Pneumatics (Wolverhampton) Ltd	
G-BHNP	Eiri PIK-20E-1	D. A. Sutton/Riseley	
G-BHNV	Westlan-Bell 47G-3B1	Leyline Helicopters Ltd	
G-BHNX	Jodel D.117	A. J. Chalkley	
G-BHOA	Robin DR.400/160	M. L. Sargeant	
G-BHOH	Sikorsky S-61N Mk.II	Bristow Helicopters Ltd	
G-BHOJ	Colt 12A balloon	J. A. Folkes	
G-BHOL	Jodel DR.1050	J. E. Sharkey	
G-BHOM	PA-18 Super Cub 95	Oscar Mike Flying Group/Andrewsfield	
G-BHOO	Thunder Ax7-65 balloon	D. Livesey & J. M. Purves Scraps	
G-BHOR	PA-28-161 Warrior II	Oscar Romeo Flying Group/Biggin Hill	
G-BHOT	Cameron V-65 balloon	Dante Balloon Group	
G-BHOZ	SOCATA TB.9 Tampico	A. N. Hendley/Blackbushe	
G-BHPK	Piper J-3C-65 Cub (236800)	L-4 Group	
G-BHPL	C.A.S.A. 1.131E Jungmann 1000 (E3B-350)	R. G. Gray/North Weald	
G-BHPM	PA-18 Super Cub 95	P. I. Morgans	
G-BHPN	Colt 14A balloon	Lindstrand Balloons Ltd/Sweden	
G-BHPS	Jodel D.120A	T. J. Price	
G-BHPY	Cessna 152 II	Halegreen Associates	
G-BHPZ	Cessna 172N	O'Brien Properties Ltd/Redhill	
G-BHRB	Cessna F.152 II	LAC (Enterprises) Ltd/Barton	
G-BHRC	PA-28-161 Warrior II	Sherwood Flying Club Ltd/Tollerton	
G-BHRH	Cessna FA.150K	Merlin Flying Club Ltd/Hucknall	
G-BHRI	Saffery S.200 balloon	N. J. & H. L. Dunnington	
G-BHRM	Cessna F.152	Aerohire Ltd/Wolverhampton	
G-BHRN	Cessna F.152	Fraggle Leasing Ltd/Edinburgh	
G-BHRO	R. Commander 112A	John Raymond Transport Ltd/Cardiff	
G-BHRR	PA-44-180 Seminole	M. S. Farmers	
G-BHRR	CP.301A Emeraude	T. W. Offen	
G-BHRW	Jodel DR.221	Dauphin Flying Group	
G-BHRY	Colt 56A balloon	A. S. Davidson	
G-BHSA	Cessna 152 II	D. Copley	
G-BHSB	Cessna 172N	ABK Aviation Services Ltd	
G-BHSD	Scheibe SF.25E Super Falke	Lasham Gliding Soc Ltd	
G-BHSE	R. Commander 114	604 Sqdn Flying Group Ltd	
G-BHSN	Cameron N-56 balloon	I. Bentley	
G-BHSP	Thunder Ax7-77Z balloon	Out-Of-The-Blue	
G-BHSS	Pitts S-1C Special	S. P. A. Hill	

Notes	Reg.	Type	Owner or Operator
	G-BHSY	Jodel DR.1050	T. R. Allebone
	G-BHTA	PA-28-236 Dakota	Dakota Ltd
	G-BHTC	Jodel DR.1050/M1	G. Clark
	G-BHTG	Thunder Ax6-56 balloon	F. R. & Mrs S. H. MacDonald
	G-BHTH	NA T-6G Texan (2807)	J. J. Woodhouse
	G-BHUB	Douglas C-47A (315509) ★	Imperial War Museum/Duxford
	G-BHUE	Jodel DR.1050	M. J. Harris
	G-BHUG	Cessna 172N	FGT Aircraft Hire
	G-BHUI	Cessna 152	Galair International Ltd
	G-BHUJ	Cessna 172N	Flightline Ltd/Southend
	G-BHUM	D.H.82A Tiger Moth	S. G. Towers
	G-BHUR	Thunder Ax3 balloon	B. F. G. Ribbans
	G-BHUU	PA-25 Pawnee 235	Booker Gliding Club Ltd
	G-BHVB	PA-28-161 Warrior II	Caine Aviation Ltd/Wolverhampton
	G-BHVF	Jodel 150A	J. D. Walton
	G-BHVP	Cessna 182Q	R. J. W. Wood
	G-BHVR	Cessna 172N	G-BHVR Group
	G-BHVV	Piper J-3C-65 Cub	I. J. M. Donnelly
	G-BHWA	Cessna F.152	Lincoln Aviation/Wickenby
	G-BHWB	Cessna F.152	Lincoln Aviation/Wickenby
	G-BHWH	Weedhopper JC-24A	G. A. Clephane
	G-BHWK	M.S.880B Rallye Club	L. L. Gayther
	G-BHWY	PA-28R Cherokee Arrow 200-II	Kilo Foxtrot Flying Group/Sandown
	G-BHWZ	PA-28-181 Archer II	M. A. Abbott
	G-BHXA	SA Bulldog Srs 120/1210	Air Plan Flight Equipment Ltd/Barton
	G-BHXD	Jodel D.120	P. H. C. Hall
	G-BHXK	PA-28 Cherokee 140	GXK Flying Group
	G-BHXL	Evans VP-2	R. S. Wharton
	G-BHXS	Jodel D.120	I. R. Willis
	G-BHXY	Piper J-3C-65 Cub (44-79609)	F. W. Rogers/Aldergrove
	G-BHYA	Cessna R.182RG II	Card Tech Ltd
	G-BHYC	Cessna 172RG II	IB Aeroplanes Ltd
	G-BHYD	Cessna R.172K XP II	Sylmar Aviation Services Ltd
	G-BHYE	PA-34-200T Seneca II	Oxford Aviation Services Ltd/Kidlington
	G-BHYF	PA-34-200T Seneca II	Oxford Aviation Services Ltd/Kidlington
	G-BHYG	PA-34-200T Seneca II	Oxford Aviation Services Ltd/Kidlington
	G-BHYI	SNCAN Stampe SV-4A	P. Chamberlain
	G-BHYO	Cameron N-77 balloon	Adventure Balloon Co Ltd
	G-BHYP	Cessna F.172M	Avior Ltd/Biggin Hill
	G-BHYR	Cessna F.172M	G-BHYR Group
	G-BHYV	Evans VP-1	L. Chiappi/Blackpool
	G-BHYX	Cessna 152 II	Stapleford Flying Club Ltd
	G-BHZE	PA-28-181 Archer II	Zegruppe Ltd
	G-BHZH	Cessna F.152	Plymouth School of Flying Ltd
	G-BHZK	AA-5B Tiger	ZK Group/Elstree
	G-BHZO	AA-5A Cheetah	Scotia Safari Ltd/Prestwick
	G-BHZR	SA Bulldog Srs 120/1210	M. A. Elobeid
	G-BHZS	SA Bulldog Srs 120/1210	Air Plan Flight Equipment Ltd/Hawarden
	G-BHZT	SA Bulldog Srs 120/1210	D. M. Curties
	G-BHZU	Piper J-3C-65 Cub	J. K. Tomkinson
	G-BHZV	Jodel D.120A	K. J. Scott
	G-BHZX	Thunder Ax7-65A balloon	R. J. & H. M. Beattie
	G-BIAC	SOCATA Rallye 235E	A. Pound
	G-BIAH	Jodel D.112	D. Mitchell
	G-BIAI	WMB.2 Windtracker balloon	I. Chadwick
	G-BIAK	SOCATA TB.10 Tobago	Westmead Business Group Ltd
	G-BIAP	PA-16 Clipper	P. J. Bish/White Waltham
	G-BIAR	Rigg Skyliner II balloon	I. A. Rigg
	G-BIAU	Sopwith Pup (replica) (N6452) ★	F.A.A. Museum/Yeovilton
	G-BIAX	Taylor JT.2 Titch	J. T. Everest
	G-BIAY	AA-5 Traveler	M. D. Dupay & ptnrs
	G-BIBA	SOCATA TB.9 Tampico	TB Aviation Ltd
	G-BIBB	Mooney M.20C	P. M. Breton
	G-BIBJ	Enstrom 280C-UK-2	Tindon Ltd/Little Snoring
	G-BIBN	Cessna FA.150K	B. V. Mayo
	G-BIBO	Cameron V-65 balloon	I. Harris
	G-BIBS	Cameron P-20 balloon	Cameron Balloons Ltd
	G-BIBT	AA-5B Tiger	Vizor Tempered Glass Ltd
	G-BIBW	Cessna F.172N	P. T. Fellows & J. C. Waller
	G-BIBX	WMB.2 Windtracker balloon	I. A. Rigg
	G-BICD	Auster 5	R. T. Parsons
	G-BICE	AT-6C Harvard IIA (41-33275)	C. M. L. Edwards

Reg.	Type	Owner or Operator	Notes
G-BICG	Cessna F.152 II	Falcon Flying Services/Biggin Hill	
G-BICJ	Monnett Sonerai II	I. Parr	
G-BICM	Colt 56A balloon	Avon Advertiser Balloon Club	
G-BICP	Robin DR.360	A. E. Smith/Breighton	
G-BICR	Jodel D.120A	Beehive Flying Group/White Waltham	
G-BICS	Robin R.2100A	I. Young/Sandown	
G-BICU	Cameron V-56 balloon	S. D. Bather & D. Scott	
G-BICW	PA-28-161 Warrior II	D. Gellhorn/Blackbushe	
G-BICX	Maule M5-235C Lunar Rocket	A. T. Jeans & J. F. Clarkson/Old Sarum	
G-BICY	PA-23 Apache 160	A. M. Lynn/Sibson	
G-BIDD	Evans VP-1	J. Hodgkinson	
G-BIDF	Cessna F.172P	E. Alexander	
G-BIDG	Jodel 150A	D. R. Gray/Barton	
G-BIDH	Cessna 152 II	C. Clark-Monks (G-DONA)	
G-BIDI	PA-28R-201 Arrow III	Ambrit Ltd	
G-BIDJ	PA-18A Super Cub 150	Flight Solutions Ltd	
G-BIDK	PA-18 Super Cub 150	J. & M. A. McCullough	
G-BIDU	Cameron V-77 balloon	E. Eleazor	
G-BIDV	Colt 14A balloon ★	British Balloon Museum/Newbury	
G-BIDW	Sopwith 1 1/2 Strutter (replica) (A8226) ★	RAF Museum/Hendon	
G-BIDX	Jodel D.112	P. Turton & H. C. Peake-Jones	
G-BIEF	Cameron V-77 balloon	D. S. Bush	
G-BIEJ	Sikorsky S-76A	Bristow Helicopters Ltd	
G-BIEO	Jodel D.112	Clipgate Flyers	
G-BIES	Maule M5-235C Lunar Rocket	William Proctor Farms	
G-BIET	Cameron O-77 balloon	G. M. Westley	
G-BIEY	PA-28-151 Warrior	Falcon Flying Services/Biggin Hill	
G-BIFA	Cessna 310R II	J. S. Lee	
G-BIFB	PA-28 Cherokee 150C	N. A. Ayub	
G-BIFN	Bensen B.8MR	B. Gunn	
G-BIFO	Evans VP-1	R. Broadhead	
G-BIFY	Cessna F.150L	Astra Associates/Elstree	
G-BIFZ	Partenavia P.68C	Eil Sud SRL/Italy	
G-BIGJ	Cessna F.172M	V. D. Speck/Clacton	
G-BIGK	Taylorcraft BC-12D	N. P. S. Ramsay	
G-BIGL	Cameron O-65 balloon	P. L. Mossman	
G-BIGP	Bensen B.8M	R. H. S. Cooper	
G-BIGR	Avenger T.200-2112 balloon	R. Light	
G-BIGU	Bensen B.8MR	C. G. Ponsford	
G-BIGZ	Scheibe SF.25B Falke	G-BIGZ Syndicate/Saltby	
G-BIHD	Robin DR.400/160	A. J. Fieldman	
G-BIHF	SE-5A (replica) (F943)	S. H. O'connell/White Waltham	
G-BIHG	PA-28 Cherokee 140	Madley Flying Group/Shobdon	
G-BIHI	Cessna 172M	Fenland Flying School	
G-BIHO	D.H.C.6 Twin Otter 310	Isles of Scilly Skybus Ltd/St. Just	
G-BIHP	Van Den Bemden gas balloon	J. J. Harris	
G-BIHT	PA-17 Vagabond	W. E. Willets	
G-BIHU	Saffrey S.200 balloon	B. L. King	
G-BIHW	Aeronca A65TAC Defender	T. J. Ingrouille	
G-BIHX	Bensen B.8M	P. P. Willmott	
G-BIIA	Fournier RF-3	P. K. Jenkins	
G-BIIB	Cessna F.172M	Civil Service Flying Club (Biggin Hill) Ltd	
G-BIID	PA-18 Super Cub 95	D. A. Lacey	
G-BIIE	Cessna F.172P	Sterling Helicopters Ltd	
G-BIIK	M.S.883 Rallye 115	K. M. Bowen	
G-BIIL	Thunder Ax6-56 balloon	G. W. Reader	
G-BIIP	BN-2B-27 Islander	Hebridean Air Services Ltd/Glasgow	
G-BIIT	PA-28-161 Warrior II	Tayside Aviation Ltd/Dundee	
G-BIIV	PA-28-181 Archer II	E. Bensoussan/France	
G-BIIZ	Great Lakes 2T-1A Sport Trainer	Circa 42 Ltd	
G-BIJB	PA-18 Super Cub 150	Essex Gliding Club Ltd/North Weald	
G-BIJD	Bo 208C Junior	C. G. Stone	
G-BIJE	Piper J-3C-65 Cub	R. L. Hayward & A. G. Scott	
G-BIJS	Luton LA-4A Minor	I. J. Smith	
G-BIJU	CP-301A Emeraude	Eastern Taildraggers Flying Group (G-BHTX)	
G-BIJV	Cessna F.152 II	Falcon Flying Services/Biggin Hill	
G-BIJW	Cessna F.152 II	Falcon Flying Services/Biggin Hill	
G-BIJX	Cessna F.152 II	Falcon Flying Services/Biggin Hill	
G-BIKE	PA-28R Cherokee Arrow 200	R. V. Webb Ltd/Elstree	
G-BILB	WMB.2 Windtracker balloon	B. L. King	
G-BILE	Scruggs BL.2B balloon	P. D. Ridout	

Notes	Reg.	Type	Owner or Operator
	G-BILG	Scruggs BL.2B balloon	P. D. Ridout
	G-BILI	Piper J-3C-65 Cub (454467)	G-BILI Flying Group
	G-BILJ	Cessna FA.152	Bflying Ltd
	G-BILL	PA-25 Pawnee 235	Pawnee Aviation
	G-BILR	Cessna 152 II	Shropshire Aero Club Ltd/Sleap
	G-BILS	Cessna 152 II	Keen Leasing (IOM) Ltd
	G-BILU	Cessna 172RG	Full Sutton Flying Centre Ltd
	G-BILZ	Taylor JT.1 Monoplane	A. Petherbridge
	G-BIMK	Tiger T.200 Srs 1 balloon	M. K. Baron
	G-BIMM	PA-18 Super Cub 150	Fairmont Investments Ltd/Clacton
	G-BIMN	Steen Skybolt	D. Watt
	G-BIMO	SNCAN Stampe SV-4C	R. A. Roberts
	G-BIMT	Cessna FA.152	Staverton Flying Services Ltd
	G-BIMU	Sikorsky S-61N	Bristow Helicopters Ltd
	G-BIMX	Rutan Vari-Eze	D. G. Crow/Biggin Hill
	G-BIMZ	Beech 76 Duchess	Firfax Systems Ltd
	G-BING	Cessna F.172P	M. P. Dolan
	G-BINL	Scruggs BL.2B balloon	P. D. Ridout
	G-BINM	Scruggs BL.2B balloon	P. D. Ridout
	G-BINR	Unicorn UE.1A balloon	Unicorn Group
	G-BINS	Unicorn UE.2A balloon	Unicorn Group
	G-BINT	Unicorn UE.1A balloon	D. E. Bint
	G-BINX	Scruggs BL.2B balloon	P. D. Ridout
	G-BINY	Oriental balloon	J. L. Morton
	G-BIOA	Hughes 369D	AH Helicopter Services Ltd
	G-BIOB	Cessna F.172P	Aerofilms Ltd/Elstree
	G-BIOC	Cessna F.150L	Southside Flyers
	G-BIOI	Jodel DR.1051/M	R. Pidcock
	G-BIOJ	R. Commander 112TCA	A. T. Dalby
	G-BIOK	Cessna F.152	Tayside Aviation Ltd/Dundee
	G-BIOM	Cessna F.152	Falcon Flying Services/Luton
	G-BIOR	M.S.880B Rallye Club	R. L. & K. P. McLean/Rufforth
	G-BIOU	Jodel D.117A	Dubious Group/Booker
	G-BIOW	Slingsby T.67A	A. B. Slinger/Sherburn
	G-BIPA	AA-5B Tiger	J. Campbell/Walney Island
	G-BIPH	Scruggs BL.2B balloon	C. M. Dewsnap
	G-BIPI	Everett gyroplane	C. A. Reeves
	G-BIPN	Fournier RF-3	J. C. R. Rogers & I. F. Fairhead
	G-BIPO	Mudry/CAARP CAP.20LS-200M.	C. Sandford
	G-BIPS	SOCATA Rallye 100ST	McAully Flying Group/Little Snoring
	G-BIPT	Jodel D.112	C. R. Davies
	G-BIPV	AA-5B Tiger	Airtime Aviation Ltd
	G-BIPW	Avenger T.200-2112 balloon	B. L. King
	G-BIPY	Montgomerie-Bensen B.8MR	C. G. Ponsford
	G-BIRD	Pitts S-1D Special	Pitts Artists Flying Group
	G-BIRE	Colt 56 Bottle SS balloon	K. R. Gafney
	G-BIRH	PA-18 Super Cub 135 (R-163)	Aquila Gliding Club Ltd
	G-BIRI	C.A.S.A. 1.131E Jungmann 1000	M. G. & J. R. Jeffries
	G-BIRK	Avenger T.200-2112 balloon	D. Harland
	G-BIRL	Avenger T.200-2112 balloon	R. Light
	G-BIRP	Arena Mk 17 Skyship balloon	A. S. Viel
	G-BIRS	Cessna 182P	–(G-BBBS)/Liverpool
	G-BIRT	Robin R.1180TD	W. D'A. Hall/Booker
	G-BIRW	M.S.505 Criquet (F+IS) ★	Museum of Flight/E. Fortune
	G-BIRY	Cameron V-77 balloon	P. & H. Mann
	G-BIRZ	Zenair CH.250	L. D. Johnston
	G-BISG	FRED Srs 3	T. Littlefair
	G-BISH	Cameron O-42 balloon	Zebedee Balloon Service
	G-BISJ	Cessna 340A	Midland Airline Transport Services Ltd
	G-BISK	R. Commander 112B ★	P. A. Warner
	G-BISL	Scruggs BL.2B balloon	P. D. Ridout
	G-BISM	Scruggs BL.2B balloon	P. D. Ridout
	G-BISS	Scruggs BL.2C balloon	P. D. Ridout
	G-BIST	Scruggs BL.2C balloon	P. D. Ridout
	G-BISX	Colt 56A balloon	C. D. Steel
	G-BISZ	Sikorsky S-76A	Bristow Helicopters Ltd
	G-BITA	PA-18 Super Cub 150	Intrepid Aviation Co/North Weald
	G-BITE	SOCATA TB.10 Tobago	M. A. Smith & R. J. Bristow/Fairoaks
	G-BITF	Cessna F.152 II	Tayside Aviation Ltd/Dundee
	G-BITH	Cessna F.152 II	Tayside Aviation Ltd/Dundee
	G-BITK	FRED Srs 2	D. J. Wood
	G-BITM	Cessna F.172P	Dreamtrade Ltd
	G-BITO	Jodel D.112D	A. Dunbar/Barton

Reg.	Type	Owner or Operator	Notes
G-BITS	Drayton B-56 balloon	M. J. Betts	
G-BITY	FD.31T balloon	A. J. Bell	
G-BIUM	Cessna F.152	Sheffield Aero Club Ltd/Netherthorpe	
G-BIUP	SNCAN NC.854S	BIUP Flying Group	
G-BIUU	PA-23 Aztec 250D ★	G. Cormack/Glasgow	
G-BIUV	H.S.748 Srs 2A	Emerald Airways Ltd *City of Liverpool* (G-AYYH)/Liverpool	
G-BIUW	PA-28-161 Warrior II	D. R. Staley	
G-BIUY	PA-28-181 Archer II	J. S. Devlin & Z. Islam	
G-BIVA	Robin R.2112	P. A. Richardson	
G-BIVB	Jodel D.112	M. J. Hayman	
G-BIVC	Jodel D.112	M. J. Barmby/Cardiff	
G-BIVF	CP.301C-3 Emeraude	R. J. Moore	
G-BIVK	Bensen B.8M	K. Balch	
G-BIVT	Saffery S.80 balloon	L. F. Guyot	
G-BIVV	AA-5A Cheetah	Robert Afia Consulting Engineer	
G-BIWB	Scruggs RS.5000 balloon	P. D. Ridout	
G-BIWC	Scruggs RS.5000 balloon	P. D. Ridout	
G-BIWF	Warren balloon	P. D. Ridout	
G-BIWG	Zelenski Mk 2 balloon	P. D. Ridout	
G-BIWJ	Unicorn UE.1A balloon	B. L. King	
G-BIWK	Cameron V-65 balloon	I. R. Williams & R. G. Bickerdike	
G-BIWL	PA-32-301 Saratoga	A. R. Ward	
G-BIWN	Jodel D.112	C. R. Coates	
G-BIWR	Mooney M.20F	A. C. Brink	
G-BIWU	Cameron V-65 balloon	L. P. Hooper	
G-BIWW	AA-5 Traveler	B & K Aviation/Cranfield	
G-BIWY	Westland WG.30 ★	*Instructional airframe*/Yeovil	
G-BIXA	SOCATA TB.9 Tampico	W. & K. J. C. Maxwell	
G-BIXB	SOCATA TB.9 Tampico	L. B. W. & F. H. Hancock	
G-BIXH	Cessna F.152	Cambridge Aero Club Ltd	
G-BIXI	Cessna 172RG Cutlass	J. F. P. Lewis/Sandown	
G-BIXL	P-51D Mustang (472216)	R. Lamplough/North Weald	
G-BIXN	Boeing Stearman A.75N1	V. S. E. Norman/Rendcomb	
G-BIXS	Avenger T.200-2112 balloon	M. Stuart	
G-BIXV	Bell 212	Bristow Helicopters Ltd	
G-BIXW	Colt 56B balloon	N. A. P. Bates	
G-BIXX	Pearson Srs 2 balloon	D. Pearson	
G-BIXZ	Grob G-109	D. L. Nind & I. Allum/Booker	
G-BIYI	Cameron V-65 balloon	Sarnia Balloon Group	
G-BIYJ	PA-18 Super Cub 95	S. Russell	
G-BIYK	Isaacs Fury II	C. W. Wilkins	
G-BIYP	PA-20 Pacer 125	A. W. Hoy & S. W. M. Johnson	
G-BIYR	PA-18 Super Cub 150 (R-151)	Delta Foxtrot Flying Group	
G-BIYT	Colt 17A balloon	J. M. Francois/France	
G-BIYU	Fokker S.11.1 Instructor (E-15)	C. Briggs	
G-BIYW	Jodel D.112	Pollard/Balaam/Bye Flying Group	
G-BIYX	PA-28 Cherokee 140	W. B. Bateson/Blackpool	
G-BIYY	PA-18 Super Cub 95	A. E. & W. J. Taylor/Ingoldmells	
G-BIZE	SOCATA TB.9 Tampico	C. Fordham	
G-BIZF	Cessna F.172P	R. S. Bentley/Bourn	
G-BIZG	Cessna F.152	M. A. Judge	
G-BIZI	Robin DR.400/120	Headcorn Flying School Ltd	
G-BIZK	Nord 3202	A. I. Milne/Swanton Morley	
G-BIZM	Nord 3202	Magnificent Obsessions Ltd	
G-BIZO	PA-28R Cherokee Arrow 200	Bizo Air Ltd	
G-BIZR	SOCATA TB.9 Tampico	R. C. Walker (G-BSEC)	
G-BIZU	Thunder Ax6-56Z balloon	M. J. Loades	
G-BIZV	PA-18 Super Cub 95 (18-2001)	S. J. Pugh & R. L. Wademan	
G-BIZW	Champion 7GCBC Citabria	G. Read & Sons	
G-BIZY	Jodel D.112	Wayland Tunley & Associates/Cranfield	
G-BJAD	FRED Srs 2	C. Allison	
G-BJAE	Lavadoux Starck AS.80	D. J. & S. A. E. Phillips/Coventry	
G-BJAF	Piper J-3C-65 Cub	P. J. Cottle	
G-BJAG	PA-28-181 Archer II	J. F. Clark	
G-BJAJ	AA-5B Tiger	A. H. McVicar/Prestwick	
G-BJAL	C.A.S.A. 1.131E Jungmann 1000	I. C. Underwood & S. B. J. Chandler/ Breighton	
G-BJAO	Bensen B.8M	A. P. Lay	
G-BJAP	D.H.82A Tiger Moth (K2587)	K. Knight	
G-BJAS	Rango NA.9 balloon	A. Lindsay	
G-BJAV	GY-80 Horizon 160	P. L. Lovegrove	

Notes	Reg.	Type	Owner or Operator
	G-BJAW	Cameron V-65 balloon	G. W. McCarthy
	G-BJAX	Pilatus P2-05 (U-108) ★	(stored)
	G-BJAY	Piper J-3C-65 Cub	J. H. A. Clarke
	G-BJBK	PA-18 Super Cub 95	M. S. Bird/Old Sarum
	G-BJBO	Jodel DR.250/160	Wiltshire Flying Group
	G-BJBW	PA-28-161 Warrior II	152 Group
	G-BJBX	PA-28-161 Warrior II	Haimoss Ltd
	G-BJCA	PA-28-161 Warrior II	QBS Trading Co Ltd
	G-BJCF	CP.1310-C3 Super Emeraude	K. M. Hodson & C. G. H. Gurney
	G-BJCI	PA-18 Super Cub 150 (modified)	The Borders (Milfield) Aero-Tour Club Ltd
	G-BJCW	PA-32R-301 Saratoga SP	Golf Charlie Whisky Ltd
	G-BJDE	Cessna F.172M	Cranfield Aircraft Partnership
	G-BJDF	M.S.880B Rallye 100T	G-BJDF Group
	G-BJDI	Cessna FR.182RG	JSE Systems
	G-BJDJ	H.S.125 Srs 700B	Falcon Jet Centre Ltd (G-RCDI)
	G-BJDK	European E.14 balloon	Aeroprint Tours
	G-BJDO	AA-5A Cheetah	Flying Services
	G-BJDT	SOCATA TB.9 Tampico	A. Watson
	G-BJDW	Cessna F.172M	J. Rae
	G-BJEI	PA-18 Super Cub 95	H. J. Cox
	G-BJEL	SNCAN NC.854	N. F. & S. G. Hunter
	G-BJEN	Scruggs RS.5000 balloon	N. J. Richardson
	G-BJEV	Aeronca 11AC Chief (897)	R. F. Willcox
	G-BJEX	Bo 208C Junior	G. D. H. Crawford/Thruxton
	G-BJFB	Mk 1A balloon	Aeroprint Tours
	G-BJFC	European E.8 balloon	P. D. Ridout
	G-BJFE	PA-18 Super Cub 95	P. H. Wilmot-Allistone
	G-BJFL	Sikorsky S-76A	Bristow Helicopters Ltd
	G-BJFM	Jodel D.120	J. V. George & P. A. Smith/Popham
	G-BJGK	Cameron V-77 balloon	T. J. Orchard & ptnrs
	G-BJGM	Unicorn UE.1A balloon	D. Eaves & P. D. Ridout
	G-BJGX	Sikorsky S-76A	Bristow Helicopters Ltd
	G-BJGY	Cessna F.172P	Lucca Wines Ltd
	G-BJHB	Mooney M.20J	Zitair Flying Club Ltd/Redhill
	G-BJHK	EAA Acro Sport	M. R. Holden
	G-BJHP	Osprey 1C balloon	N. J. Richardson
	G-BJHV	Voisin Replica ★	Brooklands Museum of Aviation /Weybridge
	G-BJHW	Osprey 1C balloon	N. J. Richardson
	G-BJIA	Allport balloon	D. J. Allport
	G-BJIC	Dodo 1A balloon	P. D. Ridout
	G-BJID	Osprey 1B balloon	P. D. Ridout
	G-BJIG	Slingsby T.67A	G-BJIG Slingsby Syndicate
	G-BJIR	Cessna 550 Citation II	Gator Aviation Ltd
	G-BJIV	PA-18 Super Cub 180	Yorkshire Gliding Club (Pty) Ltd/ Sutton Bank
	G-BJKF	SOCATA TB.9 Tampico	Venue Solutions
	G-BJKW	Wills Aera II	J. K. S. Wills
	G-BJKY	Cessna F.152	Air Charter & Travel Ltd/Ronaldsway
	G-BJLB	SNCAN NC.854S	M. J. Barnaby
	G-BJLC	Monnett Sonerai IIL	A. R. Ansell
	G-BJLH	PA-18 Super Cub 95 (44)	Felthorpe Flying Group Ltd
	G-BJLO	PA-31-310 Turbo Navajo	RJ Aviation Ltd
	G-BJLX	Cremer balloon	P. W. May
	G-BJLY	Cremer balloon	P. Cannon
	G-BJML	Cessna 120	D. F. Lawlor/Inverness
	G-BJMO	Taylor JT.1 Monoplane	R. C. Mark
	G-BJMR	Cessna 310R	J. McL. Robinson/Sherburn
	G-BJMW	Thunder Ax8-105 balloon	G. M. Westley
	G-BJMX	Jarre JR.3 balloon	P. D. Ridout
	G-BJMZ	European EA.8A balloon	P. D. Ridout
	G-BJNA	Arena Mk 117P balloon	P. D. Ridout
	G-BJND	Osprey Mk 1E balloon	A. Billington & D. Whitmore
	G-BJNF	Cessna F.152	Exeter Flying Club Ltd
	G-BJNG	Slingsby T.67AM	D. F. Hodgkinson
	G-BJNN	PA-38-112 Tomahawk	Scotia Safari Ltd/Prestwick
	G-BJNY	Aeronca 11CC Super Chief	P. I. & D. M. Morgans
	G-BJNZ	PA-23 Aztec 250F	Bonus Aviation Ltd (G-FANZ)/Cranfield
	G-BJOA	PA-28-181 Archer II	Channel Islands Aero Services Ltd
	G-BJOB	Jodel D.140C	T. W. M. Beck & M. J. Smith
	G-BJOE	Jodel D.120A	Forth Flying Group
	G-BJOP	BN-2B-26 Islander	Loganair Ltd/BA Express
	G-BJOT	Jodel D.117	R. Meares-Davies & ptnrs

Reg.	Type	Owner or Operator	Notes
G-BJOV	Cessna F.150K	J. A. Boyd	
G-BJPI	Bede BD-5G	M. D. McQueen	
G-BJRA	Osprey Mk 4B balloon	E. Osborn	
G-BJRG	Osprey Mk 4B balloon	A. E. de Gruchy	
G-BJRH	Rango NA.36 balloon	N. H. Ponsford	
G-BJRP	Cremer balloon	M. D. Williams	
G-BJRR	Cremer balloon	M. D. Williams	
G-BJRV	Cremer balloon	M. D. Williams	
G-BJSC	Osprey Mk 4D balloon	N. J. Richardson	
G-BJSD	Osprey Mk 4D balloon	N. J. Richardson	
G-BJSF	Osprey Mk 4B balloon	N. J. Richardson	
G-BJSI	Osprey Mk 1E balloon	N. J. Richardson	
G-BJSP	Guido 1A Srs 61 balloon	G. A. Newsome	
G-BJSS	Allport balloon	D. J. Allport	
G-BJST	CCF T-6J Harvard IV	Tuplin Holdings Ltd	
G-BJSV	PA-28-161 Warrior II	Airways Flight Training (Exeter) Ltd	
G-BJSW	Thunder Ax7-65 balloon	Sandicliffe Garage Ltd	
G-BJSX	Unicorn UE-1C balloon	N. J. Richardson	
G-BJTB	Cessna A.150M	V. D. Speck/Clacton	
G-BJTO	Piper J-3C-65 Cub	K. R. Nunn	
G-BJTP	PA-18 Super Cub 95 (115302)	J. T. Parkins	
G-BJTW	European E.107 balloon	C. J. Brealey	
G-BJTY	Osprey Mk 4B balloon	A. E. de Gruchy	
G-BJUB	BVS Special 01 balloon	P. G. Wild	
G-BJUC	Robinson R-22HP	Heli Services	
G-BJUD	Robin DR.400/180R	Lasham Gliding Soc Ltd	
G-BJUR	PA-38-112 Tomahawk	Truman Aviation Ltd/Tollerton	
G-BJUS	PA-38-112 Tomahawk	Panshanger School of Flying	
G-BJUV	Cameron V-20 balloon	P. Spellward	
G-BJUY	Colt Ax7-77 Golf Ball SS balloon	Balloon Sports HB/Sweden	
G-BJVC	Evans VP-2	C. J. Morris	
G-BJVH	Cessna F.182Q	R. J. de Courcy Cuming/ Wellesbourne	
G-BJVJ	Cessna F.152	Cambridge Aero Club Ltd	
G-BJVK	Grob G-109	B. Kimberley/Enstone	
G-BJVM	Cessna 172N	I. C. MacLennan	
G-BJVS	CP.1310-C3 Super Emeraude	BJVS Group	
G-BJVT	Cessna F.152	Cambridge Aero Club Ltd	
G-BJVU	Thunder Ax6-56 Bolt SS balloon	G. V. Beckwith	
G-BJVV	Robin R.1180	Medway Flying Group Ltd/Rochester	
G-BJVX	Sikorsky S-76A	Bristow Helicopters Ltd	
G-BJWC	Saro Skeeter AOP.12 (XK 482) ★	Sloane Helicopters Ltd/Sywell	
G-BJWH	Cessna F.152 II	Plane Talking Ltd/Elstree	
G-BJWI	Cessna F.172P	Bflying Ltd	
G-BJWJ	Cameron V-65 balloon	R. G. Turnbull & S. G. Forse	
G-BJWO	BN-2A-26 Islander	Peterborough Parachute Centre Ltd (G-BAXC)/Sibson	
G-BJWT	Wittman W.10 Tailwind	Tailwind Group	
G-BJWV	Colt 17A balloon	D. T. Meyes	
G-BJWW	Cessna F.172N	Air Charter & Travel Ltd/Blackpool	
G-BJWX	PA-18 Super Cub 95	G-BJWX Syndicate	
G-BJWY	S-55 Whirlwind HAR.21 (WV198) ★	Solway Aviation Museum/Carlisle	
G-BJWZ	PA-18 Super Cub 95	G-BJWZ Syndicate/Redhill	
G-BJXA	Slingsby T.67A	Comed Aviation Ltd/Blackpool	
G-BJXB	Slingsby T.67A	X-Ray Bravo Ltd/Barton	
G-BJXK	Fournier RF-5	G-BJXK Syndicate/Usk	
G-BJXP	Colt 56B balloon	H. J. Anderson	
G-BJXX	PA-23 Aztec 250E	V. Bojovic	
G-BJXZ	Cessna 172N	T. M. Jones/Egginton	
G-BJYD	Cessna F.152 II	Cleveland Flying School Ltd/Teesside	
G-BJYF	Colt 56A balloon	H. Dos Santos	
G-BJYG	PA-28-161 Warrior II	S. R. Mitchell/Liverpool	
G-BJYK	Jodel D.120A	T. Fox & D. A. Thorpe	
G-BJYN	PA-38-112 Tomahawk	Panshanger School of Flying Ltd (G-BJTE)	
G-BJZA	Cameron N-65 balloon	A. D. Pinner	
G-BJZB	Evans VP-2	G. A. Shaw	
G-BJZF	D.H.82A Tiger Moth	R. Blast	
G-BJZN	Slingsby T.67A	A. R. T. Marsland	
G-BJZR	Colt 42A balloon	Selfish Balloon Group	
G-BJZX	Grob G.109	Oxfordshire Sport Flying Ltd/Enstone	

Notes	Reg.	Type	Owner or Operator
	G-BKAE	Jodel D.120	M. P. Wakem
	G-BKAF	FRED Srs 2	J. Mc. D. Robinson
	G-BKAM	Slingsby T.67M Firefly160	A. J. Daley
	G-BKAO	Jodel D.112	R. Broadhead
	G-BKAS	PA-38-112 Tomahawk	St. George Flying Club/Teesside
	G-BKAY	R. Commander 114	The Rockwell Group
	G-BKAZ	Cessna 152	L. W. Scattergood
	G-BKBB	Hawker Fury Mk I (replica)	Brandish Holdings Ltd/O. Warden
	G-BKBD	Thunder Ax3 balloon	M. J. Casson
	G-BKBF	M.S.894A Rallye Minerva 220	J. A. Gibbs
	G-BKBN	SOCATA TB.10 Tobago	David Newby Associates
	G-BKBO	Colt 17A balloon	J. Armstrong & ptnrs
	G-BKBP	Bellanca 7GCBC Scout	M. G. & J. R. Jefferies
	G-BKBV	SOCATA TB.10 Tobago	The Studio People Ltd
	G-BKBW	SOCATA TB.10 Tobago	Merlin Aviation
	G-BKCC	PA-28 Cherokee 180	Aeroshow Ltd
	G-BKCE	Cessna F.172P II	M. O. Loxton
	G-BKCI	Brügger MB.2 Colibri	E. R. Newall
	G-BKCJ	Oldfield Baby Great Lakes	S. V. Roberts/Sleap
	G-BKCL	PA-30 Twin Comanche 160C	Yorkair Ltd/Leeds
	G-BKCN	Currie Wot	N. A. A. Podmore
	G-BKCR	SOCATA TB.9 Tampico	A. Whitehouse
	G-BKCV	EAA Acro Sport II	T. N. Jinks
	G-BKCW	Jodel D.120	Dundee Flying Group (G-BMYF)
	G-BKCX	Mudry/CAARP CAP.10B	R. Ingleton
	G-BKCY	PA-38-112 Tomahawk II ★	*(stored)*/Welshpool
	G-BKCZ	Jodel D.120A	M. R. Baker/Shoreham
	G-BKDC	Monnett Sonerai II	K. J. Towell
	G-BKDH	Robin DR.400/120	Dauphin Flying Group Ltd
	G-BKDI	Robin DR.400/120	Cotswold Aero Club Ltd/Gloucestershire
	G-BKDJ	Robin DR.400/120	I. H. Taylor
	G-BKDK	Thunder Ax7-77Z balloon	A. J. Byrne
	G-BKDP	FRED Srs 3	M. Whittaker
	G-BKDR	Pitts S-1S Special	T. J. Reeve
	G-BKDT	SE-5A (replica) (F943) ★	Yorkshire Air Museum/Elvington
	G-BKDX	Jodel DR.1050	DX Group
	G-BKEK	PA-32 Cherokee Six 300	S. W. Turley
	G-BKEP	Cessna F.172M	Bob Crowe Aircraft Sales Ltd
	G-BKER	SE-5A (replica) (F5447)	N. K. Geddes
	G-BKET	PA-18 Super Cub 95	H. M. MacKenzie
	G-BKEU	Taylor JT.1 Monoplane	R. J. Whybrow & J. M. Springham
	G-BKEV	Cessna F.172M	Echo Victor Group
	G-BKEW	Bell 206B JetRanger 3	N. R. Foster
	G-BKEY	FRED Srs 3	G. S. Taylor
	G-BKFC	Cessna F.152 II	Sulby Aerial Surveys Ltd
	G-BKFI	Evans VP-1	P. L. Naylor
	G-BKFK	Isaacs Fury II	G. G. C. Jones
	G-BKFL	Aerosport Scamp	J. Sherwood
	G-BKFM	QAC Quickie 1	G. E. Meakin
	G-BKFN	Bell 214ST	Bristow Helicopters Ltd
	G-BKFR	CP.301C Emeraude	J. J. Beall
	G-BKFW	P.56 Provost T.1 (XF597)	Sylmar Aviation & Services Ltd
	G-BKFZ	PA-28R Cherokee Arrow 200	Shacklewell Flying Group
	G-BKGA	M.S.892E Rallye 150GT	BJJ Aviation
	G-BKGB	Jodel D.120	B. A. Ridgway
	G-BKGC	Maule M.6-235	D. W. Pennell
	G-BKGD	Westland WG.30 Srs.100 ★	IHM/Weston-s-Mare
	G-BKGL	Beech D.18S (1164)	Propshop Ltd & T. Darrah/Duxford
	G-BKGM	Beech D.18S (HB275)	A. E. Hutton/North Weald
	G-BKGR	Cameron O-65 balloon	K. Kidner & L. E. More
	G-BKGT	SOCATA Rallye 110ST	Long Marston Flying Group
	G-BKGW	Cessna F.152-II	Leicestershire Aero Club Ltd
	G-BKHA	W.S.55 Whirlwind HAR.10 (XJ763) ★	C. J. Evans
	G-BKHG	Piper J-3C-65 Cub (479766)	K. G. Wakefield
	G-BKHJ	Cessna 182P	Augur Films Ltd
	G-BKHR	Luton LA-4 Minor	C. B. Buscombe & R. Goldsworthy
	G-BKHW	Stoddard-Hamilton Glasair IIRG	G. R. W. Monksfield & ptnrs
	G-BKHY	Taylor JT.1 Monoplane	B. C. J. O'Neill
	G-BKHZ	Cessna F.172P	L. R. Leader
	G-BKIA	SOCATA TB.10 Tobago	M. F. McGinn
	G-BKIB	SOCATA TB.9 Tampico	G. A. Vickers
	G-BKIC	Cameron V-77 balloon	C. A. Butler

Reg.	Type	Owner or Operator	Notes
G-BKIF	Fournier RF-6B	D. J. Taylor & J. T. Flint	
G-BKII	Cessna F.172M	M. S. Knight/Goodwood	
G-BKIJ	Cessna F.172M	V. Speck	
G-BKIK	Cameron DG-19 airship ★	Balloon Preservation Group/Lancing	
G-BKIN	Alon A.2A Aircoupe	D. W. Vernon	
G-BKIR	Jodel D.117	R. Shaw & D. M. Hardaker/Sherburn	
G-BKIS	SOCATA TB.10 Tobago	Wessex Flyers Group	
G-BKIT	SOCATA TB.9 Tampico	D. N. Garlick & ptnrs	
G-BKIY	Thunder Ax3 balloon ★	Balloon Preservation Group/Lancing	
G-BKIZ	Cameron V-31 balloon	A. P. S. Cox	
G-BKJB	PA-18 Super Cub 135	Haimoss Ltd/O. Sarum	
G-BKJF	M.S.880B Rallye 100T	Journeyman Aviation Ltd	
G-BKJR	Hughes 269C	March Helicopters Ltd/Sywell	
G-BKJS	Jodel D.120A	Clipgate Flying Group	
G-BKJW	PA-23 Aztec 250E	Alan Williams Entertainments Ltd	
G-BKKN	Cessna 182R	R A. Marven/Elstree	
G-BKKO	Cessna 182R	B. & G. Jebson Ltd/Crosland Moor	
G-BKKZ	Pitts S-1D Special	J. A. Coutts	
G-BKLJ	Westland Scout AH.1 ★	N. R. Windley	
G-BKLO	Cessna F.172M	Stapleford Flying Club Ltd	
G-BKLP	Cessna F.172N	M. J. Jones	
G-BKMA	Mooney M.20J Srs 201	Foxtrot Whisky Aviation	
G-BKMB	Mooney M.20J Srs 201	W. A. Cook & ptnrs	
G-BKMG	Handley Page O/400 (replica)	Paralyser Group	
G-BKMI	V.S.359 Spitfire HF.VIIIc (MT928)	Aerial Museum (North Weald) Ltd/Filton	
G-BKMT	PA-32R-301 Saratoga SP	Severn Valley Aviation Group	
G-BKMX	Short SD3-60 Variant 100	BAC Leasing Ltd	
G-BKNB	Cameron V-42 balloon	D. N. Close	
G-BKNI	GY-80 Horizon 160D	A. Hartigan & ptnrs/Fenland	
G-BKNO	Monnett Sonerai IIL	S. Hardy	
G-BKNP	Cameron V-77 balloon	E. K. K. & C. E. Odman	
G-BKNZ	CP.301A Emeraude	C. J. Bellworthy	
G-BKOA	SOCATA M.S.893E Rallye 180GT	P. Howick	
G-BKOB	Z.326 Trener Master	W. G. V. Hall	
G-BKOT	Wassmer WA.81 Piranha	B. N. Rolfe	
G-BKOU	P.84 Jet Provost T.3 (XN637)	Seagull Formation Ltd/North Weald	
G-BKPA	Hoffmann H-36 Dimona	A. Mayhew	
G-BKPB	Aerosport Scamp	B. R. Thompson	
G-BKPC	Cessna A.185F	Black Knights Parachute Centre	
G-BKPD	Viking Dragonfly	E. P. Browne & G. J. Sargent	
G-BKPE	Jodel DR.250/160	J. S. & J. D. Lewer	
G-BKPK	Everett gyroplane	J. C. McHugh	
G-BKPN	Cameron N-77 balloon	R. H. Sanderson	
G-BKPS	AA-5B Tiger	A. E. T. Clarke	
G-BKPX	Jodel D.120A	N. H. Martin	
G-BKPY	SAAB 91B/2 Safir (56321) ★	Newark Air Museum	
G-BKPZ	Pitts S-1T Special	M. A. Frost	
G-BKRA	NA T-6G Texan (51-15227)	Pulsegrove Ltd/Shoreham	
G-BKRB	Cessna 172N	Saunders Caravans Ltd	
G-BKRF	PA-18 Super Cub 95	K. M. Bishop	
G-BKRH	Brügger MB.2 Colibri	M. R. Benwell	
G-BKRI	Cameron V-77 balloon	D. W. & J. M. Westlake	
G-BKRK	SNCAN Stampe SV-4C	Strathgadie Stampe Group	
G-BKRL	Chichester-Miles Leopard ★	(stored)/Cranfield	
G-BKRN	Beechcraft D.18S	A. A. Marshall & P. L. Turland	
G-BKRS	Cameron V-56 balloon	D. N. & L. J. Close	
G-BKRZ	Dragon G-77 balloon	J. R. Barber	
G-BKSB	Cessna T.310Q II	G. H. Smith & Son	
G-BKSC	Saro Skeeter AOP.12 (XN351) ★	R. A. L. Falconer	
G-BKSD	Colt 56A balloon	M. J. Casson	
G-BKSE	QAC Quickie Q.1	M. D. Burns	
G-BKSP	Schleicher ASK.14	J. H. Bryson/Bellarena	
G-BKSS	Jodel D.150	D. H. Wilson-Spratt/Ronaldsway	
G-BKST	Rutan Vari-Eze	R. Towle	
G-BKSX	SNCAN Stampe SV-4C	C. A. Bailey & J. A. Carr	
G-BKTA	PA-18 Super Cub 95	M. J. Dyson & M. T. Clark	
G-BKTH	CCF Hawker Sea Hurricane IB (Z7015)	The Shuttleworth Collection/Duxford	
G-BKTM	PZL SZD-45A Ogar	Repclif Chemical Services Ltd	
G-BKTR	Cameron V-77 balloon	C. Wilson	
G-BKTV	Cessna F.152	A. Jahanfar/Southend	
G-BKTZ	Slingsby T.67M Firefly	D. C. Mayle & M. V. Pettifer (G-SFTV)	
G-BKUE	SOCATA TB.9 Tampico	Pool Aviation (NW) Ltd/Blackpool	

Notes	Reg.	Type	Owner or Operator
	G-BKUR	CP.301A Emeraude	R. Wells
	G-BKUU	Thunder Ax7-77-1 balloon	M. A. Mould
	G-BKVA	SOCATA Rallye 180T	Buckminster Gliding Club Syndicate
	G-BKVB	SOCATA Rallye 110ST	A. & K. Bishop
	G-BKVC	SOCATA TB.9 Tampico	H. P. Aubin-Parvu
	G-BKVE	Rutan Vari-Eze	K. Cox (G-EZLT)
	G-BKVF	FRED Srs 3	A. R. Hawes
	G-BKVG	Scheibe SF.25E Super Falke	G-BKVG Ltd
	G-BKVK	Auster AOP.9 (WZ662)	J. D. Butcher
	G-BKVL	Robin DR.400/160	Tatenhill Aviation
	G-BKVM	PA-18 Super Cub 150 (115684)	D. G. Caffrey
	G-BKVO	Pietenpol Air Camper	M. C. Hayes
	G-BKVP	Pitts S-1D Special	S. W. Doyle
	G-BKVS	Campbell Cricket (modified)	K. Hughes
	G-BKVT	PA-23 Aztec 250E	BKS Surveys Ltd (G-HARV)
	G-BKVW	Airtour 56 balloon	L. D. & H. Vaughan
	G-BKVX	Airtour 56 balloon	P. Aldridge
	G-BKVY	Airtour 31 balloon	M. Davies
	G-BKWD	Taylor JT.2 Titch	E. H. Booker
	G-BKWE	Colt 17A balloon	Flying Pictures Ltd
	G-BKWR	Cameron V-65 balloon	K. J. Foster
	G-BKWW	Cameron O-77 balloon	A. M. Marten
	G-BKWY	Cessna F.152	Cambridge Aero Club
	G-BKXA	Robin R.2100	M. Wilson
	G-BKXD	SA.365N Dauphin 2	CHC Scotia Ltd
	G-BKXF	PA-28R Cherokee Arrow 200	P. L. Brunton/Caernarfon
	G-BKXM	Colt 17A balloon	R. G. Turnbull
	G-BKXN	ICA-Brasov IS-28M2A	D. C. Wellard
	G-BKXO	Rutan LongEz	D. F. P. Finan
	G-BKXP	Auster AOP.6	B. J. & W. J. Ellis
	G-BKXR	D.31A Turbulent	M. B. Hill
	G-BKZB	Cameron V-77 balloon	K. B. Chapple
	G-BKZE	AS.332L Super Puma	CHC Scotia Ltd
	G-BKZF	Cameron V-56 balloon	A. D. Brice
	G-BKZG	AS.332L Super Puma	CHC Scotia Ltd
	G-BKZH	AS.332L Super Puma	CHC Scotia Ltd
	G-BKZI	Bell 206B JetRanger 2	Dolphin Property (Management) Ltd
	G-BKZM	Isaacs Fury II (K2060)	B. Jones
	G-BKZT	FRED Srs 2	U. Chakravorty
	G-BKZV	Bede BD-4A	G. I. J. Thomson
	G-BLAA	Fournier RF-5	A. D. Wren/Southend
	G-BLAC	Cessna FA.152	D. C. C. Handley
	G-BLAD	Thunder Ax7-77-1 balloon	P. J. Bish
	G-BLAF	Stolp SA.900 V-Star	P. R. Skeels
	G-BLAG	Pitts S-1D Special	P. M. Ambrose
	G-BLAH	Thunder Ax7-77-1 balloon	T. M. Donnelly
	G-BLAI	Monnett Sonerai IIL	T. Simpon
	G-BLAM	Jodel DR.360	D. J. Durell
	G-BLAT	Jodel 150	D. J. Dulborough & A. J. Court
	G-BLAX	Cessna FA.152	Bflying Ltd
	G-BLAY	Robin HR.100/200B	B. A. Mills
	G-BLCA	Bell 206B JetRanger 3	R.M.H. Stainless Ltd
	G-BLCG	SOCATA TB.10 Tobago	Charlie Golf Flying Group (G-BHES)/ Shoreham
	G-BLCH	Colt 65D balloon	Balloon Flights Club Ltd
	G-BLCI	EAA Acro Sport	M. R. Holden
	G-BLCM	SOCATA TB.9 Tampico	Repclif Aviation Ltd/Liverpool
	G-BLCT	Jodel DR.220 2+2	Christopher Robin Flying Group
	G-BLCU	Scheibe SF.25B Falke	C. F. Sellers
	G-BLCV	Hoffmann H-36 Dimona	R. L. Braithwaite
	G-BLCW	Evans VP-1	M. Flint
	G-BLCY	Thunder Ax7-65Z balloon	C. M. George
	G-BLDB	Taylor JT.1 Monoplane	C. J. Bush
	G-BLDD	WAG-Aero CUBy AcroTrainer	J. Harper
	G-BLDG	PA-25 Pawnee 260C	Ouse Gliding Club Ltd/Rufforth
	G-BLDK	Robinson R-22	Helicentre Ltd
	G-BLDN	Rand-Robinson KR-2	S. C. Solley
	G-BLDV	BN-2B-26 Islander	Loganair Ltd/BA Express
	G-BLEJ	PA-28-161 Warrior II	Eglinton Flying Club Ltd
	G-BLEP	Cameron V-65 balloon	D. Chapman
	G-BLES	Stolp SA.750 Acroduster Too	G. N. Davies
	G-BLET	Thunder Ax7-77-1 balloon	Servatruc Ltd

Reg.	Type	Owner or Operator	Notes
G-BLEW	Cessna F.182Q	Seager Publishing Ltd	
G-BLEZ	SA.365N Dauphin 2	CHC Scotia Ltd/Aberdeen	
G-BLFI	PA-28-181 Archer II	Bonus Aviation Ltd	
G-BLFW	AA-5 Traveler	Grumman Club	
G-BLFY	Cameron V-77 balloon	A. N. F. Pertwee	
G-BLFZ	PA-31-310 Turbo Navajo C	London Executive Aviation Ltd	
G-BLGH	Robin DR.300/180R	Booker Gliding Club Ltd	
G-BLGO	Bensen B.8MV	F. Vernon	
G-BLGR	Bell 47G-4A	Courteenhall Farms	
G-BLGS	SOCATA Rallye 180T	A. Waters	
G-BLGT	PA-18 Super Cub 95	Liddell Aircraft Ltd	
G-BLGV	Bell 206B JetRanger 3	Heliflight (UK) Ltd	
G-BLHH	Jodel DR.315	Central Certification Service Ltd	
G-BLHI	Colt 17A balloon	J. A. Folkes	
G-BLHJ	Cessna F.172P	Fraggle Leasing Ltd	
G-BLHK	Colt 105A balloon	Hale Hot-Air Balloon Club	
G-BLHM	PA-18 Super Cub 95	A. G. Edwards	
G-BLHN	Robin HR.100/285	N. A. Onions	
G-BLHR	GA-7 Cougar	T. E. Westley	
G-BLHS	Bellanca 7ECA Citabria	N. J. F. Campbell	
G-BLHW	Varga 2150A Kachina	Kachina Hotel Whiskey Group	
G-BLID	D.H.112 Venom FB.50 (J-1605) ★	P. G. Vallance Ltd/Charlwood	
G-BLIH	PA-18 Super Cub 135	I. R. F. Hammond	
G-BLIK	Wallis WA-116/F/S	K. H. Wallis	
G-BLIT	Thorp T-18 CW	A. P. Tyrwhitt-Drake	
G-BLIW	P.56 Provost T.51 (177)	Provost Flying Group/Shoreham	
G-BLIX	Saro Skeeter Mk 12 (XL809)	K. M. Scholes	
G-BLIY	M.S.892A Rallye Commodore	A. J. Brasher & K. R. Haynes	
G-BLJD	Glaser-Dirks DG.400	M. I. Gee	
G-BLJF	Cameron O-65 balloon	M. D. & C. E. C. Hammond	
G-BLJH	Cameron N-77 balloon ★	Balloon Preservation Group/Lancing	
G-BLJM	Beech 95-B55 Baron	R. A. Perrot	
G-BLJO	Cessna F.152	Redhill School of Flying Ltd	
G-BLKA	D.H.112 Venom FB.54 (WR410)★	De Havilland Aviation Ltd/Swansea	
G-BLKK	Evans VP-1	N. Wright	
G-BLKL	D.31 Turbulent	D. L. Ripley	
G-BLKM	Jodel DR.1051	T. C. Humphreys	
G-BLKP	BAe Jetstream 3102	BAE Systems (Corporate Air Travel) Ltd/ Warton	
G-BLKY	Beech 95-58 Baron	J. C. Hall	
G-BLKZ	Pilatus P2-05	R. W. Hinton	
G-BLLA	Bensen B.8M	K. T. Donaghey	
G-BLLB	Bensen B.8M	D. H. Moss	
G-BLLD	Cameron O-77 balloon	G. Birchall	
G-BLLH	Jodel DR.220A 2+2	M. D. Hughes	
G-BLLM	PA-23 Aztec 250E	C. & M. Thomas (G-BBNM)/Cardiff	
G-BLLN	PA-18 Super Cub 95	P. L. Pilch & C. G. Fisher	
G-BLLP	Slingsby T.67B	Cleveland Flying School Ltd/Teesside	
G-BLLR	Slingsby T.67B	R. L. Brinklow/Biggin Hill	
G-BLLS	Slingsby T.67B	Western Air (Thruxton) Ltd	
G-BLLV	Slingsby T.67C	R. L. Brinklow	
G-BLLW	Colt 56B balloon	G. Fordyce & ptnrs	
G-BLLZ	Rutan LongEz	R. S. Stoddart-Stones	
G-BLMA	Zlin 326 Trener Master	G. P. Northcott/Redhill	
G-BLMC	Avro 698 Vulcan B.2A (XM575) ★	Aeropark/E. Midlands	
G-BLME	Robinson R-22HP	Heli Air Ltd/Wellesbourne	
G-BLMG	Grob G.109B	Mike Golf Syndicate	
G-BLMI	PA-18 Super Cub 95	B. J. Borsberry	
G-BLMN	Rutan LongEz	G-BLMN Flying Group	
G-BLMP	PA-17 Vagabond	M. Austin/Popham	
G-BLMR	PA-18 Super Cub 150	Transport Command Ltd	
G-BLMT	PA-18 Super Cub 135	I. S. Runnalls	
G-BLMW	T.66 Nipper 3	S. L. Millar	
G-BLMZ	Colt 105A balloon	M. D. Dickinson	
G-BLNJ	BN-2B-26 Islander	Loganair Ltd/BA Express	
G-BLNO	FRED Srs 3	L. W. Smith	
G-BLNW	BN-2B-26 Islander	Loganair Ltd/BA Express	
G-BLOB	Colt 31A balloon	Jacques W. Soukup Enterprises Ltd/USA	
G-BLOR	PA-30 Twin Comanche 160	R. L. C. Appleton	
G-BLOS	Cessna 185A (also flown with floats)	E. Brun	
G-BLOT	Colt Ax6-56B balloon	H. J. Anderson	
G-BLOV	Thunder Ax5-42 Srs 1 balloon	A. G. R. Calder	

Notes	Reg.	Type	Owner or Operator
	G-BLPA	Piper J-3C-65 Cub	A. C. Frost
	G-BLPB	Turner TSW Hot Two Wot	I. R. Hannah
	G-BLPE	PA-18 Super Cub 95	A. A. Haig-Thomas
	G-BLPF	Cessna FR.172G	G. E. McFarlane
	G-BLPG	J/1N Alpha (16693)	D. Taylor (G-AZIH)
	G-BLPH	Cessna FRA.150L	New Aerobat Group/Shoreham
	G-BLPI	Slingsby T.67B	RAF Wyton Flying Group Ltd
	G-BLPP	Cameron V-77 balloon	L. P. Purfield
	G-BLRA	BAe 146-100	BAE Systems (Operations) Ltd
	G-BLRC	PA-18 Super Cub 135	A. J. McBurnie
	G-BLRD	MBB Bo 209 Monsun 150FV	T. G. Lloyd
	G-BLRF	Slingsby T.67C	R. C. Nicholls
	G-BLRG	Slingsby T.67B	R. L. Brinklow
	G-BLRJ	Jodel DR.1051	M. P. Hallam
	G-BLRL	CP.301C-1 Emeraude	N. Thorne
	G-BLRM	Glaser-Dirks DG.400	J. A. & W. S. Y. Stephen
	G-BLRN	D.H.104 Dove 8 (WB531) ★	J. F. M. Bleeker/Netherlands
	G-BLRW	Cameron 77 Elephant SS balloon	Forbes Europe Inc/France
	G-BLRY	AS.332L Super Puma	Bristow Helicopters Ltd
	G-BLSD	D.H.112 Venom FB.54 (J-1758)★	R. Lamplough/North Weald
	G-BLSF	AA-5A Cheetah	J. P. E. Walsh (G-BGCK)
	G-BLSM	H.S.125 Srs 700B	Dravidian Air Services Ltd/Heathrow
	G-BLST	Cessna 421C	Cecil Aviation Ltd/Cambridge
	G-BLSX	Cameron O-105 balloon	B. J. Petteford
	G-BLTA	Thunder Ax7-77A	K. A. Schlussler
	G-BLTC	D.31A Turbulent	G. P. Smith & A. W. Burton
	G-BLTF	Robinson R-22A	Brian Seedle Helicopters Ltd
	G-BLTK	R. Commander 112TC	B. Rogalewski/Denham
	G-BLTM	Robin HR.200/100	Barton Robin Group
	G-BLTN	Thunder Ax7-65 balloon	J. A. Liddle
	G-BLTP	H.S.125 Srs 700B	Dravidian Air Services Ltd/Heathrow
	G-BLTR	Scheibe SF.25B Falke	V. Mallon/Germany
	G-BLTS	Rutan LongEz	R. W. Cutler
	G-BLTT	Slingsby T.67B	C. W. Ward
	G-BLTU	Slingsby T.67B	RAF Wyton Flying Club Ltd
	G-BLTV	Slingsby T.67B	R. L. Brinklow
	G-BLTW	Slingsby T.67B	Cheshire Air Training Services Ltd/ Liverpool
	G-BLTY	Westland WG.30 Srs 160	D. Drem-Wilson
	G-BLTZ	SOCATA TB.10 Tobago	Martin Ltd/Biggin Hill
	G-BLUI	Thunder Ax7-65 balloon	S. Johnson
	G-BLUL	CEA Jodel DR.1051/M1	J. Owen
	G-BLUM	SA.365N Dauphin 2	CHC Scotia Ltd
	G-BLUN	SA.365N Dauphin 2	CHC Scotia Ltd
	G-BLUV	Grob G.109B	The 109 Flying Group/North Weald
	G-BLUX	Slingsby T.67M Firefly 200	R. L. Brinklow
	G-BLUZ	D.H.82 Queen Bee (LF858)	The Bee Keepers Group
	G-BLVA	Airtour AH-56 balloon	A. Van Wyk
	G-BLVB	Airtour AH-56 balloon	R. W. Guild
	G-BLVI	Slingsby T.67M Firefly Mk II	Hunting Aviation Ltd/Barkston Heath
	G-BLVK	CAARP CAP-10B	E. K. Coventry/Earls Colne
	G-BLVL	PA-28-161 Warrior II	Marair (Jersey) Ltd
	G-BLVS	Cessna 150M	Tindon Ltd
	G-BLVW	Cessna F.172H	R. & D. Holloway Ltd
	G-BLWD	PA-34-200T Seneca	Acre 123 Ltd
	G-BLWE	Colt 90A balloon	Huntair Ltd/Germany
	G-BLWF	Robin HR.100/210	Starguide Ltd
	G-BLWH	Fournier RF-6B-100	I. R. March
	G-BLWM	Bristol M.1C (replica) (C4994) ★	RAF Museum/Hendon
	G-BLWP	PA-38-112 Tomahawk	J. C. Dodd & ptnrs/Panshanger
	G-BLWT	Evans VP-1	J. S. Peplow
	G-BLWV	Cessna F.152	Redhill Flying Club
	G-BLWY	Robin 2161D	K. D. Boardman
	G-BLXA	SOCATA TB.20 Trinidad	Tango Bravo Aviation Ltd
	G-BLXG	Colt 21A balloon	A. Walker
	G-BLXH	Fournier RF-3	A. Rawicz-Szczerbo
	G-BLXI	CP.1310-C3 Super Emeraude	R. Howard
	G-BLXO	Jodel 150	P. R. Powell
	G-BLXP	PA-28R Cherokee Arrow 200	M. B. Hamlett
	G-BLXR	AS.332L Super Puma	Bristow Helicopters Ltd
	G-BLXY	Cameron V-65 balloon	Gone With The Wind Ltd/Tanzania
	G-BLYD	SOCATA TB.20 Trinidad	Yankee Delta Corporation Ltd
	G-BLYE	SOCATA TB.10 Tobago	G. Hatton

Reg.	Type	Owner or Operator	Notes
G-BLYK	PA-34-220T Seneca III	Oxford Aviation Services Ltd/Kidlington	
G-BLYP	Robin 3000/120	Weald Air Services/Headcorn	
G-BLYT	Airtour AH-77 balloon	I. J. Taylor & R. C. Kincaid	
G-BLZA	Scheibe SF.25B Falke	Chiltern Gliding Club	
G-BLZE	Cessna F.152 II	Flairhire Ltd (G-CSSC)/Redhill	
G-BLZF	Thunder Ax7-77 balloon	H. M. Savage	
G-BLZH	Cessna F.152 II	Plane Talking Ltd/Elstree	
G-BLZJ	AS.332L Super Puma	Bristow Helicopters Ltd (G-PUMJ)	
G-BLZM	Rutan LongEz	Zulu Mike Group	
G-BLZN	Bell 206B JetRanger	Biggin Hill Helicopters	
G-BLZP	Cessna F.152	E. Midlands Flying School Ltd	
G-BLZS	Cameron O-77 balloon	M. M. Cobbold	
G-BLZT	Short SD3-60 Variant 100	BAC Express Airlines	
G-BMAD	Cameron V-77 balloon	M. A. Stelling	
G-BMAL	Sikorsky S-76A	CHC Scotiia Ltd	
G-BMAO	Taylor JT.1 Monoplane	S. J. Alston	
G-BMAV	AS.350B Ecureuil	PLM Dollar Group Ltd	
G-BMAX	FRED Srs 2	D. A. Arkley	
G-BMAY	PA-18 Super Cub 135	R. W. Davies	
G-BMBB	Cessna F.150L	LBA Aviation Ltd	
G-BMBJ	Schempp-Hirth Janus CM	RAFGSA/Dishforth	
G-BMBS	Colt 105A balloon	H. G. Davies	
G-BMBW	Bensen B.8MR	M. E. Vahdat	
G-BMBZ	Scheibe SF.25E Super Falke	Cornish Gliding & Flying Club Ltd/ Perranporth	
G-BMCC	Thunder Ax7-77 balloon	A. K. & C. M. Russell	
G-BMCD	Cameron V-65 balloon	M. C. Drye	
G-BMCG	Grob G.109B	Lagerholm Finnimport Ltd/Booker	
G-BMCI	Cessna F.172H	A. B. Davis/Edinburgh	
G-BMCN	Cessna F.152	Lincoln Aero Club Ltd/Sturgate	
G-BMCS	PA-22 Tri-Pacer 135	P. R. Deacon	
G-BMCV	Cessna F.152	Leicestershire Aero Club Ltd	
G-BMCW	AS.332L Super Puma	Bristow Helicopters Ltd	
G-BMCX	AS.332L Super Puma	Bristow Helicopters Ltd	
G-BMDB	SE-5A (replica) (F235)	D. Biggs	
G-BMDC	PA-32-301 Saratoga	MacLaren Aviation/Newcastle	
G-BMDE	Pientenpol Air Camper	P. B. Childs	
G-BMDJ	Price Ax7-77S balloon	R. A. Benham	
G-BMDK	PA-34-220T Seneca III	Air Medical Ltd/Kidlington	
G-BMDP	Partenavia P.64B Oscar 200	S. T. G. Lloyd	
G-BMDS	Jodel D.120	J. V. Thompson	
G-BMEA	PA-18 Super Cub 95	C. L. Towell	
G-BMEE	Cameron O-105 balloon	A. G. R. Calder/Los Angeles	
G-BMEG	SOCATA TB.10 Tobago	G. H. N. & R. V. Chamberlain	
G-BMEH	Jodel 150 Special Super Mascaret	R. J. & C. J. Lewis	
G-BMET	Taylor JT.1 Monoplane	M. K. A. Blyth	
G-BMEU	Isaacs Fury II	G. R. G. Smith	
G-BMEV	PA-32RT-300T Turbo Lance II	Arrow Aviation Ltd	
G-BMEX	Cessna A.150K	N. A. M. Brain & C. Butler	
G-BMFD	PA-23 Aztec 250F	Gold Air International Ltd (G-BGYY)	
G-BMFG	Dornier Do.27A-4	R. F. Warner	
G-BMFI	PZL SZD-45A Ogar	S. L. Morrey/Andreas, IoM	
G-BMFL	Rand-Robinson KR-2	E. W. B. Comber & M. F. Leusby	
G-BMFN	QAC Quickie Tri-Q.200	A. H. Hartog	
G-BMFP	PA-28-161 Warrior II	Bravo-Mike-Fox-Papa Group/Blackbushe	
G-BMFU	Cameron N-90 balloon	J. J. Rudoni	
G-BMFY	Grob G.109B	P. J. Shearer	
G-BMFZ	Cessna F.152 II	Cornwall Flying Club Ltd/Bodmin	
G-BMGB	PA-28R Cherokee Arrow 200	Malmesbury Specialist Cars	
G-BMGC	Fairey Swordfish Mk II (W5856)	F.A.A. Museum/Yeovilton	
G-BMGG	Cessna 152 II	Falcon Flying Services/Biggin Hill	
G-BMGR	Grob G.109B	M. Clarke & D. S. Hawes	
G-BMHA	Rutan LongEz	S. F. Elvins	
G-BMHC	Cessna U.206F	Fairmont Investments Ltd/Clacton	
G-BMHJ	Thunder Ax7-65 balloon	M. G. Robinson	
G-BMHL	Wittman W.8 Tailwind	T. G. Hoult	
G-BMHS	Cessna F.172M	Tango X-Ray Flying Group	
G-BMHT	PA-28RT-201T Turbo Arrow IV	White Aviation Ltd	
G-BMID	Jodel D.120	G-BMID Flying Group	
G-BMIG	Cessna 172N	J. R. Nicholls/Sibson	
G-BMIM	Rutan LongEz	R. M. Smith	

Notes	Reg.	Type	Owner or Operator
	G-BMIO	Stoddard-Hamilton Glasair RG	J. M. Ayres & S. C. Ellerton
	G-BMIP	Jodel D.112	M. T. Kinch
	G-BMIR	Westland Wasp HAS.1 (XT788)★	Park Aviation Supply/Charlwood
	G-BMIS	Monnett Sonerai II	B. A. Bower/Thruxton
	G-BMIV	PA-28R-201T Turbo Arrow III	Firmbeam Ltd
	G-BMIW	PA-28-181 Archer II	Oldbus Ltd
	G-BMIY	Oldfield Baby Great Lakes	J. B. Scott (G-NOME)
	G-BMJA	PA-32R-301 Saratoga SP	European Flyers/Blackbushe
	G-BMJC	Cessna 152 II	Cambridge Aero Club Ltd
	G-BMJD	Cessna 152 II	Donair Flying Club Ltd/E. Midlands
	G-BMJL	R. Commander 114	Wardair Ltd
	G-BMJM	Evans VP-1	M. J. Veary
	G-BMJN	Cameron O-65 balloon	P. M. Traviss
	G-BMJO	PA-34-220T Seneca III	Oxford Aviation Services Ltd/Kidlington
	G-BMJR	Cessna T.337H	John Roberts Services Ltd (G-NOVA)
	G-BMJS	Thunder Ax7-77 balloon	S. E. Burton
	G-BMJT	Beech 76 Duchess	Mike Osborne Properties Ltd
	G-BMJX	Wallis WA-116X	K. H. Wallis
	G-BMJY	Yakovlev C18M (07)	R. J. Lamplough/North Weald
	G-BMJZ	Cameron N-90 balloon	Bristol University Hot Air Ballooning Soc
	G-BMKB	PA-18 Super Cub 135	Cubair Flight Training Ltd/Redhill
	G-BMKC	Piper J-3C-65 Cub (329854)	J. W. Salter
	G-BMKD	Beech C90A King Air	A. E. Bristow
	G-BMKF	Jodel DR.221	L. Gilbert & ptnrs
	G-BMKG	PA-38-112 Tomahawk II	APB Leasing Ltd/Welshpool
	G-BMKI	Colt 21A balloon	A. C. Booth
	G-BMKJ	Cameron V-77 balloon	R. C. Thursby
	G-BMKK	PA-28R Cherokee Arrow 200	Comed Aviation Ltd
	G-BMKP	Cameron V-77 balloon	R. Bayly
	G-BMKR	PA-28-161 Warrior II	Field Flying Group (G-BGKR)/Goodwood
	G-BMKW	Cameron V-77 balloon	A. C. Garnett
	G-BMKY	Cameron O-65 balloon	A. R. Rich
	G-BMLB	Jodel D.120A	W. O. Brown
	G-BMLC	Short SD3-60 Variant 100	Aurigny Air Services Ltd
	G-BMLJ	Cameron N-77 balloon	C. J. Dunkley
	G-BMLK	Grob G.109B	Brams Syndicate/Rufforth
	G-BMLL	Grob G.109B	G-BMLL Flying Group/Denham
	G-BMLM	Beech 95-58 Baron	N. J. Webb (G-BBJF)/Cranfield
	G-BMLS	PA-28R-201 Arrow III	R. M. Shorter
	G-BMLT	Pietenpol Air Camper	W. E. R. Jenkins
	G-BMLW	Cameron O-77 balloon	M. L. & L. P. Willoughby
	G-BMLX	Cessna F.150L	J. P. A. Freeman/Headcorn
	G-BMMC	Cessna T310Q	I. T. Cooper
	G-BMMD	Rand-Robinson KR-2	D. J. Howell
	G-BMMF	FRED Srs 2	E. C. King
	G-BMMI	Pazmany PL.4A	L. Greenhough
	G-BMMK	Cessna 182P	G. G. Weston
	G-BMML	PA-38-112 Tomahawk	J. C. & C. H. Strong
	G-BMMM	Cessna 152 II	Luton Flight Training Ltd
	G-BMMP	Grob G.109B	E. W. Reynolds
	G-BMMV	ICA-Brasov IS-28M2A	F. R. Temple-Brown
	G-BMMW	Thunder Ax7-77 balloon	P. A. George
	G-BMMY	Thunder Ax7-77 balloon	S. W. Wade & S. E. Hadley
	G-BMNL	PA-28R Cherokee Arrow 200	Arrow Flying Group
	G-BMNV	SNCAN Stampe SV-4D	Wessex Aviation & Transport Ltd
	G-BMNX	Colt 56A balloon	C. N. Marshall
	G-BMOE	PA-28R Cherokee Arrow 200	E. P. C. Robson
	G-BMOF	Cessna U206G	Wild Geese Skydiving Centre
	G-BMOG	Thunder Ax7-77 balloon	R. M. Boswell
	G-BMOH	Cameron N-77 balloon	P. J. Marshall & M. A. Clarke
	G-BMOI	Partenavia P.68B	Simmette Ltd
	G-BMOK	ARV Super 2	R. E. Griffiths
	G-BMOL	PA-23 Aztec 250D	LDL Enterprises (G-BBSR)/Elstree
	G-BMOM	ICA-Brasov IS-28M2A	R. M. Cust
	G-BMOT	Bensen B.8M	Austin Trueman Ltd
	G-BMOV	Cameron O-105 balloon	C. Gillott
	G-BMPC	PA-28-181 Archer II	C. J. & R. J. Barnes
	G-BMPD	Cameron V-65 balloon	D. E. & J. M. Hartland
	G-BMPL	Optica Industries OA.7 Optica	Sunhawk Ltd/North Weald
	G-BMPP	Cameron N-77 balloon	N. A. Apsey
	G-BMPR	PA-28R-201 Arrow III	B. Edwards
	G-BMPS	Strojnik S-2A	G. J. Green
	G-BMPY	D.H.82A Tiger Moth	S. M. F. Eisenstein

Reg.	Type	Owner or Operator	Notes
G-BMSA	Stinson HW.75 Voyager	M. A. Thomas (G-BCUM)/Barton	
G-BMSB	V.S.509 Spitfire IX (MJ627)	M. S. Bayliss (G-ASOZ)/Coventry	
G-BMSC	Evans VP-2	S. Whitehead	
G-BMSD	PA-28-181 Archer II	General Airline Ltd/Blackbushe	
G-BMSE	Valentin Taifun 17E	A. J. Nurse	
G-BMSF	PA-38-112 Tomahawk	B. Catlow	
G-BMSG	SAAB 32A Lansen ★	J. E. Wilkie/Cranfield	
G-BMSL	FRED Srs 3	A. C. Coombe	
G-BMSU	Cessna 152 II	G-BMSU Group	
G-BMTA	Cessna 152 II	Alarmond Ltd	
G-BMTB	Cessna 152 II	Sky Leisure Aviation (Charters) Ltd	
G-BMTJ	Cessna 152 II	The Pilot Centre Ltd/Denham	
G-BMTN	Cameron O-77 balloon	Industrial Services (MH) Ltd	
G-BMTO	PA-38-112 Tomahawk	Falcon Flying Services/Biggin Hill	
G-BMTR	PA-28-161 Warrior II	Aeroshow Ltd/Filton	
G-BMTS	Cessna 172N	European Flyers/Blackbushe	
G-BMTU	Pitts S-1E Special	Aerodynamics Ltd	
G-BMTX	Cameron V-77 balloon	J. A. Langley	
G-BMUD	Cessna 182P	M. E. Taylor	
G-BMUG	Rutan LongEz	P. Richardson & J. Shanley	
G-BMUJ	Colt Drachenfisch balloon	Virgin Airship & Balloon Co Ltd	
G-BMUK	Colt UFO balloon	Virgin Airship & Balloon Co Ltd	
G-BMUL	Colt Kindermond balloon	Virgin Airship & Balloon Co Ltd	
G-BMUO	Cessna A.152	Sky Leisure Aviation (Charters) Ltd	
G-BMUT	PA-34-200T Seneca II	High Flyers Aviation Ltd	
G-BMUU	Thunder Ax7-77 balloon	G. Anorewartha	
G-BMUZ	PA-28-161 Warrior II	Newcastle-upon-Tyne Aero Club Ltd	
G-BMVA	Scheibe SF.25B Falke	M. L. Jackson	
G-BMVB	Cessna F.152 II	LAC (Enterprises) Ltd/Barton	
G-BMVG	QAC Quickie Q.1	P. M. Wright	
G-BMVI	Cameron O-105 balloon	Heart of England Balloons	
G-BMVJ	Cessna 172N	Green Aviation Associates Ltd	
G-BMVL	PA-38-112 Tomahawk	Airways Aero Associations Ltd/Booker	
G-BMVM	PA-38-112 Tomahawk	Airways Aero Associations Ltd/Booker	
G-BMVT	Thunder Ax7-77A balloon	M. L. & L. P. Willoughby	
G-BMVW	Cameron O-65 balloon	S. P. Richards	
G-BMWA	Hughes 269C	EBG Helicopters Ltd	
G-BMWE	ARV Super 2	R. J. N. Noble	
G-BMWF	ARV Super 2	N. R. Beale	
G-BMWM	ARV Super 2	T. C. Robson	
G-BMWN	Cameron 80 SS Temple balloon	Forbes Europe Inc/France	
G-BMWR	R. Commander 112A ★	M. & J. Edwards/Blackbushe	
G-BMWU	Cameron N-42 balloon ★	Balloon Preservation Group/Lancing	
G-BMWV	Putzer Elster B	E. A. J. Hibbard	
G-BMXA	Cessna 152 II	E. Alexander	
G-BMXB	Cessna 152 II	H. Daines Electronics Ltd	
G-BMXC	Cessna 152 II	Devon School of Flying/Dunkeswell	
G-BMXD	F.27 Friendship Mk 500	BAC Express Airlines Ltd	
G-BMXJ	Cessna F.150L	Arrow Aircraft Group	
G-BMXL	PA-38-112 Tomahawk	Airways Aero Associations Ltd/Booker	
G-BMXX	Cessna 152 II	Aerohire Ltd/Wolverhampton	
G-BMYC	SOCATA TB.10 Tobago	E. A. Grady	
G-BMYD	Beech A36 Bonanza	Seabeam Partners Ltd	
G-BMYF	Bensen B.8M	G. Callaghan	
G-BMYG	Cessna FA.152	Tayside Aviation Ltd/Dundee	
G-BMYI	AA-5 Traveler	W. C. & S. C. Westran	
G-BMYJ	Cameron V-65 balloon	J. R. Christopher & U. Feierabend	
G-BMYN	Colt 77A balloon	Spectacles Balloon Group	
G-BMYP	Fairey Gannet AEW.3 (XL502) ★	D. Copley/Sandtoft	
G-BMYS	Thunder Ax7-77Z balloon	J. E. Weidema/Netherlands	
G-BMYU	Jodel D.120	N. P. Chitty	
G-BMZA	Air Command 503 Commander	R. W. Husband	
G-BMZB	Cameron N-77 balloon	D. C. Eager	
G-BMZE	SOCATA TB.9 Tampico	R. F. Keene	
G-BMZF	WSK-Mielec LiM-2 (MiG-15bis) (01420) ★	F.A.A. Museum/Yeovilton	
G-BMZN	Everett gyroplane	K. Ashford	
G-BMZP	Everett gyroplane	M. N. Morris-Jones	
G-BMZS	Everett gyroplane	L. W. Cload	
G-BMZW	Bensen B.8MR	P. D. Widdicombe	
G-BMZX	Wolf W-II Boredom Fighter (146-11042)	A. R. Meakin & S. W. Watkins	

Notes	Reg.	Type	Owner or Operator
	G-BNAD	Rand-Robinson KR-2	P. J. Brookman
	G-BNAG	Colt 105A balloon	R. W. Batchelor
	G-BNAI	Wolf W-II Boredom Fighter (146-11083)	P. J. D. Gronow
	G-BNAJ	Cessna 152 II	Galair Ltd/Biggin Hill
	G-BNAN	Cameron V-65 balloon	A. M. Lindsay
	G-BNAR	Taylor JT.1 Monoplane	C. J. Smith
	G-BNAU	Cameron V-65 balloon	C. L. E. Lewis
	G-BNAW	Cameron V-65 balloon	A. Walker
	G-BNBL	Thunder Ax7-77 balloon	D. G. Such
	G-BNBU	Bensen B.8MV	B. A. Lyford
	G-BNBV	Thunder Ax7-77 balloon	J. M. Robinson
	G-BNBW	Thunder Ax7-77 balloon	I. S. & S. W. Watthews
	G-BNBY	Beech 95-B55A Baron	J. Butler (G-AXXR)/France
	G-BNBZ	LET L-200D Morava	C. A. Suckling/Redhill
	G-BNCB	Cameron V-77 balloon	C. W. Brown
	G-BNCC	Thunder Ax7-77 balloon	C. J. Burnhope
	G-BNCE	G.159 Gulfstream 1 ★	(stored)/Aberdeen
	G-BNCH	Cameron V-77 balloon	Royal Engineers Balloon Club
	G-BNCJ	Cameron V-77 balloon	D. Scott
	G-BNCL	WG.13 Lynx HAS.2 (XX469) ★	Lancashire Fire Brigade HQ/Lancaster
	G-BNCM	Cameron N-77 balloon	C. A. Stone
	G-BNCN	Glaser-Dirks DG.400 (421)	A. C. E. Vongontard
	G-BNCO	PA-38-112 Tomahawk	D. K. Walker
	G-BNCR	PA-38-161 Warrior II	Airways Aero Associations Ltd/Booker
	G-BNCS	Cessna 180	C. Elwell Transport Ltd
	G-BNCU	Thunder Ax7-77 balloon	P. Mann
	G-BNCX	Hawker Hunter T.7 (XL621) ★	Brooklands Museum of Aviation/Weybridge
	G-BNCZ	Rutan LongEz	P. A. Ellway
	G-BNDG	Wallis WA-201/R Srs1	K. H. Wallis
	G-BNDN	Cameron V-77 balloon	J. A. Smith
	G-BNDO	Cessna 152 II	Simair Ltd
	G-BNDP	Brügger MB.2 Colibri	J. P. Kynaston
	G-BNDR	SOCATA TB.10 Tobago	P. F. Rothwell
	G-BNDT	Brügger MB.2 Colibri	Colibri Flying Group/Waddington
	G-BNDV	Cameron N-77 balloon	R. E. Jones
	G-BNDW	D.H.82A Tiger Moth	N. D. Welch
	G-BNDY	Cessna 425-1	Standard Aviation Ltd/Newcastle
	G-BNED	PA-22 Tri-Pacer 135	P. Storey
	G-BNEE	PA-28R-201 Arrow III	Britannic Management (Aviation) Ltd
	G-BNEI	PA-34-200T Seneca II	P. J. Morrison
	G-BNEJ	PA-38-112 Tomahawk II	V. C. & S. G. Swindell
	G-BNEK	PA-38-112 Tomahawk II	APB Leasing Ltd/Welshpool
	G-BNEL	PA-28-161 Warrior II	S. C. Westran
	G-BNEN	PA-34-200T Seneca II	Warwickshire Aerocentre Ltd
	G-BNEO	Cameron V-77 balloon	J. G. O'Connell
	G-BNES	Cameron V-77 balloon	G. Wells
	G-BNET	Cameron O-84 balloon	C. & A. I. Gibson
	G-BNEV	Viking Dragonfly	N. W. Eyre
	G-BNEX	Cameron O-120 balloon	The Balloon Club Ltd
	G-BNFG	Cameron O-77 balloon	Capital Balloon Club Ltd
	G-BNFI	Cessna 150J	T. D. Aitken
	G-BNFK	Cameron 89 Egg SS balloon	Forbes Europe Inc/France
	G-BNFM	Colt 21A balloon	M. E. Dworski/France
	G-BNFN	Cameron N-105 balloon	P. Glydon
	G-BNFO	Cameron V-77 balloon	Fox Group
	G-BNFP	Cameron O-84 balloon	B. F. G. Ribbans
	G-BNFR	Cessna 152 II	Eastern Executive Air Charter Ltd/Southend
	G-BNFS	Cessna 152 II	C & S Aviation Ltd/Wolverhampton
	G-BNFV	Robin DR.400/120	J. P. A. Freeman
	G-BNGE	Auster AOP.6 (TW536)	M. Pocock
	G-BNGJ	Cameron V-77 balloon	Lathams Ltd
	G-BNGN	Cameron V-77 balloon	C. B. Leeder
	G-BNGO	Thunder Ax7-77 balloon	J. S. Finlan
	G-BNGP	Colt 77A balloon	Headland Services Ltd
	G-BNGR	PA-38-112 Tomahawk	Teesside Flight Centre Ltd
	G-BNGS	PA-38-112 Tomahawk	Teesside Flight Centre Ltd
	G-BNGT	PA-28-181 Archer II	Berry Air/Edinburgh
	G-BNGV	ARV Super 2	N. A. Onions
	G-BNGW	ARV Super 2	Southern Gas Turbines Ltd
	G-BNGY	ARV Super 2	M. T. Manwaring (G-BMWL)

Reg.	Type	Owner or Operator	Notes
G-BNHB	ARV Super 2	J. K. Davies	
G-BNHG	PA-38-112 Tomahawk II	D. A. Whitmore	
G-BNHI	Cameron V-77 balloon	C. J. Nicholls	
G-BNHJ	Cessna 152 II	The Pilot Centre Ltd/Denham	
G-BNHK	Cessna 152 II	General Airline Ltd	
G-BNHN	Colt Ariel Bottle SS balloon ★	British Balloon Museum/Newbury	
G-BNHT	Fournier RF-3	G-BNHT Group	
G-BNID	Cessna 152 II	Mercia Aircraft Leasing & Sales Ltd/ Coventry	
G-BNIF	Cameron O-56 balloon	D. V. Fowler	
G-BNII	Cameron N-90 balloon	Topless Balloon Group	
G-BNIJ	SOCATA TB.10 Tobago	Flying Start Aviation	
G-BNIK	Robin HR.200/120	A. W. Eldridge	
G-BNIM	PA-38-112 Tomahawk	Aurs Aviation Ltd	
G-BNIN	Cameron V-77 balloon	Cloud Nine Balloon Group	
G-BNIO	Luscombe 8A Silvaire	G. G. Pugh	
G-BNIP	Luscombe 8A Silvaire	D. R. C. Hunter & S. Maric	
G-BNIU	Cameron O-77 balloon	MC VH SA/Belgium	
G-BNIV	Cessna 152 II	Aerohire Ltd/Wolverhampton	
G-BNIW	Boeing Stearman PT-17	R. C. Goold	
G-BNIZ	F.27 Friendship Mk.600	Channel Express (Air Services) Ltd/ Bournemouth	
G-BNJA	WAG-Aero Wag-a-Bond	B. E. Maggs	
G-BNJB	Cessna 152 II	Aerolease Ltd/Conington	
G-BNJC	Cessna 152 II	Stapleford Flying Club Ltd	
G-BNJD	Cessna 152 II	Southern Air Ltd/Shoreham	
G-BNJF	PA-32RT-300 Lance II	PFB Aviation Ltd	
G-BNJG	Cameron O-77 balloon	A. M. Figiel	
G-BNJH	Cessna 152 II	J. McAuley	
G-BNJL	Bensen B.8	J. M. Cox	
G-BNJM	PA-28-161 Warrior II	Teesside Flight Centre Ltd	
G-BNJO	QAC Quickie Q.2	J. D. McKay	
G-BNJR	PA-28RT-201T Turbo Arrow IV	D. Croker	
G-BNJT	PA-28-161 Warrior II	Hawarden Flying Group	
G-BNJU	Cameron 80 Bust SS balloon	Ballon Team Bonn GmbH & Co Kg/ Germany	
G-BNJX	Cameron N-90 balloon	Mars UK Ltd	
G-BNJZ	Cassutt Racer IIIM	A. P. Meredith & J. R. Burry	
G-BNKC	Cessna 152 II	Herefordshire Aero Club Ltd/Shobdon	
G-BNKD	Cessna 172N	Bristol Flying Centre Ltd	
G-BNKE	Cessna 172N	Kilo Echo Flying Group	
G-BNKH	PA-38-112 Tomahawk	Goodwood Terrena Ltd	
G-BNKI	Cessna 152 II	RAF Halton Aeroplane Club Ltd	
G-BNKP	Cessna 152 II	Fairmont Investments Ltd/Clacton	
G-BNKR	Cessna 152 II	Keen Leasing (IOM) Ltd	
G-BNKS	Cessna 152 II	Shropshire Aero Club Ltd/Sleap	
G-BNKT	Cameron O-77 balloon	British Airways PLC	
G-BNKV	Cessna 152 II	S. C. Westran/Shoreham	
G-BNLA	Boeing 747-436	British Airways	
G-BNLB	Boeing 747-436	British Airways	
G-BNLC	Boeing 747-436	British Airways	
G-BNLD	Boeing 747-436	British Airways	
G-BNLE	Boeing 747-436	British Airways	
G-BNLF	Boeing 747-436	British Airways	
G-BNLG	Boeing 747-436	British Airways	
G-BNLI	Boeing 747-436	British Asia Airways	
G-BNLJ	Boeing 747-436	British Airways	
G-BNLK	Boeing 747-436	British Airways	
G-BNLL	Boeing 747-436	British Airways	
G-BNLM	Boeing 747-436	British Airways	
G-BNLN	Boeing 747-436	British Airways	
G-BNLO	Boeing 747-436	British Airways	
G-BNLP	Boeing 747-436	British Airways	
G-BNLR	Boeing 747-436	British Airways	
G-BNLS	Boeing 747-436	British Airways	
G-BNLT	Boeing 747-436	British Airways	
G-BNLU	Boeing 747-436	British Airways	
G-BNLV	Boeing 747-436	British Airways	
G-BNLW	Boeing 747-436	British Airways	
G-BNLX	Boeing 747-436	British Airways	
G-BNLY	Boeing 747-436	British Airways	
G-BNLZ	Boeing 747-436	British Airways	
G-BNMA	Cameron O-77 balloon	A. Wilkes & N. Woodham	

Notes	Reg.	Type	Owner or Operator
	G-BNMB	PA-28-151 Warrior	Britannia Airways Ltd/Luton
	G-BNMC	Cessna 152 II	M. L. Jones/Egginton
	G-BNMD	Cessna 152 II	T. M. Jones/Egginton
	G-BNME	Cessna 152 II	Northamptonshire School of Flying Ltd/ Sywell
	G-BNMF	Cessna 152 II	Aerohire Ltd
	G-BNMG	Cameron O-77 balloon	J. H. Turner
	G-BNMH	Pietenpol Air Camper	N. M. Hitchman
	G-BNMI	Colt Flying Fantasy SS balloon	Air 2 Air Ltd
	G-BNMK	Dornier Do.27A-1	G. Mackie
	G-BNML	Rand-Robinson KR-2	R. F. Cresswell
	G-BNMO	Cessna TR.182RG	Kenrye Developments Ltd
	G-BNMU	Short SD3-60 Variant 100	Loganair Ltd
	G-BNMX	Thunder Ax7-77 balloon	S. A. D. Beard
	G-BNNA	Stolp SA.300 Starduster Too	D. S. Milne
	G-BNNE	Cameron N-77 balloon	Balloon Flights International Ltd
	G-BNNG	Cessna T.337D	Somet Ltd (G-COLD)
	G-BNNI	Boeing 727-276F	Cougar Leasing Ltd
	G-BNNO	PA-28-161 Warrior II	Tindon Ltd/Little Snoring
	G-BNNR	Cessna 152	Sussex Flying Club Ltd/Shoreham
	G-BNNS	PA-28-161 Warrior II	Warrior Aircraft Syndicate
	G-BNNT	PA-28-151 Warrior	S. T. Gilbert & D. J. Kirkwood
	G-BNNU	PA-38-112 Tomahawk	Edinburgh Flying Club Ltd
	G-BNNX	PA-28R-201T Turbo Arrow III	J. G. Freeden
	G-BNNY	PA-28-161 Warrior II	Falcon Flying Services/Biggin Hill
	G-BNNZ	PA-28-161 Warrior II	European Flyers/Blackbushe
	G-BNOB	Wittman W.8 Tailwind	M. Robson-Robinson
	G-BNOE	PA-28-161 Warrior II	Sherburn Aero Club Ltd
	G-BNOF	PA-28-161 Warrior II	Tayside Aviation Ltd/Dundee
	G-BNOG	PA-28-161 Warrior II	BAE Systems Flight Training Ltd
	G-BNOH	PA-28-161 Warrior II	Sherburn Aero Club Ltd
	G-BNOI	PA-28-161 Warrior II	BAE Systems Flight Training Ltd
	G-BNOJ	PA-28-161 Warrior II	BAE Systems (Warton) Flying Club Ltd
	G-BNOK	PA-28-161 Warrior II	BAE Systems Flight Training Ltd
	G-BNOL	PA-28-161 Warrior II	BAE Systems Flight Training Ltd
	G-BNOM	PA-28-161 Warrior II	Sherburn Aero Club Ltd
	G-BNON	PA-28-161 Warrior II	Tayside Aviation Ltd/Dundee
	G-BNOO	PA-28-161 Warrior II	BAE Systems Flight Training Ltd
	G-BNOP	PA-28-161 Warrior II	BAE Systems (Warton) Flying Club Ltd
	G-BNOR	PA-28-161 Warrior II	BAE Systems Flight Training Ltd
	G-BNOS	PA-28-161 Warrior II	BAE Systems Flight Training Ltd
	G-BNOT	PA-28-161 Warrior II	BAE Systems Flight Training Ltd
	G-BNOU	PA-28-161 Warrior II	BAE Systems Flight Training Ltd
	G-BNOV	PA-28-161 Warrior II	BAE Systems Flight Training Ltd
	G-BNOW	PA-28-161 Warrior II	BAE Systems Flight Training Ltd
	G-BNOX	Cessna R.182RG II	G. T. Grimward
	G-BNOZ	Cessna 152 II	Halfpenny Green Flight Centre Ltd
	G-BNPE	Cameron N-77 balloon	Zebedee Balloon Service Ltd
	G-BNPF	Slingsby T.31M	S. Luck & ptnrs
	G-BNPH	P.66 Pembroke C.1 (WV740)	M. J. Willing/Jersey
	G-BNPI	Colt 21A balloon	Virgin Airship & Balloon Co Ltd
	G-BNPL	PA-38-112 Tomahawk	Modern Air (UK) Ltd/Fowlmere
	G-BNPM	PA-38-112 Tomahawk	Papa Mike Aviation Ltd
	G-BNPO	PA-28-181 Archer II	Bonus Aviation Ltd
	G-BNPU	P.66 Pembroke (XL929) ★	D-Day Museum/Shoreham
	G-BNPV	Bowers Fly-Baby 1B	J. G. Day & R. Gauld-Galliers
	G-BNPY	Cessna 152 II	Traffic Management Services/Gamston
	G-BNPZ	Cessna 152 II	C & S Aviation Ltd/ Wolverhampton
	G-BNRA	SOCATA TB.10 Tobago	Double D Airgroup
	G-BNRG	PA-28-161 Warrior II	RAF Brize Norton Flying Club Ltd
	G-BNRI	Cessna U.206G	Bob Crowe Aircraft Sales Ltd/Cranfield
	G-BNRK	Cessna 152 II	Redhill Flying Club
	G-BNRL	Cessna 152 II	J. R. Nicholls/Sibson
	G-BNRP	PA-28-181 Archer II	Bonua Aviation Ltd/Cranfield
	G-BNRR	Cessna 172P	PHA Aviation Ltd/Elstree
	G-BNRX	PA-34-200T Seneca II	Truman Aviation Ltd/Tollerton
	G-BNRY	Cessna 182Q	Reefly Ltd
	G-BNSG	PA-28R-201 Arrow III	Armada Aviation Ltd/Redhill
	G-BNSI	Cessna 152 II	Sky Leisure Aviation (Charters) Ltd
	G-BNSL	PA-38-112 Tomahawk II	APB Leasing Ltd/Welshpool
	G-BNSM	Cessna 152 II	Cornwall Flying Club Ltd/Bodmin
	G-BNSN	Cessna 152 II	The Pilot Centre Ltd/Denham
	G-BNSO	Slingsby T.67M Firefly Mk II	Hunting Aviation Ltd/Barkston Heath

Reg.	Type	Owner or Operator	Notes
G-BNSP	Slingsby T.67M Firefly Mk II	Hunting Aviation Ltd/Barkston Heath	
G-BNSR	Slingsby T.67M Firefly Mk II	Hunting Aviation Ltd/Barkston Heath	
G-BNST	Cessna 172N	CSG Bodyshop	
G-BNSU	Cessna 152 II	Channel Aviation Ltd/Bourn	
G-BNSV	Cessna 152 II	Channel Aviation Ltd/Bourn	
G-BNSY	PA-28-161 Warrior II	Carill Aviation Ltd/Southampton	
G-BNSZ	PA-28-161 Warrior II	Carill Aviation Ltd/Southampton	
G-BNTC	PA-28RT-201T Turbo Arrow IV	M. F. Lassan	
G-BNTD	PA-28-161 Warrior II	A. M. & F. Alam/Elstree	
G-BNTP	Cessna 172N	Westnet Ltd	
G-BNTS	PA-28RT-201T Turbo Arrow IV	Nasaire Ltd/Liverpool	
G-BNTT	Beech 76 Duchess	Aviation Rentals/Bournemouth	
G-BNTW	Cameron V-77 balloon	P. Goss	
G-BNTZ	Cameron N-77 balloon	Balloon Team	
G-BNUC	Cameron O-77 balloon	T. J. Bucknall	
G-BNUI	Rutan Vari-Eze	I. T. Kennedy & K. H. McConnell	
G-BNUL	Cessna 152 II	Exeter Air Training School Ltd	
G-BNUN	Beech 95-58PA Baron	British Midland Airways Ltd/E. Midlands	
G-BNUO	Beech 76 Duchess	G. A. F. Tilley	
G-BNUS	Cessna 152 II	Stapleford Flying Club Ltd	
G-BNUT	Cessna 152 Turbo	Stapleford Flying Club Ltd	
G-BNUV	PA-23 Aztec 250F	L. J. Martin	
G-BNUX	Hoffmann H-36 Dimona	Buckminster Dimona Syndicate/Saltby	
G-BNUY	PA-38-112 Tomahawk II	Cardiff-Wales Aviation Services Ltd	
G-BNVB	AA-5A Cheetah	Grumman Group	
G-BNVD	PA-38-112 Tomahawk	D. A. Whitmore	
G-BNVE	PA-28-181 Archer II	Steve Parrish Racing	
G-BNVT	PA-28R-201T Turbo Arrow III	Victor Tango Group	
G-BNVZ	Beech 95-B55 Baron	W. J. Forrest /White Waltham	
G-BNWA	Boeing 767-336ER	British Airways	
G-BNWH	Boeing 767-336ER	British Airways	
G-BNWI	Boeing 767-336ER	British Airways	
G-BNWM	Boeing 767-336ER	British Airways	
G-BNWN	Boeing 767-336ER	British Airways	
G-BNWO	Boeing 767-336ER	British Airways	
G-BNWR	Boeing 767-336ER	British Airways	
G-BNWS	Boeing 767-336ER	British Airways	
G-BNWT	Boeing 767-336ER	British Airways	
G-BNWU	Boeing 767-336ER	British Airways	
G-BNWV	Boeing 767-336ER	British Airways	
G-BNWX	Boeing 767-336ER	British Airways	
G-BNWZ	Boeing 767-336ER	British Airways	
G-BNXC	Cessna 152 II	Sir W. G. Armstrong Whitworth Flying Group/Coventry	
G-BNXD	Cessna 172N	I. Chaplin	
G-BNXE	PA-28-161 Warrior II	Rugby Autobody Repairs/Coventry	
G-BNXI	Robin DR.400/180R	London Gliding Club (Pty) Ltd/Dunstable	
G-BNXK	Nott-Cameron ULD-3 balloon	J. R. P. Nott (G-BLJN)	
G-BNXL	Glaser-Dirks DG.400	G-BNXL Group	
G-BNXM	PA-18 Super Cub 95	G-BNXM Group	
G-BNXR	Cameron O-84 balloon	J. A. B. Gray	
G-BNXT	PA-28-161 Warrior II	Falcon Flying Services/Manston	
G-BNXU	PA-28-161 Warrior II	Friendly Warrior Group	
G-BNXV	PA-38-112 Tomahawk	St George Flying Club/Teesside	
G-BNXX	SOCATA TB.20 Trinidad	D. M. Carr	
G-BNXZ	Thunder Ax7-77 balloon	Hale Hot Air Balloon Group	
G-BNYB	PA-28-201T Turbo Dakota	Rosetta Milestone Ltd	
G-BNYD	Bell 206B JetRanger 3	Sterling Helicopters Ltd/Norwich	
G-BNYI	Short SD3-60 Variant 100	Loganair Ltd	
G-BNYK	PA-38-112 Tomahawk	APB Leasing Ltd/Welshpool	
G-BNYL	Cessna 152 II	V. J. Freeman/Headcorn	
G-BNYM	Cessna 172N	Kestrel Syndicate	
G-BNYN	Cessna 152 II	Redhill Flying Club	
G-BNYO	Beech 76 Duchess	Harding Wragg	
G-BNYP	PA-28-181 Archer II	R. D. Cooper/Cranfield	
G-BNYV	PA-38-112 Tomahawk	Goodair Leasing Ltd	
G-BNYX	Denney Kitfox Mk 1	R. W. Husband	
G-BNYZ	SNCAN Stampe SV-4E	M. J. Heudebourck & D, A, Starkey	
G-BNZB	PA-28-161 Warrior II	EFG Flying Services Ltd/Biggin Hill	
G-BNZC	D.H.C.1 Chipmunk 22 (18671)	The Shuttleworth Collection/O.Warden	
G-BNZG	PA-28RT-201T Turbo Arrow IV	Brightday Ltd	
G-BNZK	Thunder Ax7-77 balloon	T. D. Marsden	
G-BNZL	Rotorway Scorpion 133	J. R. Wraight	

Notes	Reg.	Type	Owner or Operator
	G-BNZM	Cessna T.210N	A. J. M. Freeman
	G-BNZO	Rotorway Executive	D. Collins & R. Ayres
	G-BNZR	FRED Srs 2	R. M. Waugh/Newtownards
	G-BNZV	PA-25 Pawnee 235	Northumbria Gliding Club Ltd
	G-BNZZ	PA-28-161 Warrior II	Zoom Aviation Ltd
	G-BOAA	Concorde 102	British Airways (G-N94AA)
	G-BOAB	Concorde 102	British Airways (G-N94AB)
	G-BOAC	Concorde 102	British Airways (G-N81AC)
	G-BOAD	Concorde 102	British Airways (G-N94AD)
	G-BOAE	Concorde 102	British Airways (G-N94AE)
	G-BOAF	Concorde 102	British Airways (G-N94AF/G-BFKX)
	G-BOAG	Concorde 102	British Airways (G-BFKW)
	G-BOAH	PA-28-161 Warrior II	N. Singh & H. Kaur
	G-BOAI	Cessna 152 II	Galair Ltd/Biggin Hill
	G-BOAK	PA-22 Tri-Pacer 150	A. M. Noble
	G-BOAL	Cameron V-65 balloon	A. M. Lindsay
	G-BOAM	Robinson R-22B	Plane Talking Ltd/Elstree
	G-BOAO	Thunder Ax7-77 balloon	D. V. Fowler
	G-BOAS	Air Command 503 Commander	R. Robinson
	G-BOAU	Cameron V-77 balloon	G. T. Barstow
	G-BOBA	PA-28R-201 Arrow III	Atlantic Air Transport Ltd/Coventry
	G-BOBB	Cameron O-120 balloon	Over The Rainbow Balloon Flights Ltd
	G-BOBH	Airtour AH-77 balloon	J. & K. Francis
	G-BOBL	PA-38-112 Tomahawk	Cardiff-Wales Aviation Services Ltd
	G-BOBR	Cameron N-77 balloon	C. Bradley & M. Morris
	G-BOBT	Stolp SA.300 Starduster Too	G-BOBT Group
	G-BOBU	Colt 90A balloon	Prescott Hot Air Balloons Ltd
	G-BOBV	Cessna F.150M	Sheffield Aero Club Ltd/Netherthorpe
	G-BOBY	Monnett Sonerai II	R. G. Hallam *(stored)*/Sleap
	G-BOBZ	PA-28-181 Archer II	Trustcomms International Ltd
	G-BOCC	PA-38-112 Tomahawk	J. M. Green
	G-BOCF	Colt 77A balloon	Lindstrand Balloons Ltd
	G-BOCG	PA-34-200T Seneca II	Oxford Aviation Services Ltd/Kidlington
	G-BOCI	Cessna 140A	J. B. Bonnell
	G-BOCK	Sopwith Triplane (replica) (N6290)	The Shuttleworth Collection/O. Warden
	G-BOCL	Slingsby T.67C	Richard Brinklow Aviation Ltd
	G-BOCM	Slingsby T.67C	Richard Brinklow Aviation Ltd
	G-BOCN	Robinson R-22B	Cookie Boy Consultants Ltd
	G-BOCP	PA-34-220T Seneca III	BAE Systems Flight Training Ltd
	G-BOCR	PA-34-220T Seneca III	BAE Systems Flight Training Ltd
	G-BOCS	PA-34-220T Seneca III	BAE Systems Flight Training Ltd
	G-BOCT	PA-34-220T Seneca III	BAE Systems Flight Training Ltd
	G-BOCU	PA-34-220T Seneca III	BAE Systems Flight Training Ltd
	G-BOCV	PA-34-220T Seneca III	BAE Systems Flight Training Ltd
	G-BOCW	PA-34-220T Seneca III	BAE Systems Flight Training Ltd
	G-BOCX	PA-34-220T Seneca III	BAE Systems Flight Training Ltd
	G-BOCY	PA-34-220T Seneca III	BAE Systems Flight Training Ltd
	G-BODA	PA-28-161 Warrior II	Oxford Aviation Services Ltd/Kidlington
	G-BODB	PA-28-161 Warrior II	Oxford Aviation Services Ltd/Kidlington
	G-BODC	PA-28-161 Warrior II	Oxford Aviation Services Ltd/Kidlington
	G-BODD	PA-28-161 Warrior II	Oxford Aviation Services Ltd/Kidlington
	G-BODE	PA-28-161 Warrior II	Oxford Aviation Services Ltd/Kidlington
	G-BODF	PA-28-161 Warrior II	Oxford Aviation Services Ltd/Kidlington
	G-BODH	Slingsby Cadet III	M. M. Bain
	G-BODI	Stoddard-Hamilton SH-3R Glasair III	G. M. Howard/Switzerland
	G-BODM	PA-28 Cherokee 180	R. Emery
	G-BODO	Cessna 152	A. R. Sarson
	G-BODP	PA-38-112 Tomahawk	D. A. Whitmore
	G-BODR	PA-28-161 Warrior II	Airways Aero Associations Ltd/Booker
	G-BODS	PA-38-112 Tomahawk	M. R. Cavinder
	G-BODT	Jodel D.18	L. D. McPhillips
	G-BODU	Scheibe SF.25C Falke	Monica English Memorial Trust/Rufforth
	G-BODX	Beech 76 Duchess	Aviation Rentals/Bournemouth
	G-BODY	Cessna 310R	Atlantic Air Transport Ltd/Coventry
	G-BODZ	Robinson R-22B	Langley Construction Ltd
	G-BOEE	PA-28-181 Archer II	T. B. Parmenter
	G-BOEH	Jodel DR.340	Piper Flyers Group
	G-BOEK	Cameron V-77 balloon	A. J. E. Jones
	G-BOEM	Aerotek-Pitts S-2A	M. Murphy
	G-BOEN	Cessna 172M	G-BOEN Group

Reg.	Type	Owner or Operator	Notes
G-BOER	PA-28-161 Warrior II	M. & W. Fraser-Urquhart	
G-BOET	PA-28RT-201 Arrow IV	B. C. Chambers (G-IBEC)	
G-BOEW	Robinson R-22B	Plane Talking Ltd/Elstree	
G-BOEX	Robinson R-22B	Plane Talking Ltd/Elstree	
G-BOEZ	Robinson R-22B	Plane Talking Ltd/Elstree	
G-BOFC	Beech 76 Duchess	Magenta Ltd/Kidlington	
G-BOFD	Cessna U.206G	D. M. Penny	
G-BOFE	PA-34-200T Seneca II	Alstons Upholstery Ltd	
G-BOFF	Cameron N-77 balloon	R. C. Corcoran	
G-BOFL	Cessna 152 II	GEM Rewinds Ltd/Coventry	
G-BOFM	Cessna 152 II	GEM Rewinds Ltd/Coventry	
G-BOFW	Cessna A.150M	D. F. Donovan	
G-BOFX	Cessna A.150M	Aldergrove Flight Training Centre	
G-BOFY	PA-28 Cherokee 140	BCT Aircraft Leasing Ltd	
G-BOFZ	PA-28-161 Warrior II	R. W. Harris	
G-BOGC	Cessna 152 II	Keen Leasing (IOM) Ltd	
G-BOGG	Cessna 152 II	The Royal Artillery Aero Club Ltd/ Middle Wallop	
G-BOGI	Robin DR.400/180	A. L. M. Shepherd	
G-BOGK	ARV Super 2	D. R. Trouse	
G-BOGM	PA-28RT-201T Turbo Arrow IV	RJP Aviation	
G-BOGO	PA-32R-301T Saratoga SP	A. S. Doman/Biggin Hill	
G-BOGP	Cameron V-77 balloon	Wealden Balloon Group	
G-BOGV	Air Command 532 Elite	G. M. Hobman	
G-BOGY	Cameron V-77 balloon	R. A. Preston	
G-BOHA	PA-28-161 Warrior II	T. F. & M. I. Hall/Shoreham	
G-BOHD	Colt 77A balloon	D. B. Court	
G-BOHF	Thunder Ax8-84 balloon	J. A. Harris	
G-BOHG	Air Command 532 Elite	T. E. McDonald	
G-BOHH	Cessna 172N	T. Scott	
G-BOHI	Cessna 152 II	V. D. Speck/Clacton	
G-BOHJ	Cessna 152 II	Airlaunch/Old Buckenham	
G-BOHL	Cameron A-120 balloon	J. M. Holmes	
G-BOHM	PA-28 Cherokee 180	B. F. Keogh & R. A. Scott	
G-BOHO	PA-28-161 Warrior II	Egressus Flying Group	
G-BOHR	PA-28-151 Warrior	M. C. Wilson	
G-BOHS	PA-38-112 Tomahawk	Falcon Flying Services/Biggin Hill	
G-BOHT	PA-38-112 Tomahawk	St George Flying Club/Teesside	
G-BOHU	PA-38-112 Tomahawk	D. A. Whitmore	
G-BOHV	Wittman W.8 Tailwind	R. A. Povall	
G-BOHW	Van's RV-4	P. J. Robins	
G-BOHX	PA-44-180 Seminole	Airpart Supply Ltd/Booker	
G-BOIA	Cessna 180K	R. E. Styles & ptnrs	
G-BOIB	Wittman W.10 Tailwind	R. F. Bradshaw	
G-BOIC	PA-28R-201T Turbo Arrow III	M. J. Pearson	
G-BOID	Bellanca 7ECA Citabria	D. Mallinson	
G-BOIG	PA-28-161 Warrior II	D. Vallence-Pell/Jersey	
G-BOIJ	Thunder Ax7-77 balloon	K. Dodman	
G-BOIK	Air Command 503 Commander	F. G. Shepherd	
G-BOIL	Cessna 172N	Upperstack Ltd	
G-BOIN	Bellanca 7ECA Citabria	M. A. N. Newall	
G-BOIO	Cessna 152	AV Aviation Ltd	
G-BOIP	Cessna 152	Stapleford Flying Club Ltd	
G-BOIR	Cessna 152	Shropshire Aero Club Ltd/Sleap	
G-BOIT	SOCATA TB.10 Tobago	Buckland Newton Hire Ltd	
G-BOIU	SOCATA TB.10 Tobago	R & B Aviation Ltd	
G-BOIV	Cessna 150M	J. B. Green	
G-BOIW	Cessna 152	EFG Flying Services Ltd/Biggin Hill	
G-BOIX	Cessna 172N	JR Flying Ltd	
G-BOIY	Cessna 172N	White Aviation Ltd	
G-BOIZ	PA-34-200T Seneca II	S. F. Tebby & Son	
G-BOJB	Cameron V-77 balloon	K. L. Heron & R. M. Trotter	
G-BOJD	Cameron V-77 balloon	L. H. Ellis	
G-BOJI	PA-28RT-201 Arrow IV	Arrow Two Group/Blackbushe	
G-BOJK	PA-34-220T Seneca III	Redhill Flying Club (G-BRUF)	
G-BOJM	PA-28-181 Archer II	Fernborough Ltd	
G-BOJR	Cessna 172P	Exeter Flying Club Ltd	
G-BOJS	Cessna 172P	I. S. H. Paul	
G-BOJU	Cameron N-77 balloon	M. A. Scholes	
G-BOJW	PA-28-161 Warrior II	Brewhamfield Farm Ltd	
G-BOJZ	PA-28-161 Warrior II	Falcon Flying Services/Biggin Hill	
G-BOKA	PA-28-201T Turbo Dakota	CBG Aviation Ltd/Biggin Hill	
G-BOKB	PA-28-161 Warrior II	Premiair Engineering Ltd/Shoreham	

Notes	Reg.	Type	Owner or Operator
	G-BOKD	Bell 206B JetRanger 3	Sterling Helicopters Ltd (G-ISKY/G-PSCI)
	G-BOKF	Air Command 532 Elite	D. Beevers
	G-BOKH	Whittaker MW.7	I. D. Evans
	G-BOKL	PA-28-161 Warrior II	BAE Systems Flight Training Ltd
	G-BOKM	PA-28-161 Warrior II	BAE Systems Flight Training Ltd
	G-BOKN	PA-28-161 Warrior II	BAE Systems Flight Training Ltd
	G-BOKO	PA-28-161 Warrior II	BAE Systems Flight Training Ltd
	G-BOKP	PA-28-161 Warrior II	BAE Systems Flight Training Ltd
	G-BOKR	PA-28-161 Warrior II	BAE Systems Flight Training Ltd
	G-BOKS	PA-28-161 Warrior II	BAE Systems Flight Training Ltd
	G-BOKT	PA-28-161 Warrior II	BAE Systems Flight Training Ltd
	G-BOKU	PA-28-161 Warrior II	BAE Systems Flight Training Ltd
	G-BOKX	PA-28-161 Warrior II	Shenley Farms (Aviation) Ltd/Headcorn
	G-BOKY	Cessna 152 II	D. F. F. & J. E. Poore
	G-BOLB	Taylorcraft BC-12-65	F. J. Pacewicz & R. J. Rhys-Williams
	G-BOLC	Fournier RF-6B-100	W. H. Hendy/Dunkeswell
	G-BOLD	PA-38-112 Tomahawk	G-BOLD Group/Eaglescott
	G-BOLE	PA-38-112 Tomahawk	J. & G. Stevenson
	G-BOLF	PA-38-112 Tomahawk	Teesside Flight Centre Ltd
	G-BOLG	Bellanca 7KCAB Citabria	B. R. Pearson/Eaglescott
	G-BOLI	Cessna 172P	Boli Flying Club
	G-BOLL	Lake LA-4 Skimmer	M. C. Holmes
	G-BOLN	Colt 21A balloon	G. Everett
	G-BOLO	Bell 206B JetRanger	Hargreaves Leasing Ltd
	G-BOLP	Colt 21A balloon	J. E. Rose
	G-BOLR	Colt 21A balloon	C. J. Sanger-Davies
	G-BOLS	FRED Srs 2	I. F. Vaughan
	G-BOLT	R. Commander 114	H. Gafsen/Elstree
	G-BOLU	Robin R.3000/120	Classair/Biggin Hill
	G-BOLV	Cessna 152 II	Falcon Flying Services/Biggin Hill
	G-BOLW	Cessna 152 II	JRB Aviation Ltd/Southend
	G-BOLX	Cessna 172N	R. J. Burrough/Headcorn
	G-BOLY	Cessna 172N	D. A. T. Skidmore
	G-BOLZ	Rand-Robinson KR-2	B. Normington
	G-BOMB	Cassutt Racer IIIM	S. Adams
	G-BOMG	BN-2B-26 Islander	B-N Group Ltd/Bembridge
	G-BOMN	Cessna 150F	D. G. Williams
	G-BOMO	PA-38-112 Tomahawk II	APB Leasing Ltd/Welshpool
	G-BOMP	PA-28-181 Archer II	SRC Contractors Ltd & D. Carter
	G-BOMS	Cessna 172N	Almat Flying Club Ltd & Penchant Ltd
	G-BOMT	Cessna 172N	R. A. Mitchell
	G-BOMU	PA-28-181 Archer II	RJ Aviation/Blackbushe
	G-BOMY	PA-28-161 Warrior II	Southern Care Maintenance
	G-BOMZ	PA-38-112 Tomahawk	BOMZ Aviation/Booker
	G-BONC	PA-28RT-201 Arrow IV	Finglow Ltd
	G-BONE	Pilatus P2-06 (U-142)	G. B. E. Pearce/Shoreham
	G-BONO	Cessna 172N	Mer-Air Aviation Ltd
	G-BONP	CFM Streak Shadow	T. J. Palmer
	G-BONR	Cessna 172N	D. I. Craik/Biggin Hill
	G-BONS	Cessna 172N	BONS Group/Elstree
	G-BONT	Slingsby T.67M Mk II	Hunting Aviation Ltd/Barkston Heath
	G-BONU	Slingsby T.67B	R. L. Brinklow
	G-BONW	Cessna 152 II	Lincoln Aero Club Ltd/Sturgate
	G-BONY	Denney Kitfox Mk 1	M. J. Walker
	G-BONZ	Beech V35B Bonanza	P. M. Coulten
	G-BOOB	Cameron N-65 balloon	J. Rumming
	G-BOOC	PA-18 Super Cub 150	R. R. & S. A. Marriott
	G-BOOD	Slingsby T.31M Motor Tutor	K. A. Hale
	G-BOOE	GA-7 Cougar	N. Gardner
	G-BOOF	PA-28-181 Archer II	European Flyers/Blackbushe
	G-BOOG	PA-28RT-201T Turbo Arrow IV	Simair Ltd
	G-BOOH	Jodel D.112	J. A. Crabb
	G-BOOI	Cessna 152	Stapleford Flying Club Ltd
	G-BOOJ	Air Command 532 Elite II	Roger Savage Gyroplanes Ltd
	G-BOOL	Cessna 172N	Surrey & Kent Flying Club Ltd/Biggin Hill
	G-BOOV	AS.355F-2 Twin Squirrel	Merseyside Police Authority/Woodvale
	G-BOOW	Aerosport Scamp	I. E. Bloys
	G-BOOX	Rutan LongEz	I. R. Thomas & I. R. Wilde
	G-BOOZ	Cameron N-77 balloon	J. E. F. Kettlety
	G-BOPA	PA-28-181 Archer II	J. H. & L. F. Strutt
	G-BOPC	PA-28-161 Warrior II	Aeros Ltd
	G-BOPD	Bede BD-4	S. T. Dauncey
	G-BOPG	Cessna 182Q	G. Wimlett

Reg.	Type	Owner or Operator	Notes
G-BOPH	Cessna TR.182RG	Grandsam Investments Ltd	
G-BOPO	Brooklands OA.7 Optica	Sunhawk Ltd	
G-BOPR	Brooklands OA.7 Optica	Sunhawk Ltd	
G-BOPT	Grob G.115	LAC (Enterprises) Ltd/Barton	
G-BOPU	Grob G.115	LAC (Enterprises) Ltd/Barton	
G-BOPV	PA-34-200T Seneca II	G. J. Powell	
G-BOPX	Cessna A.152	Aerohire Ltd/Wolverhampton	
G-BORB	Cameron V-77 balloon	M. H. Wolff	
G-BORD	Thunder Ax7-77 balloon	D. D. Owen	
G-BORE	Colt 77A balloon	Little Secret Hot-Air Balloon Group	
G-BORG	Campbell Cricket	G. Davison & H. Hayes	
G-BORH	PA-34-200T Seneca II	Aerolease Ltd	
G-BORI	Cessna 152 II	Staryear Ltd	
G-BORJ	Cessna 152 II	Pool Aviation (NW) Ltd/Blackpool	
G-BORK	PA-28-161 Warrior II	A. W. Collett	
G-BORL	PA-28-161 Warrior II	Westair Flying School Ltd/Blackpool	
G-BORM	H.S.748 Srs 2B ★	Airport Fire Service/Exeter	
G-BORN	Cameron N-77 balloon	I. Chadwick	
G-BORO	Cessna 152 II	Tatenhill Aviation	
G-BORR	Thunder Ax8-90 balloon	W. J. Harris	
G-BORS	PA-28-181 Archer II	G-BORS Flying Group	
G-BORT	Colt 77A balloon	J. Triquet/France	
G-BORV	Bell 206B JetRanger 3	C. A. Rosenberg/Redhill	
G-BORW	Cessna 172P	Briter Aviation Ltd/Coventry	
G-BORY	Cessna 150L	D. G. Bell & S. J. Green	
G-BOSB	Thunder Ax7-77 balloon	M. Gallagher	
G-BOSD	PA-34-200T Seneca II	Barnes Olson Aeroleasing Ltd/Bristol	
G-BOSE	PA-28-181 Archer II	C. A. W. Godfrey	
G-BOSJ	Nord 3400 (124)	A. I. Milne	
G-BOSM	Jodel DR.253B	Sierra Mike (Ware) Group	
G-BOSN	AS.355F-1 Twin Squirrel	Helicopter Services/Booker	
G-BOSO	Cessna A.152	J. S. Develin & Z. Islam/Redhill	
G-BOSR	PA-28 Cherokee 140	Sierra Romeo Group	
G-BOSU	PA-28 Cherokee 140	R. A. Sands	
G-BOTD	Cameron O-105 balloon	P. J. Beglan/France	
G-BOTF	PA-28-151 Warrior	G-BOTF Group/Southend	
G-BOTG	Cessna 152 II	Donington Aviation Ltd/E. Midlands	
G-BOTH	Cessna 182Q	G-BOTH Group	
G-BOTI	PA-28-151 Warrior	Falcon Flying Services/Biggin Hill	
G-BOTK	Cameron O-105 balloon	F. R. & V. L. Higgins	
G-BOTM	Bell 206B JetRanger 3	David McLean Homes Ltd	
G-BOTN	PA-28-161 Warrior II	Premiair Engineering Ltd	
G-BOTO	Bellanca 7ECA Citabria	G-BOTO Group	
G-BOTP	Cessna 150J	R. F. Finnis & C. P. Williams	
G-BOTU	Piper J-3C-65 Cub	T. L. Giles	
G-BOTV	PA-32RT-300 Lance II	Robin Lance Aviation Association Ltd	
G-BOTW	Cameron V-77 balloon	M. R. Jeynes	
G-BOTZ	Bensen B.8MR	C. Jones	
G-BOUD	PA-38-112 Tomahawk	A. J. Wiggins	
G-BOUE	Cessna 172N	Aviation Access Ltd	
G-BOUF	Cessna 172N	Amber Valley Aviation	
G-BOUJ	Cessna 150M	R. D. Billins	
G-BOUK	PA-34-200T Seneca II	C. J. & R. J. Barnes	
G-BOUL	PA-34-200T Seneca II	Oxford Aviation Services Ltd/Kidlington	
G-BOUM	PA-34-200T Seneca II	Oxford Aviation Services Ltd/Kidlington	
G-BOUP	PA-28-161 Warrior II	Oxford Aviation Services Ltd/Kidlington	
G-BOUR	PA-28-161 Warrior II	Oxford Aviation Services Ltd/Kidlington	
G-BOUT	Colomban MC.12 Cri-Cri	C. K. Farley	
G-BOUV	Bensen B.8MR	G. C. Kerr	
G-BOUZ	Cessna 150G	Gordon Air Ltd/Lydd	
G-BOVB	PA-15 Vagabond	Oscar Flying Group/Shoreham	
G-BOVC	Everett gyroplane	J. W. Highton	
G-BOVK	PA-28-161 Warrior II	Air Nova PLC/Liverpool	
G-BOVR	Robinson R-22	J. O'Brien	
G-BOVS	Cessna 150M	Blue Skies Aviation Ltd	
G-BOVT	Cessna 150M	C. J. Hopewell	
G-BOVU	Stoddard-Hamilton Glasair III	B. R. Chaplin	
G-BOVV	Cameron V-77 balloon	P. Glydon	
G-BOVW	Colt 69A balloon	V. Hyland	
G-BOVX	Hughes 269C	P. E. Tornberg	
G-BOWB	Cameron V-77 balloon	R. C. Stone	
G-BOWD	Cessna F.337G	Badgehurst Ltd (G-BLSB)	
G-BOWE	PA-34-200T Seneca II	Oxford Aviation Services Ltd/Kidlington	

Notes	Reg.	Type	Owner or Operator
	G-BOWL	Cameron V-77 balloon	P. G. & G. R. Hall
	G-BOWM	Cameron V-56 balloon	C. G. Caldecutt & G. Pitt
	G-BOWN	PA-12 Super Cruiser	R. W. Bucknell
	G-BOWO	Cessna R.182	P. C. Lever (G-BOTR)
	G-BOWP	Jodel D.120A	H. W. Machell
	G-BOWU	Cameron O-84 balloon	St Elmos Fire Syndicate
	G-BOWV	Cameron V-65 balloon	R. A. Harris
	G-BOWY	PA-28RT-201T Turbo Arrow IV	A. Davies
	G-BOWZ	Bensen B.80V	W. M. Day
	G-BOXA	PA-28-161 Warrior II	Channel Islands Aero Services Ltd
	G-BOXB	PA-28-161 Warrior II	Channel Islands Aero Services Ltd
	G-BOXC	PA-28-161 Warrior II	Channel Islands Aero Services Ltd
	G-BOXG	Cameron O-77 balloon	R. A. Wicks
	G-BOXH	Pitts S-1S Special	D. Medrek/Breighton
	G-BOXJ	Piper J-3C-65 Cub	J. D. Tseliki/Shoreham
	G-BOXR	GA-7 Cougar	Plane Talking Ltd/Elstree
	G-BOXT	Hughes 269C	Goldenfly Ltd
	G-BOXU	AA-5B Tiger	Marcher Aviation Group/Welshpool
	G-BOXV	Pitts S-1S Special	G. R. Clark
	G-BOXW	Cassutt Racer Srs IIIM	D. I. Johnson
	G-BOXY	PA-28-181 Archer II	Sheffield Aero Club Ltd/Netherthorpe
	G-BOYB	Cessna A.152	Northamptonshire School of Flying Ltd/ Sywell
	G-BOYC	Robinson R-22B	Yorkshire Helicopters/Leeds
	G-BOYF	Sikorsky S-76B	Darley Stud Management Co Ltd/ Blackbushe
	G-BOYH	PA-28-151 Warrior	Superpause Ltd/Booker
	G-BOYI	PA-28-161 Warrior II	G-BOYI Group/Welshpool
	G-BOYL	Cessna 152 II	Aerohire Ltd/Wolverhampton
	G-BOYM	Cameron O-84 balloon	M. P. Ryan
	G-BOYP	Cessna 172N	Guildtons Ltd
	G-BOYS	Cameron N-77 balloon	Wye Valley Aviation Ltd
	G-BOYU	Cessna A.150L	Upperstack Ltd/Liverpool
	G-BOYV	PA-28R-201T Turbo Arrow III	Arrow Air Ltd
	G-BOYX	Robinson R-22B	R. Towle
	G-BOZI	PA-28-161 Warrior II	Aerolease Ltd/Conington
	G-BOZK	AS.332L Super Puma	CHC Scotia Ltd
	G-BOZN	Cameron N-77 balloon	Calarel Developments Ltd
	G-BOZO	AA-5B Tiger	Caslon Ltd
	G-BOZR	Cessna 152 II	GEM Rewinds Ltd/Coventry
	G-BOZS	Pitts S-1C Special	T. A. S. Rayner
	G-BOZU	Sparrow Hawk Mk II	R. V. Phillimore
	G-BOZV	CEA DR.340 Major	C. J. Turner & S. D. Kent
	G-BOZW	Bensen B.8M	M. E. Wills
	G-BOZY	Cameron RTW-120 balloon	Magical Adventures Ltd
	G-BOZZ	AA-5B Tiger	Solent Tiger Group/Southampton
	G-BPAA	Acro Advanced	Acro Engines & Airframes Ltd
	G-BPAB	Cessna 150M	M. J. Diggins/Earls Colne
	G-BPAC	PA-28-161 Warror II	G. G. Pratt
	G-BPAF	PA-28-161 Warrior II	RAF Brize Norton Flying Club Ltd
	G-BPAH	Colt 69A balloon	Justerini & Brooks Ltd
	G-BPAI	Bell 47G-3B-1 (modified)	LRC Leisure Ltd
	G-BPAJ	D.H.82A Tiger Moth	P. A. Jackson (G-AOIX)
	G-BPAL	D.H.C.1 Chipmunk 22 (WG350)	K. F. & P. Tomsett (G-BCYE)
	G-BPAS	SOCATA TB.20 Trinidad	Syndicate Clerical Services Ltd
	G-BPAU	PA-28-161 Warrior II	Lapwing Flying Group Ltd/Denham
	G-BPAV	FRED Srs 2	P. A. Valentine
	G-BPAW	Cessna 150M	P. D. Sims
	G-BPAX	Cessna 150M	The Dirty Dozen
	G-BPAY	PA-28-181 Archer II	Leicestershire Aero Club Ltd
	G-BPBG	Cessna 152 II	APB Leasing Ltd/Welshpool
	G-BPBI	Cessna 152 II	B. W. Wells & Burbage Farms Ltd
	G-BPBJ	Cessna 152 II	W. Shaw & P. G. Haines
	G-BPBK	Cessna 152 II	Sir W. G. Armstrong-Whitworth Flying Group/Coventry
	G-BPBM	PA-28-161 Warrior II	Halfpenny Green Flight Centre Ltd
	G-BPBO	PA-28RT-201T Turbo Arrow IV	Tile Holdings Ltd
	G-BPBP	Brügger MB.2 Colibri	D. A. Preston
	G-BPBU	Cameron V-77 balloon	M. C. Gibbons & J. E. Kite
	G-BPBV	Cameron V-77 balloon	S. J. Farrant
	G-BPBW	Cameron O-105 balloon	R. J. Mansfield
	G-BPBY	Cameron V-77 balloon	L. Hutley (G-BPCS)

Reg.	Type	Owner or Operator	Notes
G-BPBZ	Thunder Ax7-77 balloon	A. W. J. Weston	
G-BPCA	BN-2B-26 Islander	Loganair Ltd/BA Express (G-BLNX)	
G-BPCF	Piper J-3C-65 Cub	T. I. Williams	
G-BPCG	Colt AS-80 airship	N. Charbonnier/Italy	
G-BPCI	Cessna R.172K	P. A. Warner & E. S. Scotchbrook	
G-BPCK	PA-28-161 Warrior II	W. G. Booth	
G-BPCL	SA Bulldog Srs 120/128	Isohigh Ltd/Denham	
G-BPCM	Rotorway Executive	Aircare Group	
G-BPCR	Mooney M.20K	T. & R. Harris	
G-BPCV	Montgomerie-Bensen B.8MR	O. J. Blackbourn	
G-BPCX	PA-28-236 Dakota	G. E. J. Spooner	
G-BPDE	Colt 56A balloon	J. E. Weidema/Netherlands	
G-BPDF	Cameron V-77 balloon	The Ballooning Business Ltd	
G-BPDG	Cameron V-77 balloon	D. F. H. Smith	
G-BPDJ	Christena Mini Coupe	J. J. Morrissey/Popham	
G-BPDK	Sorrell SNS-7 Hyperbipe ★	A. J. Cable *(stored)*/Barton	
G-BPDM	C.A.S.A. 1.131E Jungmann 2000 (781-32)	J. D. Haslam	
G-BPDT	PA-28-161 Warrior II	Channel Islands Aero Services Ltd	
G-BPDU	PA-28-161 Warrior II	Shoreham Flight Centre Ltd	
G-BPDV	Pitts S-1S Special	J. Vize/Sywell	
G-BPDY	Westland-Bell 47G-3B1	Howden Helicopters/Spaldington	
G-BPEC	Boeing 757-236	British Airways	
G-BPED	Boeing 757-236	British Airways	
G-BPEE	Boeing 757-236	British Airways	
G-BPEF	Boeing 757-236	British Airways (G-BOHC)	
G-BPEI	Boeing 757-236	British Airways (G-BMRK)	
G-BPEJ	Boeing 757-236	British Airways (G-BMRL)	
G-BPEK	Boeing 757-236	British Airways (G-BMRM)	
G-BPEL	PA-28-151 Warrior	R. W. Harris & A. J. Jahanfar	
G-BPEM	Cessna 150K	R. G. Lindsey & R. Strong	
G-BPEO	Cessna 152 II	Seawing Flying Club Ltd & Eastern Executive Air Charter Ltd/Southend	
G-BPES	PA-38-112 Tomahawk II	Sherwood Flying Club Ltd/Tollerton	
G-BPEZ	Colt 77A balloon	J. E. F. Kettley & W. J. Honey	
G-BPFB	Colt 77A balloon	S. Ingram	
G-BPFC	Mooney M.20C	D. P. Wring	
G-BPFD	Jodel D.112	K. Manley	
G-BPFH	PA-28-161 Warrior II	M. H. Kleiser	
G-BPFI	PA-28-181 Archer II	F. Teagle	
G-BPFL	Davis DA-2	B. W. Griffiths	
G-BPFM	Aeronca 7AC Champion	L. A. Borrill	
G-BPFN	Short SD3-60 Variant 100	Loganair Ltd	
G-BPFZ	Cessna 152 II	C. J. Ward	
G-BPGC	Air Command 532 Elite	G. A. Speich	
G-BPGD	Cameron V-65 balloon	Gone With The Wind Ltd	
G-BPGE	Cessna U.206C	Scottish Parachute Club/Strathallan	
G-BPGF	Thunder Ax7-77 balloon	M. Schiavo	
G-BPGH	EAA Acro Sport II	G. M. Bradley	
G-BPGK	Aeronca 7AC Champion	D. A. Crompton	
G-BPGM	Cessna 152 II	Fraggle Leasing Ltd/Edinburgh	
G-BPGT	Colt AS-80 Mk II airship	P. Porati/Italy	
G-BPGU	PA-28-181 Archer II	G. Underwood/Tollerton	
G-BPGV	Robinson R-22B	Plane Talking Ltd/Elstree	
G-BPGX	SOCATA TB.9 Tampico	D. A. Lee	
G-BPGY	Cessna 150H	Premiair Engineering Ltd	
G-BPGZ	Cessna 150G	J. B. Scott	
G-BPHB	PA-28-161 Warrior II	M. J. Wade	
G-BPHD	Cameron N-42 balloon	P. J. Marshall & M. A. Clarke	
G-BPHE	PA-28-161 Warrior II	APB Leasing Ltd/Welshpool	
G-BPHG	Robin DR.400/180	K. J. & M. B. White/Redhill	
G-BPHH	Cameron V-77 balloon	C. D. Aindow	
G-BPHI	PA-38-112 Tomahawk	J. S. Devlin & Z. Islam/Redhill	
G-BPHJ	Cameron V-77 balloon	C. W. Brown	
G-BPHL	PA-28-161 Warrior II	Teesside Flight Centre Ltd	
G-BPHO	Taylorcraft BC-12	A. A. Alderdice	
G-BPHP	Taylorcraft BC-12-65	D. C. Stephens	
G-BPHR	D.H.82A Tiger Moth (A17-48)	N. Parry	
G-BPHT	Cessna 152	Evensport Ltd	
G-BPHU	Thunder Ax7-77 balloon	R. P. Waite	
G-BPHW	Cessna 140	M. Day	
G-BPHX	Cessna 140	M. McChesney	
G-BPHZ	M.S.505 Criquet (TA+RC)	The Aircraft Restoration Co/Duxford	

Notes	Reg.	Type	Owner or Operator
	G-BPID	PA-28-161 Warrior II	K. J. Newman
	G-BPIF	Bensen-Parsons 2-place gyroplane	B. J. L. P. de Saar
	G-BPIH	Rand-Robinson KR-2	J. R. Rowley
	G-BPII	Denney Kitfox	G-BPII Group
	G-BPIJ	Brantly B.2B	R. B. Payne
	G-BPIK	PA-38-112 Tomahawk	Metropolitan Services Ltd
	G-BPIL	Cessna 310B	A. L. Brown & R. A. Parsons
	G-BPIN	Glaser-Dirks DG.400	J. N. Stevenson
	G-BPIO	Cessna F.152 II	I. D. McClelland
	G-BPIP	Slingsby T.31 Motor Cadet III	J. H. Beard
	G-BPIR	Scheibe SF.25E Super Falke	K. E. Ballington
	G-BPIT	Robinson R-22B	NA Air Ltd
	G-BPIU	PA-28-161 Warrior II	P. G. Doble & P. G. Stewart
	G-BPIV	B.149 Bolingbroke Mk IVT (R3821)	The Aircraft Restoration Co/Duxford
	G-BPIZ	AA-5B Tiger	D. A. Horsley
	G-BPJB	Schweizer 269C	Elborne Holdings Ltd/Portugal
	G-BPJD	SOCATA Rallye 110ST	G-BPJD Rallye Group
	G-BPJE	Cameron A-105 balloon	J. S. Eckersley
	G-BPJG	PA-18 Super Cub 150	M. W. Stein
	G-BPJH	PA-18 Super Cub 95	P. J. Heron
	G-BPJK	Colt 77A balloon	Saran UK Ltd
	G-BPJL	Cessna 152 II	Seawing Flying Club/Southend
	G-BPJO	PA-28-161 Cadet	Plane Talking Ltd/Elstree
	G-BPJP	PA-28-161 Cadet	Aviation Rentals/Bournemouth
	G-BPJR	PA-28-161 Cadet	Walsh Aviation
	G-BPJU	PA-28-161 Cadet	Aviation Rentals/Bournemouth
	G-BPJV	Taylorcraft F-21	TC Flying Group
	G-BPJW	Cessna A.150K	G. & S. A. Jones
	G-BPJZ	Cameron O-160 balloon	M. L. Gabb
	G-BPKF	Grob G.115	Steventon Morgan Aviation
	G-BPKK	Denney Kitfox Mk 1	D. Moffat
	G-BPKM	PA-28-161 Warrior II	M. J. Greasby
	G-BPKO	Cessna 140	M. J. Patrick
	G-BPKR	PA-28-151 Warrior	Aeroshow Ltd
	G-BPLF	Cameron V-77 balloon	I. R. Warrington & R. A. MacMillan
	G-BPLH	Jodel DR.1051	D. W. Tovey
	G-BPLM	AIA Stampe SV-4C	C. J. Jesson/Redhill
	G-BPLR	BN-2B-26 Islander	Hebridean Air Services Ltd
	G-BPLV	Cameron V-77 balloon	MC VH SA/Belgium
	G-BPLY	Christen Pitts S-2B Special	J. D. Haslam/Breighton
	G-BPLZ	Hughes 369HS	Pyramid Helicopters Ltd
	G-BPMB	Maule M5-235C Lunar Rocket	Earth Products Ltd/Crosland Moor
	G-BPME	Cessna 152 II	Seawing Flying Club/Southend
	G-BPMF	PA-28-151 Warrior	L. & A. Hill
	G-BPMH	Schempp-Hirth Nimbus 3DM	Southern Sailplanes/Membury
	G-BPML	Cessna 172M	N. A. Bilton & P. R. Bennett
	G-BPMM	Champion 7ECA Citabria	J. Murray
	G-BPMR	PA-28-161 Warrior II	B. McIntyre
	G-BPMU	Nord 3202B	A. I. Milne (G-BIZJ)
	G-BPMV	PA-28-161 Warrior II	Oxford Aviation Services Ltd/Kidlington
	G-BPMW	QAC Quickie Q.2	P. M. Wright (G-OICI/G-OGKN)
	G-BPMX	ARV Super 2	C. R. James
	G-BPNA	Cessna 150L	BBC Air Ltd/Compton Abbas
	G-BPND	Boeing 727-2D3	Cougar Airlines
	G-BPNI	Robinson R-22B	Heliflight (UK) Ltd
	G-BPNL	QAC Quickie Q.2	J. R. Jensen
	G-BPNN	Montgomerie-Bensen B.8MR	M. E. Vahdat
	G-BPNO	Zlin Z.326 Trener Master	J. A. S. Bailey & S. T. Logan
	G-BPNT	BAe 146-300	Flightline Ltd
	G-BPNU	Thunder Ax7-77 balloon	M. J. Barnes
	G-BPOA	Gloster Meteor T.7 (WF877) ★	39 Restoration Group/North Weald
	G-BPOB	Sopwith Camel F.1 (replica) (B2458)	Bianchi Aviation Film Services Ltd/Booker
	G-BPOL	Pietenpol Air Camper	G. W. Postance
	G-BPOM	PA-28-161 Warrior II	APB Leasing Ltd/Welshpool
	G-BPON	PA-34-200T Seneca II	Aeroshare Ltd/Staverton
	G-BPOO	Montgomerie-Bensen B.8MR	M. E. Vahdat
	G-BPOS	Cessna 150M	K. J. Goggins
	G-BPOT	PA-28-181 Archer II	P. Fraser
	G-BPOU	Luscombe 8A Silvaire	M. J. Negus & R. Hardley

Reg.	Type	Owner or Operator	Notes
G-BPOV	Cameron 90 Magazine SS balloon	Forbes Europe Inc/France	
G-BPPA	Cameron O-65 balloon	Rix Petroleum Ltd	
G-BPPD	PA-38-112 Tomahawk	Belting Products/Cardiff	
G-BPPE	PA-38-112 Tomahawk	D. J. Woodnutt	
G-BPPF	PA-38-112 Tomahawk	Bristol Strut Flying Group	
G-BPPJ	Cameron A-180 balloon	H. R. Evans	
G-BPPK	PA-28-151 Warrior	UK Technical Consultants Ltd	
G-BPPL	Enstrom F-28A	M. & P. Food Products Ltd	
G-BPPM	Beech B200 Super King Air	Gama Aviation Ltd/Fairoaks	
G-BPPO	Luscombe 8A Silvaire	I. K. Ratcliffe	
G-BPPP	Cameron V-77 balloon	Sarnia Balloon Group	
G-BPPS	Mudry CAARP CAP.21	N. B. Gray & L. Van Vuuren	
G-BPPU	Air Command 532 Elite	J. Hough	
G-BPPY	Hughes 269B	A. Harvey & R. C. S. Timbrell	
G-BPPZ	Taylorcraft BC-12D	Zulu Warriors Flying Group	
G-BPRA	Aeronca 11AC Chief	R. M. C. Hunter	
G-BPRC	Cameron 77 Elephant SS balloon	A. Schneider/Germany	
G-BPRD	Pitts S-1C Special	S. M. Trickey	
G-BPRI	AS.355F-1 Twin Squirrel	Quay Contracts Ltd (G-TVPA)	
G-BPRJ	AS.355F-1 Twin Squirrel	PLM Dollar Group Ltd/Inverness	
G-BPRL	AS.355F-1 Twin Squirrel	Gas & Air Ltd	
G-BPRM	Cessna F.172L	M. R. H. Wishart (G-AZKG)	
G-BPRN	PA-28-161 Warrior II	Air Navigation & Trading Co Ltd/ Blackpool	
G-BPRR	Rand-Robinson KR-2	A. M. Witt	
G-BPRX	Aeronca 11AC Chief	D. J. Dumolo & C. R. Barnes/Breighton	
G-BPRY	PA-28-161 Warrior II	White Wings Aviation	
G-BPSA	Luscombe 8A Silvaire	K. P. Gorman/Staverton	
G-BPSH	Cameron V-77 balloon	P. G. Hossack	
G-BPSI	Thunder Ax10-160 balloon	M. E. White	
G-BPSJ	Thunder Ax6-56 balloon	Capricorn Balloons Ltd	
G-BPSK	Montgomerie-Bensen B.8M	P. T. Ambrozik	
G-BPSL	Cessna 177	G-BPSL Group	
G-BPSO	Cameron N-90 balloon	J. Oberprieler/Germany	
G-BPSP	Cameron 90 Ship SS balloon	Forbes Europe Inc/France	
G-BPSR	Cameron V-77 balloon	K. J. A. Maxwell	
G-BPSS	Cameron A-120 balloon	Anglian Countryside Balloons	
G-BPTA	Stinson 108-2	M. L. Ryan	
G-BPTD	Cameron V-77 balloon	J. Lippett	
G-BPTE	PA-28-181 Archer II	J. S. Develin & Z. Islam	
G-BPTF	Cessna 152 II	Falcon Flying Services/Biggin Hill	
G-BPTG	R. Commander 112TC	M. A. Watteau	
G-BPTI	SOCATA TB.20 Trinidad	N. Davis	
G-BPTL	Cessna 172N	Cleveland Flying School Ltd/Teesside	
G-BPTO	Zenith CH.200-AA	B. Philips	
G-BPTS	C.A.S.A. 1.131E Jungmann 1000 (E3B-153)	Aerobatic Displays Ltd/Duxford	
G-BPTU	Cessna 152	A. M. Alam/Panshanger	
G-BPTV	Bensen B.8	C. Munro	
G-BPTX	Cameron O-120 balloon	Skybus Ballooning	
G-BPUA	EAA Sport Biplane	Skyview Systems Ltd	
G-BPUB	Cameron V-31 balloon	M. T. Evans	
G-BPUC	QAC Quickie Q.200	S. R. Harvey	
G-BPUE	Air Command 532 Elite	A. H. Brent	
G-BPUF	Thunder Ax6-56Z balloon	R. C. & M. A. Trimble (G-BHRL)	
G-BPUG	Air Command 532 Elite	T. A. Holmes	
G-BPUJ	Cameron N-90 balloon	D. Grimshaw	
G-BPUL	PA-18 Super Cub 150	C. D. Duthy-James	
G-BPUM	Cessna R.182RG	R. C. Chapman	
G-BPUP	Whittaker MW-7	J. H. Beard	
G-BPUR	Piper J-3L-65 Cub★	H. A. D. Monro	
G-BPUU	Cessna 140	Sherburn Aero Club Ltd	
G-BPUW	Colt 90A balloon	Huntair Ltd	
G-BPUX	Cessna 150J	BCT Aircraft Leasing Ltd	
G-BPVA	Cessna 172F	S. Lancashire Flyers Group	
G-BPVE	Bleriot IX (replica) (1197) ★	Bianchi Aviation Film Services Ltd/Booker	
G-BPVH	Cub Aircraft J-3C-65 Prospector	D. E. Cooper-Maguire	
G-BPVI	PA-32R-301 Saratoga SP	M. T. Coppen/Booker	
G-BPVK	Varga 2150A Kachina	H. W. Hall	
G-BPVM	Cameron V-77 balloon	Royal Engineers Balloon Club	
G-BPVN	PA-32R-301T Turbo Saratoga SP	Y. Leysen	
G-BPVO	Cassutt Racer IIIM	A. J. Brown	

Notes	Reg.	Type	Owner or Operator
	G-BPVP	Pitts S-2B Special	J. A. Harris
	G-BPVU	Thunder Ax7-77 balloon	B. J. Hammond
	G-BPVW	C.A.S.A. 1.131E Jungmann 2000	C. & J-W. Labeij/Netherlands
	G-BPVX	Cassutt Racer IIIM	D. D. Milne
	G-BPVY	Cessna 172D	O. Scott-Tomlin
	G-BPVZ	Luscombe 8E Silvaire	W. E. Gillham & P. Ryman
	G-BPWA	PA-28-161 Warrior II	Proudpixie Productions Ltd
	G-BPWB	Sikorsky S-61N	Bristow Helicopters Ltd/HM Coastguard
	G-BPWC	Cameron V-77 balloon	H. B. Roberts
	G-BPWD	Cessna 120	Peregrine Flying Group
	G-BPWE	PA-28-161 Warrior II	RPR Associates Ltd/Swansea
	G-BPWF	PA-28 Cherokee 140 ★	(Static display)/1244 Sqdn ATC/Swindon
	G-BPWG	Cessna 150M	W. R. Spicer & I. D. Carling
	G-BPWI	Bell 206B JetRanger 3	Warren Aviation
	G-BPWK	Sportavia Fournier RF-5B	S. L. Reed/Usk
	G-BPWL	PA-25 Pawnee 235	Tecair Aviation Ltd/Shipdham
	G-BPWM	Cessna 150L	M. E. Creasey
	G-BPWN	Cessna 150L	International Aerospace Engineering Ltd
	G-BPWP	Rutan LongEz (modified)	D. A. Field
	G-BPWR	Cessna R.172K	A. M. Skelton
	G-BPWS	Cessna 172P	Chartstone Ltd
	G-BPXA	PA-28-181 Archer II	Cherokee Flying Group/Netherthorpe
	G-BPXB	Glaser-Dirks DG.400	G. C. Westgate & Ptnrs/Parham Park
	G-BPXE	Enstrom 280C Shark	A. Healy
	G-BPXF	Cameron V-65 balloon	D. Pascall
	G-BPXH	Colt 17A balloon	Sport Promotion SRL/Italy
	G-BPXJ	PA-28RT-201T Turbo Arrow IV	K. M. Hollamby/Biggin Hill
	G-BPXX	PA-34-200T Seneca II	Laden Project Management Services
	G-BPXY	Aeronca 11AC Chief	S. Hawksworth
	G-BPYI	Cameron O-77 balloon	N. J. Logue
	G-BPYJ	Wittman W.8 Tailwind	J. Dixon
	G-BPYK	Thunder Ax7-77 balloon	A. R. Swinnerton
	G-BPYL	Hughes 369D	Morcorp (BVI) Ltd
	G-BPYN	Piper J-3C-65 Cub	The Aquila Group/White Waltham
	G-BPYO	PA-28-181 Archer II	Sherburn Aero Club Ltd
	G-BPYR	PA-31-310 Turbo Navajo	Multi Ltd (G-ECMA)
	G-BPYS	Cameron O-77 balloon	D. J. Goldsmith
	G-BPYT	Cameron V-77 balloon	M. H. Redman
	G-BPYV	Cameron V-77 balloon	R. J. Shortall
	G-BPYY	Cameron A-180 balloon	G. D. Fitzpatrick
	G-BPYZ	Thunder Ax7-77 balloon	J. E. Astall
	G-BPZA	Luscombe 8A Silvaire	T. P. W. Hyde
	G-BPZB	Cessna 120	C. & M. A. Grime
	G-BPZC	Luscombe 8A Silvaire	C. C. & J. M. Lovell
	G-BPZD	SNCAN NC.858S	S. J. Gaveston & ptnrs/Headcorn
	G-BPZE	Luscombe 8E Silvaire	WFG Luscombe Associates
	G-BPZI	Christen Eagle II	R. J. Allan & A. J. Maxwell
	G-BPZK	Cameron O-120 balloon	D. L. Smith
	G-BPZM	PA-28RT-201 Arrow IV	Airways Flight Training (Exeter) Ltd (G-ROYW/G-CRTI)
	G-BPZP	Robin DR.400/180R	Lasham Gliding Soc. Ltd
	G-BPZS	Colt 105A balloon	Magical Adventures Ltd
	G-BPZU	Scheibe SF.25C Falke	G-BPZU Group/Parham Park
	G-BPZY	Pitts S-1C Special	J. S. Mitchell
	G-BPZZ	Thunder Ax8-105 balloon	Capricorn Balloons Ltd
	G-BRAA	Pitts S-1C Special	D. Richardson
	G-BRAF	V.S.394 Spitfire FR.XVIII (SM969)	Wizard Investments Ltd
	G-BRAJ	Cameron V-77 balloon	A. W. J. & C. Weston
	G-BRAK	Cessna 172N	Masonair/Kemble
	G-BRAM	Mikoyan MiG-21PF (503) ★	Jet Heritage/Bournemouth
	G-BRAR	Aeronca 7AC Champion	C. D. Ward
	G-BRAW	Pitts S-1C Special	P. G. Bond & P. B. Hunter
	G-BRAX	Payne Knight Twister 85B	R. Earl
	G-BRBA	PA-28-161 Warrior II	S. H. Pearce
	G-BRBB	PA-28-161 Warrior II	Aeros Leasing Ltd
	G-BRBC	NA T-6G Texan	A. P. Murphy
	G-BRBD	PA-28-151 Warrior	Bravo Delta Group/Bournemouth
	G-BRBE	PA-28-161 Warrior II	Solo Services Ltd/Shoreham
	G-BRBG	PA-28 Cherokee 180	Ken MacDonald & Co
	G-BRBH	Cessna 150H	J. Maffia & H. Merkado/Panshanger
	G-BRBI	Cessna 172N	G-BRBI Flying Group
	G-BRBJ	Cessna 172M	L. C. MacKnight

Reg.	Type	Owner or Operator	Notes
G-BRBK	Robin DR.400/180	R. Kemp	
G-BRBL	Robin DR.400/180	C. A. Merren	
G-BRBM	Robin DR.400/180	R. W. Davies/Headcorn	
G-BRBN	Pitts S-1S Special	D. R. Evans	
G-BRBO	Cameron V-77 balloon	M. B. Murby	
G-BRBP	Cessna 152	Staverton Flying Services Ltd	
G-BRBS	Bensen B.8M	K. T. MacFarlane	
G-BRBT	Trotter Ax3-20 balloon	R. M. Trotter	
G-BRBW	PA-28 Cherokee 140	Cherokee Cruiser Aircraft Group/ Shoreham	
G-BRBX	PA-28-181 Archer II	M. J. Ireland	
G-BRBY	Robinson R-22B	Abraxas Aviation Ltd	
G-BRCA	Jodel D.112	R. C. Jordan	
G-BRCD	Cessna A.152	D. E. Simmons/Shoreham	
G-BRCE	Pitts S-1C Special	R. O. Rogers	
G-BRCF	Montgomerie-Bensen B.8MR	J. S. Walton	
G-BRCG	Grob G.109	I. R. Taylor	
G-BRCI	Pitts S-1C Special	G. L. A. Vandormael/Belgium	
G-BRCJ	Cameron NS-20 balloon	P. de Cock/Belgium	
G-BRCM	Cessna 172L	S. G. E. Plessis & D. C. C. Handley	
G-BRCT	Denney Kitfox Mk 2	M. L. Roberts	
G-BRCV	Aeronca 7AC Champion	J. M. Gale	
G-BRCW	Aeronca 11AC Chief	R. B. McComish	
G-BRDB	Zenair CH.701 STOL	D. L. Bowtell	
G-BRDC	Thunder Ax7-77 balloon	Zebedee Balloon Service	
G-BRDD	Avions Mudry CAP.10B	R. D. Dickson/Gamston	
G-BRDE	Thunder Ax7-77 balloon	C. C. Brash	
G-BRDF	PA-28-161 Warrior II	White Waltham Airfield Ltd	
G-BRDG	PA-28-161 Warrior II	White Waltham Airfield Ltd	
G-BRDJ	Luscombe 8A Silvaire	J. D. Parker	
G-BRDM	PA-28-161 Warrior II	White Waltham Airfield Ltd	
G-BRDN	M.S.880B Rallye Club	B. J. D. Peatfield	
G-BRDO	Cessna 177B	Cardinal Aviation	
G-BRDT	Cameron DP-70 airship	Tim Balloon Promotion Airships Ltd	
G-BRDV	Viking Wood Products Spitfire Prototype replica (K5054) ★	Southampton Hall of Aviation	
G-BRDW	PA-24 Comanche 180	I. P. Gibson/Southampton	
G-BREA	Bensen B.8MR	T. J. Deane	
G-BREB	Piper J-3C-65 Cub	L. W. & O. Usherwood	
G-BREE	Whittaker MW.7	G. Hawkins	
G-BREH	Cameron V-65 balloon	S. E. & V. D. Hurst	
G-BREL	Cameron O-77 balloon	R. A. Patey	
G-BRER	Aeronca 7AC Champion	Rabbit Flight	
G-BREU	Montgomerie-Bensen B.8MR	J. S. Firth	
G-BREX	Cameron O-84 balloon	Ovolo Ltd	
G-BREY	Taylorcraft BC-12D	BREY Group	
G-BRFB	Rutan LongEz	R. Young	
G-BRFE	Cameron V-77 balloon	Esmerelda Balloon Syndicate	
G-BRFF	Colt 90A balloon	Amber Valley Aviation	
G-BRFI	Aeronca 7DC Champion	A. C. Lines	
G-BRFJ	Aeronca 11AC Chief	J. M. Mooney	
G-BRFL	PA-38-112 Tomahawk	Teesside Flight Centre Ltd	
G-BRFM	PA-28-161 Warrior II	Atlantic Air Transport Ltd/Coventry	
G-BRFN	PA-38-112 Tomahawk	Light Aircraft Leasing (UK) Ltd	
G-BRFO	Cameron V-77 balloon	Hedge Hoppers Balloon Group	
G-BRFW	Montgomerie-Bensen B.8 2-seat	A. J. Barker	
G-BRFX	Pazmany PL.4A	D. E. Hills	
G-BRGD	Cameron O-84 balloon	J. R. H. & M. A. Ashworth	
G-BRGE	Cameron N-90 balloon	Oakfield Farm Products Ltd	
G-BRGF	Luscombe 8E Silvaire	Luscombe Flying Group	
G-BRGG	Luscombe 8A Silvaire	M. A. Lamprell	
G-BRGI	PA-28 Cherokee 180	Golf India Aviation Ltd/Redhill	
G-BRGN	BAe Jetstream 3102	BAE Systems (Corporate Air Travel) Ltd (G-BLHC)/Warton	
G-BRGO	Air Command 532 Elite	A. McCredie	
G-BRGT	PA-32 Cherokee Six 260	P. Cowley	
G-BRGW	GY-201 Minicab	R. G. White	
G-BRGX	Rotorway Executive	D. W. J. Lee	
G-BRHA	PA-32RT-300 Lance II	Lance G-BRHA Group	
G-BRHB	Boeing Stearman B.75N1	D. Calabritto	
G-BRHG	Colt 90A balloon	Bath University Students' Union	
G-BRHL	Montgomerie-Bensen B.8MR	R. M. Savage & T. M. Jones	
G-BRHO	PA-34-200 Seneca	D. A. Lewis/Luton	

Notes	Reg.	Type	Owner or Operator
	G-BRHP	Aeronca O-58B Grasshopper (31923)	C. J. Willis/Italy
	G-BRHR	PA-38-112 Tomahawk	J. Davies
	G-BRHT	PA-38-112 Tomahawk	–/Liverpool
	G-BRHW	D.H.82A Tiger Moth	P. J. & A. J. Borsberry
	G-BRHX	Luscombe 8E Silvaire	J. Lakin
	G-BRHY	Luscombe 8E Silvaire	D. Lofts & A. R. W. Taylor/Sleap
	G-BRIA	Cessna 310L	B. J. Tucker & R. C. Pugsley
	G-BRIE	Cameron N-77 balloon	S. F. Redman
	G-BRIF	Boeing 767-204ER	Britannia Airways Ltd *Horatio Nelson*
	G-BRIG	Boeing 767-204ER	Britannia Airways Ltd *Eglantyne Jebb*
	G-BRIH	Taylorcraft BC-12D	A. D. Duke
	G-BRII	Zenair CH.600 Zodiac	A. C. Bowdrey
	G-BRIJ	Taylorcraft F-19	K. E. Ballington
	G-BRIK	T.66 Nipper 3	P. R. Bentley
	G-BRIL	Piper J-5A Cub Cruiser	P. L. Jobes
	G-BRIO	Turner Super T-40A	D. McIntyre
	G-BRIR	Cameron V-56 balloon	H. G. Davies & C. Dowd
	G-BRIS	Steen Skybolt	Little Bear Ltd
	G-BRIV	SOCATA TB.9 Tampico Club	P. M. Harrison
	G-BRIY	Taylorcraft DF-65 (42-58678)	T. G. Solomon
	G-BRJA	Luscombe 8A Silvaire	A. D. Keen
	G-BRJB	Zenair CH.600 Zodiac	D. Collinson
	G-BRJC	Cessna 120	One Twenty Flyers Ltd
	G-BRJK	Luscombe 8A Silvaire	C. J. L. Peat & M. Richardson
	G-BRJL	PA-15 Vagabond	C. P. Ware & A. R. Williams
	G-BRJN	Pitts S-1C Special	W. Chapel
	G-BRJR	PA-38-112 Tomahawk	Chester Aviation Ltd
	G-BRJT	Cessna 150H	Pink Panther Flying Group
	G-BRJV	PA-28-161 Cadet	Newcastle-upon-Tyne Aero Club Ltd
	G-BRJW	Bellanca 7GCBC Citabria	F. A. L. Castleden & A. J. Sillis
	G-BRJY	Rand-Robinson KR-2	R. E. Taylor
	G-BRKC	J/1 Autocrat	J. W. Conlon
	G-BRKH	PA-28-236 Dakota	Dateworld Ltd
	G-BRKN	Robinson R-22 Mariner	Sloane Helicopters Ltd/Sywell
	G-BRKO	Oldfield Baby Great Lakes	R. Trickett
	G-BRKR	Cessna 182R	A. R. D. Brooker
	G-BRKW	Cameron V-77 balloon	T. J. Parker
	G-BRKX	Air Command 532 Elite	K. Davis
	G-BRKY	Viking Dragonfly Mk II	G. D. Price
	G-BRLB	Air Command 532 Elite	F. G. Shepherd
	G-BRLF	Campbell Cricket (replica)	D. Wood
	G-BRLG	PA-28RT-201T Turbo Arrow IV	C. G. Westwood/Welshpool
	G-BRLI	Piper J-5A Cub Cruiser	Little Bear Ltd
	G-BRLJ	Evans VP-2	R. L. Jones
	G-BRLL	Cameron A-105 balloon	A. J. Street
	G-BRLO	PA-38-112 Tomahawk	A. H. McVicar/Prestwick
	G-BRLP	PA-38-112 Tomahawk	D. A. Whitmore
	G-BRLR	Cessna 150G	D. Carr & M. R. Muter
	G-BRLS	Thunder Ax7-77 balloon	E. C. Meek
	G-BRLT	Colt 77A balloon	D. Bareford
	G-BRLV	CCF Harvard IV (93542)	Extraviation Ltd/North Weald
	G-BRMA	W.S.51 Dragonfly HR.5 (WG719) ★	IHM/Weston-s-Mare
	G-BRMB	B.192 Belvedere HC.1 (XG452)★	IHM/Weston-s-Mare
	G-BRME	PA-28-181 Archer II	Keen Leasing Ltd
	G-BRMG	V.S.384 Seafire XVII (SX336)	T. J. Manna/Cranfield
	G-BRMI	Cameron V-65 balloon	M. Davies
	G-BRML	PA-38-112 Tomahawk	P. H. Rogers/Coventry
	G-BRMS	PA-28RT-201 Arrow IV	Fleetbridge Ltd
	G-BRMT	Cameron V-31 balloon	T. C. Hinton
	G-BRMU	Cameron V-77 balloon	K. J. & G. R. Ibbotson
	G-BRMV	Cameron O-77 balloon	P. D. Griffiths
	G-BRMW	Whittaker MW.7	N. Crisp
	G-BRNC	Cessna 150M	D. C. Bonsall
	G-BRND	Cessna 152 II	T. M. & M. L. Jones/Egginton
	G-BRNE	Cessna 152 II	Redhill Air Services Ltd
	G-BRNJ	PA-38-112 Tomahawk	Cardiff-Wales Aviation Services Ltd
	G-BRNK	Cessna 152 II	Sheffield Aero Club Ltd/Netherthorpe
	G-BRNM	Chichester-Miles Leopard	Chichester-Miles Consultants Ltd
	G-BRNN	Cessna 152 II	Sheffield Aero Club Ltd/Netherthorpe
	G-BRNT	Robin DR.400/180	M. J. Cowham

Reg.	Type	Owner or Operator	Notes
G-BRNU	Robin DR.400/180	November Uniform Travel Syndicate Ltd/ Booker	
G-BRNV	PA-28-181 Archer II	B. S. Hobbs	
G-BRNW	Cameron V-77 balloon	N. Robertson & G. Smith	
G-BRNX	PA-22 Tri-Pacer 150	C. A. Robbins	
G-BRNZ	PA-32 Cherokee Six 300B	Longfellow Flying Group	
G-BROB	Cameron V-77 balloon	R. W. Richardson	
G-BROE	Cameron N-65 balloon	R. H. Sanderson	
G-BROG	Cameron V-65 balloon	R. Kunert	
G-BROH	Cameron O-90 balloon	P. A. Wenlock	
G-BROI	CFM Streak Shadow Srs SA	G. W. Rowbotham	
G-BROJ	Colt 31A balloon	Virgin Airship & Balloon Co Ltd	
G-BROL	Cameron Colt AS-105 airship	Ballonwerbung Hamburg GmbH	
G-BROP	Vans RV-4	K. E. Armstrong	
G-BROR	Piper J-3C-65 Cub	White Hart Flying Group	
G-BROX	Robinson R-22B	Richmond Helicopters	
G-BROY	Cameron V-77 balloon	T. G. S. Dixon	
G-BROZ	PA-18 Super Cub 150	P. G. Kynsey	
G-BRPE	Cessna 120	J. M. Fowler/Tollerton	
G-BRPF	Cessna 120	D. Sharp/Breighton	
G-BRPG	Cessna 120	I. C. Lomax	
G-BRPH	Cessna 120	J. A. Cook	
G-BRPJ	Cameron N-90 balloon	Cloud Nine Balloon Co	
G-BRPK	PA-28 Cherokee 140	J. P. A. Gomes	
G-BRPL	PA-28 Cherokee 140	Comed Aviation Ltd/Blackpool	
G-BRPM	T.66 Nipper 3	T. C. Horner	
G-BRPO	Enstrom 280C Shark	C. M. Evans & J. W. Blaylock	
G-BRPP	Brookland Hornet (modified)	B. J. L. P. & W. J. A. L. de Saar	
G-BRPR	Aeronca O-58B Grasshopper (31952)	C. S. Tolchard	
G-BRPS	Cessna 177B	R. C. Tebbett	
G-BRPT	Rans S.10 Sakota	B. G. Morris	
G-BRPU	Beech 76 Duchess	Leeds Flying School Ltd/Leeds-Bradford	
G-BRPV	Cessna 152	GEM Rewinds Ltd/Coventry	
G-BRPX	Taylorcraft BC-12D	The BRPX Group	
G-BRPY	PA-15 Vagabond	D. J. Palmer	
G-BRPZ	Luscombe 8A Silvaire	S. L. & J. P. Waring	
G-BRRA	V.S.361 Spitfire LF.IXe (MK912)	Historic Flying Ltd	
G-BRRD	Scheibe SF.25B Falke	The G-BRRD Syndicate	
G-BRRF	Cameron O-77 balloon	Mid-Bucks Farmers Balloon Group	
G-BRRG	Glaser-Dirks DG.500M	Glider Syndicate/Sutton Bank	
G-BRRJ	PA-28RT-201T Turbo Arrow IV	M. Stower	
G-BRRK	Cessna 182Q	Werewolf Aviation Ltd	
G-BRRL	PA-18 Super Cub 95	Acebell G-BRRL Syndicate/Redhill	
G-BRRN	PA-28-161 Warrior II	Spinseal Ltd	
G-BRRO	Cameron N-77 balloon	B. Birch	
G-BRRR	Cameron V-77 balloon	L. M. Heal & A. P. Wilcox	
G-BRRS	Pitts S-1C Special	R. C. Atkinson	
G-BRRU	Colt 90A balloon	Reach For The Sky Ltd	
G-BRRW	Cameron O-77 balloon	D. V. Fowler	
G-BRRY	Robinson R-22B	P. W. Vellacott	
G-BRSA	Cameron N-56 balloon	C. Wilkinson	
G-BRSC	Rans S.10 Sakota	P. Wilkinson	
G-BRSD	Cameron V-77 balloon	T. J. Porter & J. E. Kelly	
G-BRSE	PA-28-161 Warrior II	Aerohire Ltd	
G-BRSG	PA-28-161 Cadet	Holmes Rentals/Denham	
G-BRSH	C.A.S.A. 1.131E Jungmann 2000 (781-25)	L. Ness/Norway	
G-BRSJ	PA-38-112 Tomahawk II	APB Leasing Ltd/Welshpool	
G-BRSK	Boeing Stearman N2S-3 (1180)	Wymondham Engineering	
G-BRSL	Cameron N-56 balloon	S. Budd	
G-BRSN	Rand-Robinson KR-2	K. W. Darby	
G-BRSO	CFM Streak Shadow Srs SA	D. J. Smith	
G-BRSP	Air Command 532 Elite	G. M. Hobman	
G-BRSW	Luscombe 8A Silvaire	Bloody Mary Aviation/Fenland	
G-BRSX	PA-15 Vagabond	C. Milne-Fowler	
G-BRSY	Hatz CB-1	G. A. Barrett & Son/Breighton	
G-BRTD	Cessna 152 II	152 Group	
G-BRTH	Cameron A-180 balloon	The Ballooning Business Ltd	
G-BRTJ	Cessna 150F	Avon Aviation Ltd	
G-BRTK	Boeing Stearman E.75 (217786)	Eastern Stearman Ltd/Swanton Morley	
G-BRTL	Hughes 369E	Crewhall Ltd	
G-BRTM	PA-28-161 Warrior II	Oxford Aviation Services Ltd/Kidlington	

Notes	Reg.	Type	Owner or Operator
	G-BRTN	Beech 95-B58 Baron	Colneway Ltd/Guernsey
	G-BRTP	Cessna 152 II	Tatenhill Aviation
	G-BRTT	Schweizer 269C	Fairthorpe Ltd/Denham
	G-BRTV	Cameron O-77 balloon	C. Vening
	G-BRTW	Glaser-Dirks DG.400	I. J. Carruthers
	G-BRTX	PA-28-151 Warrior	Spectrum Flying Group
	G-BRTZ	Slingsby T.31 Motor Cadet III	R. R. Walters
	G-BRUA	Cessna 152 II	BBC Air Ltd/Compton Abbas
	G-BRUB	PA-28-161 Warrior II	Flytrek Ltd/Bournemouth
	G-BRUD	PA-28-181 Archer II	Wilkins & Wilkins Special Auctions Ltd
	G-BRUG	Luscombe 8E Silvaire	P. A. Cain & N. W. Barratt
	G-BRUH	Colt 105A balloon	D. C. Chipping/Portugal
	G-BRUI	PA-44-180 Seminole	Tatenhill Aviation
	G-BRUJ	Boeing Stearman A.75N1 (6136)	M. Walker/Liverpool
	G-BRUM	Cessna A.152	Aerohire Ltd/Wolverhampton
	G-BRUN	Cessna 120	O. C. Brun (G-BRDH)
	G-BRUO	Taylor JT.1 Monoplane	P. M. Beresford
	G-BRUU	EAA Biplane Model P.1	E. C. Murgatroyd
	G-BRUV	Cameron V-77 balloon	T. W. & R. F. Benbrook
	G-BRUX	PA-44-180 Seminole	Hambrair Ltd/Tollerton
	G-BRVB	Stolp SA.300 Starduster Too	M. N. Petchey & S. Turner
	G-BRVC	Cameron N-180 balloon	The Balloon Club Ltd
	G-BRVE	Beech D.17S	P. A. Teichman/North Weald
	G-BRVF	Colt 77A balloon	The Ballooning Business Ltd
	G-BRVG	NA SNJ-7 Texan (27)	Intrepid Aviation Co/North Weald
	G-BRVH	Smyth Model S Sidewinder	I. C. Whyte
	G-BRVI	Robinson R-22B	P. M. Whitaker
	G-BRVJ	Slingsby T.31 Motor Cadet III	B. Outhwaite
	G-BRVL	Pitts S-1C Special	M. F. Pocock
	G-BRVN	Thunder Ax7-77 balloon	D. L. Beckwith
	G-BRVO	AS.350B Ecureuil	Gama Leasing Ltd
	G-BRVR	Barnett J4B-2 Rotorcraft	Ilkeston Contractors
	G-BRVS	Barnett J4B-2 Rotorcraft	Ilkeston Contractors
	G-BRVT	Pitts S-2B Special	A. Caramella
	G-BRVU	Colt 77A balloon	J. K. Woods
	G-BRVV	Colt 56B balloon	S. J. Hollingsworth
	G-BRVY	Thunder Ax8-90 balloon	G. E. Morris
	G-BRVZ	Jodel D.117	J. G. Patton
	G-BRWA	Aeronca 7AC Champion	D. D. Smith & J. R. Edwards
	G-BRWB	NA T-6G Texan (51-14526)	A. Edie/Shoreham
	G-BRWD	Robinson R22B	Matrix Aviation Ltd
	G-BRWF	Thunder Ax7-77 balloon	D. R. & C. L. Firkins
	G-BRWO	PA-28 Cherokee 140	Spitfire Aviation Ltd/Bournemouth
	G-BRWP	CFM Streak Shadow	R. Biffin
	G-BRWR	Aeronca 11AC Chief	A. W. Crutcher
	G-BRWT	Scheibe SF.25C Falke	Booker Gliding Club Ltd
	G-BRWU	Luton LA-4A Minor	R. B. Webber & P. K. Pike
	G-BRWV	Brügger MB.2 Colibri	R. W. Chatterton
	G-BRWX	Cessna 172P	D. A. Abels
	G-BRWZ	Cameron 90 Macaw SS balloon	Forbes Europe Inc/France
	G-BRXA	Cameron O-120 balloon	Gone With The Wind Ltd & R. J. Mansfield
	G-BRXB	Thunder Ax7-77 balloon	H. Peel
	G-BRXC	PA-28-161 Warrior II	Oxford Aviation Services Ltd/Kidlington
	G-BRXD	PA-28-181 Archer II	D. D. Stone
	G-BRXE	Taylorcraft BC-12D	W. J. Durrad
	G-BRXF	Aeronca 11AC Chief	Aeronca Flying Group
	G-BRXG	Aeronca 7AC Champion	X-Ray Golf Flying Group
	G-BRXH	Cessna 120	BRXH Group
	G-BRXL	Aeronca 11AC Chief (42-78044)	G. Taylor
	G-BRXN	Montgomerie-Bensen B.8MR	G. Robertson
	G-BRXO	PA-34-200T Seneca II	Aviation Services Ltd
	G-BRXP	SNCAN Stampe SV-4C (modified)	T. Brown
	G-BRXS	Howard Special T Minus	A. Shuttleworth
	G-BRXU	AS.332L Super Puma	Bristow Helicopters Ltd
	G-BRXV	Robinson R-22B	Tukair Aircraft Charter
	G-BRXW	PA-24 Comanche 260	Oak Group
	G-BRXY	Pietenpol Air Camper	P. S. Ganczakowski
	G-BRYI	D.H.C.8-311 Dash Eight	Brymon/British Airways Citiexpress
	G-BRYJ	D.H.C.8-311 Dash Eight	Brymon/British Airways Citiexpress
	G-BRYM	D.H.C.8-311 Dash Eight	Brymon/British Airways Citiexpress
	G-BRYO	D.H.C.8-311 Dash Eight	Brymon/British Airways Citiexpress

Reg.	Type	Owner or Operator	Notes
G-BRYP	D.H.C.8-311 Dash Eight	Brymon/British Airways Citiexpress	
G-BRYS	D.H.C.8-311 Dash Eight	Brymon/British Airways Citiexpress	
G-BRYT	D.H.C.8-311 Dash Eight	Brymon/British Airways Citiexpress	
G-BRYU	D.H.C.8-311 Dash Eight	Brymon/British Airways Citiexpress	
G-BRYV	D.H.C.8-311 Dash Eight	Brymon/British Airways Citiexpress	
G-BRYW	D.H.C.8-311 Dash Eight	Brymon/British Airways Citiexpress	
G-BRYX	D.H.C.8-311 Dash Eight	Brymon/British Airways Citiexpress	
G-BRYY	D.H.C.8-311 Dash Eight	Brymon/British Airways Citiexpress	
G-BRYZ	D.H.C.8-311 Dash Eight	Brymon/British Airways Citiexpress	
G-BRZA	Cameron O-77 balloon	L. & R. J. Mold	
G-BRZB	Cameron A-105 balloon	Headland Services Ltd	
G-BRZD	Hapi Cygnet SF-2A	C. I. Coghill	
G-BRZE	Thunder Ax7-77 balloon	G. V. Beckwith & F. Schoeder/Germany	
G-BRZG	Enstrom F-28A	Metropolitan Services Ltd	
G-BRZI	Cameron N-180 balloon	Eastern Balloon Rides	
G-BRZK	Stinson 108-2	Voyager G-BRZK Syndicate	
G-BRZO	Jodel D.18	J. D. Anson	
G-BRZS	Cessna 172P	YP Flying Group/Blackpool	
G-BRZT	Cameron V-77 balloon	B. Drawbridge	
G-BRZV	Colt Flying Apple SS balloon	Obst Vom Bodensee Marketing Gbr/ Germany	
G-BRZW	Rans S.10 Sakota	D. L. Davies	
G-BRZX	Pitts S-1S Special	J. L. Dixon	
G-BRZZ	CFM Streak Shadow	Shetland Flying Group	
G-BSAI	Stoddard-Hamilton Glasair III	K. J. & P. J. Whitehead	
G-BSAJ	C.A.S.A. 1.131E Jungmann 2000	P. G. Kynsey/Redhill	
G-BSAK	Colt 21A balloon	Northern Flights	
G-BSAS	Cameron V-65 balloon	J. R. Barber	
G-BSAV	Thunder Ax7-77 balloon	E. A. Evans & ptnrs	
G-BSAW	PA-28-161 Warrior II	Carill Aviation Ltd/Southampton	
G-BSAZ	Denney Kitfox Mk 2	A. J. Lloyd & ptnrs	
G-BSBA	PA-28-161 Warrior II	London Transport Flying Club Ltd	
G-BSBG	CCF Harvard IV (20310)	A. P. St John/Liverpool	
G-BSBH	Short SD3-30 ★	Ulster Aviation Soc Museum (stored)	
G-BSBI	Cameron O-77 balloon	D. M. Billing	
G-BSBN	Thunder Ax7-77 balloon	B. Pawson	
G-BSBP	Jodel D.18	R. T. Pratt	
G-BSBR	Cameron V-77 balloon	R. P. Wade	
G-BSBT	Piper J-3C-65 Cub	R. W. H. Watson	
G-BSBV	Rans S.10 Sakota	R. V. Cameron	
G-BSBW	Bell 206B JetRanger 3	D. T. Sharpe	
G-BSBX	Montgomerie-Bensen B.8MR	R. J. Roan	
G-BSBZ	Cessna 150M	DTG Aviation	
G-BSCA	Cameron N-90 balloon	P. J. Marshall & M. A. Clarke	
G-BSCB	Air Command 532 Elite	P. H. Smith	
G-BSCC	Colt 105A balloon	Capricorn Balloons Ltd	
G-BSCE	Robinson R-22B	H. Sugden	
G-BSCF	Thunder Ax7-77 balloon	V. P. Gardiner	
G-BSCG	Denney Kitfox Mk 2	N. L. Beever/Breighton	
G-BSCH	Denney Kitfox Mk 2	M. P. M. Read	
G-BSCI	Colt 77A balloon	J. L. & S. Wrigglesworth	
G-BSCK	Cameron H-24 balloon	J. D. Shapland	
G-BSCL	Robinson R-22B	Flightworks Sales & Leasing Ltd	
G-BSCM	Denney Kitfox Mk 2	S. A. Hewitt	
G-BSCN	SOCATA TB.20 Trinidad	B. W. Dye	
G-BSCO	Thunder Ax7-77 balloon	F. J. Whalley	
G-BSCP	Cessna 152 II	Moray Flying Club (1990) Ltd/Kinloss	
G-BSCS	PA-28-181 Archer II	Wingtask 1995 Ltd	
G-BSCV	PA-28-161 Warrior II	Southwood Flying Group/Southend	
G-BSCW	Taylorcraft BC-65	S. Leach	
G-BSCX	Thunder Ax8-105 balloon	Balloon Flights Club Ltd	
G-BSCY	PA-28-151 Warrior	Falcon Flying Services/Biggin Hill	
G-BSCZ	Cessna 152 II	Seawing Flying Club/Southend	
G-BSDA	Taylorcraft BC-12D	D. G. Edwards	
G-BSDB	Pitts S-1C Special	J. T. Mielech/Germany	
G-BSDD	Denney Kitfox Mk 2	J. Windmill	
G-BSDG	Robin DR.400/180	P. A. Stephens	
G-BSDH	Robin DR.400/180	R. L. Brucciani	
G-BSDI	Corben Junior Ace Model E	T. K. Pullen & A. J. Staplehurst	
G-BSDJ	Piper J-4E Cub Coupé	B. M. Jackson	
G-BSDK	Piper J-5A Cub Cruiser	S. Haughton & I. S. Hodge	
G-BSDL	SOCATA TB.10 Tobago	Delta Lima Group/Sherburn	

Notes	Reg.	Type	Owner or Operator
	G-BSDN	PA-34-200T Seneca II	McCormick Consulting Ltd
	G-BSDO	Cessna 152 II	J. Vickers//Humberside
	G-BSDP	Cessna 152 II	I. S. H. Paul
	G-BSDS	Boeing Stearman E.75 (118)	A. Basso/Switzerland
	G-BSDV	Colt 31A balloon	C. D. Monk
	G-BSDW	Cessna 182P	Glanwith Ltd
	G-BSDZ	Enstrom 280FX	Avalon Group Ltd (G-ODSC)
	G-BSED	PA-22 Tri-Pacer 160 (modified)	B. W. Haston
	G-BSEE	Rans S.9	P. M. Semler
	G-BSEF	PA-28 Cherokee 180	I. D. Wakeling
	G-BSEG	Ken Brock KB-2 gyroplane	S. J. M. Ledingham
	G-BSEJ	Cessna 150M	I. Shackleton/Wolverhampton
	G-BSEK	Robinson R-22	Helicentre Ltd
	G-BSEL	Slingsby T.61G Super Falke	RAFGSA/Hullavington
	G-BSEP	Cessna 172	R. J. Tyson & Ptnrs/Redhill
	G-BSER	PA-28 Cherokee 160	Yorkair Ltd
	G-BSET	B.206 Srs 1 Basset (XS765)	Lawgra (No.386) Ltd/Cranfield
	G-BSEU	PA-28-181 Archer II	Euro Aviation 91 Ltd
	G-BSEV	Cameron O-77 balloon	The Ballooning Business Ltd
	G-BSEX	Cameron A-180 balloon	Heart of England Balloons
	G-BSEY	Beech A36 Bonanza	K. Phillips Ltd
	G-BSFA	Aero Designs Pulsar	S. A. Gill
	G-BSFB	C.A.S.A. 1.131E Jungmann 2000 (S5-B06)	C. D. Beal
	G-BSFD	Piper J-3C-65 Cub	AJD Engineering Ltd
	G-BSFE	PA-38-112 Tomahawk II	Mopps (UK) Ltd/Perth
	G-BSFF	Robin DR.400/180R	Lasham Gliding Soc Ltd
	G-BSFK	PA-28-161 Warrior II	Oxford Aviation Services Ltd/Kidlington
	G-BSFP	Cessna 152T	J. R. Nicholls/Sibson
	G-BSFR	Cessna 152 II	Galair Ltd/Biggin Hill
	G-BSFV	Woods Woody Pusher	M. J. Wells
	G-BSFW	PA-15 Vagabond	J. R. Kimberley
	G-BSFX	Denney Kitfox Mk 2	T. A. Crone
	G-BSFY	Denney Kitfox Mk 2	C. I. Bates
	G-BSGB	Gaertner Ax4 Skyranger balloon	B. Gaertner
	G-BSGD	PA-28 Cherokee 180	R. J. Cleverley
	G-BSGF	Robinson R-22B	Direct Helicopters
	G-BSGG	Denney Kitfox Mk 2	C. G. Richardson
	G-BSGH	Airtour AH-56B balloon	A. R. Hardwick
	G-BSGJ	Monnett Sonerai II	G. A. Brady
	G-BSGK	PA-34-200T Seneca II	GK Aviation
	G-BSGL	PA-28-161 Warrior II	Keywest Air Charter Ltd/Liverpool
	G-BSGP	Cameron N-65 balloon	G. J. Bell
	G-BSGS	Rans S.10 Sakota	M. R. Parr
	G-BSGT	Cessna T.210N	B. J. Sharpe/Booker
	G-BSGY	Thunder Ax7-77 balloon	P. B. Kenington
	G-BSHA	PA-34-200T Seneca II	Justgold Ltd/Blackpool
	G-BSHC	Colt 69A balloon	Magical Adventures Ltd
	G-BSHD	Colt 69A balloon	D. B. Court
	G-BSHE	Cessna 152 II	J. A. Pothecary/Shoreham
	G-BSHH	Luscombe 8E Silvaire	G. M. Whiteman
	G-BSHI	Luscombe 8F Silvaire	Calcott Garage Ltd
	G-BSHK	Denney Kitfox Mk 2	D. Doyle & C. Aherne
	G-BSHO	Cameron V-77 balloon	D. J. Duckworth & J. C. Stewart
	G-BSHR	Cessna F.172N	Deep Cleavage Ltd (G-BFGE)
	G-BSHT	Cameron V-77 balloon	ECM Construction Ltd
	G-BSHV	PA-18 Super Cub 135	G. T. Fisher
	G-BSHW	Hawker Tempest II (MW800)	P. Y. C. Denis/France
	G-BSHX	Enstrom F-28A	Stephenson Aviation Ltd/Goodwood
	G-BSHY	EAA Acro Sport I	R. J. Hodder
	G-BSHZ	Enstrom F-28F	G. Birchmore
	G-BSIF	Denney Kitfox Mk 2	P. Annable
	G-BSIG	Colt 21A balloon	E. C. & A. J. Moore
	G-BSIH	Rutan LongEz	W. S. Allen
	G-BSII	PA-34-200T Seneca II	N. H. N. Gardner
	G-BSIJ	Cameron V-77 balloon	A. S. Jones
	G-BSIK	Denney Kitfox Mk 1	S. P. Collins
	G-BSIM	PA-28-181 Archer II	Bobbington Air Training School Ltd
	G-BSIN	Robinson R-22B	Griffin Helicopters Ltd
	G-BSIO	Cameron 80 Shed SS balloon	R. E. Jones
	G-BSIU	Colt 90A balloon	S. Travaglia/Italy
	G-BSIY	Schleicher ASK.14	Winwick Flying Group
	G-BSIZ	PA-28-181 Archer II	A. M. L. Maxwell

Reg.	Type	Owner or Operator	Notes
G-BSJB	Bensen B.8	J. W. Limbrick	
G-BSJU	Cessna 150M	A. C. Williamson	
G-BSJW	Everett Srs 2 gyroplane	R. Sarwan	
G-BSJX	PA-28-161 Warrior II	D. A. Shields & L. C. Brekkeflat	
G-BSJZ	Cessna 150J	BCT Aircraft Leasing Ltd	
G-BSKA	Cessna 150M	H. Daines Electronics Ltd	
G-BSKD	Cameron V-77 balloon	M. J. Gunston	
G-BSKE	Cameron O-84 balloon	The Blunt Arrows Balloon Team	
G-BSKG	Maule MX-7-180	J. R. Surbey	
G-BSKI	Thunder Ax8-90 balloon	G-BSKI Balloon Group	
G-BSKK	PA-38-112 Tomahawk	Falcon Flying Services/Biggin Hill	
G-BSKL	PA-38-112 Tomahawk	Falcon Flying Services/Biggin Hill	
G-BSKO	Maule MXT-7-180	M. A. Ashmole	
G-BSKP	V.S.379 Spitfire F.XIV (SG-3)	Historic Flying Ltd	
G-BSKU	Cameron O-84 balloon	Alfred Bagnall & Sons (West) Ltd	
G-BSKW	PA-28-181 Archer II	Shropshire Aero Club Ltd/Sleap	
G-BSLA	Robin DR.400/180	A. B. McCoig/Biggin Hill	
G-BSLE	PA-28-161 Warrior II	Oxford Aviation Services Ltd/Kidlington	
G-BSLH	C.A.S.A. 1.131E Jungmann 2000	P. Warden/France	
G-BSLI	Cameron V-77 balloon	J. D. C. & F. E. Bevan	
G-BSLK	PA-28-161 Warrior II	R. A. Rose	
G-BSLM	PA-28 Cherokee 160	Old Sarum Cherokee Group	
G-BSLT	PA-28-161 Warrior II	APB Leasing Ltd/Welshpool	
G-BSLU	PA-28 Cherokee 140	D. J. Budden Ltd/Shobdon	
G-BSLV	Enstrom 280FX	Beaufort Securities Ltd	
G-BSLW	Bellanca 7ECA Citabria	Shoreham Citabria Group	
G-BSLX	WAR Focke-Wulf Fw.190 (replica) (4+)	Fw.190 Gruppe	
G-BSMB	Cessna U.206E	London Parachute School Ltd	
G-BSMD	Nord 1101 Noralpha (+114)	R. J. Lamplough/North Weald	
G-BSME	Bo 208C1 Junior	D. J. Hampson	
G-BSMG	Montgomerie-Bensen B.8M	A. C. Timperley	
G-BSMK	Cameron O-84 balloon	G-BSMK Shareholders	
G-BSML	Schweizer 269C	K. P. Foster & B. I. Winsor	
G-BSMM	Colt 31A balloon	D. V. Fowler	
G-BSMN	CFM Streak Shadow	P. J. Porter	
G-BSMO	Denney Kitfox	Kitfox Group	
G-BSMS	Cameron V-77 balloon	Sade Balloons Ltd	
G-BSMT	Rans S.10 Sakota	P. J. Barker	
G-BSMU	Rans S.6 Coyote II	G. C. Hutchinson (G-MWJE)	
G-BSMV	PA-17 Vagabond (modified)	A. Cheriton	
G-BSMX	Bensen B.8MR	J. S. E. R. McGregor	
G-BSND	Air Command 532 Elite	K. Brogden & W. B. Lumb	
G-BSNE	Luscombe 8E Silvaire	N. Reynolds & C. Watts	
G-BSNF	Piper J-3C-65 Cub	D. A. Hammant	
G-BSNG	Cessna 172N	A. J. & P. C. MacDonald/Edinburgh	
G-BSNJ	Cameron N-90 balloon	D. P. H. Smith/France	
G-BSNL	Bensen B.8MR	A. C. Breane	
G-BSNN	Rans S.10 Sakota	O. & S. D. Barnard	
G-BSNP	PA-28-201T Turbo Arrow III	D. F. K. Singleton/Germany	
G-BSNR	BAe 146-300A	K.L.M.uk/Buzz/Stansted	
G-BSNT	Luscombe 8A Silvaire	A. L. Nightingale	
G-BSNU	Colt 105A balloon	Sun Life Assurance Soc PLC	
G-BSNV	Boeing 737-4Q8	British Airways/Gatwick	
G-BSNW	Boeing 737-4Q8	British Airways/Gatwick	
G-BSNX	PA-28-181 Archer II	Halfpenny Green Flight Centre Ltd	
G-BSNY	Bensen B.8M	H. McCartney	
G-BSNZ	Cameron O-105 balloon	W. O. Hawkins	
G-BSOE	Luscombe 8A Silvaire	S. B. Marsden	
G-BSOF	Colt 25A balloon	H. C. J. Williams	
G-BSOG	Cessna 172M	B. Chapman & A. R. Budden/Goodwood	
G-BSOI	AS.332L Super Puma	CHC Scotia Ltd/Aberdeen	
G-BSOJ	Thunder Ax7-77 balloon	R. J. S. Jones	
G-BSOK	PA-28-161 Warrior II	Aeroshow Ltd/Gloucestershire	
G-BSOM	Glaser-Dirks DG.400	G-BSOM Group/Tibenham	
G-BSON	Green S.25 balloon	J. J. Green	
G-BSOO	Cessna 172F	Double Oscar Flying Group	
G-BSOR	CFM Streak Shadow Srs SA	J. P. Sorenson	
G-BSOT	PA-38-112 Tomahawk II	APB Leasing Ltd/Welshpool	
G-BSOU	PA-38-112 Tomahawk II	Mopps (UK) Ltd/Perth	
G-BSOX	Luscombe 8AE Silvaire	P. S Lanary	
G-BSOY	PA-34-220T Seneca III	BAe Flying College	
G-BSOZ	PA-28-161 Warrior II	The Moray Flying Club 1990)/Kinloss	

Notes	Reg.	Type	Owner or Operator
	G-BSPA	QAC Quickie Q.2	G. V. McKirdy & B. K. Glover
	G-BSPB	Thunder Ax8-84 balloon	Nigs Pertwee Ltd
	G-BSPE	Cessna F.172P	A. M. J. Clark
	G-BSPG	PA-34-200T Seneca II	D. P. Hughes
	G-BSPI	PA-28-161 Warrior II	Halegreen Associates
	G-BSPJ	Bensen B.8	C. M. Jones
	G-BSPK	Cessna 195A	A. G. & D. L. Bompas
	G-BSPL	CFM Streak Shadow Srs SA	MEL (Aviation Oxygen) Ltd
	G-BSPM	PA-28-161 Warrior II	White Waltham Airfield Ltd
	G-BSPN	PA-28R-201T Turbo Arrow III	V. E. H. Taylor
	G-BSPX	Lancair 320	C. H. Skelt
	G-BSRH	Pitts S-1C Special	M. R. Janney
	G-BSRI	Lancair 235	G. Lewis/Liverpool
	G-BSRK	ARV Super 2	D. M. Blair
	G-BSRL	Campbell Cricket Mk.4 gyroplane	I. Rosewall
	G-BSRP	Rotorway Executive	R. J. Baker
	G-BSRR	Cessna 182Q	Select Management Services Ltd/ Germany
	G-BSRT	Denney Kitfox Mk 2	A. J. Lloyd
	G-BSRX	CFM Streak Shadow	P. Williams
	G-BSRZ	Air Command 532 Elite 2-seat	A. S. G. Crabb
	G-BSSA	Luscombe 8E Silvaire	Luscombe Aircraft Ltd/White Waltham
	G-BSSB	Cessna 150L	D. T. A. Rees
	G-BSSC	PA-28-161 Warrior II	Oxford Aviation Services Ltd/Kidlington
	G-BSSE	PA-28 Cherokee 140	Comed Aviation Ltd/Blackpool
	G-BSSF	Denney Kitfox Mk 2	S. G. Moores
	G-BSSI	Rans S.6 Coyote II	J. Currell (G-MWJA)
	G-BSSK	QAC Quickie Q.2	D. G. Greatrex
	G-BSSO	Cameron O-90 balloon	R. R. & J. E. Hatton
	G-BSSP	Robin DR.400/180R	Soaring (Oxford) Ltd
	G-BSST	Concorde 002 ★	F.A.A. Museum/Yeovilton
	G-BSSV	CFM Streak Shadow	R. W. Payne
	G-BSSW	PA-28-161 Warrior II	R. L. Hayward
	G-BSSX	PA-28-161 Warrior II	Airways Aero Associations Ltd/Booker
	G-BSTC	Aeronca 11AC Chief	B. Bridgman & N. J. Mortimore
	G-BSTE	AS.355F-2 Twin Squirrel	Hygrade Foods Ltd
	G-BSTH	PA-25 Pawnee 235	Scottish Gliding Union Ltd/Portmoak
	G-BSTI	Piper J-3C-65 Cub	I. Fraser & G. L. Nunn
	G-BSTK	Thunder Ax8-90 balloon	M. Williams
	G-BSTL	Rand-Robinson KR-2	C. S. Hales
	G-BSTM	Cessna 172L	G-BSTM Group/Cambridge
	G-BSTO	Cessna 152 II	Plymouth School of Flying Ltd
	G-BSTP	Cessna 152 II	FR Aviation Ltd/Bournemouth
	G-BSTR	AA-5 Traveler	James Allan (Aviation & Engineering) Ltd/ Dundee
	G-BSTT	Rans S.6 Coyote II	D. G. Palmer
	G-BSTV	PA-32 Cherokee Six 300	B. C. Hudson
	G-BSTX	Luscombe 8A Silvaire	G. R. Nicholson
	G-BSTY	Thunder Ax8-90 balloon	Shere Balloon Group
	G-BSTZ	PA-28 Cherokee 140	Air Navigation & Trading Co Ltd/ Blackpool
	G-BSUA	Rans S.6 Coyote II	A. J. Todd
	G-BSUB	Colt 77A balloon	R. R. J. Wilson & M. P. Hill
	G-BSUD	Luscombe 8A Silvaire	I. G. Harrison/Egginton
	G-BSUE	Cessna U.206G II	R. D. Masters
	G-BSUF	PA-32RT-300 Lance II	S. T. Laffin
	G-BSUJ	Brügger MB.2 Colibri	M. A. Farrelly
	G-BSUK	Colt 77A balloon	A. J. Moore
	G-BSUO	Scheibe SF.25C Falke	British Gliding Association Ltd
	G-BSUR	Rotorway Executive 90	Psion Manufacturing Ltd
	G-BSUT	Rans S.6-ESA Coyote II	J. Bell
	G-BSUU	Colt 180A balloon	British School of Ballooning
	G-BSUV	Cameron O-77 balloon	R. Moss
	G-BSUW	PA-34-200T Seneca II	TG Aviation Ltd/Manston
	G-BSUX	Carlson Sparrow II	J. Stephenson
	G-BSUZ	Denney Kitfox Mk 3	M. J. Clark
	G-BSVB	PA-28-181 Archer II	Datewold Ltd
	G-BSVE	Binder CP.301S Smaragd	Smaragd Flying Group
	G-BSVF	PA-28-161 Warrior II	Airways Aero Associations Ltd/Booker
	G-BSVG	PA-28-161 Warrior II	Airways Aero Associations Ltd/Booker
	G-BSVH	Piper J-3C-65 Cub	A. R. Meakin
	G-BSVI	PA-16 Clipper	I. R. Blakemore
	G-BSVJ	Piper J-3C-65 Cub	V. S. E. Norman/Rendcomb

Reg.	Type	Owner or Operator	Notes
G-BSVK	Denney Kitfox Mk 2	C. M. Looney	
G-BSVM	PA-28-161 Warrior II	EFG Flying Services/Biggin Hill	
G-BSVN	Thorp T-18	J. H. Kirkham	
G-BSVP	PA-23 Aztec 250	Time Electronics Ltd/Biggin Hill	
G-BSVR	Schweizer 269C	Martinair Ltd	
G-BSVS	Robin DR.400/100	D. McK. Chalmers	
G-BSVV	PA-38-112 Tomahawk	E. & H. Merkado/Panshanger	
G-BSVW	PA-38-112 Tomahawk	Goodair Leasing Ltd/Cardiff-Wales	
G-BSVX	PA-38-112 Tomahawk	Cristal Air Ltd	
G-BSVZ	Pietenpol Air Camper	G. F. M. Garner	
G-BSWB	Rans S.10 Sakota	F. A. Hewitt	
G-BSWC	Boeing Stearman E.75 (112)	R. J. Thwaites	
G-BSWF	PA-16 Clipper	T. M. Storey	
G-BSWG	PA-17 Vagabond	P. E. J. Sturgeon	
G-BSWH	Cessna 152 II	Airspeed Aviation Ltd	
G-BSWI	Rans S.10 Sakota	J. M. Mooney	
G-BSWL	Slingsby T.61F Venture T.2	K. Richards	
G-BSWM	Slingsby T.61F Venture T.2	Venture Gliding Group/Bellarena	
G-BSWR	BN-2T-26 Turbine Islander	Police Authority for Northern Ireland	
G-BSWV	Cameron N-77 balloon	S. Charlish	
G-BSWX	Cameron V-90 balloon	B. J. Burrows	
G-BSWY	Cameron N-77 balloon	Nottingham Hot Air Balloon Club	
G-BSWZ	Cameron A-180 balloon	G. C. Ludlow	
G-BSXA	PA-28-161 Warrior II	Falcon Flying Services/Biggin Hill	
G-BSXB	PA-28-161 Warrior II	Aeroshow Ltd	
G-BSXC	PA-28-161 Warrior II	L. T. Halpin/Booker	
G-BSXD	Soko P-2 Kraguj (30146)	L. C. MacKnight	
G-BSXI	Mooney M.20E	A. N. Pain	
G-BSXM	Cameron V-77 balloon	C. A. Oxby	
G-BSXN	Robinson R-22B	J. G. Gray	
G-BSXS	PA-28-181 Archer II	Jaxx Landing Ltd	
G-BSXT	Piper J-5A Cub Cruiser	M. G. & K. J. Thompson	
G-BSXX	Whittaker MW.7	H. J. Stanley	
G-BSYA	Jodel D.18	S. Harrison	
G-BSYB	Cameron N-120 balloon	M. Buono/Italy	
G-BSYC	PA-32R-300 Lance	M. N. Pinches	
G-BSYD	Cameron A-180 balloon	A. A. Brown	
G-BSYF	Luscombe 8A Silvaire	Atlantic Aviation	
G-BSYG	PA-12 Super Cruiser	Fat Cub Group	
G-BSYH	Luscombe 8A Silvaire	N. R. Osborne	
G-BSYI	AS.355F-1 Twin Squirrel	Signature Aircraft Charter	
G-BSYJ	Cameron N-77 balloon	Chubb Fire Ltd	
G-BSYO	Piper J-3C-90 Cub	C. R. Reynolds & J. D. Fuller (G-BSMJ/G-BRHE)	
G-BSYU	Robin DR.400/180	K. J. J. Jarman & P. D. Smoothy	
G-BSYV	Cessna 150M	Fenland Flying School	
G-BSYZ	PA-28-161 Warrior II	Yankee Zulu Group	
G-BSZB	Stolp SA.300 Starduster Too	D. T. Gethin/Swansea	
G-BSZC	Beech C-45H (51-11701A)	A. A. Hodgson	
G-BSZD	Robin DR.400/180	R. J. Hitchman & M. Rowland	
G-BSZF	Jodel DR.250/160	J. B. Randle	
G-BSZG	Stolp SA.100 Starduster	D. F. Chapman	
G-BSZH	Thunder Ax7-77 balloon	K. E. Viney & L. J. Weston	
G-BSZI	Cessna 152 II	Eglinton Flying Club Ltd	
G-BSZJ	PA-28-181 Archer II	M. L. A. Pudney & R. D. Fuller	
G-BSZM	Montgomerie-Bensen B.8MR	A. McCredie	
G-BSZN	Bücker Bü133D-1 Jungmeister	Norman Aeroplane Trust/Rendcomb	
G-BSZO	Cessna 152	Direct Helicopters/Southend	
G-BSZS	Robinson R-22B	Blade Runner Helicopters	
G-BSZT	PA-28-161 Warrior II	Jade Air PLC	
G-BSZU	Cessna 150F	M. J. Tarrant	
G-BSZV	Cessna 150F	Kirmington Aviation Ltd	
G-BSZW	Cessna 152	Haimoss Ltd	
G-BTAB	BAe 125 Srs 800B	Dean Finance Co Ltd (G-BOOA)	
G-BTAG	Cameron O-77 balloon	R. A. Shapland	
G-BTAH	Bensen B.8M	C. J. Toner	
G-BTAK	EAA Acro Sport II	P. G. Harrison	
G-BTAL	Cessna F.152 II	Thanet Flying Club/Manston	
G-BTAN	Thunder Ax7-65Z balloon	A. S. Newham	
G-BTAP	PA-38-112 Tomahawk	Western Air (Thruxton) Ltd	
G-BTAR	PA-38-112 Tomahawk	Aerohire Ltd/Wolverhampton	
G-BTAS	PA-38-112 Tomahawk	Goodair Leasing Ltd/Cardiff-Wales	

Notes	Reg.	Type	Owner or Operator
	G-BTAT	Denney Kitfox Mk 2	M. K. Ashmore
	G-BTAW	PA-28-161 Warrior II	A. J. Wiggins
	G-BTAZ	Evans VP-2	G. S. Poulter
	G-BTBA	Robinson R-22B	Heliflight (UK) Ltd/Wolverhampton
	G-BTBB	Thunder Ax8-90 balloon	W. J. Brogan
	G-BTBC	PA-28-161 Warrior II	M. J. L. MacDonald
	G-BTBF	Super Koala	E. A. Taylor (G-MWOZ)
	G-BTBG	Denney Kitfox	L. A. James
	G-BTBH	Ryan ST3KR (854)	Ryan Group
	G-BTBI	WAR P-47 Thunderbolt (replica) (85)	E. C. Murgatroyd
	G-BTBJ	Cessna 195B	P. Camus
	G-BTBL	Montgomerie-Bensen B.8MR	AES Radionic Surveillance Systems
	G-BTBN	Denney Kitfox Mk 2	R. C. Bowley
	G-BTBP	Cameron N-90 balloon	Chianti Balloon Club/Italy
	G-BTBR	Cameron DP-80 airship	Cameron Balloons Ltd
	G-BTBU	PA-18 Super Cub 150	G-BTBU Syndicate
	G-BTBV	Cessna 140	A. Brinkley
	G-BTBW	Cessna 120	M. J. Willies
	G-BTBX	Piper J-3C-65 Cub	Henlow Taildraggers
	G-BTBY	PA-17 Vagabond	G. J. Smith
	G-BTCA	PA-32R-300 Lance	P. Taylor
	G-BTCB	Air Command 582 Sport	G. Scurrah
	G-BTCC	Grumman F6F-5 Hellcat (40467)	Patina Ltd/Duxford
	G-BTCD	P-51D-25-NA Mustang (463221)	Pelham Ltd/Duxford
	G-BTCE	Cessna 152	S. T. Gilbert
	G-BTCH	Luscombe 8E Silvaire	J. Grewcock & R. C. Carroll
	G-BTCI	PA-17 Vagabond	T. R. Whittome
	G-BTCJ	Luscombe 8AE Silvaire	J. M. Lovell
	G-BTCM	Cameron N-90 balloon	Zeberdee Balloon Service Ltd (G-BMPW)
	G-BTCR	Rans S.10 Sakota	B. J. Hewitt
	G-BTCS	Colt 90A balloon	R. C. Stone
	G-BTCW	Cameron A-180 balloon	Bristol Balloons
	G-BTCZ	Cameron 84 Chateau SS balloon	Forbes Europe Inc/France
	G-BTDA	Slingsby T.61G Falke	RAFGSA/Bicester
	G-BTDC	Denney Kitfox Mk 2	O. Smith
	G-BTDD	CFM Streak Shadow	N. D. Ewer
	G-BTDE	Cessna C-165 Airmaster	G. S. Moss
	G-BTDF	Luscombe 8A Silvaire	Delta Foxtrot Group
	G-BTDN	Denney Kitfox Mk 2	Foxy Flyers Group
	G-BTDP	TBM-3R Avenger (53319)	A. Haig-Thomas/North Weald
	G-BTDR	Aero Designs Pulsar	M. Jordan
	G-BTDS	Colt 77A balloon	C. P. Witter Ltd
	G-BTDT	C.A.S.A. 1.131E Jungmann 2000	T. A. Reed
	G-BTDV	PA-28-161 Warrior II	Southern Flight Centre Ltd/Shoreham
	G-BTDW	Cessna 152 II	J. A. Blenkharn/Carlisle
	G-BTDX	PA-18 Super Cub 150	Hammond Aviation
	G-BTDZ	C.A.S.A. 1.131E Jungmann 2000	R. J. Pickin & I. M. White
	G-BTEA	Cameron N-105 balloon	M. W. A. Shemilt
	G-BTEE	Cameron O-120 balloon	W. H. & J. P. Morgan
	G-BTEK	SOCATA TB.20 Trinidad	M. Northwood
	G-BTEL	CFM Streak Shadow	J. E. Eatwell
	G-BTES	Cessna 150H	R. A. Forward
	G-BTET	Piper J-3C-65 Cub	R. M. Jones/Blackpool
	G-BTEU	SA.365N-2 Dauphin	CHC Scotia Ltd
	G-BTEW	Cessna 120	K. F. Mason
	G-BTEX	PA-28 Cherokee 140	McAully Flying Group Ltd/Little Snoring
	G-BTFA	Denney Kitfox Mk 2	K. R. Peek
	G-BTFC	Cessna F.152 II	Tayside Aviation Ltd/Dundee
	G-BTFE	Bensen-Parsons 2-seat gyroplane	J. R. Goldspink
	G-BTFF	Cessna T.310R II	United Sales Equipment Dealers Ltd
	G-BTFG	Boeing Stearman A.75N1 (441)	D. S. Milne/North Weald
	G-BTFJ	PA-15 Vagabond	Vagabond FJ Flying Group
	G-BTFK	Taylorcraft BC-12D	M. Gibson
	G-BTFL	Aeronca 11AC Chief	BTFL Group
	G-BTFM	Cameron O-105 balloon	Edinburgh University Hot Air Balloon Club
	G-BTFO	PA-28-161 Warrior II	Flyfar Ltd
	G-BTFP	PA-38-112 Tomahawk	Teesside Flight Centre Ltd
	G-BTFS	Cessna A.150M	P. A. James
	G-BTFT	Beech 58 Baron	Fastwing Air Charter Ltd
	G-BTFU	Ciameron N-90 balloon	J. J. Rudoni & A. C. K. Rawson
	G-BTFV	Whittaker MW.7	S. J. Luck

Reg.	Type	Owner or Operator	Notes
G-BTFW	Montgomerie-Bensen B.8MR	J. R. J. Read	
G-BTFX	Bell 206B JetRanger 2	J. Selwyn Smith (Shepley) Ltd	
G-BTFY	Bell 206B JetRanger 2	Biggin Hill Helicopters	
G-BTGA	Boeing Stearman A.751N1	Classic Aviation Ltd/Duxford	
G-BTGD	Rand-Robinson KR-2 (modified)	A. M. Chester	
G-BTGG	Rans S.10 Sakota	A. R. Cameron	
G-BTGH	Cessna 152 II	C & S Aviation Ltd/Wolverhampton	
G-BTGI	Rearwin 175 Skyranger	A. H. Hunt/St Just	
G-BTGJ	Smith DSA-1 Miniplane	G. J. Knowles	
G-BTGL	Light Aero Avid Flyer	A. F. Vizoso	
G-BTGM	Aeronca 7AC Champion	G. P. Gregg/France	
G-BTGN	Cessna 310R II	Turnhouse Flying Club	
G-BTGO	PA-28 Cherokee 140	Halegreen Associates Ltd	
G-BTGP	Cessna 150M	Billins Air Service Ltd	
G-BTGR	Cessna 152 II	A. J. Gomes/Shoreham	
G-BTGS	Stolp SA.300 Starduster Too	G. N. Elliott & ptnrs (G-AYMA)	
G-BTGT	CFM Streak Shadow	G. D. Bailey (G-MWPY)	
G-BTGU	PA-34-220T Seneca III	Carill Aviation Ltd	
G-BTGV	PA-34-200T Seneca II	MS 124 Ltd/Shobdon	
G-BTGW	Cessna 152 II	Stapleford Flying Club Ltd	
G-BTGX	Cessna 152 II	Stapleford Flying Club Ltd	
G-BTGY	PA-28-161 Warrior II	Stapleford Flying Club Ltd	
G-BTGZ	PA-28-181 Archer II	Allzones Travel Ltd/Biggin Hill	
G-BTHA	Cessna 182P	Hotel Alpha Flying Group/Liverpool	
G-BTHD	Yakovlev Yak-3U	Patina Ltd/Duxford	
G-BTHE	Cessna 150L	Humberside Police Flying Club	
G-BTHF	Cameron V-90 balloon	N. J. & S. J. Langley	
G-BTHH	Jodel DR.100A	H. R. Leefe	
G-BTHI	Robinson R-22B	Yorkshire Helicopters	
G-BTHJ	Evans VP-2	C. J. Moseley	
G-BTHK	Thunder Ax7-77 balloon	M. J. Chandler	
G-BTHM	Thunder Ax8-105 balloon	J. K. Woods	
G-BTHN	Murphy Renegade 912	F. A. Purvis	
G-BTHP	Thorp T.211	M. Gardner	
G-BTHR	SOCATA TB.10 Tobago	P., A., & J. McRae/White Waltham	
G-BTHU	Light Aero Avid Flyer	R. C. Bowley	
G-BTHV	MBB Bo 105DBS/4	Bond Air Services/Aberdeen	
G-BTHW	Beech F33C Bonanza	Robin Lance Aviation Associates Ltd	
G-BTHX	Colt 105A balloon	R. Ollier	
G-BTHY	Bell 206B JetRanger 3	Sterling Helicopters Ltd	
G-BTHZ	Cameron V-56 balloon	C. N. Marshall/Kenya	
G-BTID	PA-28-161 Warrior II	Plymouth School of Flying Ltd	
G-BTIE	SOCATA TB.10 Tobago	I. M. D. Weston	
G-BTIF	Denney Kitfox Mk 3	D. A. Murchie	
G-BTIG	Montgomerie-Bensen B.8MR	K. Jarvis	
G-BTII	AA-5B Tiger	B. D. Greenwood	
G-BTIJ	Luscombe 8E Silvaire	S. J. Hornsby	
G-BTIK	Cessna 152 II	P. R. Edwards & E. Alexandert	
G-BTIL	PA-38-112 Tomahawk	B. J. Pearson/Eaglescott	
G-BTIM	PA-28-161 Cadet	JMS Janetorial Supplies	
G-BTIO	SNCAN Stampe SV-4C	M. D. & C. F. Garratt	
G-BTIR	Denney Kitfox Mk 2	R. B. Wilson	
G-BTIS	AS.355F-1 Twin Squirrel	Walsh Aviation (G-TALI)/Elstree	
G-BTIU	M.S.892A Rallye Commodore 150	W. H. Cole	
G-BTIV	PA-28-161 Warrior II	Warrior Group/Eaglescott	
G-BTIW	Jodel DR.1050/M1 ★	(stored)/Crosland Moor	
G-BTIX	Cameron V-77 balloon	D. J. Cook	
G-BTIZ	Cameron A-105 balloon	W. A. Board	
G-BTJA	Luscombe 8E Silvaire	M. W. Rudkin	
G-BTJB	Luscombe 8E Silvaire	M. Loxton	
G-BTJC	Luscombe 8F Silvaire	A. M. Noble	
G-BTJD	Thunder Ax8-90 S2 balloon	R. E. Vinten	
G-BTJF	Thunder Ax10-180 balloon	Airborne Adventures Ltd	
G-BTJH	Cameron O-77 balloon	H. Stringer	
G-BTJK	PA-38-112 Tomahawk	Western Air (Thruxton) Ltd	
G-BTJL	PA-38-112 Tomahawk	J. S. Devlin & Z. Islam/Redhill	
G-BTJS	Montgomerie-Bensen B.8MR	T. C. & P. K. Jackson	
G-BTJU	Cameron V-90 balloon	C. W. Jones (Floorings) Ltd	
G-BTJX	Rans S.10 Sakota	W. C. Dobson	
G-BTKA	Piper J-5A Cub Cruiser	J. M. Lister	
G-BTKB	Renegade Spirit 912	G. S. Blundell	
G-BTKD	Denney Kitfox Mk 4	J. F. White	
G-BTKG	Light Aero Avid Flyer	I. Holt	

Notes	Reg.	Type	Owner or Operator
	G-BTKL	MBB Bo 105DB-4	Veritair Ltd
	G-BTKP	CFM Streak Shadow	G. D. Martin
	G-BTKT	PA-28-161 Warrior II	Eastern Executive Air Charter Ltd
	G-BTKV	PA-22 Tri-Pacer 160	R. A. Moore
	G-BTKW	Cameron O-105 balloon	P. Spellward
	G-BTKX	PA-28-181 Archer II	D. J. Perkins
	G-BTKZ	Cameron V-77 balloon	S. P. Richards
	G-BTLB	Wassmer WA.52 Europa	M. D. O'Brien/Shoreham
	G-BTLE	PA-31-350 Navajo Chieftain	Boal Air Services (UK) Ltd
	G-BTLG	PA-28R Cherokee Arrow 200	W. B. Bateson/Blackpool
	G-BTLL	Pilatus P3-03 (A-806) ★	(stored)/Headcorn
	G-BTLM	PA-22 Tri-Pacer 160	F & H (Aircraft)
	G-BTLP	AA-1C Lynx	Partlease Ltd
	G-BTMA	Cessna 172N	East of England Flying Group Ltd
	G-BTMH	Colt 90A balloon	European Balloon Corporation
	G-BTMJ	Maule MX-7-180	C. M. McGill/Biggin Hill
	G-BTMK	Cessna R.172K XPII	S. P. & A. C. Barker
	G-BTMO	Colt 69A balloon	Thunder & Colt
	G-BTMP	Campbell Cricket	P. W. McLaughlin
	G-BTMR	Cessna 172M	Linley Aviation Ltd
	G-BTMS	Light Aero Avid Speedwing	F. Sayyah
	G-BTMT	Denney Kitfox Mk 1	Skulk Flying Group
	G-BTMV	Everett Srs 2 gyroplane	L. Armes
	G-BTMW	Zenair CH.701 STOL	L. Lewis
	G-BTMX	Denney Kitfox Mk 3	P. B. Lowry
	G-BTNA	Robinson R-22B	Heli Charter Ltd
	G-BTNB	Robinson R-22B	Kuki Helicopters Ltd
	G-BTNC	AS.365N-2 Dauphin 2	CHC Scotia Ltd
	G-BTND	PA-38-112 Tomahawk	R. B. Turner
	G-BTNE	PA-28-161 Warrior II	D. Rowe/Wellesbourne
	G-BTNL	Thunder Ax10-180 balloon	M. P. A. Sevrin/Belgium
	G-BTNN	Colt 21A balloon	Cameron Balloons Ltd
	G-BTNO	Aeronca 7AC Champion	November Oscar Group/Netherthorpe
	G-BTNP	Light Aero Avid Flyer Commuter	N. Evans
	G-BTNR	Denney Kitfox Mk 3	H. Thompson
	G-BTNS	PZL-104 Wilga 80	D. Rowland
	G-BTNT	PA-28-151 Warrior	Britannia Airways Ltd/Luton
	G-BTNV	PA-28-161 Warrior II	D. E. Peet
	G-BTNW	Rans S.6-ESA Coyote II	B. Read
	G-BTOC	Robinson R-22B	N. Parkhouse
	G-BTOD	PA-38-112 Tomahawk	S. M. P. & D. A. Adams
	G-BTOG	D.H.82A Tiger Moth	P. T. Szluha
	G-BTOI	Cameron N-77 balloon	The Nestle Co Ltd
	G-BTOL	Denney Kitfox Mk 3	P. J. Gibbs
	G-BTON	PA-28 Cherokee 140	S. G. Woodsford
	G-BTOO	Pitts S-1C Special	G. H. Matthews
	G-BTOP	Cameron V-77 balloon	J. J. Winter
	G-BTOS	Cessna 140	J. L. Kaiser/France
	G-BTOT	PA-15 Vagabond	Vagabond Flying Group
	G-BTOU	Cameron O-120 balloon	R. M. Horn
	G-BTOW	SOCATA Rallye 180GT	Cambridge University Gliding Trust Ltd/ Gransden Lodge
	G-BTOZ	Thunder Ax9-120 S2 balloon	H. G. Davies
	G-BTPB	Cameron N-105 balloon	Test Valley Balloon Group
	G-BTPT	Cameron N-77 balloon	Derbyshire Building Soc
	G-BTPX	Thunder Ax8-90 balloon	E. Cordall
	G-BTPZ	Isaacs Fury II	M. A. Farrelly
	G-BTRB	Thunder Colt Mickey Mouse SS balloon	Benedikt Haggeney GmbH/Germany
	G-BTRC	Light Aero Avid Speedwing	Grangecote Ltd
	G-BTRE	Cessna F.172H	M. L. J. Warwick
	G-BTRF	Aero Designs Pulsar	C. Smith
	G-BTRG	Aeronca 65C Super Chief	H. J. Cox
	G-BTRH	Aeronca 7AC Champion	J. Horan
	G-BTRI	Aeronca 11CC Super Chief	P. A. Wensak
	G-BTRK	PA-28-161 Warrior II	Stapleford Flying Club Ltd
	G-BTRL	Cameron N-105 balloon	J. Lippett
	G-BTRN	Thunder Ax9-120 S2 balloon	P. B. D. Bird
	G-BTRO	Thunder Ax8-90 balloon	Capital Balloon Club Ltd
	G-BTRP	Hughes 369E	P. C. Shann
	G-BTRR	Thunder Ax7-77 balloon	S. M. Roberts
	G-BTRS	PA-28-161 Warrior II	Airwise Flying Group
	G-BTRT	PA-28R Cherokee Arrow 200-II	C. E. Yates/Barton

Reg.	Type	Owner or Operator	Notes
G-BTRU	Robin DR.400/180	R. & M. Engineering Ltd	
G-BTRW	Slingsby T.61F Venture T.2	The Falke Syndicate	
G-BTRY	PA-28-161 Warrior II	Oxford Aviation Services Ltd/Kidlington	
G-BTRZ	Jodel D.18	R. M. Johnson & R. Collin	
G-BTSB	Corben Baby Ace D	J. A. MacLeod	
G-BTSC	Evans VP-2	G. B. O'Neill	
G-BTSJ	PA-28-161 Warrior II	Plymouth School of Flying Ltd	
G-BTSL	Cameron 70 Glass SS balloon	M. R. Humphrey & J. R .Clifton	
G-BTSM	Cessna 180A	C. Couston	
G-BTSN	Cessna 150G	N. A. Bilton/Norwich	
G-BTSP	Piper J-3C-65 Cub	J. A. Walshe & A. Corcoran	
G-BTSR	Aeronca 11AC Chief	R. D. & E. G. N. Morris	
G-BTST	Bensen B.9	V. Scott	
G-BTSV	Denney Kitfox Mk 3	M. G. Dovey	
G-BTSW	Colt AS-80 Mk II airship	Gefa-Flug GmbH/Germany	
G-BTSX	Thunder Ax7-77 balloon	C. Moris-Gallimore	
G-BTSY	EE Lightning F.6 (XR724)	Lightning Association	
G-BTSZ	Cessna 177A	K. D. Harvey	
G-BTTB	Cameron V-90 balloon	Royal Engineers Balloon Club	
G-BTTD	Montgomerie-Bensen B.8MR	K. B. Gutridge	
G-BTTE	Cessna 150L	W. E. Rodwell/Shoreham	
G-BTTK	Thunder Ax8-105 balloon	Tempowish Ltd	
G-BTTL	Cameron V-90 balloon	A. J. Baird	
G-BTTP	BAe 146-300	K.L.M.uk/Buzz/Stansted	
G-BTTR	Aerotek Pitts S-2A Special	P. Shaw	
G-BTTS	Colt 77A balloon	Rutland Balloon Club	
G-BTTW	Thunder Ax7-77 balloon	J. Kenny	
G-BTTY	Denney Kitfox Mk 2	K. J. Fleming	
G-BTTZ	Slingsby T.61F Venture T.2	M. W. Olliver	
G-BTUA	Slingsby T.61F Venture T.2	Shenington Gliding Club	
G-BTUB	Yakovlev C.11	M. G. & J. R. Jefferies	
G-BTUC	EMB-312 Tucano ★	Ulster Aviation Heritage/Langford Lodge	
G-BTUG	SOCATA Rallye 180T	Herefordshire Gliding Club Ltd/Shobdon	
G-BTUH	Cameron N-65 balloon	B. J. Godding	
G-BTUJ	Thunder Ax9-120 balloon	ECM Construction Ltd	
G-BTUK	Aerotek Pitts S-2A Special	S. H. Elkington/Wickenby	
G-BTUL	Aerotek Pitts S-2A Special	J. M. Adams	
G-BTUM	Piper J-3C-65 Cub	G-BTUM Syndicate	
G-BTUR	PA-18 Super Cub 95 (modified)	Liddell Aircraft Ltd	
G-BTUS	Whittaker MW.7	J. D. Webb	
G-BTUU	Cameron O-120 balloon	J. L. Guy	
G-BTUV	Aeronca A65TAC Defender	M. B. Hamlett & R. E. Coates/France	
G-BTUW	PA-28-151 Warrior	T. S. Kemp	
G-BTUX	AS.365N-2 Dauphin 2	CHC Scotia Ltd	
G-BTUZ	American General AG-5B Tiger	Grocontinental Ltd/Tilstock	
G-BTVA	Thunder Ax7-77 balloon	A. H. Symonds	
G-BTVB	Everett Srs 3 gyroplane	J. Pumford	
G-BTVC	Denney Kitfox Mk 2	P. Mitchell	
G-BTVE	Hawker Demon I (K8203)	Demon Displays Ltd	
G-BTVF	Rotorway Executive 90	E. P. Sadler	
G-BTVG	PA-28 Cherokee 140	Full Sutton Flying Centre Ltd	
G-BTVU	Robinson R-22B	B. Enzo/Italy	
G-BTVV	Cessna FA.337G	C. Keane	
G-BTVW	Cessna 152 II	Halegreen Associates Ltd	
G-BTVX	Cessna 152 II	Traffic Management Services	
G-BTWC	Slingsby T.61F Venture T.2	RAFGSA/Bicester	
G-BTWD	Slingsby T.61F Venture T.2	York Gliding Centre/Rufforth	
G-BTWE	Slingsby T.61F Venture T.2	RAFGSA/Syerston	
G-BTWF	D.H.C.1 Chipmunk 22 (WK549)	J. A. & V. G. Sims	
G-BTWI	EAA Acro Sport I	WI Group	
G-BTWJ	Cameron V-77 balloon	S. J. & J. A. Bellaby	
G-BTWL	WAG-Aero Acro Sport Trainer	I. M. Ashpole	
G-BTWM	Cameron V-77 balloon	R. C. Franklin	
G-BTWN	Maule MXT-7-180	C. T. Rolls/Redhill	
G-BTWU	PA-22 Tri-Pacer 135	Prestige Air (Engineers) Ltd	
G-BTWV	Cameron O-90 balloon	S. F. Hancke	
G-BTWX	SOCATA TB.9 Tampico	British Car Rentals	
G-BTWY	Aero Designs Pulsar	M. Stevenson	
G-BTWZ	Rans S.10 Sakota	D. G. Hey	
G-BTXB	Colt 77A balloon	A. Derbyshire	
G-BTXD	Rans S.6-ESA Coyote II	M. Isterling	
G-BTXF	Cameron V-90 balloon	G. Thompson	
G-BTXG	BAe Jetstream 3102	Highland Airways Ltd/Inverness	

Notes	Reg.	Type	Owner or Operator
	G-BTXH	Colt AS-56 airship	L. Kiefer/Germany
	G-BTXI	Noorduyn AT-16 Harvard IIB (FE695)	Patina Ltd/Duxford
	G-BTXK	Thunder Ax7-65 balloon	T. M. Dawson
	G-BTXS	Cameron O-120 balloon	Southern Balloon Group
	G-BTXT	Maule MXT-7-180	H. Balfour-Paul
	G-BTXV	Cameron A-210 balloon	The Ballooning Business Ltd
	G-BTXW	Cameron V-77 balloon	P. C. Waterhouse
	G-BTXX	Bellanca 8KCAB Decathlon	Tatenhill Aviation
	G-BTXZ	Zenair CH.250	I. Parris & P. W. J. Bull
	G-BTYC	Cessna 150L	Polestar Aviation Ltd
	G-BTYE	Cameron A-180 balloon	K. J. A. Maxwell & D. S. Messmer
	G-BTYF	Thunder Ax10-180 S2 balloon	P. Glydon
	G-BTYH	Pottier P.80S	R. Pickett
	G-BTYI	PA-28-181 Archer II	C. E. Wright
	G-BTYK	Cessna 310R	Revere Aviation Ltd
	G-BTYW	Cessna 120	G-BTYW Group
	G-BTYY	Curtiss Robin C-2	R. R. L. Windus
	G-BTYZ	Colt 210A balloon	T. M. Donnelly
	G-BTZA	Beech F33A Bonanza	G-BTZA Group/Edinburgh
	G-BTZB	Yakovlev Yak-50 (69)	J. S. & J. S. Allison
	G-BTZD	Yakovlev Yak-1	Historic Aircraft Collection Ltd
	G-BTZE	LET Yakovlev C.11	Bianchi Aviation Film Services Ltd/Booker
	G-BTZG	BAe ATP	Trident Aviation Leasing Services
	G-BTZK	BAe ATP	Trident Aviation Leasing Services
	G-BTZL	Oldfield Baby Lakes	K. P. Rusling
	G-BTZO	SOCATA TB.20 Trinidad	M. R. Munn
	G-BTZP	SOCATA TB.9 Tampico	M. W. Orr
	G-BTZR	Colt 77B balloon	P. J. Fell
	G-BTZS	Colt 77A balloon	P. T. R. Ollivere
	G-BTZU	Cameron Concept SS balloon	A. C. Rackham
	G-BTZV	Cameron V-77 balloon	A. W. Sumner/Belgium
	G-BTZX	Piper J-3C-65 Cub	D. A. Woodhams & J. T. Coulthard
	G-BTZY	Colt 56A balloon	T. M. Donnelly
	G-BTZZ	CFM Streak Shadow	D. R. Stennett
	G-BUAA	Corben Baby Ace D	M. W. Chamberlain
	G-BUAB	Aeronca 11AC Chief	J. Reed
	G-BUAC	Slingsby T.31 Motor Cadet III	D. A. Wilson
	G-BUAF	Cameron N-77 balloon	T. H. Wadden
	G-BUAG	Jodel D.18	A. L. Silcox
	G-BUAI	Everett Srs 3 gyroplane	Pop-Corn Group
	G-BUAJ	Cameron N-90 balloon	J. R. & S. J. Huggins
	G-BUAM	Cameron V-77 balloon	N. Florence
	G-BUAN	Cessna 172N	R. J. Cawdell
	G-BUAO	Luscombe 8A Silvaire	D. Sweeney & G. R. Thomas
	G-BUAR	V.S.358 Seafire LF.IIIc (PP972)	Wizzard Investments Ltd
	G-BUAT	Thunder Ax9-120 balloon	J. Fenton
	G-BUAW	Pitts S-1C Special	D. G. Crawley
	G-BUAX	Rans S.10 Sakota	S. P. Wakeham
	G-BUAY	Cameron A-210 balloon	Virgin Balloon Flights Ltd
	G-BUBA	PA-18S Super Cub 150 (floatplane)	Liddell Aircraft Ltd/Bournemouth
	G-BUBC	QAC Quickie Tri-Q.200	D. J. Clarke
	G-BUBL	Thunder Ax8-105 balloon ★	British Balloon Museum/Newbury
	G-BUBN	BN-2B-26 Islander	Isles of Scilly Skybus Ltd/St Just
	G-BUBR	Cameron A-250 balloon	Bath Hot-Air Balloon Club
	G-BUBS	Lindstrand LBL-77B balloon	B. J. Bower
	G-BUBT	Stoddard-Hamilton Glasair IIRGS	M. D. Evans
	G-BUBU	PA-34-220T Seneca III	Brinor (Holdings) Ltd
	G-BUBW	Robinson R-22B	Forth Helicopter Services Ltd/Edinburgh
	G-BUBY	Thunder Ax8-105 S2 balloon	T. M. Donnelly
	G-BUCA	Cessna A.150K	BUCA Group
	G-BUCB	Cameron H-34 balloon	A. S. Jones
	G-BUCC	C.A.S.A. 1.131E Jungmann 2000 (BU+CC)	P. L. Gaze (G-BUEM)
	G-BUCG	Schleicher ASW.20L (modified)	W. B. Andrews
	G-BUCH	Stinson V-77 Reliant	Pullmerit Ltd
	G-BUCI	Auster AOP.9 (XP242)	Historic Aircraft Flight Reserve Collection/Middle Wallop
	G-BUCJ	D.H.C.2 Beaver 1 (XP772)	British Aerial Museum/Duxford
	G-BUCK	C.A.S.A. 1.131E Jungmann 1000 (BU+CK)	Jungmann Flying Group/White Waltham

Reg.	Type	Owner or Operator	Notes
G-BUCM	Hawker Sea Fury FB.11 (WE724)	Patina Ltd/Duxford	
G-BUCO	Pietenpol Air Camper	A. James	
G-BUCS	Cessna 150F	Gordon Air Ltd/Lydd	
G-BUCT	Cessna 150L	Gordon Air Ltd/Lydd	
G-BUDA	Slingsby T.61F Venture T.2	RAFGSA/Bicester	
G-BUDB	Slingsby T.61F Venture T.2	RAFGSA/Bicester	
G-BUDC	Slingsby T.61F Venture T.2	T.61 Group	
G-BUDE	PA-22 Tri-Pacer 135 (tailwheel)	B. A. Bower/Thruxton	
G-BUDF	Rand-Robinson KR-2	E. C. King	
G-BUDI	Aero Designs Pulsar	R. W. L. Oliver	
G-BUDK	Thunder Ax7-77 balloon	W. Evans	
G-BUDL	Auster 3 (NX534)	M. Pocock	
G-BUDN	Cameron 90 Shoe SS balloon	Magical Adventures Ltd	
G-BUDO	PZL-110 Koliber 150	A. S. Vine/Goodwood	
G-BUDR	Denney Kitfox Mk 3	N. J. P. Mayled	
G-BUDS	Rand-Robinson KR-2	D. W. Munday	
G-BUDT	Slingsby T.61F Venture T.2	G-BUDT Group	
G-BUDU	Cameron V-77 balloon	T. M. G. Amery	
G-BUDW	Brügger MB.2 Colibri	J. M. Hoblyn (G-GODS)	
G-BUEC	Van's RV-6	R. D. Harper	
G-BUED	Slingsby T.61F Venture T.2	SE Kent Civil Service Flying Club	
G-BUEE	Cameron A-210 balloon	Bristol Balloons	
G-BUEF	Cessna 152 II	Channel Aviation	
G-BUEG	Cessna 152 II	Plymouth School of Flying Ltd	
G-BUEI	Thunder Ax8-105 balloon	Imagination Balloon Flights	
G-BUEK	Slingsby T.61F Venture T.2	Norfolk Gliding Club Ltd/Tibenham	
G-BUEN	VPM M.14 Scout	F. G. Shepherd	
G-BUEP	Maule MX-7-180	G. M. Bunn	
G-BUEV	Cameron O-77 balloon	R. R. McCormack	
G-BUEX	Schweizer 269C	Fenland Helicopter Centre (G-HFLR)	
G-BUFA	Cameron R-77 gas balloon	Noble Adventures Ltd	
G-BUFC	Cameron R-77 gas balloon	Noble Adventures Ltd	
G-BUFE	Cameron R-77 gas balloon	Noble Adventures Ltd	
G-BUFG	Slingsby T.61F Venture T.2	Halegreen Associates Ltd	
G-BUFH	PA-28-161 Warrior II	The Tiger Leisure Group	
G-BUFJ	Cameron V-90 balloon	S. P. Richards	
G-BUFK	Cassutt Racer IIIM	D. I. H. Johnstone & W. T. Barnard	
G-BUFN	Slingsby T.61F Venture T.2	BUFN Group	
G-BUFO	Cameron 70 UFO SS balloon	Virgin Airship & Balloon Co Ltd	
G-BUFR	Slingsby T.61F Venture T.2	East Sussex Gliding Club Ltd	
G-BUFT	Cameron O-120 balloon	N. D. Hicks	
G-BUFV	Light Aero Avid Speedwing Mk.4	M. & B. Gribbin	
G-BUFX	Cameron N-90 balloon	Kerridge Computer Co Ltd	
G-BUFY	PA-28-161 Warrior II	Bickertons Aerodromes Ltd/Denham	
G-BUGB	Stolp SA.750 Acroduster Too	R. M. Chaplin	
G-BUGD	Cameron V-77 balloon	Cameron Balloons Ltd	
G-BUGE	Bellanca 7GCAA CItabria	P. White	
G-BUGG	Cessna 150F	C. P. J. Taylor & D. M. Forshaw/ Panshanger	
G-BUGI	Evans VP-2	D. G. Gibson	
G-BUGJ	Robin DR.400/180	W. M. Patterson	
G-BUGL	Slingsby T.61F Venture T.2	VMG Group	
G-BUGM	CFM Streak Shadow	The Shadow Group	
G-BUGO	Colt 56B balloon	Escuela de Aerostacion Mica/Spain	
G-BUGP	Cameron V-77 balloon	R. Churcher	
G-BUGS	Cameron V-77 balloon	T. J. Orchard Bugs Bunny	
G-BUGT	Slingsby T.61F Venture T.2	R. W. Hornsey/Rufforth	
G-BUGV	Slingsby T.61F Venture T.2	Oxfordshire Sportflying Ltd/Enstone	
G-BUGW	Slingsby T.61F Venture T.2	Halegreen Associates Ltd	
G-BUGY	Cameron V-90 balloon	Dante Balloon Group	
G-BUGZ	Slingsby T.61F Venture T.2	Dishforth Flying Group	
G-BUHA	Slingsby T.61F Venture T.2 (ZA634)	G-BUHA Group	
G-BUHJ	Boeing 737-4Q8	British Airways	
G-BUHK	Boeing 737-4Q8	British Airways	
G-BUHL	Boeing 737-4S3	GB Airways Ltd/Gatwick	
G-BUHM	Cameron V-77 balloon	L. A. Watts	
G-BUHO	Cessna 140	W. B. Bateson/Blackpool	
G-BUHR	Slingsby T.61F Venture T.2	Denbigh Falke Group/Lleweni Parc	
G-BUHS	Stoddard-Hamilton Glasair SH-TD-1	E. J. Spalding	
G-BUHU	Cameron N-105 balloon	Unipart Balloon Club	
G-BUHY	Cameron A-210 balloon	Adventure Balloon Co Ltd	

Notes	Reg.	Type	Owner or Operator
	G-BUHZ	Cessna 120	J. Redfarn
	G-BUIC	Denney Kitfox Mk 2	C. R. Northrop & B. M. Chilvers
	G-BUIE	Cameron N-90 balloon	Flying Pictures Ltd
	G-BUIF	PA-28-161 Warrior II	Newcastle-upon-Tyne Aero Club Ltd
	G-BUIG	Campbell Cricket (replica)	T. A. Holmes
	G-BUIH	Slingsby T.61F Venture T.2	Yorkshire Gliding Club (Pty) Ltd/
			Sutton Bank
	G-BUIJ	PA-28-161 Warrior II	Tradecliff Ltd/Blackbushe
	G-BUIK	PA-28-161 Warrior II	Falcon Flying Services/Biggin Hill
	G-BUIL	CFM Streak Shadow	P. N. Bevan & L. M. Poor
	G-BUIN	Thunder Ax7-77 balloon	Free Flight Aerostat Group
	G-BUIO	BAe Jetstream 3202	Eastern Airways Ltd
	G-BUIP	Denney Kitfox Mk 2	Avcomm Developments Ltd
	G-BUIR	Light Aero Avid Speedwing Mk 4	K. N. Pollard/Sturgate
	G-BUIU	Cameron V-90 balloon	H. Micketeit/Germany
	G-BUJA	Slingsby T.61F Venture T.2	RAFGSA/Cosford
	G-BUJB	Slingsby T.61F Venture T.2	Falke Syndicate/Shobdon
	G-BUJE	Cessna 177B	FG93 Group
	G-BUJH	Colt 77B balloon	R. P. Cross & R. Stanley
	G-BUJI	Slingsby T.61F Venture T.2	Solent Venture Syndicate Ltd
	G-BUJK	Montgomerie-Bensen B.8MR	K. J. Robinson
	G-BUJL	Aero Designs Pulsar	J. J. Lynch
	G-BUJM	Cessna 120	Cessna 120 Flying Group
	G-BUJN	Cessna 172N	Aerohire Ltd/Wolverhampton
	G-BUJO	PA-28-161 Warrior II	Channel Islands Aero Services Ltd
	G-BUJP	PA-28-161 Warrior II	White Waltham Airfield Ltd
	G-BUJR	Cameron A-180 balloon	W. I. Hooker & C. Parker
	G-BUJV	Light Aero Avid Speedwing Mk 4	C. Thomas
	G-BUJW	Thunder Ax8-90 S2 balloon	R. T. Fagan
	G-BUJX	Slingsby T.61F Venture T.2	J. R. Chichester-Constable
	G-BUJY	D.H.82A Tiger Moth	P. Winters
	G-BUJZ	Rotorway Executive 90 (modified)	M. P. Swoboda
	G-BUKA	Fairchild SA227AC Metro III	Atlantic Air Transport Ltd/Coventry
	G-BUKB	Rans S.10 Sakota	M. K. Blatch & M. P. Lee
	G-BUKF	Denney Kitfox Mk 4	Kilo Foxtrot Group
	G-BUKH	D.31 Turbulent	P. M. Newman
	G-BUKI	Thunder Ax7-77 balloon	Virgin Airship & Balloon Co Ltd
	G-BUKK	Bücker Bü133C Jungmeister	E. J. F. McEntee/White Waltham
		(U-80)	
	G-BUKN	PA-15 Vagabond	B. F. & M. A. Goddard
	G-BUKP	Denney Kitfox Mk 2	S. Moreton
	G-BUKR	M.S.880B Rallye Club 100T	G-BUKR Flying Group
	G-BUKS	Colt 77B balloon	R. & M. Bairstow
	G-BUKT	Luscombe 8A Silvaire	M. G. Talbot & J. N. Willshaw
	G-BUKU	Luscombe 8E Silvaire	F. G. Miskelly
	G-BUKV	Colt AS-105 Mk II Airship	A. Ockelmann/Germany
	G-BUKX	PA-28-161 Warrior II	LNP Ltd
	G-BUKZ	Evans VP-2	P. R. Farnell
	G-BULB	Thunder Ax7-77 balloon	Richard Nash Cars Ltd
	G-BULC	Light Aero Avid Flyer Mk 4	C. Nice
	G-BULD	Cameron N-105 balloon	C. L. Jenkins
	G-BULF	Colt 77A balloon	P. Goss & T. C. Davies
	G-BULG	Van's RV-4	M. J. Aldridge/Tibenham
	G-BULH	Cessna 172N	Touchdown Properties Ltd/Blackpool
	G-BULJ	CFM Steak Shadow	C. C. Brown
	G-BULK	Thunder Ax9-120 S2 balloon	Skybus Ballooning/Austria
	G-BULL	SA Bulldog Srs 120/128	Solo Leisure Ltd
	G-BULM	Aero Designs Pulsar	J. Lloyd
	G-BULN	Colt 210A balloon	H. G. Davies
	G-BULO	Luscombe 8A Silvaire	A. F. S. Caldecourt
	G-BULR	PA-28 Cherokee 140	R. & H. Wale (General Woodworks) Ltd
	G-BULT	Campbell Cricket	A. T. Pocklington
	G-BULY	Light Aero Avid Flyer	D. R. Piercy
	G-BULZ	Denney Kitfox Mk 2	T. G. F. Trenchard
	G-BUMP	PA-28-181 Archer II	Marnham Investments Ltd
	G-BUMB	Slingsby T.61F Venture T.2	RAFGSA Cranwell Gliding Club
	G-BUNC	PZL-104 Wilga 35	Fast Aerospace Ltd
	G-BUND	PA-28RT-201T Turbo Arrow IV	Jenrick Ltd & A. Somerville/Blackbushe
	G-BUNG	Cameron N-77 balloon	The Bungle Balloon Group
	G-BUNH	PA-28RT-201T Turbo Arrow IV	JB Consultants (Aviation)
	G-BUNI	Cameron 90 Bunny SS balloon	Virgin Airship & Balloon Co Ltd
	G-BUNJ	Squarecraft SA.102-5 Cavalier	J. A. Smith
	G-BUNM	Denney Kitfox Mk 3	P. N. Akass

Reg.	Type	Owner or Operator	Notes
G-BUNO	Lancair 320	J. Softley	
G-BUNS	Cessna F.150K	R. W. H. Cole	
G-BUNV	Thunder Ax7-77 balloon	J. A. Lister	
G-BUNZ	Thunder Ax10-180 S2 balloon	T. M. Donnelly	
G-BUOA	Whittaker MW.6-S Fatboy Flyer	R. Blackburn	
G-BUOB	CFM Streak Shadow	A. M. Simmons	
G-BUOC	Cameron A-210 balloon	Bailey Balloons	
G-BUOD	SE-5A (replica) (B595)	M. D. Waldron/Belgium	
G-BUOE	Cameron V-90 balloon	Dusters & Co	
G-BUOF	D.62B Condor	R. P. Loxton	
G-BUOI	PA-20 Pacer	Foley Farm Flying Group	
G-BUOJ	Cessna 172N	EFG Flying Services Ltd/Biggin Hill	
G-BUOK	Rans S.6-ESA Coyote II	M. Morris	
G-BUOL	Denney Kitfox Mk 3	J. G. D. Barbour	
G-BUON	Light Aero Avid Aerobat	N. T. Hawkins	
G-BUOR	C.A.S.A. 1.131E Jungmann 2000	M. I. M. S. Voest/Netherlands	
G-BUOS	V.S.394 Spitfire FR.XVIII (SM845)	Historic Flying Ltd	
G-BUOW	Aero Designs Pulsar XP	T. J. Hartwell	
G-BUOX	Cameron V-77 balloon	R. M. Pursey & C. M. Richardson	
G-BUOZ	Thunder Ax10-180 balloon	Zebedee Balloon Service Ltd	
G-BUPA	Rutan LongEz	G. J. Banfield	
G-BUPB	Stolp SA.300 Starduster Too	Starduster PB Group	
G-BUPC	Rollason Beta B.2	C. A. Rolph	
G-BUPF	Bensen B.8R	P. W. Hewitt-Dean	
G-BUPG	Cessna 180K	T. P. A. Norman/Rendcomb	
G-BUPI	Cameron V-77 balloon	S. A. Masey (G-BOUC)	
G-BUPJ	Fournier RF-4D	M. R. Shelton	
G-BUPM	VPM M.16 Tandem Trainer	Roger Savage (Gyroplanes) Ltd	
G-BUPP	Cameron V-42 balloon	L. J. Schoeman	
G-BUPR	Jodel D.18	R. W. Burrows	
G-BUPS	Aérospatiale ATR-42-300	Titan Airways Ltd/Stansted	
G-BUPT	Cameron O-105 balloon	Chiltern Balloons	
G-BUPU	Thunder Ax7-77 balloon	R. C. Barkworth & D. G. Maguire/USA	
G-BUPV	Great Lakes 2T-1A	R. J. Fray	
G-BUPW	Denney Kitfox Mk 3	Kitfox Group	
G-BURD	Cessna F.172N	M. O. Loxton	
G-BURE	Jodel D.9	L. J. Kingsford	
G-BURF	Rand-Robinson KR-2	P. J. H. Moorhouse & B. L. Hewart	
G-BURG	Colt 77A balloon	S. T. Humphreys	
G-BURH	Cessna 150E	BURH Flying Group	
G-BURI	Enstrom F-28C	India Helicopters Group	
G-BURL	Colt 105A balloon	J. E. Rose	
G-BURN	Cameron O-120 balloon	Innovation Ballooning Ltd	
G-BURP	Rotorway Executive 90	N. K. Newman	
G-BURS	Sikorsky S-76A	Signature Aircraft Charter (G-OHTL)	
G-BURT	PA-28-161 Warrior II	J. D. F. Fendick	
G-BURU	BAe Jetstream 3202	Trident Aviation Leasing Services	
G-BURZ	Hawker Nimrod II (K3661)	Historic Aircraft Collection Ltd	
G-BUSB	Airbus A.320-111	British Airways	
G-BUSC	Airbus A.320-111	British Airways	
G-BUSD	Airbus A.320-111	British Airways	
G-BUSE	Airbus A.320-111	British Airways	
G-BUSF	Airbus A.320-111	British Airways	
G-BUSG	Airbus A.320-211	British Airways	
G-BUSH	Airbus A.320-211	British Airways	
G-BUSI	Airbus A.320-211	British Airways	
G-BUSJ	Airbus A.320-211	British Airways	
G-BUSK	Airbus A.320-211	British Airways	
G-BUSN	Rotorway Executive 90	J. A. McGinley	
G-BUSR	Aero Designs Pulsar	S. S. Bateman & R. A. Watts	
G-BUSS	Cameron 90 Bus SS balloon	Magical Adventures Ltd	
G-BUST	Lancair IV	C. C. Butt	
G-BUSV	Colt 105A balloon	M. N. J. Kirby	
G-BUSW	R. Commander 114	P. A. Nesbitt/USA	
G-BUSY	Thunder Ax6-56A balloon	M. E. Hooker	
G-BUSZ	Light Aero Avid Speedwing Mk 4	T. J. Allan	
G-BUTA	C.A.S.A. 1.131E Jungmann 2000	A. G. Dunkerley/Breighton	
G-BUTB	CFM Streak Shadow	S. Vestuti	
G-BUTD	Van's RV-6	N. W. Beadle	
G-BUTE	Anderson EA-1 Kingfisher	T. Crawford (G-BRCK)	
G-BUTF	Aeronca 11AC Chief	N. J. Mortimore	
G-BUTG	Zenair CH.601HD	J. M. Palmer	

Notes	Reg.	Type	Owner or Operator
	G-BUTH	CEA DR.220 2+2	A. A. M. & C. W. N. Huke
	G-BUTJ	Cameron O-77 balloon	A. J. A. Bubb
	G-BUTK	Murphy Rebel	L. D. Johnston (stored)
	G-BUTL	PA-24 Comanche 250	D. Heater (G-ARLB)/Blackbushe
	G-BUTM	Rans S.6-116 Coyote II	G-BUTM Group
	G-BUTW	BAe Jetstream 3202	Trident Aviation Leasing Services
	G-BUTX	C.A.S.A. 1.133C Jungmeister	A. J. E. Smith/Breighton
	G-BUTY	Brügger MB.2 Colibri	R. M. Lawday
	G-BUTZ	PA-28 Cherokee 180C	A. J. & J. M. Davis (G-DARL)
	G-BUUA	Slingsby T.67M Firefly Mk II	Hunting Aviation Ltd/Barkston Heath
	G-BUUB	Slingsby T.67M Firefly Mk II	Hunting Aviation Ltd/Newton
	G-BUUC	Slingsby T.67M Firefly Mk II	Hunting Aviation Ltd/Barkston Heath
	G-BUUD	Slingsby T.67M Firefly Mk II	Hunting Aviation Ltd/Newton
	G-BUUE	Slingsby T.67M Firefly Mk II	Hunting Aviation Ltd/Newton
	G-BUUF	Slingsby T.67M Firefly Mk II	Hunting Aviation Ltd/Newton
	G-BUUG	Slingsby T.67M Firefly Mk II	Hunting Aviation Ltd/Barkston Heath
	G-BUUI	Slingsby T.67M Firefly Mk II	Hunting Aviation Ltd/Newton
	G-BUUJ	Slingsby T.67M Firefly Mk II	Hunting Aviation Ltd/Newton
	G-BUUK	Slingsby T.67M Firefly Mk II	Hunting Aviation Ltd/Newton
	G-BUUL	Slingsby T.67M Firefly Mk II	Hunting Aviation Ltd/Barkston Heath
	G-BUUM	PA-28RT-201 Arrow IV	Bluebird Flying Group
	G-BUUN	Lindstrand LBL-105A balloon	Flying Pictures Ltd
	G-BUUO	Cameron N-90 balloon	Gone Ballooning Group
	G-BUUP	BAe ATP	Trident Aviation Leasing Ltd (G-MANU)
	G-BUUT	Interavia 70TA balloon	Aero Vintage Ltd
	G-BUUX	PA-28 Cherokee 180D	Aero Group 78/Netherthorpe
	G-BUUZ	BAe Jetstream 3202	Trident Aviation Leasing Services
	G-BUVA	PA-22 Tri-Pacer 135	Oaksey VA Group
	G-BUVC	BAe Jetstream 3206	Eastern Airways Ltd
	G-BUVD	BAe Jetstream 3206	Eastern Airways Ltd
	G-BUVE	Colt 77B balloon	G. D. Philpot
	G-BUVG	Cameron N-56 balloon	Cameron Balloons Ltd
	G-BUVL	Fisher Super Koala	A. D. Malcolm
	G-BUVM	CEA DR.250/160	G. G. Milton
	G-BUVN	C.A.S.A. 1.131E Jungmann 2000 (Bl-005)	W. Van Egmond/Netherlands
	G-BUVO	Cessna F.182P	BUVO Group (G-WTFA)/Southend
	G-BUVP	C.A.S.A. 1.131E Jungmann 2000	M. I. M. S. Voest/Netherlands
	G-BUVR	Christen A.1 Husky	A. E. Poulson
	G-BUVS	Colt 77A balloon	S. J. Chatfield
	G-BUVT	Colt 77A balloon	N. A. Carr
	G-BUVW	Cameron N-90 balloon	Bristol Balloon Fiestas Ltd
	G-BUVX	CFM Streak Shadow	G. K. R. Linney
	G-BUVZ	Thunder Ax10-180 S2 balloon	A. Van Wyk
	G-BUWE	SE-5A (replica) (C9533)	P. N. Davis
	G-BUWF	Cameron N-105 balloon	R. E. Jones
	G-BUWH	Parsons 2-seat gyroplane	R. V. Brunskill
	G-BUWI	Lindstrand LBL-77A balloon	Capital Balloon Club Ltd
	G-BUWJ	Pitts S-1C Special	J. I. Greenshields
	G-BUWK	Rans S.6-116 Coyote II	R. Warriner
	G-BUWR	CFM Streak Shadow	T. Harvey
	G-BUWS	Denney Kitfox Mk 2	J. E. Brewis
	G-BUWT	Rand-Robinson KR-2	C. M. Coombe
	G-BUWU	Cameron V-77 balloon	G. Thompson
	G-BUWY	Cameron V-77 balloon	P. A. Sachs
	G-BUWZ	Robin HR.200/120B	A. Cox
	G-BUXA	Colt 210A balloon	Balloon School International Ltd
	G-BUXB	Sikorsky S-76A	Signature Aircraft Charter
	G-BUXC	CFM Streak Shadow	J. P. Mimnagh
	G-BUXD	Maule MXT-7-160	S. Baigent
	G-BUXI	Steen Skybolt	M. Frankland/Liverpool
	G-BUXJ	Slingsby T.61F Venture T.2	Venture Motor Glider Club/Halton
	G-BUXK	Pietenpol Air Camper	B. P. Hogan
	G-BUXL	Taylor JT.1 Monoplane	M. W. Elliott
	G-BUXM	QAC Quickie Q.2	A. J. Ross & D. Ramwell
	G-BUXN	Beech C23 Sundowner	Private Pilots Syndicate
	G-BUXO	Pober P-9 Pixie	P-9 Flying Group
	G-BUXR	Cameron A-250 balloon	Celebration Balloon Flights
	G-BUXS	MBB Bo 105DBS/4	Bond Air Services (G-PASA/G-BGWP)
	G-BUXT	Dornier Do.228-202K	Air Wales Ltd
	G-BUXU	Beech D.17S	S. J. Ellis
	G-BUXV	PA-22 Tri-Pacer 160 (tailwheel)	Bogavia Two
	G-BUXW	Thunder Ax8-90 S2 balloon	J. M. Percival

Reg.	Type	Owner or Operator	Notes
G-BUXX	PA-17 Vagabond	R. H. Hunt/Old Sarum	
G-BUXY	PA-25 Pawnee 235	Bath, Wilts & North Dorset Gliding Club Ltd/Kingston Deverill	
G-BUYB	Aero Designs Pulsar	A. P. Fenn/Shobdon	
G-BUYC	Cameron 80 Concept balloon	P. J. Dorward	
G-BUYD	Thunder Ax8-90 balloon	Anglia Balloons	
G-BUYE	Aeronca 7AC Champion	R. Mazey	
G-BUYF	Falcon XP	G-BUYF Syndicate	
G-BUYJ	Lindstrand LBL-105A balloon	D. K. Fish	
G-BUYK	Denney Kitfox Mk 4	A. W. Shellis	
G-BUYL	RAF 2000GT gyroplane	Newtonair Gyroplanes Ltd	
G-BUYM	Thunder Ax8-105 balloon	Scotair Balloons	
G-BUYN	Cameron O-84 balloon	Reach For The Sky Ltd	
G-BUYO	Colt 77A balloon	S. F. Burden/Netherlands	
G-BUYR	Mooney M.20C	C. R. Weldon/Eire	
G-BUYS	Robin DR.400/180	F. A. Spear	
G-BUYU	Bowers Fly-Baby 1A	J. A. Nugent	
G-BUYY	PA-28 Cherokee 180	G-BUYY Group	
G-BUZA	Denney Kitfox Mk 3	J. Thomas	
G-BUZB	Aero Designs Pulsar XP	S. M. Lancashire	
G-BUZC	Everett Srs 3A gyroplane	M. P. L'Hermette	
G-BUZD	AS.332L Super Puma	CHC Scotia Ltd	
G-BUZE	Light Aero Avid Speedwing	J. M. Fforde	
G-BUZF	Colt 77B balloon	A. E. Austin	
G-BUZG	Zenair CH.601HD	N. C. White	
G-BUZH	Aero Designs Star-Lite SL-1	C. A. McDowall	
G-BUZJ	Lindstrand LBL-105A balloon	Eastgate Mazda	
G-BUZK	Cameron V-77 balloon	J. T. Wilkinson	
G-BUZL	VPM M.16 Tandem Trainer	Roger Savage (Photography)/Carlisle	
G-BUZM	Light Aero Avid Flyer Mk 3	R. McLuckie & O. G. Jones	
G-BUZN	Cessna 172H	H. Jones/Barton	
G-BUZO	Pietenpol Air Camper	D. A. Jones	
G-BUZR	Lindstrand LBL-77A balloon	Lindstrand Balloons Ltd	
G-BUZS	Colt Flying Pig SS balloon	Banco Bilbao Vizcaya/Spain	
G-BUZT	Kölb Twinstar Mk 3	A. C. Goadby	
G-BUZV	Ken Brock KB-2 gyroplane	K. Hughes	
G-BUZY	Cameron A-250 balloon	P. J. D. Kerr	
G-BUZZ	AB-206B JetRanger 2	European Skytime Ltd	
G-BVAA	Light Aero Avid Aerobat Mk 4	D. T. Searchfield	
G-BVAB	Zenair CH.601HDS	T. J. Smith	
G-BVAC	Zenair CH.601HD	A. G. Cozens	
G-BVAF	Piper J-3C-65 Cub	N. M. Hitchman/France	
G-BVAG	Lindstrand LBL-90A balloon	T. Moult & ptnrs	
G-BVAH	Denney Kitfox Mk.3	D. A. Lord	
G-BVAI	PZL-110 Koliber 150	N. J. & R. F. Morgan	
G-BVAM	Evans VP-1	R. F. Selby	
G-BVAN	M.S.892E Rallye 150	D. R. Stringer/Elstree	
G-BVAO	Colt 25A balloon	J. M. Frazer	
G-BVAW	Staaken Z-1 Flitzer (D-692)	D. J. Evans & L. R. Williams	
G-BVAX	Colt 77A balloon	P. H. Porter	
G-BVAY	Rutan Vari-Eze	D. A. Young	
G-BVAZ	Montgomerie-Bensen B.8MR	Great Orton Group	
G-BVBD	Sikorsky S-52-3	J. Windmill	
G-BVBF	PA-28-151 Warrior	R. K. Spence/Cardiff	
G-BVBG	PA-32R Cherokee Lance 300	R. K. Spence/Cardiff	
G-BVBN	Cameron A-210 balloon	Heart of England Balloons	
G-BVBO	Sikorsky S-52-3	Ilkeston Contractors	
G-BVBP	Avro 683 Lancaster X (KB994)★	D. Copley/Sandtoft	
G-BVBR	Light Aero Avid Speedwing	J. K. Cook	
G-BVBS	Cameron N-77 balloon	Marley Building Materials Ltd	
G-BVBT	D.H.C.1 Chipmunk T.10 (WK511)	T. J. Manna/Cranfield	
G-BVBU	Cameron V-77 balloon	J. Manclark	
G-BVBV	Light Aero Avid Flyer	L. W. M. Summers	
G-BVCA	Cameron N-105 balloon	Unipart Balloon Club	
G-BVCB	Rans S.10 Sakota	M. D. T. Barley	
G-BVCC	Monnett Sonerai 2LT	J. Eggleston	
G-BVCG	Van's RV-6	C. J. F. Flint	
G-BVCJ	Agusta A.109A-II	Castle Air Charters Ltd (G-CLRL/G-EJCB)	
G-BVCL	Rans S.6-116 Coyote II	R. A. Blackbourn & I. H. Clarke	
G-BVCM	Cessna 525 CitationJet	Kwik Fit PLC/Edinburgh	
G-BVCO	FRED Srs 2	I. W. Bremner	

Notes	Reg.	Type	Owner or Operator
	G-BVCP	Piper CP.1 Metisse	C. W. R. Piper
	G-BVCS	Aeronca 7BCM Champion	P. C. Isbell
	G-BVCT	Denney Kitfox Mk 4	A. F. Reid
	G-BVCY	Cameron H-24 balloon	Bryant Group PLC
	G-BVDB	Thunder Ax7-77 balloon	M. J. Smith & J. Towler (G-ORDY)
	G-BVDC	Van's RV-3	J. A. A. Schofield
	G-BVDD	Colt 69A balloon	R. M. Cambridge & D. Harrison-Morris
	G-BVDE	Taylor JT.1 Monoplane	S. G. Hammond
	G-BVDH	PA-28RT-201 Arrow IV	Goodair Leasing Ltd
	G-BVDI	Van's RV-4	D. F. Brown
	G-BVDJ	Campbell Cricket (replica)	S. Jennings
	G-BVDM	Cameron 60 Concept balloon	M. P. Young
	G-BVDN	PA-34-220T Seneca III	Convergence Aviation Ltd (G-IGHA/G-IPUT)
	G-BVDO	Lindstrand LBL-105A balloon	J. Burlinson
	G-BVDP	Sequoia F.8L Falco	T. G. Painter
	G-BVDR	Cameron O-77 balloon	T. Duggan
	G-BVDS	Lindstrand LBL-69A balloon	Lindstrand Balloons Ltd
	G-BVDT	CFM Streak Shadow	H. J. Bennet
	G-BVDW	Thunder Ax8-90 balloon	S. C. Vora
	G-BVDX	Cameron V-90 balloon	R. K. Scott
	G-BVDY	Cameron 60 Concept balloon	K. A. & G. N. Connolly
	G-BVDZ	Taylorcraft BC-12D	P. N. W. England
	G-BVEA	Mosler Motors N.3 Pup	N. Lynch (G-MWEA)/Breighton
	G-BVEH	Jodel D.112	M. L. Copland
	G-BVEJ	Cameron V-90 balloon	J. D. A. Snields & A. R. Craze
	G-BVEK	Cameron 80 Concept balloon	A. D. Malcolm
	G-BVEN	Cameron 80 Concept balloon	Hildon Associates
	G-BVEP	Luscombe 8A Master	B. H. Austen
	G-BVER	D.H.C.2 Beaver 1 (XV268)	Seaflite Ltd (G-BTCM)/Duxford
	G-BVES	Cessna 340A	K. P. Gibbin & I. M. Worthington
	G-BVEU	Cameron O-105 balloon	H. C. Wright
	G-BVEV	PA-34-200 Seneca	R. W. Harris & ptnrs
	G-BVEW	Lindstrand LBL-150A balloon	A. Van Wyk
	G-BVEY	Denney Kitfox Mk 4-1200	J. H. H. Turner
	G-BVEZ	P.84 Jet Provost T.3A (XM479)	Newcastle Jet Provost Co Ltd
	G-BVFA	Rans S.10 Sakota	J. Holme
	G-BVFB	Cameron N-31 balloon	Bath City Council
	G-BVFF	Cameron V-77 balloon	I. R. Warrington
	G-BVFM	Rans S.6-116 Coyote II	J. Gorman
	G-BVFO	Light Aero Avid Speedwing	P. Chisman
	G-BVFP	Cameron V-90 balloon	C. Duppa-Miller
	G-BVFR	CFM Streak Shadow	R. W. Chatterton
	G-BVFS	Slingsby T.31M Cadet	V. M. Crabb
	G-BVFT	Maule M5-235C	Avon Air Services
	G-BVFU	Cameron 105 Sphere SS balloon	Lascar Investments Ltd/Luxembourg
	G-BVFY	Colt 210A balloon	Cheshire Balloon Flights
	G-BVFZ	Maule M5-180C Lunar Rocket	C. N. White
	G-BVGA	Bell 206B JetRanger 3	Findon Air Services/Shoreham
	G-BVGB	Thunder Ax8-105 S2 balloon	M. E. Dunstan-Sewell
	G-BVGE	W.S.55 Whirlwind HAR.10 (XJ729)	J. F. Kelly
	G-BVGF	Shaw Europa	A. Graham & G. G. Beal
	G-BVGG	Lindstrand LBL-69A balloon	Lindstrand Balloons Ltd
	G-BVGH	Hawker Hunter T.7 (XL573)	DAT Enterprises Ltd/North Weald
	G-BVGI	Pereira Osprey II	A. A. Knight
	G-BVGJ	Cameron C-80 balloon	D. T. Watkins
	G-BVGO	Denney Kitfox Mk 4-1200	A. Morgan
	G-BVGR	RAF BE-2e (A1325)	Aero Vintage Ltd
	G-BVGS	Robinson R-22B	Bristol & Wessex Helicopters Ltd
	G-BVGT	Auster J/1 (modified)	P. N. Birch
	G-BVGW	Luscombe 8A Silvaire	L. A. Groves
	G-BVGX	Thunder Ax8-90 S2 balloon	G-BVGX Group/New Zealand
	G-BVGY	Luscombe 8E Silvaire	T. Groves
	G-BVGZ	Fokker Dr.1 (replica) (450/17) ★	Taildragger Classics
	G-BVHC	Grob G.115D-2 Heron	VT Aerospace Ltd/Plymouth
	G-BVHD	Grob G.115D-2 Heron	VT Aerospace Ltd/Plymouth
	G-BVHE	Grob G.115D-2 Heron	VT Aerospace Ltd/Plymouth
	G-BVHF	Grob G.115D-2 Heron	VT Aerospace Ltd/Plymouth
	G-BVHG	Grob G.115D-2 Heron	VT Aerospace Ltd/Plymouth
	G-BVHI	Rans S.10 Sakota	P. D. Rowley
	G-BVHJ	Cameron A-180 balloon	S. J. Boxall
	G-BVHK	Cameron V-77 balloon	A. R. Rich

Reg.	Type	Owner or Operator	Notes
G-BVHL	Nicollier HN.700 Menestrel II	W. Goldsmith	
G-BVHM	PA-38-112 Tomahawk	A. J. Gomes (G-DCAN)	
G-BVHO	Cameron V-90 balloon	N. W. B. Bews	
G-BVHP	Colt 42A balloon	Huntair Ltd	
G-BVHR	Cameron V-90 balloon	G. P. Walton	
G-BVHS	Murphy Rebel	J. R. Malpass	
G-BVHT	Light Aero Avid Speedwing Mk 4	R. S. Holt	
G-BVHV	Cameron N-105 balloon	Flying Pictures Ltd	
G-BVHY	BN-2T-4R Defender 4000	B-N Group Ltd/Bembridge	
G-BVIA	Rand-Robinson KR-2	K. Atkinson	
G-BVIC	EE Canberra B.6 (XH568)	Classic Aviation Projects Ltd/ Bruntingthorpe	
G-BVID	Lindstrand Lozenge SS balloon	Respatex International Ltd	
G-BVIE	PA-18 Super Cub 95 (modified)	J. C. Best (G-CLIK/G-BLMB)	
G-BVIF	Montgomerie-Bensen B.8MR	R. M. & D. Mann	
G-BVIG	Cameron A-250 balloon	Balloon Flights International Ltd	
G-BVIH	PA-28-161 Warrior II	Ocean Developments Ltd (G-GFCE/ G-BNJP)	
G-BVIK	Maule MXT-7-180 Star Rocket	R. D. Masters	
G-BVIL	Maule MXT-7-180 Star Rocket	K. & S. C. Knight	
G-BVIM	Cameron V-77 balloon	The Ballooning Business Ltd	
G-BVIN	Rans S.6-ESA Coyote II	T. J. Wilkinson	
G-BVIR	Lindstrand LBL-69A balloon	Aerial Promotions Ltd	
G-BVIS	Brügger MB.2 Colibri	B. H. Shaw	
G-BVIT	Campbell Cricket	D. R. Owen	
G-BVIV	Light Aero Avid Speedwing	M. Burton	
G-BVIW	PA-18-Super Cub 150	C. H. Rodger	
G-BVIX	Lindstrand LBL-180A balloon	European Balloon Display Co Ltd	
G-BVIZ	Shaw Europa	T. J. Punter & P. G. Jeffers	
G-BVJA	Fokker 100	bmi regional	
G-BVJB	Fokker 100	bmi regional	
G-BVJC	Fokker 100	bmi regional	
G-BVJD	Fokker 100	bmi regional	
G-BVJE	AS.350B-1 Ecureuil	PLM Dollar Group Ltd	
G-BVJF	Montgomerie-Bensen B.8MR	D. M. F. Harvey	
G-BVJG	Cyclone AX3/K	T. D. Reid (G-MYOP)	
G-BVJH	Aero Designs Pulsar	J. P. Kynaston	
G-BVJK	Glaser-Dirks DG.800A	B. A. Eastwell/Ringmer	
G-BVJN	Shaw Europa	JN Europa Group	
G-BVJT	Cessna F.406	Nor Leasing	
G-BVJU	Evans VP-1	BVJU Flying Club & Associates	
G-BVJX	Marquart MA.5 Charger	M. L. Martin/Redhill	
G-BVJZ	PA-28-161 Warrior II	A. R. Fowkes/Denham	
G-BVKA	Boeing 737-59D	bmi british midland	
G-BVKB	Boeing 737-59D	bmi british midland	
G-BVKC	Boeing 737-59D	bmi british midland	
G-BVKD	Boeing 737-59D	bmi british midland	
G-BVKF	Shaw Europa	T. R. Sinclair	
G-BVKG	Colt Flying Hot Dog SS balloon	Longbreak Ltd/USA	
G-BVKH	Thunder Ax8-90 balloon	R. G. Gruzelier	
G-BVKJ	Bensen B.8	A. G. Foster	
G-BVKK	Slingsby T.61F Venture T.2	K. E. Ballington	
G-BVKL	Cameron A-180 balloon	W. I. & C. Hooker	
G-BVKM	Rutan Vari-Eze	J. P. G. Lindquist/Switzerland	
G-BVKR	Sikorsky S-76A	Bristow Helicopters Ltd	
G-BVKU	Slingsby T.61F Venture T.2	G-BVKU Syndicate	
G-BVKX	Colt 14A balloon	H. C. J. Williams	
G-BVKZ	Thunder Ax9-120 balloon	D. J. Head	
G-BVLC	Cameron N-42 balloon	Cameron Balloons Ltd	
G-BVLD	Campbell Cricket (replica)	C. Berry	
G-BVLE	McCandless M.4 gyroplane	H. Walls	
G-BVLF	CFM Starstreak Shadow SS-D	B. R. Johnson	
G-BVLG	AS.355F-1 Twin Squirrel	PLM Dollar Group PLC	
G-BVLH	Shaw Europa	D. Barraclough	
G-BVLI	Cameron V-77 balloon	J. Lewis-Richardson/New Zealand	
G-BVLK	Rearwin 8125 Cloudster	M. C. Hiscock	
G-BVLL	Lindstrand LBL-210A balloon	A. G. E. Faulkner	
G-BVLP	PA-38-112 Tomahawk	D. A. Whitmore	
G-BVLR	Van's RV-4	RV4 Group	
G-BVLS	Thunder Ax8-90 S2 balloon	J. R. Henderson	
G-BVLT	Bellanca 7GCBC Citabria	M. D. Hinge	
G-BVLU	D.31 Turbulent	C. D. Bancroft	
G-BVLV	Shaw Europa	Euro 39 Group	

Notes	Reg.	Type	Owner or Operator
	G-BVLW	Light Aero Avid Flyer Mk 4	D. M. Johnstone/Shobdon
	G-BVLX	Slingsby T.61F Venture T.2	Fulmar Gliding Club/Kinloss
	G-BVLZ	Lindstrand LBL-120A balloon	Balloon Flights Club Ltd
	G-BVMA	Beech 200 Super King Air	Manhattan Air Ltd (G-VPLC)/Blackbushe
	G-BVMC	Robinson R-44 Astro	E. Wooton
	G-BVMD	Luscombe 8E Silvaire	G. M. Scott
	G-BVMF	Cameron V-77 balloon	P. A. Meecham
	G-BVMH	WAG-Aero Sport Trainer (39624)	R. A. Durance
	G-BVMI	PA-18 Super Cub 150	S. Sampson
	G-BVMJ	Cameron 95 Eagle SS balloon	R. D. Sargeant
	G-BVML	Lindstrand LBL-210A balloon	Ballooning Adventures Ltd
	G-BVMM	Robin HR.200/100	R. H. Ashforth
	G-BVMN	Ken Brock KB-2 gyroplane	S. McCullagh
	G-BVMR	Cameron V-90 balloon	I. R. Comley
	G-BVMU	Yakovlev Yak-52 (09)	A. L. Hall-Carpenter
	G-BVMZ	Robin HR.100/210	Chiltern Handbags (London) Ltd/Booker
	G-BVNG	D.H.60G-III Moth Major	J. A. Pothecary/Shoreham
	G-BVNI	Taylor JT-2 Titch	T. V. Adamson/Rufforth
	G-BVNL	R. Commander 114	S. J. Healey
	G-BVNM	Boeing 737-4S3	British Airways (G-BPKA)
	G-BVNN	Boeing 737-4S3	British Airways (G-BPKB)
	G-BVNO	Boeing 737-4S3	British Airways (G-BPKE)
	G-BVNR	Cameron N-105 balloon	Liquigas SPA/Italy
	G-BVNS	PA-28-181 Archer II	Scottish Airways Flyers (Prestwick) Ltd
	G-BVNU	FLS Aerospace Sprint Club	Sunhawk Ltd/North Weald
	G-BVNY	Rans S.7 Courier	G- Doyle & P. Morris
	G-BVOA	PA-28-181 Archer II	Millen Aviation Services
	G-BVOB	F.27 Friendship Mk 500	BAC Express Airlines Ltd
	G-BVOC	Cameron V-90 balloon	S. A. Masey
	G-BVOG	Cameron RN-9 balloon	Cameron Balloons Ltd
	G-BVOH	Campbell Cricket (replica)	G. A. Speich
	G-BVOI	Rans S.6-116 Coyote II	A. P. Bacon
	G-BVOK	Yakovlev Yak-52 (55)	D. J. Gilmour/North Weald
	G-BVON	Lindstrand LBL-105A balloon	P. A. Lindstrand/USA
	G-BVOO	Lindstrand LBL-105A balloon	T. G. Church
	G-BVOP	Cameron N-90 balloon	Cambury Ltd
	G-BVOR	CFM Streak Shadow	K. Fowler
	G-BVOS	Shaw Europa	Durham Europa Group
	G-BVOU	H.S.748 Srs 2A	Emerald Airways Ltd/Liverpool
	G-BVOV	H.S.748 Srs 2A	Emerald Airways Ltd/Liverpool
	G-BVOW	Shaw Europa	Europa Syndicate
	G-BVOX	Taylorcraft F-22	Jones Samuel Ltd
	G-BVOY	Rotorway Executive 90	Southern Helicopters Ltd
	G-BVOZ	Colt 56A balloon	British School of Ballooning
	G-BVPA	Thunder Ax8-105 S2 balloon	Firefly Balloon Promotions
	G-BVPD	C.A.S.A. 1.131E Jungmann 2000	D. Bruton
	G-BVPK	Cameron O-90 balloon	D. V. Fowler
	G-BVPL	Zenair CH.601HD	A. F. Walters
	G-BVPM	Evans VP-2 Coupé	P. Marigold
	G-BVPN	Piper J-3C-65 Cub	C. Willoughby (G-TAFY)
	G-BVPP	Folland Gnat T.1 (XR993)	T. J. Manna/Cranfield
	G-BVPR	Robinson R-22B	E. Bailey (G-KNIT)/Staverton
	G-BVPS	Jodel D.112	P. J. Sharp
	G-BVPV	Lindstrand LBL-77B balloon	A. R. Greensides
	G-BVPW	Rans S.6-116 Coyote II	J. G. Beesley
	G-BVPX	Bensen B.8 (modified) Tyro Gyro	A. W. Harvey
	G-BVPY	CFM Streak Shadow	R. J. Mitchell
	G-BVRA	Shaw Europa	N. E. Stokes
	G-BVRH	Taylorcraft BL.65	M. J. Smith
	G-BVRI	Thunder Ax6-56 balloon	A. Van Wyk
	G-BVRK	Rans S.6-ESA Coyote II	J. Secular (G-MYPK)
	G-BVRL	Lindstrand LBL-21A balloon	Exclusive Ballooning
	G-BVRN	F.27 Friendship Mk 500	Compania Canaria de Transporte Aereo SA/Tenerife
	G-BVRR	Lindstrand LBL-77A balloon	G. C. Elson/Spain
	G-BVRU	Lindstrand LBL-105A balloon	Flying Pictures Ltd
	G-BVRV	Van's RV-4	A. Troughton
	G-BVRY	Cyclone Ax3/582	A. N. Bowerman
	G-BVRZ	PA-18 Super Cub 95	R. G. Warwick
	G-BVSB	Team Minimax	D. G. Palmer
	G-BVSD	SE.3130 Alouette II (V-54)	M. J. Cuttell
	G-BVSF	Aero Designs Pulsar	S. N. & R. J. Freestone
	G-BVSJ	BN-2T Turbine Islander	B-N Group Ltd/Bembridge

Reg.	Type	Owner or Operator	Notes
G-BVSM	RAF 2000 gyroplane	K. Quigley	
G-BVSN	Light Aero Avid Speedwing	A. S. Markey	
G-BVSO	Cameron A-120 balloon	J. F. Till	
G-BVSP	P.84 Jet Provost T.3A (XM370)	H. G. Hodges & Son Ltd	
G-BVSS	Jodel D.150	A. P. Burns	
G-BVST	Jodel D.150	A. Shipp/Breighton	
G-BVSX	Team Minimax 91	G. N. Smith	
G-BVSY	Thunder Ax9-120 balloon	G. R. Elson/Spain	
G-BVSZ	Pitts S-1E (S) Special	R. C. F. Bailey	
G-BVTA	Tri-R Kis	P. J. Webb	
G-BVTC	P.84 Jet Provost T.5A (XW333)	Global Aviation Ltd/Binbrook	
G-BVTD	CFM Streak Shadow	M. Walton	
G-BVTE	Fokker 70	bmi regional	
G-BVTF	Fokker 70	bmi regional	
G-BVTG	Fokker 70	bmi regional	
G-BVTJ	Aérospatiale ATR-72-202	CityFlyer Express Ltd/BA Express	
G-BVTK	Aérospatiale ATR-72-202	CityFlyer Express Ltd/BA Express	
G-BVTL	Colt 31A balloon	A. Lindsay	
G-BVTM	Cessna F.152 II	RAF Halton Aeroplane Club (G-WACS)	
G-BVTN	Cameron N-90 balloon	P. Zulehner/Austria	
G-BVTO	PA-28-151 Warrior	Falcon Flying Services (G-SEWL)/ Biggin Hill	
G-BVTV	Rotorway Executive 90	Southern Helicopters Ltd	
G-BVTW	Aero Designs Pulsar	J. D. Webb	
G-BVTX	D.H.C.1 Chipmunk 22A (WP809)	TX Flying Group	
G-BVUA	Cameron O-105 balloon	D. C. Eager	
G-BVUC	Colt 56A balloon	Thunder & Colt	
G-BVUG	Betts TB.1 (Stampe SV-4C)	William Tomkins Ltd (G-BEUS)	
G-BVUH	Thunder Ax6-65B balloon	N. C. A. Crawley	
G-BVUI	Lindstrand LBL-25A balloon	J. W. Hole	
G-BVUJ	Ken Brock KB-2 gyroplane	R. J. Hutchinson	
G-BVUK	Cameron V-77 balloon	H. G. Griffiths & W. A. Steel	
G-BVUM	Rans S.6-116 Coyote II	M. A. Abbott	
G-BVUN	Van's RV-4	A. E. Kay	
G-BVUO	Cameron 'R-150 balloon	M. Sevrin/Belgium	
G-BVUU	Cameron C-80 balloon	T. M. C. McCoy	
G-BVUV	Shaw Europa	R. J. Mills	
G-BVUZ	Cessna 120	N. O. Anderson	
G-BVVA	Yakovlev Yak-52	T. W. Freeman/Little Gransden	
G-BVVB	Carlson Sparrow Mk II	L. M. McCullen	
G-BVVC	Hawker Hunter F.6A (XF516)	Classic Jet Aircraft Co	
G-BVVE	Jodel D.112	G. W. Jarvis	
G-BVVG	Nanchang CJ-6A	G. Beda/France	
G-BVVH	Shaw Europa	T. G. Hoult	
G-BVVI	Hawker Audax I (K5600)	Aero Vintage Ltd	
G-BVVK	D.H.C.6 Twin Otter 310	Loganair Ltd/BA Express	
G-BVVL	EAA Acro Sport II	G. A. Breen/Portugal	
G-BVVM	Zenair CH.601HD	A. Rooker	
G-BVVN	Brügger MB.2 Colibri	N. F. Andrews	
G-BVVP	Shaw Europa	W. Komm/Germany	
G-BVVR	Stits SA-3A Playboy	A. D. Pearce	
G-BVVS	Van's RV-4	E. G. & N. S. C. English	
G-BVVT	Colt 240A balloon	R. W. Keron	
G-BVVU	Lindstrand LBL Four SS balloon	Magical Adventures Ltd	
G-BVVW	Yakovlev Yak-52	J. E. Blackman	
G-BVVX	Yakovlev Yak-18A	J. M. & E. M. Wicks	
G-BVVZ	Corby CJ-1 Starlet	P. V. Flack	
G-BVWA	M. S. 880B Rallye Club	G. K. Brunwin	
G-BVWB	Thunder Ax8-90 S2 balloon	S. C. Clayton	
G-BVWC	EE Canberra B.6 (WK163)	Classic Aviation Projects Ltd/ Bruntingthorpe	
G-BVWE	Cameron C-80 balloon	Mid-Bucks Farmers Balloon Group	
G-BVWM	Shaw Europa	Europa Syndicate	
G-BVWP	D.H.C.1 Chipmunk 22 (WP856)	T. W. M. Beck	
G-BVWW	Lindstrand LBL-90A balloon	Drawflight Ltd	
G-BVWX	VPM M.16 Tandem Trainer	M. L. Smith	
G-BVWY	Porterfield CP.65	B. Morris	
G-BVWZ	PA-32-301 Saratoga	N. N. Kenny	
G-BVXA	Cameron N-105 balloon	R. E. Jones	
G-BVXB	Cameron V-77 balloon	J. A. Lawton	
G-BVXC	EE Canberra B.6 (WT333)	Classic Aviation Projects Ltd/ Bruntingthorpe	
G-BVXD	Cameron O-84 balloon	N. J. Langley	

Notes	Reg.	Type	Owner or Operator
	G-BVXE	Steen Skybolt	J. Buglass (G-LISA)
	G-BVXF	Cameron O-120 balloon	Gone With The Wind Ltd/Chile
	G-BVXG	Lindstrand LBL-90A balloon	G. C. Elson/Spain
	G-BVXJ	C.A.S.A. 1.133 Jungmeister	J. D. Haslam
	G-BVXK	Yakovlev Yak-52 (26)	E. Gavazzi
	G-BVXM	AS.350B Ecureuil	The Berkeley Leisure Group Ltd
	G-BVXR	D.H.104 Devon C.2 (XA880)	M. Whale & M. W. A. Lunn
	G-BVXS	Taylorcraft BC-12D	J. M. Allison
	G-BVXW	SC.7 Skyvan Srs 3A Variant 100	Hunting Aviation Ltd/ Weston-on-the-Green
	G-BVYA	Airbus A.320-231	jmc Airlines Ltd
	G-BVYB	Airbus A.320-231	jmc Airlines Ltd
	G-BVYC	Airbus A.320-231	jmc Airlines Ltd
	G-BVYF	PA-31-350 Navajo Chieftain	J. A. Rees & ptnrs (G-SAVE)
	G-BVYG	CEA DR.300/180	Ulster Gliding Club Ltd/
	G-BVYK	Team Minimax	S. B. Churchill
	G-BVYM	CEA DR. 300/180	London Gliding Club (Pty) Ltd/Dunstable
	G-BVYO	Robin R.2160	Aviation Rentals
	G-BVYP	PA-25 Pawnee 235B	Bidford Airfield Ltd
	G-BVYR	Cameron A-250 balloon	Voyager Balloons Ltd
	G-BVYT	QAC Quickie Q.2	C. A. McGee
	G-BVYU	Cameron A-140 balloon	Sky Operations
	G-BVYX	Light Aero Avid Speedwing Mk 4	G. J. Keen
	G-BVYY	Pietenpol Air Camper	J. R. Orchard
	G-BVYZ	Stemme S.10V	L. Gubbay & S. Sagar
	G-BVZD	Tri-R Kis Cruiser	D. R. Morgan
	G-BVZE	Boeing 737-59D	bmi british midland
	G-BVZG	Boeing 737-5Q8	bmi british midland
	G-BVZH	Boeing 737-5Q8	bmi british midland
	G-BVZI	Boeing 737-5Q8	bmi british midland
	G-BVZJ	Rand-Robinson KR-2	J. P. McConnell-Wood
	G-BVZM	Cessna 210M	J. J. M. Feeney
	G-BVZN	Cameron C-80 balloon	Sky Fly Balloons
	G-BVZO	Rans S.6-116 Coyote II	P. Atkinson
	G-BVZR	Zenair CH.601HD	J. D. White/Tollerton
	G-BVZT	Lindstrand LBL-90A balloon	Pork Farms Bowyers
	G-BVZV	Rans S.6-116 Coyote II	A. G. Cameron & W. G. Dunn
	G-BVZX	Cameron H-34 balloon	Chianti Balloon Club/Italy
	G-BVZZ	D.H.C.1 Chipmunk 22 (WP795)	Portsmouth Naval Gliding Club/ Lee-on-Solent
	G-BWAA	Cameron N-133 balloon	Bailey Balloons
	G-BWAB	Jodel D.14	W. A. Braim
	G-BWAC	Waco YKS-7	D. N. Peters
	G-BWAD	RAF 2000GT gyroplane	Newtonair Gyroplanes Ltd
	G-BWAE	RAF 2000GT gyroplane	D. P. Kearns
	G-BWAF	Hawker Hunter F.6A (XG160)	R. V. Aviation Ltd/Bournemouth
	G-BWAG	Cameron O-120 balloon	P. M. Skinner
	G-BWAH	Montgomerie-Bensen B.8MR	J. B. Allan
	G-BWAI	CFM Streak Shadow	N. J. Mines
	G-BWAJ	Cameron V-77 balloon	R. S. & S. H. Ham
	G-BWAK	Robinson R-22B	Caudwell Communications Ltd
	G-BWAO	Cameron C-80 balloon	Virgin Airship & Balloon Co Ltd
	G-BWAP	FRED Srs 3	G. A. Shepherd
	G-BWAR	Denney Kitfox Mk 3	I. Wightman
	G-BWAT	Pietenpol Air Camper	P. W. Aitchison
	G-BWAU	Cameron V-90 balloon	K. M. & A. M. F. Hall
	G-BWAV	Schweizer 269C	Helihire
	G-BWAW	Lindstrand LBL-77A balloon	D. Bareford
	G-BWBA	Cameron V-65 balloon	Dante Balloon Group
	G-BWBB	Lindstrand LBL-14A balloon	Oxford Promotions (UK) Ltd
	G-BWBC	Cameron N-90AS balloon	Wetterauer Montgolfieren/Germany
	G-BWBE	Colt Flying Ice Cream Cone SS balloon	Benedikt Haggeney GmbH/Germany
	G-BWBF	Colt Flying Ice Cream Cone SS balloon	Benedikt Haggeney GmbH/Germany
	G-BWBG	Cvjetkovic CA-65 Skyfly	T. White & M. C. Fawkes
	G-BWBH	Colt Fork Lift Truck SS balloon	Jungheinrich AG/Germany
	G-BWBI	Taylorcraft F-22A	P. J. Wallace
	G-BWBJ	Colt 21A balloon	U. Schneider/Germany
	G-BWBT	Lindstrand LBL-90A balloon	British Telecommunications PLC
	G-BWBY	Schleicher ASH.26E	J. S. Ward

Reg.	Type	Owner or Operator	Notes
G-BWBZ	ARV Super 2	J. N. C. Shields & D. J. Millar (G-BMWG)/ Newtownards	
G-BWCA	CFM Streak Shadow	S. Woolmington	
G-BWCC	Van Den Bemden Gas balloon	Piccard Balloon Group	
G-BWCG	Lindstrand LBL-42A balloon	Oxford Promotions (UK) Ltd	
G-BWCK	Everett Srs 2 gyroplane	A. C. S. M. Hart	
G-BWCO	Dornier Do.28D-2	Wingglider Ltd/Hibaldstow	
G-BWCS	P.84 Jet Provost T.5 (XW293)	R. E. Todd/Sandtoft	
G-BWCT	Tipsy T.66 Nipper 1	J. S. Hemmings & C. R. Steer	
G-BWCV	Shaw Europa	G. C. McKirdy	
G-BWCW	Barnett J4B rotorcraft	S. H. Kirkby	
G-BWCY	Murphy Rebel	A. Konieczek	
G-BWDE	PA-31P Pressurised Navajo	Tomkat Aviation Ltd (G-HWKN)	
G-BWDF	PZL-104 Wilga 35A	Shivair Ltd	
G-BWDH	Cameron N-105 balloon	Bridges Van Hire Ltd	
G-BWDM	Lindstrand LBL-120A balloon	G. D. & L. Fitzpatrick	
G-BWDO	Sikorsky S-76B	Haughey Air Ltd	
G-BWDP	Shaw Europa	W. Hueltz/Germany	
G-BWDR	P.84 Jet Provost T.3A (XM376)	W. O. Bayazid/North Weald	
G-BWDS	P.84 Jet Provost T.3A (XM424)	J. Sinclair	
G-BWDT	PA-34-220T Seneca II	H. R. Chambers (G-BKHS)/Biggin Hill	
G-BWDU	Cameron V-90 balloon	Bath & West Security	
G-BWDV	Schweizer 269C	Oxford Aviation Services Ltd/Kidlington	
G-BWDX	Shaw Europa	J. B. Crane	
G-BWDZ	Sky 105-24 balloon	Skyride Balloons Ltd	
G-BWEA	Lindstrand LBL-120A balloon	S. R. Seager	
G-BWEB	P.84 Jet Provost T.5A	D. W. N. Johnson	
G-BWEC	Cassutt-Colson Variant	N. R. Thomason & M. P. J. Hill	
G-BWED	Thunder Ax7-77 balloon	J. Tod	
G-BWEE	Cameron V-42 balloon	Aeromantics Ltd	
G-BWEF	SNCAN Stampe SV-4C	Acebell BWEF Syndicate (G-BOVL)	
G-BWEG	Shaw Europa	Wessex Europa Group	
G-BWEH	HOAC Katana DV.20	Lowlog Ltd/Elstree	
G-BWEL	Sky 200-24 balloon	H-O-T Air Balloons	
G-BWEM	V.S.358 Seafire L.IIIC (RX168)	C. J. Warrilow & S. W. Atkins	
G-BWEN	Macair Merlin GT	B. W. Davies	
G-BWEO	Lindstrand AM400 balloon	Lindstrand Balloons Ltd	
G-BWER	Lindstrand AM400 balloon	Lindstrand Balloons Ltd	
G-BWEU	Cessna F.152 II	Flight Ltd	
G-BWEV	Cessna 152 II	Haimoss Ltd	
G-BWEW	Cameron N-105 balloon	Unipart Balloon Club	
G-BWEY	Bensen B.8	F. G. Shepherd	
G-BWEZ	Piper J-3C-65 Cub (436021)	J. G. McTaggart/Cumbernauld	
G-BWFD	HOAC Katana DV.20	Cumberauld Flying School Ltd	
G-BWFE	HOAC Katana DV.20	Airways Ltd	
G-BWFG	Robin HR.200/120B	Atlantic Air Transport Ltd/Coventry	
G-BWFH	Shaw Europa	B. L. Wratten	
G-BWFI	HOAC Katana DV.20	Lowlog Ltd/Elstree	
G-BWFJ	Evans VP-1	P. A. West	
G-BWFM	Yakovlev Yak-50	Classic Aviation Ltd/Duxford	
G-BWFN	Hapi Cygnet SF-2A	T. Crawford	
G-BWFO	Colomban MC.15 Cri-Cri	O. G. Jones	
G-BWFP	Yakovlev Yak-52	M. C. Lee/Manchester	
G-BWFR	Hawker Hunter F.58 (J-4031)	The Old Flying Machine Co. Ltd/Duxford	
G-BWFS	Hawker Hunter F.58 (J-4058)	The Old Flying Machine Co. Ltd/Duxford	
G-BWFT	Hawker Hunter T.8M (XL602)	T8M Group	
G-BWFV	HOAC Katana DV.20	Plane Talking Ltd/Elstree	
G-BWFX	Shaw Europa	A. D. Stewart	
G-BWFY	AS.350B-1 Ecureuil	PLM Dollar Group Ltd/Inverness	
G-BWFZ	Murphy Rebel	I. E. Spencer (G-SAVS)	
G-BWGF	P.84 Jet Provost T.5A (XW325)	Specialscope Jet Provost Group/ Woodford	
G-BWGG	MH.1521C-1 Broussard	M. J. Burnett & R. B. Maalouf/France	
G-BWGH	Shaw Europa	M. H. B. Heathman	
G-BWGJ	Chilton DW.1A	T. J. Harrison	
G-BWGK	Hawker Hunter GA.11 (XE689)	GA11 Group/Exeter	
G-BWGL	Hawker Hunter T.8C (XJ615)	Classic Aviation Ltd/Duxford	
G-BWGM	Hawker Hunter T.8C (XE665)	The Admirals Barge/Exeter	
G-BWGN	Hawker Hunter T.8C (WT722)	T8C Group	
G-BWGO	Slingsby T.67M Firefly 200	R. Gray	
G-BWGP	Cameron C-80 balloon	D. J. Groombridge	
G-BWGR	NA TB-25N Mitchell (151632) ★	D. Copley/Sandtoft	
G-BWGS	P.84 Jet Provost T.5A	K. K. Gerstorfer	

Notes	Reg.	Type	Owner or Operator
	G-BWGT	P.84 Jet Provost T.4	R. E. Todd/Sandtoft
	G-BWGU	Cessna 150F	Goodair Leasing Ltd
	G-BWGX	Cameron N-42 balloon	Newbury Building Soc.
	G-BWGY	HOAC Katana DV.20	Plane Talking Ltd/Elstree
	G-BWGZ	HOAC Katana DV.20	HOAC Austria Weiner Neustadt GmbH
	G-BWHA	Hawker Hurricane IIB (Z5252)	Historic Flying Ltd/Duxford
	G-BWHB	Cameron O-65 balloon	G. Aimo/Italy
	G-BWHC	Cameron N-77 balloon	Travelsphere Ltd
	G-BWHD	Lindstrand LBL-31A balloon	Army Air Corps Balloon Club
	G-BWHF	PA-31-325 Navajo	Awyr Cymru Cyf/Welshpool
	G-BWHG	Cameron N-65 balloon	M. Stefanini & F. B. Alaoui
	G-BWHH	PA-18 Super Cub 135 (44)	JME Ltd
	G-BWHI	D.H.C.1 Chipmunk 22A (WK624)	N. E. M. Clare
	G-BWHK	Rans S.6-116 Coyote II	M. Knowles
	G-BWHM	Sky 140-24 balloon	C. J. S. Limon
	G-BWHP	C.A.S.A. 1.131E Jungmann (S4+A07)	J. F. Hopkins
	G-BWHR	Tipsy Nipper T.66 Srs 1	L. R. Marnef
	G-BWHS	RAF 2000 gyroplane	J. M. Cox
	G-BWHT	Everett Campbell Cricket	D. Brown
	G-BWHU	Westland Scout AH.1 (XR595)	N. J. F. Boston
	G-BWHV	Denney Kitfox Mk 2	A. C. Dove
	G-BWHW	Cameron A-180 balloon	Societe Bombard SARL/France
	G-BWHY	Robinson R-22	Finnigan-Wood Ltd
	G-BWIA	Rans S.10 Sakota	P. A. Beck
	G-BWIB	SA Bulldog Srs 120/122	Aerofab Restorations
	G-BWID	D.31 Turbulent	A. M. Turney
	G-BWII	Cessna 150G	J. D. G. Hicks (G-BSKB)
	G-BWIK	D.H.82A Tiger Moth (NL985)	B. J. Ellis
	G-BWIL	Rans S.10 Sakota	J. C. Longmore (G-WIEN)
	G-BWIP	Cameron N-90 balloon	Noble Adventures Ltd
	G-BWIR	Dornier Do.328-100	ScotAirways Ltd
	G-BWIT	QAC Quickie 1	D. E. Johnson & ptnrs/Coventry
	G-BWIU	Hawker Hunter F.58 (XG232)	Classic Aviation Ltd/Duxford
	G-BWIV	Shaw Europa	T. G. Ledbury
	G-BWIW	Sky 180-24 balloon	J. A. Cooper
	G-BWIX	Sky 120-24 balloon	J. M. Percival
	G-BWJB	Thunder Ax8-105 balloon	Justerini & Brooks Ltd
	G-BWJG	Mooney M.20J	Samic Ltd
	G-BWJH	Shaw Europa	D. P. Cripps & P. J. Rudling
	G-BWJI	Cameron V-90 balloon	Calarel Developments Ltd
	G-BWJM	Bristol M.1C (replica) (C4918)	The Shuttleworth Collection/O. Warden
	G-BWJN	Montgomerie-Bensen B.8	M. Johnston
	G-BWJP	Cessna 172C	T. W. R. Case
	G-BWJT	Yakovlev Yak-50 (01385)	D. Bonucchi
	G-BWJW	Westland Scout AH.1 (XV130)	C. L. Holdsworth
	G-BWJY	D.H.C.1 Chipmunk 22 (WG469)	K. J. Thompson
	G-BWKB	Hawker Hunter F.58 (J-4081)	Classic Aviation Ltd/Duxford
	G-BWKD	Cameron O-120 balloon	K.E. Viney
	G-BWKE	Cameron AS-105GD airship	W. Arnold/Germany
	G-BWKF	Cameron N-105 balloon	R. M. M. Botti/Italy
	G-BWKG	Shaw Europa	T. C. Jackson
	G-BWKJ	Rans S.7 Courier	R. W. Skelton
	G-BWKK	Auster A.O.P.9 (XP279)	C. A. Davis & D. R. White
	G-BWKR	Sky 90-24 balloon	B. Drawbridge
	G-BWKT	Stephens Akro Laser	P. D. Begley
	G-BWKU	Cameron A-250 balloon	British School of Ballooning
	G-BWKV	Cameron V-77 balloon	Poppies (UK) Ltd
	G-BWKW	Thunder Ax8-90 balloon	Venice Simplon Orient Express Ltd
	G-BWKX	Cameron A-250 balloon	Hot Airlines/Thailand
	G-BWKZ	Lindstrand LBL-77A balloon	J. H. Dobson
	G-BWLA	Lindstrand LBL-69A balloon	Virgin Airship & Balloon Co Ltd
	G-BWLD	Cameron O-120 balloon	D. Pedri & ptnrs/Italy
	G-BWLF	Cessna 404	Nor Leasing (G-BNXS)
	G-BWLJ	Taylorcraft DCO-65	C. Evans
	G-BWLL	Murphy Rebel	F. W. Parker
	G-BWLM	Sky 65-24 balloon	Dachstein Tauern Balloons KG/Austria
	G-BWLN	Cameron O-84 balloon	Reggiana Riduttori SRL/Italy
	G-BWLP	HOAC Katana DV.20	Plane Talking Ltd/Elstree
	G-BWLR	MH.1521M Broussard (185)	Chicory Crops Ltd
	G-BWLS	HOAC Katana DV.20-100	Shadow Aviation/Elstree
	G-BWLT	HOAC Katana DV.20	Plane Talking Ltd/Elstree
	G-BWLV	HOAC Katana DV.20	Plane Talking Ltd/Elstree

Reg.	Type	Owner or Operator	Notes
G-BWLW	Light Aero Avid Speedwing Mk4	P. C. & S. A. Creswick	
G-BWLX	Westland Scout AH.1 (XV134)	R. E. Dagless	
G-BWLY	Rotorway Executive 90	P. W. & I. P. Bewley	
G-BWLZ	Wombat gyroplane	M. R. Harrisson	
G-BWMA	Colt 105A balloon	C. C. Duppa-Miller	
G-BWMB	Jodel D.119	C. Hughes	
G-BWMC	Cessna 182P	Eggesford Eagles Flying Group	
G-BWMD	Enstrom 480	Lamindene Ltd	
G-BWMF	Gloster Meteor T.7 (WA591)	Meteor Flight (Yatesbury)	
G-BWMG	AS.332L Super Puma	Bristow Helicopters Ltd	
G-BWMH	Lindstrand LBL-77B balloon	J. W. Hole	
G-BWMI	PA-28RT-201T Turbo Arrow IV	Oxford Aviation Services Ltd/Kidlington	
G-BWMJ	Nieuport 17/2B (replica) (B3459)	R. Gauld-Galliers & L. J. Day	
G-BWMK	D.H.82A Tiger Moth (T8191)	Schneider Trophy Ltd/Welshpool	
G-BWML	Cameron A-275 balloon	A. J. Street	
G-BWMN	Rans S.7 Courier	G. J. Knee & G. Keyser	
G-BWMO	Oldfield Baby Lakes	P. J. Tanulak (G-CIII)	
G-BWMS	D.H.82A Tiger Moth	Foundation Early Birds/Netherlands	
G-BWMU	Cameron 105 Monster Truck SS balloon	Magical Adventures Ltd/Canada	
G-BWMV	Colt AS-105 Mk II airship	D. Stuber/Germany	
G-BWMX	D.H.C.1 Chipmunk 22 (WG407)	407th Flying Group	
G-BWMY	Cameron Bradford & Bingley SS balloon	Magical Adventures Ltd/USA	
G-BWNB	Cessna 152 II	Galair International Ltd	
G-BWNC	Cessna 152 II	Galair International Ltd	
G-BWND	Cessna 152 II	Galair International Ltd	
G-BWNH	Cameron A-375 balloon	Noble Adventures Ltd	
G-BWNI	PA-24 Comanche 180	T. D. Cooper & D. F. Hurn	
G-BWNJ	Hughes 269C	L. R. Fenwick	
G-BWNK	D,H,C,1 Chipmunk 22 (WD390)	B. Whitworth	
G-BWNM	PA-28R Cherokee Arrow 180	D. Houghton	
G-BWNO	Cameron O-90 balloon	M. A. Pratt & T. Knight	
G-BWNP	Cameron 90 Club SS balloon	C. J. Davies & P. Spellward	
G-BWNR	PA-38-112 Tomahawk	APB Leasing Ltd/Liverpool	
G-BWNS	Cameron O-90 balloon	Smithair Ltd	
G-BWNT	D.H.C.1 Chipmunk 22 (WP901)	Three Point Aviation	
G-BWNU	PA-38-112 Tomahawk	G-BWNU Group	
G-BWNX	Thunder Ax10-180 S2 balloon	MJN Balloon Management Ltd (G-OWBC)	
G-BWNY	Aeromot AMT-200 Super Ximango	H. G. Nicklin	
G-BWNZ	Agusta A.109C	Anglo Beef Processors Ltd	
G-BWOA	Sky 105-24 balloon	Akhter Group Holdings PLC	
G-BWOB	Luscombe 8F Silvaire	P. J. Tanulak & H. T. Law	
G-BWOD	Yakovlev Yak-52 (139)	Insurefast Ltd/Sywell	
G-BWOE	Yakovlev Yak-3U	R. G. Hanna/Duxford (G-BUXZ)	
G-BWOF	P.84 Jet Provost T.5	Techair London Ltd	
G-BWOK	Lindstrand LBL GB-1000 balloon	Lindstrand Balloons Ltd	
G-BWOM	Cessna 550 Citation II	Ferron Trading Ltd	
G-BWON	Shaw Europa	G. T. Birks	
G-BWOR	PA-18 Super Cub 135	C. D. Baird	
G-BWOT	P.84 Jet Provost T.3A (XN459)	Red Pelicans Formation Ltd/North Weald	
G-BWOU	Hawker Hunter F.58A (XF303)	Old Flying Machine Co. Ltd/Duxford	
G-BWOV	Enstrom F-28A	A. P. Goddard	
G-BWOW	Cameron N-105 balloon	S. J. Colin & A. S. Pinder	
G-BWOX	D.H.C.1 Chipmunk 22 (WP844)	J. St. Clair-Quentin	
G-BWOY	Sky 31-24 balloon	C. Wolstenholme	
G-BWOZ	CFM Streak Shadow SA	N. P. Harding	
G-BWPA	Cameron A-340 balloon	A. A. Brown	
G-BWPB	Cameron V-77 balloon	Fair Weather Friends Ballooning Co	
G-BWPC	Cameron V-77 balloon	H. Vaughan	
G-BWPE	Murphy Renegade Spirit UK	G. Wilson	
G-BWPF	Sky 120-24 balloon	H. & R. T. Revel	
G-BWPH	PA-28-181 Archer II	E. & H. Merkado	
G-BWPJ	Steen Skybolt	W. R. Penaluna	
G-BWPP	Sky 105-24 balloon	The Sarnia Balloon Group	
G-BWPR	BN-2T-4S Defender 4000	B-N Group Ltd/Bembridge	
G-BWPS	CFM Streak Shadow SA	P. M. E. D. McNair-Wilson	
G-BWPT	Cameron N-90 balloon	G. Burrows	
G-BWPY	HOAC Katana DV.20	SAS Flight Services	
G-BWPZ	Cameron N-105 balloon	Flying Pictures Ltd	

Notes	Reg.	Type	Owner or Operator
	G-BWRA	Sopwith LC-1T Triplane (replica) (N500)	S. M. Truscott & J. M. Hoblyn (G-PENY)
	G-BWRC	Light Aero Avid Speedwing	B. Williams
	G-BWRM	Colt 105A balloon	N. Charbonnier/Italy
	G-BWRO	Shaw Europa	J. G. M. McDiarmid
	G-BWRP	Beech 58 Baron	Astra Aviation Ltd
	G-BWRR	Cessna 182Q	D. O. Halle
	G-BWRS	SNCAN Stampe SV-4C	G. P. J. M. Valvekens/Belgium
	G-BWRT	Cameron 60 Concept balloon	W. R. Teasdale
	G-BWRV	Lindstrand LBL-90A balloon	Flying Pictures Ltd Audi
	G-BWRW	Sky 220-24 balloon	Sky Trek Ballooning Ltd
	G-BWRY	Cameron N-105 balloon	G. Aimo/Italy
	G-BWRZ	Lindstrand LBL-105A balloon	Flying Pictures Ltd Rover
	G-BWSB	Lindstrand LBL-105A balloon	Flying Pictures Ltd MG
	G-BWSC	PA-38-112 Tomahawk II	APB Leasing Ltd/Welshpool
	G-BWSD	Campbell Cricket	R. F. G. Moyle
	G-BWSG	P.84 Jet Provost T.5 (XW324)	R. M. Kay
	G-BWSH	P.84 Jet Provost T.3A (XN498)	Global Aviation Ltd/Binbrook
	G-BWSI	K & S SA.102.5 Cavalier	B. W. Shaw
	G-BWSJ	Denney Kitfox Mk 3	J. M. Miller
	G-BWSK	Enstrom 280FX	M. A. & M. Gradwell
	G-BWSL	Sky 77-24 balloon	The Balloon Co Ltd
	G-BWSN	Denney Kitfox Mk 3	W. J. Forrest
	G-BWSO	Cameron 90 Apple SS balloon	Flying Pictures Ltd
	G-BWSP	Cameron 80 Carrots SS balloon	Flying Pictures Ltd
	G-BWST	Sky 200-24 balloon	S. A. Townley
	G-BWSU	Cameron N-105 balloon	A. M. Marten
	G-BWSV	Yakovlev Yak-52	P. Traynor
	G-BWSX	PA-28-236 Dakota	C. & C. Bowie
	G-BWSY	BAe 125 Srs 800B	BAE Systems (Operations) Ltd (G-OCCI)/ Warton
	G-BWSZ	Montgomerie-Bensen B.8MR	D. Cawkwell
	G-BWTA	HOAC Katana DV.20	Diamond Aircraft Industries GmbH/ Austria
	G-BWTB	Lindstrand LBL-105A balloon	Servatruc Ltd
	G-BWTC	Zlin Z.242L	Oxford Aviation Services Ltd/Kidlington
	G-BWTD	Zlin Z.242L	Oxford Aviation Services Ltd/Kidlington
	G-BWTE	Cameron O-140 balloon	R. J. & A. J. Mansfield
	G-BWTF	Lindstrand LBL Bear SS balloon	Free Enterprise Balloons Ltd/USA
	G-BWTG	D.H.C.1 Chipmunk 22 (WB671)	Chipmunk 4 Ever Foundation/ Netherlands
	G-BWTH	Robinson R-22B	Helicopter Services
	G-BWTJ	Cameron V-77 balloon	A. J. Montgomery
	G-BWTK	RAF 2000 GTX-SE gyroplane	Terrafirma Services Ltd
	G-BWTN	Lindstrand LBL-90A balloon	Clarks Drainage Ltd
	G-BWTO	D.H.C.1 Chipmunk 22 (WP984)	A. C. Eltis & P. L. Reilly
	G-BWTR	Slingsby T.61F Venture T.2	P. R. Williams
	G-BWTU	Lindstrand LBL-77A balloon	Virgin Airship & Balloon Co Ltd
	G-BWTW	Mooney M.20C	R. C. Volkers
	G-BWUA	Campbell Cricket	R. T. Lancaster
	G-BWUB	PA-18S Super Cub 135	Caledonian Seaplanes Ltd/Cumbernauld
	G-BWUE	Hispano HA.1112M1L	R. A. Fleming(G-AWHK)/Breighton
	G-BWUF	WSK-Mielec LiM-5 (1211)	–/Duxford
	G-BWUH	PA-28-181 Archer III	R. Paston
	G-BWUJ	Rotorway Executive 162F	Southern Helicopters Ltd
	G-BWUK	Sky 160-24 balloon	Blagdon Balloons Ltd
	G-BWUL	Noorduyn AT-16 Harvard IIB	Aereo Servizi Bresciana SRL/Italy
	G-BWUM	Sky 105-24 balloon	P. Stern & F. Kirchberger/Germany
	G-BWUN	D.H.C.1 Chipmunk 22 (WD310)	T. Henderson
	G-BWUP	Shaw Europa	T. J. Harrison
	G-BWUR	Thunder Ax10-210 S2 balloon	T. J. Bucknall
	G-BWUS	Sky 65-24 balloon	N. A. P. Bates
	G-BWUT	D.H.C.1 Chipmunk 22 (WZ879)	Aero Vintage Ltd
	G-BWUU	Cameron N-90 balloon	South Western Electricity PLC
	G-BWUV	D.H.C.1 Chipmunk 22A (WK640)	P. Ray
	G-BWUW	P.84 Jet Provost T.5A (XW423)	Tinton Ltd/Little Snoring
	G-BWUZ	Campbell Cricket	M. A. Concannon
	G-BWVB	Pietenpol Air Camper	M. J. Whatley
	G-BWVC	Jodel D.18	R. W. J. Cripps
	G-BWVH	Robinson R-44 Astro	Glenwood Transport Ltd
	G-BWVI	Stern ST.80	M. P. Wakem
	G-BWVL	Cessna 150M	A. H. Shaw
	G-BWVM	Colt AA-1050 balloon	B. B. Baxter Ltd

Reg.	Type	Owner or Operator	Notes
G-BWVN	Whittaker MW.7	R. S. Willcox	
G-BWVR	Yakovlev Yak-52 (52)	J. H. Askew/Barton	
G-BWVS	Shaw Europa	D. R. Bishop	
G-BWVT	D.H.A.82A Tiger Moth	R. Jewitt	
G-BWVU	Cameron O-90 balloon	J. Atkinson	
G-BWVV	Jodel D.18	P. Cooper	
G-BWVX	Yakovlev Yak-52	C. J. M. Van Den Broek &	
		R. V. De Vries/Netherlands	
G-BWVY	D.H.C.1 Chipmunk 22 (WP896)	P. W. Portelli	
G-BWVZ	D.H.C.1 Chipmunk 22A (WK590)	D. Campion/Belgium	
G-BWWA	Pelican Club GS	T. J. Franklin & D. S. Simpson	
G-BWWB	Shaw Europa	M. G. Dolphin	
G-BWWC	D.H.104 Dove 7 (XM223)	Air Atlantique Ltd/Coventry	
G-BWWE	Lindstrand LBL-90A balloon	B. J. Newman	
G-BWWF	Cessna 185A	S. M. C. Harvey	
G-BWWG	SOCATA Rallye 235E	J. McEleney	
G-BWWH	Yakovlev Yak-50	De Cadenet Motor Racing Ltd	
G-BWWI	AS.332L Super Puma	Bristow Helicopters Ltd	
G-BWWJ	Hughes 269C	Dave Nieman Models Ltd (G-BMYZ)	
G-BWWK	Hawker Nimrod I (S1581)	Historic Aircraft Collection Ltd	
G-BWWL	Colt Flying Egg SS balloon	Magical Adventures Ltd/USA	
G-BWWN	Isaacs Fury II (K8303)	R. I. Warman	
G-BWWP	Rans S.6-116 Coyote II	S. A. Beddus	
G-BWWS	RAF 2000 GTX-SE gyroplane	R. I. Grant	
G-BWWT	Dornier Do.328-100	ScotAirways Ltd	
G-BWWU	PA-22 Tri-Pacer 150	Aerocars Ltd	
G-BWWW	BAe Jetstream 3102	British Aerospace PLC/Warton	
G-BWWX	Yakovlev Yak-50	J. L. Pfundt/Netherlands	
G-BWWY	Lindstrand LBL-105A balloon	M. J. Smith	
G-BWWZ	Denney Kitfox Mk 3	A. I. Eskander	
G-BWXA	Slingsby T.67M Firefly 260	Hunting Aviation Ltd/Barkston Heath	
G-BWXB	Slingsby T.67M Firefly 260	Hunting Aviation Ltd/Barkston Heath	
G-BWXC	Slingsby T.67M Firefly 260	Hunting Aviation Ltd/Barkston Heath	
G-BWXD	Slingsby T.67M Firefly 260	Hunting Aviation Ltd/Barkston Heath	
G-BWXE	Slingsby T.67M Firefly 260	Hunting Aviation Ltd/Barkston Heath	
G-BWXF	Slingsby T.67M Firefly 260	Hunting Aviation Ltd/Barkston Heath	
G-BWXG	Slingsby T.67M Firefly 260	Hunting Aviation Ltd/Barkston Heath	
G-BWXH	Slingsby T.67M Firefly 260	Hunting Aviation Ltd/Barkston Heath	
G-BWXI	Slingsby T.67M Firefly 260	Hunting Aviation Ltd/Barkston Heath	
G-BWXJ	Slingsby T.67M Firefly 260	Hunting Aviation Ltd/Newton	
G-BWXK	Slingsby T.67M Firefly 260	Hunting Aviation Ltd/Newton	
G-BWXL	Slingsby T.67M Firefly 260	Hunting Aviation Ltd/Barkston Heath	
G-BWXM	Slingsby T.67M Firefly 260	Hunting Aviation Ltd/Barkston Heath	
G-BWXN	Slingsby T.67M Firefly 260	Hunting Aviation Ltd/Barkston Heath	
G-BWXO	Slingsby T.67M Firefly 260	Hunting Aviation Ltd/Barkston Heath	
G-BWXP	Slingsby T.67M Firefly 260	Hunting Aviation Ltd/Barkston Heath	
G-BWXR	Slingsby T.67M Firefly 260	Hunting Aviation Ltd/Barkston Heath	
G-BWXS	Slingsby T.67M Firefly 260	Hunting Aviation Ltd/Barkston Heath	
G-BWXT	Slingsby T.67M Firefly 260	Hunting Aviation Ltd/Barkston Heath	
G-BWXU	Slingsby T.67M Firefly 260	Hunting Aviation Ltd/Barkston Heath	
G-BWXV	Slingsby T.67M Firefly 260	Hunting Aviation Ltd/Barkston Heath	
G-BWXW	Slingsby T.67M Firefly 260	Hunting Aviation Ltd/Barkston Heath	
G-BWXX	Slingsby T.67M Firefly 260	Hunting Aviation Ltd/Barkston Heath	
G-BWXY	Slingsby T.67M Firefly 260	Hunting Aviation Ltd/Barkston Heath	
G-BWXZ	Slingsby T.67M Firefly 260	Hunting Aviation Ltd/Barkston Heath	
G-BWYB	PA-28 Cherokee 160	I. M. Latiff	
G-BWYC	Cameron N-90 balloon	Cameron Balloons Ltd	
G-BWYD	Shaw Europa	H. J. Bendiksen	
G-BWYE	Cessna 310R II	Air Charter Scotland Ltd/Edinburgh	
G-BWYG	Cessna 310R II	Kissair Aviation	
G-BWYH	Cessna 310R II	Air Charter Scotland Ltd/Edinburgh	
G-BWYI	Denney Kitfox Mk3	J. Adamson	
G-BWYK	Yakovlev Yak-50	Titan Airways Ltd/Stansted	
G-BWYM	HOAC Katana DV.20	Plane Talking Ltd/Elstree	
G-BWYN	Cameron O-77 balloon	W. H. Morgan (G-ODER)	
G-BWYO	Sequoia F.8L Falco	N. G. Abbott & J. Copeland	
G-BWYP	Sky 56-24 balloon	Sky High Leisure	
G-BWYR	Rans S.6-116 Coyote II	R. C. Burden	
G-BWYS	Cameron O-120 balloon	Aire Valley Balloons	
G-BWYU	Sky 120-24 balloon	D. J. Tofton	
G-BWYY	BN-2B-20 Islander	B-N Group Ltd/Bembridge	
G-BWZA	Shaw Europa	M. C. Costin	
G-BWZD	Light Aero Avid Flyer Mk 4	B. Moore	

Notes	Reg.	Type	Owner or Operator
	G-BWZG	Robin R.2160	Sherburn Aero Club Ltd
	G-BWZI	Agusta A. 109A-II	Pendley Farm
	G-BWZJ	Cameron A-250 balloon	Balloon Club of Great Britain
	G-BWZK	Cameron A-210 balloon	Balloon Club of Great Britain
	G-BWZP	Cameron 105 Home Special SS balloon	Flying Pictures Ltd
	G-BWZT	Shaw Europa	G-BWZT Group
	G-BWZU	Lindstrand LBL-90B balloon	K. D. Pierce
	G-BWZW	Bell 206B JetRanger 2	R. & M. International Engineering Ltd (G-CTEK)
	G-BWZX	AS.332L Super Puma	Bristow Helicopters Ltd
	G-BWZY	Hughes 269A	K. B. Elliott (G-FSDT)
	G-BWZZ	P.84 Jet Provost T.3A (XM470)	R. G. Schreiber & J. P. Trevor
	G-BXAB	PA-28-161 Warrior II	TG Aviation Ltd (G-BTGK)
	G-BXAC	RAF 2000 GTX-SE gyroplane	D. C. Fairbrass
	G-BXAD	Thunder Ax11-225 S2 balloon	C. E. Wood
	G-BXAF	Pitts S-1D Special	N. J. Watson
	G-BXAH	CP.301A Emeraude	G. E. Valler
	G-BXAI	Colt 120A balloon	E. F. & R. F. Casswell
	G-BXAJ	Lindstrand LBL-14A balloon	Oscair Project AB/Sweden
	G-BXAK	Yakovlev Yak-52	J. G. McTaggart
	G-BXAL	Cameron 90 Bertie Bassett SS balloon	Trebor Bassett Ltd
	G-BXAM	Cameron N-90 balloon	Trebor Bassett Ltd
	G-BXAN	Scheibe SF-25C Falke	C. Falke Syndicate/Winthorpe
	G-BXAO	Avtech Jabiru SK	P. J. Thompson
	G-BXAR	Avro RJ100	CityFlyer Express Ltd/BA Express
	G-BXAS	Avro RJ100	CityFlyer Express Ltd/BA Express
	G-BXAU	Pitts S-1 Special	P. Tomlinson
	G-BXAV	Yakovlev Yak-52 (72)	Skytrace (UK) Ltd
	G-BXAX	Cameron N-77 balloon	Flying Pictures Ltd Citroen
	G-BXAY	Bell 206B JetRanger 3	Viewdart Ltd
	G-BXBA	Cameron A-210 balloon	Reach For The Sky Ltd
	G-BXBB	PA-20 Pacer 150	M. E. R. Coghlan
	G-BXBC	EA.1 Kingfisher amphibian	S. Bichan
	G-BXBD	C.A.S.A. 1.131E Jungmann	P. B. Childs & B. L. Robinson
	G-BXBG	Cameron A-275 balloon	M. L. Gabb
	G-BXBH	P.84 Jet Provost T.3A (XM365)	G-BXBH Provost Ltd
	G-BXBI	P.84 Jet Provost T.3A	Global Aviation Ltd/Binbrook
	G-BXBK	Avions Mudry CAP-10B	S. Skipworth
	G-BXBL	Lindstrand LBL-240A balloon	Firefly Balloon Promotions
	G-BXBM	Cameron O-105 balloon	Bristol University Hot Air Ballooning Soc
	G-BXBN	Rans S.6-116 Coyote II	A. G. Foster
	G-BXBP	Denney Kitfox	G. S. Adams
	G-BXBR	Cameron A-120 balloon	M. G. Barlow
	G-BXBT	AS.355F-1 Twin Squirrel	McAlpine Helicopters Ltd (G-TMMC/G-JLCO)/Kidlington
	G-BXBU	Avions Mudry CAP.10B	J. F. Cosgrave & H. R. Pearson
	G-BXBY	Cameron A-105 balloon	S. P. Watkins
	G-BXBZ	PZL-104 Wilga 80	P. G. Marks/Luxembourg
	G-BXCA	Hapi Cygnet SF-2A	G. E. Collard
	G-BXCC	PA-28-201T Turbo Dakota	Greer Aviation Ltd
	G-BXCD	Team Minimax 91A	R. Davies
	G-BXCG	Jodel DR.250/160	G-BXCG Group
	G-BXCH	Shaw Europa	D. M. Stevens
	G-BXCJ	Campbell Cricket (replica)	J. R. Cooper
	G-BXCK	Cameron 110 Douglas SS balloon	Flying Pictures Ltd
	G-BXCL	Montgomerie-Bensen B.8MR	A. D. Gordon
	G-BXCM	Lindstrand LBL-150A balloon	Blown Away (UK) Ltd
	G-BXCN	Sky 105-24 balloon	Capricorn Balloons Ltd
	G-BXCO	Colt 120A balloon	G. C. Ludlow
	G-BXCP	D.H.C.1 Chipmunk 22 (WP859)	S. Conlan
	G-BXCS	Cameron N-90 balloon	Flying Pictures (Balloons) Ltd
	G-BXCT	D.H.C.1 Chipmunk 22 (WB697)	Wickenby Aviation Ltd
	G-BXCU	Rans S.6-116 Coyote II	M. R. McNeil
	G-BXCV	D.H.C.1 Chipmunk 22 (WP929)	Ocean Flight Holdings Ltd/Hong Kong
	G-BXCW	Denney Kitfox Mk 3	M. J. Blanchard
	G-BXCX	Robinson R-22B	European Living Ltd
	G-BXDA	D.H.C.1 Chipmunk 22 (WP860)	S. R. Cleary
	G-BXDB	Cessna U.206F	Tindon Ltd (G-BMNZ)/Little Snoring
	G-BXDD	RAF 2000 GTX-SE gyroplane	Roger Savage (Photography)/Carlisle

Reg.	Type	Owner or Operator	Notes
G-BXDE	RAF 2000 GTX-SE gyroplane	A. McRedie	
G-BXDF	Beech 95-B55 Baron	Chesh-Air Ltd	
G-BXDG	D.H.C.1 Chipmunk 22 (WK630)	R. E. Dagless	
G-BXDH	D.H.C.1 Chipmunk 22 (WD331)	Victory Workware Ltd	
G-BXDI	D.H.C.1 Chipmunk 22 (WD373)	J. R. Gore/Perth	
G-BXDL	P.84 Jet Provost T.3A (XM478)	Seagull Formation Ltd/North Weald	
G-BXDM	D.H.C.1 Chipmunk 22 (WP840)	RAF Halton Aeroplane Club Ltd	
G-BXDN	D.H.C.1 Chipmunk 22 (WK609)	W. D. Lowe & L. A. Edwards	
G-BXDO	Rutan Cozy	C. R. Blackburn	
G-BXDP	D.H.C.1 Chupmunk 22 (WK642)	J. S. J. Valentine & J. P. Conlan	
G-BXDR	Lindstrand LBL-77A balloon	British Telecommunications PLC	
G-BXDS	Bell 206B JetRanger 3	Sterling Helicopters Ltd (G-OVBJ)	
G-BXDT	Robin HR.200/120B	Multiflight Ltd/Leeds-Bradford	
G-BXDU	Aero Designs Pulsar	M. P. Board	
G-BXDV	Sky 105-24 balloon	J. Skinner	
G-BXDW	Sky 105-24 balloon	M. & S. M. Sarti	
G-BXDY	Shaw Europa	D. G. & S. Watts	
G-BXEA	RAF 2000 GTX-SE gyroplane	R. Firth	
G-BXEB	RAF 2000 GTX-SE gyroplane	Penny Hydraulics Ltd	
G-BXEC	D.H.C.1 Chipmunk 22 (WK633)	M.A.D. Flying Group	
G-BXEE	Enstrom 280C	S. T. Raby	
G-BXEF	Shaw Europa	C. & W. P. Busuttil-Reynaud	
G-BXEJ	VPM M.16 Tandem Trainer	AES Radionic Surveillance Systems	
G-BXEL	MDH MD.500N	Ford Helicopters Ltd/Sywell	
G-BXEN	Cameron N-105 balloon	G. Aimo/Italy	
G-BXEP	Lindstrand LBL-14M balloon	Lindstrand Balloons Ltd	
G-BXER	PA-46-350P Malibu Mirage	Glasdon Group Ltd	
G-BXES	P.66 Pembroke C.1 (XL954)	Atlantic Air Transport Ltd/Coventry	
G-BXET	PA-38-112 Tomahawk II	APB Leasing Ltd/Welshpool	
G-BXEX	PA-28-181 Archer II	R. Mayle	
G-BXEY	Colt AS-105GD airship	D. Mayer/Germany	
G-BXEZ	Cessna 182P	Forhawk Ltd	
G-BXFB	Pitts S-1 Special	D. Dobson	
G-BXFC	Jodel D.18	B. S. Godbold	
G-BXFD	Enstrom 280C	R. Collenette	
G-BXFE	Avions Mudry CAP.10B	Avion Aerobatic Ltd	
G-BXFG	Shaw Europa	A. Rawicz-Szczerbo	
G-BXFI	Hawker Hunter T.7 (WV372)	Fox-One Ltd/Bournemouth	
G-BXFK	CFM Streak Shadow	D. Adcock	
G-BXFN	Colt 77A balloon	Cameron Balloons Ltd	
G-BXFP	BAC.145 Strikemaster 87 (NZ6361)	C. J. & S. M. Thompson/North Weald	
G-BXFU	BAC.167 Strikemaster 83	Global Aviation Ltd/Binbrook	
G-BXFV	BAC.167 Strikemaster 83	Global Aviation Ltd/Binbrook	
G-BXFY	Cameron 90 Bierkrug SS balloon	Ballooning Bavaria	
G-BXGA	AS.350B-2 Ecureuil	PLM Dollar Group Ltd/Inverness	
G-BXGC	Cameron N-105 balloon	Cliveden Ltd	
G-BXGD	Sky 90-24 balloon	Servo & Electronic Sales Ltd	
G-BXGE	Cessna 152	APB Leasing Ltd/Welshpool	
G-BXGG	Shaw Europa	C. J. H. & P. A. J. Richardson	
G-BXGH	Diamond Katana DA.20-A1	Diamond Aircraft Industries Gmbh	
G-BXGK	Lindstrand LBL-203M balloon	Lindstrand Balloons Ltd	
G-BXGL	D.H.C.1 Chipmunk 22	Airways Aero Associations Ltd/Booker	
G-BXGM	D.H.C.1 Chipmunk 22 (WP928)	M. A. Petrie	
G-BXGO	D.H.C.1 Chipmunk 22 (WB654)	Trees Group/Booker	
G-BXGP	D.H.C.1 Chipmunk 22 (WZ882)	Eaglescott Chipmunk Group	
G-BXGS	RAF 2000 gyroplane	C. R. Gordon	
G-BXGT	I.I.I. Sky Arrow 650T	Sky Arrow (Kits) UK Ltd/Old Sarum	
G-BXGV	Cessna 172R	Billingshurst Holdings Ltd	
G-BXGW	Robin HR.200/120B	Multiflight Ltd/Leeds-Bradford	
G-BXGX	D.H.C.1 Chipmunk 22 (WK586)	Interflight (Air Charter) Ltd	
G-BXGY	Cameron V-65 balloon	Gone With The Wind Ltd	
G-BXGZ	Stemme S.10V	D. Tucker & K. Lloyd	
G-BXHA	D.H.C.1 Chipmunk 22 (WP925)	F. A. de Munck & C. S. Huijers/ Netherlands	
G-BXHD	Beech 76 Duchess	Aviation Rentals/Bournemouth	
G-BXHE	Lindstrand LBL-105A balloon	Independent Insurance Co Ltd	
G-BXHF	D.H.C.1 Chipmunk 22 (WP930)	R. Beresford	
G-BXHH	AA-5A Cheetah	Oaklands Flying/Biggin Hill	
G-BXHJ	Hapi Cygnet SF-2A	I. J. Smith	
G-BXHL	Sky 77-24 balloon	R. K. Gyselynck	
G-BXHO	Lindstrand Telewest Sphere SS balloon	Flying Pictures Ltd	

UK IN-SEQUENCE

Notes	Reg.	Type	Owner or Operator
	G-BXHP	Lindstrand LBL-105A balloon	Flying Pictures Ltd
	G-BXHR	Stemme S.10V	J. H. Rutherford
	G-BXHT	Bushby-Long Midget Mustang	P. P. Chapman
	G-BXHU	Campbell Cricket Mk 6	P. J. Began
	G-BXHY	Shaw Europa	Jupiter Flying Group
	G-BXHZ	V.S.361 Spitfire HF.IX	A. G. Dunkerley
	G-BXIA	D.H.C.1 Chipmunk 22 (WB615)	Dales Aviation/Blackpool
	G-BXIC	Cameron A-275 balloon	A. J. Street
	G-BXID	Yakovlev Yak-52 (74)	E. S. Ewen
	G-BXIE	Colt 77B balloon	The Aerial Display Co Ltd
	G-BXIF	PA-28-161 Warrior II	Piper Flight Ltd
	G-BXIG	Zenair CH.701 STOL	A. J. Perry
	G-BXIH	Sky 200-24 balloon	G. C. Ludlow
	G-BXII	Shaw Europa	D. A. McFadyean
	G-BXIJ	Shaw Europa	D. G. & E. A. Bligh
	G-BXIM	D.H.C.1 Chipmunk 22 (WK512)	A. B. Ashcroft & P. R. Joshua
	G-BXIO	Jodel DR.1050M	D. N. K. & M. A. Symon
	G-BXIT	Zebedee V-31 balloon	Zebedee Balloon Service Ltd
	G-BXIV	Agusta A.109A	Heli-Tele Ltd/North Weald
	G-BXIW	Sky 105-24 balloon	L. A. Watts
	G-BXIX	VPM M.16 Tandem Trainer	D. Beevers
	G-BXIY	Blake Bluetit (BAPC37)	J. Bryant
	G-BXJA	Cessna 402B	Air Charter Scotland Ltd/Edinburgh
	G-BXJB	Yakovlev Yak-52 (15)	A. M. Playford & ptnrs
	G-BXJC	Cameron A-210 balloon	British School of Ballooning
	G-BXJD	PA-28 Cherokee 180C	BCT Aircraft Leasing Ltd/Filton
	G-BXJG	Lindstrand LBL-105B balloon	C. E. Wood
	G-BXJH	Cameron N-42 balloon	Flying Pictures Ltd
	G-BXJI	Tri-R Kis	R. M. Wakeford
	G-BXJJ	PA-28-161 Cadet	Plane Talking Ltd (G-GFCC)/Elstree
	G-BXJK	SA.341G Gazelle 1	MW Helicopters Ltd
	G-BXJM	Cessna 152	E. Alexander
	G-BXJO	Cameron O-90 balloon	W. I. & C. Hooker
	G-BXJP	Cameron C-80 balloon	AR. Cobaleno Pasta Fresca SRL/Italy
	G-BXJS	Schempp-Hirth Janus CM	Janus Syndicate
	G-BXJT	Sky 90-24 balloon	J. G. O'Connell
	G-BXJV	Diamond Katana DA.20-A1	Tayside Aviation Ltd/Dundee
	G-BXJW	Diamond Katana DA.20-A1	Tayside Aviation Ltd/Dundee
	G-BXJY	Van's RV-6	D. J. Sharland
	G-BXJZ	Cameron C-60 balloon	R. S. Mohr
	G-BXKA	Airbus A.320-214	jmc Airlines Ltd
	G-BXKB	Airbus A.320-214	jmc Airlines Ltd
	G-BXKC	Airbus A.320-214	jmc Airlines Ltd
	G-BXKD	Airbus A.320-214	jmc Airlines Ltd
	G-BXKF	Hawker Hunter T.7(XL577)	R. F. Harvey
	G-BXKH	Colt 90 Sparkasse Box SS balloon	Westfalisch-Lippischer Sparkasse UND/ Germany
	G-BXKJ	Cameron A-275 balloon	The Balloon Club Ltd
	G-BXKK	Colt 105 Golf Ball SS balloon	Longbreak Ltd/USA
	G-BXKL	Bell 206B JetRanger 3	Swattons Aviation Ltd
	G-BXKM	RAF 2000 GTX-SE gyroplane	J. R. Huggins
	G-BXKO	Sky 65-24 balloon	J-M. Reck/France
	G-BXKU	Colt AS-120 Mk II airship	D. C. Chipping/Portugal
	G-BXKW	Slingsby T.67M Firefly 200	W. R. Tandy
	G-BXKX	Auster V	A. L. Jubb
	G-BXLA	Robinson R-22B	Fast Helicopters Ltd
	G-BXLC	Sky 120-24 balloon	A. F. Selby
	G-BXLF	Lindstrand LBL-90A balloon	Variohm Components
	G-BXLG	Cameron C-80 balloon	D. & L. S. Litchfield
	G-BXLI	Bell 206B JetRanger 3	Williams Grand Prix Engineering Ltd (G-JODY)
	G-BXLK	Shaw Europa	R. G. Fairall
	G-BXLN	Fournier RF-4D	E. H. Booker
	G-BXLO	P.84 Jet Provost T.4 (XR673)	HCR Aviation Ltd
	G-BXLP	Sky 90-24 balloon	G. B. Lescott
	G-BXLR	PZL-110 Koliber 160A	PZL International Aviation Marketing & Sales PLC
	G-BXLS	PZL-110 Koliber 160A	P. A. Rickells
	G-BXLT	SOCATA TB.200 Tobago XL	R. M. Shears/Blackbushe
	G-BXLV	Enstrom F-28F	Solent Projects Ltd
	G-BXLW	Enstrom F-28F	M. & P. Food Products Ltd
	G-BXLY	PA-28-151 Warrior	Air Nova PLC (G-WATZ)/Liverpool
	G-BXLZ	Shaw Europa	A. R. Round

Reg.	Type	Owner or Operator	Notes
G-BXMF	Cassutt Racer IIIM	J. F. Bakewell	
G-BXMG	RAF 2000 GTX gyroplane	R. Paolone	
G-BXMH	Beech 76 Duchess	R. Clarke	
G-BXML	Mooney M.20A	G. Kay	
G-BXMM	Cameron A-180 balloon	Flying Pictures Ltd	
G-BXMU	PZL-104 Wilga 80	G-BXMU Group	
G-BXMV	Scheibe SF.25C Falke 1700	Falcon Flying Group/Shrivenham	
G-BXMW	Cameron A-275 balloon	Balloon Flights International Ltd	
G-BXMX	Currie Wot	M. J. Hayman	
G-BXMY	Hughes 269C	DS Air Ltd	
G-BXMZ	Diamond Katana DA.20-A1	Tayside Aviation Ltd/Dundee	
G-BXNC	Shaw Europa	J. K. Cantwell	
G-BXND	Cameron 110 Thomas SS balloon	Virgin Airship & Balloon Co. Ltd	
G-BXNG	Beech 58 Baron	Bonanza Flying Club Ltd	
G-BXNH	PA-28-161 Warrior II	CC Management Associates Ltd/Redhill	
G-BXNL	Cameron A-120 balloon	R. G. Griffin	
G-BXNM	Cameron A-210 balloon	Horizon Ballooning	
G-BXNN	D.H.C.1 Chipmunk 22 (WP983)	J. N. Robinson	
G-BXNS	Bell 206B JetRanger 3	Sterling Helicopters Ltd/Norwich	
G-BXNT	Bell 206B JetRanger 3	Sterling Helicopters Ltd/Norwich	
G-BXNU	Jabiru SK	J. Smith	
G-BXNV	Colt AS-105GD airship	The Sleeping Soc./Belgium	
G-BXNX	Lindstrand LBL-210A balloon	J. H. Cuthbert	
G-BXNZ	Hawker Hunter F.58 (J-4066)	Classic Aviation Ltd/Duxford	
G-BXOA	Robinson R-22B	MG Group Ltd	
G-BXOB	Shaw Europa	S. J. Willett	
G-BXOC	Evans VP-2	H. J. & E. M. Cox	
G-BXOF	Diamond Katana DA.20-A1	Diamond Aircraft UK Ltd	
G-BXOI	Cessna 172R	J. S. & J. Q. Malcolm	
G-BXOJ	PA-28-161 Warrior III	Plane Talking Ltd/Elstree	
G-BXOM	Isaacs Spitfire	J. H. Betton	
G-BXON	Auster AOP.9	C. J. & D. J. Baker	
G-BXOO	AA-5A Cheetah	ENS-Entire Network Solutions Ltd/ Blackbushe	
G-BXOR	Robin HR.200/120B	Multiflight Ltd	
G-BXOS	Cameron A-200 balloon	Airborne Balloon Management	
G-BXOT	Cameron C-70 balloon	Gone With The Wind Ltd	
G-BXOU	CEA DR.360	S. H. & J. A. Williams/Blackpool	
G-BXOV	Colt 105A balloon	The Aerial Display Co Ltd	
G-BXOW	Colt 105A balloon	The Aerial Display Co Ltd	
G-BXOX	AA-5A Cheetah	A. J. Radford/Tattenhill	
G-BXOY	QAC Quickie Q.235	C. C. Clapham	
G-BXOZ	PA-28-181 Archer II	Spritetone Ltd	
G-BXPB	Diamond Katana DA.20-A1	Diamond Aircraft (UK) Ltd/Gamston	
G-BXPC	Diamond Katana DA.20-A1	Cubair Flight Training Ltd/Redhill	
G-BXPD	Diamond Katana DA.20-A1	Cubair Flight Training Ltd/Redhill	
G-BXPE	Diamond Katana DA.20-A1	Tayside Aviation Ltd/Dundee	
G-BXPF	Thorp T.211	AD Aviation Ltd/Barton	
G-BXPH	Sky 220-24 balloon	J. Nolte/Germany	
G-BXPI	Van's RV-4	Cavendish Aviation Ltd	
G-BXPK	Cameron A-250 balloon	Richard Nash Cars Ltd	
G-BXPL	PA-28 Cherokee 140	C. R. Guggenheim	
G-BXPM	Beech 58 Baron	Foyle Flyers Ltd	
G-BXPO	Thorp T.211	AD Aviation Ltd/Barton	
G-BXPP	Sky 90-24 balloon	Adam Associates Ltd	
G-BXPR	Colt 110 Can SS balloon	FRB Fleishwarenfabrik Rostock-Bramow/ Germany	
G-BXPS	PA-23 Aztec 250C	W. A. Moore (G-AYLY)	
G-BXPT	Ultramagic H-77 balloon	G. D. O. Bartram/Andorra	
G-BXPV	PA-34-220T Seneca IV	Oxford Aviation Services Ltd/Kidlington	
G-BXPW	PA-34-220T Seneca IV	Oxford Aviation Services Ltd/Kidlington	
G-BXPY	Robinson R-44	O. Desmet & B. Mornie/Belgium	
G-BXRA	Avions Mudry CAP.10B	P. A. Soper	
G-BXRB	Avions Mudry CAP.10B	T. T. Duhig	
G-BXRC	Avions Mudry CAP.10B	Group Alpha/Sibson	
G-BXRD	Enstrom 280FX	Eastern Atlantic Helicopters	
G-BXRF	CP.1310-C3 Super Emeraude	D. T. Gethin	
G-BXRG	PA-28-181 Archer II	Alderney Flying Training Ltd	
G-BXRH	Cessna 185A	R. E. M. Holmes	
G-BXRM	Cameron A-210 balloon	W. & C. Hooker	
G-BXRO	Cessna U.206G	M. Penny	
G-BXRP	Schweizer 269C	C. W. Larner	

Notes	Reg.	Type	Owner or Operator
	G-BXRR	Westland Scout AH.1	T. K. Phillips
	G-BXRS	Westland Scout AH.1	R. P. Coplestone
	G-BXRT	Robin DR.400-180	R. A. Ford
	G-BXRV	Van's RV-4	Cleeve Flying Grouip
	G-BXRY	Bell 206B JetRanger	John Mann International
	G-BXRZ	Rans S.6-116 Coyote II	C. M. White
	G-BXSA	Cameron PM-80 balloon	Flying Pictures Ltd/Dubai
	G-BXSB	Cameron PM-80 balloon	Flying Pictures Ltd/Dubai
	G-BXSC	Cameron C-80 balloon	S. J. Coates
	G-BXSD	Cessna 172R	K. K. Freeman
	G-BXSE	Cessna 172R	MK Aero Support Ltd/Andrewsfield
	G-BXSG	Robinson R-22B-2	R. M. Goodenough
	G-BXSH	Glaser-Dirks DG.800B	D. S. McKay
	G-BXSI	Avtech Jabiru SK	M. H. Molyneux
	G-BXSJ	Cameron C-80 balloon	British School of Ballooning
	G-BXSL	Westland Scout AH.1	B. J. Green
	G-BXSM	Cessna 172R	East Midlands Flying School Ltd
	G-BXSO	Lindstrand LBL-105A balloon	Lindstrand Balloons Ltd
	G-BXSP	Grob G.109B	I. M. Donnelly/Aboyne
	G-BXSR	Cessna F172N	S. A. Parkes
	G-BXST	PA-25 Pawnee 235C	P. Channon
	G-BXSU	Team Minimax 91A	M. R. Overall (G-MYGL)
	G-BXSX	Cameron V-77 balloon	D. R. Metcalf
	G-BXSY	Robinson R-22B-2	N. M. G. Pearson
	G-BXTB	Cessna 152	Haimoss Ltd
	G-BXTC	Taylor JT.1 Monoplane	R. Holden-Rushworth
	G-BXTD	Shaw Europa	P. R. Anderson
	G-BXTE	Cameron A-275 balloon	Adventure Balloon Co Ltd
	G-BXTF	Cameron N-105 balloon	Flying Pictures Ltd *Salisbury's Strawberry*
	G-BXTG	Cameron N-42 balloon	Flying Pictures Ltd
	G-BXTH	Westland Gazelle HT.1 (XW866)	Flightline Ltd/Southend
	G-BXTI	Pitts S-1S Special	A. B. Treherne-Pollock
	G-BXTJ	Cameron N-77 balloon	Chubb Fire Ltd *Chubb*
	G-BXTK	Dornier Do.28D-2	R. Ebke/Germany
	G-BXTL	Schweizer 269C-1	Oxford Aviation Services Ltd/Kidlington
	G-BXTN	Aérospatiale ATR-72-202	CityFlyer Express Ltd/BA Express
	G-BXTO	Hindustan HAL-6 Pushpak	Pushpak Flying Group
	G-BXTP	Diamond Katana DA.20-A1	Diamond Aircraft UK Ltd/Gamston
	G-BXTR	Diamond Katana DA.20-A1	Diamond Aircraft UK Ltd/Gamston
	G-BXTS	Diamond Katana DA.20-A1	Avon Aviation Ltd
	G-BXTT	AA-5B Tiger	G-BXTT Group/Gamston
	G-BXTU	Robinson R-22B-2	TDR Aviation Ltd
	G-BXTV	Bug	B. R. Cope
	G-BXTW	PA-28-181 Archer III	Davison Plant Hire
	G-BXTY	PA-28-161 Cadet	Bflying Ltd
	G-BXTZ	PA-28-161 Cadet	Bflying Ltd
	G-BXUA	Campbell Cricket Mk.5	R. N. Bodley
	G-BXUB	Lindstrand Syrup Bottle SS balloon	Free Enterprise Balloons Ltd
	G-BXUC	Robinson R-22B	Hields Aviation
	G-BXUE	Sky 240-24 balloon	Scotair Balloons
	G-BXUF	AB-206B JetRanger 3	SJ Contracting Services Ltd
	G-BXUG	Lindstrand Baby Bel SS balloon	Virgin Airship & Balloon Co Ltd
	G-BXUH	Lindstrand LBL-31A balloon	Virgin Airship & Balloon Co Ltd
	G-BXUI	Glaser-Dirks DG.800B	J. Le Coyte
	G-BXUK	Robinson R-44	Hertfordshire Helicopters Ltd
	G-BXUL	Goodyear FG-1D Corsair (NZ5648)	Old Flying Machine (Air Museum) Co Ltd/Duxford
	G-BXUM	Shaw Europa	D. Bosomworth
	G-BXUO	Lindstrand LBL-105A balloon	Lindstrand Balloons Ltd
	G-BXUP	Schweizer 269C	J. N. Crewdson
	G-BXUS	Sky 65-24 balloon	K. Coate-Bond
	G-BXUU	Cameron V-65 balloon	D. I. Gray-Fisk
	G-BXUW	Cameron Colt 90A balloon	Zycomm Electronics Ltd
	G-BXUX	Fountain Cherry BX-2	M. F. Fountain
	G-BXUY	Cessna 310Q	D. A. D. Rowntree
	G-BXUZ	Cessna 152 II	Stapleford Flying Club Ltd
	G-BXVA	SOCATA TB.200 Tobago XL	H. R. Palser/Cardiff-Wales
	G-BXVB	Cessna 152 II	PJC (Leasing) Ltd
	G-BXVC	PA-28RT-201T Turbo Arrow IV	J. S. Develin & I. Zahurul
	G-BXVD	CFM Streak Shadow SA	CFM Aircraft Ltd
	G-BXVE	Lindstrand LBL-330A balloon	Adventure Balloon Co Ltd
	G-BXVF	Thunder Ax11-250 S2 balloon	Anglian Countryside Balloons

Reg.	Type	Owner or Operator	Notes
G-BXVG	Sky 77-24 balloon	M. Wolf	
G-BXVH	Sky 25-16 balloon	Flying Pictures Ltd	
G-BXVJ	Cameron O-120 balloon	MJN Balloon Management Ltd (G-IMAX)	
G-BXVK	Robin HR.200/120B	Northamptonshire School of Flying Ltd/ Sywell	
G-BXVL	Sky 180-24 balloon	Purple Balloons	
G-BXVM	Van's RV-6A	J. G. Small	
G-BXVO	Van's RV-6A	P. J. Hynes & M. E. Holden	
G-BXVP	Sky 31-24 balloon	L. Greaves	
G-BXVR	Sky 90-24 balloon	P. Hegarty	
G-BXVS	Brügger MB.2 Colibri	G. T. Snoddon	
G-BXVT	Cameron O-77 balloon	R. P. Wade	
G-BXVU	PA-28-161 Warrior II	Gordon Air Ltd/Lydd	
G-BXVV	Cameron V-90 balloon	Floating Sensations Ltd	
G-BXVW	Colt Piggy Bank SS balloon	G. Binder/Germany	
G-BXVX	Rutan Cozy	G. E. Murray	
G-BXVY	Cessna 152	Stapleford Flying Club Ltd	
G-BXVZ	WSK-PZL Mielec TS-11 Iskra	J.Ziubrzynski	
G-BXWA	Beech 76 Duchess	Plymouth School of Flying Ltd	
G-BXWB	Robin HR.100/200B	W. A. Brunwin	
G-BXWC	Cessna 152	PJC (Leasing) Ltd/Stapleford	
G-BXWD	Agusta A.109A-II	Castle Air Charters Ltd	
G-BXWE	Fokker 100	bmi regional	
G-BXWF	Fokker 100	bmi regional	
G-BXWG	Sky 120-24 balloon	Airborne Adventures Ltd	
G-BXWH	Denney Kitfox Mk.4-1200	B. J. Finch	
G-BXWI	Cameron N-120 balloon	Flying Pictures Ltd	
G-BXWK	Rans S.6-ESA Coyote II	R. J. Teal	
G-BXWL	Sky 90-24 balloon	The Shropshire Hills Balloon Co	
G-BXWO	PA-28-181 Archer II	J. S. Develin & Z. Islam	
G-BXWP	PA-32 Cherokee Six 300	Alliance Aviation	
G-BXWR	CFM Streak Shadow	M. A. Hayward (G-MZMI)	
G-BXWT	Van's RV-6	R. C. Owen	
G-BXWU	FLS Aerospace Sprint 160	Sunhawk Ltd/North Weald	
G-BXWV	FLS Aerospace Sprint 160	Sunhawk Ltd/North Weald	
G-BXWX	Sky 25-16 balloon	Zebedee Balloon Service Ltd	
G-BXWY	Cameron A-105 balloon	Richard Nash Cars Ltd	
G-BXXC	Scheibe SF.25C Falke 1700	K. E. Ballantine	
G-BXXD	Cessna 172R	Oxford Aviation Services Ltd/Kidlington	
G-BXXE	Rand-Robinson KR-2	N. Rawlinson	
G-BXXG	Cameron N-105 balloon	Allen Owen Ltd	
G-BXXH	Hatz CB-1	R. D. Shingler	
G-BXXI	Grob G.109B	M. N. Martin	
G-BXXJ	Colt Flying Yacht SS balloon	Magical Adventures Ltd/USA	
G-BXXK	Cessna FR.172N	E. Alexander	
G-BXXL	Cameron N-105 balloon	Flying Pictures Ltd	
G-BXXN	Robinson R-22B	Murray Galloway	
G-BXXO	Lindstrand LBL-90B balloon	K. Temple	
G-BXXP	Sky 77-24 balloon	C. J. James	
G-BXXR	Lovegrove AV-8 gyroplane	P. C. Lovegrove	
G-BXXS	Sky 105-24 balloon	Flying Pictures Ltd	
G-BXXT	Beech 76 Duchess	Aviation Rentals	
G-BXXU	Colt 31A balloon	Sade Balloons Ltd	
G-BXXW	Enstrom F-28F	G. Kidger (G-SCOX)	
G-BXXZ	CFM Starstreak Shadow SA-II	A. V. & B. T. Orchard	
G-BXYC	Schweizer 269C	Foremans Aviation Ltd	
G-BXYD	Eurocopter EC.120B	Airmac Ltd	
G-BXYE	CP.301-C1 Emeraude	D. T. Gethin	
G-BXYF	Colt AS-105 GD airship	LN Flying Ltd	
G-BXYG	Cessna 310D	Equitus SARL/France	
G-BXYH	Cameron N-105 balloon	Virgin Airship & Balloon Co Ltd	
G-BXYI	Cameron H-34 balloon	Virgin Airship & Balloon Co Ltd	
G-BXYJ	Jodel DR.1050	R. Manning	
G-BXYK	Robinson R-22B	D. N. Whittlestone	
G-BXYL	Cameron A-275 balloon	Bristol Balloons	
G-BXYM	PA-28 Cherokee 235	Ashurst Aviation Ltd/Shoreham	
G-BXYN	Van's RV-6	J. A. Tooley & R. M. Austin	
G-BXYO	PA-28RT-201 Arrow IV	Oxford Aviation Services Ltd/Kidlington	
G-BXYP	PA-28RT-201 Arrow IV	Oxford Aviation Services Ltd/Kidlington	
G-BXYR	PA-28RT-201 Arrow IV	Oxford Aviation Services Ltd/Kidlington	
G-BXYS	PA-28RT-201 Arrow IV	Oxford Aviation Services Ltd/Kidlington	
G-BXYT	PA-28RT-201 Arrow IV	Oxford Aviation Services Ltd/Kidlington	
G-BXYX	Van's RV-6A	A. G. Palmer	

Notes	Reg.	Type	Owner or Operator
	G-BXYY	Cessna FR.172E	Haimoss Ltd/Old Sarum
	G-BXZA	PA-38-112 Tomahawk	P. D. Brooks/Inverness
	G-BXZB	Nanchang CJ-6A (2632016)	Wingglider Ltd/Hibaldstow
	G-BXZD	Westland Gazelle HT.2 (XW895)	Middleton Miniature Mouldings Ltd
	G-BXZE	Westland Gazelle HT.3 (XW910)	Leisure Park Management Ltd
	G-BXZF	Lindstrand LBL-90A balloon	L. Van Den Avyle/Portugal
	G-BXZG	Cameron A-210 balloon	Societe Bombard SARL/France
	G-BXZH	Cameron A-210 balloon	Societe Bombard SARL/France
	G-BXZI	Lindstrand LBL-90A balloon	Purple Balloons
	G-BXZK	MDH MD-900 Explorer	Dorset Police Air Support Unit
	G-BXZM	Cessna 182S	Oxford Aviation Services Ltd/Kidlington
	G-BXZN	CH1 ATI	Intora-Firebird PLC
	G-BXZO	Pietenpol Air Camper	P. J. Cooke
	G-BXZS	Sikorsky S-76A (modified)	Bristow Helicopters Ltd
	G-BXZT	M.S.880B Rallye Club	K. P. Snipe
	G-BXZU	Bantam B.22-S	M. R. M. Welch
	G-BXZV	CFM Streak Shadow	CFM Aircraft Ltd
	G-BXZY	CFM Streak Shadow Srs DD	Cloudbase Aviation Services Ltd
	G-BXZZ	Sky 160-24 balloon	Skybus Ballooning
	G-BYAA	Boeing 767-204ER	Britannia Airways Ltd *Sir Matt Busby CBE*
	G-BYAB	Boeing 767-204ER	Britannia Airways Ltd *Brian Johnston CBE MC*
	G-BYAD	Boeing 757-204	Britannia Airways Ltd
	G-BYAE	Boeing 757-204	Britannia Airways Ltd
	G-BYAF	Boeing 757-204	Britannia Airways Ltd
	G-BYAH	Boeing 757-204	Britannia Airways Ltd
	G-BYAI	Boeing 757-204	Britannia Airways Ltd
	G-BYAJ	Boeing 757-204	Britannia Airways Ltd
	G-BYAK	Boeing 757-28A	Britannia Airways Ltd
	G-BYAL	Boeing 757-28A	Britannia Airways Ltd
	G-BYAN	Boeing 757-204	Britannia Airways Ltd
	G-BYAO	Boeing 757-204	Britannia Airways Ltd
	G-BYAP	Boeing 757-204	Britannia Airways Ltd
	G-BYAR	Boeing 757-204	Britannia Airways Ltd
	G-BYAS	Boeing 757-204	Britannia Airways Ltd
	G-BYAT	Boeing 757-204	Britannia Airways Ltd
	G-BYAU	Boeing 757-204	Britannia Airways Ltd
	G-BYAV	Taylor JT.1 Monoplane	T. Adams
	G-BYAW	Boeing 757-204	Britannia Airways Ltd *Eric Morecambe OBE*
	G-BYAX	Boeing 757-204	Britannia Airways Ltd
	G-BYAY	Boeing 757-204	Britannia Airways Ltd
	G-BYAZ	CFM Streak Shadow	A. G. Wright
	G-BYBA	AB-206B JetRanger 3	R. Forests Ltd (G-BHXV/G-OWJM)
	G-BYBC	AB-206B JetRanger 2	Mainstreet Aviation (G-BTWW)
	G-BYBD	Cessna F.172H	R. Ross (G-OBHX/G-AWMU)
	G-BYBE	Jodel D.120A	R. J. Page
	G-BYBF	Robin R.2160i	D. J. R. Lloyd-Evans
	G-BYBH	PA-34-200T Seneca II	Goldspear (UK) Ltd
	G-BYBI	Bell 206B JetRanger 3	Winkburn Air Ltd
	G-BYBJ	Medway Hybred 44XLR	M. Gardner
	G-BYBK	Murphy Rebel	D. Webb
	G-BYBL	GY-80 Horizon 160D	P. T. Harmsworth
	G-BYBM	Avtech Jabiru SK	P. J. Hatton
	G-BYBN	Cameron N-77 balloon	M. G. & R. D. Howard
	G-BYBO	Medway Hybred 44XLR Eclipser	R. Skene
	G-BYBP	Cessna A.185F	G. M. S. Scott
	G-BYBR	Rans S.6-116 Coyote II	J. B. Robinson/Blackpool
	G-BYBS	Sky 80-16 balloon	K. B. Chapple
	G-BYBU	Renegade Spirit UK	L. C. Cook
	G-BYBV	Mainair Rapier	M. W. Robson
	G-BYBW	Team Minimax	N. E. Johnson
	G-BYBX	Slingsby T.67M Firefly 260	Slingsby Aviation Ltd
	G-BYBY	Thorp T.18C Tiger	L. J. Joyce
	G-BYBZ	Avtech Jabiru SK	A. W. Harris
	G-BYCA	PA-28 Cherokee 140D	I. J. Sixsmith
	G-BYCB	Sky 21-16 balloon	Zebedee Balloon Service Ltd
	G-BYCD	Cessna 140 (modified)	G. P. James
	G-BYCE	Robinson R-44	Walters Plant Hire Ltd
	G-BYCF	Robinson R-22B-2	Teleology Ltd
	G-BYCJ	CFM Shadow Srs DD	J. W. E. Pearson
	G-BYCL	Raj Hamsa X'Air 582 (2)	D. O'Keefe & ptnrs

Reg.	Type	Owner or Operator	Notes
G-BYCM	Rans S.6-ES Coyote II	E. W. McMullan	
G-BYCN	Rans S.6-ES Coyote II	J. K. & R. L. Dunseath	
G-BYCP	Beech B200 Super King Air	Comex Services Ltd	
G-BYCS	Jodel DR.1051	Fire Defence PLC	
G-BYCT	Aero L-29 Delfin	M. Beesley	
G-BYCU	Robinson R-22B	K. S. & S. A. Faria (G-OCGJ)	
G-BYCV	Meridian Maverick	J. M. Swash	
G-BYCX	Westland Wasp HAS.1	Austen Associates	
G-BYCY	I.I.I. Sky Arrow 650T	K. A. Daniels	
G-BYCZ	Avtech Jabiru SK	R. Scroby	
G-BYDA	Douglas DC-10-30	My Travel Airways (Airtours)	
G-BYDB	Grob G.115B	J. B. Baker	
G-BYDD	Mooney M.20J	A. D. E. Eade	
G-BYDE	V.S.361 Spitfire LF. IX (PT879)	A. H. Soper	
G-BYDF	Sikorsky S-76A	Brecqhou Development Ltd	
G-BYDG	Beech C24R Sierra	Professional Air Training Ltd	
G-BYDI	Cameron A-210 balloon	First Flight	
G-BYDJ	Colt 120A balloon	D. K. Hempleman-Adams	
G-BYDK	SNCAN Stampe SV-4C	Bianchi Aviation Film Services Ltd/Booker	
G-BYDL	Hawker Hurricane IIB (Z5207)	R. A. Roberts	
G-BYDM	Pegasus Quantum 15-912	B. J. Fallows	
G-BYDR	NA B-25D-3-ND Mitchell (KL161)	Patina Ltd/Duxford	
G-BYDT	Cameron N-90 balloon	N. J. Langley	
G-BYDV	Van's RV-6	B. F. Hill	
G-BYDW	RAF 2000 GTX-SE gyroplane	R. G. Turck	
G-BYDX	American General AG-5B Tiger	Bibit Group	
G-BYDY	Beech 58 Baron	J. F. Britten	
G-BYDZ	Pegasus Quantum 15-912	W.McCormack	
G-BYEA	Cessna 172P	Plane Talking Ltd/Elstree	
G-BYEB	Cessna 172P	Plane Talking Ltd/Elstree	
G-BYEC	Glaser-Dirks DG.800B	P. R. Redshaw	
G-BYEE	Mooney M.20K	Double Echo Flying Group	
G-BYEH	CEA Jodel DR.250	E. J. Horsfall/Blackpool	
G-BYEI	Cameron 90 Chick SS balloon	Virgin Airship & Balloon Co Ltd	
G-BYEJ	Scheibe SF-28A Tandem Falke	D. Shrimpton	
G-BYEK	Stoddard-Hamilton Glastar	B. M. New	
G-BYEL	Van's RV-6	D. Millar	
G-BYEM	Cessna R.182 RG	Wycombe Air Centre Ltd/Booker	
G-BYEO	Zenair CH.601HDS	Cloudbase Flying Group	
G-BYEP	Lindstrand LBL-90B balloon	R. C. Barkworth & D. G. Maguire	
G-BYER	Cameron C-80 balloon	Cameron Balloons Ltd	
G-BYES	Cessna 172P	Plane Talking Ltd/Elstree	
G-BYET	Cessna 172P	Plane Talking Ltd/Elstree	
G-BYEU	Pegasus Quantum 15	T. C. Brown	
G-BYEW	Pegasus Quantum 15-912	P. M. Coppola	
G-BYEX	Sky 120-24 balloon	Ballongflyg Upp & Ner AB/Sweden	
G-BYEY	Lindstrand LBL-21 Silver Dream balloon	Oscair Project Ltd/Sweden	
G-BYEZ	Dyn' Aero MCR-01	J. P. Davis	
G-BYFA	Cessna F.152 II	A. J. Gomes (G-WACA)	
G-BYFB	Cameron N-105 balloon	Cameron Balloons Ltd	
G-BYFC	Avtech Jabiru SK	A. C. N. Freeman	
G-BYFD	Grob G.115A	D. Lewis (G-BSGE)	
G-BYFE	Pegasus Quantum 15-912	G-BYFE Flying Group	
G-BYFF	Pegasus Quantum 15-912	Kemble Flying Club	
G-BYFG	Shaw Europa XS	P. R. Brodie	
G-BYFH	Bede BD-5B	G. M. J. Monaghan	
G-BYFI	CFM Starstreak Shadow SA	D. G. Cook	
G-BYFJ	Cameron N-105 balloon	R. R. McCormack	
G-BYFK	Cameron Printer SS balloon	Flying Pictures Ltd	
G-BYFL	Diamond HK.36 TTS	Seahawk Gliding Club/Culdrose	
G-BYFM	Jodel DR.1050M-1 (replica)	P. M. Standen & A. J. Roxburgh	
G-BYFN	Thruster T.600N	J. S. Manning	
G-BYFP	PA-28-181 Archer II	B. Badley	
G-BYFR	PA-32R-301 Saratoga II HP	Buckleton Ltd	
G-BYFS	Airbus A.320-231	My Travel Airways (Airtours)	
G-BYFT	Pietenpol Air Camper	M. W. Elliott	
G-BYFU	Lindstrand LBL-105B balloon	Balloons Lindstrand France	
G-BYFV	Team Minimax 91	W. E. Gillham	
G-BYFX	Colt 77A balloon	Flying Pictures Ltd	
G-BYFY	Avions Mudry CAP.10B	Cole Aviation	
G-BYGA	Boeing 747-436	British Airways	
G-BYGB	Boeing 747-436	British Airways	

Notes	Reg.	Type	Owner or Operator
	G-BYGC	Boeing 747-436	British Airways
	G-BYGD	Boeing 747-436	British Airways
	G-BYGE	Boeing 747-436	British Airways
	G-BYGF	Boeing 747-436	British Airways
	G-BYGG	Boeing 747-436	British Airways
	G-BYHC	Cameron Z-90 balloon	Exclusive Ballooning
	G-BYHD	Robinson R-22B	C. G. P. Holden
	G-BYHE	Robinson R-22B	Helicopter Services
	G-BYHG	Dornier Do.328-100	ScotAirways Ltd
	G-BYHH	PA-28-161 Warrior III	Stapleford Flying Club Ltd
	G-BYHI	PA-28-161 Warrior II	Haimoss Ltd
	G-BYHJ	PA-28R-201 Arrow	Bflying Ltd/Bournemouth
	G-BYHK	PA-28-181 Archer III	Southnet Ltd
	G-BYHL	D.H.C.1 Chipmunk 22 (WG308)	M. R. & I. D. Higgins
	G-BYHM	BAe 125 Srs 800B	Corporate Aircraft Leasing Ltd
	G-BYHN	Mainair Blade 912	R. Stone
	G-BYHO	Mainair Blade 912	P. J. Morton
	G-BYHP	CEA DR.253B	D. A. Hood
	G-BYHR	Pegasus Quantum 15-912	I. D. Chantler
	G-BYHS	Mainair Blade 912	D. A. Bolton
	G-BYHT	Robin DR.400/180R	M. A. Recht
	G-BYHU	Cameron N-105 balloon	Freeup Ltd
	G-BYHV	Raj Hamsa X'Air 582	B. J. Bowditch
	G-BYHW	Cameron A-160 balloon	R. H. Etherington/Italy
	G-BYHX	Cameron A-250 balloon	Global Ballooning
	G-BYHY	Cameron V-77 balloon	P. Spellward
	G-BYHZ	Sky 160-24 balloon	Skyride Balloons Ltd
	G-BYIA	Avtech Jabiru SK	G. M. Geary
	G-BYIB	Rans S.6-ES Coyote II	G. A. Clayton
	G-BYIC	Cessna U.206G	Wild Geese Parachute Club
	G-BYID	Rans S.6-ES Coyote II	D. J. Brotherhood/Tollerton
	G-BYIE	Robinson R-22B	Jepar Rotorcraft
	G-BYIF	Avtech Jabiru XL	J. A. Moss
	G-BYIG	Murphy Renegade Spirit	J. Hatswell
	G-BYII	Team Minimax	J. S. R. Moodie
	G-BYIJ	C.A.S.A. 1.131E Jungmann 2000	P. R. Teager & R. N. Crosland
	G-BYIK	Shaw Europa	P. M. Davis
	G-BYIL	Cameron N-105 balloon	Oakfield Farm Products Ltd
	G-BYIM	Avtech Jabiru UL	W. J. Dale & R. F. Hinton/Tollerton
	G-BYIN	RAF 2000 gyroplane	J. R. Legge
	G-BYIO	Colt 105A balloon	N. Charbonnier/Italy
	G-BYIP	Aerotek Pitts S-2A Special	D. P. Heather-Hayes
	G-BYIR	Aerotek Pitts S-1S Special	Hampshire Aeroplane Co Ltd/St Just
	G-BYIS	Pegasus Quantum 15-912	A. J. Ridell
	G-BYIT	Robin DR.400/500	P. R. Liddle
	G-BYIU	Cameron V-90 balloon	H. Micketeit/Germany
	G-BYIV	Cameron PM-80 balloon	A. Schneider/Germany
	G-BYIW	Cameron PM-80 balloon	A. Schneider/Germany
	G-BYIX	Cameron PM-80 balloon	A. Schneider/Germany
	G-BYIY	Lindstrand LBL-105B balloon	J. H. Dobson
	G-BYIZ	Pegasus Quantum 15-912	J. D. Gray
	G-BYJA	RAF 2000 GTX-SE gyroplane	B. Errington-Weddle
	G-BYJB	Mainair Blade 912	J. H. Bradbury
	G-BYJC	Cameron N-90 balloon	D. E. Bentley Ltd
	G-BYJD	Avtech Jabiru UL	M. W. Knights
	G-BYJE	Team Minimax 91	A. W. Austin
	G-BYJF	Thorpe T.211	AD Aviation Ltd/Barton
	G-BYJG	Lindstrand LBL-77A balloon	Lindstrand Balloons Ltd
	G-BYJH	Grob G.109B	J. D. Scott
	G-BYJI	Shaw Europa	P. S. Jones (G-ODTI)
	G-BYJJ	Cameron C-80 balloon	Proximm Franchising SRL/Italy
	G-BYJK	Pegasus Quantum 15-912	B. S. Smy
	G-BYJL	Aero Designs Pulsar	F. A. H. Ashmead
	G-BYJM	Cyclone AX2000	Caunton AX2000 Syndicate
	G-BYJN	Lindstrand LBL-105A balloon	B. Meeson
	G-BYJO	Rans S.6-ES Coyote II	G. Ferguson
	G-BYJP	Aerotek Pitts S-1S Special	Eaglescott Pitts Group
	G-BYJR	Lindstrand LBL-77B balloon	C. D. Duthy-James
	G-BYJS	SOCATA TB-20 Trinidad	J. K. Sharkey
	G-BYJT	Zenair CH.601HD	J. D. T. Tannock
	G-BYJU	Raj Hamsa X'Air 582	C. W. Payne
	G-BYJV	Cameron A-210 balloon	Societe Bombard SRL/France
	G-BYJW	Cameron 105 Sphere SS balloon	Forbes Europe Inc/USA

Reg.	Type	Owner or Operator	Notes
G-BYJX	Cameron C-70 balloon	B. Perona	
G-BYJZ	Lindstrand LBL-105A balloon	M. A. Webb	
G-BYKA	Lindstrand LBL-69A balloon	Aerial Promotions Ltd	
G-BYKB	R. Commander 114	A. Walton	
G-BYKC	Mainair Blade 912	D. Gabott	
G-BYKD	Mainair Blade 912	D. C. Boyle	
G-BYKE	Rans S.6-ESA Coyote II	C. Townsend	
G-BYKF	Enstrom F-28F	Battle Helicopters Ltd	
G-BYKG	Pietenpol Air Camper	K. B. Hodge	
G-BYKI	Cameron N-105 balloon	Flying Pictures Ltd	
G-BYKJ	Westland Scout AH.1	Austen Associates	
G-BYKK	Robinson R-44	Banner Helicopters Ltd	
G-BYKL	PA-28-181 Archer II	Alliance Aerolink Ltd	
G-BYKM	PA-34-220T Seneca III	Oxford Aviation Services Ltd/Kidlington	
G-BYKN	PA-28-161 Warrior II	Oxford Aviation Services Ltd/Kidlington	
G-BYKO	PA-28-161 Warrior II	Oxford Aviation Services Ltd/Kidlington	
G-BYKP	PA-28R-201T Turbo Arrow IV	Oxford Aviation Services Ltd/Kidlington	
G-BYKR	PA-28-161 Warrior II	Oxford Aviation Services Ltd/Kidlington	
G-BYKS	Leopoldoff L-6 Colibri	I. M. Callier	
G-BYKT	Pegasus Quantum 15-912	D. A. Bannister & N. J. Howarth	
G-BYKU	BFC Challenger II	K. W. Seedhouse	
G-BYKV	Avro 504K (replica)	Hawker Restorations Ltd	
G-BYKW	Lindstrand LBL-77B balloon	P.-J. Fuseau/France	
G-BYKX	Cameron N-90 balloon	G. Davis	
G-BYKY	Avtech Jabiru SK	N. C. Cowell	
G-BYKZ	Sky 140-24 balloon	D. J. Head	
G-BYLA	FRED Srs 3	R. Holden-Rushworth	
G-BYLB	D.H.82A Tiger Moth	P. W. Payne	
G-BYLC	Pegasus Quantum 15-912	T. Marriott	
G-BYLD	Pietenpol Air Camper	S. Bryan	
G-BYLE	PA-38-112 Tomahawk	Surrey & Kent Flying Club Ltd/Biggin Hill	
G-BYLF	Zenair CH.601HDS	M. Thomas	
G-BYLG	Robin HR.200/120B	Building & Commercial Ltd/ Gloucestershire	
G-BYLH	Robin HR.200/120B	Multiflight Ltd	
G-BYLI	Nova Vertex 22	M. N. Maclean	
G-BYLJ	Letov LK-2M Sluka	N. E. Stokes	
G-BYLK	Mainair Blade	Hummingbird Microlight Flight Training Ltd	
G-BYLL	Sequoia F.8L Falco	N. J. Langrick/Breighton	
G-BYLM	PA-46-350P Malibu Mirage	Polestar Holdings Ltd	
G-BYLN	Raj Hamsa X'Air 582	R. Gillespie & S. P. McGirr	
G-BYLO	T.66 Nipper Srs 1	M. J. A. Trudgill	
G-BYLP	Rand-Robinson KR-2	C. S. Hales	
G-BYLR	Cessna 404	Air Charter Scotland Ltd/Edinburgh	
G-BYLS	Bede BD-4	G. H. Bayliss/Shobdon	
G-BYLT	Raj Hamsa X'Air 582	T. W. Phipps & B. G. Simons	
G-BYLU	Cameron A-140 balloon	Cameron Balloons Ltd	
G-BYLV	Thunder Ax8-105 S2 balloon	Wind Line SRL/Italy	
G-BYLW	Lindstrand LBL-77A balloon	Associazione Gran Premio Italiano	
G-BYLX	Lindstrand LBL-105A balloon	Italiana Aeronavi/Italy	
G-BYLY	Cameron V-77 balloon (1)	R. Bayly (G-ULIA)/Italy	
G-BYLZ	Rutan Cozy	E. R. Allen	
G-BYMA	BAe Jetstream 3202	Eastern Airways Ltd	
G-BYMB	Diamond Katana DA.20-C1	Enstone Flying Club	
G-BYMC	PA-38-112 Tomahawk II	Surrey & Kent Flying Club Ltd/Biggin Hill	
G-BYMD	PA-38-112 Tomahawk II	Surrey & Kent Flying Club Ltd/Biggin Hill	
G-BYME	GY-80 Horizon 180	Air Venturas Ltd	
G-BYMF	Pegasus Quantum 15-912	G. R. Stockdale	
G-BYMG	Cameron A-210 balloon	Cloud Nine Balloon Co	
G-BYMH	Cessna 152	PJC (Leasing) Ltd/Stapleford	
G-BYMI	Pegasus Quantum 15	N. C. Grayson	
G-BYMJ	Cessna 152	PJC (Leasing) Ltd/Stapleford	
G-BYMK	Dornier Do.328-100	ScotAirways Ltd	
G-BYML	Dornier Do.328-100	ScotAirways Ltd	
G-BYMM	Raj Hamsa X'Air 582 (1)	R. W. F. Boarder	
G-BYMN	Rans S.6-ESA Coyote II	H. Smith	
G-BYMO	Campbell Cricket	D. G. Hill	
G-BYMP	Campbell Cricket Mk 1	J. J. Fitzgerald	
G-BYMR	Raj Hamsa X'Air 582	W. M. McMinn	
G-BYMT	Pegasus Quantum 15-912	S. A. Owen	
G-BYMU	Rans S.6-ES Coyote II	I. R. Russell & B. Frogley	
G-BYMV	Rans S.6-ES Coyote II	G. A. Squires	

Notes	Reg.	Type	Owner or Operator
	G-BYMW	Boland 52-12 balloon	C. Jones
	G-BYMX	Cameron A-105 balloon	H. Reis/Germany
	G-BYMY	Cameron N-90 balloon	Cameron Balloons Ltd
	G-BYNA	Cessna F.172H	Heliview Ltd (G-AWTH)/Blackbushe
	G-BYNB	Boeing 737-804	Britannia Airways Ltd
	G-BYND	Pegasus Quantum 15	M. C. Kerr
	G-BYNE	Pilatus PC-6/B2-H4 Turbo Porter	D. M. Penny
	G-BYNF	NA-64 Yale I	R. S. Van Dijk
	G-BYNH	Rotorway Executive 162F	R. C. MacKenzie
	G-BYNI	Rotorway Exec 90	M. Bunn
	G-BYNJ	Cameron N-77 balloon	A. Giovanni/Italy
	G-BYNK	Robin HR.200/160	M. & K. A. Whittaker
	G-BYNL	Avtech Jabiru SK	R. C. Daykin
	G-BYNM	Mainair Blade 912	M. W. Holmes
	G-BYNN	Cameron V-90 balloon	M. K. Grigson
	G-BYNO	Pegasus Quantum 15-912	R. J. Newsham & G. J. Slater
	G-BYNP	Rans S.6-ES Coyote II	R. J. Lines
	G-BYNR	Avtech Jabiru UL	A. Parker
	G-BYNS	Avtech Jabiru SK	D. K. Lawry
	G-BYNT	Raj Hamsa X'Air 582 (1)	G. R. Wallis
	G-BYNU	Cameron Thunder Ax7-77 balloon	Aerial Promotions Ltd
	G-BYNV	Sky 105-24 balloon	Par Rovelli Construzioni SRL/Italy
	G-BYNW	Cameron H-34 balloon	Flying Pictures Ltd
	G-BYNX	Cameron RX-105 balloon	Cameron Balloons Ltd
	G-BYNY	Beech 76 Duchess	Magenta Ltd
	G-BYOA	Slingsby T.67M Firefly 260	Hunting Aviation Ltd/Barkston Heath
	G-BYOB	Slingsby T.67M Firefly 260	Hunting Aviation Ltd/Barkston Heath
	G-BYOD	Slingsby T.67C	Slingsby Aviation Ltd/Kirkbymoorside
	G-BYOF	Robin R.2160I	Mistral Aviation Ltd
	G-BYOG	Pegasus Quantum 15-912	A. Foote & M. Fizelle
	G-BYOH	Raj Hamsa X'Air 582 (1)	P. H. J. Kent
	G-BYOI	Sky 80-16 balloon	I. S. & S. W. Watthews
	G-BYOJ	Raj Hamsa X'Air 582 (1)	R. R. Hadley
	G-BYOK	Cameron V-90 balloon	D. S. Wilson
	G-BYOM	Sikorsky S-76C (modified)	Starspeed Ltd (G-IJCB)/Blackbushe
	G-BYON	Mainair Blade	S. Mills & G. M. Hobman
	G-BYOO	CFM Streak Shadow	C. I. Chegwen
	G-BYOR	Raj Hamsa X'Air 582 (1)	A. R. Walker
	G-BYOS	Mainair Blade 912	Baxby Airsports Club
	G-BYOT	Rans S.6-ES Coyote II	H. F. Blakeman
	G-BYOU	Rans S.6-ES Coyote II	R. Germany
	G-BYOV	Pegasus Quantum 15-912	K. W. A. Ballinger
	G-BYOW	Mainair Blade	N. Forster
	G-BYOY	Canadair T-33AN	K. K. Gerstorfer/North Weald
	G-BYOZ	Mainair Rapier	M. Morgan
	G-BYPA	AS.355F-2 Twin Squirrel	Aeromega Aviation Ltd (G-NWPI)
	G-BYPB	Pegasus Quantum 15-912	S. Graham
	G-BYPC	Lindstrand LBL-AS2 balloon	Lindstrand Balloons Ltd
	G-BYPD	Cameron A-105 balloon	Headland Hotel Ltd
	G-BYPE	GY-80 Horizon 160D	H. I. Smith & P. R. Hendry-Smith
	G-BYPF	Thruster T.600N	G. E. Hillyer-Jones
	G-BYPG	Thruster T.600N	A. Stanford
	G-BYPH	Thruster T.600N	A. H. Wooley
	G-BYPJ	Pegasus Quantum 15-912	P. J. Manders
	G-BYPL	Pegasus Quantum 15-912	K. J. Hard
	G-BYPM	Shaw Europa XS	P. Mileham
	G-BYPN	M.S.880B Rallye Club	R. & T. C. Edwards
	G-BYPO	Raj Hamsa X'Air 582 (1)	N. G. Woodall & A. S. Leach
	G-BYPP	Medway Rebel SS	J. L. Gowens
	G-BYPT	Rans S.6-ES Coyote II	G. R. & J. A. Pritchard
	G-BYPU	PA-32R-301 Saratoga SP	Thornfield Enterprises Ltd
	G-BYPW	Raj Hamsa X'Air 582 (3)	P. A. Mercer
	G-BYPY	Ryan ST3KR	P. B. Rice/Brighton
	G-BYPZ	Rans S.6-116 Super 6	P. G. Hayward
	G-BYRA	BAe Jetstream 3201	Eastern Airways Ltd
	G-BYRC	WS.58 Wessex HC.2 (XT671)	D. Rrem-Wilson
	G-BYRF	Cameron N-77 balloon	AAA Entertainments Ltd
	G-BYRG	Rans S.6-ES Coyote II	W. H. Mills
	G-BYRH	Medway Hybred 44XLR	M. R. Holland
	G-BYRJ	Pegasus Quantum 15-912	Light Flight Ltd
	G-BYRK	Cameron V-42 balloon	Gone With The Wind Ltd/USA
	G-BYRM	BAe Jetstream 3201	Eastern Airways Ltd
	G-BYRO	Mainair Blade	P. W. F. Coleman

Reg.	Type	Owner or Operator	Notes
G-BYRP	Mainair Blade 912	M. P. Middleton	
G-BYRR	Mainair Blade 912	G. R. Sharples	
G-BYRS	Rans S.6-ES Coyote II	R. Beniston	
G-BYRT	Beech F33A Bonanza	Barmoor Aviation	
G-BYRU	Pegasus Quantum 15-912	Sarum QTM 912 Group	
G-BYRV	Raj Hamsa X'Air 582 (1)	A, Hipkin	
G-BYRX	Westland Scout AH.1 (XT634)	Historic Helicopters Ltd	
G-BYRY	Slingsby T.67M Firefly 200	D. S. Balman & W. R. Tandy	
G-BYRZ	Lindstrand LBL-77M balloon	Challenge Transatlantique/France	
G-BYSA	Shaw Europa XS	B. Allsop	
G-BYSE	AB-206B JetRanger 2	Alspath Properties Ltd (G-BFND)	
G-BYSF	Avtech Jabiru UL	S. J. Marshall	
G-BYSG	Robin HR.200/120B	Anglian Flight Centres Ltd	
G-BYSI	WSK-PZL Koliber 160A	J. & D. F. Evans	
G-BYSJ	D.H.C.1 Chipmunk 22 (WB569)	Silver Victory BVBA/Belgium	
G-BYSK	Cameron A-275 balloon	Balloon School (International) Ltd	
G-BYSM	Cameron A-210 balloon	Balloon School (International) Ltd	
G-BYSN	Rans S.6-ES Coyote II	A. L. & A. R. Roberts	
G-BYSP	PA-28-181 Archer II	Aerohire Ltd	
G-BYSR	Pegasus Quantum 15-912	J. Lane & P. R. Thomas	
G-BYSS	Medway Rebel SS	C. R. Stevens	
G-BYSV	Cameron N-120 balloon	Cameron Balloons Ltd	
G-BYSW	Enstrom 280FX	S. G. Oliphant-Hope	
G-BYSX	Pegasus Quantum 15-912	RAF Microlight Flying Association	
G-BYSY	Raj Hamsa X'Air 582 (1)	J. M. Davidson	
G-BYTA	Kölb Twinstar Mk 3 (modified)	R. E. Gray	
G-BYTB	SOCATA TB-20 Trinidad	Jeff Brown Ltd	
G-BYTC	Pegasus Quantum 15-912	J. Hood	
G-BYTD	Robinson R-22B-2	Ace Air Flights Ltd	
G-BYTE	Robinson R-22B	Burman Aviation Ltd/Cranfield	
G-BYTG	Glaser-Dirks DG.400	P. R. Williams	
G-BYTH	Airbus A.320-231	My Travel Airways (Airtours)	
G-BYTI	PA-24 Comanche 250	G-BYTI Syndicate	
G-BYTJ	Cameron C-80 balloon	M. White	
G-BYTK	Avtech Jabiru UL	K. A. Fagan & S. Pike	
G-BYTL	Mainair Blade 912	M. E. Keefe	
G-BYTM	Dyn' Aero MCR-01	I. Lang	
G-BYTN	D.H.82A Tiger Moth	B. D. Hughes	
G-BYTO	Aérospatiale ATR-72-212	CityFlyer Express Ltd (G-OILA)	
G-BYTP	Aérospatiale ATR-72-212	CityFlyer Express Ltd (G-OILB)	
G-BYTR	Raj Hamsa X'Air 582 (1)	A. P. Roberts & R. Dunn	
G-BYTS	Montgomerie-Bensen B.8MR gyroplane	M. G. Mee	
G-BYTT	Raj Hamsa X'Air 582 (1)	J. L. Pearson	
G-BYTU	Mainair Blade 912	L. Chesworth	
G-BYTV	Avtech Jabiru UK	E. Bentley	
G-BYTW	Cameron O-90 balloon	Sade Balloons Ltd	
G-BYTY	Dornier Do.328-100	ScotAirways Ltd	
G-BYTZ	Raj Hamsa X'Air 582 (1)	K. C. Millar	
G-BYUA	Grob G.115E Tutor	VT Aerospace Ltd/Wyton	
G-BYUB	Grob G.115E Tutor	VT Aerospace Ltd/Cranwell	
G-BYUC	Grob G.115E Tutor	VT Aerospace Ltd/Cranwell	
G-BYUD	Grob G.115E Tutor	VT Aerospace Ltd/Cranwell	
G-BYUE	Grob G.115E Tutor	VT Aerospace Ltd/Wyton	
G-BYUF	Grob G.115E Tutor	VT Aerospace Ltd/Cranwell	
G-BYUG	Grob G.115E Tutor	VT Aerospace Ltd/Cranwell	
G-BYUH	Grob G.115E Tutor	VT Aerospace Ltd/Cranwell	
G-BYUI	Grob G.115E Tutor	VT Aerospace Ltd/Wyton	
G-BYUJ	Grob G.115E Tutor	VT Aerospace Ltd/Wyton	
G-BYUK	Grob G.115E Tutor	VT Aerospace Ltd/Cranwell	
G-BYUL	Grob G.115E Tutor	VT Aersoapce Ltd/Wyton	
G-BYUM	Grob G.115E Tutor	VT Aerospace Ltd/Wyton	
G-BYUN	Grob G.115E Tutor	VT Aerospace Ltd/Wyton	
G-BYUO	Grob G.115E Tutor	VT Aerospace Ltd/Wyton	
G-BYUP	Grob G.115E Tutor	VT Aerospace Ltd/Leuchars	
G-BYUR	Grob G.115E Tutor	VT Aerospace Ltd/Glasgow	
G-BYUS	Grob G.115E Tutor	VT Aerospace Ltd/Benson	
G-BYUT	Grob G.115E Tutor	VT Aerospace Ltd/Benson	
G-BYUU	Grob G.115E Tutor	VT Aerospace Ltd/Glasgow	
G-BYUV	Grob G.115E Tutor	VT Aerospace Ltd	
G-BYUW	Grob G.115E Tutor	VT Aerospace Ltd	
G-BYUX	Grob G.115E Tutor	VT Aerospace Ltd	
G-BYUY	Grob.G.115E Tutor	VT Aerospace Ltd	

Notes	Reg.	Type	Owner or Operator
	G-BYUZ	Grob G.115E Tutor	VT Aerospace Ltd
	G-BYVA	Grob G.115E Tutor	VT Aerospace Ltd
	G-BYVB	Grob G.115E Tutor	VT Aerospace Ltd
	G-BYVC	Grob G.115E Tutor	VT Aerospace Ltd
	G-BYVD	Grob G.115E Tutor	VT Aerospace Ltd
	G-BYVE	Grob G.115E Tutor	VT Aerospace Ltd
	G-BYVF	Grob G.115E Tutor	VT Aerospace Ltd
	G-BYVG	Grob G.115E Tutor	VT Aerospace Ltd
	G-BYVH	Grob G.115E Tutor	VT Aerospace Ltd
	G-BYVI	Grob G.115E Tutor	VT Aerospace Ltd
	G-BYVJ	Grob G.115E Tutor	VT Aerospace Ltd
	G-BYVK	Grob G.115E Tutor	VT Aerospace Ltd
	G-BYVL	Grob G.115E Tutor	VT Aerospace Ltd
	G-BYVM	Grob G.115E Tutor	VT Aerospace Ltd
	G-BYVN	Grob G.115E Tutor	VT Aerospace Ltd
	G-BYVO	Grob G.115E Tutor	VT Aerospace Ltd
	G-BYVP	Grob G.115E Tutor	VT Aerospace Ltd
	G-BYVR	Grob G.115E Tutor	VT Aerospace Ltd
	G-BYVS	Grob G.115E Tutor	VT Aerospace Ltd
	G-BYVT	Grob G.115E Tutor	VT Aerospace Ltd
	G-BYVU	Grob G.115E Tutor	VT Aerospace Ltd
	G-BYVV	Grob G.115E Tutor	VT Aerospace Ltd
	G-BYVW	Grob G.115E Tutor	VT Aerospace Ltd
	G-BYVX	Grob G.115E Tutor	VT Aerospace Ltd
	G-BYVY	Grob G.115E Tutor	VT Aerospace Ltd
	G-BYVZ	Grob G.115E Tutor	VT Aerospace Ltd
	G-BYWA	Grob G.115E Tutor	VT Aerospace Ltd
	G-BYWB	Grob G.115E Tutor	VT Aerospace Ltd
	G-BYWC	Grob G.115E Tutor	VT Aerospace Ltd
	G-BYWD	Grob G.115E Tutor	VT Aerospace Ltd
	G-BYWE	Grob G.115E Tutor	VT Aerospace Ltd
	G-BYWF	Grob G.115E Tutor	VT Aerospace Ltd
	G-BYWG	Grob G.115E Tutor	VT Aerospace Ltd
	G-BYWH	Grob G.115E Tutor	VT Aerospace Ltd
	G-BYWI	Grob G.115E Tutor	VT Aerospace Ltd
	G-BYWJ	Grob G.115E Tutor	VT Aerospace Ltd
	G-BYWK	Grob G.115E Tutor	VT Aerospace Ltd
	G-BYWL	Grob G.115E Tutor	VT Aerospace Ltd
	G-BYWM	Grob G.115E Tutor	VT Aerospace Ltd
	G-BYWN	Grob G.115E Tutor	VT Aerospace Ltd
	G-BYWO	Grob G.115E Tutor	VT Aerospace Ltd
	G-BYWP	Grob G.115E Tutor	VT Aerospace Ltd
	G-BYWR	Grob G.115E Tutor	VT Aerospace Ltd
	G-BYWS	Grob G.115E Tutor	VT Aerospace Ltd
	G-BYWT	Grob G-115E Tutor	VT Aerospace Ltd
	G-BYWU	Grob G.115E Tutor	VT Aerospace Ltd
	G-BYWV	Grob G.115E Tutor	VT Aerospace Ltd
	G-BYWW	Grob G.115E Tutor	VT Aerospace Ltd
	G-BYWX	Grob G.115E Tutor	VT Aerospace Ltd
	G-BYWY	Grob G.115E Tutor	VT Aerospace Ltd
	G-BYWZ	Grob G.115E Tutor	VT Aerospace Ltd
	G-BYXA	Grob G.115E Tutor	VT Aerospace Ltd
	G-BYXB	Grob G.115E Tutor	VT Aerospace Ltd
	G-BYXC	Grob G.115E Tutor	VT Aerospace Ltd
	G-BYXD	Grob G.115E Tutor	VT Aerospace Ltd
	G-BYXE	Grob G.115E Tutor	VT Aerospace Ltd
	G-BYXF	Grob G.115E Tutor	VT Aerospace Ltd
	G-BYXG	Grob G.115E Tutor	VT Aerospace Ltd
	G-BYXH	Grob G.115E Tutor	VT Aerospace Ltd
	G-BYXI	Grob G.115E Tutor	VT Aerospace Ltd
	G-BYXJ	Grob G.115E Tutor	VT Aerospace Ltd/Cranwell
	G-BYXK	Grob G.115E Tutor	VT Aerospace Ltd/Cranwell
	G-BYXL	Grob G.115E Tutor	VT Aerospace Ltd/Cranwell
	G-BYXM	Grob G.115E Tutor	VT Aerospace Ltd/Cranwell
	G-BYXN	Grob G.115E Tutor	VT Aerospace Ltd
	G-BYXO	Grob G.115E Tutor	VT Aerospace Ltd
	G-BYXP	Grob G.115E Tutor	VT Aerospace Ltd
	G-BYXR	Grob G.115E Tutor	VT Aerospace Ltd
	G-BYXS	Grob G.115E Tutor	VT Aerospace Ltd
	G-BYXT	Grob G.115E Tutor	VT Aerospace Ltd
	G-BYXU	PA-28-161 Warrior II	F. P. McGovern (G-BNUP)
	G-BYXV	Medway Eclipser	K. Swann
	G-BYXW	Medway Eclipser	J. Swann

Reg.	Type	Owner or Operator	Notes
G-BYXX	Grob G.115E Tutor	VT Aerospace Ltd	
G-BYXY	Grob G.115E Tutor	VT Aerospace Ltd	
G-BYXZ	Grob G.115E Tutor	VT Aerospace Ltd	
G-BYYA	Grob G.115E Tutor	VT Aerospace Ltd	
G-BYYB	Grob G.115E Tutor	VT Aerospace Ltd	
G-BYYC	Hapi Cygnet SF-2A	C. D. Hughes	
G-BYYD	Cameron A-250 balloon	C. & J. M. Bailey	
G-BYYE	Lindstrand LBL-77A balloon	D. J. Cook	
G-BYYF	Boeing 737-229C	European Aviation Air Charter Ltd	
G-BYYG	Slingsby T.67C	S. E. Marples & B. Dixon	
G-BYYH	AS.350B Ecureuil	RCR Aviation Ltd/Thruxton	
G-BYYI	BAe Jetstream 3107	Vale Aviation Ltd	
G-BYYK	Boeing 737-229C	European Aviation Air Charter Ltd	
G-BYYM	Raj Hamsa X'Air 582 (1)	B. Pilling & D. J. McCall	
G-BYYN	Pegasus Quantum 15-912	E. Clarke	
G-BYYO	PA-28R -201 Arrow III	Stapleford Flying Club Ltd	
G-BYYP	Pegasus Quantum 15	D. A. Linsey-Bloom	
G-BYYR	Raj Hamsa X'Air 582 (1)	T. D. Bawden	
G-BYYT	Avtech Jabiru UL	T. D. Saveker	
G-BYYW	D.H.C.1 Chipmunk 20	R. Farrer	
G-BYYX	Team Minimax 91	P. L. Turner	
G-BYYY	Pegasus Quantum 15-912	C. J. Finnigan	
G-BYYZ	Staaken Z-21A Flitzer	A. E. Morris	
G-BYZA	AS.355F-2 Twin Squirrel	Aeromega Aviation PLC	
G-BYZB	Mainair Blade	O. Grati	
G-BYZD	Kis Cruiser	R. T. Clegg	
G-BYZE	AS.350B-2 Ecureuil	V. H. L. Ellis	
G-BYZF	Raj Hamsa X'Air 582 (1)	S. W. Grainger	
G-BYZG	Cameron A-275 balloon	Horizon Ballooning Ltd	
G-BYZH	Cessna 208B Caravan	Army Parachute Association/Netheravon	
G-BYZJ	Boeing 737-3Q8	bmi british midland (G-COLE)	
G-BYZL	Cameron GP-65 balloon	P. Thibo	
G-BYZM	PA-28-161 Warrior II	Goodair Leasing Ltd	
G-BYZO	Rans S.6-ES Coyote II	A. J. Boulton	
G-BYZP	Robinson R-22B	Coleraine Landscape Services	
G-BYZR	I.I.I. Sky Arrow 650TC	G. H. Jackson & R. Moncrieff	
G-BYZS	Avtech Jabiru UL-450	N. Fielding	
G-BYZT	Nova Vertex 26	M. N. Maclean	
G-BYZU	Pegasus Quantum 15	N. I. Clifton	
G-BYZV	Sky 90-24 balloon	P. Farmer	
G-BYZW	Raj Hamsa X'Air 582 (2)	H. C. Lowther	
G-BYZX	Cameron R-90 balloon	D. K. Hempleman-Adams	
G-BYZZ	Robinson R-22B-2	Astra Helicopters Ltd	
G-BZAA	Mainair Blade	R. Locke	
G-BZAB	Mainair Rapier	G. Verity	
G-BZAD	Cessna 152	Cristal Air Ltd	
G-BZAE	Cessna 152	Jaxx Landing Ltd	
G-BZAF	Raj Hamsa X'Air 582 (1)	Y. A. Evans	
G-BZAG	Lindstrand LBL-105A balloon	R. J. Mold	
G-BZAI	Pegasus Quantum 15	D. Paget	
G-BZAJ	WSK PZL Koliber 160A	PZL International Marketing & Sales PLC/North Weald	
G-BZAK	Raj Hamsa X'Air 582 (1)	R. J. Ripley	
G-BZAL	Mainair Blade 912	K. Worthington	
G-BZAO	Rans S.12XL	M. L. Robinson	
G-BZAP	Avtech Jabiru UL-450	S. Derwin	
G-BZAR	Denny Kitfox 4-1200 Speedster	C. E. Brookes (G-LEZJ)	
G-BZAS	Isaacs Fury II	H. A. Brunt & H. Frick	
G-BZAT	Avro RJ100	CityFlyer Express Ltd/BA Express	
G-BZAU	Avro RJ100	CityFlyer Express Ltd/BA Express	
G-BZAV	Avro RJ100	CityFlyer Express Ltd/BA Express	
G-BZAW	Avro RJ100	CityFlyer Express Ltd/BA Express	
G-BZAX	Avro RJ100	CityFlyer Express Ltd/BA Express	
G-BZAY	Avro RJ100	CityFlyer Express Ltd/BA Express	
G-BZAZ	Avro RJ100	CityFlyer Express Ltd/BA Express	
G-BZBC	Rans S.6-ES Coyote II	A. J. Baldwin	
G-BZBE	Cameron A-210 balloon	Dragon Balloon Co.	
G-BZBF	Cessna 172M	F. & H. Aircraft	
G-BZBG	Thruster T.600N	Mainair Microlight School Ltd	
G-BZBH	Thunder Ax6-65 balloon	R. B. & G. Clarke	
G-BZBI	Cameron V-77 balloon	B. Smallwood	
G-BZBJ	Lindstrand LBL-77A balloon	The Cancer Research Campaign	

Notes	Reg.	Type	Owner or Operator
	G-BZBL	Lindstrand LBL-120A balloon	Flying Pictures Ltd
	G-BZBM	Cameron A-315 balloon	Listers of Coventry (Motors) Ltd
	G-BZBN	Thunder Ax9-120 balloon	K. Willie
	G-BZBO	Stoddard-Hamilton Glasair III	M. B. Hamlett/France
	G-BZBP	Raj Hamsa X'Air 582 (1)	D. F. Hughes
	G-BZBR	Pegasus Quantum 15-912	N.C.Stevenson
	G-BZBS	PA-28-161 Warrior III	Aviation Rentals
	G-BZBT	Cameron H-34 Hopper balloon	British Telecommunications PLC
	G-BZBU	Robinson R-22	J. N. A. Cawood
	G-BZBW	Rotorway Executive 162F	M. Gardiner
	G-BZBX	Rans S.6-ES Coyote II	R. Johnstone
	G-BZBZ	Jodel D.9	S. Marom
	G-BZDA	PA-28-161 Warrior III	Aviation Rentals
	G-BZDB	Thruster T.600T	Thruster Air Services Ltd
	G-BZDC	Mainair Blade	L. J. Dickson
	G-BZDD	Mainair Blade 912	Barton Blade Group
	G-BZDE	Lindstrand LBL-210A balloon	Toucan Travel Ltd
	G-BZDF	CFM Streak Shadow SA	J. W. Beckett
	G-BZDH	PA-28R Cherokee Arrow 200-II	E. Alexander
	G-BZDI	Aero L-39C Albatros	M. Gainza & E. Gavazzi/North Weald
	G-BZDJ	Cameron Z-105 balloon	BWS Security Systems Ltd
	G-BZDK	Raj Hamsa X'Air 582 (4)	B. Park & R. Barnes
	G-BZDL	Pegasus Quantum 15-912	D. M. Holman
	G-BZDM	Stoddard-Hamilton Glastar	F. G. Miskelly
	G-BZDN	Cameron N-105 balloon	J. D. & K. Griffiths
	G-BZDP	SA Bulldog Srs 120/121	D. M. Squires/Wellesbourne
	G-BZDR	Tri-R Kis	T. J. Johnson
	G-BZDS	Pegasus Quantum 15-912	J. M. Hardstaff
	G-BZDT	Maule MXT-7-180	D. J. Brook
	G-BZDU	D.H.C.1 Chipmunk 22	M. R. Clark
	G-BZDX	Cameron Colt 90 Sugarbox SS balloon	Stratos Ballooning GmbH & Co KG/ Germany
	G-BZDY	Cameron Colt 90 Sugarbox SS balloon	Stratos Ballooning GmbH & Co KG/ Germany
	G-BZDZ	Avtech Jabiru SP	R. M. Whiteside
	G-BZEA	Cessna A.152	Sky Leisure Aviation (Charters) Ltd
	G-BZEB	Cessna 152	Sky Leisure Aviation (Charters) Ltd
	G-BZEC	Cessna 152	Sky Leisure Aviation (Charters) Ltd
	G-BZED	Pegasus Quantum 15-912	M. P. Wimsey
	G-BZEE	AB-206B JetRanger 2	Yateley Helicopters Ltd (G-OJCB)
	G-BZEG	Mainair Blade	R. P. Cookson
	G-BZEH	PA-28 Cherokee 235B	A. D. Wood
	G-BZEI	Agusta A.109E	JJB Sports PLC
	G-BZEJ	Raj Hamsa X'Air 582 (7)	H. Hall
	G-BZEK	Cameron C-70 balloon	Ballooning 50 Degrees Nord/Luxembourg
	G-BZEL	Mainair Blade	M. W. Bush
	G-BZEN	Avtech Jabiru UL-450	B. W. Stockil
	G-BZEP	SA Bulldog Srs 120/121	I. D. McClelland
	G-BZER	Raj Hamsa X'Air R100 (1)	N. P. Lloyd & H. Lloyd-Jones
	G-BZES	Rotorway Executive 90	Southern Helicopters Ltd (G-LUFF)
	G-BZET	Robin HR.200/120B	Anglian Flight Centres Ltd
	G-BZEU	Raj Hamsa X'Air 582 (2)	B. P. Percy
	G-BZEV	Semicopter 1	M. E. Vahdat
	G-BZEW	Rans S.6-ES Coyote II	J. E. Gattrell & A. R. Trace
	G-BZEX	Raj Hamsa X'Air R.200 (2)	J. M. McCullough & R. T. Henry
	G-BZEY	Cameron N-90 balloon	The Ballooning Business Ltd
	G-BZEZ	CFM Streak Shadow	G. J. Pearce
	G-BZFB	Robin R.2112A	M. R. Brown
	G-BZFC	Pegasus Quantum 15-912	G. Brown
	G-BZFD	Cameron N-90 balloon	David Hathaway Transport Ltd
	G-BZFF	Raj Hamsa X'Air 582 (2)	G-BZFF Flying Group
	G-BZFG	Sky 105 balloon	Virgin Airship & Balloon Co. Ltd
	G-BZFH	Pegasus Quantum 15-912	Kent Scout Microlights
	G-BZFI	Avtech Jabiru UL	Group Family
	G-BZFJ	Westland Gazelle HT.2	European Marine Ltd
	G-BZFK	Team Minimax	H. P. Brooks
	G-BZFN	SA Bulldog Srs 120/121	Towerdrive Ltd
	G-BZFO	Mainair Blade	J. E. Walendowski
	G-BZFP	D.H.C.6 Twin Otter 310	Loganair Ltd
	G-BZFR	Extra EA.300/L	Powerhunt Ltd/Biggin Hill
	G-BZFS	Mainair Blade 912	S. P. Stone & F. A. Stephens
	G-BZFT	Murphy Rebel	N. A. Evans
	G-BZFU	Lindstrand LBL HS-110 airship	PNB Entreprenad AB/Sweden

Reg.	Type	Owner or Operator	Notes
G-BZFV	Zenair CH.601UL	T. R. Sinclair & T. Clyde	
G-BZGA	D.H.C.1 Chipmunk 22	Propshop Ltd/Duxford	
G-BZGB	D.H.C.1 Chipmunk 22	Chipmunk Aviation Ltd	
G-BZGC	AS.355F-1 Twin Squirrel	McAlpine Helicopters Ltd (G-CCAO/G-SETA/G-NEAS/ G-CMMM/G-BNBJ)/Kidlington	
G-BZGD	PA-18 Super Cub 150	Proline Aviation	
G-BZGE	Medway Eclipser	J. A. McGill	
G-BZGF	Rans S.6-ES Coyote II	D. F. Castle	
G-BZGH	Cessna F.172N	Golf Hotel Group	
G-BZGI	Ultramagic M-145 balloon	European Balloon Co Ltd	
G-BZGJ	Thunder Ax10-180 S2 balloon	Merlin Balloons	
G-BZGK	NA OV-10B Bronco	Aircraft Restoration Co Ltd/Duxford	
G-BZGL	NA OV-10B Bronco	Aircraft Restoration Co Ltd/Duxford	
G-BZGM	Mainair Blade 912	P. Ryder	
G-BZGN	Raj Hamsa X'Air 582 (2)	C. S. Warr & P. A. Pilkington	
G-BZGO	Robinson R-44	P. Durkin	
G-BZGP	Thruster T.600N 460	M. L. Smith/Popham	
G-BZGR	Rans S.6-ES Coyote II	J. M. Benton	
G-BZGS	Mainair Blade 912	S. C. Reeve	
G-BZGT	Avtech Jabiru UL-450	P. H. Ronfell	
G-BZGU	Raj Hamsa X'Air 582 (4)	C. Kiernan	
G-BZGV	Lindstrand LBL-77A balloon	J. H. Dryden	
G-BZGW	Mainair Blade	C. S. M. Hallam	
G-BZGX	Raj Hamsa X'Air 202 (1)	A. Crowe	
G-BZGY	Dyn'Aero CR.100	D. Hayes	
G-BZGZ	Pegasus Quantum 15-912	W. H. J. Knowles	
G-BZHA	Boeing 767-336ER	British Airways	
G-BZHB	Boeing 767-336ER	British Airways	
G-BZHC	Boeing 767-336ER	British Airways	
G-BZHE	Cessna 152	Two Seven Aviation Ltd	
G-BZHF	Cessna 152	Two Seven Aviation Ltd	
G-BZHG	Tecnam P.92 Echo	M. Rudd	
G-BZHH	Eurocopter EC.120B	Airtrol Ltd	
G-BZHI	Enstrom F-28A-UK	Tindon Ltd (G-BPOZ)	
G-BZHJ	Raj Hamsa X'Air 582 (8)	A. P. Harvey & B. Barker	
G-BZHK	PA-28-181 Archer III	Premiair Engineering Ltd/Shoreham	
G-BZHL	Noorduyn AT-16 Harvard IIB	R. H. Cooper & S. Swallow	
G-BZHN	Pegasus Quantum 15-912	Eaglescott Microlights	
G-BZHO	Pegasus Quantum 15	N. D. Meer	
G-BZHP	Quad City Challenger II	F. Payne	
G-BZHR	Avtech Jabiru UL-450	G. W. Rowbotham	
G-BZHS	Shaw Europa	P. Waugh	
G-BZHT	PA-18A Super Cub 150	B. Walker & Co (Dursley) Ltd	
G-BZHU	Wag-Aero CUBy Sport Trainer	B. Walker & Co (Dursley) Ltd	
G-BZHV	PA-28-181 Archer III	Anglo American Airmotive Ltd/ Bournemouth	
G-BZHW	PA-28-181 Archer III	Anglo American Airmotive Ltd/ Bournemouth	
G-BZHX	Thunder Ax11-250 S2 balloon	T. H. Wilson	
G-BZHY	Mainair Blade 912	M. Morris	
G-BZIA	Raj Hamsa X'Air 700 (1)	A. V. I. Hudson	
G-BZIB	Denney Kitfox Mk 3	S. L. Symons	
G-BZIC	Lindstrand LBL Sun SS balloon	Ballongaventyr 1 Sakne AB/Sweden	
G-BZID	Montgomerie-Bensen B.8MR	A. Gault	
G-BZIF	Dornier Do.328-100	ScotAirways Ltd	
G-BZIG	Thruster T.600N	Ultra Air Ltd	
G-BZII	Extra EA.300/1	J. A. Carr	
G-BZIJ	Robin DR.400/500	Rob Airways Ltd	
G-BZIK	Cameron A-250 balloon	Breckland Balloons Ltd	
G-BZIL	Colt 120A balloon	Champagne Flights	
G-BZIM	Pegasus Quantum 15-912	H. J. W. Munckton	
G-BZIN	Robinson R-44	Helicentre Ltd	
G-BZIP	Montgomerie-Bensen B.8MR	S. J. Boxall	
G-BZIR	Mainair Blade 912	D. M. Law	
G-BZIS	Raj Hamsa X'Air 582 (2)	X'Air Group	
G-BZIT	Beech 95-B55 Baron	Pye Consulting Group Ltd/Blackpool	
G-BZIV	Avtech Jabiru UL	V. R. Leggott	
G-BZIW	Pegasus Quantum 15-912	J. M. Hodgson	
G-BZIX	Cameron N-90 balloon	Infosteada SpA/Italy	
G-BZIY	Raj Hamsa X'Air 582 (2)	I. K. Hogg	
G-BZIZ	Ultramagic H-31 balloon	G. D. O. Bartram	
G-BZJA	Cameron 90 Fire SS balloon	Chubb Fire Ltd	

Notes	Reg.	Type	Owner or Operator
	G-BZJB	Aerostar Yakovlev Yak-52	A. D. Heath
	G-BZJC	Thruster T.600N	Thruster Air Services Ltd
	G-BZJD	Thruster T.600T	Heart Of The Ocean Ltd
	G-BZJE	PA-46-350P Malibu Mirage	Palace Aviation Ltd
	G-BZJF	Pegasus Quantum 15	A. M. Dalgetty
	G-BZJG	Cameron A-400 balloon	Cameron Balloons Ltd
	G-BZJH	Cameron Z-90 balloon	Cameron Balloons Ltd
	G-BZJI	Nova X-Large 37 paraplane	M. N. MacLean
	G-BZJJ	Robinson R-22B	Helicentre Ltd
	G-BZJK	Robinson R-22B	Helicentre Ltd
	G-BZJL	Mainair Blade 912S	D. N. Powell
	G-BZJM	VPM M.16 Tandem Trainer	J. Musil
	G-BZJN	Mainair Blade 912	R. M. Pickwick
	G-BZJO	Pegasus Quantum 15	J. D. Doran
	G-BZJP	Zenair CH.701UL	D. Jerwood
	G-BZJR	Montgomerie-Bensen B.8MR	AES Radionic Surveillance Systems
	G-BZJS	Taylor JT.2 Titch	R. W. Clarke
	G-BZJU	Cameron A-200 balloon	Leeds Castle Enterprises Ltd
	G-BZJV	C.A.S.A. 1-131E Jungmann 1000	J. A. Sykes
	G-BZJW	Cessna 150F	R. J. Scott
	G-BZJX	Ultramagic N-250 balloon	Hot Air Balloons
	G-BZJY	Lindstrand LBL-69A balloon	J. J. C. Bernardin/France
	G-BZJZ	Pegasus Quantum 15	S. Baker
	G-BZKB	Cessna F.172N	Stapleford Flying Club Ltd
	G-BZKC	Raj Hamsa X'Air 582 (2)	P. J. Cheney
	G-BZKD	Stolp Starduster Too	P. & C. Edmunds
	G-BZKE	Lindstrand LBL-77B balloon	P. M. Harrison
	G-BZKF	Rans S.6-ES Coyote II	A. W. Hodder
	G-BZKG	Extreme/Silex	R. M. Hardy
	G-BZKH	Flylight Airsports Doodle Bug/Target	B. Tempest
	G-BZKI	Flylight Airsports Doodle Bug/Target	S. Bond
	G-BZKJ	Flylight Airsports Doodle Bug/Target	Flylight Airsports Ltd/Sywell
	G-BZKK	Cameron V-56 balloon	P. J. Green & C. Bosley Gemini II
	G-BZKL	PA-28R-201 Arrow III	Van Diemen International Racing Service Ltd
	G-BZKN	Campbell Cricket Mk 4	C. G. Hooghkirk
	G-BZKO	Rans S.6-ES Coyote II	J. A. R. Hartley
	G-BZKP	Boeing 737-229C	European Aviation Ltd/Bournemouth
	G-BZKR	Cameron 90 Sugarbox SS balloon	Stratos Ballooning GmbH & Co KG
	G-BZKS	Ercoupe 415CD	M. D. & W. R. Horler
	G-BZKT	Pegasus Quantum 15	K. J. Reynolds
	G-BZKU	Cameron Z-105 balloon	Cameron Balloons Ltd
	G-BZKV	Cameron Sky 90-24 balloon	Omega Selction Services Ltd
	G-BZKW	Ultramagic M-27 balloon	T. G. Church
	G-BZKX	Cameron V-90 balloon	Cameron Balloons Ltd
	G-BZKY	Focke Wulf Fw.189A-1	G. B. E. Pearce
	G-BZKZ	Lindstrand LBL-25A balloon	Lindstrand Balloons Ltd
	G-BZLA	SA.341G Gazelle 1	Highfield Developments (Yorkshire) Ltd
	G-BZLB	SA Bulldog Srs 120/121	L. Bax
	G-BZLC	WSK-PZL Koliber 160A	PZL International Aviation Marketing & Sales PLC/North Weald
	G-BZLD	Raj Hamsa X'Air 582 (2)	C. Blackburn
	G-BZLE	Rans S.6-ES Coyote II	W. S. Long
	G-BZLF	CFM Shadow Srs CD	D. W. Stacey
	G-BZLG	Robin HR.200/120B	G. S. McNaughton
	G-BZLH	PA-28-161 Warrior II	Aviation Rentals
	G-BZLI	SOCATA TB-21 Trinidad TC	K. B. Hallam
	G-BZLJ	Cameron N-90 balloon	Gone With The Wind Ltd
	G-BZLK	Slingsby T.31M Motor Tutor	I. P. Manley
	G-BZLL	Pegasus Quantum 15-912	J. J. Smith
	G-BZLM	Mainair Blade	K. Bull
	G-BZLO	Denney Kitfox Mk 2	M. W. Hanley
	G-BZLP	Robinson R-44	Scotia Helicopters Ltd
	G-BZLS	Cameron Sky 77-24 balloon	D. W. Young
	G-BZLT	Raj Hamsa X'Air (1)	G. Millar
	G-BZLU	Lindstrand LBL-90A balloon	A. E. Lusty
	G-BZLV	Avtech Jabiru UL-450	G. Dalton
	G-BZLX	Pegasus Quantum 15-912	J. McCormack
	G-BZLY	Grob G.109B	M. Tolson

Reg.	Type	Owner or Operator	Notes
G-BZLZ	Pegasus Quantum 15-912	A. R. Way	
G-BZMB	PA-28R-201 Arrow III	D. S. Seex	
G-BZMC	Avtech Jabiru UL	J. R. Banks	
G-BZMD	SA Bulldog Srs 120/121	J. Cooper	
G-BZME	SA Bulldog Srs 120/121	B. Whitworth/Breighton	
G-BZMF	Rutan LongEz	R. A. Gardiner & A. McLaughlin	
G-BZMG	Robinson R-44	Ramsgill Aviation Ltd	
G-BZMH	SA Bulldog Srs 120/121	M. E. J. Hingley & Co Ltd	
G-BZMI	Pegasus Quantum 15-912	T. W. Thiele	
G-BZMJ	Rans S.6-ES Coyote II	Heskin Flying Group	
G-BZML	SA Bulldog Srs 120/121	I. D. Anderson	
G-BZMM	Robin DR.400/180R	N. A. C. Norman	
G-BZMO	Robinson R-22B	Sloane Helicopters Ltd/Sywell	
G-BZMR	Raj Hamsa X'Air 582 (2)	M. Grime	
G-BZMS	Mainair Blade	A. J. Tyler	
G-BZMT	PA-28-161 Warrior III	Aviation Rentals	
G-BZMV	Cameron 80 Concept balloon	Latteria Soresinese Soc. Coop SRL/Italy	
G-BZMW	Pegasus Quantum 15-912	J. I. Greenshields	
G-BZMX	Cameron Z-90 balloon	Cameron Balloons Ltd	
G-BZMY	SPP Yakovlev Yak C-11	E. G. Gavazzi/North Weald	
G-BZMZ	CFM Streak Shadow	J. F. F. Fouche	
G-BZNA	Lindstrand 90A balloon	Lindstrand Balloons Ltd	
G-BZNB	Pegasus Quantum 15	R. C. Whittall	
G-BZNC	Pegasus Quantum 15-912	D. E. Wall	
G-BZND	Sopwith Pup (replica)	B. F. Goddard	
G-BZNE	Beech B300 Super King Air	G. Davies	
G-BZNF	Colt 120A balloon	N. Charbonnier/Italy	
G-BZNG	Raj Hamsa X'Air 700 (1)	G. L. Craig	
G-BZNH	Rans S.6-ES Coyote II	R. E. Quine & R. W. Cooper	
G-BZNI	Bell 206B JetRanger 2	Trimax Ltd (G-ODIG/G-NEEP)	
G-BZNJ	Rans S.6-ES Coyote II	S. P. Read & M. H. Wise	
G-BZNK	Morane Saulnier M.S.315-D2	R. H. Cooper & S. Swallow	
G-BZNM	Pegasus Quantum 15	M. Tomlinson	
G-BZNN	Beech 76 Duchess	Aviation Rentals/Bournemouth	
G-BZNO	Ercoupe 415C	D. K. Tregilgas	
G-BZNP	Thruster T.600N	R. S. O'Carroll	
G-BZNR	BAe 125 Srs 800B	RMC Group Services Ltd (G-XRMC)	
G-BZNS	Mainair Blade	M. K. B. Molyneux	
G-BZNT	Aero L-29 Delfin	Jet Centre Sales Ltd/North Weald	
G-BZNU	Cameron A-300 balloon	D. K. Hempleman-Adams	
G-BZNV	Lindstrand LBL-31A balloon	G. R. Down	
G-BZNW	Isaacs Fury II (K2048)	J. E. D. Rogerson	
G-BZNX	SOCATA M.S.880B Rallye Club	R. E. Knapton	
G-BZNY	Shaw Europa XS	A. K. Middlemas	
G-BZNZ	Lindstrand LBL Cake SS balloon	Oxford Promotions (UK) Ltd	
G-BZOB	Slepcev Storch	J. E. & A. Ashby	
G-BZOC	Pegasus Quantum 15-912	S. J. Doyle	
G-BZOD	Pegasus Quantum 15-912	N. F. MacKenzie	
G-BZOE	Pegasus Quantum 15	W. E. Richards	
G-BZOF	Montgomerie-Bensen B.8MR gyroplane	S. J. M. Ledingham	
G-BZOG	Dornier Do.328-100	ScotAirways Ltd	
G-BZOH	Cameron 110 Bull SS balloon	Ballon Team Bonn GmbH & Co KG/ Germany	
G-BZOI	Nicollier HN.700 Menestrel II	S. J. McCollum	
G-BZOL	Robin R.3000/140	Building & Commercial Ltd	
G-BZOM	Rotorway Executive 162F	J. A. Jackson	
G-BZON	SA Bulldog Srs 120/121	Towerdrive Ltd	
G-BZOO	Pegasus Quantum 15-912	C. R. Ashley	
G-BZOP	Robinson R-44	20:20 Logistics Ltd	
G-BZOR	Team Minimax 91	A. Watt	
G-BZOS	Westland Gazelle HT.2	South West Aviation Services Ltd	
G-BZOT	Westland Gazelle HT.2	South West Aviation Services Ltd	
G-BZOU	Pegasus Quantum 15-912	A. J. Gordon	
G-BZOV	Pegasus Quantum 15-912	D. Turner	
G-BZOW	Whittaker MW-7	G. W. Peacock	
G-BZOX	Cameron Colt 90B balloon	D. J. Head	
G-BZOZ	Van's RV-6	V. Edmondson	
G-BZPA	Mainair Blade 912S	J. McGoldrick	
G-BZPB	Hawker Hunter GA.11 (WB188 duckegg green)	B. R. Pearson	
G-BZPC	Hawker Hunter GA.11 (WB188 red)	B. R. Pearson	

Notes	Reg.	Type	Owner or Operator
	G-BZPD	Cameron V-65 balloon	Gone-With-The-Wind Ltd
	G-BZPE	Lindstrand LBL-310 balloon	A. J. Street
	G-BZPF	Scheibe SF.24B Motorspatz 1	D. Shrimpton
	G-BZPG	Beech C24R Sierra	Aviation Rentals
	G-BZPH	Van's RV-4	G-BZPH RV-4 Group
	G-BZPI	SOCATA TB.20 Trinidad	P. W. Bentley
	G-BZPJ	Beech 76 Duchess	Aviation Rentals
	G-BZPK	Cameron C-80 balloon	Horizon Ballooning Ltd
	G-BZPL	Robinson R-44	M. K. Shaw
	G-BZPM	Cessna 172S	TDR Aviation Ltd
	G-BZPN	Mainair Blade 912S	M. Lovelidge
	G-BZPP	Westland Wasp HAS.1	G. P. Winkley
	G-BZPR	Ultramagic N-210 balloon	European Balloon Display Co. Ltd
	G-BZPS	SA Bulldog Srs 120/121	D. M. Squires
	G-BZPT	Ultramagic N-210 balloon	European Balloon Display Co Ltd
	G-BZPU	Cameron V-77 balloon	J. Vonka
	G-BZPV	Lindstrand LBL-90B balloon	D. P. Hopkins
	G-BZPW	Cameron V-77 balloon	J. Vonka
	G-BZPX	Ultramagic S-105 balloon	Scotair Balloons
	G-BZPY	Ultramagic H-31 balloon	Scotair Balloons
	G-BZPZ	Mainair Blade	M. C. W. Robertson
	G-BZRA	Rans S.6-ES Coyote II	A. W. Fish
	G-BZRB	Mainair Blade	S. B. Brady
	G-BZRC	D.H.115 Vampire T.11	D. Copley/Sandtoft
	G-BZRD	D.H.115 Vampire T.11	D. Copley/Sandtoft
	G-BZRE	P.56 Provost T.1	D. Copley/Sandtoft
	G-BZRF	P.56 Provost T.1	D. Copley/Sandtoft
	G-BZRG	Hunt Wing	W. G. Reynolds
	G-BZRJ	Pegasus Quantum 15-912	R. W. Goddin
	G-BZRM	Eurocopter EC.135T-1	Eurocopter Deutschland GmbH
	G-BZRN	Robinson R-44	Toriamos Ltd
	G-BZRO	PA-30 Twin Comanche C	Comanche Hire Ltd
	G-BZRP	Pegasus Quantum 15-912	RAF Microlight Flying Association
	G-BZRR	Pegasus Quantum 15-912	Syndicate Romeo Romeo
	G-BZRS	Eurocopter EC.135T-1	Bond Air Services Ltd
	G-BZRU	Cameron V-90 balloon	Close Invoice Finance Ltd
	G-BZRV	Van's RV-6	E. Hicks & N. M. Hitchman
	G-BZRW	Mainair Blade 912S	N. D. Kube
	G-BZRX	Ultramagic M-105 balloon	Specialist Recruitment Group PLC
	G-BZRY	Rans S.6-ES Coyote II	S. Forman
	G-BZRZ	Thunder Ax11-250 S2 balloon	Cheshire Balloon Flights
	G-BZSA	Pegasus Quantum 15	Cyclone Airsports Ltd
	G-BZSB	Pitts S-1S Special	A. D. Ingold
	G-BZSC	Sopwith Camel F.1 (replica)	The Shuttleworth Collection/O.Warden
	G-BZSD	PA-46-350P Malibu Mirage	Hairpin Ltd
	G-BZSE	Hawker Hunter T.8B	Towerdrive Ltd
	G-BZSF	Hawker Hunter T.8B	Towerdrive Ltd
	G-BZSG	Pegasus Quantum 15-912	K. J. Gay
	G-BZSH	Ultramagic H-77 balloon	J. L. Hutsby
	G-BZSI	Pegasus Quantum 15	B. & K. Yoxall
	G-BZSL	Sky 25-16 balloon	Zebedee Balloon Service Ltd
	G-BZSM	Pegasus Quantum 15	S. J. Mawman
	G-BZSP	Stemme S.10	A. Flewelling & L. Bleaken
	G-BZSR	Hawker Hunter T.7	Stick & Rudder Aviation Ltd
	G-BZSS	Pegasus Quantum 15-912	T. R. Marsh
	G-BZST	Avtech Jabiru UL	G. Hammond
	G-BZSU	Cameron A-315 balloon	Balloon Flights International Ltd
	G-BZSV	Barracuda	M. J. Aherne
	G-BZSX	Pegasus Quantum 15-912	J. B. Greenwood
	G-BZSY	SNCAN Stampe SV-4A	D. T. Kaberry
	G-BZSZ	Avtech Jabiru UL-450	M. C. J. Ludlow
	G-BZTA	Robinson R-44	Ash Aviation Ltd
	G-BZTC	Team Minimax 91	G. G. Clayton
	G-BZTD	Thruster T.600T JAB	Thruster Air Services Ltd
	G-BZTE	Cameron A-275 balloon	Richard Nash Cars Ltd
	G-BZTF	Yakovlev Yak-52	M. S. Davy
	G-BZTG	PA-34-220T Seneca V	L. R. Chiswell
	G-BZTH	Shaw Europa	T. J. Houlihan
	G-BZTI	Shaw Europa XS	W. Hoolachan
	G-BZTJ	C.A.S.A. Bu.133C Jungmeister	R. A. Seeley
	G-BZTK	Cameron V-90 balloon	Cameron Balloons Ltd
	G-BZTL	Cameron Colt Flying Ice Cream Cone SS balloon	Stratos Ballooning GmbH & Co. KG/Germany

Reg.	Type	Owner or Operator	Notes
G-BZTM	Mainair Blade	L. Hogan	
G-BZTN	Shaw Europa XS	W. Pringle & J. Dewberry	
G-BZTO	Lindstrand LBL-150A balloon	A. M. Holly	
G-BZTP	PA-46-500TP Malibu Meridian	Sunseeker Sales (UK) Ltd	
G-BZTR	Mainair Blade	A. Rees & M. Liptrot	
G-BZTS	Cameron 90 Bertie Bassett SS balloon	Trebor Bassett Ltd	
G-BZTT	Cameron A-275 balloon	Spotlight Group Ltd	
G-BZTU	Mainair Blade 912	Mainair Sports Ltd	
G-BZTV	Mainair Blade 912S	S. Dornan	
G-BZTW	Hunt Wing	T. S. Walker	
G-BZTX	Mainair Blade 912	K. A. Ingham	
G-BZTY	Avtech Jabiru UL	R. P. Lewis	
G-BZTZ	MDH MD.600N	Helicorp Ltd	
G-BZUB	Mainair Blade	A. J. Lindsay	
G-BZUC	Pegasus Quantum 15-912	G. Breen/Portugal	
G-BZUD	Lindstrand LBL-105A balloon	P. N. Rhodes	
G-BZUE	Pegasus Quantum 15	D. J. & M. E. Walcraft	
G-BZUF	Mainair Rapier	S. J. Perry	
G-BZUG	RL.7A XP Sherwood Ranger	S. P. Sharp	
G-BZUH	Rans S.6-ES Coyote II	G. M. Prowling	
G-BZUI	Pegasus Quantum 15-912	R. Clarke/Rufforth	
G-BZUK	Lindstrand LBL-31A balloon	G. R. J. Luckett/USA	
G-BZUL	Avtech Jabiru UL	P. Hawkins	
G-BZUM	Mainair Blade 912	R. B. Milton	
G-BZUN	Mainair Blade 912	E. Paxton & A. Jones	
G-BZUO	Cameron A-340HL balloon	Anglian Countryside Balloons	
G-BZUP	Raj Hamsa X'Air 582 (5)	A. A. A. Lappin	
G-BZUU	Cameron C-90 balloon	D. C. Ball & C. F. Pooley	
G-BZUV	Cameron H-24 balloon	J. N. Race	
G-BZUX	Pegasus Quantum 15	K. M. MacRae & ptnrs	
G-BZUY	Van's RV-6	D. M. Gale & K. F. Crumplin	
G-BZUZ	Hunt Avon-Blade R.100 (1)	J. A. Hunt	
G-BXVA	Zenair CH.701UL	M. W. Taylor	
G-BZVB	Cessna FR.172H	Tindon Ltd (G-BLMX)/Little Snoring	
G-BZVC	Mickleburgh L.107	D. R. Mickleburgh	
G-BZVD	Cameron Colt 105 Forklift SS balloon	Stratos Ballooning GmbH & Co KG/Germany	
G-BZVE	Cameron N-133 balloon	Flying Pictures Ltd	
G-BZVF	Cessna 182T	Denston Hall Estate	
G-BZVG	Eurocopter AS.350B-3 Ecureuil	Finlay (Holdings) Ltd	
G-BZVH	Raj Hamsa X'Air 582 (1)	B. & D. Bergin	
G-BZVI	Nova Vertex 24 hang glider	M. N. Maclean	
G-BZVJ	Pegasus Quantum 15	W. T. Davis	
G-BZVK	Raj Hamsa X'Air 582 (2)	K. P. Taylor	
G-BZVM	Rans S.6-ES Coyote II	N. N. Ducker	
G-BZVN	Van's RV-6	J. A. Booth	
G-BZVO	Cessna TR.182 RG	Swiftair Ltd	
G-BZVP	Robinson R-44	Heli Air Ltd/Wellesbourne	
G-BZVR	Raj Hamsa X'Air 582 (8)	R. P. Sims	
G-BZVS	C.A.S.A. 1-131E Jungmann 2000	W. R. M. Beesley	
G-BZVT	I.I.I. Sky Arrow 650TC	R. W. Seabrook & R. N. Wright	
G-BZVU	Cameron Z-105 balloon	Prudential Investment Managers Ltd	
G-BZVV	Pegasus Quantum 15-912	A. Featherstone & D. C. Mott	
G-BZVW	Ilyushin IL-2 Stormovik	S. Swallow & R. H. Cooper/Sandtoft	
G-BZVX	Ilyushin IL-2 Stormovik	S. Swallow & R. H. Cooper/Sandtoft	
G-BZVZ	Eurocopter AS.355N Twin Squirrel	Iiona Ltd	
G-BZWB	Mainair Blade 912	Mainair Sports Ltd	
G-BZWC	Raj Hamsa X'Air Falcon 912 (1)	G. A. J. Salter	
G-BZWG	PA-28 Cherokee 140	E. & H. Merkado	
G-BZWH	Cessna 152	J. & H. Aviation Services Ltd	
G-BZWI	Medway Eclipser	R. A. Keene	
G-BZWJ	CFM Streak Shadow SA	T. A. Morgan	
G-BZWK	Avtech Jabiru SK	R. Thompson	
G-BZWM	Pegasus XL-Q	D. T. Evans	
G-BZWN	Van's RV-8	A. J. Symms & R. D. Harper	
G-BZWR	Mainair Rapier	W. E. Ross	
G-BZWS	Pegasus Quantum 15-912	Cyclone Airsports Ltd	
G-BZWT	Technam P.92-EM Echo	R. F. Cooper	
G-BZWU	Pegasus Quantum 15-912	P. C. Hogg	
G-BZWV	Steen Skybolt	P. D. & K. Begley	
G-BZWX	Whittaker MW.5D Sorcerer	P. G. Depper	
G-BZWY	CFM Streak Shadow SA	B. Cartwright	

Notes	Reg.	Type	Owner or Operator
	G-BZWZ	Van's RV-6	J. Shanley
	G-BZXA	Raj Hamsa X'Air V2 (1)	D. W. Mullin
	G-BZXB	Van's RV-6	B. J. King-Smith & D. J. Akerman
	G-BZXC	SA Bulldog Srs 120/121	G. Jones
	G-BZXD	Rotorway Executive 162F	P. G. King
	G-BZXE	D.H.C.1 Chipmunk 22	K. Moore
	G-BZXG	Dyn' Aero MCR-01	G-BZXG Group
	G-BZXH	Jodel D.150	E. J. Horsfall/Blackpool
	G-BZXI	Nova Philou 26 hang glider	M. N. Maclean
	G-BZXJ	Schweizer 269-1	Helicentre Ltd/Blackpool
	G-BZXK	Robin HR.200/120B	Aviation Rentals
	G-BZXL	Whittaker MW.5D Sorcerer	K. Wright
	G-BZXM	Mainair Blade 912	P. Harper
	G-BZXN	Avtech Jabiru UL-450	A. R. Silvester
	G-BZXO	Cameron Z-105 balloon	Virgin Airship & Balloon Co. Ltd
	G-BZXP	Kiss 400-582	P. M. Dewhurst
	G-BZXR	Cameron N-90 balloon	Derbyshire Building Soc.
	G-BZXS	SA Bulldog Srs 120/121	K. J. Thompson
	G-BZXT	Mainair Blade 912	Barton 912 Flyers
	G-BZXU	Pegasus XL-R	E. Spain
	G-BZXV	Pegasus Quantum 15-912	S. Laws
	G-BZXW	VPM M.16 Tandem Trainer	S. J. Tyler (G-NANA)
	G-BZXX	Pegasus Quantum 15-912	R. R. Nichol
	G-BZXY	Robinson R-44	Extraviation Ltd/North Weald
	G-BZXZ	SA Bulldog Srs 120/121	Air & Ground Aviation Ltd
	G-BZYA	Rans S.6-ES Coyote II	D. J. Clack
	G-BZYB	Westland Gazelle HT.3	Aerocars Ltd
	G-BZYC	Westland Gazelle AH.1	Aerocars Ltd
	G-BZYD	Westland Gazelle AH.1	Aerocars Ltd
	G-BZYE	Robinson R-22B	Plane Talking Ltd/Elstree
	G-BZYF	BAC.167 Strikemaster Mk.80	R. J. Everett
	G-BZYG	Glaser-Dirks DG.500MB	R. C. Bromwich
	G-BZYH	BAC.167 Strikemaster Mk.80A	R. J. Everett
	G-BZYI	Nova Phocus 123 hang glider	N. M. Maclean
	G-BZYK	Avtech Jabiru UL	A. S. Forbes
	G-BZYL	Rans S.6-ES Coyote II	J. D. Harris
	G-BZYM	Raj Hamsa X'Air 700 (1A)	G. Fleck
	G-BZYN	Pegasus Quantum 15-912	K. Roberts
	G-BZYO	Colt 210A balloon	P. M. Forster
	G-BZYP	BAe Jetstream 3200	Trident Aviation Leasing (Ireland) Ltd
	G-BZYR	Cameron N-31 balloon	Virgin Balloon & Airship Co Ltd
	G-BZYS	Micro Aviation Bantam B.22-S	D. L. Howell
	G-BZYT	Interavia 80TA	N. G. Cranham
	G-BZYU	Whittaker MW.6 Merlin	K. J. Cole
	G-BZYV	Snowbird Mk.V 582 (1)	S. Jones
	G-BZYW	Cameron N-90 balloon	Bailey Balloons
	G-BZYX	Raj Hamsa X'Air 700 (1A)	A. G. Marsh
	G-BZYY	Cameron N-90 balloon	Mason Zimbler Ltd
	G-BZYZ	Robin R.2120U	Aviation Rentals
	G-BZZA	Boeing 737-3L9	K.L.M.uk/Buzz/Stansted
	G-BZZB	Boeing 737-3L9	K.L.M.uk/Buzz/Stansted
	G-BZZD	Cessna F.172M	R. H. M. Richardson-Bunbury (G-BDPF)

Having reached the end of the G-BZ series, the in-sequence allocations continue from G-CBAA instead of G-CAAA. The latter block was used for Canadian registrations during the 1920s and although a number have subsequently been issued as out-of-sequence marks in the UK, all were previously unused.

	G-CBAB	SA Bulldog Srs 120/121	Propshop Ltd/Duxford
	G-CBAC	Short SD3-60 Variant 200	BAC Leasing Ltd (G-BLYH)
	G-CBAD	Mainair Blade 912	D. Sykes
	G-CBAF	Lancair 320	R. W. Fairless
	G-CBAG	RAF 2000 GTX-SE gyroplane	G. R. French
	G-CBAH	Raj Hamsa X'Air 582 (5)	D. N. B. Hearn
	G-CBAI	Flight Design CT.2K	Cyclone Airsports Ltd
	G-CBAJ	D.H.C.1 Chipmunk 22	J. Lamb
	G-CBAK	Robinson R-44	Swift Frame Ltd
	G-CBAL	PA-28-161 Warrior II	Britannia Airways Ltd
	G-CBAN	SA Bulldog Srs 120/121	C. J. D. Howcroft & C. Hilliker
	G-CBAP	Zenair CH.601UL	L. J. Lowry
	G-CBAR	Stoddard-Hamilton Glastar	C. M. Barnes
	G-CBAS	Rans S.6-ES Coyote II	S. R. Green
	G-CBAT	Cameron Z-90 balloon	British Telecommunications PLC

Reg.	Type	Owner or Operator	Notes
G-CBAU	Rand Robinson KR-2	B. Normington	
G-CBAV	Raj Hamsa X'Air V.2 (1)	D. W. Stamp & G. J. Lampitt	
G-CBAX	Tecnam P.92-EM Exho	R. P. Reeves	
G-CBAY	Pegasus Quantum 15-912	P. R. Jones	
G-CBAZ	Rans S.6-ES Coyote II	G. V. Willder	
G-CBBA	Robin DR.400/180	A. P. Loch	
G-CBBB	Pegasus Quantum 15-912	Light Flight Ltd	
G-CBBC	SA Bulldog Srs 120/121	Bulldog Support Ltd	
G-CBBD	Pegasus Quantum 15-912	T. D. Grieve	
G-CBBF	Beech 76 Duchess	Liddell Aircraft Ltd	
G-CBBG	Mainair Blade	P. J. Donoghue	
G-CBBH	Raj Hamsa X'Air V2 (1)	W. G. Colyer	
G-CBBK	Robinson R-22B	Heli Air Ltd/Wellesbourne	
G-CBBL	SA Bulldog Srs 120/121	I. R. Bates	
G-CBBM	MXP-740 Savannah J (1)	Sandtoft Ultralights Partnership	
G-CBBN	Pegasus Quantum 15-912	C. D. Hogbourne	
G-CBBO	Whittaker MW.5D Sorcerer	P. J. Gripton	
G-CBBP	Pegasus Quantum 15-912	V. Causey & F. G. Green	
G-CBBR	SA Bulldog Srs 120/121	Elite Consultancy Corporation Ltd	
G-CBBS	SA Bulldog Srs 120/121	Elite Consultancy Corporation Ltd	
G-CBBT	SA Bulldog Srs 120/121	Elite Consultancy Corporation Ltd	
G-CBBU	SA Bulldog Srs 120/121	Elite Consultancy Corporation Ltd	
G-CBBV	Westland Gazelle HT.3	Elite Consultancy Corporation Ltd	
G-CBBW	SA Bulldog Srs 120/121	S. E. Robottom-Scott	
G-CBBX	Lindstrand LBL-69A balloon	J. L. F. Garcia	
G-CBBY	Westland Gazelle HT.3	Southwest Aviation Services Ltd	
G-CBBZ	Pegasus Quantum 15-912	A. J. Irving	
G-CBCA	PA-32R-301T Saratoga IITC	Branksome Aircraft Leasing Ltd	
G-CBCB	SA Bulldog Srs 120/121	The General Aviation Trading Co. Ltd	
G-CBCD	Pegasus Quantum 15	I. A. Lumley	
G-CBCE	C.A.S.A. 1-131E Jungmann (replica)	E. B. Toulson/Breighton	
G-CBCF	Pegasus Quantum 15-912	D. Seiler	
G-CBCH	Zenair CH.701UL	L. G. Millen	
G-CBCI	Raj Hamsa X'Air 582 (2)	P. A. Gilford	
G-CBCJ	RAF 2000 GTX-SE gyroplane	J. P. Comerford	
G-CBCK	Tipsy T.66 Nipper Srs 3	N. M. Bloom (G-TEDZ)	
G-CBCL	Stoddard-Hamilton Glastar	C. F. M. Norman	
G-CBCM	Raj Hamsa X'Air 700 (1A)	A. Hipkin	
G-CBCO	SA Bulldog Srs 120/121	P. Stephenson	
G-CBCP	Van's RV-6A	G-CBCP Group	
G-CBCR	SA Bulldog Srs 120/121	S. C. Smith	
G-CBCS	BAe Jetstream 3202	Eastern Airways Ltd	
G-CBCT	SA Bulldog Srs 120/121	T. Brun/France	
G-CBCU	H.S. Harrier GR.3	Y. Dumortier/Belgium	
G-CBCV	SA Bulldog Srs 120/121	Cheshire Aviators Ltd	
G-CBCW	Cameron N-90 balloon	Flying Pictures Ltd	
G-CBCX	Pegasus Quantum 15	D. V. Lawrence	
G-CBCY	Beech C24R Sierra Super	Liddell Aircraft Ltd	
G-CBCZ	CFM Streak Shadow SLA	J. A. Hambleton	
G-CBDA	BAe Jetstream 3217	Eastern Airways Ltd	
G-CBDB	Robinson R-22B	Heli Air Ltd/Wellesbourne	
G-CBDC	Thruster T.600N 450-JAB	David Clarke Microlight Aircraft	
G-CBDD	Mainair Blade	R. E. Dugmore	
G-CBDF	Bell 206B JetRanger 3	R & M International Engineering Ltd	
G-CBDG	Zenair CH.601HD	R. E. Lasnier	
G-CBDH	Flight Design CT.2K	J. Hosier	
G-CBDI	Denney Kitfox Mk.2	J. G. D. Barbour	
G-CBDJ	Flight Design CT.2K	P. J. Walker	
G-CBDK	SA Bulldog Srs 120/121	J. N. Randle	
G-CBDL	Mainair Blade	D. Lightwood	
G-CBDM	Tecnam P.92-EM Echo	C. J. Willy & J. J. Cozens	
G-CBDN	Mainair Blade	P. N. Gibson	
G-CBDO	Raj Hamsa X'Air 582 (1)	R. T. Henry	
G-CBDP	Mainair Blade 912	D. S. Parker	
G-CBDR	Agusta A.109A-II	Castle Air Charters Ltd	
G-CBDS	SA Bulldog Srs 120/121	Bulldog Support Ltd	
G-CBDT	Zenair CH.601HD	D. G. Watt	
G-CBDU	Quad City Challenger II	Hiscox Cases Ltd	
G-CBDV	Raj Hamsa X'Air 582	D. J. Prothero	
G-CBDW	Raj Hamsa X'Air Jabiru	P. R & V. C. Reynolds	
G-CBDX	Pegasus Quantum 15	C. C. Beck	
G-CBDY	Raj Hamsa X'Air V.2 (2)	D. Mahajan	

Notes	Reg.	Type	Owner or Operator
	G-CBDZ	Pegasus Quantum 15-912	C. I. D. H. Garrison
	G-CBEB	Kiss 400-582 (1)	P. R. J. & A. R. R. Williams
	G-CBEC	Cameron Z-105 balloon	A. L. Ballarino/Italy
	G-CBED	Cameron Z-90 balloon	John Aimo Balloons SAS/Italy
	G-CBEE	PA-28R Cherokee Arrow 200	Falcon Flying Services/Biggin Hill
	G-CBEF	SA Bulldog Srs 120/121	M. A. Wilkinson
	G-CBEG	Robinson R-44	Heli Air Ltd/Wellesbourne
	G-CBEH	SA Bulldog Srs 120/121	R. E. Dagless
	G-CBEJ	Colt 120A balloon	Cameron Balloons Ltd
	G-CBEK	SA Bulldog Srs 120/121	S. Landregan
	G-CBEL	Hawker Fury FB.11	J. A. D. Bradshaw
	G-CBEM	Mainair Blade	M. Earp
	G-CBEN	Pegasus Quantum 15-912	B. J. Syson
	G-CBEP	BAe Jetstream 3206	Trident Aviation Leasing Services Ltd
	G-CBES	Shaw Europa XS	M. R. Hexley
	G-CBET	Mainair Blade 912S	R. Neale
	G-CBEU	Pegasus Quantum 15-912	C. Lee
	G-CBEV	Pegasus Quantum 15-912	T. Lee
	G-CBEW	Flight Design CT.2K	M. Clare
	G-CBEX	Flight Design CT.2K	B. W. T. Rood
	G-CBEY	Cameron C-80 balloon	D. V. Fowler
	G-CBFA	Diamond DA.40 Star	Diamond Aircraft (UK) Ltd/Gamston
	G-CBFC	Diamond DA.40 Star	Diamond Aircraft (UK) Ltd/Gamston
	G-CBFD	Westland Gazelle HT.2	Aerocars Ltd
	G-CBFE	Raj Hamsa X'Air V.2 (1)	S. Whittle & M. L. Powell
	G-CBFF	Cameron O-120 balloon	T. M. C. McCoy
	G-CBFG	Thunder Ax8-105 S2 balloon	Master Ad (UK) Ltd
	G-CBFH	Thunder Ax8-105 S2 balloon	Master Ad (UK) Ltd
	G-CBFI	PA-18 Super Cub 150	L. F. Appelbeck
	G-CBFJ	Robinson R-44	Heli Air Ltd/Wellesbourne
	G-CBFK	Murphy Rebel	D. Webb
	G-CBFL	BAe 146-200	BAE Systems (Operations) Ltd/Woodford
	G-CBFM	SOCATA TB.21 Trinidad	Exec Flight Ltd
	G-CBFO	Cessna 172S	Oxford Aviation Services Ltd/Kidlington
	G-CBFP	SA Bulldog Srs 120/121	I. D. McClelland/Biggin Hill
	G-CBFS	Beech 200 Super King Air	Bevair Services Ltd (G-PLAT)
	G-CBFT	Raj Hamsa X'Air 582 (5)	T. Collins
	G-CBFU	SA Bulldog Srs 120/121	J. R. & S. J. Huggins
	G-CBFV	Ikarus C.42	P. A. D. Chubb
	G-CBFW	Bensen B.8	B. F. Pearson
	G-CBFX	Rans S.6-ES Coyote II	Sport Air (UK) Ltd
	G-CBFY	Cameron Z-250 balloon	Cameron Balloons Ltd
	G-CBFZ	Avtech Jabiru UL-450	A. H. King
	G-CBGA	PZL-110 Koliber 160A	PZL International Aviation Marketing & Sales PLC/North Weald
	G-CBGB	Zenair CH.601UL	R. Germany
	G-CBGC	SOCATA TB.10 Tobago	Air Touring Ltd/Biggin Hill
	G-CBGD	Zenair CH.701UL	I. S. Walsh
	G-CBGE	Tecnam P.92-EM Echo	T. C. Robson
	G-CBGF	PA-31-310 Navajo B	S. J. Skilton
	G-CBGG	Pegasus Quantum 15	A. R. Cundill
	G-CBGH	Teverson Bisport	R. C. Teverson
	G-CBGI	CFM Streak Shadow	M. W. W. Clotworthy
	G-CBGJ	Aeroprakt A.22 Foxbat	W. R. Davis-Smith
	G-CBGK	H.S. Harrier GR.3	Y- Dumortier/Belgium
	G-CBGL	MH.1521M Broussard	A. I. Milne
	G-CBGM	Mainair Blade 912	J. R. Pearce
	G-CBGN	Van's RV-4	G. A. Nash
	G-CBGO	Murphy Maverick 430	C. R. Ellis & E. A. Wrathall
	G-CBGP	Ikarus C.42 FB UK	A. R. Lloyd
	G-CBGR	Avtech Jabiru UL	K. R. Emery
	G-CBGT	Mainair Blade 912	J. A. Cresswell
	G-CBGU	Thruster T.600N 450-JAB	Thruster Air Services Ltd
	G-CBGV	Thruster T.600N 450-JAB	Thruster Air Services Ltd
	G-CBGW	Thruster T.600N 450-JAB	Thruster Air Services Ltd
	G-CBGX	SA Bulldog Srs 120/121 (XX622)	R. B. Black
	G-CBGZ	Westland Gazelle HT.2	D. Weatherhead Ltd
	G-CBHA	SOCATA TB.10 Tobago	Air Touring Ltd/Biggin Hill
	G-CBHB	Raj Hamsa X'Air Jabiru (1)	Marine Power Scotland Ltd
	G-CBHC	RAF 2000 GTX-SE gyroplane	A. J. Thomas
	G-CBHE	Slingsby T.67M Firefly 260	R. Swann
	G-CBHG	Mainair Blade 912S	J. A. Horn
	G-CBHI	Shaw Europa XS	B. Price

Reg.	Type	Owner or Operator	Notes
G-CBHK	Pegasus Quantum 15 (HKS)	Cyclone Airsports Ltd	
G-CBHO	Gloster Gladiator II	Retro Track & Air (UK) Ltd	
G-CBHP	Corby CJ-1 Starlet	J. D. Muldowney	
G-CBHM	Mainair Blade 912	Mainair Sports Ltd	
G-CBHN	Pegasus Quantum 15-912	Cyclone Airsports Ltd	
G-CBHR	Stephens Akro Z	D. T. Karberry	
G-CBHS	Eurocopter EC.120B	McAlpine Helicopters Ltd/Kidlington	
G-CBHT	Dassault Falcon 900EX	TAG Aviation (UK) Ltd (G-GPWH)	
G-CBHU	RL.5A Sherwood Ranger	M. J. Gooch	
G-CBHV	Raj Hamsa X'Air 582 (5)	J. D. Buchanan	
G-CBHX	Cameron V-77 balloon	N. A. Apsey	
G-CBHZ	RAF 2000 GTX-SE gyroplane	M. P. Donnelly	
G-CBIC	Raj Hamsa X'Air V2 (2)	J. T. Blackburn	
G-CBID	SA Bulldog Srs 120/121	D. A. Steven	
G-CBIF	Avtech Jabiru UL-450	J. A, Iszard	
G-CBIG	Mainair Blade 912	J. H. Bradbury	
G-CBIH	Cameron Z-31 balloon	Cameron Balloons Ltd	
G-CBIJ	Ikarus C.42	A. Jones	
G-CBIL	Cessna 182K	E. Bannister & J. R. C. Spooner (G-BFZZ)/E. Midlands	
G-CBIT	RAF 2000 GTX-SE gyroplane	Terrafirma Services Ltd	
G-CBIX	Zenair CH.601UL	M. F. Cottam	
G-CBIZ	Pegasus Quantum 15-912	P. A. Bass	
G-CBJA	Kiss 400-582 (1)	C. W. Lark	
G-CBJJ	SA Bulldog Srs 120/121 (XX525)	Elite Consultancy Corporation Ltd	
G-CBJK	SA Bulldog Srs 120/121 (XX713)	Elite Consultancy Corporation Ltd	
G-CBJM	Avtech Jabiru SP-470	A. T. Moyce	
G-CBJO	Pegasus Quantum 15-912	J. E. Borrill	
G-CBJT	Mainair Blade	B. Hunter & K. D. Taylor	
G-CBNB	Eurocopter EC.120B	Arenberg Consultadoria E Servicos LDA/Madeira	
G-CBOB	PA-34-220T Seneca V	Blackbrook Nominee 30 Ltd	
G-CBOR	Cessna F.172N	P. Seville	
G-CBUG	Technam P.92-EM Echo	R. C. Mincik	

G-BYML Dornier Do.328-100 of ScotAirways.

G-DHDV D.H.100 Dove of Air Atlantique.

Reg.	Type	Owner or Operator	Notes
G-CAHA	PA-34-200T Seneca II	H. & R. Marshall	
G-CAIN	CFM Shadow Srs CD	S. K. Starling (G-MTKU)	
G-CALL	PA-23 Aztec 250F	Woodgate Aviation (IOM) Ltd	
G-CAMB	AS.355F-2 Twin Squirrel	Cambridgeshire & Essex Air Support	
G-CAMM	Hawker Cygnet (replica)	D. M. Cashmore	
G-CAMP	Cameron N-105 balloon	Hong Kong Balloon & Airship Club	
G-CAMR	BFC Challenger II	P. R. A. Walker	
G-CAPI	Mudry/CAARP CAP.10B	I. Valentine (G-BEXR)	
G-CAPX	Avions Mudry CAP.10B	Cole Aviation	
G-CARS†	Pitts S-2A Special (replica) (BAPC134) ★	Toyota Ltd	
G-CCAR	Cameron N-77 balloon	D. P. Turner	
G-CCAT	AA-5A Cheetah	Plane Talking Ltd (G-OAJH/G-KILT/ G-BJFA)/Elstree	
G-CCAU	Eurocopter EC.135T-1	West Mercia Constabulary	
G-CCCC	Cessna 172H	Springbank Aviation Ltd	
G-CCCP	Yakovlev Yak-52	R. J. N. Howarth	
G-CCLY	Bell 206B JetRanger 3	Ciceley Ltd (G-TILT/G-BRJO)	
G-CCMV	Chance Vought FG-1D Corsair (92399)	Aircraft Restoration Co/Duxford	
G-CCOA	SA Bulldog Srs 120/122	Cranfield University (G-BCUU)	
G-CCOZ	Monnett Sonerai II	P. R. Cozens	
G-CCSC	Cameron N-77 balloon	C. J. Royden	
G-CCST	PA-32R-301 Saratoga IIHP	Dorset Aircraft Leasing Ltd	
G-CCUB	Piper J-3C-65 Cub	Cormack (Aircraft Services) Ltd	
G-CDAV	PA-34-220T Seneca V	Neric Ltd	
G-CDBS	MBB Bo 105DBS	Bond Air Services/Aberdeen	
G-CDET	Culver LCA Cadet	H. B. Fox/Booker	
G-CDGA	Taylor JT.1 Monoplane	R. M. Larimore	
G-CDON	PA-28-161 Warrior II	East Midlands Flying School Ltd	
G-CDPY	Shaw Europa	A. Burrill	
G-CDRU	C.A.S.A. 1.131E Jungmann 2000	P. Cunniff/White Waltham	
G-CDUO	Boeing 757-236	Britannia Airways Ltd (SE-DUO)	
G-CDUP	Boeing 757-236	Britannia Airways Ltd (SE-DUP)	
G-CEAA	Airbus A.300B2-1C	European Aviation Ltd/Bournemouth	
G-CEAB	Airbus A.300B2-1C	European Aviation Ltd/Bournemouth	
G-CEAC	Boeing 737-229	Palmair European/Bournemouth	
G-CEAD	Boeing 737-229	Palmair European/Bournemouth	
G-CEAE	Boeing 737-229	European Aviation Ltd/Bournemouth	
G-CEAF	Boeing 737-229	European Aviation Ltd (G-BYRI)/ Bournemouth	
G-CEAG	Boeing 737-229	European Aviation Ltd/Bournemouth	
G-CEAH	Boeing 737-229	European Aviation Ltd/Bournemouth	
G-CEAI	Boeing 737-229	European Aviation Ltd/Bournemouth	
G-CEAJ	Boeing 737-229	European Aviation Ltd/Bournemouth	
G-CEAL	Short SD3-60 Variant 100	BAC Express Airlines Ltd (G-BPXO)	
G-CEGA	PA-34-200T Seneca II	Oxford Aviation Services Ltd/Kidlington	
G-CEGR	Beech 200 Super King Air	CEGA Aviation Ltd (G-BXMA)	
G-CEGR	Beech 200 Super King Air	CEGA Aviation Ltd	
G-CEJA	Cameron V-77 balloon	L. & C. Gray (G-BTOF)	
G-CERT	Mooney M.20K	K. A. Hemming/Fowlmere	
G-CEXA	F.27 Friendship Mk 500	Channel Express (Air Services) Ltd	
G-CEXB	F.27 Friendship Mk 500	Channel Express (Air Services) Ltd	
G-CEXD	F.27 Friendship Mk 600	Channel Express (Air Services) Ltd	
G-CEXE	F.27 Friendship Mk 500	Channel Express (Air Services) Ltd	
G-CEXF	F.27 Friendship Mk 500	Channel Express (Air Services) Ltd	
G-CEXG	F.27 Friendship Mk 500	Channel Express (Air Services) Ltd (G-JEAP)	
G-CEXH	Airbus A.300B4-203F	Channel Express (Air Services) Ltd	
G-CEXI	Airbus A.300B4-203F	Channel Express (Air Services) Ltd	
G-CEXJ	Airbus A.300B4-203F	Channel Express (Air Services) Ltd	
G-CEXP	HPR-7 Herald 209 ★	Spectators' Terrace/Gatwick	
G-CEXS	L.188C Electra	Channel Express (Air Services) Ltd	
G-CFAA	Avro RJ100	CityFlyer Express Ltd/BA Express	
G-CFAB	Avro RJ100	CityFlyer Express Ltd/BA Express	
G-CFAC	Avro RJ100	CityFlyer Express Ltd/BA Express	
G-CFAD	Avro RJ100	CityFlyer Express Ltd/BA Express	
G-CFAE	Avro RJ100	CityFlyer Express Ltd/BA Express	
G-CFAF	Avro RJ100	CityFlyer Express Ltd/BA Express	
G-CFAH	Avro RJ100	CityFlyer Express Ltd/BA Express	
G-CFBI	Colt 56A balloon	G. A. Fisher	
G-CFME	SOCATA TB.10 Tobago	Charles Funke Associates Ltd	
G-CFRA	Cessna 560XL Citation Excel	Chauffair Ltd	

Notes	Reg.	Type	Owner or Operator
	G-CGHM	PA-28 Cherokee 140	I. J. Sixsmith
	G-CGOD	Cameron N-77 balloon	G. P. Lane
	G-CHAA	Cameron O-90 balloon	The Balloon Club Ltd
	G-CHAM	Cameron 90 Pot SS balloon	High Exposure Balloons
	G-CHAP	Robinson R-44	Brierley Lifting Tackle Co Ltd
	G-CHAR	Grob G.109B	RAFGSA/Bicester
	G-CHAS	PA-28-181 Archer II	C. H. Elliott
	G-CHAV	Shaw Europa	Chavenage Flying Group
	G-CHCD	Sikorsky S-76A (modified)	CHC Scotia Ltd (G-CBJB)
	G-CHCE	Sikorsky S-76A II Plus	CHC Scotia Ltd (G-BOND)
	G-CHCF	AS.332L-2 Super Puma	CHC Scotia Ltd
	G-CHEB	Shaw Europa	C. H. P. Bell
	G-CHEL	Colt 77B balloon	Chelsea Financial Services PLC
	G-CHEM	PA-34-200T Seneca II	London Executive Aviation Ltd
	G-CHER	PA-38-112 Tomahawk II	Aerohire Ltd (G-BVBL)/Wolverhampton
	G-CHES	BN-2A-26 Islander	Cormack (Aircraft Services) Ltd (G-PASY/G-BPCB/G-BEXA/G-MALI/ G-DIVE)/Cumbernauld
	G-CHET	Shaw Europa	H. P. Chetwynd-Talbot
	G-CHEZ	BN-2B-20 Islander	Cheshire Police Authority (G-BSAG)/ Liverpool
	G-CHIK	Cessna F.152	Stapleford Flying Club Ltd (G-BHAZ)
	G-CHIP	PA-28-181 Archer II	C. M. Hough/Fairoaks
	G-CHIS	Robinson R-22B	Bradmore Helicopter Leasing
	G-CHIX	Robin DR.400/500	P. A. & R. Stephens
	G-CHKL	Cameron 120 Kookaburra SS balloon	Eagle Ltd/Australia
	G-CHKN	Kiss 400-582 (1)	I. Tomkins
	G-CHLT	Stemme S.10	J. Abbess
	G-CHMP	Bellanca 7ACA Champ	I. J. Langley
	G-CHNX	L.188AF Electra	Channel Express (Air Services) Ltd
	G-CHOK	Cameron V-77 balloon	A. J. Moore
	G-CHOP	Westland-Bell 47G-3B1	Dolphin Property (Management) Ltd
	G-CHPY	D.H.C.1 Chipmunk 22 (WB652)	J. G. H. Computer Services Ltd
	G-CHSU	Eurocopter EC.135T-1	Thames Valley Police Authority Chiltern Air Support Unit/Benson
	G-CHTA	AA-5A Cheetah	Quick Spin Ltd (G-BFRC)
	G-CHTG	Rotorway Executive 90	G. Cooper (G-BVAJ)
	G-CHUG	Shaw Europa	C. A. Pratt
	G-CHUK	Cameron O-77 balloon	L. C. Taylor
	G-CHUM	Robinson R-44	Vitapage Ltd
	G-CHYL	Robinson R-22B	C. M. Gough-Cooper
	G-CHZN	Robinson R-22B	Cloudbase Ltd (G-GHZM/G-FENI)
	G-CIAO	I.I.I. Sky Arrow 1450-L	G. Arscott
	G-CIAS	BN-2B-21 Islander	Channel Island Air Search Ltd (G-BKJM)
	G-CICI	Cameron R-15 balloon	Ballooning Endeavours Ltd
	G-CIDD	Bellanca 7ECA Citabria	A. & P. West
	G-CIFR	PA-28-181 Archer II	Aeroshow Ltd
	G-CIGY	Westland-Bell 47G-3B1	R. A. Perrot (G-BGXP)
	G-CITI	Cessna 501 Citation	Euro Executive Jet Ltd
	G-CITY	PA-31-350 Navajo Chieftain	Woodgate Aviation (IOM) Ltd
	G-CITZ	Bell 206B JetRanger 2	Euro Executive Jet Ltd (G-BRTB)
	G-CIVA	Boeing 747-436	British Asia Airways
	G-CIVB	Boeing 747-436	British Asia Airways
	G-CIVC	Boeing 747-436	British Airways
	G-CIVD	Boeing 747-436	British Airways
	G-CIVE	Boeing 747-436	British Airways
	G-CIVF	Boeing 747-436	British Airways
	G-CIVG	Boeing 747-436	British Airways
	G-CIVH	Boeing 747-436	British Airways
	G-CIVI	Boeing 747-436	British Airways
	G-CIVJ	Boeing 747-436	British Airways
	G-CIVK	Boeing 747-436	British Airways
	G-CIVL	Boeing 747-436	British Airways
	G-CIVM	Boeing 747-436	British Airways
	G-CIVN	Boeing 747-436	British Airways
	G-CIVO	Boeing 747-436	British Airways
	G-CIVP	Boeing 747-436	British Airways
	G-CIVR	Boeing 747-436	British Airways
	G-CIVS	Boeing 747-436	British Airways
	G-CIVT	Boeing 747-436	British Airways
	G-CIVU	Boeing 747-436	British Airways
	G-CIVV	Boeing 747-436	British Airways

Reg.	Type	Owner or Operator	Notes
G-CIVW	Boeing 747-436	British Airways	
G-CIVX	Boeing 747-436	British Airways	
G-CIVY	Boeing 747-436	British Airways	
G-CIVZ	Boeing 747-436	British Airways	
G-CJBC	PA-28 Cherokee 180	J. B. Cave/Halfpenny Green	
G-CJCI	Pilatus P2-06 (CC+43)	Pilatus P2 Flying Group	
G-CJUD	Denney Kitfox Mk 3	D. M. Garrett	
G-CKCK	Enstrom 280FX	Farmax Ltd	
G-CLAC	PA-28-161 Warrior II	M. A. Steadman/Blackbushe	
G-CLAS	Short SD3-60 Variant 100	BAC Express Ltd (G-BLED)	
G-CLAX	Jurca MJ.5 Sirocco F2/39	G. D. Claxton (G-AWKB)	
G-CLEA	PA-28-161 Warrior II	R. J. Harrison & A. R. Carpenter	
G-CLEE	Rans S.6-ES Coyote II	R. Holt	
G-CLEM	Bo 208A2 Junior	Bolkow Group (G-ASWE)	
G-CLEO	Zenair CH.601HD	K. M. Bowen	
G-CLHA	BAe 146-200	bmi regional/CityLine (G-DEBC)	
G-CLHB	BAe 146-200	bmi regional/CityLine (G-GNTZ)	
G-CLHC	BAe 146-200	bmi regional/CityLine (G-MANS/G-CHSR)	
G-CLHD	BAe 146-200	bmi regional/CityLine (G-DEBF)	
G-CLHE	BAe 146-200	bmi regional/CityLine (G-DEBH)	
G-CLIC	Cameron A-105 balloon	R. S. Mohr	
G-CLIP	AS.355N Twin Squirrel	Charterstyle Ltd	
G-CLKE	Robinson R-44	Clarke Business (G-HREH)	
G-CLOE	Sky 90-24 balloon	C. J. Sandell	
G-CLOS	PA-34-200 Seneca II	S. H. Kirkby	
G-CLOW	Beech 200 Super King Air	Clowes (Estates) Ltd	
G-CLRK	Sky 77-24 balloon	William Clark & Son (Parkgate) Ltd	
G-CLUB	Cessna FRA.150N	D. C. C. Handley	
G-CLUE	PA-34-200T Seneca II	Bristol Office Machines Ltd	
G-CLUX	Cessna F.172N	J. & K. Aviation	
G-CMED	SOCATA TB.9 Tampico	Enstone Flying Club	
G-CMGC	PA-25 Pawnee 235	Midland Gliding Club Ltd (G-BFEX)/ Long Mynd	
G-CNAB	Avtech Jabiru UL	W. A. Brighouse	
G-CNDY	Robinson R-22B-2	Testgate Ltd (G-BXEW)	
G-COAI	Cranfield A.1	Cranfield University (G-BCIT)	
G-COCO	Cessna F.172M	P. C. Sheard & R. C. Larder	
G-CODE	Bell 206B JetRanger 3	B. Wronski	
G-COEZ	Airbus A.320-231	My Travel Airways (Airtours)	
G-COIN	Bell 206B JetRanger 2	C. Sarno	
G-COLA	Beech F33C Bonanza	J. A.Kelman & Cola Aviation Ltd (G-BUAZ)	
G-COLH	PA-28 Cherokee 140	J. G. O'Brien (G-AVRT)	
G-COLL	Enstrom 280C-UK-2 Shark	S. P. Giddings	
G-COLR	Colt 69A balloon ★	British School of Ballooning/Lancing	
G-COMB	PA-30 Twin Comanche 160B	J. T. Bateson (G-AVBL)/Ronaldsway	
G-COMP	Cameron N-90 balloon	Computacenter Ltd	
G-CONB	Robin DR.400/180	Winchcombe Farm (G-BUPX)	
G-CONC	Cameron N-90 balloon	British Airways	
G-CONL	SOCATA TB.10 Tobago	J. M. Huntington	
G-CONV	Convair CV-440-54	Atlantic Air Transport Ltd/Coventry	
G-COOK	Cameron N-77 balloon	IAZ (International) Ltd	
G-COOT	Taylor Coot A	P. M. Napp	
G-COPS	Piper J-3C-65 Cub	R. W. Sproat & C. E. Simpson	
G-COPT	AS.350B Ecureuil	Owenlars Ltd	
G-CORB	SOCATA TB-20 Trinidad	G. D. Corbin	
G-CORD	Slingsby T.66 Nipper 3	A. V. Lamprell (G-AVTB)	
G-CORN	Bell 206B JetRanger 3	John A.Wells Ltd (G-BHTR)	
G-CORP	BAe ATP	BAe (Operations) Ltd (G-BTNK)	
G-CORT	AB-206B JetRanger 3	Helicopter Training & Hire Ltd	
G-COSY	Lindstrand LBL-56A balloon	D. D. Owen	
G-COTT	Cameron 60 Cottage SS balloon	Nottingham Hot-Air Balloon Club	
G-COUP	Ercoupe 415C	S. M. Gerrard	
G-COVE	Avtech Jabiru UL	A. A. Rowson	
G-COWS	ARV Super 2	T. C. Harrold (G-BONB)	
G-COZI	Rutan Cozy III	D. G. Machin	
G-CPCD	CEA DR.221	P. J. Taylor	
G-CPDA	D.H.106 Comet 4C	C. Walton Ltd/Bruntingthorpe	
G-CPEL	Boeing 757-236	British Airways (G-BRJE)	
G-CPEM	Boeing 757-236	British Airways	
G-CPEN	Boeing 757-236	British Airways	
G-CPEO	Boeing 757-236	British Airways	
G-CPER	Boeing 757-236	British Airways	

Notes	Reg.	Type	Owner or Operator
	G-CPES	Boeing 757-236	British Airways
	G-CPET	Boeing 757-236	British Airways
	G-CPEU	Boeing 757-236	British Airways
	G-CPEV	Boeing 757-236	British Airways
	G-CPFC	Cessna F.152 II	Willowair Flying Club (1996) Ltd/ Southend
	G-CPMK	D.H.C.1 Chipmunk 22 (WZ847)	Towerdrive Ltd
	G-CPMS	SOCATA TB.20 Trinidad	Charlotte Park Management Services Ltd
	G-CPOL	AS.355F-1 Twin Squirrel	Thames Valley Police Authority
	G-CPSF	Cameron N-90 balloon	S. A. Simington & J. D. Rigden (G-OISK)
	G-CPTM	PA-28-151 Warrior	T. J. Mackay & C. M. Pollett (G-BTOE)
	G-CPTS	AB-206B JetRanger 2	A. R. B. Aspinall
	G-CPXC	Avions Mudry CAP.10C	Cole Aviation Ltd
	G-CRAY	Robinson R-22B	W. H. Grimshaw
	G-CRES	Denney Kitfox Mk 3	K. M. James
	G-CREW	PA-46-350P Malibu Mirage	Longslow Dairy Ltd
	G-CRIC	Colomban MC.15 Cri-Cri	R. S. Stoddart-Stones
	G-CRIL	R. Commander 112B	Rockwell Aviation Group/Cardiff
	G-CRIS	Taylor JT.1 Monoplane	C. R. Steer
	G-CROL	Maule MXT-7-180	N. G. P. Evans
	G-CROW	Robinson R-44	Longmoore Ltd
	G-CROY	Shaw Europa	A. Croy
	G-CRPH	Airbus A.320-231	My Travel Airways (Airtours)
	G-CRUM	Westland Scout AH.1	Crummock Development Ltd
	G-CRUZ	Cessna T.303	Bank Farm Ltd
	G-CSBM	Cessna F.150M	Halegreen Associates Ltd
	G-CSCS	Cessna F.172N	C. Sullivan/Stapleford
	G-CSDJ	Avtech Jabiru UL	D. W. Johnston & ptnrs
	G-CSFC	Cessna 150L	Foxtrot Charlie Flying Group
	G-CSFT	PA-23 Aztec 250D ★	Aces High Ltd (G-AYKU)/North Weald
	G-CSIX	PA-32 Cherokee Six 300	G. A. Ponsford
	G-CSMK	Aerotechnik EV-97 Eurostar	Cosmik Aviation Ltd
	G-CSNA	Cessna 421C	Air Montgomery Ltd
	G-CSPJ	Hughes 369HS	The Hughes Helicopter Co. Ltd (G-BXJF)
	G-CTCL	SOCATA TB.10 Tobago	MRS Ltd (G-BSIV)
	G-CTCT	Flight Design CT.2K	Cyclone Airsports Ltd
	G-CTEC	Stoddard-Hamilton Glastar	B. N. C. Mogg
	G-CTEL	Cameron N-90 balloon	D. Triggs
	G-CTFF	Cessna T.206H	Oxford Aviation Services Ltd/Kidlington
	G-CTGR	Cameron N-77 balloon	T. G. Read (G-CCDI)
	G-CTIX	V.S.509 Spitfire T.IX (PT462)	A. A. Hodgson
	G-CTKL	Noorduyn AT-16 Harvard IIB (54137)	M. R. Simpson
	G-CTOY	Denney Kitfox Mk 3	B. McNeilly
	G-CTPW	Bell 206B JetRanger 3	Aviation Rentals
	G-CTWW	PA-34-200T Seneca II	Kensington Aviation Ltd (G-ROYZ/G-GALE)
	G-CUBB	PA-18 Super Cub 180	Bidford Airfield Ltd
	G-CUBI	PA-18 Super Cub 125	G. T. Fisher
	G-CUBJ	PA-18 Super Cub 150 (56-5395)	R. A. Fleming
	G-CUBP	PA-18 Super Cub 150	P. Grenet
	G-CUBS	Piper J-3C-65 Cub	Sunbeam Aviation (G-BHPT)
	G-CUBY	Piper J-3C-65 Cub	C. A. Bloom (G-BTZW)
	G-CUCU	Colt 180A balloon	G. M. N. & S. Spencer
	G-CUPN	PA-46-350P Malibu Mirage	Airpark
	G-CURR	Cessna 172R II	JS Aviation Ltd (G-BXOH)
	G-CURV	Avid Speedwing	K. S. Kelso
	G-CUTE	Dyn' Aero MCR-01	E. G. Shimmin
	G-CUTY	Shaw Europa	D. J. & M. Watson
	G-CVBF	Cameron A-210 balloon	Virgin Balloon Flights Ltd
	G-CVIX	D.H.110 Sea Vixen D.3 (XP924)	De Havilland Aviation Ltd/Swansea
	G-CVPM	VPM M.16 Tandem Trainer	C. S. Teuber/Germany
	G-CVYD	Airbus A.320-231	jmc Airlines Ltd
	G-CVYE	Airbus A.320-231	jmc Airlines Ltd
	G-CVYG	Airbus A.320-231	jmc Airlines Ltd
	G-CWAG	Sequoia F. 8L Falco	I. R. Court & W. Jones
	G-CWBM	Phoenix Currie Wot	K. M. Fresson (G-BTVP)
	G-CWFA	PA-38-112 Tomahawk	Cardiff-Wales Flying Club Ltd (G-BTGC)
	G-CWFB	PA-38-112 Tomahawk	Cardiff-Wales Aviation Services Ltd (G-OAAL)
	G-CWFC	PA-38-112 Tomahawk	Cardiff-Wales Flying Club Ltd (G-BRTA)
	G-CWFD	PA-38-112 Tomahawk	Cardiff-Wales Flying Club Ltd (G-BSVY)
	G-CWFE	PA-38-112 Tomahawk	Cardiff-Wales Flying Club Ltd (G-BPBR)

Reg.	Type	Owner or Operator	Notes
G-CWFY	Cessna 152 II	Cardiff-Wales Aviation Services Ltd (G-OAMY)	
G-CWFZ	PA-28-151 Warrior	Cardiff-Wales Flying Club Ltd (G-CPCH/G-BRGJ)	
G-CWIZ	AS.350B Ecureuil	PLM Dollar Group Ltd (G-DJEM/G-ZBAC/ G-SEBI/G-BMCU)	
G-CWOT	Currie Wot	G-CWOT Group	
G-CXCX	Cameron N-90 balloon	Cathay Pacific Airways (London) Ltd	
G-CXHK	Cameron N-77 balloon	Cathay Pacific Airways (London) Ltd	
G-CYLS	Cessna T.303	Gledhill Water Storage Ltd (G-BKXI)/Blackpool	
G-CYMA	GA-7 Cougar	Cyma Petroleum (UK) Ltd (G-BKOM)/ Elstree	
G-CZAG	Sky 90-24 balloon	S. McCarthy	
G-CZAR	Cessna 560 Citation V	Chauffair Ltd	
G-CZCZ	Avions Mudry CAP.10B	P. R. Moorhead & M. Farmer	
G-DAAC	Canadair CL.600-2B16 Challenger	1427 Ltd/Manchester	
G-DAAH	PA-28RT-201T Turbo Arrow IV	R. Peplow/Halfpenny Green	
G-DAAM	Robinson R-22B	County Garage (Cheltenham) Ltd	
G-DABS	Robinson R-22B-2	B. Seymour	
G-DACA	P.57 Sea Prince T.1 (WF118) ★	P. G. Vallance Ltd/Charlwood	
G-DACC	Cessna 401B	Niglon Ltd (G-AYOU)/Birmingham	
G-DACF	Cessna 152 II	T. M. & M. L. Jones (G-BURY)/Egginton	
G-DACS	Short SD3-30 Variant 100	Air Cavrel Ltd (G-BKDM)	
G-DADS	Hughes 369HS	Executive Aviation Services Ltd	
G-DAEX	Dassault Falcon 900EX	Triair (Bermuda) Ltd	
G-DAFY	Beech 58 Baron	P. R. Earp	
G-DAIR	Luscombe 8A Silvaire	D. F. Soul (G-BURK)	
G-DAIV	Ultramagic H-77 balloon	D. Harrison-Morris	
G-DAJB	Boeing 757-2T7	Monarch Airlines Ltd/Luton	
G-DAJC	Boeing 767-31KER	My Travel Airways (Airtours)	
G-DAKK	Douglas C-47A	European Flyers/Blackbushe	
G-DAKO	PA-28-236 Dakota	First European Airways Ltd	
G-DAMY	Shaw Europa	M. J. Ashby-Arnold	
G-DAND	SOCATA TB.10 Tobago	Whitemoor Engineering Co Ltd	
G-DANT	R. Commander 114	D. P. Tierney	
G-DANY	Avtech Jabiru UL	D. A. Crosbie	
G-DANZ	AS.355N Twin Squirrel	Frewton Ltd	
G-DAPH	Cessna 180K	M. R. L. Astor	
G-DARA	PA-34-220T Seneca III	SYS (Scaffolding Contractors) Ltd	
G-DARK	CFM Shadow Srs DD	P. M. Dewhurst	
G-DASH	R. Commander 112A	D. & M. Nelson (G-BDAJ)	
G-DASI	Short SD3-60 Variant 100	Aerotek Aviation Engineering Ltd (G-BKKW)/Bournemouth	
G-DAST	Jodel DR.1050/M1	D. J. & K. S. Thomas	
G-DASU	Cameron V-77 balloon	D. & L. S. Litchfield	
G-DATE	Agusta A.109C	Datel Direct Ltd (G-RNLD)	
G-DATG	Cessna F.182P	Hangar 8 Aviation Services Ltd	
G-DAVD	Cessna FR.172K	D. M. Driver	
G-DAVE	Jodel D.112	D. A. Porter/Sturgate	
G-DAVO	AA-5B Tiger	Kadala Aviation Ltd (G-GAGA/ G-BGPG/G-BGRW)/Elstree	
G-DAVT	Schleicher ASH-26E	D. A. Triplett	
G-DAYI	Shaw Europa	A. F. Day	
G-DAYS	Shaw Europa	D. J. Bowie	
G-DAYZ	Pietenpol Air Camper	J. G. Cronk	
G-DBDB	VPM M.16 Tandem Trainer	D. R. Bolsover	
G-DBHH	AB-206B JetRanger	UK Helicopter Charter Ltd (G-AWVO)	
G-DBYE	Mooney M.20M	A. J. Thomas	
G-DCAV	PA-32R-301Saratoga IIHP	Lyons Aviation	
G-DCDB	Bell 407	Paycourt Ltd	
G-DCEA	PA-34-200T Seneca II	Bristol Flying Centre Ltd	
G-DCKK	Cessna F.172N	J. Maffia/Panshanger	
G-DCOM	Robinson R-44	Burlington Publishing Ltd	
G-DCPA	MBB BK.117C-1C	Devon & Cornwall Constabulary (G-LFBA)	
G-DCSE	Robinson R-44	DCS Europe PLC	
G-DCXL	Jodel D.140C	X-Ray Lima Group	
G-DDAY	PA-28R-201T Turbo Arrow III	G-DDAY Group (G-BPDO)/Tatenhill	
G-DDMV	NA T-6G Texan (493209)	E. A. Morgan	
G-DDOD	Enstrom 280FX	Sunseeker Sales (UK) Ltd	
G-DDOG	SA Bulldog Srs 120/121	Gamit Ltd	

G-DEAN – G-DINO

Notes	Reg.	Type	Owner or Operator
	G-DEAN	Solar Wings Pegasus XL-Q	D. C. P. Cardey & G. D. Tannahill (G-MVJV)
	G-DEBR	Shaw Europa	A. J. Calvert & C. T. Smallwood
	G-DECK	Cessna T.210N	R. J. Howard
	G-DEER	Robinson R-22B-2	Mightgreat Ltd
	G-DEFK	BAe 146-200	Flightline Ltd (G-DEBK)
	G-DEFL	BAe 146-200	Flightline Ltd (G-DEBL)
	G-DEFM	BAe 146-200	Flightline Ltd (G-DEBM)
	G-DELF	Aero L-29A Delfin	B. R. Green/Manston
	G-DELT	Robinson R-22B	Jim Moodie Racing
	G-DEMH	Cessna F.172M (modified)	M. Hammond (G-BFLO)
	G-DENA	Cessna F.150G	W. M. Wilson & R. Campbell (G-AVEO)
	G-DENB	Cessna F.150G	Skytrax Aviation Ltd (G-ATZZ)/Sibson
	G-DENC	Cessna F.150G	Just Plane Trading (G-AVAP)
	G-DEND	Cessna F.150M	Deer Hill Aviation Ltd (G-WAFC/G-BDFI)
	G-DENE	PA-28 Cherokee 140	Bristol & Wessex Aeroplane Club (G-ATOS)
	G-DENH	PA-28-161 Warrior II	Plane Talking Ltd (G-BTNH)/Elstree
	G-DENI	PA-32 Cherokee Six 300	A. Bendkowski (G-BAIA)
	G-DENN	Bell 206B JetRanger 3	Abbey Flight Ltd
	G-DENR	Cessna F.172N	Den Air Aviation Ltd (G-BGNR)/Southend
	G-DENS	Binder CP.301S Smaragd	G. E. Roe & I. S. Leader
	G-DENT	Cameron N-145 balloon	Deproco UK Ltd
	G-DENZ	PA-44-180 Seminole	Den Air Aviation Ltd (G-INDE/G-BHNM)/ Southend
	G-DERB	Robinson R-22B	S. Thompson (G-BPYH)
	G-DERV	Cameron Truck SS balloon	J. M. Percival
	G-DESS	Mooney M.20J	W. E. Newnes
	G-DEST	Mooney M.20J	Allegro Aviation Ltd
	G-DESY	Cessna A.152	General Airline Ltd (G-BNJE)/Blackbushe
	G-DEVS	PA-28 Cherokee 180	180 Group (G-BGVJ)/Blackbushe
	G-DEWS	Grob G.109B	R. G. Trute
	G-DEXP	ARV Super 2	W. G. McKinnon
	G-DEXY	Beech E90 King Air	Specsavers Aviation Ltd
	G-DEZC	H.S.125 Srs 700B	Bunbury Aviation Ltd (G-BWCR)
	G-DFLY	PA-38-112 Tomahawk	P. M. Raggett
	G-DFVA	Cessna R.172K	R. A. Plowright
	G-DGCL	Glaser-Dirks DG.800B	C. J. Lowrie
	G-DGDG	Glaser-Dirks DG.400/17	DG400 Flying Group/Lasham
	G-DGIV	Glaser-Dirks DG.800B	W. R. McNair
	G-DGLM	Glaser-Dirks DG.400	L. C. McKelvie
	G-DGWW	Rand-Robinson KR-2	W. Wilson/Liverpool
	G-DHCB	D.H.C.2 Beaver 1	Seaflite Ltd (G-BTDL)
	G-DHCC	D.H.C.1 Chipmunk 22	Eureka Aviation NV/Belgium
	G-DHCI	D.H.C.1 Chipmunk 22	Felthorpe Flying Group Ltd (G-BBSE)
	G-DHDV	D.H.104 Dove 8 (VP981)	Air Atlantique Ltd/Coventry
	G-DHJH	Airbus A.321-211	My Travel Airways (Airtours)
	G-DHLB	Cameron N-90 balloon	B. A. Bower
	G-DHSS	D.H.112 Venom FB.50	D. J. L. Wood/Bournemouth
	G-DHTM	D.H.82A Tiger Moth (replica)	E. G. Waite-Roberts
	G-DHTT	D.H.112 Venom FB.50 (WR421)	Source Classic Jet Flight (G-BMOC)
	G-DHUU	D.H.112 Venom FB.50 (WR410)	Source Classic Jet Flight (G-BMOD)
	G-DHVV	D.H.115 Vampire T.55 (XE897)	Source Classic Jet Flight
	G-DHWW	D.H.115 Vampire T.55 (XG775)	Source Classic Jet Flight
	G-DHXX	D.H.100 Vampire FB.6 (VT871)	Source Classic Jet Flight
	G-DHYY	D.H.115 Vampire T.11 (WZ553)	Source Classic Jet Flight
	G-DHZF	D.H.82A Tiger Moth (N9192)	M. R. Parker (G-BSTJ)/Sywell
	G-DHZZ	D.H.115 Vampire T.55 (WZ589)	Source Classic Jet Flight
	G-DIAL	Cameron N-90 balloon	A. J. Street
	G-DIAT	PA-28 Cherokee 140	RAF Benevolent Fund's IAT/Bristol & Wessex Aeroplane Club (G-BCGK)/ Lulsgate
	G-DICE	Enstrom F-28F	Dice Aviation Services Ltd
	G-DICK	Thunder Ax6-56Z balloon	R. D. Sargeant
	G-DIGI	PA-32 Cherokee Six 300	D. Stokes
	G-DIKY	Murphy Rebel	R. J. P. Herivel
	G-DIMB	Boeing 767-31KER	My Travel Airways (Airtours)
	G-DIME	R. Commander 114	H. B. Richardson
	G-DINA	AA-5B Tiger	Portway Aviation
	G-DING	Colt 77A balloon	G. J. Bell
	G-DINK	Lindstrand Bulb SS balloon	Dinkelacker-Schwaben Brau AG/ Germany
	G-DINO	Pegasus Quantum 15	G. Van Der Gaag (G-MGMT)

Reg.	Type	Owner or Operator	Notes
G-DINT	B.156 Beaufighter IF	T. E. Moore	
G-DIPI	Cameron 80 Tub SS balloon	R. A. Preston	
G-DIRK	Glaser-Dirks DG.400	G-DIRK Syndicate	
G-DISK	PA-24 Comanche 250	A. Johnston (G-APZG)	
G-DISO	Jodel 150	P. F. Craven & J. H. Shearer	
G-DIVA	Cessna R.172K XPII	Bob Crowe Aircraft Sales Ltd	
G-DIWY	PA-32 Cherokee Six 300	IFS Chemicals Ltd	
G-DIXY	PA-28-181 Archer III	Dixyair Ltd	
G-DIZO	Jodel D.120A	D. Aldersea (G-EMKM)/Breighton	
G-DIZY	PA-28R-201T Turbo Arrow III	Calverton Flying Club Ltd/Cranfield	
G-DIZZ	Hughes 369HE	H. J. Pelham	
G-DJAE	Cessna 500 Citation	Source Group Ltd (G-JEAN)/ Bournemouth	
G-DJAR	Airbus A.320-231	My Travel Airways (Airtours)	
G-DJAY	Avtech Jabiru UL-450	D. J. Pearce	
G-DJCR	Varga 2150A Kachina	D. J. C. Robertson (G-BLWG)	
G-DJEA	Cessna 421C	Bettany Aircraft Holdings Ltd	
G-DJHB	Beech A23-19 Musketeer	Nayland Aiglet Group (G-AZZE)	
G-DJJA	PA-28-181 Archer II	Choice Aircraft/Fowlmere	
G-DJNH	Denney Kitfox Mk 3	D. J. N. Hall	
G-DKDP	Grob G.109	D. W. & J. E. Page	
G-DKGF	Viking Dragonfly	P. C. Dowbor	
G-DLCB	Shaw Europa	D. J. Lockett	
G-DLDL	Robinson R-22B	Blue Oaks Developments Ltd	
G-DLFN	Aero L-29 Delfin	T. W. Freeman & N. Gooderham/ North Weald	
G-DLOM	SOCATA TB.20 Trinidad	J. N. A. Adderley/Guernsey	
G-DLTR	PA-28 Cherokee 180E	BCT Aircraft Leasing Ltd (G-AYAV)	
G-DMAC	Avtech Jabiru UL	C. J. Pratt	
G-DMAH	SOCATA TB.20 Trinidad	D. M. A. Hutchinson	
G-DMCD	Robinson R-22B	R. W. Pomphrett (G-OOLI)	
G-DMCS	PA-28R Cherokee Arrow 200-II	Arrow Associates (G-CPAC)	
G-DMCT	Flight Design CT.2K	D. McCormack	
G-DMSS	Westland Gazelle HT.3	MSS Holdings Ltd	
G-DMWW	CFM Shadow Srs DD	Microlight Sport Aviation Ltd	
G-DNCN	AB-206A JetRanger	Flying Services/Sandown	
G-DNCS	PA-28R-201T Turbo Arrow III	BC Arrow Ltd	
G-DNGR	Colt 31A balloon	G. J. Bell	
G-DNLB	MBB Bo 105DBS/4	Bond Air Services (G-BCDH/G-BTBD/ G-BUDP)	
G-DNOP	PA-46-350P Malibu Mirage	Campbell Aviation Ltd	
G-DNVT	G.1159C Gulfstream IV	Shell Aircraft Ltd/Heathrow	
G-DOBN	Cessna 402B	Fraggle Leasing Ltd/Edinburgh	
G-DOCA	Boeing 737-436	British Airways	
G-DOCB	Boeing 737-436	British Airways	
G-DOCD	Boeing 737-436	British Airways	
G-DOCE	Boeing 737-436	British Airways	
G-DOCF	Boeing 737-436	British Airways	
G-DOCG	Boeing 737-436	British Airways	
G-DOCH	Boeing 737-436	British Airways	
G-DOCI	Boeing 737-436	British Airways	
G-DOCK	Boeing 737-436	British Airways	
G-DOCL	Boeing 737-436	British Airways	
G-DOCM	Boeing 737-436	British Airways	
G-DOCN	Boeing 737-436	British Airways	
G-DOCO	Boeing 737-436	British Airways	
G-DOCP	Boeing 737-436	British Airways	
G-DOCR	Boeing 737-436	British Airways	
G-DOCS	Boeing 737-436	British Airways	
G-DOCT	Boeing 737-436	British Airways	
G-DOCU	Boeing 737-436	British Airways	
G-DOCV	Boeing 737-436	British Airways	
G-DOCW	Boeing 737-436	British Airways	
G-DOCX	Boeing 737-436	British Airways	
G-DOCY	Boeing 737-436	British Airways (G-BVBY)	
G-DOCZ	Boeing 737-436	British Airways (G-BVBZ)	
G-DODB	Robinson R-22B	Exmoor Helicopters Ltd	
G-DODD	Cessna F.172P-II	K. Watts/Denham	
G-DODI	PA-46-350P Malibu Mirage	CAVOK SRL/Italy	
G-DODR	Robinson R-22B	Exmoor Helicopters Ltd	
G-DOEA	AA-5A Cheetah	Plane Talking Ltd (G-RJMI)/Elstree	
G-DOFY	Bell 206B JetRanger 3	Cinnamond Ltd	
G-DOGG	SA Bulldog Srs 120/121	P. Sengupta	

Notes	Reg.	Type	Owner or Operator
	G-DOGZ	Horizon 1	J. E. D. Rogerson
	G-DOIT	AS.350B-1 Ecureuil	C. C. Blakey
	G-DOLY	Cessna T.303	R. M. Jones (G-BJZK)
	G-DOME	PA-28-161 Warrior III	Wakelite Ltd
	G-DONG	Sky 105-24 balloon	G. J. Bell (G-BWKP)
	G-DONI	AA-5B Tiger	N. J. Bond (G-BLLT)
	G-DONS	PA-28RT-201T Turbo Arrow IV	D. J. Murphy/Blackbushe
	G-DONZ	Shaw Europa	D. J. Smith & D. McNicholl
	G-DOOZ	AS.355F-2 Twin Squirrel	Signature Aircraft Charter (G-BNSX)
	G-DORB	Bell 206B JetRanger 3	Dorb Crest Homes Ltd
	G-DORN	EKW C-3605	R. G. Gray
	G-DOVE	Cessna 182Q	Carel Investments Ltd
	G-DOVE†	D. H. 104 Devon C.2 ★	E. Surrey College (G-KOOL)/Gatton Point, Redhill
	G-DOWN	Colt 31A balloon	M. Williams
	G-DPPH	Agusta A.109E Power	Dyfed-Powys Police Authority (G-BYMS)
	G-DPSP	Douglas DC-10-10	My Travel Airways (Airtours)
	G-DPST	Phillips ST.2	Speedtwin Developments Ltd
	G-DPUK	Mooney M.20K	K. A. Horne (G-BNZS)
	G-DRAC	Cameron Dracula Skull SS balloon	Shiplake Investments Ltd
	G-DRAG	Cessna 152 (tailwheel)	L. A. Maynard & M. E. Scouller (G-REME/G-BRNF)
	G-DRAM	Cessna FR.172F (floatplane)	Clyde River Rats
	G-DRAW	Colt 77A balloon	C. Wolstenholme
	G-DRAY	Taylor JT.1 Monoplane	L. J. Dray
	G-DRBG	Cessna 172M	Henlow Flying Club Ltd (G-MUIL)
	G-DREX	Cameron 110 Saturn SS balloon	LRC Products Ltd
	G-DREY	Cessna 172R	C. J. & J. M. Wardill
	G-DRGN	Cameron N-105 balloon	W. I. Hooker & C. Parker
	G-DRGS	Cessna 182S	Walter Scott & Partners Ltd
	G-DRHL	AS.350B-2 Ecureuil	Lytonworth Ltd
	G-DRKJ	Schweizer 269C	Aviation Bureau (G-BPPW)
	G-DRMM	Shaw Europa	M. W. Mason
	G-DRNT	Sikorsky S-76A	CHC Scotia Ltd
	G-DROP	Cessna U.206C	Peterborough Parachute Centre Ltd (G-UKNO/G-BAMN)/Sibson
	G-DRSV	CEA DR.315 (modified)	R. S. Voice
	G-DRUM	Thruster TST Mk.1	C. C. Mercer (G-MVBR)
	G-DRYI	Cameron N-77 balloon	C. A. Butter
	G-DRYS	Cameron N-90 balloon	C. A. Butter
	G-DRZF	CEA DR.360	M. R. Parker/Sywell
	G-DSFT	PA-28R Cherokee Arrow 200-II	SFT Europe Ltd (G-LFSE/G-BAXT)
	G-DSGC	PA-25 Pawnee 235C	Devon & Somerset Gliding Club Ltd
	G-DSID	PA-34-220T Seneca III	R. Howton
	G-DSLL	Pegasus Quantum 15-912	D. Luke
	G-DSPI	Robinson R-44	D. S. Phelps (G-DPSI)
	G-DTCP	PA-32R Cherokee Lance 300	Plane Hire (G-TEEM)
	G-DUDE	Van's RV-8	W. M. Hodgkins
	G-DUDS	C.A.S.A. 1.131E Jungmann 2000	R. D. Loder
	G-DUDZ	Robin DR.400/180	D. H. Pattison (G-BXNK)
	G-DUET	Wood Duet	C. Wood
	G-DUGI	Lindstrand LBL-90A balloon	D. J. Cook
	G-DUKK	Extra EA.300/L	R. A. & K. M. Roberts
	G-DUNG	Sky 65-24 balloon	G. J. Bell
	G-DUNN	Zenair CH.250	A. Dunn
	G-DURO	Shaw Europa	D. J. Sagar
	G-DURX	Thunder 77A balloon	V. Trimble
	G-DUSK	D.H.115 Vampire T.11 (XE856)	R. M. A. Robinson & R. Horsfield
	G-DUST	Stolp SA.300 Starduster Too	J. V. George
	G-DUVL	Cessna F.172N	A. J. Simpson/Denham
	G-DVON	D.H.104 Devon C.2 (VP955)	C. L. Thatcher
	G-DWIA	Chilton D.W.1A	D. Elliott
	G-DWIB	Chilton D.W.1B (replica)	J. Jennings
	G-DWMS	Avtech Jabiru UL-450	D. H. S. Williams
	G-DWPH	Ultramagic M-77	Ultramagic UK
	G-DYNE	Cessna 414	Commair Aviation Ltd/Tollerton
	G-DYNG	Colt 105A balloon	M. J. Gunston (G-HSHS)
	G-EBJI	Hawker Cygnet (replica)	C. J. Essex
	G-ECAB	Curtiss JN-4D	V. S. E. Norman/Rendcomb
	G-ECAH	F.27 Friendship Mk 500	EuroCeltic Airways (G-JEAH)
	G-ECAN	D.H.84 Dragon	Norman Aircraft Trust/Chilbolton

Reg.	Type	Owner or Operator	Notes
G-ECAS	Boeing 737-36N	bmi british midland	
G-ECAT	F.27 Friendship Mk 500	EuroCeltic Airways (G-JEAI)	
G-ECBH	Cessna F.150K	ECBH Flying Group	
G-ECCC	Extra EA.300/L	Extraviation Ltd/North Weald	
G-ECDX	D.H.71 Tiger Moth (replica)	M. D. Souch	
G-ECGC	Cessna F.172N-II	Euroair Flying Club Ltd/Cranfield	
G-ECGO	Bo 208C1 Junior	A Flight Aviation Ltd	
G-ECHO	Enstrom 280C-UK-2 Shark	ALP Electrical (Maidenhead) Ltd (G-LONS/G-BDIB)/Booker	
G-ECJM	PA-28R-201T Turbo Arrow III	Regishire Ltd (G-FESL/G-BNRN)	
G-ECKE	Avro 504K (replica) (D8781)	Propshop Ltd/Duxford	
G-ECLI	Schweizer 269C	Eclipse (UK) Ltd	
G-ECOS	AS.355F-1 Twin Squirrel	Multiflight Ltd (G-DOLR/G-BPVB)	
G-ECOX	Grega GN.1 Air Camper	H. C. Cox	
G-ECVB	Pietenpol Air Camper	K. S. Matcham	
G-ECZZ	Eurocopter EC.120B	Kensington & Chelsea Aviation Ltd	
G-EDAV	SA Bulldog Srs 120/121	Edwalton Aviation Ltd	
G-EDEN	SOCATA TB.10 Tobago	N. G. Pistol & ptnrs	
G-EDFS	Pietenpol Air Camper	D. F. Slaughter	
G-EDGE	Jodel 150	A. D. Edge	
G-EDGI	PA-28-161 Warrior II	R. A. Forster	
G-EDMC	Pegasus Quantum 15-912	E. McCallum	
G-EDNA	PA-38-112 Tomahawk	D. J. Clucas	
G-EDRV	Van's RV-6A	E. A. Yates	
G-EDTO	Cessna FR.172F	N. G. Hopkinson	
G-EDVL	PA-28R Cherokee Arrow 200-II	J. S. Devlin & Z. Islam (G-BXIN)	
G-EECO	Lindstrand LBL-25A balloon	P. A. Bubb & A. J. Allen	
G-EEGL	Christen Eagle II	A. J. Wilson	
G-EEJE	PA-31 Navajo B	Foremans Aviation Ltd	
G-EELS	Cessna 208B Caravan 1	Glass Eels Ltd	
G-EENA	PA-32R-301 Saratoga SP	Gamit Ltd	
G-EENI	Shaw Europa	M. P. Grimshaw	
G-EENY	GA-7 Cougar	Walsh Aviation	
G-EERH	Ruschmeyer R.90-230RG	D. Sadler	
G-EERV	Van's RV-6	C. B. Stirling (G-NESI)	
G-EESA	Shaw Europa	C. B. Stirling (G-HIIL)	
G-EEST	BAe Jetstream 3102	Eastern Airways Ltd	
G-EEUP	SNCAN Stampe SV-4C	A. M. Wajih	
G-EEZS	Cessna 182P	C. M. Jones	
G-EFGH	Robinson R-22B	Foxtrot Golf Helicopters Ltd (G-ROGG)	
G-EFIR	PA-28-181 Archer II	Leicestershire Aero Club Ltd	
G-EFRY	Light Aero Avid Aerobat	P. A. Boyden	
G-EFSM	Slingsby T.67M Firefly 260	Pooler-LMT Ltd (G-BPLK)	
G-EFTE	Bolkow Bo 207	L. J. & A. A. Rice	
G-EGAL	Christen Eagle II	Eagle Partners	
G-EGEE	Cessna 310Q	Excel Automation Ltd (G-AZVY)	
G-EGEG	Cessna 172R	C. D. Lever	
G-EGGS	Robin DR.400/180	R. Foot	
G-EGHB	Ercoupe 415D	P. G. Vallance	
G-EGHH	Hawker Hunter F.58 (J-4083)	G. R. Lacey/Bournemouth	
G-EGHR	SOCATA TB.20 Trinidad	B. M. Prescott	
G-EGJA	SOCATA TB.20 Trinidad	D. A. Williamson/Alderney	
G-EGLD	PA-28-161 Cadet	J. Appleton/Denham	
G-EGLE	Christen Eagle II	R. L. Mitcham & ptnrs	
G-EGLS	PA-28-181 Archer III	D. J. Cooke	
G-EGLT	Cessna 310R	Aviation Beauport Ltd (G-BHTV)	
G-EGNR	PA-38-112 Tomahawk	Chester Aero Services Ltd/Hawarden	
G-EGTR	PA-28-161 Cadet	Plane Talking Ltd (G-BRSI)/Elstree	
G-EGUL	Christen Eagle II	G-EGUL Flying Group (G-FRYS)	
G-EGUY	Sky 220-24 balloon	Black Sheep Balloons	
G-EHBJ	C.A.S.A. 1.131E Jungmann 2000	E. P. Howard	
G-EHGF	PA-28-181 Archer II	Pegasus Flying Group/Barton	
G-EHLX	PA-28-181 Archer II	I. R. Carver & ptnrs	
G-EHMJ	Beech S35 Bonanza	A. L. Burton & A. J. Daley	
G-EHMM	Robin DR.400/180R	Booker Gliding Club Ltd	
G-EHMS	McD Douglas MDH-900	Virgin HEMS (London) Ltd	
G-EHUP	SA.341G Gazelle 1	MW Helicopters Ltd	
G-EHXP	R. Commander 112A	H. Hashimi	
G-EIBM	Robinson R-22B	XL Aviation Ltd (G-BUCL)	
G-EIII	Extra EA.300	D. Dobson (G-HIII)	
G-EIKY	Shaw Europa	J. D. Milbank	
G-EIRE	Cessna T.182T	J. Byrne	
G-EISO	M.S.892A Rallye Commodore 150	A. Head	

Notes	Reg.	Type	Owner or Operator
	G-EITE	Luscombe 8A Silvaire	J. H. Seed
	G-EIWT	Cessna FR.182RG	P. P. D. Howard-Johnston/Edinburgh
	G-EJEL	Cessna 550 Citation II	A. J. & E. A. Elliott
	G-EJGO	Z.226HE Trener	Aerotation Ltd/Biggin Hill
	G-EJMG	Cessna F.150H	Bagby Aviation
	G-EJOC	AS.350B Ecureuil	Leisure & Retail Helicopters (G-GEDS/G-HMAN/G-SKIM/G-BIVP)
	G-EKKL	PA-28-161 Warrior II	Premiair Engineering Ltd/Shoreham
	G-EKMN	Zlin Z.242L	Aeroshow Ltd
	G-EKOS	Cessna FR.182 RG	S. Charlton
	G-ELBC	PA-34-200 Seneca II	Stapleford Flying Club Ltd (G-BANS)
	G-ELEE	Cameron Z-105 balloon	D. Eliot
	G-ELEN	Robin DR.400/180	N. R. & E. Foster
	G-ELIE	Cessna 182S	V. J. R. Baring
	G-ELIT	Bell 206L LongRanger	Aeroturbine Ltd
	G-ELIZ	Denney Kitfox Mk 2	A. J. Ellis
	G-ELKA	Christen Eagle II	D. Aitken & Skydance Aviation Ltd
	G-ELKS	Avid Speedwing Mk 4	H. S. Elkins
	G-ELLA	PA-32R-301 Saratoga IIHP	C. C. W. Hart
	G-ELLE	Cameron N-90 balloon	N. D. Eliot
	G-ELLI	Bell 206B JetRanger 3	R. A. Fleming Ltd
	G-ELMH	NA AT-6D Harvard III (42-84555)	M. Hammond
	G-ELZN	PA-28-161 Warrior II	Northamptonshire School of Flying Ltd/ Sywell
	G-ELZY	PA-28-161 Warrior II	Goodwood Road Racing School Ltd
	G-EMAS	Eurocopter EC.135T-1	East Midlands Air Support Unit
	G-EMAX	PA-31-350 Navajo Chieftain	AM & T Aviation Ltd
	G-EMAZ	PA-28-181 Archer II	E. J. Stanley
	G-EMBA	Embraer RJ145EU	British Airways Citiexpress
	G-EMBB	Embraer RJ145EU	British Airways Citiexpress
	G-EMBC	Embraer RJ145EU	British Airways Citiexpress
	G-EMBD	Embraer RJ145EU	British Airways Citiexpress
	G-EMBE	Embraer RJ145EU	British Airways Citiexpress
	G-EMBF	Embraer RJ145EU	British Airways Citiexpress
	G-EMBG	Embraer RJ145EU	British Airways Citiexpress
	G-EMBH	Embraer RJ145EU	British Airways Citiexpress
	G-EMBI	Embraer RJ145EU	British Airways Citiexpress
	G-EMBJ	Embraer RJ145EU	British Airways Citiexpress
	G-EMBK	Embraer RJ145EU	British Airways Citiexpress
	G-EMBL	Embraer RJ145EU	British Airways Citiexpress
	G-EMBM	Embraer RJ145EU	British Airways Citiexpress
	G-EMBN	Embraer RJ145EU	British Airways Citiexpress
	G-EMBO	Embraer RJ145EU	British Airways Citiexpress
	G-EMBP	Embraer RJ145EU	British Airways Citiexpress
	G-EMBS	Embraer RJ145EU	British Airways Citiexpress
	G-EMBT	Embraer RJ145EU	British Airways Citiexpress
	G-EMBU	Embraer RJ145EU	British Airways Citiexpress
	G-EMBV	Embraer RJ145EU	British Airways Citiexpress
	G-EMBW	Embraer RJ145EU	British Airways Citiexpress
	G-EMBX	Embraer RJ145EU	British Airways Citiexpress
	G-EMBY	Embraer RJ145EU	British Airways Citiexpress
	G-EMCM	Eurocopter EC.120B	C. R. W. Morrell
	G-EMER	PA-34-200 Seneca II	Haimoss Ltd/Old Sarum
	G-EMHH	AS.355F-2 Twin Squirrel	Hancocks Holdings Ltd (G-BYKH)
	G-EMIN	Shaw Europa	S. A. Lamb
	G-EMJA	C.A.S.A. 1.131E Jungmann 2000	P. J. Brand
	G-EMLY	Pegasus Quantum 15	A. R. White
	G-EMMS	PA-38-112 Tomahawk	Ravenair/Liverpool
	G-EMMY	Rutan Vari-Eze	M. J. Tooze
	G-EMSI	Shaw Europa	P. W. L. Thomas
	G-EMSY	D.H.82A Tiger Moth	B. E. Micklewright (G-ASPZ)
	G-ENCE	Partenavia P.68B	Bicton Aviation (G-OROY/G-BFSU)
	G-ENEE	CFM Streak Shadow SA	T. Green
	G-ENGO	Steen Skybolt	C. Docherty
	G-ENIE	Tipsy T.66 Nipper 3	E. J. Clarke
	G-ENII	Cessna F.172M	J. Howley
	G-ENNI	Robin R.3000/180	P. F. Taylor
	G-ENNK	Cessna 172S	AK Enterprises Ltd
	G-ENNY	Cameron V-77 balloon	B. G. Jones
	G-ENOA	Cessna F.172F	M. K. Acors (G-ASZW)
	G-ENRE	Avtech Jabiru UL	J. C. Harris
	G-ENRI	Lindstrand LBL-105A balloon	P. G. Hall
	G-ENRY	Cameron N-105 balloon	P. G. & G. R. Hall

Reg.	Type	Owner or Operator	Notes
G-ENSI	Beech F33A Bonanza	J. M. Eskes	
G-ENTT	Cessna F.152 II	Plane Talking Ltd (G-BHHI)/Elstree	
G-ENTW	Cessna F.152 II	Firecrest Aviation Ltd & ptnrs (G-BFLK)	
G-ENUS	Cameron N-90 balloon	Wye Valley Aviation Ltd	
G-ENVY	Mainair Blade 912	D. L. Pollitt & P. Millership	
G-EOFM	Cessna F.172N	20th Air Training Group Ltd	
G-EOFS	Shaw Europa	G. T. Leedham	
G-EOFW	Pegasus Quantum 15-912	G. C. Weighell	
G-EOHL	Cessna 182L	G. B. Dale & M. C. Terris	
G-EOIN	Zenair CH.701UL	D. G. Palmer	
G-EOLD	PA-28-161 Warrior II	Goodwood Road Racing Co Ltd	
G-EOMA	Airbus A.330-243	Monarch Airlines Ltd	
G-EORG	PA-38-112 Tomahawk	Airways Aero Association/Booker	
G-EORJ	Shaw Europa	P. E. George	
G-EPAR	Robinson R-22B-2	Jepar Rotorcraft	
G-EPDI	Cameron N-77 balloon	R. Moss	
G-EPED	PA-31-350 Navajo Chieftain	Pedley Furniture International Ltd (G-BMCJ)	
G-EPFR	Airbus A.320-231	My Travel Airways (G-BVJV) (Airtours)	
G-EPOL	AS.355F-1 Twin Squirrel	Cambridge & Essex Air Support Unit (G-SASU/G-BSSM/G-BMTC/G-BKUK)	
G-EPOX	Aero Designs Pulsar XP	K. F. Farey	
G-EPTR	PA-28R Cherokee Arrow 200-II	T. I. Moore	
G-ERAD	Beech C90A King Air	GKL Management Services Ltd	
G-ERBL	Robinson R-22B-2	G. V. Maloney	
G-ERCO	Ercoupe 415D	A. R. & M. V. Tapp	
G-ERDS	D.H.82A Tiger Moth	W. A. Gerdes	
G-ERIC	R. Commander 112TC	Atomchoice Ltd	
G-ERIK	Cameron N-77 balloon	T. M. Donnelly	
G-ERIS	Hughes 369D	R. J. Howard (G-PJMD/G-BMJV)	
G-ERIX	Boeing Stearman A75N-1	Flight Incentives NV/Belgium	
G-ERJA	Embraer RJ145EU	Brymon/British Airways Citiexpress	
G-ERJB	Embraer RJ145EU	Brymon/British Airways Citiexpress	
G-ERJC	Embraer RJ145EU	Brymon/British Airways Citiexpress	
G-ERJD	Embraer RJ145EU	Brymon/British Airways Citiexpress	
G-ERJE	Embraer RJ145EU	Brymon/British Airways Citiexpress	
G-ERJF	Embraer RJ145EU	Brymon/British Airways Citiexpress	
G-ERJG	Embraer RJ145EU	Brymon/British Airways Citiexpress	
G-ERMO	ARV Super 2	T. Pond (G-BMWK)	
G-ERMS	Thunder Ax3 balloon	B. R. & M. Boyle	
G-ERNI	PA-28-181 Archer II	P. C. & M. A. Greenaway (G-OSSY)	
G-EROS	Cameron H-34 balloon	Evening Standard Co Ltd	
G-ERRY	AA-5B Tiger	Gemini Aviation (G-BFMJ)/Shobdon	
G-ESAM	MBB Bo 105DBS/4	Bond Air Services Ltd (G-BUIB/G-BDYZ)	
G-ESFT	PA-28-161 Warrior II	SFT Europe Ltd (G-ENNA)/ Bournemouth	
G-ESKY	PA-23 Aztec 250D	Systems & Research Ltd (G-BBNN)	
G-ESSX	PA-28-161 Warrior II	Courtenay Enterprises (G-BHYY)	
G-ESTA	Cessna 550 Citation II	Executive Aviation Services Ltd (G-GAUL)	
G-ESTE	AA-5A Cheetah	Plane Talking Ltd(G-GHNC)/Elstree	
G-ESTR	Van's RV-6	R. M. Johnson	
G-ESUS	Rotorway Executive 162F	J. Tickner	
G-ETAV	PA-32 Cherokee Six 300D	Erintech Ltd (G-MCAR/G-LADA/ G-AYWK)	
G-ETBY	PA-32 Cherokee Six 260	G-ETBY Group (G-AWCY)	
G-ETCW	Stoddard-Hamilton Glastar	P. G. Hayward	
G-ETDA	PA-28-161 Warrior II	T. Griffiths	
G-ETDC	Cessna 172P	Osprey Air Services Ltd	
G-ETFT	Colt Financial Times SS balloon	Financial Times Ltd (G-BSGZ)	
G-ETHY	Cessna 208	N. A. Moore	
G-ETIN	Robinson R-22B	Forestdale Hotels Ltd	
G-ETIV	Robin DR.400/180	J. MacGilvray	
G-ETME	Nord 1002 Pingouin (KG+EM)	108 Flying Group	
G-EUGN	Robinson R-44	Twinlite Developments Ltd	
G-EUOA	Airbus A.319-131	British Airways	
G-EUOB	Airbus A.319-131	British Airways	
G-EUOC	Airbus A.319-131	British Airways	
G-EUOD	Airbus A.319-131	British Airways	
G-EUOE	Airbus A.319-131	British Airways	
G-EUOF	Airbus A.319-131	British Airways	
G-EUOG	Airbus A.319-131	British Airways	
G-EUOH	Airbus A.319-131	British Airways	

Notes	Reg.	Type	Owner or Operator
	G-EUOI	Airbus A.319-131	British Airways
	G-EUOJ	Airbus A.319-131	British Airways
	G-EUOK	Airbus A.319-131	British Airways
	G-EUOL	Airbus A.319-131	British Airways
	G-EUPA	Airbus A.319-131	British Airways
	G-EUPB	Airbus A.319-131	British Airways
	G-EUPC	Airbus A.319-131	British Airways
	G-EUPD	Airbus A.319-131	British Airways
	G-EUPE	Airbus A.319-131	British Airways
	G-EUPF	Airbus A.319-131	British Airways
	G-EUPG	Airbus A.319-131	British Airways
	G-EUPH	Airbus A.319-131	British Airways
	G-EUPJ	Airbus A.319-131	British Airways
	G-EUPK	Airbus A.319-131	British Airways
	G-EUPL	Airbus A.319-131	British Airways
	G-EUPM	Airbus A.319-131	British Airways
	G-EUPN	Airbus A.319-131	British Airways
	G-EUPO	Airbus A.319-131	British Airways
	G-EUPP	Airbus A.319-131	British Airways
	G-EUPR	Airbus A.319-131	British Airways
	G-EUPS	Airbus A.319-131	British Airways
	G-EUPT	Airbus A.319-131	British Airways
	G-EUPU	Airbus A.319-131	British Airways
	G-EUPV	Airbus A.319-131	British Airways
	G-EUPW	Airbus A.319-131	British Airways
	G-EUPX	Airbus A.319-131	British Airways
	G-EUPY	Airbus A.319-131	British Airways
	G-EUPZ	Airbus A.319-131	British Airways
	G-EUUA	Airbus A.320-232	British Airways
	G-EUUB	Airbus A.320-232	British Airways
	G-EUUC	Airbus A.320-232	British Airways
	G-EUUD	Airbus A.320-232	British Airways
	G-EUUE	Airbus A.320-232	British Airways
	G-EUUF	Airbus A.320-232	British Airways
	G-EUUG	Airbus A.320-232	British Airways
	G-EUUH	Airbus A.320-232	British Airways
	G-EUUI	Airbus A.320-232	British Airways
	G-EUUJ	Airbus A.320-232	British Airways
	G-EURX	Shaw Europa XS T-G	C. C. Napier
	G-EVES	Dassault Falcon 900B	Northern Executive Aviation Ltd
	G-EVET	Cameron 80 Concept balloon	K. J. Foster
	G-EVEY	Thruster T.600N 450-JAB	Thruster Air Services Ltd
	G-EWAN	Prostar PT-2C	C. G. Shaw
	G-EWBC	Avtec Jabiru SK	E. W. B. Comber
	G-EWFN	SOCATA TB-20 Trinidad	Trinidair Ltd (G-BRTY)
	G-EWIZ	Pitts S-2E Special	S. J. Carver
	G-EXEA	Extra EA.300/L	J. A. Carr
	G-EXEC	PA-34-200 Seneca	Sky Air Travel Ltd
	G-EXEK	Agusta A.109A-II	Knightway Aviation Ltd (G-SLNE/G-EEVS/G-OTSL)
	G-EXEX	Cessna 404	Atlantic Air Transport Ltd/Coventry
	G-EXIT	M.S.893E Rallye 180GT	M. A. Baldwin
	G-EXPD	Stemme S.10-VT	Global Gliding Expeditions
	G-EXPL	Champion 7GCBC Citabria	E. J. F. McEntee
	G-EXPR	Colt 90A balloon	Lakeside Lodge Golf Centre
	G-EXPS	Short SD3-60 Variant 100	BAC Express Airlines Ltd (G-BLRT)
	G-EXTR	Extra EA.260	D. M. Britten
	G-EYAS	Denney Kitfox Mk 2	K. Hamnett
	G-EYCO	Robin DR.400/180	Cherokee G-AVYL Flying Group Ltd
	G-EYES	Cessna 402C	Atlantic Air Transport Ltd (G-BLCE)/ Coventry
	G-EYET	Robinson R-44	Warwickshire Flight Training Centre Ltd (G-JPAD)
	G-EYLE	Bell 206L-1 LongRanger 2	Eyles Construction Ltd (G-BWCU/ G-OCRP)
	G-EYNL	MBB Bo 105DBS/5	Sterling Helicopters Ltd
	G-EYOR	Van's RV-6	S. I. Fraser
	G-EYRE	Bell 206L-1 LongRanger	Hideroute Ltd (G-STVI)
	G-EZEL	SA.341G Gazelle 1	W. R. Pitcher (G-BAZL)
	G-EZJA	Boeing 737-73V	easyJet Airline Co Ltd/Luton
	G-EZJB	Boeing 737-73V	easyJet Airline Co Ltd/Luton
	G-EZJC	Boeing 737-73V	easyJet Airline Co Ltd/Luton
	G-EZJD	Boeing 737-73V	easyJet Airline Co Ltd/Luton

Reg.	Type	Owner or Operator	Notes
G-EZJE	Boeing 737-73V	easyJet Airline Co Ltd/Luton	
G-EZJF	Boeing 737-73V	easyJet Airline Co Ltd/Luton	
G-EZJG	Boeing 737-73V	easyJet Airline Co Ltd/Luton	
G-EZJH	Boeing 737-73V	easyJet Airline Co Ltd/Luton	
G-EZJI	Boeing 737-73V	easyJet Airline Co Ltd/Luton	
G-EZJJ	Boeing 737-73V	easyJet Airline Co Ltd/Luton	
G-EZJK	Boeing 737-73V	easyJet Airline Co Ltd/Luton	
G-EZJL	Boeing 737-73V	easyJet Airline Co Ltd/Luton	
G-EZJM	Boeing 737-73V	easyJet Airline Co Ltd/Luton	
G-EZJN	Boeing 737-73V	easyJet Airline Co Ltd/Luton	
G-EZJO	Boeing 737-73V	easyJet Airline Co Ltd/Luton	
G-EZJP	Boeing 737-73V	easyJet Airline Co Ltd/Luton	
G-EZJR	Boeing 737-73V	easyJet Airline Co Ltd/Luton	
G-EZJS	Boeing 737-73V	easyJet Airline Co Ltd/Luton	
G-EZJT	Boeing 737-73V	easyJet Airline Co Ltd/Luton	
G-EZJU	Boeing 737-73V	easyJet Ailrine Co Ltd/Luton	
G-EZJV	Boeing 737-73V	easyJet Airline Co Ltd/Luton	
G-EZOS	Rutan Vari-Eze	C. Moffat	
G-EZYB	Boeing 737-3M8	easyJet Airline Co Ltd/Luton	
G-EZYC	Boeing 737-3Y0	easyJet Airline Co Ltd (G-BWJA/ G-TEAA)/Luton	
G-EZYD	Boeing 737-3M8	easyJet Airline Co Ltd/Luton	
G-EZYF	Boeing 737-375	easyJet Airline Co Ltd/Luton	
G-EZYG	Boeing 737-33V	easyJet Airline Co Ltd/Luton	
G-EZYH	Boeing 737-33V	easyJet Airline Co Ltd/Luton	
G-EZYI	Boeing 737-33V	easyJet Airline Co Ltd/Luton	
G-EZYJ	Boeing 737-33V	easyJet Airline Co Ltd/Luton	
G-EZYK	Boeing 737-33V	easyJet Airline Co Ltd/Luton	
G-EZYL	Boeing 737-33V	easyJet Airline Co Ltd/Luton	
G-EZYO	Boeing 737-33V	easyJet Airline Co Ltd/Luton	
G-EZYP	Boeing 737-33V	easyJet Airline Co Ltd/Luton	
G-EZYR	Boeing 737-33V	easyJet Airline Co Ltd/Luton	
G-EZYT	Boeing 737-3Q8	easyJet Airline Co Ltd/Luton	
G-EZYU	PA-34-200 Seneca II	P. A. S. Dyke (G-BCDB)/Elstree	
G-FABB	Cameron V-77 balloon	P. Trumper	
G-FABI	Robinson R-44 Astro	J. Froggatt	
G-FABM	Beech 95-B55 Baron	F. B. Miles (G-JOND/G-BMVC)	
G-FAGN	Robinson R-22B	C. R. Weldon	
G-FALC	Aeromere F.8L Falco	P. J. Jones (G-AROT)	
G-FAME	Starstreak Shadow SA-II	T. J. Palmer	
G-FAMH	Zenair CH.701	F. E. Telling	
G-FANC	Fairchild 24R-46 Argus III	A. T. Fines	
G-FANL	Cessna FR.172K XP-II	J. A. Rees	
G-FARM	SOCATA Rallye 235GT	Bristol Cars Ltd	
G-FARO	Aero Designs Star-Lite SL.1	M. K. Faro	
G-FARR	Jodel 150	G. H. Farr	
G-FATB	R. Commander 114B	James D.Pearce & Co	
G-FAYE	Cessna F.150M	Cheshire Air Training Services Ltd/ Liverpool	
G-FBAT	Aeroprakt A.22 Foxbat	D. G. Ashcroft	
G-FBIX	D.H.100 Vampire FB.9 (WL505)	D. G. Jones	
G-FBMW	Cameron N-90 balloon	K-J. Schwer/Germany	
G-FBPI	ANEC IV Missel Thrush	R. Trickett	
G-FBRN	PA-28-181 Archer II	Herefordshire Aero Club Ltd/Shobdon	
G-FBWH	PA-28R Cherokee Arrow 180	F. A. Short	
G-FCAL	Cessna 441	Cobham Leasing Ltd/Bournemouth	
G-FCDB	Cessna 550 Citation Bravo	Eurojet Aviation Ltd	
G-FCLA	Boeing 757-28A	jmc Airlines Ltd	
G-FCLB	Boeing 757-28A	jmc Airlines Ltd	
G-FCLC	Boeing 757-28A	jmc Airlines Ltd	
G-FCLD	Boeing 757-25F	jmc Airlines Ltd	
G-FCLE	Boeing 757-28A	jmc Airlines Ltd	
G-FCLF	Boeing 757-28A	jmc Airlines Ltd	
G-FCLG	Boeing 757-28A	jmc Airlines Ltd	
G-FCLH	Boeing 757-28A	jmc Airlines Ltd	
G-FCLI	Boeing 757-28A	jmc Airlines Ltd	
G-FCLJ	Boeing 757-2Y0	jmc Airlines Ltd	
G-FCLK	Boeing 757-2Y0	jmc Airlines Ltd	
G-FCSP	Robin DR.400/180	FCS Photochemicals	
G-FEBE	Cessna 340A	C. Dugard Ltd & E. C. Dugard	
G-FEBY	Robinson R-22B	Astra Helicopters Ltd	
G-FEDA	Eurocopter EC.120B	Federal Aviation Ltd	

Notes	Reg.	Type	Owner or Operator
	G-FEFE	Scheibe SF.25B Falke	G-FEFE Syndicate
	G-FELL	Shaw Europa	R. Barton
	G-FELT	Cameron N-77 balloon	Allan Industries Ltd
	G-FEZZ	AB-206B JetRanger 2	Helicopter Services
	G-FFAB	Cameron N-105 balloon	The Andrew Broadsword Collection
	G-FFEN	Cessna F.150M	R. J. Everett
	G-FFFT	Lindstrand LBL-31A balloon	The Aerial Display Co Ltd
	G-FFOX	Hawker Hunter T.7B (WV318)	Delta Engineering Aviation Ltd/Kemble
	G-FFRA	Dassault Falcon 20DC	FR Aviation Ltd/Bournemouth
	G-FFRI	AS.355F-1 Twin Squirrel	ATC Trading Ltd (G-GLOW/G-PAPA/ G-CNET/G-MCAH)
	G-FFTI	SOCATA TB.20 Trinidad	Romsure Ltd
	G-FFTT	Lindstrand LBL Newspaper SS balloon	The Aerial Display Co Ltd
	G-FFUN	Pegasus Quantum 15	J. B. Hobbs (G-MYMD)
	G-FFWD	Cessna 310R	Keef & Co Ltd (G-TVKE/G-EURO)
	G-FGID	Vought FG-1D Corsair (KD345)	Patina Ltd/Duxford
	G-FHAJ	Airbus A.320-231	My Travel Airways (Airtours)
	G-FHAS	Scheibe SF.25E Super Falke	Burn Gliding Club Ltd
	G-FIAT	PA-28 Cherokee 140	RAF Benevolent Fund's IAT/ Bristol & Wessex Aeroplane Club (G-BBYW)/Lulsgate
	G-FIBS	AS.350BA Ecureuil	Pristheath Ltd
	G-FIFE	Cessna FA.152	Tayside Aviation Ltd (G-BFYN)/Dundee
	G-FIFI	SOCATA TB.20 Trinidad	F. A. Saker (G-BMWS)
	G-FIGA	Cessna 152	Aerohire Ltd/Wolverhampton
	G-FIGB	Cessna 152	Aerohire Ltd/Wolverhampton
	G-FIJJ	Cessna F.177RG	Middleton Miniature Mouldings Ltd (G-AZFP)
	G-FIJR	L.188PF Electra	Atlantic Airlines Ltd/Coventry
	G-FIJV	L.188CF Electra	Atlantic Airlines Ltd/Coventry
	G-FILE	PA-34-200T Seneca	Barnes Olson Aeroleasing Ltd
	G-FILL	PA-31-310 Navajo	P. V. Naylor-Leyland
	G-FINA	Cessna F.150L	D. Norris (G-BIFT)
	G-FIND	Cessna F.406	Atlantic Air Transport Ltd/Coventry
	G-FIRM	Cessna 550 Citation Bravo	Marshall of Cambridge Aerospace Ltd
	G-FIRS	Robinson R-22B-2	M. & S. Chantler
	G-FIRZ	Murphy Renegade Spirit UK	D. M. Wood
	G-FISH	Cessna 310R-II	Air Charter Scotland Ltd/Edinburgh
	G-FITZ	Cessna 335	D. S. Hodgetts (G-RIND)
	G-FIZU	L.188CF Electra	Atlantic Airlines Ltd/Coventry
	G-FIZY	Shaw Europa XS	G. N. Holland (G-DDSC)
	G-FIZZ	PA-28-161 Warrior II	Tecair Aviation Ltd
	G-FJCE	Thruster T.600T	F. Cameron
	G-FJET	Cessna 550 Citation II	London Executive Aviation Ltd (G-DCFR/G-WYLX/G-JETD)
	G-FJMS	Partenavia P.68B	F. J. M. Sanders (G-SVHA)
	G-FKNH	PA-15 Vagabond	M. J. Mothershaw/Liverpool
	G-FLAG	Colt 77A balloon	B. A. Williams
	G-FLAK	Beech 95-E55 Baron	D. Clarke/Swanton Morley
	G-FLAV	PA-28-161 Warrior II	The Crew Flying Group/Tollerton
	G-FLCA	Fleet Model 80 Canuck	E. C. Taylor
	G-FLCT	Hallam Fleche	R. G. Hallam
	G-FLEA	SOCATA TB-10 Tobago	J. J. Berry
	G-FLEW	Lindstrand LBL-90A balloon	Lindstrand Balloons Ltd
	G-FLII	GA-7 Cougar	Plane Talking Ltd (G-GRAC)/Elstree
	G-FLIK	Pitts S-1S Special	R. P. Millinship/Leicester
	G-FLIP	Cessna FA.152	Walkbury Aviation Ltd (G-BOES)
	G-FLIT	Rotorway Executive 162F	R. F. Rhodes
	G-FLIZ	Staaken Z-21 Flitzer	M. A. Wood
	G-FLJA	PA-32 Cherokee Six 260	F. L. Avery (G-AVTJ)
	G-FLKE	Scheibe SF.25C Falke	Falkes Flying Foundation Ltd
	G-FLKS	Scheibe SF.25C Falke	Falkes Flying Foundation Ltd
	G-FLOA	Cameron O-120 balloon	Floating Sensations Ltd
	G-FLOR	Shaw Europa	A. F. C. van Eldik
	G-FLOX	Shaw Europa	DPT Group
	G-FLPI	R. Commander 112A	H. J. Freeman
	G-FLSI	FLS Aerospace Sprint 160	Sunhawk Ltd/North Weald
	G-FLTA	BAe 146-200	Flightline Ltd
	G-FLTG	Cameron A-140 balloon	Floating Sensations Ltd
	G-FLTI	Beech F90 King Air	Flightline Ltd
	G-FLTY	EMB-110P1 Bandeirante	Keenair Charter Ltd (G-ZUSS/G-REGA)/Liverpool

Reg.	Type	Owner or Operator	Notes
G-FLTZ	Beech 58 Baron	Stesco Ltd (G-PSVS)	
G-FLUF	Lindstrand Bunny SS balloon	Lindstrand Balloons Ltd	
G-FLVU	Cessna 501 Citation	Neonopal Ltd/Liverpool	
G-FLYA	Mooney M.20J	BRF Aviation Ltd	
G-FLYE	Cameron A-210 balloon	Bakers World Travel Ltd	
G-FLYI	PA-34-200 Seneca II	JBR Leisure Ltd (G-BHVO)/Southend	
G-FLYN	Cessna F.406	ILS Air Ltd	
G-FLYP	Beagle B.206 Srs 2	Key Publishing Ltd (G-AVHO)/Cranfield	
G-FLYS	Robinson R-44	Newmarket Plant Hire Ltd	
G-FLYT	Shaw Europa	K. F. & R. Richardson	
G-FLYY	BAC.167 Strikemaster 80A	B. T. Barber	
G-FLZR	Staaken Z-21 Flitzer	J. F. Govan	
G-FMAM	PA-28-151 Warrior	Lima Tango Flying Group (G-BBXV)	
G-FMKA	Diamond HK.36TC Super Dimona	A. Bailey	
G-FMSG	Cessna FA.150K	G. Owen (G-POTS/G-AYUY)/Gamston	
G-FNLD	Cessna 172N	Papa Hotel Flying Group	
G-FNLY	Cessna F.172M	C. F. Dukes (G-WACX/G-BAEX)	
G-FODI	Robinson R-44	Sanna Industries Ltd	
G-FOGG	Cameron N-90 balloon	J. P. E. Money-Kyrle	
G-FOGY	Robinson R-22B	P. Turvey	
G-FOLD	Light Aero Avid Speedwing	S. J. Higgins	
G-FOLI	Robinson R-22B-2	K. Duckworth	
G-FOLY	Aerotek Pitts S-2A Modified	A. A. Laing	
G-FOPP	Lancair 320	Airsport (UK) Ltd	
G-FORC	SNCAN Stampe SV-4C	I. A. Marsh/Elstree	
G-FORD	SNCAN Stampe SV-4C	P. H. Meeson	
G-FORR	PA-28-181 Archer III	Buchanan Partnership	
G-FORS	Slingsby T.67C	Open Skies Partnership	
G-FOSY	M.S.880B Rallye Club	A. G. Foster (G-AXAK)	
G-FOTO	PA-E23 Aztec 250F	Aerofilms Ltd (G-BJDH/G-BDXV)	
G-FOWL	Colt 90A balloon	G-FOWL Ballooning Group	
G-FOWS	Cameron N-105 balloon	Fowlers of Bristol Ltd	
G-FOXA	PA-28-161 Cadet	Leicestershire Aero Club Ltd	
G-FOXC	Denney Kitfox Mk 3	G. Hawkins	
G-FOXD	Denney Kitfox	M. Hanley	
G-FOXE	Denney Kitfox Mk 2	K. M. Pinkard	
G-FOXF	Denney Kitfox Mk 4	M. S. Goodwin	
G-FOXG	Denney Kitfox Mk 2	Kitfox Group	
G-FOXI	Denney Kitfox	B. Johns	
G-FOXM	Bell 206B JetRanger 2	Tyringham Charter & Group Services (G-STAK/G-BNIS)	
G-FOXS	Denney Kitfox Mk 2	S. P. Watkins & C. C. Rea	
G-FOXZ	Denney Kitfox	S. C. Goozee	
G-FPIG	PA-28-151 Warrior	Flying Pig Aviation Ltd (G-BSSR)	
G-FPLA	Beech 200 Super King Air	Cobham Leasing Ltd	
G-FPLB	Beech 200 Super King Air	Cobham Leasing Ltd	
G-FPLC	Cessna 441	Cobham Leasing Ltd (G-FRAX/G-BMTZ)	
G-FPLD	Beech 200 Super King Air	Cobham Leasing Ltd	
G-FRAE	Dassault Falcon 20E	FR Aviation Ltd/Bournemouth	
G-FRAF	Dassault Falcon 20E	FR Aviation Ltd/Bournemouth	
G-FRAG	PA-32 Cherokee Six 300E	T. A. Houghton	
G-FRAH	Dassault Falcon 20DC	FR Aviation Ltd/Bournemouth	
G-FRAI	Dassault Falcon 20E	FR Aviation Ltd/Bournemouth	
G-FRAJ	Dassault Falcon 20E	FR Aviation Ltd/Bournemouth	
G-FRAK	Dassault Falcon 20DC	FR Aviation Ltd/Bournemouth	
G-FRAL	Dassault Falcon 20DC	FR Aviation Ltd/Bournemouth	
G-FRAM	Dassault Falcon 20DC	FR Aviation Ltd/Bournemouth	
G-FRAN	Piper J-3C-90 Cub(480321)	Essex L-4 Group (G-BIXY)	
G-FRAO	Dassault Falcon 20DC	FR Aviation Ltd/Bournemouth	
G-FRAP	Dassault Falcon 20DC	FR Aviation Ltd/Bournemouth	
G-FRAR	Dassault Falcon 20DC	FR Aviation Ltd/Bournemouth	
G-FRAS	Dassault Falcon 20C	FR Aviation Ltd/Bournemouth	
G-FRAT	Dassault Falcon 20C	FR Aviation Ltd/Bournemouth	
G-FRAU	Dassault Falcon 20C	FR Aviation Ltd/Bournemouth	
G-FRAW	Dassault Falcon 20ECM	FR Aviation Ltd/Bournemouth	
G-FRAY	Cassutt IIIM (modified)	C. I. Fray	
G-FRAZ	Cessna 441	FR Aviation Ltd/Bournemouth	
G-FRBA	Dassault Falcon 20C	FR Aviation Ltd/Bournemouth	
G-FRBY	Beech E55 Baron	FR Aviation Ltd/Bournemouth	
G-FRCE	H.S. Gnat T.1★	stored/Cranfield	
G-FRGN	PA-28-236 Dakota	Fregon Aviation Ltd	
G-FRJB	Britten Sheriff SA-1 ★	Aeropark/E. Midlands	

Notes	Reg.	Type	Owner or Operator
	G-FROH	AS.350B-2 Ecureuil	Specialist Helicopters Ltd
	G-FRST	PA-44-180T Turbo Seminole	D. B. Ryder & Co. Ltd
	G-FRYI	Beech 200 Super King Air	London Executive Aviation Ltd (G-OAVX/ G-IBCA/G-BMCA)/London City
	G-FSFT	PA-44-180 Seminole	M. J. Love
	G-FSHA	Denney Kitfox Mk 2	P. P. Trangmar
	G-FTAX	Cessna 421C	Gold Air International Ltd (G-BFFM)
	G-FTIL	Robin DR.400/180R	RAF Wyton Flying Club Ltd
	G-FTIM	Robin DR.400/100	M. S. Bird
	G-FTIN	Robin DR.400/100	G. D. Clark & M. J. D. Theobold/ Blackpool
	G-FTSE	BN-2A Mk.III-2 Trislander	Aurigny Air Services Ltd (G-BEPI)/ Guernsey
	G-FTUO	Van's RV-4	Euroclip 2000 Ltd
	G-FTWO	AS.355F-2 Twin Squirrel	McAlpine Helicopters Ltd (G-OJOR/ G-BMUS)/Hayes
	G-FUEL	Robin DR.400/180	R. Darch/Compton Abbas
	G-FULL	PA-28R Cherokee Arrow 200-II	Stapleford Flying Club Ltd (G-HWAY/ G-JULI)
	G-FUND	Thunder Ax7-65Z balloon	Soft Sell Ltd
	G-FUNK	Yakovlev Yak-50	Intrepid Aviation Co/North Weald
	G-FUNN	Plumb BGP-1	J. D. Anson
	G-FUZY	Cameron N-77 balloon	Allan Industries Ltd
	G-FUZZ	PA-18 Super Cub 95	G. W. Cline
	G-FVBF	Lindstrand LBL-210A balloon	Virgin Balloon Flights Ltd
	G-FWPW	PA-28-236 Dakota	P. A. & F. C. Winters
	G-FWRP	Cessna 421C	Festival Property Co Ltd
	G-FXII	V.S.366 Spitfire F.XII (EN224)	P. R. Arnold
	G-FZZA	General Avia F.22-A	APB Leasing Ltd/Welshpool
	G-FZZI	Cameron H-34 balloon	Magical Adventures Ltd
	G-GABD	GA-7 Cougar	C. B. Stewart/Prestwick
	G-GACA	P.57 Sea Prince T.1 ★	P. G. Vallance Ltd/Charlwood
	G-GAFA	PA-34-200T Seneca II	SRC Contractors Ltd
	G-GAFX	Boeing 747-245F	Air Freight Express Ltd
	G-GAII	Hawker Hunter GA.11 (XE685)	DAT Enterprises Ltd/North Weald
	G-GAJB	AA-5B Tiger	G. A. J. Bowles (G-BHZN)
	G-GAJW	Bell 407	A. J. Walter (Aviation) Ltd
	G-GALA	PA-28 Cherokee 180E	E. Alexander (G-AYAP)
	G-GALB	PA-28-161 Warrior II	Goodair Leasing Ltd
	G-GALL	PA-38-112 Tomahawk	C. W. Good (G-BTEV)
	G-GAME	Cessna T.303	P. Heffron
	G-GAND	AB-206B Jet Ranger	Toms Helicopters Ltd (G-AWMK)
	G-GANE	Sequoia F.8L Falco	S. J. Gane
	G-GASC	Hughes 369HS	Crewhall Ltd (G-WELD/G-FROG)
	G-GASP	PA-28-181 Archer II	G-GASP Flying Group
	G-GASS	Thunder Ax7-77 balloon	Servowarm Balloon Syndicate
	G-GAWA	Cessna 140	E. C. Murgatroyd (G-BRSM)
	G-GAZA	SA.341G Gazelle 1	The Auster Aircraft Co Ltd (G-RALE/ G-SFTG)
	G-GAZI	SA.341G Gazelle 1	Stratton Motor Co (Norfolk) Ltd & UCC International Group Ltd (G-BKLU)
	G-GAZZ	SA.341G Gazelle 1	Stratton Motor Co (Norfolk) Ltd & UCC International Group Ltd
	G-GBAO	Robin R.1180TD	J. Kay-Movat
	G-GBAY	Bell 206L-1 LongRanger	Helixair Ltd (G-CSWL/G-SIRI)
	G-GBFF	Cessna F.172N	E. J. Watts
	G-GBHI	SOCATA TB.10 Tobago	A. B. S. Garden
	G-GBLP	Cessna F.172M	Aviate Scotland Ltd (G-GWEN)/ Edinburgh
	G-GBLR	Cessna F.150L	Blue Max Flying Group
	G-GBRB	PA-28 Cherokee 180C	G. Barker & R. Bradley
	G-GBSL	Beech 76 Duchess	M. H. Cundsy (G-BGVG)
	G-GBTA	Boeing 737-436	British Airways (G-BVHA)
	G-GBTB	Boeing 737-436	British Airways (G-BVHB)
	G-GBUE	Robin DR.400/120A	G-GBUE Group (G-BPXD)
	G-GBXS	Shaw Europa XS	Europa Aircraft Co Ltd
	G-GCAT	PA-28 Cherokee 140B	H. Skelton (G-BFRH)
	G-GCCL	Beech 76 Duchess	Aerolease Ltd
	G-GCJL	BAe Jetstream 4100	British Aerospace (Operations) Ltd
	G-GCKI	Mooney M.20K	B. Barr
	G-GCUB	PA-18 Super Cub 150	N. J. Morgan
	G-GCYC	Cessna F.182Q	G-GCYC Ltd

Reg.	Type	Owner or Operator	Notes
G-GDER	Robin R.1180TD	Berkshire Aviation Services Ltd	
G-GDEZ	BAe 125-1000B	Frewton Ltd	
G-GDGR	SOCATA TB-20 Trinidad	Willwright Aviation Ltd	
G-GDOG	PA-28R Cherokee Arrow 200-II	R. K. & S. Perry (G-BDXW)	
G-GDRV	Van's RV-6	J. R. S. Heaton & R. Feather	
G-GDTU	Avions Mudry CAP.10B	Sherburn Aero Club Ltd	
G-GEDI	Dassault Falcon 2000	Victoria Aviation Ltd	
G-GEEE	Hughes 369HS	B. P. Stein (G-BDOY)	
G-GEEP	Robin R.1180TD	Organic Concentrates Ltd/Booker	
G-GEES	Cameron N-77 balloon	N. A. Carr	
G-GEEZ	Cameron N-77 balloon	Charnwood Forest Turf Accountants Ltd	
G-GEHP	PA-28RT-201 Arrow IV	Aeros Leasing Ltd	
G-GEMS	Thunder Ax8-90 S2 balloon	B. Sevenich & ptnrs/Germany	
G-GENN	GA-7 Cougar	Abraxas Aviation Ltd (G-BNAB/G-BGYP)	
G-GEOF	Pereira Osprey 2	G. Crossley	
G-GERY	Stoddard-Hamilton Glastar	G. E. Collard	
G-GFAB	Cameron N-105 balloon	The Andrew Brownsword Collection Ltd	
G-GFCA	PA-28-161 Cadet	Aeroshow Ltd	
G-GFCB	PA-28-161 Cadet	AM & T Aviation Ltd/Bristol	
G-GFCD	PA-34-220T Seneca III	Stonehurst Aviation Ltd (G-KIDS)	
G-GFCF	PA-28-161 Cadet	Aerohire Ltd (G-RHBH)	
G-GFEY	PA-34-200T Seneca II	Topa Panama Inc	
G-GFFA	Boeing 737-59D	British Airways (G-BVZF)	
G-GFFB	Boeing 737-505	British Airways	
G-GFFC	Boeing 737-505	British Airways	
G-GFFD	Boeing 737-59D	British Airways (G-OBMY)	
G-GFFE	Boeing 737-528	British Airways	
G-GFFF	Boeing 737-53A	British Airways (G-OBMZ)	
G-GFFG	Boeing 737-505	British Airways	
G-GFFH	Boeing 737-5H6	British Airways	
G-GFFI	Boeing 737-528	British Airways	
G-GFFJ	Boeing 737-5H6	British Airways	
G-GFKY	Zenair CH.250	D. M. Edes	
G-GFLY	Cessna F.150L	Tindon Ltd	
G-GFTA	PA-28-161 Warrior III	One Zero Three Ltd	
G-GFTB	PA-28-161 Warrior III	One Zero Three Ltd	
G-GGGG	Thunder Ax7-77A balloon	T. A. Gilmour	
G-GGLE	PA-22 Colt 108 (tailwheel)	S. C. Hobden	
G-GGOW	Colt 77A balloon	G. Everett	
G-GGRR	SA Bulldog Srs 120/121	F. P. Corbett (G-CBAM)	
G-GGTT	Agusta-Bell 47G-4A	Face & Fragrance Ltd	
G-GHEE	Aerotechnik EV-97 Eurostar	C. J. Ball	
G-GHIA	Cameron N-120 balloon	J. A. Marshall	
G-GHIN	Thunder Ax7-77 balloon	N. T. Parry	
G-GHOW	Cessna F.182Q	G. How	
G-GHRW	PA-28RT-201 Arrow IV	Bonus Aviation Ltd (G-ONAB/G-BHAK)	
G-GHSI	PA-44-180T Turbo Seminole	M. G. Roberts	
G-GHZJ	SOCATA TB.9 Tampico	M. Haller	
G-GIFT	PA-28-181 Archer III	On Air Aviation Ltd (G-IMVA)	
G-GIGI	M.S.893A Rallye Commodore	D. J. Moore (G-AYVX)	
G-GILT	Cessna 421C	Air Nova PLC (G-BMZC)/Liverpool	
G-GIRY	AG-5B Tiger	Crestway Technologies Ltd	
G-GISO	PA-44-180T Turbo Seminole	G. Cockerton	
G-GIWT	Shaw Europa XS	A. Twigg	
G-GJCD	Robinson R-22B	J. C. Lane	
G-GJKK	Mooney M.20K	Pergola Ltd	
G-GKAT	Enstrom 280C	Elham Valley Aviation Ltd	
G-GKFC	RL-5A LW Sherwood Ranger	K. F. Crumplin (G-MYZI)	
G-GLAD	Gloster G.37 Gladiator II (N5903)	Patina Ltd/Duxford	
G-GLAW	Cameron N-90 balloon	George Law Ltd	
G-GLED	Cessna 150M	Firecrest Aviation Ltd/Booker	
G-GLTT	PA-31-350 Navajo Chieftain	Birchin International Ltd	
G-GLUC	Van's RV-6	Speedfreak Ltd	
G-GLUE	Cameron N-65 balloon	L. J. M. Muir & G. D. Hallett	
G-GLUG	PA-31-350 Navajo Chieftain	Champagne-Air Ltd (G-BLOE/ G-NITE)/Newcastle	
G-GMAB	BAe 125 Srs 1000A	Gama Aviation Ltd (G-BUWX)	
G-GMAX	SNCAN Stampe SV-4C	Glidegold Ltd (G-BXNW)	
G-GMPA	AS.355F-2 Twin Squirrel	Police Aviation Services Ltd (G-BPOI)	
G-GMPS	MDH MD-902 Explorer	Greater Manchester Police Authority	
G-GMSI	SOCATA TB.9 Tampico	M. L. Rhodes	
G-GNAT	H.S. Gnat T.1 (XS101)	Brutus Holdings Ltd/Cranfield	
G-GNJW	Ikarus C.42	I. R. Westrope	

Notes	Reg.	Type	Owner or Operator
	G-GNTB	SAAB SF.340A	Aurigny Air Services Ltd
	G-GNTC	SAAB SF.340A	Aurigny Air Services Ltd
	G-GNTE	SAAB SF.340A	bmi regional
	G-GNTF	SAAB SF.340A	Swedish Aircraft Holdings AB/Sweden
	G-GNTG	SAAB SF.340A	Aurigny Air Services Ltd
	G-GOBT	Colt 77A balloon	British Telecom PLC
	G-GOCX	Cameron N-90 balloon	R. D. Parry/Hong Kong
	G-GOGW	Cameron N-90 balloon	Great Western Trains Ltd
	G-GOLF	SOCATA TB.10 Tobago	E. H. Scamell & ptnrs
	G-GOMM	PA-32R-300 Lance	L. Major
	G-GONE	D.H.112 Venom FB.50	D. G. Jones/Swansea
	G-GOOD	SOCATA TB-20 Trinidad	N. J. Vetch
	G-GORE	CFM Streak Shadow	M. S. Clinton
	G-GORF	Robin HR. 200/120B	J. A. Ingram/Tollerton
	G-GOSS	Jodel DR.221	Avon Flying Group
	G-GOTC	GA-7 Cougar	Cambridge Aircraft Ltd
	G-GOTO	PA-32R-301T Turbo Saratoga II	J. A. Varndell
	G-GOUP	Robinson R-22B	Staske Construction Ltd (G-DIRE)
	G-GOZO	Cessna R.182	D. Pelling (G-BJZO)
	G-GPAG	Van's RV-6	P. A. Green
	G-GPEG	Sky 90-24 balloon	N. T. Parry
	G-GPMW	PA-28RT-201T Turbo Arrow IV	Calverton Flying Group Ltd
	G-GPST	Phillips ST.1 Speedtwin	Speedtwin Developments Ltd
	G-GPWH	Dassault Falcon 900EX	Aviation Partnership
	G-GRID	AS.355F-1 Twin Squirrel	National Grid Co PLC
	G-GRIF	R. Commander 112TCA	Nicol Aviation (G-BHXC)
	G-GRIN	Van's RV-6	A. Phillips
	G-GRIP	Colt 110 Bibendum SS balloon	The Aerial Display Co Ltd
	G-GROL	Maule MXT-7-180	D. C. Croll & ptnrs
	G-GROW	Cameron N-77 balloon	Derbyshire Building Soc.
	G-GRRC	PA-28-161 Warrior II	Goodwood Road Racing Co Ltd (G-BXJX)
	G-GRRR	SA Bulldog Srs 120/122	Horizons Europe Ltd (G-BXGU)
	G-GRYZ	Beech F33A Bonanza	J. Kawadri & M. Kaveh
	G-GSFC	Robinson R-22B	Thurston Helicopters (Engineering) Ltd/ Redhill
	G-GSFT	PA-44-180 Seminole	SFT Europe Ltd/Bournemouth
	G-GTAX	PA-31-350 Navajo Chieftain	Hadagain Investments Ltd (G-OIAS)
	G-GTHM	PA-38-112 Tomahawk	D. A. Whitmore
	G-GUAY	Enstrom 480	Heliway Aviation
	G-GUCK	Beech C23 Sundowner 180	J. T. Francis (G-BPYG)
	G-GUFO	Cameron 80 Saucer SS balloon	Magical Adventures Ltd (G-BOUB)
	G-GULF	Lindstrand LBL-105A balloon	M. A. Webb
	G-GULP	I.I.I. Sky Arrow 650T	Lord Rotherwick
	G-GUNS	Cameron V-77 balloon	Royal School of Artillery Hot Air Balloon Club
	G-GURN	PA-31 Navajo C	Neric Ltd (G-BHGA)
	G-GUSS	PA-28-151 Warrior	M. J. Cleaver & J. M. Newman (G-BJRY)
	G-GUST	AB-206B JetRanger 2	Gatehouse Estates Ltd (G-CBHH/G-AYBE)
	G-GUYS	PA-34-200T Seneca	R. J. & J. M. Z. Keel (G-BMWT)
	G-GVBF	Lindstrand LBL-180A balloon	Virgin Balloon Flights Ltd
	G-GWIZ	Colt Clown SS balloon	Magical Adventures Ltd
	G-GWYN	Cessna F.172M	D. J. Bruford
	G-GYAV	Cessna 172N	Southport & Merseyside Aero Club (1979) Ltd/Liverpool
	G-GYBO	GY-80 Horizon 180	M. J. Strother
	G-GYMM	PA-28R Cherokee Arrow 200	GYMM Group (G-AYWW)
	G-GYRO	Campbell Cricket	J. W. Pavitt
	G-GYTO	PA-38-161 Warrior III	Wellesbourne Aviation
	G-GZDO	Cessna 172N	Cambridge Hall Aviation
	G-GZLE	SA.341G Gazelle 1	R. G. Fairall (G-PYOB/G-IYOB/G-WELA/ G-SFTD/G-RIFC)
	G-HACK	PA-18 Super Cub 150	Intrepid Aviation Co/North Weald
	G-HADA	Enstrom 480	W. B. Steele
	G-HAEC	CAC-18 Mustang 23 (472218)	R. W. Davies/Duxford
	G-HAIG	Rutan LongEz	R. Carey & D. W. Parfrey/Coventry
	G-HAIR	Robin DR.400/180	Racoon International
	G-HAJJ	Glaser-Dirks DG.400	P. W. Endean
	G-HALC	PA-28R Cherokee Arrow 200	Halcyon Aviation Ltd
	G-HALE	Robinson R-44 Astro	Barhale Surveying Ltd

Reg.	Type	Owner or Operator	Notes
G-HALJ	Cessna 140	H. A. Lloyd-Jennings	
G-HALL	PA-22 Tri-Pacer 160	F. P. Hall (G-ARAH)	
G-HALO	Elisport CH-7 Angel	Taylor Woodhouse Ltd	
G-HALP	SOCATA TB.10 Tobago	D. H. Halpern (stored)/Elstree	
G-HAMA	Beech 200 Super King Air	Gama Aviation Ltd/Fairoaks	
G-HAMI	Fuji FA.200-180	K. G. Cameron (G-OISF/G-BAPT)	
G-HAMP	Bellanca 7ACA Champ	K. MacDonald	
G-HANA	WS.58 Wessex HC.2	R. A. Fidler	
G-HANS	Robin DR.400 2+2	Bagby Aviation	
G-HANY	AB-206B JetRanger 3	Swift Helicopters Ltd (G-ESAL/G-BHXW/G-JEKP)	
G-HAPI	Lindstrand LBL-105A balloon	Adventure Balloon Co. Ltd	
G-HAPR	B.171 Sycamore HR.14 (XG547) ★	IHM/Weston-s-Mare	
G-HAPY	D.H.C.1 Chipmunk 22A (WP803)	G-HAPY Ltd/Booker	
G-HARE	Cameron N-77 balloon	C. E. & J. Falkingham	
G-HARF	G.1159C Gulfstream 4	Fayair (Jersey) 1984 Ltd	
G-HARH	Sikorsky S-76B	Air Harrods Ltd/Stansted	
G-HARI	Raj Hamsa X'Air 582	D. Mahajan	
G-HARN	PA-28-181 Archer II	Harnett Air Services Ltd (G-DENK/G-BXRJ)	
G-HARP	Eurocopter EC.135T-1	Air Harrods Ltd/Stansted	
G-HART	Cessna 152 (tailwheel)	Atlantic Air Transport Ltd (G-BPBF)/ Coventry	
G-HARY	Alon A-2 Aircoupe	R. E. Dagless (G-ATWP)	
G-HASI	Cessna 421B	Hawarden Air Services Ltd (G-BTDK)	
G-HATF	Thorp T-18CW	A. T. Fraser	
G-HATZ	Hatz CB-1	S. P. Rollason	
G-HAUL	Westland WG.30 Srs 300 ★	IHM/Weston-super-Mare	
G-HAUS	Hughes 369HM	JP Aviation (Towester) (G-KBOT/G-RAMM)	
G-HAZE	Thunder Ax8-90 balloon	T. G. Church	
G-HBBC	D.H.104 Dove 8	BBC Air Ltd (G-ALFM)	
G-HBMW	Robinson R-22	Northumbria Helicopters Ltd (G-BOFA)	
G-HBOS	Scheibe SF-25C Rotax-Falke	Coventry Gliding Club Ltd	
G-HBUG	Cameron N-90 balloon	R. T. & H. Revel (G-BRCN)	
G-HCFR	BAe 125 Srs 800B	Chauffair Ltd (G-SHEA/G-BUWC)	
G-HCSL	PA-34-220T Seneca III	Shoreham Flight Centre Ltd	
G-HDEW	PA-32R-301 Saratoga SP	R. J. F. Welsh & ptnrs (G-BRGZ)	
G-HDGS	BAe Jetstream 3102	Davis Air (Pty) Ltd (G-PLAM/G-BRGL/ G-OEDC/G-LOGU)	
G-HDIX	Enstrom 280FX	J. Poupard	
G-HEBE	Bell 206B JetRanger 3	MGGR (UK) Ltd	
G-HELE	Bell 206B JetRanger 3	B. E. E. Smith (G-OJFR)	
G-HELN	PA-18 Super Cub 95	J. J. Anziani (G-BKDG)/Booker	
G-HELV	D.H.115 Vampire T.55 (215)	Hunter Wing Ltd/Bournemouth	
G-HEMH	AS.355N Twin Squirrel	McAlpine Helicopters Ltd/Kidlington	
G-HENT	SOCATA Rallye 110ST	R. J. Patton	
G-HENY	Cameron V-77 balloon	R. S. D'Alton	
G-HEPY	Robinson R-44 Astro	T. Everett	
G-HERB	PA-28R-201 Arrow III	Consort Aviation Ltd	
G-HERC	Cessna 172S	Cambridge Aero Club Ltd	
G-HERD	Lindstrand LBL-77B balloon	S. W. Herd	
G-HERO	PA-32RT-300 Lance II	Air Alize Communication (G-BOGN)/ Stapleford	
G-HEWI	Piper J-3C-90 Cub	Denham Grasshopper Group (G-BLEN)	
G-HEWS	Hughes 369D ★	Spares' use/Sywell	
G-HEYY	Cameron 72 Bear SS balloon	Magical Adventures Ltd	
G-HFBM	Curtiss Robin C-2	D. M. Forshaw	
G-HFCA	Cessna A.150L	Horizon Flying Club Ltd	
G-HFCB	Cessna F.150L	Horizon Flying Club Ltd (G-AZVR)	
G-HFCI	Cessna F.150L	Horizon Flying Club Ltd	
G-HFCL	Cessna F.152	T. H. Hird (G-BGLR)	
G-HFCT	Cessna F.152	Stapleford Flying Club Ltd	
G-HFLA	Schweizer 269C	Sterling Helicopters Ltd/Norwich	
G-HFTG	PA-23 Aztec 250E	Hawkair (G-BSOB/G-BCJR)	
G-HGAS	Cameron N-77 balloon	N. J. Tovey	
G-HGPI	SOCATA TB.20 Trinidad	M. J. Jackson/Bournemouth	
G-HIBM	Cameron N-145 balloon	P. M. Forster	
G-HIEL	Robinson R-22B	Hields Aviation/Sherburn	
G-HIJK	Cessna 421C	Oxford Aviation Services Ltd (G-OSAL)/ Kidlington	
G-HILO	R. Commander 114	F. H. Parkes	

Notes	Reg.	Type	Owner or Operator
	G-HILS	Cessna F.172H	Lowdon Aviation Group (G-AWCH)/ Blackbushe
	G-HILT	SOCATA TB.10 Tobago	Cheshire Aircraft Leasing Ltd
	G-HIND	Maule MT-7-235	R. G. Humphries
	G-HINZ	Avtec Jabiru SK	B. Faupel
	G-HIPE	Sorrell SNS-7 Hiperbipe	T. A. S. Rayner/Grenrothes
	G-HIPO	Robinson R-22B	Fleet Street Travel Ltd (G-BTGB)
	G-HIRE	GA-7 Cougar	London Aerial Tours Ltd (G-BGSZ)/ Biggin Hill
	G-HISS	Aerotek Pitts S-2A Special	L. V. Adams & J. Maffia (G-BLVU)/ Panshanger
	G-HITM	Raj Hamsa X'Air 582 (1)	G-HITM Flying Group
	G-HITS	PA-46-310P Malibu	Law 2200 Ltd (G-BMBE)
	G-HIUP	Cameron A-250 balloon	Bridges Van Hire Ltd
	G-HIVA	Cessna 337A	G. J. Banfield (G-BAES)
	G-HIVE	Cessna F.150M	M. P. Lynn (G-BCXT)/Sibson
	G-HJSM	Schempp-Hirth Nimbus 4DM	60 Group (G-ROAM)
	G-HJSS	AIA Stampe SV-4C (modified)	H. J. Smith (G-AZNF)
	G-HKHM	Hughes 369B	Heli Air Ltd/Wellsbourne
	G-HLAA	Airbus A.300B4-203F	HC Airlines/Stansted
	G-HLAB	Airbus A.300B4-203F	HC Airlines/Stansted
	G-HLAC	Airbus A.300B4-203F	HC Airlines/Stansted
	G-HLAD	Airbus A.300B4-203	HC Airlines (G-BIMB)/Stansted
	G-HLCF	Starstreak Shadow	I. P. Hutchinson
	G-HLEN	AS.350B Ecureuil	Sloane Helicopters Ltd (G-LOLY)/Sywell
	G-HLFT	SC.5 Belfast 2	HeavyLift Cargo Airlines Ltd/Stansted
	G-HMBJ	R. Commander 114B	Bravo Juliet Aviation Ltd
	G-HMED	PA-28-161 Warrior III	H. Faizal
	G-HMES	PA-28-161 Warrior II	Cleveland Flying School Ltd/Teesside
	G-HMJB	PA-34-220T Seneca III	Cross Atlantic Ventures Ltd
	G-HMMV	Cessna 525 CitationJet	Gold Star International Ltd
	G-HMPF	Robinson R-44 Astro	Mightycraft Ltd
	G-HMPH	Bell 206B JetRanger 2	Sturmer Ltd (G-BBUY)
	G-HMPT	AB-206B JetRanger 2	Helicopter Express Ltd
	G-HNRY	Cessna 650 Citation VI	Carlton Communications PLC
	G-HNTR	Hawker Hunter T.7 (XL571) ★	Yorkshire Air Museum/Elvington
	G-HOBO	Denney Kitfox Mk 4	E. M. Woods
	G-HOCK	PA-28 Cherokee 180	G-HOCK Flying Club (G-AVSH)
	G-HOFC	Shaw Europa	W. R. Mills
	G-HOFM	Cameron N-56 balloon	Magical Adventures Ltd
	G-HOGS	Cameron 90 Pig SS balloon	Flying Pictures Ltd
	G-HOHO	Colt Santa Claus SS balloon	Oxford Promotions (UK) Ltd/USA
	G-HOLY	ST.10 Diplomate	M. K. Barsham
	G-HOME	Colt 77A balloon	Anglia Balloon School Tardis
	G-HONG	Slingsby T.67M Firefly 200	Hunting Aviation Ltd/Barkston Heath
	G-HONI	Robinson R-22B	Independent Aviation Services (G-SEGO)
	G-HONY	Lilliput Type 1 Srs A balloon	A. E. & D. E. Thomas
	G-HOOD	SOCATA TB.20 Trinidad GT	M. J. Hoodless
	G-HOOV	Cameron N-56 balloon	H. R. Evans
	G-HOPE	Beech F33A Bonanza	Hurn Aviation Ltd
	G-HOPI	Cameron N-42 balloon	Ballonwerbung Hamburg GmbH/ Germany
	G-HOPS	Thunder Ax8-90 balloon	A. C. & B. Munn
	G-HOPY	Van's RV-6A	R. C. Hopkinson
	G-HORN	Cameron V-77 balloon	S. Herd
	G-HOTI	Colt 77A balloon	R. Ollier
	G-HOTT	Cameron O-120 balloon	D. L. Smith
	G-HOTZ	Colt 77B balloon	C. J. & S. M. Davies
	G-HOUS	Colt 31A balloon	Anglia Balloons Ltd
	G-HOWE	Thunder Ax7-77 balloon	M. F. Howe
	G-HOWL	RAF 2000 GTX-SE gyroplane	C. J. Watkinson
	G-HPOL	MDH MD-902 Explorer	Humberside Police Authority
	G-HPSB	R. Commander 114B	S. P. Wakeham
	G-HPSE	R. Commander 114B	Al Nisr Ltd
	G-HPUX	Hawker Hunter T.7 (XL587)	Classic Aviation Ltd/Duxford
	G-HPWH	Agusta A.109E Power	Aviation Partnership (G-HWPH)
	G-HRHE	Robinson R-22B	R. Whitear (G-BTWP)
	G-HRHI	B.206 Srs 1 Basset (XS770)	Lawgra (No.386) Ltd/Cranfield
	G-HRHS	Robinson R-44	Stratus Aviation Ltd/Hong Kong
	G-HRIO	Robin HR.100/120	T. W. Evans
	G-HRLK	SAAB 91D/2 Safir	Sylmar Aviation & Services Ltd (G-BRZY)

UK OUT OF SEQUENCE

Reg.	Type	Owner or Operator	Notes
G-HRLM	Brügger MB.2 Colibri	S. J. Perkins & D. Dobson	
G-HRNT	Cessna 182S	Dingle Star Ltd	
G-HROI	R. Commander 112A	Intereuropean Aviation Ltd	
G-HRON	D.H.114 Heron 2 (XR442)	M. E. R. Coghlan (G-AORH)	
G-HRVD	CCF Harvard IV	Anglia Flight (G-BSBC)	
G-HRZN	Colt 77A balloon	A. J. Spindler	
G-HSDW	Bell 206B JetRanger	Winfield Shoe Co Ltd	
G-HSFT	PA-44-180 Seminole	Magenta Ltd	
G-HSLA	Robinson R-22B	Helicopter Support Ltd (G-BRTI)	
G-HSOO	Hughes 369HE	Edwards Aviation (G-BFYJ)	
G-HSTH	Lindstrand LBL HS-110 balloon	Ballonsport Helmut Seitz/Germany	
G-HTAX	PA-31-350 Navajo Chieftain	Hadagain Investments Ltd	
G-HTRL	PA-34-220T Seneca III	Air Medical Ltd (G-BXXY)	
G-HUBB	Partenavia P.68B	G-HUBB Ltd	
G-HUCH	Cameron 80 Carrots SS balloon	Magical Adventures Ltd (G-BYPS)	
G-HUEY	Bell UH-1H ★	Bournemouth Aviation Museum	
G-HUFF	Cessna 182P	A. E. G. Cousins	
G-HUGG	Learjet 35A	Northern Executive Aviation Ltd	
G-HUGO	Colt 240A balloon	P. G. Hall	
G-HULL	Cessna F.150M	A. D. McLeod	
G-HUMF	Robinson R-22B	Plane Talking Ltd/Elstree	
G-HUNI	Bellanca 7GCBC Scout	T. I. M. Paul	
G-HUNK	Lindstrand LBL-77A balloon	Lindstrand Balloons Ltd	
G-HUPW	Hawker Hurricane 1	Minmere Farm Partnership	
G-HURI	CCF Hawker Hurricane XIIA (Z7381)	Historic Aircraft Collection/Duxford	
G-HURN	Robinson R-22B	R. M. Weyman	
G-HURR	Hawker Hurricane XIIB (BE417)	R. A. Fleming/Breighton	
G-HURY	Hawker Hurricane IV (KZ321)	Patina Ltd/Duxford	
G-HUTT	Denney Kitfox Mk 2	L. A. James	
G-HVAN	RL-5A LW Sherwood Ranger	H. T. H. van Neck	
G-HVBF	Lindstrand LBL-210A balloon	Virgin Balloon Flights Ltd	
G-HVIP	Hawker Hunter T.68	Golden Europe Jet De Luxe Club Ltd/Bournemouth	
G-HVRD	PA-31-350 Navajo Chieftain	Opal Aviation Ltd (G-BEZU)	
G-HWKR	Colt 90A balloon	P. A. Henderson	
G-HXTD	Robin DR.400/180	Hayley Aviation Ltd	
G-HYLT	PA-32R-301 Saratoga SP	H. Young Transport Ltd	
G-HYST	Enstrom 280FX	Patten Helicopter Services Ltd	
G-IAFT	Cessna 152 II	Marnham Investments Ltd	
G-IAGD	Robinson R-22B	A & M Engineering Ltd (G-DRAI)	
G-IANG	Bell 206L LongRanger	Lothian Helicopters Ltd	
G-IANH	SOCATA TB.10 Tobago	Harland Aviation Ltd	
G-IANI	Shaw Europa XS T-G	I. F. Rickard & I. A. Watson	
G-IANJ	Cessna F.150K	Messrs Rees of Poyston West (G-AXVW)	
G-IANW	AS.350B-3 Ecureuil	McAlpine Helicopters Ltd/Kidlington	
G-IARC	Stoddard-Hamilton Glastar	A. A. Craig	
G-IASL	Beech 60 Duke	Applied Sweepers Ltd (G-SING)	
G-IBBC	Cameron 105 Sphere SS balloon	Virgin Airship & Balloon Co Ltd	
G-IBBO	PA-28-181 Archer II	M. Gibbon	
G-IBBS	Shaw Europa	R. H. Gibbs	
G-IBED	Robinson R-22A	Brian Seedle Helicopters (G-BMHN)/ Blackpool	
G-IBET	Cameron 70 Can SS balloon	M. R. Humphrey & J. R. Clifton	
G-IBFC	BFC Challenger II	K. N. Dickinson	
G-IBFW	PA-28R-201 Arrow III	A. W. Collett	
G-IBHH	Hughes 269C	Biggin Hill Helicopters (G-BSCD)	
G-IBKA	Robinson R-44	Bon Accord Glass Ltd (G-USTE)	
G-IBLU	Cameron Z-90 balloon	Blu Spa/Italy	
G-IBRO	Cessna F.152 II	Leicestershire Aero Club Ltd	
G-IBSF	Dassault Falcon 2000	Marconda Services Ltd	
G-IBZS	Cessna 182S	Patrick Eddery Ltd/Kidlington	
G-IBZT	Cessna 182T	Oxford Aviation Services Ltd/Kidlington	
G-ICAB	Robinson R-44	J. R. Clark Ltd	
G-ICAS	Pitts S-2B Special	J. C. Smith	
G-ICBM	Stoddard-Hamilton Glasair III Turbine	G. V. Walters & D. N. Brown	
G-ICCL	Robinson R-22B	JK Aviation Services Ltd (G-ORZZ)	
G-ICES	Thunder Ax6-56 balloon	British Balloon Museum & Library Ltd	
G-ICEY	Lindstrand LBL-77A balloon	G. C. Elson/Spain	
G-ICFR	BAe 125 Srs 800A	Chauffair Ltd (G-BUCR)	

Notes	Reg.	Type	Owner or Operator
	G-ICKY	Lindstrand LBL-77A balloon	Blown Away UK Ltd
	G-ICOI	Lindstrand LBL-105A balloon	Virgin Airship & Balloon Co Ltd
	G-ICOM	Cessna F.172M	C. G. Elesmore (G-BFXI)
	G-ICON	Rutan LongEz	S. J. & M. A. Carradice
	G-ICOZ	Lindstrand LBL-105A balloon	Virgin Airship & Balloon Co Ltd
	G-ICSG	AS.355F-1 Twin Squirrel	MW Helicopters Ltd (G-PAMI/G-BUSA)
	G-ICWT	Pegasus Quantum 15-912	C. W. Taylor
	G-IDAY	Skyfox CA-25N Gazelle	The Anglo-Pacific Aircraft Co & G. Horne
	G-IDDI	Cameron N-77 balloon	Allen & Harris Ltd
	G-IDEA	AA-5A Cheetah	Plane Talking Ltd (G-BGNO)/Elstree
	G-IDII	Dan Rihn DR.107 One Design	C. Darlow
	G-IDUP	Enstrom 280C Shark	Antique Buildings Ltd (G-BRZF)
	G-IDWR	Hughes 369HS	Copley Electrical Contractors (G-AXEJ)
	G-IEJH	Jodel 150A	A. Turner & D. Worth (G-BPAM)/ Crowfield
	G-IEYE	Robin DR. 400/180	E. Hopper
	G-IFDM	Robinson R-44	Bedgbury Aviation Ltd
	G-IFFR	PA-32 Cherokee Six 300	D. J. D. Ritchie & ptnrs (G-BWVO)
	G-IFIT	PA-31-350 Navajo Chieftain	Dart Group PLC (G-NABI/ G-MARG)/Bournemouth
	G-IFLI	AA-5A Cheetah	I-Fly Ltd
	G-IFLP	PA-34-200T Seneca II	Tayflite Ltd/Perth
	G-IFTC	H.S.125 Srs F3B/RA	Albion Aviation Management Ltd (G-OPOL/G-BXPU/G-IBIS/G-AXPU)
	G-IFTE	H.S.125 Srs 700B	Albion Aviation Management Ltd (G-BFVI)
	G-IFTS	Robinson R-44	Context GB Ltd
	G-IGEL	Cameron N-90 balloon	Computacenter Ltd
	G-IGGL	SOCATA TB-10 Tobago	G-IGGL Flying Group (G-BYDC)/ White Waltham
	G-IGHH	Enstrom 480	G. H. Harding
	G-IGLA	Colt 240A balloon	Heart of England Balloons
	G-IGLE	Cameron V-90 balloon	A. A. Laing
	G-IGOA	Boeing 737-3Y0	Go-Fly Ltd/Stansted
	G-IGOB	Boeing 737-36Q	Go-Fly Ltd/Stansted
	G-IGOC	Boeing 737-3Y0	Go-Fly Ltd/Stansted
	G-IGOE	Boeing 737-3Y0	Go-Fly Ltd/Stansted
	G-IGOF	Boeing 737-3Q8	Go-Fly Ltd/Stansted
	G-IGOG	Boeing 737-3Y0	Go-Fly Ltd/Stansted
	G-IGOH	Boeing 737-3Y0	Go-Fly Ltd/Stansted
	G-IGOI	Boeing 737-33A	Go-Fly Ltd (G-OBMD)/Stansted
	G-IGOJ	Boeing 737-36N	Go-Fly Ltd/Stansted
	G-IGOK	Boeing 737-36N	Go-Fly Ltd/Stansted
	G-IGOL	Boeing 737-36N	Go-Fly Ltd/Stansted
	G-IGOM	Boeing 737-36N	Go-Fly Ltd/Stansted
	G-IGOP	Boeing 737-36N	Go-Fly Ltd/Stansted
	G-IGOR	Boeing 737-36N	Go-Fly Ltd/Stansted
	G-IGOS	Boeing 737-3L9	Go-Fly Ltd/Stansted
	G-IGOT	Boeing 737-3L9	Go-Fly Ltd/Stansted
	G-IGOU	Boeing 737-3L9	Go-Fly Ltd/Stansted
	G-IGOV	Boeing 737-3M8	Go-Fly Ltd/Stansted
	G-IGOW	Boeing 737-3Y0	Go-Fly Ltd (G-TEAB)/Stansted
	G-IGOX	Boeing 737-3L9	Go-Fly Ltd/Stansted
	G-IGPW	Eurocopter EC.120B	Helihopper Ltd (G-CBRI)
	G-IHSB	Robinson R-22B	M. Walker
	G-IIAC	Aeronca 11AC Chief	C. P. Whitwell (G-BTPY)
	G-IIAN	Aero Designs Pulsar	I. G. Harrison
	G-IICM	Extra EA.300/L	Phonetiques Ltd
	G-IIDI	Extra EA.300/L	Power Aerobatics Ltd (G-XTRS)
	G-IIFR	Robinson R-22B-2	Hields Aviation
	G-IIID	Dan Rihn DR.107 One Design	A. J. & M. A. N. Newall
	G-IIIG	Boeing Stearman A.75N1	F. & S. Vormezeele (G-BSDR)/Belgium
	G-IIII	Aerotek Pitts S-2B Special	B. K. Lecomber
	G-IIIL	Pits S-1T Special	The Sywell Boys Toy Box Ltd
	G-IIIR	Pitts S-1S Special	R. O. Rogers
	G-IIIT	Aerotek Pitts S-2A Special	Aerobatic Displays Ltd
	G-IIIV	Pitts Super Stinker 11-260	G. G. Ferriman
	G-IIIX	Pitts S-1S Special	Jenks Ltd (G-LBAT/G-UCCI/G-BIYN)
	G-IILI	Extra EA.300/L	Firebird Aerobatics Ltd/Denham
	G-IIMI	Extra EA.300/L	Firebird Aerobatics Ltd/Denham
	G-IIPM	AS.350B Ecureuil	Kis Associates Ltd (G-GWIL)
	G-IIPT	Robinson R-22B	P. R. Thorne (G-FUSI)

Reg.	Type	Owner or Operator	Notes
G-IIRG	Stoddard-Hamilton Glasair IIS RG	A. C. Lang	
G-IISI	Extra EA.300/200	S. G. Jones	
G-IITI	Extra EA.300	Aerobatic Displays Ltd/Booker	
G-IIXX	Parsons 2-seat gyroplane	J. M. Montgomerie	
G-IIZI	Extra EA.300	11-21 Flying Group	
G-IJAC	Light Aero Avid Speedwing Mk 4	I. J. A. Charlton	
G-IJBB	Enstrom 480	J. B. Booth (G-LIVA/G-PBTT)	
G-IJMC	VPM M.16 Tandem Trainer	I. J. McTear (G-POSA/G-BVJM)	
G-IJOE	PA-28RT-201T Turbo Arrow IV	P. Randall	
G-IJYS	BAe Jetstream 3102	Eastern Airways Ltd (G-BTZT)	
G-IKAP	Cessna T.303	T. M. Beresford	
G-IKBP	PA-28-161 Warrior II	K. B. Page	
G-IKIS	Cessna 210M	Chapple Investment Trust	
G-IKPS	PA-31-310 Navajo C	Channel Aviation Ltd	
G-IKRS	Ikarus C.42	P. G. Walton	
G-ILEA	PA-31-310 Navajo C	I. G. Fletcher	
G-ILEE	Colt 56A balloon	G. I. Lindsay	
G-ILES	Cameron O-90 balloon	G. N. Lantos	
G-ILLE	Boeing Stearman A.75L3 (379)	J. Griffin	
G-ILLY	PA-28-181 Archer II	A. G. & K. M. Spiers	
G-ILSE	Corby CJ-1 Starlet	S. Stride	
G-ILTS	PA-32 Cherokee Six 300	Foremans Aviation Ltd (G-CVOK)	
G-ILUM	Shaw Europa XS	A. R. Haynes	
G-IMAB	Shaw Europa XS	A. H. Brown	
G-IMAG	Colt 77A balloon	Flying Pictures Ltd	
G-IMAN	Colt 31A balloon	Benedikt Haggeney GmbH/Germany	
G-IMBY	Pietenpol Air Camper	P. F. Bockh	
G-IMGL	Beech B200 Super King Air	IM Aviation Ltd	
G-IMLI	Cessna 310Q	W. R. M. Beesley (G-AZYK)/Breighton	
G-IMOK	Hoffmann HK-36R Super Dimona	A. L. Garfield	
G-IMPX	R. Commander 112B	T. L. & S. Hull	
G-IMPY	Light Aero Avid Flyer C	T. R. C. Griffin	
G-INAV	Aviation Composites Mercury	I. Shaw	
G-INCA	Glaser-Dirks DG.400	K. D. Hook	
G-INDC	Cessna T.303	Crusader Aviation Ltd	
G-INDY	Robinson R-44	Lincoln Aviation	
G-INGA	Thunder Ax8-84 balloon	M. L. J. Ritchie	
G-INGE	Thruster T.600N	Thruster Air Services Ltd)	
G-INIS	Robinson R-22B	J. W. Lanchbury (G-UPMW)	
G-INNI	Jodel D.112	R. G. Andrews	
G-INNY	SE-5A (replica) (F5459)	K. S. Matcham	
G-INOW	Monnett Moni	W. C. Brown	
G-INSR	Cameron N-90 balloon	M. J. Betts & The Smith & Pinching Group Ltd	
G-INTL	Boeing 747-245F (SCD)	Air Freight Express Ltd	
G-INVU	AB-206B JetRanger 2	Burman Aviation Ltd (G-XXII/G-GGCC/ G-BEHG)	
G-IOCO	Beech 58 Baron	Arenberg Consultadoria E Servicos LDA/ Madeira	
G-IOIO	Bell 206B JetRanger 3	Lynton Air Ltd/Denham	
G-IOOI	Robin DR.400/160	N. B. Mason & S. J. O'Rourke	
G-IOPT	Cessna 182P	M. J. Valentine & P. R. Davis	
G-IORB	Bell 407	Robard Consultants Ltd	
G-IORG	Robinson R-22B	G. M. Richardson (G-ZAND)	
G-IOSI	Jodel DR.1051	Sicile Flying Group	
G-IOSO	Jodel DR.1050	A. E. Jackson	
G-IOWE	Shaw Europa XS	P. A. Lowe	
G-IPSI	Grob G.109B	D. G. Margetts (G-BMLO)	
G-IPSY	Rutan Vari-Eze	R. A. Fairclough/Biggin Hill	
G-IPUP	B.121 Pup 2	Skyway Group/Elstree	
G-IRAF	RAF 2000 GTX-SE gyroplane	M. S. R. Allen	
G-IRAN	Cessna 152	E. Alexander	
G-IRIS	AA-5B Tiger	Carlisle Flight Centre (G-BIXU)	
G-IRJX	Avro RJX-100	BAE Systems (Operations) Ltd/Woodford	
G-IRKB	PA-28R-201 Arrow III	R. K. Brierley	
G-IRLY	Colt 90A balloon	S. A. Burnett & L. P. Purfield	
G-IRPC	Cessna 182Q	J. W. Halfpenny (G-BSKM)	
G-ISAX	PA-28-181 Archer III	Anglo American Airmotive Ltd/ Bournemouth	
G-ISCA	PA-28RT-201 Arrow IV	D. J. & P. Pay	
G-ISDB	PA-28-161 Warrior II	Action Air Services Ltd (G-BWET)	
G-ISDN	Boeing Stearman A.75N1	D. R. L. Jones	
G-ISEH	Cessna 182R	Hadsley Ltd (G-BIWS)	

Notes	Reg.	Type	Owner or Operator
	G-ISFC	PA-31-310 Turbo Navajo B	G. R. E. Evans (G-BNEF)
	G-ISIS	D.H.82A Tiger Moth	D. R. & M. Wood (G-AODR)
	G-ISKA	WSK-PZL Mielec TS-11 Iskra	P. C. Harper
	G-ISLA	BN-2A-26 Islander	Hoe Leasing Ltd (G-BNEA)
	G-ISMO	Robinson R-22B	Moy Motorsport Ltd
	G-ISSY	Eurocopter EC.120B	McAlpine Helicopters Ltd (G-CBCG)
	G-ISTT	Thunder Ax8-84 balloon	RAF Halton Hot Air Balloon Club
	G-ITEX	BN-2A Mk III-2 Trislander	Aurigny Air Services Ltd (G-OCTA/G-BCXW)
	G-ITII	Aerotech Pitts S-2A Special	Aerobatic Displays Ltd/Booker
	G-ITOI	Cameron N-90 balloon	Flying Pictures Ltd
	G-ITON	Maule MX-7-235	J. R. S. Heaton
	G-IUAN	Cessna 525 CitationJet	R. F. Celada SPA/Italy
	G-IVAC	Airtour AH-77B balloon	T. D. Gibbs
	G-IVAN	Shaw TwinEze	A. M. Aldridge
	G-IVAR	Yakovlev Yak-50	Foley Farm Flying Group
	G-IVEL	Fournier RF-4D	V. S. E. Norman (G-AVNY)/Rendcomb
	G-IVER	Shaw Europa XS	I. Phillips
	G-IVET	Shaw Europa	K. J. Fraser
	G-IVIV	Robinson R-44	Rahtol Ltd
	G-IVOR	Aeronca 11AC Chief	South Western Aeronca Group/Plymouth
	G-IVYS	Parsons 2-seat gyroplane	R. M. Harris
	G-IWON	Cameron V-90 balloon	D. P. P. Jenkinson (G-BTCV)
	G-IXIX	I.I.I. Sky Arrow 650T	W. J. De Gier
	G-IXTI	Extra EA.300/1	Sundance Aviation Ltd
	G-IYAK	Yakovlev C-11	E. K. Coventry/Earls Colne
	G-IYCO	Robin DR.400/500	L. M. Gould
	G-IZIT	Rans S.6-116 Coyote II	Sport Air (UK) Ltd
	G-IZOD	Avtec Jabiru UL	D. A. Izod
	G-IZZS	Cessna 172S	Rankart Ltd
	G-IZZY	Cesna 172R	T. J. & P. S. Nicholson (G-BXSF)
	G-JABA	Avtech Jabiru SK	A. P. Gornall
	G-JABB	Avtech Jabiru UL	D. J. Royce
	G-JABO	WAR Focke-Wulf Fw.190A-3 (replica)	S. P. Taylor
	G-JABY	Avtech Jabiru UL	J. T. Grant
	G-JACK	Cessna 421C	JCT 600 Ltd
	G-JACO	Avtech Jabiru UL	S. Jackson
	G-JACS	PA-28-181 Archer III	Vector Air Ltd
	G-JADJ	PA-28-181 Archer III	Aviation Rentals
	G-JAGS	Cessna FRA.150L	RAF Coltishall Flying Club (G-BAUY)
	G-JAHL	Bell 206B JetRanger 3	Jet Air Helicopters
	G-JAIR	Mainair Blade	J. Loughran
	G-JAJK	PA-31-350 Navajo Chieftain	Keen Leasing (IOM) Ltd (G-OLDB/G-DIXI)
	G-JAJP	Avtech Jabiru UL	J. W. E. Pearson & J. Anderson
	G-JAKE	D.H.C.1 Chipmunk 22	K. Ritter (G-BBMY)
	G-JAKI	Mooney M.20R	J. M. Moss & D. M. Abrahamson
	G-JAKS	PA-28 Cherokee 160	K. Harper (G-ARVS)
	G-JALC	Boeing 757-225	My Travel Airways (Airtours)
	G-JAMP	PA-28-151 Warrior	ANP Ltd (G-BRJU)/White Waltham
	G-JAMY	Shaw Europa XS	J. P. Sharp
	G-JANA	PA-28-181 Archer II	Croaker Aviation/Stapleford
	G-JANB	Colt Flying Bottle SS balloon	Justerini & Brooks Ltd
	G-JANN	PA-34-220T Seneca III	MBC Aviation Ltd/Headcorn
	G-JANO	PA-28RT-201 Arrow IV	Abertawe Aviation Ltd
	G-JANS	Cessna FR.172J	I. G. Aizlewood/Luton
	G-JANT	PA-28-181 Archer II	Janair Aviation Ltd
	G-JARA	Robinson R-22B	S. G. Simpson
	G-JARV	AS.355F-1 Twin Squirrel	PLM Dollar Group (G-OGHL)
	G-JASE	PA-28-161 Warrior II	Mid-Anglia School of Flying
	G-JAVO	PA-28-161 Warrior II	I. N. T. Thornhill (G-BSXW)
	G-JAWC	Pegasus Quantum 15-912	A. W. Chester
	G-JAWZ	Pitts S-1S Special	A. R. Harding
	G-JAXS	Avtech Jabiru UL	C. A. Palmer
	G-JAYI	J/1 Autocrat	Bravo Aviation Ltd/Coventry
	G-JAZZ	AA-5A Cheetah	Jazz Club
	G-JBBS	Robinson R-44	Fredat Ltd
	G-JBDB	AB-206B JetRanger	Brad Helicopters Ltd (G-OOPS/G-BNRD)
	G-JBDH	Robin DR.400/180	W. A. Clark
	G-JBJB	Colt 69A balloon	Justerini & Brooks Ltd
	G-JBPR	Wittman W.10 Tailwind	P. A. Rose & J. P. Broadhurst

Reg.	Type	Owner or Operator	Notes
G-JBRN	Cessna 182S	J. Byrne (G-RITZ)	
G-JBSP	Avtech Jabiru SP-470	C. R. James	
G-JCAR	PA-46-350P Malibu Mirage	J. A. Carr	
G-JCAS	PA-28-181 Archer II	Charlie Alpha Ltd	
G-JCBA	Sikorsky S-76B	J. C. Bamford Excavators Ltd/ E. Midlands	
G-JCBI	Dassault Falcon 2000	J. C. Bamford Excavators Ltd/ E. Midlands	
G-JCBJ	Sikorsky S-76C	J. C. Bamford Excavators Ltd/ E. Midlands	
G-JCFR	Cessna 550 Citation II	Chauffair Ltd (G-JETC)/Gatwick	
G-JCKT	Stemme S.10VT	J. C. Taylor	
G-JCMW	Rand-Robinson KR-2	M. Wildish & J. Cook	
G-JCUB	PA-18 Super Cub 135	N. Cummins & S. Bennett	
G-JDEE	SOCATA TB.20 Trinidad	A. W. Eldridge & J. A. Heard (G-BKLA)	
G-JDEL	Jodel 150	K. F. & R. Richardson (G-JDLI)	
G-JDIX	Mooney M.20B	A. L. Hall-Carpenter (G-ARTB)	
G-JDJM	PA-28 Cherokee 140	Hare Flying Group (G-HSJM/G-AYIF)	
G-JEAD	F.27 Friendship Mk 500	BAC Group Ltd	
G-JEAE	F.27 Friendship Mk 500	BAC Leasing Ltd	
G-JEAJ	BAe 146-200	British European (G-OLCA)	
G-JEAK	BAe 146-200	British European (G-OLCB)	
G-JEAM	BAe 146-300	British European/Air France (G-BTJT)	
G-JEAO	BAe 146-100	British European/Air France (G-UKPC/G-BKKXZ)	
G-JEAR	BAe 146-200	British European/Air France (G-HWPB/G-BSRU/G-OSKI)	
G-JEAS	BAe 146-200	British European (G-OLHB/G-BSRV/ G-OSUN)	
G-JEAT	BAe 146-100	British European/Air France (G-BVUY)	
G-JEAU	BAe 146-100	British European/Air France (G-BVUW)	
G-JEAV	BAe 146-200	British European	
G-JEAW	BAe 146-200	British European	
G-JEAX	BAe 146-200	British European	
G-JEAY	BAe-146-200	British European	
G-JEBA	BAe 146-300	British European (G-BSYR)	
G-JEBB	BAe 146-300	British European/Air France	
G-JEBC	BAe 146-300	British European	
G-JEBD	BAe 146-300	British European	
G-JEBE	BAe 146-300	British European	
G-JECA	Canadair CL.600-2B19 RJ	British European	
G-JECB	Canadair CL.600-2B19 RJ	British European	
G-JECC	Canadair CL.600-2B19 RJ	British European	
G-JECD	Canadair CL.600-2B19 RJ	British European (stored)	
G-JEDA	D.H.C.8-314 Dash Eight	British European	
G-JEDB	D.H.C.8-314 Dash Eight	British European	
G-JEDC	D.H.C.8Q-311 Dash Eight	British European	
G-JEDD	D.H.C.8Q-311 Dash Eight	British European	
G-JEDE	D.H.C.8Q-311 Dash Eight	British European	
G-JEDF	D.H.C.8Q-311B Dash Eight	British European	
G-JEDG	D.H.C.8Q-402 Dash Eight	British European	
G-JEDH	Robin DR.400/180	J. B. Hoolahan/Biggin Hill	
G-JEDI	D.H.C.8Q-402 Dash Eight	British European	
G-JEDJ	D.H.C.8Q-402 Dash Eight	British European	
G-JEDX	D.H.C.8Q-201 Dash Eight	British European	
G-JEDY	D.H.C.8Q-201 Dash Eight	British European	
G-JEDZ	D.H.C.8Q-201 Dash Eight	British European	
G-JEET	Cessna FA.152	Willowair Flying Club (1996) Ltd (G-BHMF)/Southend	
G-JEFA	Robinson R-44	Simlot Ltd	
G-JEMY	Lindstrand LBL-90A balloon	J. A. Lawton	
G-JENA	Mooney M.20K	P. Leverkuehn/Biggin Hill	
G-JENI	Cessna R.182	R. A. Bentley	
G-JENN	AA-5B Tiger	Shadow Aviation Ltd/Elstree	
G-JERL	Agusta A.109E Power	Perment Ltd	
G-JERS	Robinson R-22B	Preveda Ltd	
G-JESS	PA-28R-201T Turbo Arrow III	N. E. & M. A. Bedggood (G-REIS)	
G-JETG	Learjet 35A	Gama Aviation Ltd (G-JETN/G-JJSG)	
G-JETH	Hawker Sea Hawk FGA.6 (XE489) ★	P. G. Vallance Ltd/Charlwood	
G-JETI	BAe 125 Srs 800B	Ford Motor Co Ltd/Stansted	
G-JETJ	Cessna 550 Citation II	Citation Flying Services Ltd (G-EJET/ G-DJBE)	

Notes	Reg.	Type	Owner or Operator
	G-JETM	Gloster Meteor T.7 (VZ638) ★	P. G. Vallance Ltd/Charlwood
	G-JETU	AS.355F-2 Twin Squirrel	Summit Corporate Services Ltd
	G-JETX	Bell 206B JetRanger 3	Tripgate Ltd
	G-JETZ	Hughes 369E	John Matchett Ltd
	G-JFWI	Cessna F.172N	Staryear Ltd
	G-JGBI	Bell 206L-4 LongRanger	Dorbcrest Homes Ltd
	G-JGMN	C.A.S.A. 1.131E Jungmann 2000	P. D. Scandrett/Staverton
	G-JGSI	Pegasus Quantum 15-912	J. G. Spinks
	G-JHEW	Robinson R-22B	Burbage Farms Ltd
	G-JHYS	Shaw Europa	J. D. Boyce & G. E. Walker
	G-JIGS	Lindstrand LBL-90A balloon	Jigsaw Connections Ltd
	G-JIII	Stolp SA.300 Starduster Too	VTIO Co/Cumbernauld
	G-JILL	R. Commander 112TCA	P. M. & P. A. O'Hare
	G-JILY	Robinson R-44	N. J. Ferris
	G-JIMB	B.121 Pup 1	K. D. H. Gray & P. G. Fowler (G-AWWF)
	G-JIMW	AB-206B JetRanger 2	R. J. Watt (G-UNIK/G-TPPH/G-BCYP)
	G-JIVE	MDH Hughes 369E	First Flight (G-DRAR)
	G-JJAN	PA-28-181 Archer II	Redhill Flying Club
	G-JJEN	PA-28-181 Archer III	J. E. Jenkins
	G-JJWL	Robinson R-44	Willbeth Ltd
	G-JLCA	PA-34-200T Seneca II	C. A. S. Atha (G-BOKE)
	G-JLEE	AB-206B JetRanger 3	Lee Aviation Ltd (G-JOKE/G-CSKY/ G-TALY)
	G-JLHS	Beech A36 Bonanza	I. G. Meredith
	G-JLMW	Cameron V-77 balloon	J. L. McK. Watkins
	G-JLRW	Beech 76 Duchess	Airways Flight Training
	G-JMAA	Boeing 757-3CQ	jmc Airlines Ltd
	G-JMAB	Boeing 757-3CQ	jmc Airlines Ltd
	G-JMAC	BAe Jetstream 4100	BAe (Operations) Ltd (G-JAMD/G-JXLI)
	G-JMAN	Mainair Blade 912S	J. Manuel
	G-JMCD	Boeing 757-25F	jmc Airlines Ltd
	G-JMCE	Boeing 757-25F	jmc Airlines Ltd
	G-JMCF	Boeing 757-28A	jmc Airlines Ltd
	G-JMCG	Boeing 757-2G5	jmc Airlines Ltd
	G-JMDI	Schweizer 269C	J. J. Potter (G-FLAT)
	G-JMTS	Robin DR.400/180	J. R. Whiting
	G-JMTT	PA-28R-201T Turbo Arrow III	C. E. Passmore (G-BMHM)
	G-JNAS	AA-5A Cheetah	A. L. Shore & J. R. Nutter
	G-JNET	Robinson R-22B	Park Head Helicopters Ltd
	G-JNNB	Colt 90A balloon	Justerini & Brooks Ltd
	G-JODL	Jodel D.1050/M	D. Silsbury
	G-JOEL	Bensen B.8M	G. C. Young
	G-JOEM	Airbus A.320-231	My Travel Airways (Airtours) (G-OUZO)
	G-JOEY	BN-2A Mk III-2 Trislander	Aurigny Air Services (G-BDGG)/ Guernsey
	G-JOJO	Cameron A-210 balloon	Worcester Balloons
	G-JOLY	Cessna 120	B. V. Meade
	G-JONB	Robinson R-22B	J. Bignall
	G-JONE	Cessna 172M	A. Pierce
	G-JONH	Robinson R-22B	Scotia Helicopters Ltd
	G-JONI	Cessna FA.152	R. F. & J. S. Pooler (G-BFTU)
	G-JONO	Colt 77A balloon	The Sandcliffe Motor Group
	G-JONY	Cyclone AX2000 HKS	K. R. Matheson
	G-JONZ	Cessna 172P	Truman Aviation Ltd/Tollerton
	G-JOOL	Mainair Blade 912	J. R. Gibson
	G-JOON	Cessna 182D	G. Jackson
	G-JOPF	Smyth Model S Sidewinder	J. Furby
	G-JOSS	AS.350B Ecureuil	M. Burby (G-WILX/G-RAHM/G-UNIC/ G-COLN/G-BHIV)
	G-JOST	Shaw Europa	J. A. Austin
	G-JOYT	PA-28-181 Archer II	John K. Cathcart Ltd (G-BOVO)
	G-JOYZ	PA-28-181 Archer III	S. W. & J. E. Taylor
	G-JPAL	AS.355N Twin Squirrel	JPM Ltd
	G-JPAT	Robin HR.200/100	J. C. F. Dalton (G-BDJN)
	G-JPMA	Avtech Jabiru UL	J. P. Metcalfe
	G-JPOT	PA-32R-301 Saratoga SP	S. W. Turley (G-BIYM)
	G-JPRO	P.84 Jet Provost T.5A (XW433)	Edwalton Aviation Ltd
	G-JPSI	Dassault Falcon 50EX	Sorven Aviation Ltd
	G-JPTV	P.84 Jet Provost T.5A	Seagull Formation Ltd/North Weald
	G-JPVA	P.84 Jet Provost T.5A (XW289)	T. J. Manna (G-BVXT)/Cranfield
	G-JREE	Maule MX-7-180	J. M. P. Ree
	G-JRJR	Learjet 45	Richer Jet Ltd
	G-JRSL	Agusta A.109E Power	Perment Ltd

UK OUT OF SEQUENCE

Reg.	Type	Owner or Operator	Notes
G-JSAK	Robinson R-22B-2	Tukair Aircraft Charter	
G-JSAT	BN-2T Turbine Islander	Rhine Army Parachute Centre (G-BVFK)/ Germany	
G-JSFT	PA-44-180 Seminole	SFT Aviation Ltd/Bournemouth	
G-JSJX	Airbus A.321-211	My Travel Airways (Airtours)	
G-JSON	Cameron N-105 balloon	Up and Away Ballooning Ltd	
G-JSPC	BN-2T Turbine Islander	Rhine Army Parachute Centre (G-BUBG)/Germany	
G-JSPL	Avtech Jabiru SPL-450	J. A. Lord	
G-JSSD	H.P.137 Jetstream 3001 ★	Museum of Flight/E. Fortune	
G-JTCA	PA-23 Aztec 250E	J. D. Tighe (G-BBCU)/Sturgate	
G-JTPC	Aeromot AMT-200 Super Ximango	G-JTPC Falcon 3 Group	
G-JTWO	Piper J-2 Cub	A. T. Hooper & C. C. Silk (G-BPZR)	
G-JTYE	Aeronca 7AC Champion	G. D. Horn	
G-JUDD	Avtech Jabiru UL-450★	C. Judd	
G-JUDE	Robin DR.400/180	Bravo India Flying Group Ltd/Liverpool	
G-JUDI	AT-6D Harvard III (FX301)	A. A. Hodgson	
G-JUDY	AA-5A Cheetah	Plane Talking Ltd/Elstree	
G-JUIN	Cessna 303	M. J. & J. M. Newman/Denham	
G-JULL	Stemme S.10VT	J. P. C. Fuchs	
G-JULU	Cameron V-90 balloon	Datacentre Ltd	
G-JULZ	Shaw Europa	M. Parkin	
G-JUNG	C.A.S.A. 1.131E Jungmann 1000 (E3B-143)	K. H. Wilson/White Waltham	
G-JURA	BAe Jetstream 3102	Highland Airways Ltd/Inverness	
G-JURE	SOCATA TB.10 Tobago	P. M. Ireland	
G-JURG	R. Commander 114A	Oxford Aviation Services Ltd/Kidlington	
G-JUST	Beech F33A Bonanza	Budge It Aviation Ltd/Elstree	
G-JVBF	Lindstrand LBL-210A balloon	Virgin Balloon Flights Ltd	
G-JVMD	Cessna 172N	C. A. Morris (G-BNTV)	
G-JWBB	Jodel DR.1050	B. F. Baldock (G-LAKI)	
G-JWBI	AB-206B JetRanger 2	J. W. Bonser (Walsall) Ltd (G-RODS/ G-NOEL/G-BCWN)	
G-JWCM	SA Bulldog Srs 120/1210	M. L. J. Goff (G-BHXB)	
G-JWDG	AA-5A Cheetah	Plane Talking Ltd (G-OCML/G-JAVA)/ Elstree	
G-JWDS	Cessna F.150G	C. R. & S. A. Hardiman (G-AVNB)	
G-JWFT	Robinson R-22B	Leinster Warehousing & Distribution Ltd	
G-JWIV	Jodel DR.1051	C. M. Fitton	
G-JWLS	Bell 206B JetRanger 2	Autospeed Helicopters Ltd (G-BSXE)	
G-JWXS	Shaw Europa XS T-G	J. Wishart	
G-KAAT	MDH MD-902 Explorer	Police Aviation Services Ltd (G-PASS)	
G-KAFE	Cameron N-65 balloon	J. R. Rivers-Scott	
G-KAIR	PA-28-181 Archer II	Keen Leasing (IOM) Ltd	
G-KAMM	Hawker Hurricane XIIA (BW881)	Alpine Deer Group Ltd/New Zealand	
G-KAMP	PA-18 Super Cub 135	A. P. Daines	
G-KAOM	Scheibe SF.25C Falke	Cambridge Gliding Club Ltd/ Gransden Lodge	
G-KAPW	P.56 Provost T.1 (XF603)	The Shuttleworth Collection/O. Warden	
G-KARA	Brügger MB.2 Colibri	C. L. Hill (G-BMUI)	
G-KARI	Fuji FA.200-160	Scottish Civil Service Flying Club (G-BBRE) Ltd	
G-KART	PA-28-161 Warrior II	Newcastle-upon-Tyne Aero Club Ltd	
G-KATA	HOAC Katana DV.20	E. van Dun	
G-KATE	Westland WG.30 Srs 100 ★	(stored)/Yeovil	
G-KATI	Rans S.7 Courier	S. M. & K. E. Hall	
G-KATS	PA-28 Cherokee 140	Airlaunch/Old Buckenham (G-BIRC)	
G-KATT	Cessna 152 II	Aerohire Ltd (G-BMTK)/Halfpenny Green	
G-KAUR	Colt 315A balloon	Balloon Safaris	
G-KAWA	Denney Kitfox Mk 2	J. W. Barr	
G-KAWW	Westland Wasp HAS.1 (NZ3908)	T. J. Manna/Cranfield	
G-KAXF	Hawker Hunter F.6A (XF515)	T. J. Manna/Cranfield	
G-KAXL	Westland Scout AH.1 (XV140)	T. J. Manna/Cranfield	
G-KBAC	Short SD3-60 Variant 100	BAC Express Ltd (G-BPXL)	
G-KAZZ	Robinson R-44	Viking Office Supplies Ltd	
G-KBKB	Thunder Ax8-90 S2 balloon	G. Boulden	
G-KBPI	PA-28-161 Warrior II	Goodwood Aerodrome & Motor Circuit Ltd (G-BFSZ)	
G-KBWW	Comper CLA.7 Swift (replica)	Hurstgate Ltd	
G-KCIG	Sportavia RF-5B	Deeside Fournier Group	

171

Notes	Reg.	Type	Owner or Operator
	G-KDET	PA-28-161 Cadet	Rapidspin Ltd/Biggin Hill
	G-KDEY	Scheibe SF.25E Super Falke	Falke Syndicate
	G-KDFF	Scheibe SF.25E Super Falke	Bowland Forest Gliding Club Ltd
	G-KDIX	Jodel D.9 Bebe	P. M. Bowden
	G-KDLN	Zlin Z.37A-2 Cmelak	J. Richards
	G-KDMA	Cessna 560 Citation V	Gamston Aviation Ltd
	G-KDOG	SA Bulldog Srs 120/121	Gamit Ltd
	G-KEAB	Beech 65-B80 Queen Air ★	Instructional airframe (G-BSSL/ G-BFEP)/Shoreham
	G-KEEN	Stolp SA.300 Starduster Too	Sharp Aerobatics Ltd/Netherlands
	G-KEES	PA-28 Cherokee 180	C. N. Ellerbrook
	G-KELL	Van's RV-6	J. D. Kelsall
	G-KEMC	Grob G.109	Eye-Fly
	G-KEMI	PA-28-181 Archer III	K. B. Kempster
	G-KENB	Air Command 503 Commander	K. Brogden
	G-KENI	Rotorway Executive	A. J. Wheatley
	G-KENM	Luscombe 8EF Silvaire	M. G. Waters
	G-KERY	PA-28 Cherokee 180	Seawing Flying Club Ltd (G-ATWO)/ Southend
	G-KEST	Steen Skybolt	G-KEST Syndicate
	G-KEVB	PA-28-181 Archer III	Palmair Ltd
	G-KEYS	PA-23 Aztec 250F	T. M. Tuke & W. T. McCarter/Eglinton
	G-KEYY	Cameron N-77 balloon	B. N. Trowbridge (G-BORZ)
	G-KFAN	Scheibe SF.25B Falke	R. G. & J. A. Boyes
	G-KFOX	Denney Kitfox	I. R. Lawrence
	G-KFRA	PA-32 Cherokee Six 300	West India Flying Group (G-BGII)
	G-KFZI	KFZ-1 Tigerfalck	L. R. Williams
	G-KGAO	Scheibe SF.25C Falke 1700	Falke 2000 Group
	G-KHOM	Aeromot AMT-200 Super Ximango	O. C. Masters & K. M. Haslett
	G-KHRE	M.S.893E Rallye 150SV	D. M. Gale & K. F. Crumplin
	G-KICK	Pegasus Quantum 15-912	G. D. Hall
	G-KIMB	Robin DR.340/140	R. M. Kimbell
	G-KIMK	Partenavia P.68B	Kamair Ltd (G-BCPO)
	G-KIMM	Shaw Europa XS	P. A. D. Clarke
	G-KIMY	Robin DR.400/140B	P. W. & K. C. Johnson
	G-KINE	AA-5A Cheetah	Walsh Aviation
	G-KIRK	Piper J-3C-65 Cub	M. J. Kirk
	G-KISS	Rand-Robinson KR-2	E. A. Rooney
	G-KITE	PA-28-181 Archer II	L. G. Kennedy
	G-KITF	Denney Kitfox	M. Leavesley
	G-KITI	Pitts S-2E Special	B. R. Cornes
	G-KITS	Shaw Europa	H. E. Perkins/Spain
	G-KITT	Curtiss P-40M Kittyhawk (43-5802)	Patina Ltd/Duxford
	G-KITY	Denney Kitfox Mk 2	Kitfox KFM Group/Tollerton
	G-KITZ	Shaw Europa XS T-G	Europa Aircraft Ltd/Kirkbymoorside
	G-KKDL	SOCATA TB.20 Trinidad	M. S. Thompson (G-BSHU)
	G-KKER	Avtech Jabiru UL-450	W. K. Evans
	G-KKES	SOCATA TB.20 Trinidad	Polestar Holdings Ltd (G-BTLH)
	G-KKKK	SA Bulldog Srs 120/121	Drumforce Ltd
	G-KNAP	PA-28-161 Warrior II	Keen Leasing (IoM) Ltd (G-BIUX)
	G-KNEK	Grob G.109B	Syndicate 109
	G-KNIB	Robinson R-22B-2	C. G. Knibb
	G-KNOB	Lindstrand LBL-180A balloon	Wye Valley Aviation Ltd
	G-KNOT	P.84 Jet Provost T.3A (XN629)	R. S. Partridge-Hicks (G-BVEG)
	G-KNOW	PA-32 Cherokee 180	Hi Fly Ltd
	G-KNYT	Robinson R-44	Aircol
	G-KODA	Cameron O-77 balloon	N. J. Milton
	G-KOFM	Glaser-Dirks DG.600/18M	A. Mossman
	G-KOHF	Schleicher ASK.14	J. Houlihan
	G-KOKL	Hoffmann H-36 Dimona	R. Smith & R. Stembrowicz
	G-KOLB	Kölb Twinstar Mk 3A	J. L. Moar
	G-KOLI	WSK PZL-110 Koliber 150	J. R. Powell
	G-KONE	Rotorway Executive 162F	G. Kresfelder
	G-KONG	Slingsby T.67M Firefly 200	Hunting Aviation Ltd/Barkston Heath
	G-KOOL	D.H.104 Devon C.2 (G-DOVE)	D. S. & K. P. Hunt
	G-KORN	Cameron 70 Berentzen SS balloon	Balloon Preservation Flying Group
	G-KOTA	PA-28-236 Dakota	JF Packaging
	G-KPAO	Robinson R-44	Avonline Ltd (G-SSSS)
	G-KPTT	SOCATA TB.20 Trinidad	Chartfleet Ltd
	G-KRAY	Robinson R-22HP	Helisport (G-BOBO)

Reg.	Type	Owner or Operator	Notes
G-KRES	Stoddard-Hamilton Glasair IIS RG	G. Kresfelder	
G-KRII	Rand-Robinson KR-2	M. R. Cleveley	
G-KRIS	Maule M5-235C Lunar Rocket	A. C. Vermeer	
G-KRNW	Eurocopter EC.135T-1	Bond Air Services Ltd/Aberdeen	
G-KSIR	Stoddard-Hamilton Glasair IIS RG	R. Cayzer	
G-KSKS	Cameron N-54 balloon	Exclusive Ballooning	
G-KSKY	Sky 77-24 balloon	J. R. Howard	
G-KSVB	PA-24 Comanche 260	S. Juggler (G-ENIU/G-AVJU)	
G-KTEE	Cameron V-77 balloon	D. C. & N. P. Bull	
G-KTKT	Sky 260-24 balloon	T. M. Donnelly	
G-KUBB	SOCATA TB.20 Trinidad GT	Offshore Marine Consultants Ltd	
G-KUTU	Quickie Q.2	R. Nash & J. Parkinson	
G-KVBF	Cameron A-340HL balloon	Virgin Balloon Flights Ltd	
G-KWAX	Cessna 182E	D. R. Graves	
G-KWIK	Partenavia P.68B	ACD Cidra BV/Belgium	
G-KWKI	QAC Quickie Q.200	B. M. Jackson	
G-KWLI	Cessna 421C	Langley holdings PLC (G-DARR/ G-BNEZ)	
G-KYAK	Yakovlev Yak C-11	M. Gainza	
G-KYDD	Robinson R-44 Astro	EK Aviation Ltd	
G-KYNG	Aviamilano F.8L Falco Srs 1	A. E. Hutton/North Weald	
G-LABS	Shaw Europa	C. T. H. Pattinson	
G-LACA	PA-28-161 Warrior II	LAC (Enterprises) Ltd/Barton	
G-LACB	PA-28-161 Warrior II	LAC (Enterprises) Ltd/Barton	
G-LACD	PA-28-181 Archer III	David Brown Aviation (G-BYBG)	
G-LACE	Shaw Europa	J. H. Phillingham	
G-LACR	Denney Kitfox	C. M. Rose	
G-LADD	Enstrom 480	Combi-Lift Ltd	
G-LADE	PA-32 Cherokee Six 300E	B. E. Bergabo	
G-LADI	PA-30 Twin Comanche 160	S. H. Eastwood (G-ASOO)	
G-LADS	R. Commander 114	D. F. Soul	
G-LAGR	Cameron N-90 balloon	J. R. Clifton	
G-LAIN	Robinson R-22B	Deadline Programming Ltd	
G-LAIR	Stoddard-Hamilton Glasair IIS	D. L. Swallow	
G-LAKE	Lake LA-250 Renegade	P. J. McGoldrick	
G-LAMA	SA.315B Lama	PLM Dollar Group Ltd	
G-LAMM	Shaw Europa	S. A. Lamb	
G-LAMP	Cameron 110 Lampbulb SS balloon	LE Electrical Ltd	
G-LAMS	Cessna F.152 II	Jaxx Landing Ltd	
G-LANC	Avro 683 Lancaster X (KB889) ★	Imperial War Museum/Duxford	
G-LAND	Robinson R-22B	Helicopter Training & Hire Ltd/Belfast	
G-LANE	Cessna F.172N	G. C. Bantin	
G-LAOL	PA-28RT-201 Arrow IV	G. P. Aviation Ltd	
G-LAPN	Light Aero Avid Aerobat	R. M. & A. P. Shorter	
G-LARA	Robin DR.400/180	K. D. & C. A. Brackwell	
G-LARE	PA-39 Twin Comanche 160 C/R	Glareways (Neasden) Ltd	
G-LARK	Helton Lark 95	J. Fox	
G-LASR	Stoddard-Hamilton Glasair II	G. Lewis	
G-LASS	Rutan Vari-Eze	J. Mellor	
G-LAST	Cessna 340 II	Last Engineering Ltd (G-UNDY/G-BBNR)	
G-LATK	Robinson R-44	Holly Aviation Ltd (G-BVMK)	
G-LAVE	Cessna 172R	R. W. & A. M. Glaves (G-BYEV)	
G-LAWS	Sikorsky S-61N Mk.II	Laws Helicopter Ltd (G-BHOF)	
G-LAZA	Lazer Z.200	M. Hammond	
G-LAZL	PA-28-161 Warrior II	Hawk Aero Leasing/Cranfield	
G-LAZR	Cameron O-77 balloon	Laser Civil Engineering Ltd	
G-LAZY	Lindstrand Armchair SS balloon	The Air Chair Co. Ltd/USA	
G-LAZZ	Stoddard-Hamilton Glastar	A. N. Evans	
G-LBLI	Lindstrand LBL-105A balloon	Lindstrand Balloons Ltd	
G-LBMM	PA-28-161 Warrior II	Flexi-Soft Ltd	
G-LBNK	Cameron N-105 balloon	Virgin Airship & Balloon Co. Ltd	
G-LBRC	PA-28RT-201 Arrow IV	D. J. V. Morgan	
G-LCGL	CLA.7 Swift (replica)	J. M. Greenland	
G-LCOC	BN-2A Mk.III-1 Trislander	Airx Ltd (G-BCCU)	
G-LCOK	Colt 69A balloon	Hot-Air Balloon Co Ltd (G-BLWI)	
G-LCON	AS.355N Twin Squirrel	Lancashire Constabulary/Warton	
G-LCRC	Boeing 757-23A	My Travel Airways (Airtours) (G-IEAB)	
G-LDYS	Colt 56A balloon	P. Glydon & J. Coote	
G-LEAF	Cessna F.406	Atlantic Air Transport Ltd/Coventry	
G-LEAM	PA-28-236 Dakota	C. S. Doherty (G-BHLS)	

Notes	Reg.	Type	Owner or Operator
	G-LEAP	BN-2T Turbine Islander	Army Parachute Association (G-BLND)/ Netheravon
	G-LEAR	Learjet 35A	Northern Executive Aviation Ltd/ Manchester
	G-LEAS	Sky 90-24 balloon	Leasing Group PLC
	G-LEAU	Cameron N-31 balloon	P. L. Mossman
	G-LEBE	Shaw Europa	P. Atkinson
	G-LECA	AS.355F-1 Twin Squirrel	S. W. Electricity Board (G-BNBK)/Bristol
	G-LEDA	Robinson R-22B	E. D. Obeng (G-IFOX)
	G-LEED	Denney Kitfox Mk 2	A. F. Stafford
	G-LEEE	Avtech Jabiru UL-450	J. N. Fugl
	G-LEEN	Aero Designs Pulsar XP	R. B. Hemsworth (G-BZMP/G-DESI)
	G-LEES	Glaser-Dirks DG.400 (800)	J. Bradley
	G-LEEZ	Bell 206L-1 LongRanger 2	Pennine Helicopters Ltd (G-BPCT)
	G-LEGG	Cessna F.182Q	P. J. Clegg (G-GOOS)/Barton
	G-LEGO	Cameron O-77 balloon	P. M. Traviss
	G-LEIC	Cessna FA.152	Leicestershire Aero Club Ltd
	G-LELE	Lindstrand LBL-31A balloon	L. E. Electrical Ltd
	G-LENI	AS.355F-1 Twin Squirrel	Grid Aviation Ltd (G-ZFDB/G-BLEV)
	G-LENN	Cameron V-56 balloon	A. E. Austin
	G-LENS	Thunder Ax7-77Z balloon	R. S. Breakwell
	G-LENY	PA-34-220T Seneca III	Air Medical Ltd
	G-LEOS	Robin DR.400/120	P. G. Newens
	G-LESJ	Denney Kitfox Mk 3	P. Whittingham
	G-LEVI	Aeronca 7AC Champion	G-LEVI Group
	G-LEXI	Cameron N-77 balloon	T. Gilbert
	G-LEZE	Rutan LongEz	K. G. M. Loyal & ptnrs
	G-LEZZ	Stoddard-Hamilton Glastar	L. A. James (G-BYCR)
	G-LFIX	V.S.509 Spitfire T.IX (ML407)	C. S. Grace
	G-LFSA	PA-38-112 Tomahawk	Liverpool Flying School Ltd (G-BSFC)
	G-LFSB	PA-38-112 Tomahawk	Spencer Davies Engineering Ltd (G-BLYC)
	G-LFSC	PA-28 Cherokee 140	M. B. North (G-BGTR)
	G-LFSD	PA-38-112 Tomahawk II	Liverpool Flying School Ltd (G-BNPT)
	G-LFSF	Cessna 150M	Gems Europe SA (G-BSRC)/Belgium
	G-LFSG	PA-28 Cherokee 180E	Liverpool Flying School Ltd (G-AYAA)
	G-LFSH	PA-38-112 Tomahawk	Liverpool Flying School Ltd (G-BOZM)
	G-LFSI	PA-28 Cherokee 140	P. S. Hoyle & S. Merriman (G-AYKV)/ Humberside
	G-LFVB	V.S.349 Spitfire LF.Vb (EP120)	Patina Ltd/Duxford
	G-LFVC	V.S.349 Spitfire LF.Vc (JG891)	Historic Flying Ltd/Audley End
	G-LGNA	SAAB SF.340B	Loganair Ltd/BA
	G-LGNB	SAAB SF.340B	Loganair Ltd/BA
	G-LGNC	SAAB SF.340B	Loganair Ltd/BA
	G-LGND	SAAB SF.340B	Loganair Ltd/BA (G-GNTH)
	G-LGNE	SAAB SF.340B	Loganair Ltd/BA (G-GNTI)
	G-LGTD	Boeing 737-300	British Airways
	G-LGTE	Boeing 737-3Y0	British Airways
	G-LGTF	Boeing 737-382	British Airways
	G-LGTG	Boeing 737-3Q8	British Airways
	G-LGTH	Boeing 737-3Y0	British Airways (G-BNGL)
	G-LGTI	Boeing 737-3Y0	British Airways (G-BNGM)
	G-LGTJ	Boeing 737-300	British Airways
	G-LGTK	Boeing 737-300	British Airways
	G-LGTL	Boeing 737-300	British Airways
	G-LHPL	AS.350B Ecureuil	Lloyd Helicopters (Pte) Ltd
	G-LIBB	Cameron V-77 balloon	R. J. Mercer
	G-LIBS	Hughes 369HS	D. M. Stevens & A. R. Smith
	G-LIDA	Hoffmann HK-36R Super Dimona	Bidford Airfield Ltd
	G-LIDE	PA-31-350 Navajo Chieftain	Woodgate Aviation (IOM) Ltd
	G-LIDR	Hoffmann H-36 Dimona	G-LIDR Flying Group (G-BMSK)
	G-LIDS	Robinson R-22B-2	Orange Aero Engine Supplies Ltd
	G-LIFE	Thunder Ax6-56Z balloon	Lakeside Lodge Golf Centre
	G-LILY	Bell 206B JetRanger 3	T. S. Brown (G-NTBI)
	G-LINC	Hughes 369HS	Sleekform Ltd
	G-LINE	AS.355N Twin Squirrel	National Grid PLC
	G-LIOA	Lockheed 10A Electra ★ (NC5171N)	Science Museum/S. Kensington
	G-LION	PA-18 Super Cub 135 (R-167)	C. Moore
	G-LIOT	Cameron O-77 balloon	N. D. Eliot
	G-LIPE	Robinson R-22B	F. C. Owen (G-BTXJ)
	G-LIPS	Cameron 90 Lips SS balloon	Flying Pictures Ltd (G-BZBV)
	G-LISE	Robin DR.400/500	J. Marks

Reg.	Type	Owner or Operator	Notes
G-LITE	R. Commander 112A	J. E. Dixon	
G-LITZ	Pitts S-1E Special	G. G. Ferriman	
G-LIVH	Piper J-3C-65 Cub (330238)	M. D. Cowburn/Barton	
G-LIVR	Enstrom 480	Soil Tech BV/Netherlands	
G-LIZA	Cessna 340A II	Tayflight Ltd (G-BMDM)	
G-LIZI	PA-28 Cherokee 160	R. J. Walker & J. R. Lawson (G-ARRP)	
G-LIZY	Westland Lysander III (V9673) ★	G. A. Warner/Duxford	
G-LIZZ	PA-E23 Aztec 250E	T. J. Nathan (G-BBWM)	
G-LJCC	Murphy Rebel	P. H. Hyde	
G-LJET	Learjet 35A	Gama Aviation Ltd	
G-LKTB	PA-28-181 Archer III	Top Cat Aviation Ltd	
G-LLEW	Aeromot AMT-200S Super Ximango	Lleweni Parc Ltd	
G-LLYD	Cameron N-31 balloon	Virgin Airship & Balloon Co Ltd	
G-LMLV	Dyn'Aero MCR-01	L. & M. La Vecchia	
G-LNAA	MDH MD-902 Explorer	Police Aviation Services Ltd	
G-LNTI	Robinson R-44	LNT Aviation Ltd (G-TPTS)	
G-LNYS	Cessna F.177RG	J. W. Clarke (G-BDCM)	
G-LOAN	Cameron N-77 balloon	P. Lawman	
G-LOBO	Cameron O-120 balloon	Solo Aerostatics	
G-LOCH	Piper J-3C-90 Cub	J. M. Greenland	
G-LOFB	L.188CF Electra	Air Atlantique Ltd/Coventry	
G-LOFC	L.188CF Electra	Air Atlantique Ltd/Coventry	
G-LOFD	L.188CF Electra	Air Atlantique Ltd/Coventry	
G-LOFE	L.188CF Electra	Air Atlantique Ltd/Coventry	
G-LOFF	L.188CF Electra	Air Atlantique Ltd/Coventry	
G-LOFM	Maule MX-7-180A	Atlantic Air Transport Ltd/Coventry	
G-LOFT	Cessna 500 Citation I	Atlantic Air Transport Ltd/Coventry	
G-LOGO	Hughes 369E	R. M. Briggs (G-BWLC)	
G-LOIS	Avtech Jabiru UL	D. A. Chamberlain	
G-LOKM	WSK-PZL Koliber 160A	PZL International Aviation Marketing & Sales PLC (G-BYSH)/North Weald	
G-LOLL	Cameron V-77 balloon	Test Valley Balloon Group	
G-LOOP	Pitts S-1C Special	C. Butler	
G-LOOS	Cameron 100 Tissue Pack SS balloon	Flying Pictures Ltd	
G-LOOT	EMB-110P1 Bandeirante	(stored) (G-BNOC)/Southend	
G-LORA	Cameron A-250 balloon	Global Ballooning Ltd	
G-LORC	PA-28-161 Cadet	Sherburn Aero Club Ltd	
G-LORD	PA-34-200T Seneca II	Carill Aviation Ltd & ptnrs	
G-LORN	Avions Mudry CAP.10B	AWB Aeronautics Ltd	
G-LORR	PA-28-181 Archer III	S. J. Sylvester	
G-LORT	Light Aero Avid Speedwing 4	G. E. Laucht	
G-LORY	Thunder Ax4-31Z balloon	A. J. Moore	
G-LOSI	Cameron Z-105 balloon	Aeropubblicita Vicenza SRL/Italy	
G-LOSM	Gloster Meteor NF.11 (WM167)	Hunter Wing Ltd/Bournemouth	
G-LOST	Denney Kitfox Mk 3	J. H. S. Booth	
G-LOTI	Bleriot XI (replica) ★	Brooklands Museum Trust Ltd	
G-LOUN	AS.355N Twin Squirrel	Firstearl Ltd	
G-LOVB	BAe Jetstream 3102	London Flight Centre (Stansted) Ltd (G-BLCB)	
G-LOWS	Sky 77-24 balloon	A. J. Byrne & D. J. Bellinger	
G-LOYA	Cessna FR.172J	T. R. Scorer (G-BLVT)	
G-LOYD	SA.341G Gazelle 1	Apollo Manufacturing (Derby) Ltd (G-SFTC)	
G-LPAD	Lindstrand LBL-105A balloon	Line Packaging & Display Ltd	
G-LPGI	Cameron A-210 balloon	A. Derbyshire	
G-LRSN	Robinson R-44	Larsen Manufacturing Ltd	
G-LSFI	AA-5A Cheetah	G-LSFI Group (G-BGSK)	
G-LSFT	PA-28-161 Warrior II	SFT Europe Ltd (G-BXTX)/Bournemouth	
G-LSHI	Colt 77A balloon	Lambert Smith Hampton Group Ltd	
G-LSMI	Cessna F.152	Falcon Flying Services/Biggin Hill	
G-LSTR	Stoddard-Hamilton Glastar	R. Y. Kendal	
G-LTFB	PA-28 Cherokee 140	London Transport Flying Club Ltd (G-AVLU)/Fairoaks	
G-LTFC	PA-28 Cherokee 140B	London Transport Flying Club Ltd (G-AXTI)/Fairoaks	
G-LTRF	Sportavia Fournier RF-7	R. G. Trute (G-EHAP)	
G-LTSB	Cameron LTSB-90 balloon	Virgin Airship & Balloon Co Ltd	
G-LUCK	Cessna F.150M	Taylor Aviation Ltd/Elstree	
G-LUED	Aero Designs Pulsar	J. C. Anderson	
G-LUFT	Pützer Elster C	A. & E. A. Wiseman (G-BOPY)	
G-LUKE	Rutan LongEz	S. G. Busby	

G-LUKI – G-MANG

Notes	Reg.	Type	Owner or Operator
	G-LUKI	Robinson R-44	Marcella Air Ltd (G-BZLN)
	G-LUKY	Robinson R-44	English Braids Ltd
	G-LULU	Grob G.109	A. P. Bowden
	G-LUMA	Avtech Jabiru SK	B. Luyckx
	G-LUNA	PA-32RT-300T Turbo Lance II	D. C. Settrington
	G-LUSC	Luscombe 8E Silvaire	M. Fowler
	G-LUSH	PA-28-151 Warrior	J. Dunn
	G-LUSI	Luscombe 8F Silvaire	J. P. Hunt & D. M. Robinson
	G-LUST	Luscombe 8E Silvaire	M. Griffiths
	G-LUVY	AS.355F-1 Twin Squirrel	Markoss Aviation Ltd
	G-LUXE	BAe 146-300	BAE Systems (Operations) Ltd (G-SSSH)
	G-LYDA	Hoffmann H-36 Dimona	G-LYDA Flying Group/Booker
	G-LYNC	Robinson R-22B-2	Whirlybirds Ltd
	G-LYND	PA-25 Pawnee 235	York Gliding Centre Ltd (G-BSFZ)/ Rufforth
	G-LYNK	CFM Shadow Srs DD	G. Linskey
	G-LYNX	Westland WG.13 Lynx (ZB500) ★	IHM/Weston-s-Mare
	G-LYPG	Avtech Jabiru UL	P. G. Gale
	G-LYTE	Thunder Ax7-77 balloon	G. M. Bulmer
	G-LZZY	PA-28RT-201T Turbo Arrow IV	J. C. Lucas (G-BMHZ)
	G-MAAH	BAC One-Eleven 488GH	Aravco Ltd (G-BWES)
	G-MABE	Cessna F.150L	Herefordshire Aero Club Ltd (G-BLJP)/ Shobdon
	G-MABR	BAe 146-100	British Airways Citiexpress (G-DEBN)
	G-MACH	SIAI-Marchetti SF.260	Cheyne Motors Ltd/Popham
	G-MACK	PA-28R Cherokee Arrow 200-II	Haimoss Ltd
	G-MAFA	Cessna F.406	Directflight Ltd (G-DFLT)
	G-MAFB	Cessna F.406	Directflight Ltd
	G-MAFE	Dornier Do.228-202K	FR Aviation Ltd (G-OALF/G-MLDO)/ Bournemouth
	G-MAFF	BN-2T Turbine Islander	FR Aviation Ltd (G-BJEO)/Bournemouth
	G-MAFI	Dornier Do.228-202K	FR Aviation Ltd/Bournemouth
	G-MAGC	Cameron Grand Illusion SS balloon	Magical Adventures Ltd
	G-MAGG	Pitts S-1SE Special	C. A. Boardman
	G-MAGL	Sky 77-24 balloon	RCM SRL/Luxembourg
	G-MAIE	PA-32RT-301T Turbo Saratoga II TC	B. R. Sennett
	G-MAIK	PA-34-220T Seneca V	TEL (IoM) Ltd
	G-MAIN	Mainair Blade 912	J. R. Moore
	G-MAIR	PA-34-200T Seneca II	Barnes Olson Aeroleasing Ltd/Bristol
	G-MAJA	BAe Jetstream 4102	British Airways Citiexpress
	G-MAJB	BAe Jetstream 4102	British Airways Citiexpress (G-BVKT)
	G-MAJC	BAe Jetstream 4102	British Airways Citiexpress (G-LOGJ)
	G-MAJD	BAe Jetstream 4102	British Airways Citiexpress (G-WAWR)
	G-MAJE	BAe Jetstream 4102	British Airways Citiexpress (G-LOGK)
	G-MAJF	BAe Jetstream 4102	British Airways Citiexpress (G-WAWL)
	G-MAJG	BAe Jetstream 4102	British Airways Citiexpress (G-LOGL)
	G-MAJH	BAe Jetstream 4102	British Airways Citiexpress (G-WAYR)
	G-MAJI	BAe Jetstream 4102	British Airways Citiexpress (G-WAND)
	G-MAJJ	BAe Jetstream 4102	British Airways Citiexpress (G-WAFT)
	G-MAJK	BAe Jetstream 4102	British Airways Citiexpress
	G-MAJL	BAe Jetstream 4102	Eastern Airways
	G-MAJM	BAe Jetstream 4102	British Airways Citiexpress
	G-MAJR	D.H.C.1 Chipmunk 22 (WP805)	Chipmunk Shareholders
	G-MAJS	Airbus A.300-605R	Monarch Airlines Ltd/Luton
	G-MALA	PA-28-181 Archer II	M. & D. Aviation (G-BIIU)
	G-MALC	AA-5 Traveler	B. P. Hogan (G-BCPM)
	G-MALS	Mooney M.20K-231	G-MALS Group/Blackbushe
	G-MALT	Colt Flying Hop SS balloon	P. J. Stapley
	G-MAMC	Rotorway Executive 90	J. R. Carmichael
	G-MAMD	Beech B200 Super King Air	Gamston Aviation Ltd
	G-MAMO	Cameron V-77 balloon	The Marble Mosaic Co Ltd
	G-MANA	BAe ATP	Manx Airlines Ltd (G-LOGH)
	G-MANB	BAe ATP	Manx Airlines Ltd (G-LOGG/G-JATP)
	G-MANC	BAe ATP	Manx Airlines Ltd (G-LOGF)
	G-MAND	PA-28-161 Warrior II	Halfpenny Green Flight Centre Ltd (G-BRKT)
	G-MANE	BAe ATP	British Airways Citiexpress (G-LOGB)
	G-MANF	BAe ATP	British Airways Citiexpress (G-LOGA)
	G-MANG	BAe ATP	British Airways Citiexpress (G-LOGD/G-OLCD)

Reg.	Type	Owner or Operator	Notes
G-MANH	BAe ATP	British Airways Citiexpress (G-LOGC/G-OLCC)	
G-MANI	Cameron V-90 balloon	M. P. G. Papworth	
G-MANJ	BAe ATP	British Airways Citiexpress (G-LOGE/G-BMYL)	
G-MANL	BAe ATP	Manx Airlines Ltd (G-ERIN/ G-BMYK)	
G-MANM	BAe ATP	British Airways Citiexpress (G-OATP/G-BZWW)	
G-MANN	SA.341G Gazelle 1	First City Air (London) PLC (G-BKLW)	
G-MANO	BAe ATP	British Airways Citiexpress (G-UIET)	
G-MANP	BAe ATP	British Airways Citiexpress (G-PEEL)	
G-MANW	Tri-R Kis	M. T. Manwaring	
G-MANX	FRED Srs 2	S. Styles	
G-MAPP	Cessna 402B	Simmons Mapping (UK) Ltd	
G-MAPR	Beech A36 Bonanza	Moderandum Ltd	
G-MARA	Airbus A.321-231	Monarch Airlines Ltd/Luton	
G-MARE	Schweizer 269C	The Earl of Caledon	
G-MASC	Jodel 150A	K. F. & R. Richardson	
G-MASF	PA-28-181 Archer II	Mid-Anglia School of Flying	
G-MASH	Westland-Bell 47G-4A	Defence Products Ltd (G-AXKU)	
G-MASS	Cessna 152 II	MK Aero Support Ltd (G-BSHN)	
G-MASX	Masquito M.80	Masquito Aircraft NV/Belgium	
G-MASY	Masquito M.80	Masquito Aircraft NV/Belgium	
G-MASZ	Masquito M.58	Masquito Aircraft NV/Belgium	
G-MATE	Moravan Zlin Z.50LX	J. H. Askew	
G-MATS	Colt GA-42 airship	P. A. Lindstrand	
G-MATT	Robin R.2160	D. J. Nicholson (G-BKRC)	
G-MATZ	PA-28 Cherokee 140	Midland Air Training School (G-BASI)/Coventry	
G-MAUD	BAe ATP	British Airways Citiexpress (G-BMYM)	
G-MAUK	Colt 77A balloon	B. Meeson	
G-MAVI	Robinson R-22B	R. M. Weyman	
G-MAXG	Pitts S-1S Special	T. P. Jenkinson	
G-MAXI	PA-34-200T Seneca II	Draycott Seneca Syndicate Ltd	
G-MAXV	Van's RV-4	R. S. Partridge-Hicks	
G-MAYO	PA-28-161 Warrior II	Jermyk Engineering/Fairoaks	
G-MAZY†	D.H.82A Tiger Moth ★	Newark Air Museum	
G-MCCF	Thruster T.600N	C. C. F. Fuller	
G-MCEA	Boeing 757-225	My Travel Airways (Airtours)	
G-MCEL	Pegasus Quantum 15-912	F. Hodgson	
G-MCJL	Pegasus Quantum 15-912	M. C. J. Ludlow	
G-MCMS	Aero Designs Pulsar	B. R. Hunter	
G-MCOX	Fuji FA.200-180AO	W. Surrey Engineering (Shepperton) Ltd	
G-MCOY	Flight Design CT.2K	Pegasus Flight Training (Cotswolds)	
G-MCPI	Bell 206B JetRanger 3	D. A. C. Pipe (G-ONTB)	
G-MCXV	Colomban MC.15 Cri-Cri	H. A. Leek	
G-MDBC	Pegasus Quantum 15-912	D. B. Caiden	
G-MDBD	Airbus A.330-243	My Travel Airways (Airtours)	
G-MDKD	Robinson R-22B	Brian Seedle Helicopters/Blackpool	
G-MEAH	PA-28R Cherokee Arrow 200-II	Stapleford Flying Club Ltd (G-BSNM)	
G-MEDA	Airbus A.320-231	British Mediterranean Airways Ltd/BA	
G-MEDB	Airbus A.320-231	British Mediterranean Airways Ltd/BA	
G-MEDE	Airbus A.320-232	British Mediterranean Airways Ltd/BA	
G-MEDF	Airbus A.321-231	British Mediterranean Airways Ltd/BA	
G-MEDG	Airbus A.321-231	British Mediterranean Airways Ltd/BA	
G-MEGA	PA-28R-201T Turbo Arrow III	Multi Ltd	
G-MEGG	Shaw Europa XS	M. E. Mavers	
G-MELT	Cessna F.172H	A. J. M. Shepherd (G-AWTI)	
G-MELV	SOCATA Rallye 235E	J. W. Busby (G-BIND)	
G-MEME	PA-28R-201 Arrow III	Henry J. Clare Ltd	
G-MEOW	CFM Streak Shadow	G. J. Moor	
G-MERC	Colt 56A balloon	A. F. & C. D. Selby	
G-MERE	Lindstrand LBL-77A balloon	R. D. Baker	
G-MERF	Grob G.115A	G-MERF Group	
G-MERI	PA-28-181 Archer II	A. H. McVicar	
G-MERL	PA-28RT-201 Arrow IV	M. Giles/Cardiff-Wales	
G-MEUP	Cameron A-120 balloon	Innovation Ballooning Ltd	
G-MEYO	Enstrom 280FX	J. N. Ainsworth	
G-MFAC	Cessna F.172H	Springbank Aviation Ltd (G-AVGZ)	
G-MFEF	Cessna FR.172J	M. & E. N. Ford	
G-MFHI	Shaw Europa	M. F. Howe	

Notes	Reg.	Type	Owner or Operator
	G-MFHT	Robinson R-22B-2	MFH Ltd
	G-MFLI	Cameron V-90 balloon	J. M. Percival
	G-MFMF	Bell 206B JetRanger 3	S.W. Electricity Board (G-BJNJ)/Bristol
	G-MFMM	Scheibe SF.25C Falke	J. E. Selman
	G-MGAN	Robinson R-44	Meegan Motors Ltd
	G-MGWI	Robinson R-44	T. J. French (G-BZEF)
	G-MHCB	Enstrom 280C	Springbank Aviation Ltd
	G-MHCD	Enstrom 280C-UK	S. J. Ellis (G-SHGG)
	G-MHCE	Enstrom F-28A	K. Bickley (G-BBHD)/Barton
	G-MHCF	Enstrom 280C-UK	HKC Helicopter Services (G-GSML/ G-BNNV)
	G-MHCG	Enstrom 280C-UK	E. Drinkwater (G-HAYN/G-BPOX)
	G-MHCH	Enstrom 280C	J. & S. Lewis Ltd
	G-MHCI	Enstrom 280C	Charlie India Helicopters Ltd/Barton
	G-MHCJ	Enstrom F-28C-UK	Paradise Helicopters (G-CTRN)
	G-MHCK	Enstrom 280FX	Manchester Helicopter Centre (G-BXXB)
	G-MHCL	Enstrom 280C	Altolink Ltd
	G-MICH	Robinson R-22B	Tiger Helicopters Ltd (G-BNKY)/Shobdon
	G-MICI	Cessna 182S	M. J. Coleman (G-WARF)
	G-MICK	Cessna F.172N	G-MICK Flying Group
	G-MICY	Everett Srs 1 gyroplane	D. M. Hughes
	G-MICZ	PA-46-310P Malibu	Welding Alloys Group Ltd/Fowlmere
	G-MIDA	Airbus A.321-231	bmi british midland
	G-MIDC	Airbus A.321-231	bmi british midland
	G-MIDD	PA-28 Cherokee 140	Midland Air Training School (G-BBDD)/ Coventry
	G-MIDE	Airbus A.321-231	bmi british midland
	G-MIDF	Airbus A.321-231	bmi british midland
	G-MIDG	Midget Mustang	C. E. Bellhouse
	G-MIDH	Airbus A.321-231	bmi british midland
	G-MIDI	Airbus A.321-231	bmi british midland
	G-MIDJ	Airbus A.321-231	bmi british midland
	G-MIDK	Airbus A.321-231	bmi british midland
	G-MIDL	Airbus A.321-231	bmi british midland
	G-MIDM	Airbus A.321-231	bmi british midland
	G-MIDN	Airbus A.321-231	bmi british midland
	G-MIDO	Airbus A.321-231	bmi british midland
	G-MIDP	Airbus A.320-232	bmi british midland
	G-MIDR	Airbus A.320-232	bmi british midland
	G-MIDS	Airbus A.320-232	bmi british midland
	G-MIDT	Airbus A.320-232	bmi british midland
	G-MIDU	Airbus A.320-232	bmi british midland
	G-MIDV	Airbus A.320-232	bmi british midland
	G-MIDW	Airbus A.320-232	bmi british midland
	G-MIDX	Airbus A.320-232	bmi british midland
	G-MIDY	Airbus A.320-232	bmi british midland
	G-MIDZ	Airbus A.320-232	bmi british midland
	G-MIFF	Robin DR.400/180	G. E. Snushall
	G-MIII	Extra EA.300/L	Firebird Aerobatics Ltd
	G-MIKE	Brookland Hornet	M. H. J. Goldring
	G-MIKI	Rans S.6-ESA Coyote II	S. P. Slade
	G-MIKK	Robinson R-22 Mariner	Direct Timber Ltd
	G-MILA	Cessna F.172N	P. J. Miller
	G-MILE	Cameron N-77 balloon	Miles Air Ltd
	G-MILI	Bell 206B JetRanger 3	Sirius Aviation Ltd/Wolverhampton
	G-MILN	Cessna 182Q	Meon Hill Farms (Stockbridge) Ltd
	G-MILY	AA-5A Cheetah	Plane Talking Ltd (G-BFXY)/Elstree
	G-MIMA	BAe 146-200	Manx Airlines Ltd (G-CNMF)
	G-MIME	Shaw Europa	N. W. Charles
	G-MIND	Cessna 404	Atlantic Air Transport Ltd (G-SKKC/G-OHUB)/Coventry
	G-MINS	Nicollier HN.700 Menestrel II	R. Fenion
	G-MINT	Pitts S-1S Special	T. G. Sanderson/Tollerton
	G-MINX	Bell 47G-4A	R. F. Warner (G-FOOR)
	G-MIOO	M.100 Student ★	Museum of Berkshire Aviation (G-APLK)/ Woodley
	G-MISH	Cessna 182R	Kamair Ltd (G-RFAB/G-BIXT)
	G-MISS	Taylor JT.2 Titch	P. L. A. Brenen
	G-MITS	Cameron N-77 balloon	Colt Car Co Ltd
	G-MITT	Avtech Jabiru SK	N. C. Mitton
	G-MITZ	Cameron N-77 balloon	Colt Car Co Ltd
	G-MIWS	Cessna 310R II	R. W. F. Warner (G-ODNP)

Reg.	Type	Owner or Operator	Notes
G-MKAK	Colt 77A balloon	Virgin Airship & Balloon Co. Ltd	
G-MKAS	PA-28 Cherokee 140	MK Aero Support Ltd (G-BKVR)	
G-MKIA	V.S.300 Spitfire 1 (P9374)	S. J. Marsh/Italy	
G-MKSF	Agusta A.109A II	Markoss Aviation Ltd	
G-MKSS	H.S.125 Srs 700B	Markoss Aviation Ltd	
G-MKVB	V.S.349 Spitfire LF.VB (BM597)	Historic Aircraft Collection/Duxford	
G-MKVI	D.H. Vampire FB.6 (WL505)	De Havilland Aviation Ltd/Swansea	
G-MLAS	Cessna 182E ★	Parachute jump trainer/St Merryn	
G-MLFF	PA-23 Aztec 250E	Channel Islands Aero Services Ltd (G-WEBB/G-BJBU)	
G-MLJL	Airbus A.330-243	My Travel Airways (Airtours)	
G-MLTI	Dassault Falcon 900B	Multiflight Ltd/Leeds-Bradford	
G-MLTY	AS.365N-2 Dauphin 2	Multiflight Ltd/Leeds-Bradford	
G-MLWI	Thunder Ax7-77 balloon	M. L. & L. P. Willoughby	
G-MOAC	Beech F33A Bonanza	R. M. Camrass	
G-MOBI	AS.355F-1 Twin Squirrel	Faiman Aviation Ltd (G-MUFF/G-CORR)	
G-MOFB	Cameron O-120 balloon	D. M. Moffat	
G-MOFF	Cameron O-77 balloon	D. M. Moffat	
G-MOFZ	Cameron O-90 balloon	D. M. Moffat	
G-MOGI	AA-5A Cheetah	Icarus Aircraft Ltd (G-BFMU)	
G-MOGY	Robinson R-22B	HJS Helicopters	
G-MOHS	PA-31-350 Navajo Chieftain	Sky Air Travel Ltd (G-BWOC)	
G-MOJO	Airbus A.330-243	My Travel Airways (Airtours)	
G-MOKE	Cameron V-77 balloon	D. D. Owen/Luxembourg	
G-MOLE	Taylor JT.2 Titch	S. R. Mowle	
G-MOLI	Cameron A-250 balloon	J. J. Rudoni	
G-MOLL	PA-32-301T Turbo Saratoga	M. S. Bennett	
G-MOLY	PA-23 Apache 160	R. R. & M. T. Thorogood (G-APFV)/ St Just	
G-MONB	Boeing 757-2T7	Monarch Airlines Ltd/Luton	
G-MONC	Boeing 757-2T7	Monarch Airlines Ltd/Luton	
G-MOND	Boeing 757-2T7	Monarch Airlines Ltd/Luton	
G-MONE	Boeing 757-2T7	Monarch Airlines Ltd/Luton	
G-MONI	Monnett Moni	R. M. Edworthy	
G-MONJ	Boeing 757-2T7	Monarch Airlines Ltd/Luton	
G-MONK	Boeing 757-2T7	Monarch Airlines Ltd/Luton	
G-MONR	Airbus A.300-605R	Monarch Airlines Ltd/Luton	
G-MONS	Airbus A.300-605R	Monarch Airlines Ltd/Luton	
G-MONX	Airbus A.320-212	Monarch Airlines Ltd/Luton	
G-MONY	Airbus A.320-212	Monarch Airlines Ltd/Skyservice (C-GVNY)/Luton	
G-MOOR	SOCATA TB.10 Tobago	M. Watkin (G-MILK)	
G-MOOS	P.56 Provost T.1 (XF690)	T. J. Manna (G-BGKA)/Cranfield	
G-MOPB	Diamond DA.40 Star	Diamond Aircraft (UK) Ltd/Gamston	
G-MOSS	Beech 95-D55 Baron	S. C. Tysoe (G-AWAD)	
G-MOSY	Cameron O-84 balloon	P. L. Mossman	
G-MOTA	Bell 206B JetRanger 3	J. W. Sandle	
G-MOTH	D.H.82A Tiger Moth (K2567)	M. C. Russell	
G-MOTI	Robin DR.400/500	Tango India Flying Group	
G-MOTO	PA-24 Comanche 180	L. T. & S. Evans (G-EDHE/G-ASFH)/ Sandown	
G-MOUL	Maule M6-235	M. Klinge	
G-MOUR	H.S. Gnat T.1 (XR991)	D. J. Gilmour/North Weald	
G-MOVE	PA-60-601P Aerostar	A. Cazaz & A1 Hydraulics Ltd	
G-MOVI	PA-32R-301 Saratoga SP	G-BOON Ltd (G-MARI)	
G-MOZZ	Avions Mudry CAP.10B	N. Skipworth & M. B. Smith	
G-MPAC	Ultravia Pelican PL	M. J. Craven	
G-MPBH	Cessna FA.152	The Moray Flying Club (1996) Ltd (G-FLIC/G-BILV)	
G-MPBI	Cessna 310R	M. P. Bolshaw & Co Ltd	
G-MPCD	Airbus A.320-212	Monarch Airlines Ltd	
G-MPWI	Robin HR.100/210	Propwash Investments Ltd/Cardiff	
G-MPWT	PA-34-220T Seneca III	Modern Air (UK) Ltd	
G-MRAJ	Hughes 369E	A. Jardine	
G-MRAM	Mignet HM.1000 Balerit	R. A. Marven	
G-MRED	Christavia Mk 1	E. Hewett	
G-MRKT	Lindstrand LBL-90A balloon	Marketplace Public Relations (London) Ltd	
G-MRLN	Sky 240-24 balloon	Merlin Balloons	
G-MRMR	PA-31-350 Navajo Chieftain	MRMR (Flight Services) (G-WROX/ G-BNZI)	
G-MROC	Pegasus Quantum 15-912	M. Convine	

Notes	Reg.	Type	Owner or Operator
	G-MROY	Ikarus C.42	R. Beckham
	G-MRSI	Canadair CL.600-2C10 RJ	Maersk Air Ltd
	G-MRSJ	Canadair CL.600-2C10 RJ	Maersk Air Ltd
	G-MRSK	Canadair CL.600-2C10 RJ	Maersk Air Ltd
	G-MRSN	Robinson R-22B	Leeds Lighting Ltd
	G-MRST	PA-28 RT-201 Arrow IV	Calverton Flying Group Ltd
	G-MRTN	SOCATA TB.10 Tobago	Underwood Kitchens Ltd (G-BHET)
	G-MRTY	Cameron N-77 balloon	R. A. Vale & ptnrs
	G-MSAL	MS.733 Alcyon (143)	North Weald Flying Services Ltd
	G-MSFC	PA-38-112 Tomahawk	Sherwood Flying Club Ltd/Tollerton
	G-MSFT	PA-28-161 Warrior II	M. J. Love (G-MUMS)
	G-MSIX	Glaser Dirks DG.800B	G-MSIX Group
	G-MSKA	Boeing 737-5L9	Maersk Air Ltd/BA/Birmingham
	G-MSKB	Boeing 737-5L9	Maersk Air Ltd/BA/Birmingham
	G-MSKC	Boeing 737-5L9	Maersk Air Ltd/BA/Birmingham
	G-MSKO	Canadair CL.600-2B19 RJ	Maersk Air Ltd/BA/Birmingham
	G-MSKP	Canadair CL.600-2B19 RJ	Maersk Air Ltd/BA/Birmingham
	G-MSKR	Canadair CL.600-2B19 RJ	Maersk Air Ltd/BA/Birmingham
	G-MSKS	Canadair CL.600-2B19 RJ	Maersk Air Ltd/BA/Birmingham
	G-MSKT	Canadair CL.600-2B19 RJ	Maersk Air Ltd/BA/Birmingham
	G-MSKU	Canadair CL.600-2B19 RJ	Maersk Air Ltd/BA/Birmingham
	G-MSKY	Ikarus C.42	C. K. Jones
	G-MSOO	Mini-500	R. H. Ryan
	G-MSPY	Pegasus Quantum 15-912	J. Madhvani & R. K. Green
	G-MSTC	AA-5A Cheetah	Plane Talking Ltd (G-BIJT)/Elstree
	G-MSTG	NA P-51D Mustang (414419)	M. Hammond
	G-MSTR	Cameron 110 Monster SS balloon	Virgin Airship & Balloon Co. Ltd (G-OJOB)
	G-MUFY	Robinson R-22B	Rotormurf Ltd
	G-MUIR	Cameron V-65 balloon	L. C. M. Muir
	G-MUNI	Mooney M.20J	M. W. Fane
	G-MURR	Whittaker MW.6 Merlin	D. Murray
	G-MURY	Robinson R-44	Simlot Ltd
	G-MUSO	Rutan LongEz	C. J. Tadjeran/Sweden
	G-MUTE	Colt 31A balloon	Redmalt Ltd
	G-MUVG	Cessna 421C	Air Montgomery Ltd
	G-MXVI	V.S.361 Spitfire LF.XVIe (TE184)	De Cadenet Motor Racing Ltd
	G-NAAA	MBB Bo.105DBS/4	Bond Air Services (G-BUTN/ G-AZTI)/Aberdeen
	G-NAAB	MBB Bo.105DBS/4	Bond Air Services/Aberdeen
	G-NAAS	AS.355F-1 Twin Squirrel	Northumbria Ambulance Service NHS Trust (G-BPRG/G-NWPA)
	G-NACA	Norman NAC.2 Freelance 180	NDN Aircraft Ltd/Sandown
	G-NACI	Norman NAC.1 Srs 100	L. J. Martin (G-AXFB)
	G-NACL	Norman NAC.6 Fieldmaster	EPA Aircraft Co Ltd (G-BNEG)
	G-NACO	Norman NAC-6 Fieldmaster	EPA Aircraft Co Ltd
	G-NACP	Norman NAC-6 Fieldmaster	EPA Aircraft Co Ltd
	G-NADS	Team Minimax 91	G. Evans
	G-NAPO	Pegasus Quantum 15-912	D. Pick
	G-NARO	Cassutt Racer	D. A. Wirdnam (G-BTXR)
	G-NATT	R. Commander 114A	Northgleam Ltd
	G-NATX	Cameron O-65 balloon	A. G. E. Faulkner
	G-NATY	H.S. Gnat T.1 (XR537)	F. C. Hackett-Jones/Bournemouth
	G-NBAA	Avro RJ100	BAE Systems (Operations) Ltd
	G-NBDD	Robin DR.400/180	J. N. Binks
	G-NBSI	Cameron N-77 balloon	Nottingham Hot-Air Balloon Club
	G-NCFC	PA-38-112 Tomahawk II	Light Aircraft Leasing (UK) Ltd (G-BNOA)
	G-NCFE	PA-38-112 Tomahawk	R. M. Browes (G-BKMK)
	G-NCFR	H.S.125 Srs 700B	Chauffair Ltd (G-BVJY)
	G-NCUB	Piper J-3C-65 Cub	R. S. Basinger (G-BGXV)/Norwich
	G-NDGC	Grob G.109	J. E. Bedford & M. Mathieson
	G-NDNI	NDN.1 Firecracker	N. W. G. Marsh
	G-NDOL	Shaw Europa	S. Longstaff
	G-NEAL	PA-32 Cherokee Six 260	VSD Group (G-BFPY)
	G-NEAT	Shaw Europa	M. Burton
	G-NEEL	Rotorway Executive 90	M. B. Sims
	G-NEGS	Thunder Ax7-77 balloon	M. Rowlands
	G-NEIL	Thunder Ax3 balloon	N. A. Robertson
	G-NELI	PA-28R Cherokee Arrow 180	European Light Aviation Ltd
	G-NEON	PA-32 Cherokee Six 300B	S. C. A. Lever
	G-NEPB	Cameron N-77 balloon	The Post Office

Reg.	Type	Owner or Operator	Notes
G-NERC	PA-31-350 Navajo Chieftain	Natural Environment Research Council (G-BBXX)/Coventry	
G-NESA	Shaw Europa XS T-G	K. G. & V. E. Summerhill	
G-NESU	BN-2B-20 Islander	Northumbria Police Authority (G-BTVN)/ Teesside	
G-NESV	Eurocopter EC.135T-1	Northumbria Police Authority	
G-NESY	PA-18 Super Cub 95	V. Fisher	
G-NETY	PA-18 Super Cub 150	N. B. Mason	
G-NEUF	Bell 206L-1 LongRanger 2	Yendle Roberts Ltd (G-BVVV)	
G-NEVS	Aero Designs Pulsar XP	N. Warrener	
G-NEWR	PA-31-350 Navajo Chieftain	Eastern Air Executive Ltd/Sturgate	
G-NEWS	Bell 206B JetRanger 3	Abington Aviation Ltd	
G-NEWT	Beech 35 Bonanza	F. M. West (G-APVW)	
G-NEWZ	Bell 206B JetRanger 3	Peter Press Ltd	
G-NFLC	H.P.137 Jetstream 1	Cranfield University (G-AXUI)	
G-NGRM	Spezio DAL.1 Tuholer	S. H. Crook	
G-NHRH	PA-28 Cherokee 140	J. E. & I. Parkinson	
G-NHRJ	Shaw Europa XS	D. A. Lowe	
G-NHVH	Maule M5-235C Lunar Rocket	Commercial Go-Karts Ltd/Exeter	
G-NIDG	Aerotechnik EV-97 Eurostar	Skydrive Ltd	
G-NIGC	Avtech Jabiru UL-450	N. Creeney	
G-NIGE	Luscombe 8E Silvaire	Garden Party Ltd (G-BSHG)	
G-NIGL	Shaw Europa	N. M. Graham	
G-NIGS	Thunder Ax7-65 balloon	A. N. F. Pertwee	
G-NIKE	PA-28-181 Archer II	Key Properties Ltd/White Waltham	
G-NIKO	Airbus A.321-211	My Travel Airways (Airtours)	
G-NINA	PA-28-161 Warrior II	P. A. Layzell (G-BEUC)	
G-NINB	PA-28 Cherokee 180G	P. A. Layzell	
G-NINC	PA-28 Cherokee 180G	P. A. Layzell	
G-NINE	Murphy Renegade 912	R. F. Bond	
G-NIOS	PA-32R-301 Saratoga SP	Plant Aviation	
G-NIPA	Slingsby T.66 Nipper 3	R. J. O. Walker (G-AWDD)	
G-NIPP	Slingsby T.66 Nipper 3	T. Dale (G-AVKJ)	
G-NIPY	Hughes 369HS	Jet Aviation (Northwest) Ltd	
G-NITA	PA-28 Cherokee 180	T. Clifford (G-AVVG)	
G-NJAG	Cessna 207	G. H. Nolan Ltd	
G-NJIA	BAe 146-300	-	
G-NJIC	BAe 146-300	- (G-BTUY)	
G-NJIE	BAe 146-300	- (G-BVCE)	
G-NJSH	Robinson R-22B	A. J. Hawes	
G-NLEE	Cessna 182Q	J. S. Lee (G-TLTD)	
G-NLYB	Cameron N-105 balloon	P. H. E. Van Overwalle/Belgium	
G-NMHS	AS.355N Twin Squirrel	North Midlands Helicopter Support Unit (G-DPPS)	
G-NMOS	Cameron C-80 balloon	C. J. Thomas & M. C. East	
G-NNAC	PA-18 Super Cub 135	P. A. Wilde	
G-NOBI	Spezio HES-1 Tuholer Sport	A. D. Pearce	
G-NOCK	Cessna FR.182RG II	R. D. Masters (G-BGTK)	
G-NODE	AA-5B Tiger	Strategic Telecom Networks Ltd	
G-NODY	American General AG-5B Tiger	Curd & Green Ltd/Elstree	
G-NOIR	Bell 222	Arlington Securities PLC (G-OJLC/ G-OSEB/G-BNDA)	
G-NOMO	Cameron O-31 balloon	Balloon Promotion SAS/Italy	
G-NONA	SA.341G Gazelle 1	M. Persaud (G-FDAV/G-RIFA/ G-ORGE/G-BBHU)	
G-NONI	AA-5 Traveler	November India Flying Group(G-BBDA)	
G-NOOK	Mainair blade 912S	P. J. Hughes	
G-NOOR	Commander 114B	As-Al Ltd	
G-NORD	SNCAN NC.854	W. J. McCollum	
G-NOSE	Cessna 402B	Atlantic Air Transport Ltd (G-MPCU)/ Coventry	
G-NOTE	PA-28-181 Archer III	General Aviation Trading Co Ltd	
G-NOTR	MDH MD.500N	Eastern Atlantic Helicopters	
G-NOTT	Nott ULD-2 balloon	J. R. P. Nott	
G-NOTY	Westland Scout AH.1	R. P. Coplestone	
G-NOVO	Colt AS-56 airship	J. R. Huggins	
G-NOWW	Mainair Blade 912	C. Bodill	
G-NPKJ	Van's RV-6	K. Jones	
G-NROY	PA-32RT-300 Lance II	Roy West Cars (G-LYNN/G-BGNY)	
G-NRRA	SIAI-Marchetti SF.260W	G. N. Richardson	
G-NRSC	PA-23 Aztec 250E	Air Reconnaissance Ltd (G-BSFL)	
G-NSEW	Robinson R-44	Pebblestar Ltd	

Notes	Reg.	Type	Owner or Operator
	G-NSOF	Robin HR.200/120B	Northamptonshire School of Flying Ltd/ Sywell
	G-NSTG	Cessna F.150F	N. S. T. Griffin (G-ATNI)/Blackpool
	G-NSYT	Robinson R-44	F. G. Sytner
	G-NUTS	Cameron 35SS balloon ★	British Balloon Museum
	G-NUTY	AS.350B Ecureuil	Arena Aviation Ltd (G-BXKT)
	G-NVBF	Lindstrand LBL-210A balloon	Virgin Balloon Flights Ltd
	G-NVSA	D.H.C.8-311 Dash Eight	Brymon/British Airways Citiexpress
	G-NVSB	D.H.C.8-311 Dash Eight	Brymon/British Airways Citiexpress
	G-NVSC	D.H.C.8-311 Dash Eight	Brymon/British Airways Citiexpress
	G-NVSD	D.H.C.8-311 Dash Eight	Brymon/British Airways Citiexpress
	G-NWAC	PA-31-310 Turbo Navajo	North West Air Charters Ltd (G-BDUJ)/ Liverpool
	G-NWPS	Eurocopter EC.135T-1	North-West Police Authority
	G-NYTE	Cessna F.337G	I. M. Latiff (G-BATH)
	G-NZGL	Cameron O-105 balloon	R. A. Vale & ptnrs
	G-NZSS	Boeing Stearman N2S-5 (343251)	Anglian Aircraft Co Ltd
	G-OAAA	PA-28-161 Warrior II	Halfpenny Green Flight Centre Ltd
	G-OAAC	Airtour AH-77B balloon	Army Air Corps
	G-OABB	Jodel D.150	A. B. Bailey
	G-OABC	Colt 69A balloon	P. A. C. Stuart-Kregor
	G-OABO	Enstrom F-28A	ABO Ltd (G-BAIB)
	G-OABR	AG-5B Tiger	Abraxas Aviation Ltd
	G-OACE	Valentin Taifun 17E	J. E. Dallison
	G-OACG	PA-34-200T Seneca II	Cega Aviation Ltd (G-BUNR)
	G-OACI	M.S.893E Rallye 180GT	A. M. Quayle (G-DOOR)
	G-OACP	OGMA D.H.C.1 Chipmunk 20	Aeroclub de Portugal
	G-OADY	Beech 76 Duchess	Multiflight Ltd
	G-OAER	Lindstrand LBL-105A balloon	T. M. Donnelly
	G-OAFT	Cessna 152 II	Evensport Ltd (G-BNKM)
	G-OAHC	Beech F33C Bonanza	V. D. Speck (G-BTTF)/Clacton
	G-OAJB	Cyclone AX2000	G. K. R. Linney (G-MZFJ)
	G-OAJS	PA-39 Twin Comanche 160 C/R	Go-AJS Ltd (G-BCIO)
	G-OAKJ	BAe Jetstream 3202	Eastern Airways Ltd (G-BOTJ)
	G-OALB	Aero L-39C Albatros	Rocket Seat Ltd
	G-OALD	SOCATA TB.20 Trinidad	Gold Aviation/Biggin Hill
	G-OALH	Tecnam P.92-EM Echo	L. Hill
	G-OAMF	Pegasus Quantum 15-912	W. Rodham
	G-OAMG	Bell 206B JetRanger 3	Alan Mann Helicopters Ltd/Fairoaks
	G-OAMI	Bell 206B JetRanger 2	Stephenson Marine Co Ltd (G-BAUN)
	G-OAML	Cameron AML-105 balloon	Stratton Motor Co. (Norfolk) Ltd
	G-OAMP	Cessna F.177RG	Vale Aero Group (G-AYPF)
	G-OAMS	Boeing 737-37Q	British Airways Regional
	G-OAMT	PA-31-350 Navajo Chieftain	AM & T Solutions Ltd (G-BXKS)/Bristol;
	G-OANI	PA-28-161 Warrior II	J. F. Mitchell
	G-OANN	Zenair CH.601HDS	P. Noden
	G-OAPE	Cessna T.303	C. Twiston-Davies & P. L. Drew
	G-OAPR	Brantly B.2B	Helicopter International Magazine
	G-OAPW	Glaser-Dirks DG.400	J. R. Mousley
	G-OARA	PA-28R-201 Arrow III	Airsure
	G-OARG	Cameron C-80 balloon	G. & R. Madelin
	G-OARO	PA-28R-201 Arrow III	Plane Talking Ltd/Elstree
	G-OART	PA-23 Aztec 250D	Levenmere Ltd (G-AXKD)
	G-OARV	ARV Super 2	N. R. Beale (stored)
	G-OASH	Robinson R-22B	J. C. Lane
	G-OASP	AS.355F-2 Twin Squirrel	Avon & Somerset Constabulary & Gloucestershire Constabulary
	G-OATG	Advanced Technologies AT-10	Advanced Technologies Group Ltd
	G-OATS	PA-38-112 Tomahawk	Truman Aviation Ltd/Tollerton
	G-OATV	Cameron V-77 balloon	W. G. Andrews
	G-OAWS	Colt 77A balloon	Auto Windscreens Ltd
	G-OAXA	Cameron 90 Cup SS balloon	Flying Pictures Ltd
	G-OBAL	Mooney M.20J	Britannia Airways Ltd/Luton
	G-OBAM	Bell 206B JetRanger 3	Cherwell Tobacco Ltd
	G-OBAN	Jodel D.140B	S. R. Cameron (G-ATSU)/North Connel
	G-OBAX	Thruster T.600N 450-Jab	Baxby Airsports Club
	G-OBBC	Colt 90A balloon	R. A. & M. A. Riley
	G-OBBJ	Boeing 737-8DR	Multiflight Ltd
	G-OBBO	Cessna 182S	F. Friedenberg
	G-OBBY	Robinson R-44	P. C. & J. A. Twigg
	G-OBDA	Diamond Katana DA.20-A1	Oscar Papa Ltd

Reg.	Type	Owner or Operator	Notes
G-OBEN	Cessna 152 II	Airbase Aircraft Ltd (G-NALI/G-BHVM)	
G-OBET	Sky 77-24 balloon	Flying Pictures Ltd	
G-OBEV	Shaw Europa	M. B. Hill & N. I. Wingfield	
G-OBEY	PA-23 Aztec 250C	Creaton Aircraft Services (G-BAAJ)	
G-OBFC	PA-28-161 Warrior II	Bflying Ltd/Bournemouth	
G-OBFS	PA-28-161 Warrior III	Plane Talking Ltd/Elstree	
G-OBGC	SOCATA TB-20 Trinidad	Bidford Airfield Ltd	
G-OBHD	Short SD3-60 Variant 100	Emerald Airways Ltd (G-BNDK)/Liverpool	
G-OBHL	AS.355F-2 Twin Squirrel	Brands Hatch Leisure Group Ltd (G-HARO/G-DAFT/G-BNNN)	
G-OBIB	Colt 120A balloon	The Aerial Display Co Ltd	
G-OBIL	Robinson R-22B	C. A. Rosenberg	
G-OBIO	Robinson R-22B	A. E. Churchill	
G-OBJB	Lindstrand LBL-90A balloon	B. J. Bower	
G-OBJP	Pegasus Quantum 15-912	B. J. Partridge	
G-OBJT	Shaw Europa	B. J. Tarmar (G-MUZO)	
G-OBLC	Beech 76 Duchess	Pridenote Ltd	
G-OBLK	Short SD3-60 Variant 100	BAC Express Airlines Ltd (G-BNDI)	
G-OBLN	D.H.115 Vampire T.11 (XE956)	De Havilland Aviation Ltd/Swansea	
G-OBLU	Cameron H-34 balloon	Blu Spa/Italy	
G-OBMI	Mainair Blade	P. Clark	
G-OBMM	Boeing 737-4Y0	bmi british midland	
G-OBMP	Boeing 737-3Q8	bmi british midland	
G-OBMS	Cessna F.172N	D. Beverley & A. N. MacDonald	
G-OBMW	AA-5 Traveler	Fretcourt Ltd (G-BDFV)	
G-OBNA	PA-34-220T Seneca V	Anglo American Airmotive Ltd	
G-OBPL	EMB-110P2 Bandeirante	BAC Leasing Ltd (G-OEAB/G-BKWB/ G-CHEV)	
G-OBRI	Medway Eclipser	B. D. Campbell	
G-OBRY	Cameron N-180 balloon	Bryant Group PLC	
G-OBTS	Cameron C-80 balloon	Bedford Tyre Service (Chichester) Ltd	
G-OBUN	Cameron A-250 balloon	A. C. K. Rawson & J. J. Roudoni	
G-OBUY	Colt 69A balloon	Virgin Airship & Balloon Co Ltd	
G-OBWL	BAe ATP	-	
G-OBWM	BAe ATP	-	
G-OBWN	BAe ATP	- (G-BVEO)	
G-OBWO	BAe ATP	-	
G-OBWP	BAe ATP	- (G-BTPO)	
G-OBWR	BAe ATP	- (G-BUWP)	
G-OBWS	Boeing 757-23A	- (G-BXOL)	
G-OBWX	Boeing 737-3Y0	- (G-MONL)	
G-OBWY	Boeing 737-3S3	- (G-DEBZ/G-BNPB)	
G-OBWZ	Boeing 737-3Q8	-	
G-OBYA	Boeing 767-304ER	Britannia Airways Ltd	
G-OBYB	Boeing 767-304ER	Britannia Airways Ltd	
G-OBYC	Boeing 767-304ER	Britannia Airways Ltd	
G-OBYD	Boeing 767-304ER	Britannia Airways Ltd	
G-OBYE	Boeing 767-304ER	Britannia Airways Ltd	
G-OBYF	Boeing 767-304ER	Britannia Airways Ltd	
G-OBYG	Boeing 767-3Q8ER	Britannia Airways Ltd	
G-OBYH	Boeing 767-304ER	Britannia Airways Ltd	
G-OBYI	Boeing 767-304ER	Britannia Airways Ltd	
G-OBYJ	Boeing 767-304ER	Britannia Airways Ltd	
G-OBYT	AB-206A JetRanger	R. J. Everett (G-BNRC)	
G-OCAA	H.S.125 Srs 700B	MAGEC Aviation Ltd (G-BHLF)/Luton	
G-OCAD	Sequoia F.8L Falco	Falco Flying Group	
G-OCAM	AA-5A Cheetah	Plane Talking Ltd (G-BLHO)/Elstree	
G-OCAR	Colt 77A balloon	S. C. J. Derham	
G-OCAT	Eiri PIK-20E	D. Bonucchi	
G-OCAW	Lindstrand LBL Bananas SS balloon	Flying Pictures Ltd	
G-OCBS	Lindstrand LBL-210A balloon	G. Binder	
G-OCDB	Cessna 550 Citation II	Paycourt Ltd (G-ELOT)	
G-OCDS	Aviamilano F.8L Falco II	C. O. P. Barth (G-VEGL)	
G-OCEA	Short SD3-60 Variant 100	BAC Express Airlines Ltd (G-BRMX)	
G-OCFR	Learjet 35A	Chauffair Ltd (G-VIPS/G-SOVN/G-PJET)	
G-OCHM	Robinson R-44	Westleigh Developments Ltd	
G-OCJK	Schweizer 269C	P. Crawley	
G-OCJW	Cessna 182R	C. J. Ward (G-SJGM)	
G-OCMJ	SA.341G Gazelle 1	Gazelle Investments Ltd (G-HTPS/ G-BRNI)	
G-OCMM	Agusta A.109A II	The Thomas Bolton Group Ltd (G-BXCB/ G-ISEB/G-IADT/G-HBCA)	

Notes	Reg.	Type	Owner or Operator
	G-OCOV	Robinson R-22B	Flight Training Ltd
	G-OCPC	Cessna FA.152	Westward Airways (Lands End) Ltd/ St Just
	G-OCPF	PA-32 Cherokee Six 300	Syndicate Clerical Services Ltd (G-BOCH)
	G-OCPS	Colt 120A balloon	CPS Fuels Ltd
	G-OCRI	Colomban MC.15 Cri-Cri	M. J. J. Dunning
	G-OCST	AB-206B JetRanger 3	Claygate Distribution Ltd (G-BMKM)
	G-OCTI	PA-32 Cherokee Six 260	D. G. Williams (G-BGZX)
	G-OCTU	PA-28-161 Cadet	Plane Talking Ltd/Elstree
	G-OCUB	Piper J-3C-90 Cub	C. A. Foss & P. A. Brook/Shoreham
	G-ODAC	Cessna F.152 II	T. M. Jones (G-BITG)/Egginton
	G-ODAD	Colt 77A balloon	K. Meehan
	G-ODAK	PA-28-236 Dakota	Airways Aero Associations Ltd/Booker
	G-ODAM	AA-5A Cheetah	Stop & Go Ltd (G-FOUX)
	G-ODAT	Aero L-29 Delfin	Graniteweb Ltd
	G-ODBN	Lindstrand LBL Flowers SS balloon	Flying Pictures Ltd
	G-ODCS	Robinson R-22B-2	Heli Air Ltd/Wellesbourne
	G-ODDY	Lindstrand LBL-105A balloon	P. & T. Huckle
	G-ODEB	Cameron A-250 balloon	A. Derbyshire
	G-ODEE	Van's RV-6	D. Powell
	G-ODEL	Falconar F-11-3	G. F. Brummell
	G-ODEN	PA-28-161 Cadet	J. Appleton/Denham
	G-ODES	Robinson R-44	Eagle Distribution Ltd
	G-ODGS	Jabiru UL	D. G. Salt
	G-ODHG	Robinson R-44	Driver Hire Group Services Ltd
	G-ODHL	Cameron N-77 balloon	DHL International (UK) Ltd
	G-ODIN	Avions Mudry CAP.10B	T. W. Harris
	G-ODIY	Colt 69A balloon	P. Glydon
	G-ODJD	Raj Hamsa X'Air 582 (7)	D. J. Davis
	G-ODJG	Shaw Europa	D. J. Goldsmith
	G-ODJH	Mooney M.20C	R. M. Schweitzer (G-BMLH)/Netherlands
	G-ODLY	Cessna 310J	R. J. Huband (G-TUBY/G-ASZZ)
	G-ODMC	AS.350B-1 Ecureuil	D. M. Coombs (G-BPVF)/Denham
	G-ODNH	Schweizer 269C-1	Oxford Aviation Services Ltd/Kidlington
	G-ODOC	Robinson R-44	Gas & Air Ltd
	G-ODOD	MDH MD-600N Explorer	Sunseeker Sales (UK) Ltd
	G-ODOG	PA-28R Cherokee Arrow 200-II	Advanced Investments Ltd (G-BAAR)
	G-ODOT	Robinson R-22B-2	Farm Aviation Ltd
	G-ODSK	Boeing 737-37Q	bmi british midland
	G-ODTW	Shaw Europa	D. T. Walters
	G-ODUB	EMB-110P1 Bandeirante	Comed Aviation Ltd (G-BNIX)/Blackpool
	G-ODVB	CFM Shadow Srs DD	D. V. Brunt (G-MGDB)
	G-OEAC	Mooney M.20J	DR Airgroup
	G-OEAT	Robinson R-22B	C. Y. O. Seeds Ltd (G-RACH)
	G-OECH	AA-5A Cheetah	Plane Talking Ltd (G-BKBE)/Elstree
	G-OEDB	PA-38-112 Tomahawk	Metropolitan Services Ltd (G-BGGJ)
	G-OEDP	Cameron N-77 balloon	M. J. Betts
	G-OEGG	Cameron 65 Egg SS balloon	Virgin Airship & Balloon Co Ltd
	G-OEGL	Christen Eagle II	The Eagle Flight Syndicate/Shoreham
	G-OEJA	Cessna 500 Citation	Eurojet Aviation Ltd (G-BWFL)
	G-OELD	Pegasus Quantum 15-912	T. H. Filmer
	G-OERR	Lindstrand LBL-60A balloon	Lindstrand Balloons Ltd
	G-OERS	Cessna 172N	E. R. Stevens (G-SSRS)
	G-OERX	Cameron O-65 balloon	R. Roehsler/Austria
	G-OEST	BAe Jetstream 3202	Eastern Airways Ltd
	G-OESY	Easy Raider J2.2 (1)	Reality Aircraft Ltd
	G-OEWA	D.H.104 Dove 8	D. C. Hunter (G-DDCD/G-ARUM)
	G-OEYE	Rans S.10 Sakota	I. M. J. Mitchell
	G-OEZY	Shaw Europa	A. W. Wakefield
	G-OFAS	Robinson R-22B	Findon Air Services/Shoreham
	G-OFBJ	Thunder Ax7-77 balloon	N. D. Hicks
	G-OFBU	Ikarus C.42	Fly Buy Ultralights Ltd
	G-OFCH	AB-206B JetRanger 2	Fleet Coast Helicopters Ltd (G-BKDA)
	G-OFCM	Cessna F.172L	F. C. M. Aviation Ltd (G-AZUN)/Guernsey
	G-OFER	PA-18 Super Cub 150	M. S. W. Meagher/Edgehill
	G-OFFA	Pietenpol Air Camper	OFFA Group
	G-OFHL	AS.350B Ecureuil	Ford Helicopters Ltd (G-BLSP)
	G-OFIL	Robinson R-44	W. & W. Potter Ltd
	G-OFIT	SOCATA TB.10 Tobago	GFI Aviation Group (G-BRIU)
	G-OFJC	Eiri PIK-20E	M. J. Aldridge

Reg.	Type	Owner or Operator	Notes
G-OFLG	SOCATA TB.10 Tobago	Westward Airways (Lands End) Ltd (G-JMWT)	
G-OFLI	Colt 105A balloon	Virgin Airship & Balloon Co Ltd	
G-OFLT	EMB-110P1 Bandeirante	Flightline Ltd (G-MOBL/G-BGCS)/ Southend	
G-OFLY	Cessna 210M	A. P. Mothew/Stapleford	
G-OFMB	Rand-Robinson KR-2	F. M. & S. I. Burden	
G-OFOA	BAe 146-100	Formula One Administration Ltd (G-BKMN/G-ODAN)	
G-OFOM	BAe 146-100	Formula One Management Ltd (G-BSLP/ G-BRLM)	
G-OFOR	Thunder Ax3 balloon	T. J. Ellenreider & ptnrs	
G-OFOX	Denney Kitfox	P. R. Skeels	
G-OFRT	L.188C Electra	Channel Express (Air Services) Ltd/ Bournemouth	
G-OFRY	Cessna 152 II	Devon School of Flying Ltd (G-BPHS)/Dunkeswell	
G-OFTI	PA-28 Cherokee 140	P. E. Richardson (G-BRKU)	
G-OGAN	Shaw Europa	G-OGAN Group	
G-OGAR	PZL SZD-45A Ogar	N. C. Grayson	
G-OGAS	Westland WG.30 Srs 100 ★	(stored) (G-BKNW)/Yeovil	
G-OGAV	Lindstrand LBL-240A balloon	Airborne Balloon Management Ltd	
G-OGAZ	SA.341G Gazelle 1	Killochries Fold (G-OCJR/G-BRGS)	
G-OGBA	Boeing 737-4S3	GB Airways Ltd (G-OBMK)/Gatwick	
G-OGBB	Boeing 737-34S	GB Airways Ltd/Gatwick	
G-OGBC	Boeing 737-34S	GB Airways Ltd/Gatwick	
G-OGBD	Boeing 737-3L9	GB Airways Ltd/Gatwick	
G-OGBE	Boeing 737-3L9	GB Airways Ltd/Gatwick	
G-OGCA	PA-28-161 Warrior II	Cardiff-Wales Aviation Services Ltd	
G-OGEE	Pitts S-2B Special	Display Aerobatics Ltd	
G-OGEM	PA-28-181 Archer II	GEM Rewinds Ltd	
G-OGET	PA-39 Twin Comanche 160 C/R	P. G. Kitchingman (G-AYXY)	
G-OGGS	Thunder Ax8-84 balloon	G. Gamble & Sons (Quorn) Ltd	
G-OGHH	Enstrom 480	Silver Lining Finance SA	
G-OGIL	Short SD3-30 Variant 100 ★	N.E. Aircraft Museum (G-BITV)/Usworth	
G-OGJM	Cameron C-80 balloon	G. F. Madelin	
G-OGJP	Hughes 369E	Motortrak Ltd	
G-OGJS	Puffer Cozy	G. J. Stamper	
G-OGOA	AS.350B Ecureuil	Lomas Helicopters Ltd (G-PLMD/ G-NIAL)	
G-OGOB	Schweizer 269C	Kingfisher Helicopters Ltd (G-GLEE/ G-BRUW)	
G-OGOG	Robinson R-22B	Lake Services (G-TILL)	
G-OGOS	Everett gyroplane	N. A. Seymour	
G-OGPN	Thompson Cassutt Special	S. Alexander (G-OMFI/G-BKCH)	
G-OGRK	AS.355F-1 Twin Squirrel	Kelwaiver Ltd (G-BWZC/G-MOBZ)	
G-OGSA	Avtec Jabiru UL	G. J. Slater & W. Moultrie	
G-OGSS	Lindstrand LBL-120A balloon	R. Klarer/Germany	
G-OGTS	Air Command 532 Elite	GTS Engineering (Coventry) Ltd	
G-OGTX	Cessna T.310R	I. M. & S. M. Graham	
G-OHAC	Cessna F.182Q	The RAF Halton Aeroplane Club	
G-OHAJ	Boeing 737-36Q	British Airways	
G-OHAL	Pietenpol Air Camper	H. C. Danby	
G-OHAT	Cessna 525 CitationJet	Houston Air Taxis Ltd (G-OICE)	
G-OHCP	AS.355F-1 Twin Squirrel	Plane Talking Ltd (G-BTVS/ G-STVE/ G-TOFF/G-BKJX)	
G-OHDC	Colt Agfa Film Cassette SS balloon	Flying Pictures Ltd	
G-OHFT	Robinson R-22B	Heliflight (UK) Ltd (G-TYPO/G-JBWI)	
G-OHHI	Bell 206L-1 LongRanger	Bradmore Helicopters (G-BWYJ)	
G-OHIG	EMB-110P1 Bandeirante ★	Valley Nurseries (G-OPPP)/Alton	
G-OHKS	Pegasus Quantum 15-912	York Microlight Centre Ltd	
G-OHLL	Robinson R-22B	Plane Talking Ltd (G-CHAL)/Elstree	
G-OHMS	AS.355F-1 Twin Squirrel	S.W. Electricity PLC	
G-OHNA	Mainair Blade 912	P. A. Lee	
G-OHRH	Lindstrand LBL-150A balloon	Exclusive Ballooning	
G-OHSA	Cameron N-77 balloon	D. N. & L. J. Close	
G-OHSL	Robinson R-22B	Helicopter Support Ltd (G-BPNF)	
G-OHWV	Raj Hamsa X'Air 582 (5)	H. W. Vasey	
G-OIBM	R. Commander 114	I. Rosewell (G-BLVZ)	
G-OIBO	PA-28 Cherokee 180	Britannia Airways Ltd (G-AVAZ)/Luton	
G-OICO	Lindstrand LBL-42A balloon	Virgin Airship & Balloon Co Ltd	
G-OIDW	Cessna F.150G	K. J. Steel & D. J. Hewitt	

Notes	Reg.	Type	Owner or Operator
	G-OIFM	Cameron 90 Dude SS balloon	Magical Adventures Ltd
	G-OIMC	Cessna 152 II	E. Midlands Flying School Ltd
	G-OING	AA-5A Cheetah ★	Abraxas Aviation Ltd (G-BFPD)/Denham
	G-OINK	Piper J-3C-65 Cub	A. R. Harding (G-BILD/G-KERK)
	G-OINV	BAe 146-300	British Airways Citiexpress/BA
	G-OIOZ	Thunder Ax9-120 S2 balloon	The Flying Doctors Hot Air Balloon Co Ltd
	G-OISO	Cessna FRA.150L	V. J. Wilce & D. A. Miller (G-BBJW)
	G-OITN	AS.355F-1 Twin Squirrel	Lynton Aviation Ltd/Denham
	G-OITV	Enstrom 280C-UK-2	C. W. Brierley Jones (G-HRVY/G-DUGY/G-BEEL)
	G-OIZI	Shaw Europa XS T-G	K. S. Duddy
	G-OJAB	Avtec Jabiru SK	P. A. Brigstock
	G-OJAC	Mooney M.20J	Hornet Engineering Ltd
	G-OJAE	Hughes 269C	J. A. & C. M. Wilson
	G-OJAN	Robinson R-22B	Heliflight (UK) Ltd (G-SANS/G-BUHX)
	G-OJAS	Auster J/1U Workmaster (Lycoming)	K. P. & D. S. Hunt
	G-OJAV	BN-2A Mk III-2 Trislander	Lyddair (G-BDOS)
	G-OJBB	Enstrom 280FX	Adenstar Developments Ltd
	G-OJBM	Cameron N-90 balloon	P. Spinlove
	G-OJBS	Cameron N-105A balloon	Up & Away Ballooning Ltd
	G-OJBW	Lindstrand LBL J & B Bottle SS balloon	Justerini & Brooks Ltd
	G-OJCW	PA-32RT-300 Lance II	CW Group
	G-OJDA	EAA Acrosport II	D. B. Almey
	G-OJDC	Thunder Ax7-77 balloon	J. Crosby
	G-OJEG	Airbus A.321-231	Monarch Airlines Ltd/Luton
	G-OJGT	Maule M.5-235C	J. G. Townsend
	G-OJHB	Colt Flying Ice Cream Cone SS balloon	Benedikt Haggeney GmbH/Germany
	G-OJHL	Shaw Europa	J. H. Lace
	G-OJIL	PA-31-350 Navajo Chieftain	Redhill Aviation Ltd
	G-OJIM	PA-28R-201T Turbo Arrow III	Piper Arrow Group
	G-OJJB	Mooney M.20K	Fly Over Ltd
	G-OJJF	D.31 Turbulent	J. J. Ferguson
	G-OJKM	Rans S.7 Courier	M. Jackson
	G-OJLH	Team Minimax 91	J. L. Hamer (G-MYAW)
	G-OJMB	Airbus A.330-243	-
	G-OJMC	Airbus A.330-243	-
	G-OJMF	Enstrom 280FX	JMF Ltd (G-DDOD)
	G-OJMR	Airbus A.300-605R	Monarch Airlines Ltd/Luton
	G-OJNB	Linsdstrand LBL-21A balloon	Justerini & Brooks Ltd
	G-OJON	Taylor JT.2 Titch	J. H. Fell
	G-OJPB	H.S.125 Srs F600B	Widehawk Aviation Ltd (G-BFAN/G-AZHS)
	G-OJRH	Robinson R-44	Holgate Construction Ltd
	G-OJRM	Cessna T.182T	SPD Ltd/Old Sarum
	G-OJSH	Thruster T.600N 450 Jab	S. J. Holden
	G-OJTA	Stemme S.10V	OJT Associates
	G-OJTW	Boeing 737-36N	bmi british midland (G-JTWF)
	G-OJVA	Van's RV-6	J. A. Village
	G-OJVH	Cessna F.150H	A. W. Cairns (G-AWJZ)
	G-OJWS	PA-28-161 Warrior II	P. J. Ward
	G-OKAG	PA-28R Cherokee Arrow 180	N. F. & B. R. Green/Stapleford
	G-OKAY	Pitts S-1E Special	D. S. T. Eggleton
	G-OKBT	Colt 25A Mk II balloon	British Telecommunications PLC
	G-OKCC	Cameron N-90 balloon	D. J. Head
	G-OKED	Cessna 150L	Haimoss Ltd/Old Sarum
	G-OKEN	PA-28R-201T Turbo Arrow III	W. B. Bateson/Blackpool
	G-OKES	Robinson R-44	Direct Helicopters/Southend
	G-OKEV	Shaw Europa	K. R. Pilcher
	G-OKEY	Robinson R-22B	Key Properties Ltd/Booker
	G-OKIS	Tri-R Kis	B. W. Davies
	G-OKJN	Boeing 727-225RE	Cougar Airlines
	G-OKMA	Tri-R Kis	K. Miller
	G-OKPW	Tri-R Kis	K. P. Wordsworth
	G-OKYA	Cameron V-77 balloon	Army Balloon Club
	G-OKYM	PA-28 Cherokee 140	B. Marshall (G-AVLS)
	G-OLAU	Robinson R-22B	MPW Aviation Ltd
	G-OLAW	Lindstrand LBL-25A balloon	George Law Plant
	G-OLDC	Learjet 45	Gold Air International Ltd
	G-OLDD	BAe 125 Srs 800B	Gold Air International Ltd

Reg.	Type	Owner or Operator	Notes
G-OLDJ	Learjet 45	Gold Air International Ltd	
G-OLDL	Learjet 45	Gold Air International Ltd	
G-OLDM	Pegasus Quantum 15-912	P. Simpson	
G-OLDN	Bell 206L LongRanger	Von Essen Aviation Ltd (G-TBCA/ G-BFAL)	
G-OLEE	Cessna F.152	Redhill Air Services Ltd	
G-OLEL	American Blimp Corp. A-60 airship	Lightship Europe Ltd	
G-OLEO	Thunder Ax10-210 S2 balloon	P. J. Waller	
G-OLEZ	Piper J-3C-65 Cub	L. Powell (G-BSAX)	
G-OLFB	Pegasus Quantum 15-912	A. J. Boyd	
G-OLFC	PA-38-112 Tomahawk	M. W. Glencross (G-BGZG)	
G-OLFT	R. Commander 114	D. A. Tubby (G-WJMN)	
G-OLGA	CFM Starstreak Shadow SA-II	N. F. Smith	
G-OLIZ	Robinson R-22B	R. S. Forsyth & L. T. W. Alderman	
G-OLJT	Mainair Gemini Flash IIA	K. D. Taylor (G-MTKY)	
G-OLLE	Cameron O-84 balloon	N. A. Robertson	
G-OLLI	Cameron O-31 SS balloon	N. A. Robertson	
G-OLMA	Partenavia P.68B	C. M. Evans (G-BGBT)	
G-OLOW	Robinson R-44	Morris Transport	
G-OLPG	Colt 77A balloon	D. J. Farrar	
G-OLRT	Robinson R-22B	First Degree Air/Tatenhill	
G-OLSF	PA-28-161 Cadet	Bflying Ltd (G-OTYJ)	
G-OLYD	Beech 58 Baron	I. G. Lloyd	
G-OLYN	Sky 260-24 balloon	Airborne Balloon Management Ltd=	
G-OMAC	Cessna FR.172E	S. G. Shilling	
G-OMAF	Dornier Do.228-200	FR Aviation Ltd/Bournemouth	
G-OMAK	Airbus A.319-132	Twinjet Aircraft Sales Ltd	
G-OMAL	Thruster T.600N 450	Thruster Air Services Ltd	
G-OMAP	R. Commander 685	Cooper Aerial Surveys Ltd/Sandtoft	
G-OMAT	PA-28 Cherokee 140	Midland Air Training School (G-JIMY/ G-AYUG)/Coventry	
G-OMAX	Brantly B.2B	P. D. Benmax (G-AVJN)	
G-OMDD	Thunder Ax8-90 S2 balloon	M. D. Dickinson	
G-OMDG	Hoffmann H-36 Dimona	P. Turner/Halesland	
G-OMDH	Hughes 369E	Stilgate Ltd/Booker	
G-OMDR	AB-206B JetRanger 3	Aeromega Ltd (G-HRAY/G-VANG/ G-BIZA)	
G-OMEC	AB-206B JetRanger 3	Kallas Ltd (G-OBLD)/Monaco	
G-OMEL	Robinson R-44	Nedair Ltd (G-BVPB)	
G-OMEX	Zenair CH.701 STOL	S. J. Perry	
G-OMEZ	Zenair CH.601HDS	C. J. Gow	
G-OMFG	Cameron A-120 balloon	M. F. Glue	
G-OMGD	H.S.125 Srs 700B	MAGEC Aviation Ltd/Luton	
G-OMGE	BAe 125 Srs 800B	Marconda Services Ltd (G-BTMG)/Luton	
G-OMGG	BAe 125 Srs 800B	Aviation One Co. Ltd/Cayman Islands	
G-OMHC	PA-28RT-201 Arrow IV	Tatenhill Aviation	
G-OMHI	Mills MH-1	J. P. Mills	
G-OMHP	Avtech Jabiru UL	M. H. Player	
G-OMIA	M.S.893A Rallye Commodore 180	P. W. Portelli	
G-OMIK	Shaw Europa	M. J. Clews	
G-OMJT	Rutan LongEz	M. J. Timmons	
G-OMKF	Aero Designs Pulsar	M. K. Faro	
G-OMMG	Robinson R-22B	R. D. Masters (G-BPYX)	
G-OMMM	Colt 90A balloon	V. Trimble	
G-OMNH	Beech 200 Super King Air	Maynard & Harris Holdings Ltd	
G-OMNI	PA-28R Cherokee Arrow 200D	The Blue Book (G-BAWA)	
G-OMOL	Maule MX-7-180C	Aeromarine Ltd	
G-OMRB	Cameron V-77 balloon	M. R. Bayne	
G-OMRG	Hoffmann H-36 Dimona	M. R. Grimwood (G-BLHG)	
G-OMSG	Robinson R-22B-2	Morhire	
G-OMST	PA-28-161 Warrior III	Mid-Sussex Timber Co. Ltd (G-BZUA)	
G-OMUC	Boeing 737-36Q	British Airways	
G-OMUM	R. Commander 114	C. E. Campbell	
G-OMWE	Zenair CH.601HD	Mid-West Engines Ltd (G-BVXU)/ Staverton	
G-OMXS	Lindstrand LBL-105A balloon	Virgin Airship & Balloon Co Ltd	
G-ONAF	Naval Aircraft Factory N3N-3	R. P. W. Steel & J. E. Hutchinson	
G-ONAV	PA-31-310 Turbo Navajo C	Panther Aviation Ltd (G-IGAR)	
G-ONCB	Lindstrand LBL-31A balloon	Flying Pictures Ltd	
G-ONCL	Colt 77A balloon	D. R. Pearce	
G-ONCM	Partenavia P.68C	Millair Ltd (G-TELE/G-DORE)	
G-ONEB	Westland Scout AH.1	N. E. Bailey (G-BXOE)	

Notes	Reg.	Type	Owner or Operator
	G-ONES	Slingsby T.67M Firefly 200	L. J. Jones
	G-ONET	PA-28 Cherokee 180E	J. Blackburn (G-AYAU)
	G-ONEW	EMB-110P1 Bandeirante	Sky Service/Belgium
	G-ONFL	Meridian Maverick	K. M. Dando (G-MYUJ)
	G-ONGC	Robin DR.400/180R	Norfolk Gliding Club Ltd/Tibenham
	G-ONHH	Forney F-1A Aircoupe	R. D. I. Tarry (G-ARHA)
	G-ONIX	Cameron C-80 balloon	Hillwalk Ltd
	G-ONKA	Aeronca K	N. J. R. Minchin
	G-ONMT	Robinson R-22B-2	Redcourt Enterprises Ltd
	G-ONON	RAF 2000 GTX-SE gyroplane	M. S. R. Allen
	G-ONOW	Bell 206A JetRanger 2	J. Lucketti (G-AYMX)
	G-ONPA	PA-31-350 Navajo Chieftain	Anglo American Airmotive Ltd/ Bournemouth
	G-ONSF	PA-28R-201 Arrow III	Northamptonshire School of Flying Ltd (G-EMAK)
	G-ONTV	AB-206B JetRanger 3	Castle Air Charters Ltd
	G-ONUN	Van's RV-6A	R. E. Nunn
	G-ONUP	Enstrom F-28C-UK	R. E. Harvey (G-MHCA/G-SHWW/ G-SMUJ/G-BHTF)
	G-ONYX	Bell 206B JetRanger 3	N. C. Wheelwright (G-BXPN)
	G-ONZO	Cameron N-77 balloon	K. Temple
	G-OOAE	Airbus A.321-211	Air 2000 Ltd (G-UNIF)
	G-OOAF	Airbus A.321-211	Air 2000 Ltd (G-UNID/G-UKLO)
	G-OOAH	Airbus A.321-211	Air 2000 Ltd (G-UNIE)
	G-OOAI	Airbus A.321-213	Air 2000 Ltd
	G-OOAJ	Airbus A.321-213	Air 2000 Ltd
	G-OOAL	Boeing 767-38AER	Air 2000 Ltd
	G-OOAM	Boeing 767-38AER	Air 2000 Ltd
	G-OOAN	Boeing 767-39HER	Air 2000 Ltd (G-UKLH)
	G-OOAP	Airbus A.320-214	Air 2000 Ltd
	G-OOAR	Airbus A.320-214	Air 2000 Ltd
	G-OOAS	Airbus A.320-214	Air 2000 Ltd
	G-OOAT	Airbus A.320-214	Air 2000 Ltd
	G-OOBA	Boeing 757-28A	Air 2000 Ltd
	G-OOBB	Boeing 757-28A	Air 2000 Ltd
	G-OODE	SNCAN Stampe SV-4C	A. R. Radford (G-AZNN)
	G-OODH	Schemmp-Hirth Ventus 2CM	D. J. M. Hill
	G-OODI	Pitts S-1D Special	R. M. Buchan (G-BBBU)
	G-OODW	PA-28-181 Archer II	Goodwood Terrena Ltd
	G-OOER	Lindstrand LBL-25A balloon	Airborne Adventures Ltd
	G-OOFT	PA-28-161 Warrior III	Lyrical Computing Ltd
	G-OOGA	GA-7 Cougar	Cougar Aviation Ltd/Elstree
	G-OOGI	GA-7 Cougar	Plane Talking Ltd (G-PLAS/G-BGHL)
	G-OOGO	GA-7 Cougar	Leonard F. Jollye (Brookmans Park) Ltd /Elstree
	G-OOGS	GA-7 Cougar	Bflying Ltd (G-BGJW)
	G-OOJC	Bensen B.8MR	J. R. Cooper
	G-OOJP	Commander 114B	Plato Management Ltd
	G-OOHO	Bell 206B JetRanger 3	Into Space Ltd (G-OCHC/G-KLEE/ G-SIZL/G-BOSW)
	G-OOIO	AS.350B-3 Ecureuil	McAlpine Helicopters Ltd/Kidlington
	G-OOLE	Cessna 172M	P. S. Eccersley (G-BOSI)
	G-OONE	Mooney M.20J	J. H. Donald & K. B. Moore
	G-OONI	Thunder Ax7-77 balloon	Fivedata Ltd
	G-OONY	PA-28-161 Warrior II	D. A. Field & P. B. Jenkins
	G-OOOA	Boeing 757-28A	Air 2000 Ltd
	G-OOOB	Boeing 757-28A	Air 2000 Ltd
	G-OOOC	Boeing 757-28A	Air 2000 Ltd
	G-OOOD	Boeing 757-28A	Air 2000 Ltd
	G-OOOG	Boeing 757-23A	Air 2000 Ltd
	G-OOOI	Boeing 757-23A	Air 2000 Ltd
	G-OOOJ	Boeing 757-23A	Air 2000 Ltd
	G-OOOM	Boeing 757-225	Air 2000 Ltd
	G-OOOO	Mooney M.20J	Pergola Ltd
	G-OOOS	Boeing 757-236	Air 2000 Ltd (G-BRJD)
	G-OOOU	Boeing 757-2Y0	Air 2000 Ltd
	G-OOOV	Boeing 757-225	Air 2000 Ltd
	G-OOOW	Boeing 757-225	Air 2000 Ltd
	G-OOOX	Boeing 757-2Y0	Air 2000 Ltd
	G-OOOY	Boeing 757-2Q8	Air 2000 Ltd
	G-OOSE	Rutan Vari-Eze	B. O. Smith & J. A. Towers
	G-OOSY	D.H.82A Tiger Moth	M. Goosey
	G-OOTC	PA-28R-201T Turbo Arrow III	R. Noble Ltd (G-CLIV)

Reg.	Type	Owner or Operator	Notes
G-OOUT	Colt Flying Shuttlecock SS balloon	Shiplake Investments Ltd	
G-OOXP	Aero Designs Pulsar XP	T. D. Baker	
G-OPAG	PA-34-200 Seneca II	A. H. Lavender (G-BNGB)/Biggin Hill	
G-OPAL	Robinson R-22B	Hell Air Ltd/Wellesbourne	
G-OPAM	Cessna F.152 II (tailwheel)	PJC Leasing Ltd (G-BFZS)	
G-OPAT	Beech 76 Duchess	R. D. J. Axford (G-BHAO)	
G-OPAZ	Pazmany PL.2	K. Morris	
G-OPCS	Hughes 369E	Productivity Computer Solutions Ltd	
G-OPDM	Enstrom 280FX	Lamindene Ltd	
G-OPDS	Denney Kitfox Mk 4	P. D. Sparling	
G-OPEP	PA-28RT-201T Turbo Arrow IV	Oxford Aviation Services Ltd/Kidlington	
G-OPET	PA-28-181 Archer II	Its Just Plane Fun Ltd	
G-OPFT	Cessna 172R	Rankart Ltd	
G-OPFW	H.S.748 Srs 2A	Emerald Airways Ltd (G-BMFT)/Liverpool	
G-OPHA	Robinson R-44	Simax Services Ltd	
G-OPHR	Diamond DA.40 Star	Diamond Aircraft UK Ltd/Gamston	
G-OPHT	Schleicher ASH-26E	Scheibler Filters Ltd	
G-OPIC	Cessna FRA.150L	Air Survey (G-BGNZ)	
G-OPIK	Eiri PIK-20E	A. J. McWilliam/Newtownards	
G-OPIT	CFM Streak Shadow Srs SA	W. M. Kilner	
G-OPJC	Cessna 152 II	PJC Leasing Ltd/Stapleford	
G-OPJD	PA-28RT-201T Turbo Arrow IV	J. M. McMillan	
G-OPJH	D.62B Condor	P. J. Hall (G-AVDW)	
G-OPJK	Shaw Europa	P. J. Kember	
G-OPJS	Pietenpol Air Camper	P. J. Shenton	
G-OPLB	Cessna 340A II	Ridgewood Ltd (G-FCHJ/G-BJLS)	
G-OPLC	D.H.104 Dove 8 ★	W. G. T. Pritchard & I. Darcy-Bean (G-BLRB)	
G-OPME	PA-23 Aztec 250D	S. G. Shilling (G-ODIR/G-AZGB)	
G-OPMN	Boeing 727-225RE	Cougar Airlines	
G-OPMT	Lindstrand LBL-105A balloon	Pace Micro Technology PLC	
G-OPNH	Stoddard-Hamilton Glasair IIRG	P. N. Haigh (G-CINY)	
G-OPPL	AA-5A Cheetah	London School of Flying Ltd (G-BGNN)/Elstree	
G-OPRC	Shaw Europa XS	I. R. Chaplin	
G-OPSF	PA-38-112 Tomahawk	Panshanger School of Flying (G-BGZI)	
G-OPSL	PA-32R-301 Saratoga SP	Photonic Science Ltd (G-IMPW)	
G-OPST	Cessna 182R	Lota Ltd/Shoreham	
G-OPTS	Robinson R-22B-2	T. A. Knox (Shopfitters) Ltd	
G-OPUB	Slingsby T.67M Firefly 160	P. M. Barker (G-DLTA/G-SFTX)	
G-OPUP	B.121 Pup 2	Brinkley Light Aircraft Services (G-AXEU)	
G-OPUS	Avtech Jabiru SK	H. H. R. Lagache	
G-OPWK	AA-5A Cheetah	A. H. McVicar (G-OAEL)/Prestwick	
G-OPWS	Mooney M.20K	A. R. Mills	
G-OPYE	Cessna 172S	Far North Aviation/Wick	
G-ORAC	Cameron 110 RAC Van SS balloon	Virgin Airship & Balloon Co Ltd	
G-ORAF	CFM Streak Shadow	A. P. Hunn	
G-ORAL	H.S.748 Srs 2A	Emerald Airways Ltd (G-BPDA/G-GLAS) /Liverpool	
G-ORAR	PA-28-181 Archer III	P. N. & S. M. Thornton	
G-ORAS	Clutton FRED Srs 2	A. I. Sutherland	
G-ORAY	Cessna F.182Q II	G. A. Barrett (G-BHDN)	
G-ORBD	Van's RV-6A	C. M. Dixon (G-BVRE)	
G-ORDO	PA-30 Twin Comanche B	C. A. Ringrose	
G-ORED	BN-2T Turbine Islander	The Red Devils Aviation Ltd (G-BJYW)	
G-OREV	Mini -500	R. H. Everett	
G-ORFC	Jurca MJ.5 Sirocco	D. J. Phillips	
G-ORFH	Aérospatiale ATR-42-300	-	
G-ORHE	Cessna 500 Citation	R. H. Everett (G-OBEL/G-BOGA)	
G-ORIG	Glaser-Dirks DG.800A	I. Godfrey	
G-ORIX	ARV K1 Super 2	T. M. Lyons (G-BUXH/G-BNVK)	
G-ORJB	Cessna 500 Citation	L'Equipe Air Ltd (G-OKSP)	
G-ORJW	Laverda F.8L Falco Srs 4	W. R. M. Sutton	
G-ORJX	Avro RJX85	BAE Systems (Operations) Ltd/Woodford	
G-ORMA	AS.355F-1 Twin Squirrel	Stratton Motor Co (Norfolk) Ltd (G-SITE/G-BPHC)	
G-ORMB	Robinson R-22B	R. M. Bailey	
G-ORMG	Cessna 172R II	J. R. T. Royle	
G-OROB	Robinson R-22B	Corniche Helicopters (G-TBFC)	
G-OROD	PA-18 Super Cub 150	B. W. Faulkner	
G-ORON	Cameron 77A balloon	Orion Hot Air Balloon Group	

Notes	Reg.	Type	Owner or Operator
	G-ORPR	Cameron O-77 balloon	T. Strauss & A. Sheehan
	G-ORRR	Hughes 369HS	The Lower Mill Estate Ltd (G-BKTK/ G-STEF)
	G-ORSP	Beech A36 Bonanza	Makins
	G-ORTM	Glaser-Dirks DG.400	M. A. Recht
	G-ORVB	McCulloch J-2	R. V. Bowles (G-BLGI/G-BKKL)
	G-ORVG	Van's RV-6	R. J. Fray
	G-ORVR	Partenavia P.68B	Ravenair (G-BFBD)/Liverpool
	G-OSCC	PA-32 Cherokee Six 300	BG & G Airlines Ltd (G-BGFD)
	G-OSCH	Cessna 421C	Sureflight Aviation Ltd (G-SALI)
	G-OSCO	Team Minimax 91	P. J. Schofield
	G-OSDI	Beech 95-58 Baron	D. Darling (G-BHFY)
	G-OSEA	BN-2B-26 Islander	W. T. Johnson & Sons (Huddersfield) Ltd (G-BKOL)
	G-OSEE	Robinson R-22B	Aero-Charter Ltd
	G-OSFA	Diamond HK.36TC Super Dimona	Oxfordshire Sportflying Ltd
	G-OSFC	Cessna F.152	Stapleford Flying Club Ltd (G-BIVJ)
	G-OSGB	PA-31-350 Navajo Chieftain	Gold Air International Ltd (G-YSKY)
	G-OSHL	Robinson R-22B	Sloane Helicopters Ltd/Sywell
	G-OSII	Cessna 172N	K. J. Abrams (G-BIVY)
	G-OSIP	Robinson R-22B-2	Heli Air Ltd
	G-OSIS	Pitts S-1S Special	C. Butler
	G-OSIT	Pitts S-1T Special	G. C. J. Cooper
	G-OSIX	PA-32 Cherokee Six 260	A. E. Whittle (G-AZMO)
	G-OSKP	Enstrom 480	Churchill Stairlifts Ltd
	G-OSKY	Cessna 172M	Skyhawk Leasing Ltd/Wellesbourne
	G-OSLD	Shaw Europa XS	Opus Sofware Ltd
	G-OSLO	Schweizer 269C	A. H. Helicopter Services Ltd
	G-OSMD	Bell 206B JetRanger 2	Stuart Aviation Ltd (G-LTEK/G-BMIB)
	G-OSMS	Robinson R-22B	Heliflight (UK) Ltd (G-BXYW)
	G-OSND	Cessna FRA.150M	Wilkins & Wilkins Special Auctions Ltd (G-BDOU)
	G-OSNI	PA-23 Aztec 250C	Marham Investments Ltd (G-AWER)
	G-OSOE	H.S.748 Srs 2A	Emerald Airways Ltd (G-AYYG)/Liverpool
	G-OSOO	Hughes 369E	Methan Aviation Ltd
	G-OSPS	PA-18 Super Cub 95	T. Gale & ptnrs
	G-OSSF	AA-5A Cheetah	Direct Helicopters (G-MELD/G-BHCB)
	G-OSST	Colt 77A balloon	British Airways PLC
	G-OSTA	J/1 Autocrat	D. & M. Nelson (G-AXUJ)
	G-OSTC	AA-5A Cheetah	5th Generation Designs Ltd
	G-OSTU	AA-5A Cheetah	Direct Helicopters (G-BGCL)
	G-OSTY	Cessna F.150G	C. R. Guggenheim (G-AVCU)
	G-OSUP	Lindstrand LBL-90A balloon	British Airways Balloon Club
	G-OSUS	Mooney M.20K	J. B. King/Goodwood
	G-OTAC	Robinson R-22B-2	Direct Helicopters (Southend) Ltd
	G-OTAF	Aero L-39ZO Albatros (111)	C. P. B. Horsley/Duxford
	G-OTAL	ARV Super 2	N. R. Beale (G-BNGZ)
	G-OTAM	Cessna 172M	G. V. White
	G-OTAN	PA-18 Super Cub 135	S. D. Turner
	G-OTBA	H.S.748 Srs 2A	Emerald Airways Ltd/Liverpool
	G-OTBY	PA-32 Cherokee Six 300	GOTBY Ltd
	G-OTCH	CFM Streak Shadow	H. E. Gotch
	G-OTDB	MDH Hughes 369E	D. E. McDowell(G-BXUR)
	G-OTED	Robinson R-22HP	Andrews Heli-Lease Ltd (G-BMYR)
	G-OTEL	Thunder Ax8-90 balloon	D. N. Belton
	G-OTFT	PA-38-112 Tomahawk	N. Papadroushotis (G-BNKW)
	G-OTGA	PA-28R-201 Arrow III	TG Aviation Ltd
	G-OTHE	Enstrom 280C-UK Shark	GTS Engineering (Coventry) Ltd (G-OPJT/G-BKCO)
	G-OTIB	Robin DR.400/180R	Norfolk Gliding Club Ltd/Tibenham
	G-OTIG	AA-5B Tiger	Albatross Ltd (G-PENN)/Elstree
	G-OTIM	Bensen B.8MV	T. J. Deane
	G-OTIS	Cessna 550 Citation II	The Streamline Partnership Ltd
	G-OTJB	Robinson R-44	Heli Air Ltd/Wellesbourne
	G-OTJH	Pegasus Quantum 15-912	T. J. Hector
	G-OTOE	Aeronca 7AC Champion	J. M. Gale (G-BRWW)
	G-OTOO	Stolp SA.300 Starduster Too	I. M. Castle
	G-OTOY	Robinson R-22B	Tickstop Ltd (G-BPEW)
	G-OTRG	Cessna TR.182RG	Middleton Miniature Mouldings Ltd
	G-OTRV	Van's RV-6	W. R. C. Williams-Wynne
	G-OTSP	AS.355F-1 Twin Squirrel	Aeromega Aviation PLC (G-XPOL/G-BPRF)

Reg.	Type	Owner or Operator	Notes
G-OTTI	Cameron 34 Otti SS balloon	Ballonwerbung Hamburg GmbH/ Germany	
G-OTTO	Cameron 82 Katalog SS balloon	Ballonwerbung Hamburg GmbH/ Germany	
G-OTUG	PA-18 Super Cub 150	B. F. Walker	
G-OTUP	Lindstrand LBL-180A balloon	Airborne Adventures Ltd	
G-OTWO	Rutan Defiant	A. J. Baggerley	
G-OUCH	Cameron N-105 balloon	Flying Pictures Ltd	
G-OUHI	Shaw Europa XS T-G	Europa Aircraft Co Ltd	
G-OUMC	Lindstrand LBL-105A balloon	Executive Ballooning	
G-OURO	Shaw Europa	D. Pitt	
G-OURS	Sky 120-24 balloon	M. P. A. Sevrin	
G-OUVI	Cameron O-105 balloon	Bristol University Hot Air Ballooning Soc	
G-OVAA	Colt Jumbo SS balloon	Virgin Airship & Balloon Co Ltd	
G-OVAX	Colt AS-80 Mk II airship	Gefa-Flug GmbH/Germany	
G-OVBF	Cameron A-250 balloon	Virgin Balloon Flights Ltd	
G-OVET	Cameron O-56 balloon	E. J. A. Macholc	
G-OVFM	Cessna 120	E. G. & R. B. Woods	
G-OVFR	Cessna F.172N	Western Air (Thruxton) Ltd	
G-OVID	Light Aero Avid Flyer	L. G. Horne	
G-OVMC	Cessna F.152 II	Staverton Flying School	
G-OVNR	Robinson R-22B	Rally Repaints/Breighton	
G-OWAC	Cessna F.152	K. McDonald (G-BHEB)	
G-OWAK	Cessna F.152	Falcon Flying Services (G-BHEA)	
G-OWAL	PA-34-220T Seneca III	R. G. & W. Allison	
G-OWAR	PA-28-161 Warrior II	Bickertons Aerodromes Ltd	
G-OWAX	Beech 200 Super King Air	Context GB Ltd/Blackpool	
G-OWAZ	Pitts S-1C Special	P. E. S. Latham (G-BRPI)	
G-OWCG	Bell 222	Phoenix Helicopter Charters Ltd (G-VERT/G-JLBZ/G-BNDB)	
G-OWDB	H.S.125 Srs 700B	Bizair Ltd (G-BYFO/G-OWEB)	
G-OWEL	Colt 105A balloon	S. R. Seager	
G-OWEN	K & S Jungster	R. C. Owen	
G-OWET	Thurston TSC-1A2 Teal	D. Nieman	
G-OWGC	Slingsby T.61F Venture T.2	Wolds Gliding Club Ltd/Pocklington	
G-OWLC	PA-31 Turbo Navajo	Channel Airways Ltd (G-AYFZ)	
G-OWND	Robinson R-44 Astro	W. N. Dore	
G-OWOW	Cessna 152 II	Falcon Flying Services (G-BMSZ)/ Biggin Hill	
G-OWRC	Cessna 525 CitationJet	Softbreeze Ltd (G-OCSB)	
G-OWRT	Cessna 182G	Blackpool & Flyde Aero Club Ltd (G-ASUL)	
G-OWYE	Lindstrand LBL-240A balloon	Wye Valley Aviation Ltd	
G-OWYN	Aviamilano F.14 Nibbio	D. Kynaston	
G-OXBC	Cameron A-140 balloon	J. E. Rose	
G-OXBY	Cameron N-90 balloon	C. A. Oxby	
G-OXKB	Cameron 110 Sports Car SS balloon	Flying Pictures Ltd	
G-OXTC	PA-23 Aztec 250D	Falcon Flying Services (G-AZOD)/ Biggin Hill	
G-OXVI	V.S.361 Spitfire LF.XVIe (TD248)	Silver Victory BVBA/Belgium	
G-OYAK	Yakovlev C-11 (27)	A. H. Soper/Earls Colne	
G-OYES	Mainair Blade 912	J. Crowe	
G-OZAR	Enstrom 480	Lancroft Air Ltd (G-BWFF)	
G-OZBA	Airbus A.320-212	Monarch Airlines Ltd (G-MALE)/Luton	
G-OZBB	Airbus A.320-212	Monarch Airlines Ltd/Luton	
G-OZBD	Airbus A.321-231	Monarch Airlines Ltd/Luton	
G-OZBE	Airbus A.321-231	Monarch Airlines Ltd/Luton	
G-OZBF	Airbus A.321-231	Monarch Airlines Ltd/Luton	
G-OZEE	Light Aero Avid Speedwing Mk 4	S. C. Goozee	
G-OZEG	Cameron 65 Egg SS balloon	Cameron Balloons Ltd	
G-OZLN	Zlin Z.242L	R. L. McDonald	
G-OZOI	Cessna R.182	J. R. G. & F. L. G. Fleming (G-ROBK)	
G-OZOO	Cessna 172N	Gordon Air Ltd (G-BWEI)/Lydd	
G-OZRH	BAe 146-200	Flightline Ltd	
G-OZZI	Jabiru SK	A. H. Godfrey	
G-PACE	Robin R.1180T	Millicron Instruments Ltd/Coventry	
G-PACL	Robinson R-22B	R. Wharam	
G-PADI	Cameron V-77 balloon	R. F. Penney	
G-PADS	R. Commander 114B	New Media Holdings Ltd	
G-PAGS	SA.341G Gazelle 1	P. A. G. Seers (G-OAFY/G-SFTH/ G-BLAP)	

Notes	Reg.	Type	Owner or Operator
	G-PAIZ	PA-12 Super Cruiser	B. R. Pearson/Eaglescott
	G-PALL	PA-46-350P Malibu Mirage	Pressurised Aircraft Leasing Ltd (G-RMST)
	G-PALS	Enstrom 280C-UK-2 Shark	G. Firbank
	G-PAPS	PA-32R-301T Turbo Saratoga SP	W. J. Forrest
	G-PARI	Cessna 172RG Cutlass	Applied Signs Ltd/Tatenhill
	G-PART	Partenavia P.68B	Springbank Aviation Ltd
	G-PASF	AS.355F-1 Twin Squirrel	Police Aviation Services Ltd (G-SCHU)/Newcastle
	G-PASG	MBB Bo 105DBS/4	Police Aviation Services Ltd (G-MHSL)/Staverton
	G-PASH	AS.355F-1 Twin Squirrel	Police Aviation Services Ltd/Staverton
	G-PASV	BN-2B-21 Islander	Police Aviation Services Ltd (G-BKJH)/Teesside
	G-PASX	MBB Bo 105DBS/4	Police Aviation Services Ltd/Shoreham
	G-PATF	Shaw Europa	E. P. Farrell
	G-PATG	Cameron O-90 balloon	P. A. & A. J. A. Bubb
	G-PATI	Cessna F.172M	Professional Air Training Ltd (G-WACZ/G-BCUK)
	G-PATN	SOCATA TB.10 Tobago	M. D. Bond (G-LUAR)
	G-PATP	Lindstrand LBL-77A balloon	P. Pruchnickyj
	G-PATS	Shaw Europa	D. J. D. Kesterton
	G-PATX	Lindstrand LBL-90A balloon	P. A. Bubb
	G-PATZ	Shaw Europa	H. P. H. Griffin
	G-PAVL	Robin R.3000/120	Newcharter (UK) Ltd
	G-PAWL	PA-28 Cherokee 140	G-PAWL Group (G-AWEU)
	G-PAWN	PA-25 Pawnee 260C	A. P. Meredith (G-BEHS)/Lasham
	G-PAWS	AA-5A Cheetah	Direct Helicopters
	G-PAZY	Pazmany PL.4A	C. R. Nash (G-BLAJ)
	G-PBEE	Robinson R-44	P. Barnard
	G-PBEL	CFM Shadow Srs DD	P. C. Bell
	G-PBES	Robinson R-22B	M. Horrell (G-EXOR/G-CMCM)
	G-PBUS	Avtech Jabiru SK	G. R. Pybus
	G-PBYY	Enstrom 280FX	J. J. Woodhouse (G-BXKV)
	G-PCAF	Pietenpol Air Camper	C. C. & F. M. Barley
	G-PCAM	BN-2A Mk.III-2 Trislander	Aurigny Air Services Ltd (G-BEPH)
	G-PCAR	PA-46-500TP Malibu Meridian	J. A. Carr
	G-PCDP	Zlin Z.526F Trener Master	Zlin Group
	G-PCOM	PA-30 Twin Comanche 160B	P. & H. Robinson
	G-PDGE	Eurocopter EC.120B	McAlpine Helicopters Ltd/Kidlington
	G-PDGG	Aeromere F.8L Falco Srs 3	P. D. G. Grist
	G-PDGN	SA.365N Dauphin 2	PLM Dollar Group Ltd (G-TRAF/G-BLDR)
	G-PDHJ	Cessna T.182R	P. G. Vallance Ltd
	G-PDOC	PA-44-180 Seminole	Medicare (G-PVAF)/Newcastle
	G-PDOG	Cessna 305C Bird Dog	N. D. Needham
	G-PDSI	Cessna 172N	DA Flying Group
	G-PDWI	Mini-500	P. Waterhouse
	G-PEAK	AB-206B JetRanger 2	Leisure Park Management Ltd (G-BLJE)
	G-PEAL	Aerotek Pitts S-2A	Plymouth Executive Aviation Ltd
	G-PEGA	Pegasus Quantum 15-912	J. J. Bowen
	G-PEGG	Colt 90A balloon	Ballon Vole Association/France
	G-PEGI	PA-34-200T Seneca II	Tayflite Ltd
	G-PEGY	Shaw Europa	M. T. Dawson
	G-PEJM	PA-28-181 Archer III	E. J. Moorey/Bournemouth
	G-PEKT	SOCATA TB.20 Trinidad	A. J. Dales
	G-PELG	Avions Mudry CAP.231	J. P. M. Groot (G-OPPS)/Netherlands
	G-PENT	Bell 206B JetRanger 3	Flying Tonight Ltd (G-IIRB)
	G-PEPL	MDH MD.600N	Helidirect UK Ltd
	G-PERC	Cameron N-90 balloon	Stanton Marris Ltd
	G-PERR	Cameron 60 Bottle SS balloon ★	British Balloon Museum/Newbury
	G-PERZ	Bell 206B JetRanger 3	C. P. Lockyer
	G-PEST	Hawker Tempest II (MW401)	Tempest Two Ltd
	G-PETR	PA-28 Cherokee 140	Marnham Investments Ltd (G-BCJL)
	G-PFAA	EAA Biplane Model P	S. Alexander & M. Coffee
	G-PFAF	FRED Srs 2	M. S. Perkins
	G-PFAG	Evans VP-1	J. A. Hatch
	G-PFAH	Evans VP-1	J. A. Scott
	G-PFAL	FRED Srs 2	J. McD. Robinson/Bann Foot
	G-PFAO	Evans VP-1	P. W. Price
	G-PFAP	Currie Wot/SE-5A (C1904)	J. H. Seed
	G-PFAR	Isaacs Fury II (K2059)	J. W. Hale & R. Cooper
	G-PFAT	Monnett Sonerai II	H. B. Carter

Reg.	Type	Owner or Operator	Notes
G-PFAW	Evans VP-1	R. F. Shingler	
G-PFFN	Beech 200 Super King Air	The Puffin Club Ltd	
G-PFML	Robinson R-44	Helicopter Training & Hire Ltd	
G-PFSL	Cessna F.152	P. A. Simon	
G-PGAC	Dyn Aero MCR-01	D. T. S. Walsh & G. A. Coatesworth	
G-PGFG	Tecnam P.92-EM Echo	P. G. Fitzgerald	
G-PGSA	Thruster T.600N	G. J. Slater	
G-PGSI	Robin R.2160	P. Spencer	
G-PGUY	Sky 70-16 balloon	Black Sheep Balloons (G-BXZJ)	
G-PHAA	Cessna F.150M	PHA Aviation Ltd (G-BCPE)	
G-PHEL	Robinson R-22B	Focal Point Communications Ltd (G-RUMP)	
G-PHIL	Brookland Hornet	A. J. Philpotts	
G-PHOT	Thunder Film Cassette SS balloon	Flying Pictures Ltd	
G-PHSI	Colt 90A balloon	P. H. Strickland & Simpson (Piccadilly) Ltd	
G-PHTG	SOCATA TB.10 Tobago	A. J. Baggarley	
G-PHYL	Denney Kitfox Mk 4	J. Dunn	
G-PIAF	Thunder Ax7-65 balloon	L. Battersley	
G-PICT	Colt 180A balloon	J. L. Guy	
G-PIDG	Robinson R-44	First Degree Air	
G-PIDS	Boeing 757-225	My Travel Airways (Airtours)	
G-PIEL	CP.301A Emeraude	P. R. Thorne (G-BARY)	
G-PIES	Thunder Ax7-77Z balloon	Pork Farms Ltd	
G-PIET	Pietenpol Air Camper	N. D. Marshall	
G-PIGG	Lindstrand LBL Pig SS balloon	I. Heidenreich/Germany	
G-PIGS	SOCATA Rallye 150ST	Boonhill Flying Group (G-BDWB)	
G-PIGY	SC.7 Skyvan Srs 3A Variant 100	Hunting Contract Services/ Weston-on-the-Green	
G-PIIX	Cessna P.210N	J. R. Colthurst (G-KATH)	
G-PIKE	Robinson R-22 Mariner	Sloane Helicopters Ltd/Sywell	
G-PIKK	PA-28 Cherokee 140	O. D. Atkinson & ptnrs (G-AVLA)	
G-PILE	Rotorway Executive 90	J. B. Russell	
G-PILL	Light Aero Avid Flyer Mk 4	D. R. Meston	
G-PINE	Thunder Ax8-90 balloon	J. A. Pine	
G-PING	AA-5A Cheetah	Plane Talking Ltd (G-OCWC/G-WULL)/ Elstree	
G-PINT	Cameron 65 Barrel SS balloon	D. K. Fish	
G-PINX	Lindstrand Pink Panther SS balloon	Magical Adventures Ltd/USA	
G-PIPR	PA-18 Super Cub 95	D. S. Sweet (G-BCDC)	
G-PIPS	Van's RV-4	C. J. Marsh	
G-PIPY	Cameron 105 Pipe SS balloon	Cameron Balloons Ltd	
G-PITS	Pitts S-2AE Special	The Eitlean Group	
G-PITZ	Pitts S-2A Special	A. K. Halvorsen	
G-PIXE	Colt 31A balloon	N. D. Eliot	
G-PIXI	Pegasus Quantum 15-912	D. L. Goode	
G-PIXS	Cessna 336	Atlantic Bridge Aviation Ltd/Lydd	
G-PIZZ	Lindstrand LBL-105A balloon	HD Bargain SRL/Italy	
G-PJMT	Lancair 320	M. T. Holland	
G-PJTM	Cessna FR.172K II	Jane Air (G-BFIF)	
G-PKPK	Schweizer 269C	C. H. Dobson	
G-PLAC	PA-31-350 Navajo Chieftain	D. B. Harper (G-OLDA/ G-BNDS)	
G-PLAH	BAe Jetstream 3102	Vale Aviation PLAH Ltd (G-LOVA/ G-OAKA/G-BUFM/G-LAKH)	
G-PLAJ	BAe Jetstream 3102	-	
G-PLAN	Cessna F.150L	G-PLAN Flying Group	
G-PLAY	Robin R.2100A	D. R. Austin	
G-PLBI	Cessna 172S	Grandfort Properties Ltd/Booker	
G-PLEE	Cessna 182Q	Peterlee Parachute Centre	
G-PLIV	Pazmany PL.4A	B. P. North	
G-PLMB	AS.350B Ecureuil	PLM Dollar Group Ltd (G-BMMB)	
G-PLMH	AS.350B-2 Ecureuil	PLM Dollar Group Ltd	
G-PLMI	SA.365C-1 Dauphin	PLM Dollar Group Ltd	
G-PLOW	Hughes 269B	Sulby Aerial Surveys Ltd (G-AVUM)	
G-PLPC	Schweizer Hughes 269C	Power Lines, Pipes & Cables Ltd (G-JMAT)	
G-PLPM	Shaw Europa XS	P. L. P. Mansfiled	
G-PLXI	BAe ATP/Jetstream 61	BAe (Operations) Ltd (G-MATP)/ Woodford	
G-PMAM	Cameron V-65 balloon	P. A. Meecham	
G-PMAX	PA-31-350 Navajo Chieftain	AM & T Aviation Ltd (G-GRAM/G-BRHF)	
G-PMNF	V.S.361 Spitfire HF.IX (TA805)	P. R. Monk	

Notes	Reg.	Type	Owner or Operator
	G-PNEU	Colt 110 Bibendum SS balloon	The Aerial Display Co Ltd
	G-PNNI	PA-28-181 Archer III	Total Entertainments
	G-POAH	Sikorsky S-76B	Signature Aircraft Charter
	G-POAJ	Canadair CL.604 Challenger	P & O Containers (Assets) Ltd
	G-POGO	Flight Design CT.2K	P. A. & M. W. Aston
	G-POLY	Cameron N-77 balloon	Empty Wallets Balloon Group
	G-POND	Oldfield Baby Lakes	C. Bellmer/Germany
	G-POOH	Piper J-3C-65 Cub	P. & H. Robinson
	G-POOL	ARV Super 2	P. A. Dawson (G-BNHA)
	G-POOP	Dyn Aero MCR-01	Eurodata Computer Supplies
	G-POPA	Beech A36 Bonanza	C. J. O'Sullivan
	G-POPE	Eiri PIK-20E-1	C. J. Hadley
	G-POPI	SOCATA TB.10 Tobago	I. S. Hacon & C. J. Earle (G-BKEN)
	G-POPS	PA-34-220T Seneca III	Alpine Ltd
	G-POPW	Cessna 182S	D. L. Price
	G-PORK	AA-5B Tiger	C. M. M. Grange & D. Thomas (G-BFHS)
	G-PORT	Bell 206B JetRanger 3	Image Computer System Ltd
	G-POSE	SE.3130 Alouette II	Alouette Aviation (G-BZGG)
	G-POSH	Colt 56A balloon	B. K. Rippon (G-BMPT)
	G-POTT	Robinson R-44 Astro	Ranc Care Homes Ltd
	G-POWL	Cessna 182R	Hillhouse Estates Ltd
	G-PPAH	Enstrom 480	D. S. Tunnicliffe
	G-PPPP	Denney Kitfox Mk 3	R. Powers
	G-PPTS	Robinson R-44	Superstore Ltd
	G-PRAG	Brügger MB.2 Colibri	Colibri Flying Group
	G-PRAH	Flight Design CT.2K	P. R. A. Hammond
	G-PRET	Robinson R-44	R. W. Raymond
	G-PREY	Pereira Osprey II	D. W. Gibson (G-BEPB)
	G-PRII	Hawker Hunter PR.11	Stick & Rudder Aviation Ltd/Belgium
	G-PRIM	PA-38-112 Tomahawk	Braddock Ltd
	G-PRIT	Cameron N-90 balloon	B. J. Hammond (G-HTVI)
	G-PRNT	Cameron V-90 balloon	E. K. Gray
	G-PROB	AS.350B-2 Ecureuil	Irvine Aviation Ltd (G-PROD)
	G-PROF	Lindstrand LBL-90A balloon	S. J. Wardle
	G-PROM	AS.350B Ecureuil	JPM Ltd (G-MAGY/G-BIYC)
	G-PROP	AA-5A Cheetah	Fortune Technology Ltd (G-BHKU)
	G-PROV	P.84 Jet Provost T.52A (T.4)	Provost Group
	G-PRSI	Pegasus Quantum 15-912	S. Morris
	G-PRTT	Cameron N-31 balloon	J. M. Albury
	G-PSIC	NA P-51C Mustang (2106449)	Patina Ltd/Duxford
	G-PSRT	PA-28-151 Warrior	P. A. S. Dyke (G-BSGN)
	G-PSST	Hunter F.58A	Heritage Aviation Developments Ltd/ Bournemouth
	G-PSUE	CFM Shadow Srs CD	P. F. Lorroman (G-MYAA)
	G-PTAG	Shaw Europa	R. C. Harrison
	G-PTRE	SOCATA TB.20 Trinidad	Trantshore Ltd (G-BNKU)
	G-PTWB	Cessna T.303	F. Kratky (G-BYNG)
	G-PTWO	Pilatus P2-05 (U-110)	Bulldog Aviation Ltd/Earls Colne
	G-PTYE	Shaw Europa	J. Tye
	G-PUDL	PA-18 Super Cub 150	R. A. Roberts
	G-PUDS	Shaw Europa	I. Milner
	G-PUFF	Thunder Ax7-77A balloon	Intervarsity Balloon Club
	G-PUFN	Cessna 340A	The Puffin Club
	G-PUGS	Cessna 182H	N. C. & M. F. Shaw
	G-PUMA	AS.332L Super Puma	CHC Scotia Ltd
	G-PUMB	AS.332L Super Puma	CHC Scotia Ltd
	G-PUMD	AS.332L Super Puma	CHC Scotia Ltd
	G-PUME	AS.332L Super Puma	CHC Scotia Ltd
	G-PUMG	AS.332L Super Puma	CHC Scotia Ltd
	G-PUMH	AS.332L Super Puma	Bristow Helicopters Ltd
	G-PUMI	AS.332L Super Puma	Bristow Helicopters Ltd
	G-PUMK	AS.332L Super Puma	CHC Scotia Ltd
	G-PUML	AS.332L Super Puma	CHC Scotia Ltd
	G-PUMM	AS.332L-2 Super Puma	CHC Scotia Ltd
	G-PUMN	AS.332L Super Puma	CHC Scotia Ltd
	G-PUMO	AS.332L-2 Super Puma	CHC Scotia Ltd
	G-PUMS	AS.332L-2 Super Puma	CHC Scotia Ltd
	G-PUPP	B.121 Pup 2	P. A. Teichman (G-BASD)/Elstree
	G-PURR	AA-5A Cheetah	Nabco Retail Display (G-BJDN)
	G-PURS	Rotorway Executive	J. E. Houseman
	G-PUSH	Rutan LongEz	E. G. Peterson
	G-PUSI	Cessna T.303	Crusader Aviation Ltd/Kidlington
	G-PUSK	PA-32R-301 Saratoga IIHP	HN Consultancy (UK) Ltd

Reg.	Type	Owner or Operator	Notes
G-PUSS	Cameron N-77 balloon	L. D. Thurgar	
G-PUSY	RL-5A LW Sherwood Ranger	B. J. Chester-Master (G-MZNF)	
G-PUTT	Cameron 76 Golf SS balloon	Lakeside Lodge Golf Centre	
G-PVBF	Lindstrand LBL-260S balloon	Virgin Balloon Flights Ltd	
G-PVCU	Cameron N-77 balloon	R. G. March & T. J. Maycock	
G-PVET	D.H.C.1 Chipmunk 22 (WB565)	Connect Properties Ltd	
G-PWBE	D.H.82A Tiger Moth	P. W. Beales	
G-PWEL	Robinson R-22B-2	DJP Ltd	
G-PWER	Agusta A.109E	Powersense Ltd	
G-PWIT	Bell 206L-1 LongRanger	Formal Graphics Ltd (G-DWMI)	
G-PYRO	Cameron N-65 balloon	A. C. Booth	
G-PZAZ	PA-31-350 Navajo Chieftain	Air Medical Ltd (G-VTAX/G-UTAX)	
G-PZIZ	PA-31-350 Navajo Chieftain	Air Medical Ltd (G-CAFZ/G-BPPT)	
G-RACA	P.57 Sea Prince T.1 (571/CU)	(stored)/Long Marston	
G-RACO	PA-28R Cherokee Arrow 200-II	Graco Group Ltd	
G-RACY	Cessna 182S	N. J. Fuller	
G-RADA	Soko P-2 Kraguj (30140)	Steerworld Ltd	
G-RADI	PA-28-181 Archer II	G. S. & D. V. Foster	
G-RAEM	Rutan LongEz	G. F. H. Singleton	
G-RAES	Boeing 777-236	British Airways	
G-RAFA	Grob G.115	RAF College Flying Club Ltd/Cranwell	
G-RAFB	Grob G.115	RAF College Flying Club Ltd/Cranwell	
G-RAFC	Robin R.2112	RAF Charlie Group	
G-RAFE	Thunder Ax7-77 balloon	Giraffe Balloon Syndicate	
G-RAFF	Learjet 35A	Graff Aviation Ltd/Heathrow	
G-RAFG	Slingsby T.67C Firefly	Arrow Flying Ltd	
G-RAFI	P.84 Jet Provost T.4 (XP672)	R. J. Everett/North Weald	
G-RAFT	Rutan LongEz	B. Wronski	
G-RAFW	Mooney M.20E	Vinola (Knitwear) Manufacturing Co. Ltd (G-ATHW)	
G-RAGG	Maule M5-235C Lunar Rocket	P. Ragg	
G-RAGS	Pietenpol Air Camper	R. F. Billington	
G-RAID	AD-4NA Skyraider (126922)	Patina Ltd/Duxford	
G-RAIL	Colt 105A balloon	Ballooning World Ltd	
G-RAIN	Maule M5-235C Lunar Rocket	D. S. McKay & J. A. Rayment/ Hinton-in-the-Hedges	
G-RAIX	CCF AT-16 Harvard 4 (KF584)	M. R. Paul & P. A. Shaw (G-BIWX)	
G-RAJA	Raj Hamsa X'Air 582 (2)	Priory Flyers	
G-RALD	Robinson R-22HP	Heli Air Ltd (G-CHIL)	
G-RAMI	Bell 206B JetRanger 3	Yorkshire Helicopters/Leeds	
G-RAMP	Piper J-3C-65 Cub	J. Whittall	
G-RAMS	PA-32R-301 Saratoga SP	Air Tobago Ltd/Netherthorpe	
G-RAMY	Bell 206B JetRanger 2	Lincair Ltd	
G-RANS	Rans S.10 Sakota	J. D. Weller	
G-RANZ	Rans S-10 Sakota	P. Whittingham	
G-RAPA	BN-2T-4R Defender 4000	B-N Group Ltd (G-BJBH)/Bembridge	
G-RAPH	Cameron O-77 balloon	P. B. D. Bird & M. E. Mason	
G-RAPP	Cameron H-34 balloon	Cameron Balloons Ltd	
G-RARB	Cessna 172N	Richlyn Aviation Ltd (G-BOII)	
G-RARE	Thunder Ax5-42 SS balloon	Justerini & Brooks Ltd	
G-RASC	Evans VP-2	K. A. Stewart & G. Oldfield	
G-RATE	AA-5A Cheetah	Holmes Rentals (G-BIFF)/Blackbushe	
G-RATZ	Shaw Europa	W. Goldsmith	
G-RAVE	Southdown Raven X	M. J. Robbins (G-MNZV)	
G-RAVN	Robinson R-44	Heli Air Ltd/Wellesbourne	
G-RAWS	Rotorway Executive 162F	Raw Sports Ltd	
G-RAYA	Denney Kitfox Mk 4	A. K. Ray	
G-RAYE	PA-32 Cherokee Six 260	G-RAYE Group (G-ATTY)	
G-RAYS	Zenair CH.250	M. J. Malbon	
G-RBBB	Shaw Europa	T. J. Hartwell	
G-RBCI	BN-2A Mk.III-2 Trislander	Aurigny Air Services Ltd (G-BDWV)	
G-RBMV	Cameron O-31 balloon	P. D. Griffiths	
G-RBOS	Colt AS-105 airship ★	Science Museum/Wroughton	
G-RBOW	Thunder Ax-7-65 balloon	A. C. Hall	
G-RCED	R. Commander 114	Echo Delta Ltd	
G-RCEJ	BAe 125 Srs 800B	Aravco Ltd (G-GEIL)/Farnborough	
G-RCMC	Murphy Renegade 912	R. C. M. Collisson	
G-RCMF	Cameron V-77 balloon	Mouldform Ltd	
G-RCML	Sky 77-24 balloon	R. C. M. Sarl/Luxembourg	
G-RDBS	Cessna 550 Citation II	Albion Aviation Management Ltd (G-JETA)	
G-RDCI	R. Commander 112A	P. Turner (G-BFWG)	

Notes	Reg.	Type	Owner or Operator
	G-RDEL	Robinson R-44	GRB Developments Ltd
	G-RDVE	Airbus A.320-231	My Travel Airways (Airtours)
	G-READ	Colt 77A balloon	J. Keena
	G-REAH	PA-32R-301 Saratoga SP	M. Q. Tolbod & S. J. Rogers (G-CELL)
	G-REAP	Pitts S-1S Special	R. Dixon
	G-REAS	Van's RV-6A	E. J. D. Proctor
	G-REAT	GA-7 Cougar	Goodtechnique Ltd
	G-REBA	RAF 2000 GTX-SE gyroplane	D. J. Pearce
	G-REBK	Beech B200 Super King Air	Planstable Enterprises Ltd
	G-REBL	Hughes 269B	Farmax Ltd
	G-RECK	PA-28 Cherokee 140B	R. J. Grantham & D. Boatswain (G-AXJW)
	G-RECO	Jurca MJ-5L Sirocco	J. D. Tseliki
	G-REDA	Robinson R-22B	Simax Services Ltd
	G-REDB	Cessna 310Q	Red Baron Haulage Ltd (G-BBIC)
	G-REDC	Pegasus Quantum 15-912	Red Communications Ltd
	G-REDD	Cessna 310R II	G. Wightman (G-BMGT)
	G-REDI	Robinson R-44	Redeye.com Ltd
	G-REDX	Experimental Aviation Berkut	G. V. Waters
	G-REEC	Sequoia F.8L Falco	J. D. Tseliki
	G-REED	Mainair Blade 912S	P. A. B. Morgan
	G-REEF	Mainair Blade 912S	G. B. Shaw
	G-REEK	AA-5A Cheetah	J. & A. Pearson
	G-REEM	AS.355F-1 Twin Squirrel	Heliking Ltd (G-EMAN/G-WEKR/ G-CHLA)
	G-REEN	Cessna 340	E. & M. Green (G-AZYR)/Guernsey
	G-REES	Jodel D.140C	W. H. Greenwood
	G-REKO	Pegasus Quasar IITC	G. S. Stokes (G-MWWA)
	G-RENE	Murphy Renegade 912	P. M. Whitaker
	G-RENO	SOCATA TB.10 Tobago	Lamond Ltd
	G-RENT	Robinson R-22B	Rentatruck Self Drive Ltd
	G-REPH	Pegasus Quantum 15-912	R. S. Partridge-Hicks
	G-REST	Beech P35 Bonanza	C. R. Taylor (G-ASFJ)
	G-RETA	C.A.S.A. 1.131 Jungmann 2000	N. S. C. & G. English (G-BGZC)
	G-REXS	PA-28-181 Archer II	Tatenhill Aviation
	G-REYS	Canadair CL.604 Challenger	Greyscape Ltd
	G-RFDS	Agusta A.109A-II	Castle Air Charters Ltd (G-BOLA)
	G-RFIL	Thunder Colt 77A balloon	G. Davis
	G-RFIO	Aeromot AMT-200 Super Ximango	M. D. Evans
	G-RFSB	Sportavia RF-5B	S. W. Brown
	G-RGDT	Dornier Do.228-201K	Air Wales Ltd
	G-RGEE	Extra EA.300/L	Skylane Aviation Ltd
	G-RGEN	Cessna T.337D	Legoprint SpA (G-EDOT/G-BJIY)/Italy
	G-RGUS	Fairchild 24A-46A Argus III (44-83184)	Fenlands Ltd
	G-RHCB	Schweizer 269C-1	Aviation Rentals
	G-RHHT	PA-32RT-300 Lance II	R. W. & M. Struth
	G-RHYS	Rotorway Executive 90	A. K. Voase & K. Matthews
	G-RIAN	AB-206A JetRanger	Thorneygrove Ltd (G-SOOR/G-FMAL/ G-BHSG)
	G-RIAT	Robinson R-22B-2	RMJ Helicopters
	G-RIBS	Diamond Katana DA.20-A1	Phantom Air Ltd (G-BWWM)
	G-RIBV	Cessna 560 Citation V. Ultra	Houston Air Taxis Ltd/Kidlington
	G-RICA	AG-5B Tiger	Gowad Aviation Ltd
	G-RICC	AS.350B-2 Ecureuil	Specialist Helicopters Ltd (G-BTXA)
	G-RICE	Robinson R-22B	Heli Air Ltd/Wellesbourne
	G-RICK	Beech 95-B55 Baron	James Jack (Invergordon) Ltd (G-BAAG)
	G-RICO	AG-\5B Tiger	Dynasty Trading Ltd
	G-RICS	Shaw Europa	The Flying Property Doctor
	G-RIDE	Stephens Akro	R. Mitchell/Coventry
	G-RIDL	Robinson R-22B	G. Riddell
	G-RIFB	Hughes 269C	J. McHugh & Son (Civil Engineering Contractors) Ltd
	G-RIFN	Avion Mudry CAP.10B	S. A. W. Becker
	G-RIGB	Thunder Ax7-77 balloon	N. J. Bettin
	G-RIGH	PA-32R-301 Saratoga IIHP	Rentair
	G-RIGS	PA-60 Aerostar 601P	G. G. Caravatti & P. G. Penati/Italy
	G-RIIN	WSK PZL-104M Wilga 2000	PZL International Aviation Marketing & Sales PLC/North Weald
	G-RIKI	Mainair Blade 912	R. Cook
	G-RIKS	Shaw Europa XS	R. Morris
	G-RIMM	Westland Wasp HAS.1 (NZ3907)	M. P. Grimshaw & T. Martin

Reg.	Type	Owner or Operator	Notes
G-RINN	Mainair Blade	J. P. Lang	
G-RINO	Thunder Ax7-77 balloon	D. J. Head	
G-RINS	Rans S.6-ESD Coyote II	D. Watt	
G-RINT	CFM Streak Shadow	D. Grint	
G-RIPE	Pitts S-1S Special	J. A. Harris	
G-RIPS	Cameron 110 Parachutist SS balloon	Virgin Airship & Balloon Co Ltd	
G-RISE	Cameron V-77 balloon	D. L. Smith	
G-RIST	Cessna 310R II	J. M. Jackson (G-DATS)	
G-RIVR	Thruster T.600N	Thruster Air Services Ltd	
G-RIVT	Van's RV-6	N. Reddish	
G-RIZE	Cameron O-90 balloon	S. F. Burden/Netherlands	
G-RIZI	Cameron N-90 balloon	R. Wiles	
G-RIZZ	PA-28-161 Warrior II	Northamptonshire School of Flying Ltd/ Sywell	
G-RJAH	Boeing Stearman A.75N1	R. J. Horne	
G-RJAM	Sequoia F.8C Falco	R. J. Marks	
G-RJCP	R. Commander 114B	Heltor Ltd	
G-RJGR	Boeing 757-225	My Travel Airways (Airtours)	
G-RJMS	PA-28R-201 Arrow III	M. G. Hill	
G-RJTT	Bell 206B JetRanger 3	Air Deluxe	
G-RJWW	Maule M5-235C Lunar Rocket	Paw Flying Services Ltd (G-BRWG)	
G-RJWX	Shaw Europa XS	J. R. Jones	
G-RJXA	Embraer RJ145EP	bmi regional	
G-RJXB	Embraer RJ145EP	bmi regional	
G-RJXC	Embraer RJ145EP	bmi regional	
G-RJXD	Embraer RJ145EP	bmi regional	
G-RJXE	Embraer RJ145EP	bmi regional	
G-RJXF	Embraer RJ145EP	bmi regional	
G-RJXG	Embraer RJ145EP	bmi regional	
G-RJXH	Embraer RJ145EP	bmi regional	
G-RJXI	Embraer RJ145EP	bmi regional	
G-RJXJ	Embraer RJ135LR	bmi regional	
G-RJXK	Embraer RJ135LR	bmi regional	
G-RJ	Embraer RJ135LR	bmi regional	
G-RJ	Embraer RJ135LR	bmi regional	
G-RKET	Taylor JT.2 Titch	P. A. Dunkley (G-BIBK)	
G-RKEL	AB-206B JetRanger 3	Nunkeeling Ltd	
G-RLFI	Cessna FA.152	Tayside Aviation Ltd (G-DFTS)/Aberdeen	
G-RLMC	Cessna 421C	R. D. Lygo	
G-RMAC	Shaw Europa	P. J. Lawless	
G-RMAN	Aero Designs Pulsar	M. B. Redman	
G-RMAX	Cameron C-80 balloon	M. Quinn & D. Curtain	
G-RMIE	Bell 206B JetRanger 3	R & M International Engineering Ltd (G-BPIE)	
G-RMIT	Van's RV-4	J. P. Kloos	
G-RMUG	Cameron 90 Mug SS balloon	Nestle UK Ltd	
G-RNAS	D.H.104 Sea Devon C.20 (XK896) ★	Airport Fire Service/Filton	
G-RNBW	Bell 206B JetRanger 2	Rainbow Helicopters Ltd	
G-RNGO	Robinson R-22B-2	B. E. Llewellyn	
G-RNIE	Cameron 70 Ball SS balloon	N. J. Bland	
G-RNLI	V.S.236 Walrus I (W2718) ★	R. E. Melton	
G-RNRM	Cessna A.185F	Skydive St. Andrews Ltd	
G-ROAR	Cessna 401	Special Scope Ltd (G-BZFL/G-AWSF)	
G-ROBD	Shaw Europa	R. D. Davies	
G-ROBN	Robin R.1180T	Bustard Flying Club Ltd	
G-ROBT	Hawker Hurricane I	R. A. Roberts	
G-ROBY	Colt 17A balloon	Virgin Airship & Balloon Co Ltd	
G-ROCH	Cessna T.303	R. S. Bentley	
G-ROCK	Thunder Ax7-77 balloon	M. A. Green	
G-ROCR	Schweizer 269C	Oxford Aviation Services Ltd/Kidlington	
G-RODD	Cessna 310R II	R. J. Herbert Engineering Ltd (G-TEDD/ G-MADI)	
G-RODG	Avtech Jabiru UL	S. Jackson	
G-RODI	Isaacs Fury (K3731)	M. R. Baker/Shoreham	
G-ROGY	Cameron 60 Concept balloon	A. A. Laing	
G-ROLA	PA-34-200T Seneca	Deer Hill Aviation Ltd & Goss Challenges Ltd	
G-ROLF	PA-32R-301 Saratoga SP	P. F. Larkins	
G-ROLL	Pitts S-2A Special	Aerial & Aerobatic Services	
G-ROLO	Robinson R-22B	Plane Talking Ltd/Elstree	
G-ROME	I.I.I. Sky Arrow 650TC	Sky Arrow (Kits) UK Ltd	

Notes	Reg.	Type	Owner or Operator
	G-ROMW	Cyclone AX2000	Financial Planning (Wells) Ltd
	G-RONA	Shaw Europa	C. M. Noakes
	G-ROND	Short SD3-60 Variant 100	Emerald Airways Ltd (G-OLAH/G-BPCO/
			G-RMSS/G-BKKU)/Liverpool
	G-RONG	PA-28R Cherokee Arrow 200-II	E. Tang
	G-RONI	Cameron V-77 balloon	R. E. Simpson
	G-RONN	Robinson R-44 Astro	R. Hallam & S. E. Watts
	G-RONS	Robin DR.400/180	R. & K. Baker
	G-RONW	FRED Srs 2	K. Atkinson
	G-ROOK	Cessna F.172P	Rolim Ltd
	G-ROOV	Shaw Europa XS	E. Sheridan & P. W. Hawkins
	G-RORI	Folland Gnat T.1 (XR538)	D, S, Milne
	G-RORO	Cessna 337B	H. D. Hezlett (G-AVIX)
	G-RORY	Piaggio FWP.149D	Bushfire Investments Ltd (G-TOWN)/
			North Weald
	G-ROSE	Evans VP-1	A. P. M. Long
	G-ROSI	Thunder Ax7-77 balloon	J. E. Rose
	G-ROTI	Luscombe 8A Silvaire	A. L. Chapman & R. Ludgate
	G-ROTR	Brantly B.2B	P. G. R. Brown
	G-ROTS	CFM Streak Shadow Srs SA	K. K. Kenealy
	G-ROUP	Cessna F.172M	Stapleford Flying Club Ltd (G-BDPH)
	G-ROUS	PA-34-200T Seneca II	Oxford Aviation Services Ltd/Kidlington
	G-ROUT	Robinson R-22B	Preston Associatres Ltd
	G-ROVE	PA-18 Super Cub 135	S. J. Gaveston
	G-ROVY	Robinson R-22B-2	R. Rice
	G-ROWE	Cessna F.182P	D. Rowe/Liverpool
	G-ROWI	Shaw Europa XS	R. M. Carson
	G-ROWL	AA-5B Tiger	Airhouse Corporation Ltd/Elstree
	G-ROWN	Beech 200 Super King Air	Valentia Air Ltd (G-BHLC)
	G-ROWR	Robinson R-44	R. A. Oldworth
	G-ROWS	PA-28-151 Warrior	Mustarrow Ltd/Woodford
	G-ROZI	Robinson R-44	Milford Garage Ltd
	G-ROZY	Cameron R.36 balloon	Jacques W. Soukup Enterprises Ltd/USA
	G-RPEZ	Rutan LongEz	B. A. Fairston & D. Richardson
	G-RRCU	CEA DR.221B Dauphin	Merlin Flying Club Ltd
	G-RRFC	SOCATA TB.20 Trinidad GT	A. T. Paton
	G-RRGN	V.S.390 Spitfire PR.XIX (PS853)	Rolls-Royce PLC (G-MXIX)/Filton
	G-RRIN	WSK PZL-104M Wilga 2000	PZL International Marketing & Sales PLC
	G-RROD	PA-30 Twin Comanche 160B	R. P. Coplestone (G-SHAW)
	G-RSCJ	Cessna 525 CitationJet	SMD Investments Ltd
	G-RSFT	PA-28-161 Warrior II	SFT Europe Ltd (G-WARI)/Bournemouth
	G-RSKR	PA-28-161 Warrior II	Krown Group (G-BOJY)
	G-RSSF	Denney Kitfox Mk 2	R. W. Somerville
	G-RSVP	Robinson R-22B-2	Pearce Enterprise Ltd
	G-RSWO	Cessna 172R	AC Management Associates Ltd
	G-RSWW	Robinson R-22B	Woodstock Enterprises
	G-RTBI	Thunder Ax6-56 balloon	P. J. Waller
	G-RTWW	Robinson R-44 Astro	Rotorvation
	G-RUBB	AA-5B Tiger	D. E. Gee/Blackbushe
	G-RUBI	Thunder Ax7-77 balloon	Warren & Johnson
	G-RUBY	PA-28RT-201T Turbo Arrow IV	Arrow Aircraft Group (G-BROU)
	G-RUDD	Cameron V-65 balloon	N. A. Apsey
	G-RUFF	Mainair Blade 912	C. G. P. Holden
	G-RUFS	Avtech Jabiru UL	J. W. Holland
	G-RUGS	Campbell Cricket Mk 4 gyroplane	J. L. G. McLane
	G-RUIA	Cessna F.172N	Knockin Flying Club Ltd
	G-RUMM	Grumman F8F-2P Bearcat (21714)	Patina Ltd/Duxford
	G-RUMN	AA-1A Trainer	T. J. White/Stapleford
	G-RUMT	Grumman F7F-3P Tigercat (80425)	Patina Ltd/Duxford
	G-RUMW	Grumman FM-2 Wildcat (JV579)	Patina Ltd/Duxford
	G-RUNG	SAAB SF.340A	Aurigny Air Services Ltd
	G-RUNT	Cassutt Racer IIIM	N. A. Scully
	G-RUSA	Pegasus Quantum 15-912	A. D. Stewart
	G-RUSL	Van's RV-6A	G. R. Russell
	G-RUSO	Robinson R-22B	R. M. Barnes-Gorell
	G-RUSS	Cessna 172N ★	Leisure Lease (stored)/Southend
	G-RUVY	Van's RV-9A	R. Taylor
	G-RVAL	Van's RV-8	R. N. York
	G-RVAN	Van's RV-6	D. Broom
	G-RVAW	Van's RV-6	A. A. Wordsworth
	G-RVBA	Van's RV-8A	S. Hawksworth

Reg.	Type	Owner or Operator	Notes
G-RVBC	Van's RV-6A	B. J. Clifford	
G-RVCE	Van's RV-6A	M. D. Barnard & C. Voelger	
G-RVCG	Van's RV-6A	C. J. Griffin	
G-RVCL	Van's RV-6	C. T. Lamb	
G-RVDJ	Van's RV-6	J. D. Jewitt	
G-RVDP	Van's RV-4	D. H. Pattison	
G-RVDR	Van's RV6A	D. W. Reast	
G-RVEE	Van's RV-6	J. C. A. Wheeler	
G-RVET	Van's RV-6	D. R. Coleman	
G-RVGA	Van's RV-6A	D. P. Dawson	
G-RVHT	Cessna 550 Citation 2	Ravenheat Manufacturing Ltd	
G-RVIA	Van's RV-6A	A. N. Tyers	
G-RVIB	Van's RV-6	I. M. Belmore	
G-RVII	Van's RV-7	P. H. C. Hall	
G-RVIN	Van's RV-6	N. Reddish	
G-RVIT	Van's RV-6	P. J. Shotbolt	
G-RVIV	Van's RV-4	G. S. Scot	
G-RVIX	Van's RV-9A	R. E. Garforth	
G-RVMJ	Van's RV-4	M. J. de Ruiter	
G-RVMT	Van's RV-6	M. R. Tingle	
G-RVMZ	Van's RV-8	M. W. Zipfell	
G-RVRA	PA-28 Cherokee 140	Ravenair (G-OWVA)/Liverpool	
G-RVRB	PA-34-200T Seneca II	Ravenair (G-BTAJ)/Liverpool	
G-RVRC	PA-23 Aztec 250E	Ravenair (G-BNPD)/Liverpool	
G-RVRD	PA-23 Aztec 250E	Ravenair (G-BRAV/G-BBCM)/Liverpool	
G-RVRF	PA-38-112 Tomahawk	Ravenair (G-BGEL)/Liverpool	
G-RVRG	PA-38-112 Tomahawk	Ravenair (G-BHAF)/Liverpool	
G-RVRS	Robinson R-22B	Holly Aviation Ltd (G-BYCK/G-XTEC)	
G-RVRV	Van's RV-4	P. Jenkins	
G-RVSA	Van's RV-6A	W. H. Knott	
G-RVSX	Van's RV-6	R. L. & V. A. West	
G-RVVI	Van's RV-6	J. E. Alsford & J. N. Parr	
G-RWHC	Cameron A-180 balloon	Wickers World Hot Air Balloon Co	
G-RWIN	Rearwin 175	G. Kay	
G-RWLY	Shaw Europa XS	C. R. Arcle	
G-RWSS	Denney Kitfox Mk 2	R. W. Somerville	
G-RWWW	W.S.55 Whirlwind HCC.12 (XR486) ★	IHM/Weston-s-Mare	
G-RXUK	Lindstrand LBL-105A balloon	P. A. Hames	
G-RYAL	Avtech Jabiru UL	A. C. Ryall	
G-RYPH	Mainair Blade 912	R. J. Griffiths	
G-RZPH	CFM Streak Shadow SLA	CFM Aircraft Ltd	
G-SAAB	R. Commander 112TC	M. R. J. Hill (G-BEFS)	
G-SAAM	Cessna T.182R	M. D. Harvey & ptnrs (G-TAGL)	
G-SABA	PA-28R-201T Turbo Arrow III	D. Booth (G-BFEN)	
G-SABB	Eurocopter EC.135T-1	Bond Air Services Ltd	
G-SABR	NA F-86A Sabre (8178)	Golden Apple Operations Ltd/Bournemouth	
G-SACB	Cessna F.152 II	Flight Ltd (G-BFRB)	
G-SACD	Cessna F.172H	Northbrook College of Design & Technology (G-AVCD)/Shoreham	
G-SACH	Stoddard-Hamilton Glastar	R. S. Holt	
G-SACI	PA-28-161 Warrior II	PJC (Leasing) Ltd	
G-SACK	Robin R.2160	Sherburn Aero Club Ltd	
G-SACO	PA-28-161 Warrior II	M. & D. C. Brooks	
G-SACR	PA-28-161 Cadet	Sherburn Aero Club Ltd	
G-SACS	PA-28-161 Cadet	Sherburn Aero Club Ltd	
G-SACT	PA-28-161 Cadet	Sherburn Aero Club Ltd	
G-SACZ	PA-28-161 Warrior II	Lima Delta Aviation Ltd	
G-SADE	Cessna F.150L	N. E. Sams (G-AZJW)	
G-SAFE	Cameron N-77 balloon	P. J. Waller	
G-SAFI	CP.1320 Super Emeraude	C. S. Carleton-Smith	
G-SAFR	SAAB 91D Safir	Sylmar Aviation & Services Ltd	
G-SAGA	Grob G.109B	G-GROB Ltd/Booker	
G-SAGE	Luscombe 8A Silvaire	R. J. P. Herivel (G-AKTL)	
G-SAHI	Trago Mills SAH-1	Sunhawk Ltd/North Weald	
G-SAIR	Cessna 421C	Air Support Aviation Services Ltd (G-OBCA)	
G-SAIX	Cameron N-77 balloon	C. Walther & ptnrs	
G-SALA	PA-32 Cherokee Six 300E	Stonebold Ltd	
G-SALL	Cessna F.150L (Tailwheel)	D. & P. A. Hailey	
G-SAMG	Grob G.109B	RAFGSA/Bicester	

Notes	Reg.	Type	Owner or Operator
	G-SAMI	Cameron N-90 balloon	Flying Pictures Ltd (G-BWSE)
	G-SAMJ	Partenavia P.68B	G-SAMJ Group
	G-SAMM	Cessna 340A	M. R. Cross
	G-SAMY	Shaw Europa	K. R. Tallent
	G-SAND	Schweizer 269C	Hields Aviation
	G-SARA	PA-28-181 Archer II	R. P. Lewis
	G-SARH	PA-28-161 Warrior II	Sussex Flying Club Ltd/Shoreham
	G-SARK	BAC.167 Strikemaster Mk 84 (311)	Sark International Airways Ltd
	G-SARO	Saro Skeeter Mk 12 (XL812)	B. Chamberlain
	G-SARV	Van's RV-4	S. N. Aston
	G-SASA	Eurocopter EC.135T-1	Bond Air Services Ltd
	G-SASB	Eurocopter EC.135T-1	Bond Air Services Ltd
	G-SASK	PA-31P Pressurised Navajo	Middle East Business Club Ltd (G-BFAM)
	G-SATL	Cameron 105 Sphere SS balloon	Ballonwerbung Hamburg GmbH/ Germany
	G-SAUF	Colt 90A balloon	K. H. Medau
	G-SAWI	PA-32RT-300T Turbo Lance II	S. A. & K. J. Williams
	G-SAXO	Cameron N-105 balloon	Flying Pictures Ltd
	G-SAYS	RAF 2000 GTX-SE gyroplane	Aziz Corporation Ltd
	G-SAZZ	CP.328 Super Emeraude	D. J. Long
	G-SBAE	Cessna F.172P	Warton Flying Club/Blackpool
	G-SBAS	Beech B200 Super King Air	Gama Aviation Ltd (G-BJJV)
	G-SBLT	Steen Skybolt	Skybolt Group
	G-SBMO	Robin R.2160I	D. Henderson & ptnrs
	G-SBUS	BN-2A-26 Islander	Isles of Scilly Skybus Ltd (G-BMMH)/ St Just
	G-SBUT	Robinson R-22B-2	Princepro Ltd (G-BXMT)
	G-SCAN	Vinten-Wallis WA-116/100	K. H. Wallis
	G-SCAT	Cessna F.150F (tailwheel)	G. D. Cooper (G-ATRN)
	G-SCBI	SOCATA TB.20 Trinidad	Ace Services
	G-SCFO	Cameron O-77 balloon	M. K. Grigson
	G-SCHI	AS.350B-2 Ecureuil	Patriot Aviation Ltd
	G-SCIP	SOCATA TB-20 Trinidad GT	J. C. White
	G-SCLX	FLS Aerospace Sprint 160	Sunhawk Ltd (G-PLYM)/North Weald
	G-SCOO	Bell 206B JetRanger 2	Biggin Hill Helicopters (G-CORC/ G-CJHI/G-BBFB)
	G-SCOW	AS.355F-2 Twin Squirrel	B. K. Scowcroft (G-POON/G-MCAL)
	G-SCPL	PA-28 Cherokee 140	Aeroshow Ltd (G-BPVL)/Staverton
	G-SCRU	Cameron A-250 balloon	Societe Bombard SARL (G-BWWO)/ France
	G-SCTA	Westland Scout AH.1 (XV126)	G. R. Harrison
	G-SCUB	PA-18 Super Cub 135 (542447)	N. D. Needham Farms
	G-SCUD	Montgomerie-Bensen B.8MR	D. Taylor
	G-SCUL	Rutan Cozy	K. R. W. Scull
	G-SCUR	Eurocopter EC.120B	JS Aviation Ltd
	G-SDCI	Bell 206B JetRanger 2	S. D. Coomes (G-GHCL/G-SHVV)
	G-SDEV	D.H.104 Sea Devon C.20 (XK895)	Wyndeham Press Group PLC/Shoreham
	G-SDLW	Cameron O-105 balloon	P. J. Smart
	G-SEAB	Republic RC-3 Seabee	B. A. Farries/Tollerton
	G-SEAI	Cessna U.206G (amphibian)	Aerofloat Ltd
	G-SEAT	Colt 42 balloon	Virgin Airship & Balloon Co Ltd
	G-SEED	Piper J-3C-65 Cub	J. H. Seed
	G-SEEK	Cessna T.210N	A. Hopper
	G-SEJW	PA-28-161 Warrior II	Keen Leasing Ltd
	G-SELF	Shaw Europa	N. D. Crisp & ptnrs
	G-SELL	Robin DR.400/180	G-SELL Regent Group
	G-SELY	AB-206B JetRanger 3	Petrochem Aviation Services Ltd
	G-SEMI	PA-44-180 Seminole	T. Hiscox (G-DENW)
	G-SENA	Rutan LongEz	G. Bennett
	G-SEND	Colt 90A balloon	B. Nigrowsky
	G-SENX	PA-34-200T Seneca II	Katotech Ltd (G-DARE/G-WOTS/ G-SEVL)
	G-SEPA	AS.355N Twin Squirrel	Metropolitan Police (G-METD/G-BUJF)
	G-SEPB	AS.355N Twin Squirrel	Metropolitan Police (G-BVSE)
	G-SEPC	AS.355N Twin Squirrel	Metropolitan Police (G-BWGV)
	G-SEPT	Cameron N-105 balloon	P. Gooch
	G-SERA	Enstrom F-28A-UK	W. R. Pitcher (G-BAHU)
	G-SERL	SOCATA TB.10 Tobago	R. J. Searle (G-LANA)/Rochester
	G-SETI	Cameron Sky 80-16 balloon	R. P. Allan
	G-SEUK	Cameron 80 TV SS balloon	Flying Pictures Ltd

Reg.	Type	Owner or Operator	Notes
G-SEVA	SE-5A (replica) (F141)	I. D. Gregory	
G-SEVE	Cessna 172N	MK Aero Support Ltd	
G-SEVN	Van's RV-7	N. Reddish	
G-SEWP	AS.355F-2 Twin Squirrel	Veritair Ltd (G-OFIN/G-DANS/G-BTNM)	
G-SEXI	Cessna 172M	European Flyers/Blackbushe	
G-SEXY	AA-1 Yankee ★	(stored)/Liverpool (G-AYLM)	
G-SFBH	Boeing 737-46N	bmi british midland	
G-SFHR	PA-23 Aztec 250F	Comed Aviation Ltd (G-BHSO)/Blackpool	
G-SFOX	Rotorway Executive 90	Magpie Computer Services Ltd (G-BUAH)	
G-SFPA	Cessna F.406	Scottish Fisheries Protection Agency	
G-SFPB	Cessna F.406	Scottish Fisheries Protection Agency	
G-SFRY	Thunder Ax7-77 balloon	K. J. Baxter & P. Szczepanski	
G-SFTZ	Slingsby T.67M Firefly 160	Western Air (Thruxton) Ltd	
G-SGAS	Colt 77A balloon	A. Derbyshire	
G-SGSE	PA-28-181 Archer II	Mountune Racing Ltd (G-BOJX)	
G-SHAA	Enstrom 280-UK	ELT Radio Telephones	
G-SHAH	Cessna F.152	E. Alexander	
G-SHAM	Beech C90 King Air (modified)	Aerospeed Ltd	
G-SHAY	PA-28R-201T Turbo Arrow III	R. J. Shay (G-BFDG/G-JEFS)	
G-SHCB	Schweizer 269C-1	Oxford Aviation Services Ltd/Kidlington	
G-SHED	PA-28-181 Archer II	P. T. Crouch & R. M. Gingell (G-BRAU)	
G-SHEP	SOCATA TB.20 Trinidad	L. W. Shepherd	
G-SHIM	CFM Streak Shadow	K. R. Anderson	
G-SHIP	PA-23 Aztec 250F ★	Midland Air Museum/Coventry	
G-SHIV	GA-7 Cougar	Westley Aircraft Ltd/Cranfield	
G-SHNN	Enstrom 280C	W. R. Pitcher	
G-SHOG	Colomban MC.15 Cri-Cri	V. S. E. Norman (G-PFAB)/Rendcomb	
G-SHOW	M.S.733 Alcyon	Vintage Aircraft Team/Cranfield	
G-SHPP	Hughes TH-55A	R. P. Bateman	
G-SHRK	Enstrom 280C-UK	Aviation Bureau (G-BGMX)	
G-SHSH	Shaw Europa	D. G. Hillam	
G-SHSP	Cessna 172S	Shropshire Aero Club Ltd/Sleap	
G-SHSS	Enstrom 280C-UK	St. Angelo Helicopters (G-BENO)	
G-SHUF	Mainair Blade	J. A. Shufflebotham	
G-SHUG	PA-28R-201T Turbo Arrow III	N. E. Rennie	
G-SHUU	Enstrom 280C-UK-2	D. Ellis (G-OMCP/G-KENY/G-BJFG)	
G-SIAI	SIAI-Marchetti SF.260W	D. Gage	
G-SIAL	Hawker Hunter F.58 (J-4090)	Classic Aviation Ltd/Duxford	
G-SIAM	Cameron V-90 balloon	D. Tuck (G-BXBS)	
G-SIGN	PA-39 Twin Comanche 160 C/R	D. Buttle/Blackbushe	
G-SIIA	Pitts S-2A Special	B. Brown	
G-SIIB	Pitts S-2B Special	T. H. Bishop & J. H. Milne (G-BUVY)	
G-SIIC	Pitts S-2C Special	Technoforce Ltd	
G-SIII	Extra EA.300	Callmast Ltd	
G-SIJW	SA Bulldog Srs 120/121 (XX630)	M. Miles	
G-SILS	Pietenpol Skyscout	D. Silsbury	
G-SIMI	Cameron A-315 balloon	Balloon Safaris	
G-SIMN	Robinson R-22B-2	Flight Training Ltd/Coventry	
G-SIMP	Avtech Jabiru SP	J. C. Simpson	
G-SION	PA-38-112 Tomahawk II	Naiad Air Services	
G-SIPA	SIPA 903	Mersey SIPA Group (G-BGBM)	
G-SIRR	NA P-51D Mustang (474008)	Intrepid Aviation Co/North Weald	
G-SIRS	Cessna 560XL Citation Excel	Amsail Ltd	
G-SITA	Pegasus Quantum 15-912	A. R. Oliver	
G-SIVC	Agusta A.109E Power	Mandarin Aviation Ltd/Redhill	
G-SIVX	Robinson R-22B	Mandarin Aviation Ltd	
G-SIXC	Douglas DC-6A	Atlantic Air Transport Ltd/Coventry	
G-SIXD	PA-32 Cherokee Six 300D	M. B. Paine & I. Gordon	
G-SIXX	Colt 77A balloon	M. Dear & M. Taylor	
G-SIXY	Van's RV-6	C. J. Hall & C. R. P. Hamlett	
G-SJCH	BN-2T-4S Defender 4000	Hampshire Police Authority (G-BWPK)	
G-SJDI	Robinson R-44	R. Kibble	
G-SJKR	Lindstrand LBL-90A balloon	S. J. Roake	
G-SJMC	Boeing 767-31KER	My Travel Airways (Airtours)	
G-SKAN	Cessna F.172M	Bustard Flying Club Ltd (G-BFKT)	
G-SKCI	Rutan Vari-Eze	S. K. Cockburn	
G-SKID	Lake LA-4-200 Buccaneer	D. J. Lindsey Wood (G-BMGY/G-BWKS/ G-BDDI)	
G-SKIE	Steen Skybolt	S. Gray	
G-SKIL	Cameron N-77 balloon	S. P. Johnston	
G-SKOT	Cameron V-42 balloon	A. A. Laing	
G-SKYC	Slingsby T.67M Firefly	T. W. Cassells (G-BLDP)	

Notes	Reg.	Type	Owner or Operator
	G-SKYD	Pitts S-2B Special	SHYD Syndicate
	G-SKYE	Cessna TU.206G	RAF Sport Parachute Association
	G-SKYF	SOCATA TB.10 Tobago	Air Touring Ltd/Biggin Hill
	G-SKYG	I.I.I. Sky Arrow 650TC	G. F. Smith
	G-SKYK	Cameron A-275 balloon	Cameron Flights Southern Ltd
	G-SKYL	Cessna 182S	Skylane Aviation Ltd/Sherburn
	G-SKYM	Cessna F.337E	Bencray Ltd (G-AYHW) (stored)/ Blackpool
	G-SKYO	Slingsby T.67M-200	T. W. Cassells
	G-SKYR	Cameron A-180 balloon	Cameron Flights Southern Ltd
	G-SKYT	I.I.I. Sky Arrow 650TC	I. R. Malby
	G-SKYU	Cameron A-210 balloon	PSH Skypower Ltd
	G-SKYX	Cameron A-210 balloon	PSH Skypower Ltd
	G-SKYY	Cameron A-275 balloon	Cameron Flights Southern Ltd
	G-SLCE	Cameron C-80 balloon	Z. Bayat
	G-SLEA	Mudry/CAARP CAP.10B	P. D. Southerington/Sturgate
	G-SLII	Cameron O-90 balloon	R. B. & A. M. Harris
	G-SLOW	Pietenpol Air Camper	C. Newton
	G-SLTN	SOCATA TB.20 Trinidad	S. N. Adamson
	G-SLYN	PA-28-161 Warrior II	G. E. Layton
	G-SMAF	Sikorsky S-76A	Air Harrods Ltd/Stansted
	G-SMAN	Airbus A.330-243	Monarch Airlines Ltd
	G-SMBM	Pegasus Quantum 15-912	B. J. Mould
	G-SMDB	Boeing 737-36N	bmi british midland
	G-SMDH	Shaw Europa XS	S. W. Pitt
	G-SMDJ	AS.350B-2 Ecureuil	Denis Ferranti Hoverknights Ltd
	G-SMIG	Cameron O-65 balloon	Hong Kong Balloon & Airship Club
	G-SMJH	Robinson R-44	M. J. Hayward (G-NTEE)
	G-SMJJ	Cessna 414A	Gull Air Ltd/Guernsey
	G-SMTC	Colt Flying Hut SS balloon	Shiplake Investments Ltd/Switzerland
	G-SMTH	PA-28 Cherokee 140	Masonair (G-AYJS)
	G-SNAK	Lindstrand LBL-105A balloon	Ballooning Adventures Ltd
	G-SNAP	Cameron V-77 balloon	C. J. S. Limon
	G-SNAZ	Enstrom F-28F	Thornhill Aviation Ltd (G-BRCP)
	G-SNEV	CFM Streak Shadow SA	N. G. Smart
	G-SNOW	Cameron V-77 balloon	M. J. Ball
	G-SNUZ	PA-28-161 Warrior II	J. C. O. & C. A. Adams (G-PSFT/G-BPDS)
	G-SOAR	Eiri PIK-20E	F. W. Fay
	G-SOAY	Cessna T.303	Bulldog Aviation Ltd
	G-SOBI	PA-28-181 Archer II	Alliance Aerolink Ltd
	G-SOEI	H.S.748 Srs 2A	Emerald Airways Ltd/Liverpool
	G-SOFT	Thunder Ax7-77 balloon	A. J. Bowen
	G-SOHI	Agusta A.109E	Tri-Ventures Group Ltd
	G-SOKO	Soko P-2 Kraguj (30149)	J. A. Keen (G-BRXK)/Liverpool
	G-SOLA	Aero Designs Star-Lite SL.1	J. P. Roberts-Lethaby
	G-SOLD	Robinson R-22A	J. F. H. James
	G-SOLH	Bell 47G-5	SOL Helicopters Ltd (G-AZMB)
	G-SOLO	Pitts S-2S Special	Landitfast Ltd
	G-SONA	SOCATA TB.10 Tobago	M. Kelly (G-BIBI)/Breighton
	G-SONY	Aero Commander 200D	General Airline Ltd (G-BGPS)/ Blackbushe
	G-SOOC	Hughes 369HS	Helicopter Experience (G-BRRX)
	G-SOOE	Hughes 369E	R. W. Nash
	G-SOOS	Colt 21A balloon	P. J. Stapley
	G-SOOT	PA-28 Cherokee 180	J. A. Bridger (G-AVNM/Exeter
	G-SOPP	Enstrom 280FX	F. J. Sopp (G-OSAB)
	G-SORT	Cameron N-90 balloon	A. Brown
	G-SOUL	Cessna 310R	Atlantic Air Transport Ltd/Coventry
	G-SPAM	Light Aero Avid Aerobat	J. Lee
	G-SPAU	Eurocopter EC.135T-1	Bond Air Services Ltd
	G-SPDR	D.H.115 Sea Vampire T.22 (XG766)	M. J. Cobb/Bournemouth
	G-SPEE	Robinson R-22B	Verve Systems Ltd (G-BPJC)
	G-SPEL	Sky 220-24 balloon	Pendle Balloon Co
	G-SPEY	AB-206B JetRanger 3	Castle Air Charters Ltd (G-BIGO)
	G-SPFX	Rutan Cozy	B. D. Tutty
	G-SPIN	Aerotek Pitts S-2A Special	N. M. R. Richards
	G-SPIT	V.S.379 Spitfire FR.XIV (MV268)	Patina Ltd (G-BGHB)/Duxford
	G-SPOG	Jodel DR.1050	A. C. Frost (G-AXVS)
	G-SPOL	MBB Bo 105CBS/4	Bond Air Services Ltd/Aberdeen
	G-SPUR	Cessna 550 Citation II	Amsail Ltd
	G-SPYI	Bell 206B JetRanger 3	A. J. Sinclair (G-BVRC/G-BSJC)

Reg.	Type	Owner or Operator	Notes
G-SROE	Westland Scout AH.1 (XP907)	Bolenda Engineering Ltd	
G-SRVO	Cameron N-90 balloon	Servo & Electronic Sales Ltd	
G-SSAS	Airbus A.320-231	My Travel Airways (Airtours)	
G-SSCL	MDH Hughes 369E	Shaun Stevens Contractors Ltd	
G-SSFC	PA-34-200 Seneca II	SFC (Air Taxis) Ltd (G-BBXG)/Stapleford	
G-SSFT	PA-28-161 Warrior II	SFT Europe Ltd (G-BHIL/Bournemouth	
G-SSGS	Shaw Europa	G. Szurovy	
G-SSIX	Rans S.6-116 Coyote II	T. J. Bax	
G-SSKY	BN-2B-26 Islander	Isles of Scilly Skybus Ltd (G-BSWT)	
G-SSLF	Lindstrand LBL-210A balloon	Exclusive Ballooning	
G-SSPP	Sky Science Powerhawk L70/500	Sky Science Powered Parachutes Ltd	
G-SSSC	Sikorsky S-76C	CHC Scotia Ltd	
G-SSSD	Sikorsky S-76C	CHC Scotia Ltd	
G-SSSE	Sikorsky S-76C	CHC Scotia Ltd	
G-SSTI	Cameron N-105 balloon	British Airways	
G-SSWA	Short SD3-30 Variant 100	Streamline Aviation (SW) Ltd (G-BHHU)	
G-SSWB	Short SD3-60 Variant 100	Streamline Aviation (SW) Ltd (G-BMLE)	
G-SSWC	Short SD3-60 Variant 100	Streamline Aviation (SW) Ltd (G-BMHX)	
G-SSWM	Short SD3-60 Variant 100	Freshleave Ltd (G-OAAS/G-BLIL)	
G-SSWO	Short SD3-60 Variant 100	Streamline Aviation (SW) Ltd	
G-SSWP	Short SD3-60 Variant 100	Freshleave Ltd (G-BGNB)	
G-SSWR	Short SD3-60 Variant 100	Freshleave Ltd (G-BLWJ)	
G-SSWT	Short SD3-30 Variant 100	Freshleave Ltd (G-BNYA/G-BKSU)	
G-SSWU	Short SD3-30 Variant 100	Streamline Aviation (SW) Ltd (G-BIYH)	
G-SSWV	Sportavia Fournier RF-5B	Skylark Flying Group	
G-SSWX	Short SD3-60 Variant 200	Streamline Aviation (SW) Ltd	
G-STAT	Cesna U.206F	Wingglider Ltd/Hibaldstow	
G-STAY	Cessna FR.172K	Staywhite (UK) Ltd	
G-STEF	Hughes 369HS	Source Group Ltd (G-BKTK)/ Bournemouth	
G-STEM	Stemme S.10V	Warwickshire Aerocentre Ltd	
G-STEN	Stemme S.10 (4)	W. A. H. Kahn	
G-STEP	Schweizer 269C	M. Johnson	
G-STER	Bell 206B JetRanger 3	P. J. Brown	
G-STEV	Jodel DR.221	S. W. Talbot/Long Marston	
G-STMP	SNCAN Stampe SV-4A	A,. C. Thorne	
G-STOK	Colt 77B balloon	Christows Ltd	
G-STOW	Cameron 90 Wine Box SS balloon	Flying Enterprise Partnership	
G-STOX	Bell 206B JetRanger 2	Burman Aviation Ltd (G-BNIR)/Cranfield	
G-STPI	Cameron A-210 balloon	A. D. Pinner	
G-STRK	CFN Streak Shadow Srs SA	E. J. Hadley/Switzerland	
G-STRM	Cameron N-90 balloon	High Profile Balloons	
G-STUA	Aerotek Pitts S-2A Special (modified)	Rollquick Ltd/Stapleford	
G-STUB	Christen Pitts S-2B Special	R. N. Goode & T. L. P. Delaney/ White Waltham	
G-STWO	ARV Super 2	G. E. Morris	
G-STYL	Pitts S-1S Special	C. A. Wills	
G-SUCH	Cameron V-77 balloon	D. G. Such (G-BIGD)	
G-SUEE	Airbus A.320-231	My Travel Airways (G-IEAG)	
G-SUEZ	AB-206B JetRanger 2	Aerospeed Ltd	
G-SUFF	Eurocopter EC.135T-1	Suffolk Constabulary Air Support Unit	
G-SUKI	PA-38-112 Tomahawk	Western Air (Thruxton) Ltd (G-BPNV)	
G-SUMT	Robinson R-22B	Sloane Helicopters Ltd/Sywell (G-BUKD)	
G-SUMX	Robinson R-22B	Frankham Bros Ltd	
G-SUPA	PA-18 Super Cub 150	Supa Group	
G-SURG	PA-30 Twin Comanche 160B	A. R. Taylor (G-VIST/G-AVHG)/Kidlington	
G-SURV	BN-2T-4R Defender 4000	Atlantic Air Transport Ltd (G-BVHZ/ Coventry	
G-SUSI	Cameron V-77 balloon	J. H. Dryden	
G-SUSX	MDH MD-902 Explorer	Sussex Police Authority	
G-SUSY	P-51D-25-NA Mustang (472773)	P. J. Morgan	
G-SUTN	I.I.I. Sky Arrow 650TC	G. C. Sutton	
G-SUZI	Beech 95-B55 Baron	Bebecar (UK) Ltd (G-BAXR)	
G-SUZN	PA-28-161 Warrior II	The St. George Flying Club/Teesside	
G-SUZY	Taylor JT.1 Monoplane	N. C. Stone	
G-SVBF	Cameron A-180 balloon	Virgin Balloon Flights Ltd	
G-SVEA	PA-28-161 Warrior II	Avion Aviation	
G-SVIP	Cessna 421B	Stephenson Marine Co. Ltd (G-BNYJ)	
G-SVIV	SNCAN Stampe SV-4C	R. Taylor	
G-SWEB	Cameron N-90 balloon	South Western Electricity PLC	
G-SWEL	Hughes 369HS	I. C. & L. E. Stigwell (G-RBUT)	
G-SWIF	V.S.541 Swift F.7 (XF114)	Heritage Aviation Developments Ltd	

Notes	Reg.	Type	Owner or Operator
	G-SWIS	D.H.100 Vampire FB.6 (J-1149)★	Jet Heritage Museum/Bournemouth
	G-SWJW	Airbus A.300B4-203	OY Air Scandic International Aviation AB
	G-SWOT	Currie Wot (C3011)	D. Watt
	G-SWPR	Cameron N-56 balloon	A. Brown
	G-SWUN	Pitts S-1 Special (modified)	T. G. Lloyd (G-BSXH)
	G-SYCO	Shaw Europa	J. T. Fillingham
	G-SYFW	Focke-Wulf Fw.190 replica (2+1)	M. R. Parr
	G-SYPA	AS.355F-2 Twin Squirrel	South Yorkshire Police Authority (G-BPRE)
	G-TAAL	Cessna 172R	Eagle Cruise Aviation Ltd
	G-TABS	EMB-110P1 Bandeirante	Skydrift Ltd (G-PBAC)
	G-TACK	Grob G.109B	A. P. Mayne
	G-TAFF	C.A.S.A. 1.131E Jungmann 1000	A. Horsfall (G-BFNE)/Breighton
	G-TAFI	Bücher Bü133 Jungmeister	R. P. Lamplough
	G-TAGS	PA-28-161 Warrior II	Oxford Aviation Services Ltd/Kidlington
	G-TAIL	Cessna 150J	L. I. D. Denham-Brown
	G-TAIR	PA-34-200T Seneca II	Branksome Dene Garage/Bournemouth
	G-TAMR	Cessna 172S	Tamair Leasing
	G-TAMS	Beech A23-24 Musketeer Super	Aerograde Ltd
	G-TAMY	Cessna 421B	Malcolm Enamellers (Midlands) Ltd
	G-TAND	Robinson R-44	Southwest Helicharter Ltd
	G-TANI	GA-7 Cougar	S. Spier (G-VJAI/G-OCAB/G-BICF)/Elstree
	G-TANK	Cameron N-90 balloon	Hoyers (UK) Ltd
	G-TANS	SOCATA TB-20 Trinidad	Tettenhall Leisure
	G-TAOS	Douglas DC-10-10	My Travel Airways (Airtours)
	G-TAPE	PA-23 Aztec 250D	D. J. Hare (G-AWVW)
	G-TARN	Pietenpol Air Camper	P. J. Heilbron
	G-TART	PA-28-236 Dakota	Prescot Planes Ltd
	G-TARV	ARV Super 2	M. F. Filer (G-OARV)
	G-TASH	Cessna 172N (modified)	A. Ashplet
	G-TASK	Cessna 404	Bravo Aviation Ltd
	G-TATT	GY-20 Minicab	Tatt's Group
	G-TATY	Robinson R-44	W. R. Walker
	G-TAXI	PA-23 Aztec 250E	SWL Leasing Ltd/Leeds
	G-TAYI	Grob G.115	K. P. Widdowson (G-DODO
	G-TAYS	Cessna F.152 II	Tayside Aviation Ltd (G-LFCA)/Aberdeen
	G-TBAG	Murphy Renegade II	M. R. Tetley
	G-TBAH	Bell 206B JetRanger 2	Murray Galloway Ltd (G-OMJB)
	G-TBBC	Pegasus Quantum 15-912	Big Bamboo Co. Ltd
	G-TBEE	Dyn'Aero MCR-01	A. D. S. Baker
	G-TBGL	Agusta A.109A-II	Bulford Holdings Ltd (G-VJCB/G-BOUA)
	G-TBGT	SOCATA TB.10 Tobago GT	P. G. Sherry & A. J. Simmonds/Liverpool
	G-TBIC	BAe 146-200	Flightline Ltd
	G-TBMW	Murphy Renegade Spirit	S. J. Spavins (G-MYIG)
	G-TBRD	Lockheed T-33A (54-21261)	Golden Apple Operations Ltd (G-JETT/G-OAHB)/Duxford
	G-TBXX	SOCATA TB.20 Trinidad	D. A. Phillips & Co
	G-TBZI	SOCATA TB.21 Trinidad TC	W. R. M. Beesley
	G-TBZO	SOCATA TB.20 Tobago	D. L. Clark & M. J. M. Hopper/Shoreham
	G-TCAN	Colt 69A balloon	H. C. J. Williams
	G-TCAP	BAe 125 Srs 800B	BAE Systems Ltd
	G-TCDI	H.S.125 Srs 403B	Aravco Ltd (G-SHOP/G-BTUF)
	G-TCOM	PA-30 Twin Comanche 160B	C. A. C. Burrough
	G-TCTC	PA-28RT-200 Arrow IV	T. Haigh
	G-TCUB	Piper J-3C-65 Cub	C. Kirk
	G-TDFS	IMCO Callair A.9	Dollarhigh Ltd (G-AVZA)
	G-TDOG	SA Bulldog Srs 120/121	G. S. Taylor
	G-TDTW	Douglas DC-10-10	My Travel Airways (Airtours)
	G-TEAL	Thurston TSC-1A1 Teal	K. Heeley/Crosland Moor
	G-TEBZ	PA-28R-201 Arrow III	S. F. Tebby & Son
	G-TECC	Aeronca 7AC Champion	G. S. Claybourn
	G-TECH	R. Commander 114	P. A. Reed (G-BEDH)/Denham
	G-TECK	Cameron V-77 balloon	G. M. N. Spencer
	G-TECM	Tecnam P.92-EM ECHO	D. A. Lawrence
	G-TEDF	Cameron N-90 balloon	Fort Vale Engineering Ltd
	G-TEDS	SOCATA TB.10 Tobago	E. W. Lyon (G-BHCO)
	G-TEDY	Evans VP-1	N. K. Marston (G-BHGN)
	G-TEEZ	Cameron N-90 balloon	Fresh Air Ltd
	G-TEFC	PA-28 Cherokee 140	P. M. Havard
	G-TEHL	CFM Streak Shadow Srs M	A. K. Paterson (G-MYJE)
	G-TELY	Agusta A.109A-II	Castle Air Charters Ltd

Reg.	Type	Owner or Operator	Notes
G-TEMP	PA-28 Cherokee 180	BEV Group (G-AYBK)/Andrewsfield	
G-TEMT	Hawker Tempest II (MW763)	Tempest Two Ltd/Gamston	
G-TENT	J/1N Alpha	R. Callaway-Lewis (G-AKJU)	
G-TERN	Shaw Europa	J. E. J. Lundesjo	
G-TERY	PA-28-181 Archer II	T. Barlow (G-BOXZ)/Barton	
G-TEST	PA-34-200 Seneca	Stapleford Flying Club Ltd (G-BLCD)	
G-TETI	Cameron N-90 balloon	Teti SPA/Italy	
G-TEWS	PA-28 Cherokee 140	G-TEWS Flying Group (G-KEAN/ G-AWTM)/Liverpool	
G-TFCI	Cessna FA-152	Tayside Aviation Ltd/Dundee	
G-TFOX	Denney Kitfox Mk.2	F. A. Bakir	
G-TFRB	Air Command 532 Elite	F. R. Blennerhassett	
G-TFUN	Valentin Taifun 17E	NW Taifun Group	
G-TFYN	PA-32RT-300 Lance II	Fynair Ltd	
G-TGAS	Cameron O-160 balloon	Zebedee Balloon Service	
G-TGER	AA-5B Tiger	Photonic Science Ltd (G-BFZP)/ Biggin Hill	
G-TGRS	Robinson R-22B	Tiger Helicopters Ltd (G-DELL)/Shobdon	
G-TGRZ	Bell 206B JetRanger 3	Tiger Helicopters Ltd (G-BXZX)/Shobdon	
G-THEL	Robinson R-44	N. Parkhouse (G-OCCB/G-STMM)	
G-THEO	Team Minimax 91	T. Willford	
G-THLS	MBB Bo 105DBS/4	Bond Air Services Ltd (G-BCXO)/ Aberdeen	
G-THOM	Thunder Ax-6-56 balloon	T. H. Wilson	
G-THOS	Thunder Ax7-77 balloon	C. E. A. Breton	
G-THOT	Avtech Jabiru SK	D. J. Reed	
G-THRE	Cessna 182S	S. J. Mole	
G-THSL	PA-28R-201 Arrow III	D. M. Markscheffe	
G-THUN	Republic P-47D Thunderbolt (226671)	Patina Ltd/Duxford	
G-THZL	SOCATA TB.20 Trinidad	Ewan Ltd	
G-TICL	Airbus A.320-231	My Travel Airways (Airtours)	
G-TIDS	Jodel 150	J. B. Dovey	
G-TIGA	D.H.82 Tiger Moth	D. E. Leatherland (G-AOEG)/Tollerton	
G-TIGB	AS.332L Super Puma	Bristow Helicopters Ltd (G-BJXC)	
G-TIGC	AS.332L Super Puma	Bristow Helicopters Ltd (G-BJYH)	
G-TIGE	AS.332L Super Puma	Bristow Helicopters Ltd (G-BJYJ)	
G-TIGF	AS.332L Super Puma	Bristow Helicopters Ltd	
G-TIGG	AS.332L Super Puma	Bristow Helicopters Ltd	
G-TIGI	AS.332L Super Puma	Bristow Helicopters Ltd	
G-TIGJ	AS.332L Super Puma	Bristow Helicopters Ltd	
G-TIGL	AS.332L Super Puma	Bristow Helicopters Ltd	
G-TIGM	AS.332L Super Puma	Bristow Helicopters Ltd	
G-TIGO	AS.332L Super Puma	Bristow Helicopters Ltd	
G-TIGP	AS.332L Super Puma	Bristow Helicopters Ltd	
G-TIGR	AS.332L Super Puma	Bristow Helicopters Ltd	
G-TIGS	AS.332L Super Puma	Bristow Helicopters Ltd	
G-TIGT	AS.332L Super Puma	Bristow Helicopters Ltd	
G-TIGV	AS.332L Super Puma	Bristow Helicopters Ltd	
G-TIGZ	AS.332L Super Puma	Bristow Helicopters Ltd	
G-TIII	Aerotek Pitts S-2A Special	D. G. Cowden (G-BGSE)	
G-TIKO	Hatz CB-1	Tiko Architecture	
G-TILE	Robinson R-22B	M. J. Webb & C. R. Woodwise	
G-TILI	Bell 206B JetRanger 2	CIM Helicopters	
G-TIMB	Rutan Vari-Eze	T. M. Bailey (G-BKXJ)	
G-TIME	Ted Smith Aerostar 601P	T & G Engineering Co. Ltd	
G-TIMK	PA-28-181 Archer II	T. Baker	
G-TIMM	Folland Gnat T.1 (XM693)	T. J. Manna/Cranfield	
G-TIMP	Aeronca 7BCM Champion	T. E. Phillips	
G-TIMS	Falconar F-12A	T. Sheridan	
G-TIMY	GY080 Horizon 160	R. G. Whyte	
G-TINA	SOCATA TB.10 Tobago	A. Lister	
G-TING	Cameron O-120 balloon	Floating Sensations Ltd	
G-TINS	Cameron N-90 balloon	J. R. Clifton	
G-TINY	Z.526F Trener Master	D. Evans	
G-TIPS	Tipsy T.66 Nipper Srs 5	R. F. L. Cuypers/Belgium	
G-TJAY	PA-22 Tri-Pacer 135	D. D. Saint	
G-TKAY	Shaw Europa	A. M. Kay	
G-TKGR	Lindstrand LBL Racing Car SS balloon	Brown & Williams Tobacco Corporation (Export) Ltd/USA	
G-TKIS	Tri-R Kis	T. J. Bone	
G-TKPZ	Cessna 310R	Fraggle Leasing Ltd (G-BRAH)	
G-TLDK	PA-22 Tri-Pacer 150	A. M. Thomson	

Notes	Reg.	Type	Owner or Operator
	G-TMCC	Cameron N-90 balloon	Prudential Assurance Co. Ltd
	G-TMDP	Airbus A.320-231	My Travel Airways (Airtours)
	G-TMKI	P.56 Provost T.1 (WW453)	B. L. Robinson
	G-TMOL	SOCATA TB.20 Trinidad	West Wales Airport Ltd
	G-TNTN	Thunder Ax6-56 balloon	H. M. Savage & J. F. Trehern
	G-TOAD	Jodel D.140B	J. H. Stevens
	G-TOAK	SOCATA TB.20 Trinidad	Phoenix Group
	G-TOBA	SOCATA TB.10 Tobago	E. Downing
	G-TOBI	Cessna F.172K	G. Hall (G-AYVB)
	G-TODD	ICA IS-28M2A	C. I. Roberts & C. D. King/Shobdon
	G-TODE	Ruschmeyer R.90-230RG	A. I. D. Rich
	G-TOFT	Colt 90A balloon	C. S. Perceval
	G-TOGO	Van's RV-6	G. Schwetz
	G-TOLL	PA-28R-201 Arrow III	Plymouth School of Flying Ltd
	G-TOLY	Robinson R-22B	K. N. Tolley (G-NSHR)
	G-TOMS	PA-38-112 Tomahawk	Juno Estates Ltd
	G-TOMZ	Denney Kitfox Mk.2	P. T. Knight
	G-TOOL	Thunder Ax8-105 balloon	W. J. Honey
	G-TOOT	Dyn'Aero MCR-01	E. K. Griffin
	G-TOPC	AS.355F-1 Twin Squirrel	Bridge Street Nominees Ltd
	G-TOPS	AS.355F-1 Twin Squirrel	Sterling Helicopters (G-BPRH)
	G-TORE	P.84 Jet Provost T.3A (XM405)	R. J. Everett
	G-TORS	Robinson R-22B	GT Investigations (International) Ltd
	G-TOSH	Robinson R-22B	Heli Air Ltd/Wellesbourne
	G-TOTO	Cessna F.177RG	W. G. Walton (G-OADE/G-AZKH)
	G-TOUR	Robin R.2112	Mardenair Ltd
	G-TOWS	PA-25 Pawnee 260	Lasham Gliding Soc Ltd
	G-TOYS	Enstrom 280C-UK-2 Shark	Stephenson Aviation Ltd (G-BISE)
	G-TOYZ	Bell 206B JetRanger 3	P. B. Ellis (G-RGER)
	G-TPSL	Cessna 182S	A. N. Purslow/Blackbushe
	G-TPTT	Airbus A.320-212	My Travel Airways (Airtours)
	G-TRAC	Robinson R-44	C. J. Sharples
	G-TRAM	Pegasus Quantum 15-912	T. F. J. Roach
	G-TRAN	Beech 76 Duchess	Multiflight Ltd (G-NIFR)
	G-TRCY	Robinson R-44	T. Fletcher
	G-TRDM	SOCATA TB.20 Trinidad	Mann Organisation Ltd
	G-TREC	Cessna 421C	C. P. Lockyer (G-TLOL)
	G-TRED	Colt 110 Bibendum balloon	The Aerial Display Co. Ltd
	G-TREE	Bell 206B JetRanger 3	LGH Aviation Ltd
	G-TREK	Jodel D.18	R. H. Mole/Leicester
	G-TREN	Boeing 737-4S3	GB Airways Ltd (G-BRKG)/Gatwick
	G-TRIB	Lindstrand HS-110 airship	J. Addison
	G-TRIC	D.H.C.1 Chipmunk 22A (18013)	D. M. Barnett (G-AOSZ)
	G-TRIM	Monnett Moni	J. E. Bennell
	G-TRIN	SOCATA TB.20 Trinidad	TL Aviation Ltd
	G-TRIO	Cessna 172M	C. M. B. Reid (G-BNXY)
	G-TROP	Cessna 310R II	D. E. Carpenter/Shoreham
	G-TROY	NA T-28A Fennec (51-7692)	S. G. Howell & S. Tilling
	G-TRUD	Enstrom 480	Ardore Ltd
	G-TRUE	MDH Hughes 369E	Horizon Helicopter Hire
	G-TRUK	Stoddard-Hamilton Glasair RG	M. P. Jackson
	G-TRUX	Colt 77A balloon	Highway Truck Rental Ltd
	G-TRYG	Robinson R-44	Productive Investments Ltd
	G-TRYK	Kiss 400-582 (1)	S. Elsbury
	G-TSAM	BAe 125 Srs 800B	BAE Systems (Operations) Ltd/Warton
	G-TSFT	PA-28-161 Warrior II	SFT Europe Ltd (G-BLDJ)/Bournemouth
	G-TSGJ	PA-28-181 Archer II	Golf Juliet Flying Club
	G-TSIX	AT-6C Harvard IIA (111836)	J. M. & B. E. Adams
	G-TSKD	Raj Hamsa X'Air Jabiru (1)	T. Sexton & K. B. Dupuy
	G-TSKY	B.121 Pup 2	R. G. Hayes (G-AWDY)
	G-TSOL	EAA Acrosport 1	T. G. Solomon (G-BPKI)
	G-TTDD	Zenair CH.701 STOL	D. B. Dainton & V. D. Asque
	G-TTFN	Cessna 560 Citation V	Corporate Administration Management Ltd
	G-TTHC	Robinson R-22B	Multiflight Ltd/Leeds-Bradford
	G-TTIA	Airbus A.321-231	GB Airways Ltd
	G-TTIB	Airbus A.321-231	GB Airways Ltd
	G-TTIC	Airbus A.321-231	GB Airways Ltd
	G-TTMC	Airbus A.300B4-203	OY Air Scandic International Aviation AB
	G-TTOA	Airbus A.320-232	GB Airways Ltd
	G-TTOB	Airbus A.320-232	GB Airways Ltd
	G-TTOC	Airbus A.320-232	GB Airways Ltd
	G-TTOD	Airbus A.320-232	GB Airways Ltd

Reg.	Type	Owner or Operator	Notes
G-TTOE	Airbus A.320-232	GB Airways Ltd	
G-TTOY	CFM Streak Shadow	S. Marriott	
G-TUBB	Avtech Jabiru UL	A. H. Bower	
G-TUCH	Bell 206B JetRanger 2	Touchdown (G-OCBB/G-BASE)	
G-TUDR	Cameron V-77 balloon	Jacques W. Soukup Enterprises Ltd	
G-TUGG	PA-18 Super Cub 150	Ulster Gliding Club Ltd/Bellarena	
G-TUGY	Robin DR.400/180	Buckminster Gliding Club/Saltby	
G-TULL	Avtech Jabiru UL	W. R. Tull	
G-TULP	Lindstrand LBL Tulips SS balloon	Oxford Promotions (UK) Ltd	
G-TUNE	Robinson R-22B	Ecurie Ecosse (Scotland) Ltd (G-OJVI)	
G-TURF	Cessna F.406	Atlantic Air Transport Ltd/Coventry	
G-TURK	Cameron 80 Sultan SS balloon	Forbes Europe Inc/France	
G-TURN	Steen Skybolt	R. Bentley	
G-TURV	Robinson R-44	C. Coult	
G-TUSA	Pegasus Quantum 15-912	C. J. Cullen	
G-TUSK	Bell 206B JetRanger 3	Heli Aviation Ltd (G-BWZH)/Blackbushe	
G-TVAA	Agusta A.109E Power	Agusta SpA/Italy	
G-TVAC	Agusta A.109E Power	Sloane Helicopters Ltd/Sywell	
G-TVBF	Lindstrand LBL-310A balloon	Virgin Balloons Flights Ltd	
G-TVII	Hawker Hunter T.7 (XX467)	G. R. Montgomery/Kemble	
G-TVIJ	CCF Harvard IV (T-6J) (28521)	R. W. Davies (G-BSBE)	
G-TVIP	Cessna 404	Capital Trading (Aviation) Ltd (G-KIWI/ G-BHNI)	
G-TVSI	Campbell Cricket	C. Smith (G-AYHH)	
G-TVTV	Cameron 90 TV SS balloon	J. Krebs/Germany	
G-TWEL	PA-28-181 Archer II	International Aerospace Engineering Ltd	
G-TWEY	Colt 69A balloon	N. Bland	
G-TWIG	Cessna F.406	Highland Airways Ltd/Inverness	
G-TWIN	PA-44-180 Seminole	Bonus Aviation Ltd/Cranfield	
G-TWIZ	R. Commander 114	B. C. & P. M. Cox	
G-TXSE	RAF 2000 GTX-SE gyroplane	M. H. J. Goldring	
G-TYER	Robin DR.400/500	Alfred Graham Ltd	
G-TYGA	AA-5B Tiger	G. W. & S. Wilmshurst (G-BHNZ)	
G-TYKE	Avtech Jabiru UL	A. Parker	
G-TYNE	SOCATA TB.20 Trinidad	D. T. Watkins	
G-TYRE	Cessna F.172M	Staverton Flying School	
G-TZII	Thorp T.211B	AD Aviation Ltd/Barton	
G-UAPA	Robin DR.400/140B	Carlos Saraive Lda/Portugal	
G-UAPO	Ruschmeyer R.90-230RG	S. J. Green/Portugal	
G-UCCC	Cameron 90 Sign SS balloon	Flying Pictures Ltd	
G-UDAY	Robinson R-22B	Newmarket Plant Hire Ltd	
G-UDGE	Thruster T.600N	L. J. Appleby (G-BYPI)	
G-UEST	Bell 206B JetRanger 2	Summit Corporate Services Ltd (G- RYOB/G-BLWU)/Kidlington	
G-UESY	Robinson R-22B-2	E. W. Guess (Holdings) Ltd	
G-UFAW	Raj Hamsa X'Air 582 (5)	J. H. Goddard	
G-UFCA	Cessna 172S	Ulster Flying Club (1961) Ltd/ Newtownards	
G-UFCB	Cessna 172S	Ulster Flying Club (1961) Ltd/ Newtownards	
G-UFCC	Cessna 172S	Ulster Flying Club (1961) Ltd/ Newtownards	
G-UFCD	Cessna 172S	Ulster Flying Club (1961) Ltd (G-OYZK)/ Newtownards	
G-UFLY	Cessna F.150H	Westair Flying Services Ltd (G-AVVY)/ Blackpool	
G-UGLY	SE.313B Alouette II	S. Cox (G-BSFN)	
G-UILD	Grob G.109B	Runnymede Consultants Ltd	
G-UILE	Lancair 320	R. J. Martin	
G-UILT	Cessna T.303	Rock Seat Ltd (G-EDRY)	
G-UINN	Stolp SA.300 Starduster Too	J. D. H. Gordon	
G-UJAB	Avtech Jabiru UL	C. A. Thomas	
G-UJGK	Avtech Jabiru UL	W. G. Upton & J. G. Kosak	
G-UKAC	BAe 146-300	K.L.M. uk/Buzz/Stansted	
G-UKAG	BAe 146-300	K.L.M. uk/Buzz/Stansted	
G-UKFA	Fokker 100	K.L.M. uk/Stansted	
G-UKFB	Fokker 100	K.L.M. uk/Stansted	
G-UKFC	Fokker 100	K.L.M. uk/Stansted	
G-UKFD	Fokker 100	K.L.M. uk/Stansted	
G-UKFE	Fokker 100	K.L.M. uk/Stansted	
G-UKFF	Fokker 100	K.L.M. uk/Stansted	
G-UKFG	Fokker 100	K.L.M. uk/Stansted	

Notes	Reg.	Type	Owner or Operator
	G-UKFH	Fokker 100	K.L.M. uk/Stansted
	G-UKFI	Fokker 100	K.L.M. uk/Stansted
	G-UKFJ	Fokker 100	K.L.M. uk/Stansted
	G-UKFK	Fokker 100	K.L.M. uk/Stansted
	G-UKFM	Fokker 100	K.L.M. uk/Stansted
	G-UKFN	Fokker 100	K.L.M. uk/Stansted
	G-UKFO	Fokker 100	K.L.M. uk/Stansted
	G-UKFR	Fokker 100	K.L.M. uk/Stansted
	G-UKHP	BAe 146-300	K.L.M. uk/Buzz/Stansted
	G-UKID	BAe 146-300	K.L.M. uk/Buzz/Stansted
	G-UKOZ	Avtech Jabiru SK	D. J. Burnett
	G-UKRB	Colt 105A balloon	Virgin Airship & Balloon Co Ltd
	G-UKRC	BAe 146-300	K.L.M. uk/Buzz/Stansted
	G-UKSC	BAe 146-300	K.L.M. uk/Buzz/Stansted
	G-UKTA	Fokker 50	K.L.M. uk
	G-UKTB	Fokker 50	K.L.M. uk
	G-UKTC	Fokker 50	K.L.M. uk
	G-UKTD	Fokker 50	K.L.M. uk
	G-UKTE	Fokker 50	K.L.M. uk
	G-UKTF	Fokker 50	K.L.M. uk
	G-UKTG	Fokker 50	K.L.M. uk
	G-UKTH	Fokker 50	K.L.M. uk
	G-UKTI	Fokker 50	K.L.M. uk
	G-UKTK	Aérospatiale ATR-72-202	British Airways Citiexpress
	G-UKTM	Aérospatiale ATR-72-202	British Airways Citiexpress
	G-UKTN	Aérospatiale ATR-72-202	K.L.M. uk
	G-UKUK	Head Ax8-105 balloon	P. A. George
	G-ULAB	Robinson R-22B	Skyscraper Aviation
	G-ULAS	D.H.C.1 Chipmunk 22 (WK517)	Search & Management Services Ltd
	G-ULIA	Cameron V-77 balloon	J. M. Dean
	G-ULLS	Lindstrand LBL-90A balloon	J. R. Clifton
	G-ULPS	Everett Srs 1 gyroplane	C. J. Watkinson (G-BMNY)
	G-ULTR	Cameron A-105 balloon	P. Glydon
	G-UMBO	Thunder Ax7-77A balloon	Virgin Airship & Balloon Co Ltd
	G-UMMI	PA-31-310 Turbo Navajo	Messrs Rees of Poynston West (G-BGSO)
	G-UNDD	PA-23 Aztec 250E	G. J. & D. P. Deadman (G-BATX)
	G-UNGE	Lindstrand LBL-90A balloon	Silver Ghost Balloon Club (G-BVPJ)
	G-UNIP	Cameron Oil Container SS balloon	Flying Pictures Ltd
	G-UNIT	Partenavia P.68B	Aliservice SRL (G-BCNT)/Italy
	G-UNIV	Montgomerie-Parsons 2-seat gyroplane	University of Glasgow (G-BWTP)
	G-UNNY	BAC.167 Strikemaster 87	Transair (UK) Ltd (G-AYHR)/ North Weald
	G-UNRL	Lindstrand LBL-21A balloon	Virgin Balloon & Airship Co. Ltd
	G-UNYT	Robinson R-22B	Heli Air Ltd (G-BWZV/G-LIAN)/ Wellesbourne
	G-UORO	Shaw Europa	D. Dufton
	G-UPHL	Cameron 80 Concept SS balloon	Uphill Motor Co
	G-UPPP	Colt 77A balloon	M. Williams
	G-UPPY	Cameron DP-80 airship	Jacques W. Soukup Enterprises Ltd/ USA
	G-UPUP	Cameron V-77 balloon	S. F. Burden/Netherlands
	G-URCH	Rotorway Executive 162F	D. L. Urch
	G-UROP	Beech 95-B55 Baron	Pooler International Ltd/Sleap
	G-URRR	Air Command 582 Sport	L. Armes
	G-URUH	Robinson R-44	Heli Air Ltd/Wellesbourne
	G-USAM	Cameron Uncle Sam SS balloon	Corn Palace Balloon Club Ltd
	G-USFT	PA-23 Aztec 250F	SFT Europe Ltd (G-BEGV)/ Bournemouth
	G-USIL	Thunder Ax7-77 balloon	Window On The World Ltd
	G-USMC	Cameron 90 Chestie SS balloon	Jacques W. Soukup Enterprises Ltd/ USA
	G-USSR	Cameron 90 Doll SS balloon	Corn Palace Balloon Club Ltd
	G-USSY	PA-28-181 Archer II	Western Air (Thruxton) Ltd
	G-USTB	Agusta A.109A	Newton Aviation Ltd
	G-USTY	FRED Srs 2	Gusty Group
	G-UTSI	Rand-Robinson KR-2	K. B. Gutridge/Thruxton
	G-UTSY	PA-28R-201 Arrow III	Arrow Aviation Ltd
	G-UTTS	Robinson R-44	Heli Hire Ltd (G-ROAP)

Reg.	Type	Owner or Operator	Notes
G-UTZY	SA.341G Gazelle 1	Animal Air Ambulance Rescue Service Ltd (G-BKLV)	
G-UVIP	Cessna 421C	Capital Trading Aviation (G-BSKH)/Filton	
G-UVNR	BAC.167 Strikemaster Mk 87	Global Aviation Services Ltd (G-BXFS)	
G-UZEL	SA.341G Gazelle 1	MCC Ltd (G-BRNH)	
G-UZLE	Colt 77A balloon	Flying Pictures Ltd	
G-VAEL	Airbus A.340-311	Virgin Atlantic Airways Ltd *Maiden Toulouse*	
G-VAGA	PA-15 Vagabond	I. M. Callier/White Waltham	
G-VAIR	Airbus A.340-313	Virgin Atlantic Airways Ltd *Maiden Tokyo*	
G-VAJT	M.S.894E Rallye 220GT	W. M. Patterson	
G-VALS	Pietenpol Air Camper	I. G. & V. A. Brice	
G-VALZ	Cameron N-120 balloon	D. Ling	
G-VANS	Van's RV-4	M. Swanborough & D. Jones	
G-VANZ	Van's RV-6A	S. J. Baxter	
G-VARG	Varga 2150A Kachina	A. C. Fletcher	
G-VASA	PA-34-200 Seneca	V. Babic (G-BNNB)	
G-VAST	Boeing 747-41R	Virgin Atlantic Airways Ltd *Ladybird*	
G-VATH	Airbus A.321-211	Virgin Atlantic Airways Ltd *(stored)*	
G-VATL	Airbus A.340-642	Virgin Atlantic Airways Ltd	
G-VAUN	Cessna 340	K. L. Burnett	
G-VBAC	Short SD3-60 Variant 100	BAC Leasing Ltd (G-BOEJ)	
G-VBIG	Boeing 747-4Q8	Virgin Atlantic Airways Ltd *Tinker Belle*	
G-VBUS	Airbus A.340-311	Virgin Atlantic Airways Ltd *Lady in Red*	
G-VCED	Airbus A.320-231	My Travel Airways (Airtours)	
G-VCIO	EAA Acro Sport II	V. Millard	
G-VCML	Beech 58 Baron	St Angelo Aviation Ltd	
G-VDIR	Cessna T.310R	J. Driver	
G-VECA	Robin HR.200/120B	Aviation Rentals	
G-VECD	Robin R.1180T	Mistral Aviation Ltd	
G-VECE	Robin R.2120U	Mistral Aviation Ltd	
G-VEGA	Slingsby T.65A Vega	R. A. Rice (G-BFZN)	
G-VEIL	Airbus A.340-642	Virgin Atlantic Airways Ltd	
G-VELA	SIAI-Marchetti S.205-22R	G-VELA Partnership	
G-VELD	Airbus A.340-313	Virgin Atlantic Airways Ltd *African Queen*	
G-VENI	D.H.112 Venom FB.50 (WE402)	Lindsay Wood Promotions Ltd/ Bournemouth	
G-VENM	D.H.112 Venom FB.50 (J-1614)	T. J. Manna (G-BLIE)/Cranfield	
G-VENT	Schempp-Hirth Ventus 2CM	D. Rance	
G-VERA	GY-201 Minicab	D. K. Shipton	
G-VETA	Hawker Hunter T.7	Veta Ltd (G-BVWN)/Kemble	
G-VETS	Enstrom 280C-UK Shark	C. Upton (G-FSDC/G-BKTG)	
G-VEYE	Robinson R-22	J. B. Errington (G-BPTP)	
G-VEZE	Rutan Vari-Eze	S. D. Brown & ptnrs	
G-VFAB	Boeing 747-4Q8	Virgin Atlantic Airways Ltd *Lady Penelope*	
G-VFAR	Airbus A.340-313	Virgin Atlantic Airways Ltd *Diana*	
G-VFLY	Airbus A.340-311	Virgin Atlantic Airways Ltd *Dragon Lady*	
G-VFOX	Airbus A.340-642	Virgin Atlantic Airways Ltd	
G-VFSI	Robinson R-22B	Survey & Construction (Roofing) Ltd	
G-VGAL	Boeing 747-443	Virgin Atlantic Airways Ltd	
G-VHOL	Airbus A.340-311	Virgin Atlantic Airways Ltd *Jetstreamer*	
G-VHOT	Boeing 747-4Q8	Virgin Atlantic Airways Ltd *Tubular Belle*	
G-VIBA	Cameron DP-80 airship	Jacques W. Soukup Enterprises Ltd/ USA	
G-VIBE	Boeing 747-219B	Virgin Atlantic Airways Ltd *Spirit of New York*	
G-VICC	PA-28-161 Warrior II	Charlie Charlie Syndicate (G-JFHL)	
G-VICE	MDH Hughes 369E	Controlled Demolition Group Ltd	
G-VICI	D.H.112 Venom FB.50 (J-1573)	Lindsay Wood Promotions Ltd/ Bournemouth	
G-VICM	Beech F33C Bonanza	Velocity Engineering Ltd	
G-VICS	Commander 114B	Millennium Aviation Ltd	
G-VICT	PA-31-310 Turbo Navajo	ILS Air Ltd/Cambridge (G-BBZI)	
G-VIEW	Vinten-Wallis WA-116/100	K. H. Wallis	
G-VIIA	Boeing 777-236	British Airways	
G-VIIB	Boeing 777-236	British Airways	
G-VIIC	Boeing 777-236	British Airways	
G-VIID	Boeing 777-236	British Airways	
G-VIIE	Boeing 777-236	British Airways	
G-VIIF	Boeing 777-236	British Airways	

Notes	Reg.	Type	Owner or Operator
	G-VIIG	Boeing 777-236	British Airways
	G-VIIH	Boeing 777-236	British Airways
	G-VIIJ	Boeing 777-236	British Airways
	G-VIIK	Boeing 777-236	British Airways
	G-VIIL	Boeing 777-236	British Airways
	G-VIIM	Boeing 777-236	British Airways
	G-VIIN	Boeing 777-236	British Airways
	G-VIIO	Boeing 777-236	British Airways
	G-VIIP	Boeing 777-236	British Airways
	G-VIIR	Boeing 777-236	British Airways
	G-VIIS	Boeing 777-236	British Airways
	G-VIIT	Boeing 777-236	British Airways
	G-VIIU	Boeing 777-236	British Airways
	G-VIIV	Boeing 777-236	British Airways
	G-VIIW	Boeing 777-236	British Airways
	G-VIIX	Boeing 777-236	British Airways
	G-VIIY	Boeing 777-236	British Airways
	G-VIKE	Bellanca 1730A Viking	W. G. Prout
	G-VIKY	Cameron A-120 balloon	D. W. Pennell
	G-VILL	Lazer Z.200 (modified)	M. G. Jefferies (G-BOYZ)/ Little Gransden
	G-VINO	Sky 90-24 balloon	Fivedata Ltd
	G-VINS	Cameron N-90 balloon	PSH Skypower Ltd
	G-VIPA	Cessna 182S	Stallingborough Aviation Ltd
	G-VIPH	Agusta A.109C	Sloane Helicopters Ltd (G-BVNH/ G-LAXO)
	G-VIPI	BAe 125 Srs 800B	Yeates of Leicester Ltd
	G-VIPP	PA-31-350 Navajo Chieftain	Capital Trading Aviation (G-OGRV/ G-BMPX)/Filton
	G-VIPY	PA-31-350 Navajo Chieftain	Capital Trading Aviation (G-POLO)/ Filton
	G-VITE	Robin R.1180T	G-VITE Flying Group
	G-VITL	Lindstrand LBL-105A balloon	Vital Resources
	G-VIVA	Thunder Ax7-65 balloon	R. J. Mitchener
	G-VIVI	Taylor JT.2 Titch	D. G. Tucker
	G-VIVM	P.84 Jet Provost T.5	K. Lyndon-Dykes (G-BVWF)
	G-VIXN	D.H.110 Sea Vixen FAW.2 (XS587) ★	P. G. Vallance Ltd/Charlwood
	G-VIZZ	Sportavia RS.180 Sportsman	Exeter Fournier Group
	G-VJAB	Avtech Jabiru UL	ST Aviation Ltd
	G-VJET	Avro 698 Vulcan B.2 (XL426) ★	Vulcan Restoration Trust/Southend
	G-VJIM	Colt 77 Jumbo Jim SS balloon	Magical Adventures Ltd/USA
	G-VKID	Airbus A.320-214	Virgin Sun (stored)
	G-VKIS	Airbus A.321-211	Virgin Atlantic Airways Ltd (stored)
	G-VKIT	Shaw Europa	T. H. Crow
	G-VLAD	Yakovlev Yak-50	M. B. Smith/Booker
	G-VLCN	Avro 698 Vulcan B.2 (XH558) ★	C. Walton Ltd/Bruntingthorpe
	G-VLIP	Boeing 747-443	Virgin Atlantic Airways Ltd
	G-VMCO	Agusta A.109E Power	Unique Aviation Group Ltd
	G-VMDE	Cessna P.210N	Royton Express Deliveries (Welwyn) Ltd
	G-VMED	Airbus A.320-214	Virgin Sun (stored)
	G-VMEG	Airbus A.340-642	Virgin Atlantic Airways Ltd Mystic Maiden
	G-VMJM	SOCATA TB.10 Tobago	S. C. Brown (G-BTOK)
	G-VMPR	D.H.115 Vampire T.11 (XE920)	J. N. Kerr
	G-VMSL	Robinson R-22A	L. L. F. Smith (G-KILY)
	G-VNOM	D.H.112 Venom FB.50 (J-1632)	T. J. Manna/Cranfield
	G-VNUS	Hughes 269C	Heli Air Ltd (G-BATT)/Wellesbourne
	G-VOAR	PA-28-181 Archer III	Aviation Rentals
	G-VODA	Cameron N-77 balloon	Racal Telecom PLC
	G-VOGE	Airbus A.340-642	Virgin Atlantic Airways Ltd Cover Maiden
	G-VOID	PA-28RT-201 Arrow IV	Newbus Aviation Ltd
	G-VOLH	Airbus A.321-211	My Travel Airways (Airtours)
	G-VOSL	Robinson R-22B-2	H. Wiggins
	G-VPSJ	Shaw Europa	J. D. Bean
	G-VPUF	Boeing 747-219B	Virgin Atlantic Airways Ltd High as a Kite
	G-VROE	Avro 652A Anson T.21 (WD413)	Air Atlantique Ltd (G-BFIR)/Coventry
	G-VROM	Boeing 747-443	Virgin Atlantic Airways Ltd
	G-VROS	Boeing 747-443	Virgin Atlantic Airways Ltd
	G-VROY	Boeing 747-443	Virgin Atlantic Airways Ltd
	G-VRST	PA-46-350P Malibu Mirage	Winchfield Enterprises Ltd

Reg.	Type	Owner or Operator	Notes
G-VRUM	Boeing 747-267B	Virgin Atlantic Airways (leased to Air Atlanta)	
G-VRVI	Cameron O-90 balloon	Cooling Services Ltd	
G-VSBC	Beech B200 Super King Air	Vickers Shipbuilding & Engineering Ltd/Walney Island	
G-VSEA	Airbus A.340-311	Virgin Atlantic Airways Ltd Plane Sailing	
G-VSHY	Airbus A.340-642	Virgin Atlantic Airways Ltd	
G-VSKY	Airbus A.340-311	Virgin Atlantic Airways Ltd China Girl	
G-VSSH	Airbus A.340-642	Virgin Atlantic Airways Ltd	
G-VSSS	Boeing 747-219B	Virgin Atlantic Airways Ltd	
G-VSUN	Airbus A.340-313	Virgin Atlantic Airways Ltd Rainbow Lady	
G-VTAN	Airbus A.320-214	Virgin Sun (G-BXTA) (stored)	
G-VTII	D.H.115 Vampire T.11 (WZ507)	De Havilland Aviation Ltd/Swansea	
G-VTOL	H.S. Harrier T.52 (ZA250) ★	Brooklands Museum of Aviation/Weybridge	
G-VTOP	Boeing 747-4Q8	Virgin Atlantic Airways Ltd Virginia Plain	
G-VULC	Avro 698 Vulcan B.2A (XM655)★	Radarmoor Ltd/Wellesbourne	
G-VVBF	Colt 315A balloon	Virgin Balloon Flights Ltd	
G-VVBK	PA-34-200T Seneca II	The Mann Organisation Ltd (G-BSBS/G-BDRI)	
G-VVIP	Cessna 421C	Capital Trading Aviation (G-BMWB)/Filton	
G-VWOW	Boeing 747-41R	Virgin Atlantic Airways Ltd	
G-VXLG	Boeing 747-41R	Virgin Atlantic Airways Ltd Ruby Tuesday	
G-VYGR	Colt 120A balloon	A. van Wyk	
G-VZZZ	Boeing 747-219B	Virgin Atlantic Airways Ltd Morning Glory	
G-WAAC	Cameron N-56 balloon	N. P. Hemsley	
G-WACB	Cessna F.152 II	Wycombe Air Centre Ltd	
G-WACE	Cessna F.152 II	Wycombe Air Centre Ltd	
G-WACF	Cessna 152 II	Wycombe Air Centre Ltd	
G-WACG	Cessna 152 II	Wycombe Air Centre Ltd	
G-WACH	Cessna FA.152 II	Wycombe Air Centre Ltd	
G-WACI	Beech 76 Duchess	Wycombe Air Centre Ltd	
G-WACJ	Beech 76 Duchess	Wycombe Air Centre Ltd	
G-WACL	Cessna F.172N	Wycombe Air Centre Ltd (G-BHGG)	
G-WACM	Cessna 172S	Wycombe Air Centre Ltd	
G-WACO	Waco UPF-7	RGV (Aircraft Services) & Co/Staverton	
G-WACP	PA-28 Cherokee 180	Wycombe Air Centre Ltd (G-BBPP)	
G-WACR	PA-28 Cherokee 180	Wycombe Air Centre Ltd (G-BCZF)	
G-WACT	Cessna F.152 II	The Exeter Flying Club (G-BKFT)	
G-WACU	Cessna FA.152	Wycombe Air Centre Ltd (G-BJZU)	
G-WACW	Cessna 172P	Wycombe Air Centre Ltd	
G-WACY	Cessna F.172P	Wycombe Air Centre Ltd	
G-WADI	PA-46-350P Malibu Mirage	H. J. D. S. Baioes/Cranfield	
G-WADS	Robinson R-22B	Helicentre Ltd (G-NICO)/Blackpool	
G-WAGG	Robinson R-22B-2	N. J. Wagstaff Leasing	
G-WAHL	QAC Quickie	A. A. A. Wahlberg	
G-WAIR	PA-32-301 Saratoga	Thorne Aviation	
G-WAIT	Cameron V-77 balloon	C. P. Brown	
G-WAKE	Mainair Blade 912	J. G. Lloyd	
G-WALS	Cessna A.152	Redhill Flying Club	
G-WARB	PA-28-161 Warrior III	Muller Aircraft Leasing Ltd	
G-WARC	PA-28-161 Warrior III	Plane Talking Ltd/Elstree	
G-WARD	Taylor JT.1 Monoplane	R. P. J. Hunter	
G-WARE	PA-28-161 Warrior II	W. B. Ware/Filton	
G-WARH	PA-28-161 Warrior III	Newcastle-Upon-Tyne Aero Club Ltd	
G-WARK	Schweizer 269C	K. Sutcliffe	
G-WARP	Cessna 182F	Army Parachute Association (G-ASHB)/Netheravon	
G-WARR	PA-28-161 Warrior II	T. J. & G. M. Laundy	
G-WARS	PA-28-161 Warrior III	Blaneby Ltd	
G-WARV	PA-28-161 Warrior III	Plane Talking Ltd/Elstree	
G-WARW	PA-28-161 Warrior III	C. J. Simmonds	
G-WARX	PA-28-161 Warrior III	C. M. A. Clark	
G-WARY	PA-28-161 Warrior III	Armstrong Aviation Ltd	
G-WASP	Brantly B.2B	N. J. R. Minchin (G-ASXE)	
G-WATS	PA-34-220T Seneca III	Oxford Aviation Services Ltd (G-BOVJ)/Kidlington	
G-WAVA	Robin HR.200/120B	Wellesbourne Aviation	

G-WAVE – G-WMAN

Notes	Reg.	Type	Owner or Operator
	G-WAVE	Grob G.109B	M. L. Murdoch/Cranfield
	G-WAVI	Robin HR.200/120B	Wellesbourne Flyers Ltd (G-BZDG)
	G-WAZZ	Pitts S-1S Special	D. T. Knight (G-BRRP)
	G-WBAT	Wombat gyroplane	M. R. Harrisson (G-BSID)
	G-WBMG	Cameron N Ele-90 SS balloon	P. H. E. van Overwalle (G-BUYV)/ Belgium
	G-WBPR	BAe 125 Srs 800B	Granada Group PLC
	G-WBTS	Falconar F-11	W. C. Brown (G-BDPL)
	G-WCAT	Colt Flying Mitt SS balloon	Balloon Preservation Flying Group
	G-WCEI	M.S.894E Rallye 220GT	R. A. L. Lucas (G-BAOC)
	G-WCUB	PA-18 Super Cub 150	P. A. Walley
	G-WDEB	Thunder Ax-7-77 balloon	W. de Bock
	G-WDEV	SA.341G Gazelle 1	MW Helicopters Ltd (G-IZEL/G-BBHW)
	G-WEAC	BN-2A Mk III-2 Trislander	Keen Leasing Ltd (G-BEFP)
	G-WELI	Cameron N-77 balloon	M. A. Shannon
	G-WELL	Beech E90 King Air	Colt Transport Ltd
	G-WELS	Cameron N-65 balloon	K. J. VIckery
	G-WEND	PA-28RT-201 Arrow IV	Tayside Aviation Ltd/Dundee
	G-WERY	SOCATA TB.20 Trinidad	Fastour Aviation Ltd
	G-WEST	Agusta A.109A	Westland Helicopters Ltd/Yeovil
	G-WESX	CFM Streak Shadow	K. Kerr
	G-WETI	Cameron N-31 balloon	C. A. Butter & J. J. T. Cooke
	G-WFFW	PA-28-161 Warrior II	N. F. Duke
	G-WFOX	Robinson R-22-2	Heli Air Ltd/Wellesbourne
	G-WGAL	Bell 206B JetRanger 3	Watkiss Group Aviation Ltd (G-OICS)
	G-WGCS	PA-18 Super Cub 95	S. C. Thompson
	G-WGHB	Canadair T-33AN Silver Star 3	R. H. & G. C. Cooper
	G-WGSC	Pilatus PC-6/B2-H4 Turbo Porter	D. M. Penny
	G-WHAL	QAC Quickie	A. A, M. Wahiberg
	G-WHAT	Colt 77A balloon	M. A. Scholes
	G-WHAZ	AB-206A JetRanger 2	Heli Charter Ltd
	G-WHEE	Pegasus Quantum 15-912	PFT (Cotswolds)
	G-WHEN	Tecnam P.92-EM Echo	C. D. Marsh
	G-WHIM	Colt 77A balloon	D. L. Morgan
	G-WHOG	CFM Streak Shadow	B. R. Cannell
	G-WHOO	Rotorway Executive 162F	C. A. Saul
	G-WHRL	Schweizer 269C	Graham Wood Decorators
	G-WHST	AS.350B2 Ecureuil	Hawkrise Ltd (G-BWYA)
	G-WIBB	Jodel D.18	J. & D. Wibberley
	G-WIBS	C.A.S.A. 1-131E Jungmann 2000	C. Willoughby
	G-WIFE	Cessna R.172 RG II	Wife Group (G-BGVT).
	G-WILD	Pitts S-1T Special	The Wild Group
	G-WILG	PZL-104 Wilga 35	M. H. Bletsoe-Brown (G-AZYJ)
	G-WILS	PA-28RT-201T Turbo Arrow IV	B. Walker & Co (Dursley) Ltd
	G-WILY	Rutan LongEz	W. S. Allen
	G-WIMP	Colt 56A balloon	T. & B. Chamberlain
	G-WINE	Thunder Ax7-77Z balloon ★	Balloon Preservation Group/Lancing
	G-WINK	AA-5B Tiger	B. St J. Cooke
	G-WINS	PA-32 Cherokee Six 300	Cheyenne Ltd
	G-WIRE	AS.355F-1 Twin Squirrel	National Grid Co PLC (G-CEGB/ G-BLJL)
	G-WIRL	Robinson R-22B	T. W. Finlay
	G-WISH	Lindstrand LBL Cake SS balloon	Oxford Promotions (UK) Ltd/USA
	G-WIXI	Avions Mudry CAP.10B	J. M. & E. M. Wicks
	G-WIZA	Robinson R-22B	Burman Aviation Ltd (G-PERL)/Cranfield
	G-WIZB	Grob G.115A	A. G. Wisbey
	G-WIZD	Lindstrand LBL-180A balloon	Bignell Surgical Instruments Ltd
	G-WIZO	PA-34-220T Seneca III	B. J. Booty
	G-WIZR	Robinson R-22B-2	Clifton Helicopter Hire
	G-WIZY	Robinson R-22B	B. J. North (G-BMWX)
	G-WIZZ	AB-206B JetRanger 2	Rivermead Aviation Ltd
	G-WJAN	Boeing 757-21K	My Travel Airways (Airtours)
	G-WKRD	AS.350B-2 Ecureuil	Wickford Development Co (G-BUJG/G-HEAR)
	G-WLAC	PA-18 Super Cub 150	White Waltham Airfield Ltd (G-HAHA/G-BSWE)
	G-WLGA	PZL-104 Wilga 80	A. J. Renham
	G-WLLY	Bell 206B JetRanger	Blue Five Aviation Ltd (G-OBHH/ G-RODY/G-ROGR/G-AXMM)
	G-WLMS	Mainair Blade 912	J. R. North
	G-WMAA	MBB Bo 105DBS/4	W. Midlands Air Ambulance (G-PASB/ G-BDMC)
	G-WMAN	SA.341G Gazelle 1	J. Wightman

Reg.	Type	Owner or Operator	Notes
G-WMAS	Eurocopter EC.135T-1	Bond Air Services Ltd/Aberdeen	
G-WMID	MDH MD-900 Explorer	W. Midlands Police Authority	
G-WMPA	AS.355F-2 Twin Squirrel	Police Aviation Services Ltd	
G-WMTM	AA-5B Tiger	A. Allen	
G-WMWM	Robinson R-44 Astro	K. Cummins	
G-WNGS	Cameron N-105 balloon	Redmall Ltd	
G-WOLF	PA-28 Cherokee 140	Aircraft Management Services Ltd	
G-WOOD	Beech 95-B55A Baron	T. D. Broadhurst (G-AYID)/Sleap	
G-WOOF	Enstrom 480	Netcopter.co.uk Ltd	
G-WOOL	Colt 77A balloon	Whacko Balloon Group	
G-WORM	Thruster T.600N	R. & J. Gibson	
G-WOSY	MBB Bo.105DBS/4	Redwood Aviation Ltd (G-PASD/G-BNRS)	
G-WOTG	BN-2T Turbine Islander	RAF Sport Parachute Association (G-BJYT)	
G-WPAS	MDH MD-900 Explorer	Police Aviation Services Ltd	
G-WREN	Pitts S-2A Special	Northamptonshire School of Flying Ltd/Sywell	
G-WRFM	Enstrom 280C-UK Shark	Skywalker Enterprises (G-CTSI/G-BKIO)/Shoreham	
G-WRIT	Thunder Ax7-77A balloon	G. Pusey	
G-WRLY	Robinson R-22B	Burman Aviation Ltd (G-OFJS/G-BNXJ)/Cranfield	
G-WRWR	Robinson R-22B-2	Air Foyle Ltd	
G-WSEC	Enstrom F-28C	AJD Engineering Ltd (G-BONF)	
G-WSFT	PA-23 Aztec 250F	SFT Europe Ltd (G-BTHS)/Bournemouth	
G-WSKY	Enstrom 280C-UK-2 Shark	M. I. Edwards Engineers (G-BEEK)	
G-WUFF	Shaw Europa	M. A. Barker	
G-WULF	WAR Focke-Wulf Fw.190 (8+)	A. Howe	
G-WVBF	Lindstrand LBL-210A balloon	Virgin Balloon Flights Ltd	
G-WWAL	PA-28R Cherokee Arrow 180	White Waltham Airfield Ltd (G-AZSH)	
G-WWAS	PA-34-220T Seneca III	D. Intzevidis (G-BPPB)/Greece	
G-WWBB	Airbus A.330-243	bmi british midland	
G-WWBC	Airbus A.330-243	bmi british midland	
G-WWBD	Airbus A.330-243	bmi british midland	
G-WWBM	Airbus A.330-243	bmi british midland	
G-WWIZ	Beech 95-58 Baron	Chase Aviation Ltd (G-GAMA/G-BBSD)	
G-WWWG	Shaw Europa	C. F. Williams-Wynne	
G-WYAT	CFM Streak Shadow Srs SA	M. G. Whyatt	
G-WYCH	Cameron 90 Witch SS balloon	Corn Palace Balloon Club Ltd	
G-WYMP	Cessna F.150J	R. Hall (G-BAGW)	
G-WYMR	Robinson R-44	Heli Air Ltd/Wellesbourne	
G-WYND	Wittman W.8 Tailwind	Forge Group	
G-WYNN	Rand-Robinson KR-2	W. Thomas	
G-WYNS	Aero Designs Pulsar XP	S. L. Bauza/Majorca	
G-WYNT	Cameron N-56 balloon	S. L. G. Williams	
G-WYPA	MBB Bo 105DBS/4	Police Aviation Services Ltd/Gloucestershire	
G-WYSP	Robinson R-44	Calderbrook Estates Ltd	
G-WZOL	RL.5B LWS Sherwood Ranger	G. W. F. Webb (G-MZOL)	
G-WZZZ	Colt AS-56 airship	Lindstrand Balloons Ltd	
G-XALP	Schweizer 269C	Helicopter Experience	
G-XANT	Cameron N-105 balloon	Flying Pictures Ltd	
G-XARV	ARV Super 2	N. R. Beale (G-OPIG/G-BMSJ)	
G-XATS	Aerotek Pitts S-2A Special	Air Training Services Ltd/Booker	
G-XAXA	BN-2A-26 Islander	Airx Ltd (G-LOTO/G-BDWG)	
G-XAYR	Raj Hamsa X'Air 582 (6)	D. L. Connolly & R. Barber	
G-XBAT	Aeroprakt A.22 Foxbat	P. J. Harlow	
G-XBHX	Boeing 737-36N	British Airways Regional	
G-XCCC	Extra EA.300/L	P. T. Fellows	
G-XCEL	AS.355F-1 Twin Squirrel	R. W. Hemmings & Co (G-HBAC/G-HJET)	
G-XCUB	PA-18 Super Cub 150	M. C. Barraclough	
G-XENA	PA-28-161 Warrior II	Braddock Ltd	
G-XIIX	Robinson R-22B ★	(Static exhibit)	
G-XKEN	PA-34-200T Seneca III	Choicecircle Ltd	
G-XLAA	Boeing 737-8Q8	Excel Airways Ltd (G-OKDN)	
G-XLAB	Boeing 737-8Q8	Excel Airways Ltd (G-OJSW)	
G-XLAC	Boeing 737-81Q	Excel Airways Ltd (G-LFJB)	
G-XLAD	Boeing 737-81Q	Excel Airways Ltd (G-ODMW)	
G-XLAE	Boeing 737-8Q8	Excel Airways Ltd (G-OKJW)	
G-XLAG	Boeing 737-86N	Excel Airways Ltd	

Notes	Reg.	Type	Owner or Operator
	G-XLAH	Boeing 737-86N	Excel Airways Ltd
	G-XLIV	Robinson R-44	Defence Products Ltd
	G-XLTG	Cessna 182S	GX Aviation Ltd
	G-XLXL	Robin DR.400/160	40-40 Aero Group (G-BAUD)/Biggin Hill
	G-XMAN	Boeing 737-36N	British Airways
	G-XMGO	Aeromot AMT-200S Super Ximango	G. McLean & R. P. Beck
	G-XPBI	Letov LK-2M Sluka	B. G. M. Chapman
	G-XPSS	Short SD3-60 Variant 100	BAC Express Airlines Ltd (G-OBOH/ G-BNDJ)
	G-XPTS	Robinson R-44	Heli Air Ltd/Wellesbourne
	G-XPXP	Aero Designs Pulsar XP	B. J. Edwards
	G-XRAF	Raj Hamsa X'Air 582 (2)	X'Air Syndicate
	G-XRAY	Rand-Robinson KR-2	R. S. Smith
	G-XRLD	Cameron A-250 balloon	Red Letter Days Ltd
	G-XRXR	Raj Hamsa X'Air 582 (1)	I. S. Walsh
	G-XSDJ	Shaw Europa XS	D. N. Joyce
	G-XSFT	PA-23 Aztec 250F	T. L. B. Dykes (G-CPPC/G-BGBH)/ Goodwood
	G-XSKY	Cameron N-77 balloon	T. D. Gibbs
	G-XTEK	Robinson R-44	PLM Properties Ltd
	G-XTOR	BN-2A Mk III-2 Trislander	Aurigny Air Services Ltd (G-BAXD)
	G-XTRR	Extra EA.300/200	Taildragger Classics
	G-XTUN	Westland-Bell 47G-3B1 (XT223)	Hields Aviation (G-BGZK)
	G-XVIE	V.S.361 Spitfire LF.XVIe (TB252)	Historic Flying Ltd
	G-XVOM	Van's RV-6	A. Baker-Munton
	G-XWWF	Lindstrand LBL-56A balloon	D. D. Maimone
	G-XXEA	Sikorsky S-76C	Director of Royal Travel/Blackbushe
	G-XXIV	AB-206B JetRanger 3	Hampton Printing (Bristol) Ltd
	G-XXVI	Sukhoi Su-26M	A. N. Onn/Headcorn
	G-YAKA	Yakovlev Yak-50	R. C. Berger
	G-YAKI	Yakovlev Yak-52 (100)	Yak One Ltd/White Waltham
	G-YAKO	Yakovlev Yak-52	M. K. Shaw
	G-YAKS	Yakovlev Yak-52 (2)	Two Bees Associates Ltd
	G-YANK	PA-28-181 Archer II	G-YANK Flying Group
	G-YARR	Mainair Rapier	D. Yarr
	G-YARV	ARV Super 2	P. R. Snowden (G-BMDO)
	G-YAWW	PA-28RT-201T Turbo Arrow IV	Barton Aviation Ltd
	G-YBAA	Cessna FR.172J	A. Evans
	G-YCII	LET Yakovlev C-11	R. W. Davies
	G-YCUB	PA-18 Super Cub 150	F. W. Rogers Garage (Saltash) Ltd
	G-YEAR	Mini-500	D. J. Waddington
	G-YELL	Murphy Rebel	A. D. Keen
	G-YEOM	PA-31-350 Navajo Chieftain	Foster Yeoman Ltd/Exeter
	G-YFLY	VPM M.16 Tandem Trainer	A. J. Unwin (G-BWGI)
	G-YIII	Cessna F.150L	Sherburn Aero Club Ltd
	G-YIIK	Robinson R-44	The Websiteshop (UK) Ltd
	G-YJBM	Airbus A.320-231	My Travel Airways (Airtours) (G-IEAF)
	G-YJET	Montgomerie-Bensen B.8MR	A. Shuttleworth (G-BMUH)
	G-YKSZ	Yakovlev Yak-52	J. N. & C. J. Carter
	G-YLYB	Cameron N-105 balloon	Virgin Airship & Balloon Co Ltd
	G-YMBO	Robinson R-22M Mariner	J. Robinson
	G-YMMA	Boeing 777-236ER	British Airways
	G-YMMB	Boeing 777-236ER	British Airways
	G-YMMC	Boeing 777-236ER	British Airways
	G-YMMD	Boeing 777-236ER	British Airways
	G-YMME	Boeing 777-236ER	British Airways
	G-YMMF	Boeing 777-236ER	British Airways
	G-YMMG	Boeing 777-236ER	British Airways
	G-YMMH	Boeing 777-236ER	British Airways
	G-YMMI	Boeing 777-236ER	British Airways
	G-YMMJ	Boeing 777-236ER	British Airways
	G-YMMK	Boeing 777-236ER	British Airways
	G-YMML	Boeing 777-236ER	British Airways
	G-YMMM	Boeing 777-236ER	British Airways
	G-YMMN	Boeing 777-236ER	British Airways
	G-YMMO	Boeing 777-236ER	British Airways
	G-YMMP	Boeing 777-236ER	British Airways
	G-YNOT	D.62B Condor	T. Littlefair (G-AYFH)
	G-YOGI	Robin DR.400/140B	R. M. & A. M. Gosling (G-BDME)
	G-YORK	Cessna F.172M	H. Waetjen
	G-YOYO	Pitts S-1E Special	J. D. L. Richardson (G-OTSW/G-BLHE

Reg.	Type	Owner or Operator	Notes
G-YPOL	MDH MD-900 Explorer	West Yorkshire Police Authority	
G-YPSY	Andreasson BA-4B	R. W. Hinton	
G-YRAF	RAF 2000 GTX-SE gyroplane	C. V. King	
G-YRIL	Luscombe 8E Silvaire	C. Potter	
G-YROI	Air Command 532 Elite	W. B. Lumb	
G-YROO	RAF 2000 GTX-SE gyroplane	K. D. Rhodes & C. S. Oakes	
G-YROS	Montgomerie-Bensen B.8M	N. B. Gray	
G-YROY	Montgomerie-Bensen B.8MR	S. Brennan	
G-YSFT	PA-23 Aztec 250F	SFT Europe Ltd (G-BEJT)/Bournemouth	
G-YSON	Eurocopter EC.120B	Heli-Express Ltd	
G-YSTT	PA-32R-301 Saratoga II HP	A. W. Kendrick	
G-YTUK	Cameron A-210 balloon	Societe Bombard SRL/France	
G-YUGO	H.S.125 Srs 1B/R-522 ★	Fire Section (G-ATWH)/Dunsfold	
G-YULL	PA-28 Cherokee 180E	Fortescue Investments Ltd (G-BEAJ)	
G-YUMM	Cameron N-90 balloon	Wunderbar Ltd	
G-YUPI	Cameron N-90 balloon	MCVH SA/Belgium	
G-YURO	Shaw Europa ★	Yorkshire Air Museum/Elvington	
G-YVBF	Lindstrand LBL-317S balloon	Virgin Balloon Flights Ltd	
G-YVET	Cameron V-90 balloon	K. J. Foster	
G-YYYY	MH.1521C-1 Broussard	Aerosuperbatics Ltd/Rendcomb	
G-ZABC	Sky 90-24 balloon	J. A. Lister	
G-ZACH	Robin DR.400/100	A. P. Wellings (G-FTIO)/Sandown	
G-ZAIR	Zenair CH 601HD	Speedfreak Ltd	
G-ZAPH	Bell 206B JetRanger 4	Titan Airways Ltd (G-DBMW)	
G-ZAPJ	Aérospatiale ATR-42-300	Titan Airways Ltd	
G-ZAPK	BAe 146-200QC	Titan Airways Ltd (G-BTIA/G-PRIN)	
G-ZAPM	Boeing 737-33A	Titan Airways Ltd	
G-ZAPN	BAe 146-200QC	Titan Airways Ltd (G-BPBT)	
G-ZAPO	BAe 146-200QC	Titan Airways Ltd (G-BWLG/G-PRCS)	
G-ZAPT	Beech B.200C Super King Air	Titan Airways Ltd/Stansted	
G-ZAPY	Robinson R-22B	Heli Air Ltd (G-INGB)	
G-ZARI	AA-5B Tiger	ZARI Aviation Ltd (G-BHVY)	
G-ZARV	ARV Super 2	P. R. Snowden	
G-ZAZA	PA-18 Super Cub 95	Airborne Taxi Services Ltd	
G-ZBED	Robinson R-22B	P. D. Spinks	
G-ZBLT	Cessna 182S	Blue Line Trailers	
G-ZEBO	Thunder Ax8-105 S2 balloon	S. M. Waterton	
G-ZEIN	Slingsby T.67M Firefly 260	R.V. Aviation Ltd/Bournemouth	
G-ZENA	Zenair CH.701UL	A. N. Aston	
G-ZEPI	Colt GA-42 gas airship	P. A. Lindstrand (G-ISPY/G-BPRB)	
G-ZERO	AA-5B Tiger	G-ZERO Syndicate	
G-ZHWH	Rotorway Executive 162F	B. Alexander	
G-ZIGI	Robin DR.400/180	R. J. Dix	
G-ZIPA	R. Commander 114A	M. F. Luke (G-BHRA)	
G-ZIPI	Robin DR.400/180	H. U. & D. C. Stahlberg/Headcorn	
G-ZIPY	Wittman W.8 Tailwind	M. J. Butler	
G-ZIZI	Cessna 525 CitationJet	Ortac Air Ltd	
G-ZLIN	Z.526 Trener Master	N. J. Arthur	
G-ZLLE	SA.341G Gazelle	G-ZLLE Ltd	
G-ZLOJ	Beech A36 Bonanza	W. D. Gray	
G-ZLYN	Z.526F Trener Master	H. Philippart	
G-ZMAM	PA-28-181 Archer II	Z. Mahmood (G-BNPN)	
G-ZODI	Zenair CH.601UL	B. McFadden	
G-ZONK	Robinson R-44	CCB Aviation Ltd (G-EDIE)	
G-ZOOI	Lindstrand LBL-105A balloon	Flying Pictures Ltd	
G-ZOOL	Cessna FA.152	European Flyers (G-BGXZ)/Blackbushe	
G-ZORO	Shaw Europa	N. T. Read	
G-ZTED	Shaw Europa	J. J. Kennedy & E. W. Gladstone	
G-ZULU	PA-28-161 Warrior II	S. F. Tebby & Son	
G-ZVBF	Cameron A-400 balloon	Virgin Balloon Flights Ltd	
G-ZWAR	Eurocopter EC.120B	Hedgeton Trading Ltd	
G-ZWRC	AS.350B-3 Ecureuil	Proflight Ltd	
G-ZZAG	Cameron Z-77 balloon	T. Charlwood	
G-ZZIP	Mooney M.20J-205	H. T. El-Kasaby	
G-ZZLE	SA.341G Gazelle 1	G-ZZLE Ltd	
G-ZZOE	Eurocopter EC.120B	Loune Ltd/Kidlington	
G-ZZWW	Enstrom 280FX	A. W. Kendrick (G-BSIE)	
G-ZZZA	Boeing 777-236	British Airways	
G-ZZZB	Boeing 777-236	British Airways	
G-ZZZC	Boeing 777-236	British Airways	
G-ZZZD	Boeing 777-236	British Airways	
G-ZZZE	Boeing 777-236	British Airways	

G-DHDV D.H.104 Dove 8.

G-JEDA D.H.C.8-314 Dash Eight of British European.

G-JRJR Learjet 45. *A.S.Wright*

G-OOOX Boeing 757-2Y0 of Air 2000.

G-SSWB Short SD-360 Variant 100 of Streamline Aviation. *A.S. Wright*

Military to Civil Cross-Reference

Serial carried	Civil identity	Serial carried	Civil identity
2 (USAAC)	G-AZLE	6136 (205 USN)	G-BRUJ
2 (CIS)	G-YAKS	6232	BAPC41
09 (DOSAAF)	G-BVMU	7198/18	G-AANJ
15 (DOSAAF)	G-BXJB	7797 (USAAF)	G-BFAF
23 (USAAC)	N49272	8178 (FU-178 USAF)	G-SABR
26 (US)	G-BAVO	8449M	G-ASWJ
26 (DOSAAF)	G-BVXK	01385 (CIS)	G-BWJT
27 (CIS)	G-YAKX	01420 (Korean AF)	G-BMZF
27 (USN)	G-BRVG	02538 (USAAF)	N33870
27 (CIS)	G-OYAK	07539 (143 USN)	N63590
27 (USAAC)	G-AGYY	1/4513 (Fr AF)	G-BFYO
28 (USAAC)	N8162G	14863 (USAAF)	G-BGOR
31 (DOSAAF	RA-02209	16693 (693 RCAF)	G-BLPG
42 (DOSAAF)	LY-AMU	18013 (013 RCAF)	G-TRIC
43 (SC USAF)	G-AZSC	18263 (822 USAAF)	N38940
44 (USAAF)	G-BWHH	18393 (RCAF)	G-BCYK
44 (K-33 USAAF)	G-BJLH	18671 (671 RCAF)	G-BNZC
52 (DOSAAF)	LY-AMP	20310 (310 RCAF)	G-BSBG
52	G-BWVR	21261 (RCAF)	G-TBRD
55 (DOSAAF)	G-BVOK	21714 (201-B USN)	G-RUMM
69 (DOSAAF)	G-BTZB	28521 (TA-521 USAF)	G-TVIJ
72 (DOSAAF)	G-BXAV	30140 (Yugoslav Army)	G-RADA
74 (DOSAAF)	G-BXID	30146 (Yugoslav Army)	G-BSXD
85 (USAAF)	G-BTBI	30149 (Yugoslav Army)	G-SOKO
100 (DOSAAF)	G-YAKI	30861 (USAAF)	N9089Z
111 (Libyan Arab AF)	G-OTAF	31145 (G-26 USAAF)	G-BBLH
112 (DOSAAF)	LY-AFB	31171 (USMarines)	N7614C
112 (USAAC)	G-BSWC	31923 (USAAC)	G-BRHP
115 (DOSAAF)	RA-02293	31952 (USAAC)	G-BRPR
118 (USAAC)	G-BSDS	34037 (USAAF)	N9115Z
124 (Fr AF)	G-BOSJ	39624 (D-39 USAAF)	G-BVMH
139 (DOSAAF)	G-BWOD	40467 (19 USN)	G-BTCC
143 (Fr AF)	G-MSAL	43578 (578 USN)	N1364V
152/17	G-ATJM	46867 (USN)	N909WJ
168	G-BFDE	53319 (319/RB USN)	G-BTDP
177 (Irish AC)	G-BLIW	54137 (69 USN)	G-CTKL
185 (Fr AF)	G-BWLR	56321 (U-AB RNorAF)	G-BKPY
208 (USN)	N75664	80242 (USAF)	N196B
210/16	BAPC56	80425 (WT-14 USN)	G-RUMT
215	G-HELV	80480 (E-44 USAAF)	G-BECN
304	BAPC62	86711 (USN)	G-RUMW
311 (SingaporeAF)	G-SARK	91007 (USAF)	G-NASA
379 (USAAC)	G-ILLE	92399 (17 USN)	G-CCMV
422-15	G-AVJO	93542 (LTA-542 USAF)	G-BRLV
427 (RNorAF)	G-AMRK	111836 (JZ-6 USN)	G-TSIX
441 (USN)	G-BTFG	111989 (US Army)	N33600
450/17	G-BVGZ	115042 (TA-042 USAF)	G-BGHU
503 (Hungarian AF)	G-BRAM	115302 (TP USAAF)	G-BJTP
540 (USAAF)	G-BCNX	115684 (D-C USAAF)	G-BKVM
626/8	N6268	122179 (NP-9 USN)	N179PT
669 (USAAC)	N75TL	124485 (DF-A USAAF)	G-BEDF
781-25 (Span AF)	G-BRSH	126922 (402/AK USN)	G-RAID
781-32 (Span AF)	G-BPDM	146289 (2W USAAF)	N99153
796 (USAAC)	N43SV	150225 (123 USAF)	G-AWOX
854 (USAAC)	G-BTBH	151632 (USAAF)	G-BWGR
855 (USAAC)	N56421	18-2001 (USAAF)	G-BIZV
897 (E USN)	G-BJEV	211672 (USAAF)	N50755
1164 (USAAC)	G-BKGL	217786 (25 USAAF)	G-BRTK
1180 (USN)	G-BRSK	219993 (USAAF)	N139DP
1197	G-BPVE	2106449 (HO-W USAAF)	G-PSIC
1211(N. Korean AF)	G-BWUF	226413 (UN-Z USAAF)	N47DD
1377 (Portuguese AF)	G-BARS	226671 (MX-X USAAF)	G-THUN
1747 (Portuguese AF)	G-BGPB	231983 (IY-G USAAF)	F-BDRS
2345	G-ATVP	236800 (A-44 USAAF)	G-BHPK
2807 (V-103 USN)	G-BHTH	2632016 (China AF)	G-BXZB
3066	G-AETA	314887 (USAAF)	G-AJPI
5964	G-BFVH	315211 (J8-Z USAAF)	N1944A

Serial carried	Civil identity	Serial carried	Civil identity
315509 (W7-S USAAF)	G-BHUB	D8084	G-ACAA
329405 (A-23 USAAF)	G-BCOB	D8096 (D)	G-AEPH
329417 (USAAF)	G-BDHK	D8781	G-ECKE
329471 (F-44 USAAF)	G-BGXA	E-15 (RNethAF)	G-BIYU
329601 (D-44 USAAF)	G-AXHR	E3B-143 (Span AF)	G-JUNG
329854 (R-44 USAAF)	G-BMKC	E3B-153 (781-75 Span AF)	G-BPTS
329934 (B-72 USAAF)	G-BCPH	E3B-350 (05-97 Span AF)	G-BHPL
330238 (A-24 USAAF)	G-LIVH	E449	G-EBJE
330485 (C-44 USAAF)	G-AJES	F141 (G)	G-SEVA
343251 (27 USAAC)	G-NZSS	F235 (B)	G-BMDB
413573 (B6-V USAAF)	N6526D	F904	G-EBIA
414151 (HO-M USAAF)	NL314BG	F938	G-EBIC
414419 (LH-F USAAF)	G-MSTG	F943	G-BIHF
436021 (USAAF)	G-BWEZ	F943	G-BKDT
454467 (J-44 USAAF)	G-BILI	F5447 (N)	G-BKER
454537 (J-04 USAAF)	G-BFDL	F5459 (Y)	G-INNY
461748 (Y USAF)	G-BHDK	F8010 (Z)	G-BDWJ
463221 (G4-S USAAF)	G-BTCD	F8614	G-AWAU
472216 (HO M USAAF)	G-BIXL	G-48-1 (Class B)	G-ALSX
472218 (WZ-I USAAF)	G-HAEC	H1968	BAPC142
472773 (QP-M USAAF)	G-SUSY	H5199	G-ADEV
474008 (VF-R USAAF)	G-SIRR	J-1149 (Swiss AF)	G-SWIS
479744 (M-49 USAAF)	G-BGPD	J-1573 (Swiss AF)	G-VICI
479766 (D-63 USAAF)	G-BKHG	J-1605 (Swiss AF)	G-BLID
480015 (M-44 USAAF)	G-AKIB	J-1614 (Swiss AF)	G-VENM
480133 (B-44 USAAF)	G-BDCD	J-1632 (Swiss AF)	G-VNOM
480321 (H-44 USAAF)	G-FRAN	J-1758 (Swiss AF)	G-BLSD
480636 (A-58 USAAF)	G-AXHP	J-4031 (Swiss AF)	G-BWFR
480752 (E-39 USAAF)	G-BCXJ	J-4058 (Swiss AF)	G-BWFS
483868 (A-N USAAF)	N5237V	J-4066 (Swiss AF)	G-BXNZ
493209 (US ANG)	G-DDMV	J-4081 (Swiss AF)	G-BWKB)
41-33275 (CE USAAC)	G-BICE	J-4083 (Swiss AF)	G-EGHH
42-58678 (IY USAAC)	G-BRIY	J-4090 (Swiss AF)	G-SIAL
42-78044 (USAAC)	G-BRXL	J7326	G-EBQP
42-84555 (EP-H)	G-ELMH	J9941 (57)	G-ABMR
43-5802 (49 USAAC)	G-KITT	K-682 (RDanAF)	OY-BPB
44-14419 (LH-F USAAF)	G-MSTG	K1786	G-AFTA
44-79609 (PR USAAF)	G-BHXY	K2048	G-BZNW
44-63507 (USAAF)	N51EA	K2050	G-ASCM
44-80594 (USAAF)	G-BEDJ	K2059	G-PFAR
44-83184 (USAAF)	G-RGUS	K2060	G-BKZM
51-1585	BAPC58	K2075	G-BEER
51-7545 (113 USAF)	N14113	K2227	G-ABBB
51-7692 (Fr AF)	G-TROY	K2567	G-MOTH
51-11701A (AF258 USAF)	G-BSZC	K2572	G-AOZH
51-14526 (USAAF)	G-BRWB	K2587	G-BJAP
51-15227 (10 USN)	G-BKRA	K3215	G-AHSA
54-2447 (USAAF)	G-SCUB	K3661	G-BURZ
56-5395 (CDG Fr AF)	G-CUBJ	K3731	G-RODI
607327 (09-L USAAF)	G-ARAO	K4259 (71)	G-ANMO
A-10 (Swiss AF)	G-BECW	K5054	G-BRDV
A16-199 (SF-R RAAF)	G-BEOX	K5414 (XV)	G-AENP
A17-48 (RAAF)	G-BPHR	K5600	G-BVVI
A-57 (Swiss AF)	G-BECT	K8203	G-BTVE
A-806 (Swiss AF)	G-BTLL	K8303 (D)	G-BWWN
A1325	G-BVGR	K9853 (QV-H)	G-AIST
A1742	BAPC38	L1592	BAPC63
A8226	G-BIDW	L2301	G-AIZG
B595 (W)	G-BUOD	L6906	G-AKKY
B1807	G-EAVX	N500	G-BWRA
B2458	G-BPOB	N1854	G-AIBE
B3459	G-BWMJ	N4877 (VX-F)	G-AMDA
B6401	G-AWYY	N5182	G-APUP
B7270	G-BFCZ	N5195	G-ABOX
C1904 (Z)	G-PFAP	N5903 (H)	G-GLAD
C3011 (S)	G-SWOT	N6181	G-EBKY
C4918	G-BWJM	N6290	G-BOCK
C4994	G-BLWM	N6452	G-BIAU
C9533 (M)	G-BUWE	N6466	G-ANKZ
D-692	G-BVAW	N6532	G-ANTS
D3419	BAPC59	N6537	G-AOHY
D5397/17	G-BFXL	N6797	G-ANEH
D7889	G-AANM	N6847	G-APAL

Serial carried	Civil identity	Serial carried	Civil identity
N6965 (FL-J)	G-AJTW	DF155	G-ANFV
N6985	G-AHMN	DF198	G-BBRB
N9191	G-ALND	DG590	G-ADMW
N9192 (RCO-N)	G-DHZF	DR613	G-AFJB
P9374	G-MKIA	EJ693 (SA-J)	N7027E
N9389	G-ANJA	EM720	G-AXAN
P3059	BAPC64	EN224	G-FXII
P6382	G-AJRS	EP120 (AE-A)	G-LFVB
R-151 (RNethAF)	G-BIYR	FB226 (MT-A)	G-BDWM
R-163 (RNethAF)	G-BIRH	FE695 (94)	G-BTXI
R-167 (RNethAF)	G-LION	FE992 (K-T)	G-BDAM
R1914	G-AHUJ	FH153	G-BBHK
R3281 (UX-N)	G-BPIV	FR886	G-BDMS
R5250	G-AODT	FT391	G-AZBN
S1287	G-BEYB	FX301 (FD-NQ)	G-JUDI
S1579 (571)	G-BBVO	HB275	G-BKGM
S1581 (573)	G-BWWK	HB751	G-BCBL
T5424	G-AJOA	HD-75 (RBelAF)	G-AFDX
T5672	G-ALRI	HM580	G-ACUU
T5854	G-ANKK	JG891	G-LFVC
T5879	G-AXBW	JV579 (F)	G-RUMW
T6313	G-AHVU	KB889 (NA-I)	G-LANC
T6562	G-ANTE	KB994	G-BVBP
T6818 (91)	G-ANKT	KD345 (130)	G-FGID
T6991	G-ANOR	KF584 (RAI-X)	G-RAIX
T7230	G-AFVE	KL161 (VO-B)	G-BYDR
T7281	G-ARTL	KN556	G-AMPO
T7404 (04)	G-ANMV	KZ321	G-HURY
T7471	G-AJHU	LB294	G-AHWJ
T7793	G-ANKV	LB312	G-AHXE
T7842	G-AMTF	LB367	G-AHGZ
T7909	G-ANON	LB375	G-AHGW
T7997	G-AHUF	LF858	G-BLUZ
T8191	G-BWMK	LZ766	G-ALCK
T9707	G-AKKR	MD497	G-ANLW
T9738	G-AKAT	MH434 (PK-K)	G-ASJV
U-0247 (Class B identity)	G-AGOY	MJ627 (9G-P)	G-BMSB
U-80 (Swiss AF)	G-BUKK	MJ730 (GZ-?)	G-HFIX
U-99 (Swiss AF)	G-AXMT	MK912 (SH-L)	G-BRRA
U-108 (Swiss AF)	G-BJAX	ML407 (OU-V)	G-LFIX
U-110 (Swiss AF)	G-PTWO	MP425	G-AITB
U-142 (Swiss AF)	G-BONE	MS824 (Fr AF)	G-AWBU
V-54 (Swiss AF)	G-BVSD	MT438	G-AREI
V1075	G-AKPF	MT928 (ZX-M)	G-BKMI
V3388	G-AHTW	MV268 (JE-J)	G-SPIT
V9367 (MA-B)	G-AZWT	MW401	G-PEST
V9673 (MA-J)	G-LIZY	MW763 (HF-A)	G-TEMT
W7 (Italian AF)	G-AGFT	NJ673	G-AOCR
W2718	G-RNLI	NJ695	G-AJXV
W5856 (A2A)	G-BMGC	NJ719	G-ANFU
W9385 (YG-L)	G-ADND	NL750	G-AOBH
Z2033 (N/275)	G-ASTL	NL985	G-BWIK
Z5207	G-BYDL	NM181	G-AZGZ
Z5252 (GO-B)	G-BWHA	NP303	G-ANZJ
Z7015 (7-L)	G-BKTH	NX554	G-BUDL
Z7197	G-AKZN	NX611 (LE-C/DX-C)	G-ASXX
Z7381 (XR-T)	G-HURI	NZ3907	G-RIMM
AP506	G-ACWM	NZ3908	G-KAWW
AP507 (KX-P)	G-ACWP	NZ5648 (648 RNZAF)	G-BXUL
AR213 (PR-D)	G-AIST	NZ6361 (RNZAF)	G-BXFP
AR501 (NN-A)	G-AWII	PP972 (6M-D)	G-BUAR
BB807	G-ADWO	PB1	N18V
BE417 (LK-A)	G-HURR	PS853 (C)	G-RRGN
BI-005 (RNethAF)	G-BUVN	PT462 (SW-A)	G-CTIX
BM597 (JH-C)	G-MKVB	PT879	G-BYDE
BW881	G-KAMM	RG333	G-AIEK
DE208	G-AGYU	RG333	G-AKEZ
DE470	G-ANMY	RH377	G-ALAH
DE623	G-ANFI	RL962	G-AHED
DE673	G-ADNZ	RM221	G-ANXR
DE992	G-AXXV	RN218 (N)	G-BBJI
DF112	G-ANRM	RT486 (PF-A)	G-AJGJ
DF128 (RCO-U)	G-AOJJ	RT520	G-ALYB

Serial carried	Civil identity	Serial carried	Civil identity
RT610	G-AKWS	WD347	G-BBRV
RX168	G-BWEM	WD363 (5)	G-BCIH
SG-3 (RBelAF)	G-BSKP	WD373 (12)	G-BXDI
SM845	G-BUOS	WD379 (K)	G-APLO
SM969 (D-A)	G-BRAF	WD390 (68)	G-BWNK
SX336	G-BRMG	WD413	G-VROE
TA634 (8K-K)	G-AWJV	WE402	G-VENI
TA719 (6T)	G-ASKC	WE569	G-ASAJ
TA805	G-PMNF	WE724 (062)	G-BUCM
TB252 (GW-H)	G-XVIE	WF118	G-DACA
TD248 (D)	G-OXVI	WF877	G-BPOA
TE184 (D)	G-MXVI	WG307	G-BCYJ
TJ324	G-APAH	WG308 (8)	G-BYHL
TJ569	G-AKOW	WG316	G-BCAH
TJ672	G-ANIJ	WG348	G-BBMV
TJ704 (JA)	G-ASCD	WG350	G-BPAL
TS423	N147DC	WG407	G-BWMX
TS798	G-AGNV	WG422 (16)	G-BFAX
TW439	G-ANRP	WG465	G-BCEY
TW467 (ROD-F)	G-ANIE	WG469 (72)	G-BWJY
TW511	G-APAF	WG472	G-AOTY
TW517	G-BDFX	WG719	G-BRMA
TW536 (TS-V)	G-BNGE	WJ358	G-ARYD
TW591 (N)	G-ARIH	WJ945 (21)	G-BEDV
TW641	G-ATDN	WK126 (843)	N2138J
VF512 (PF-M)	G-ARRX	WK163	G-BVWC
VF516	G-ASMZ	WK511 (905 RN)	G-BVBT
VF526 (T)	G-ARXU	WK512 (A)	G-BXIM
VF548	G-ASEG	WK517 (84)	G-ULAS
VL348	G-AVVO	WK522	G-BCOU
VL349	G-AWSA	WK549 (Y)	G-BTWF
VM360	G-APHV	WK586	G-BXGX
VP955	G-DVON	WK590 (69)	G-BWVZ
VP981	G-DHDV	WK609 (93)	G-BXDN
VR192	G-APIT	WK611	G-ARWB
VR249 (FA-EL)	G-APIY	WK622	G-BCZH
VR259 (M)	G-APJB	WK624 (M)	G-BWHI
VS356	G-AOLU	WK628	G-BBMW
VS610 (K-L)	G-AOKL	WK630 (11)	G-BXDG
VS623	G-AOKZ	WK633 (A)	G-BXEC
VT871	G-DHXX	WK638 (83)	G-BWJZ
VX118	G-ASNB	WK640 (C)	G-BWUV
VX147	G-AVIL	WK642 (94)	G-BXDP
VZ638 (HF)	G-JETM	WL505	G-FBIX
VZ728	G-AGOS	WL505	G-MKVI
WA576	G-ALSS	WL626	G-BHDD
WA577	G-ALST	WM167	G-LOSM
WA591 (W)	G-BWMF	WP788	G-BCHL
WB188	G-BZPB (green)	WP790 (T)	G-BBNC
WB188	G-BZPC (red)	WP795 (901)	G-BVZZ
WB531	G-BLRN	WP800 (2)	G-BCXN
WB565 (X)	G-PVET	WP803	G-HAPY
WB569	G-BYSJ	WP805 (D)	G-MAJR
WB571 (34)	G-AOSF	WP808	G-BDEU
WB585 (RCU-X)	G-AOSY	WP809 (78 RN)	G-BVTX
WB588 (D)	G-AOTD	WP840 (9)	G-BXDM
WB615 (E)	G-BXIA	WP843 (F)	G-BDBP
WB652	G-CHPY	WP844 (85)	G-BWOX
WB654	G-BXGO	WP856 (904 RN)	G-BVWP
WB660	G-ARMB	WP857 (24)	G-BDRJ
WB671 (910)	G-BWTG	WP859 (E)	G-BXCP
WB697 (95)	G-BXCT	WP860 (6)	G-BXDA
WB702	G-AOFE	WP896 (M)	G-BWVY
WB703	G-ARMC	WP901 (B)	G-BWNT
WB711	G-APPM	WP903	G-BCGC
WB726 (E)	G-AOSK	WP925 (C)	G-BXHA
WD286 (J)	G-BBND	WP928	G-BXGM
WD288	G-AOSO	WP929 (F)	G-BXCV
WD292	G-BCRX	WP930	G-BXHF
WD297		WP971	G-ATHD
WD305	G-ARGG	WP983	G-BXNN
WD310 (B)	G-BWUN	WP984 (H)	G-BWTO
WD331 (J)	G-BXDH	WR410 (N)	G-BLKA

Serial carried	Civil identity	Serial carried	Civil identity
WR410	G-DHUU	XL954	G-BXES
WR421	G-DHTT	XM223 (J)	G-BWWC
WT333	G-BVXC	XM365 (37)	G-BXBH
WT722 (878/VL)	G-BWGN	XM370 (10)	G-BVSP
WT933	G-ALSW	XM376 (27)	G-BWDR
WV198 (K)	G-BJWY	XM405 (42)	G-TORE
WV318 (A)	G-FFOX	XM424	G-BWDS
WV372 (R)	G-BXFI	XM470 (12)	G-BWZZ
WV493 (29)	G-BDYG	XM478 (33)	G-BXDL
WV740	G-BNPH	XM479 (54)	G-BVEZ
WV783	G-ALSP	XM553	G-AWSV
WW453 (W-S)	G-TMKI	XM575	G-BLMC
WZ507	G-VTII	XM655	G-VULC
WZ553 (40)	G-DHYY	XM685 (513/PO)	G-AYZJ
WZ589	G-DHZZ	XM693	G-TIMM
WZ662	G-BKVK	XM819	G-APXW
WZ706	G-BURR	XN351	G-BKSC
WZ711	G-AVHT	XN435	G-BGBU
WZ847 (F)	G-CPMK	XN437	G-AXWA
WZ868 (H CUAS)	G-ARMF	XN441	G-BGKT
WZ879 (73)	G-BWUT	XN459 (N)	G-BWOT
WZ882 (K)	G-BXGP	XN498 (16)	G-BWSH
XA880	G-BVXR	XN629	G-KNOT
XD693 (Z-Q)	G-AOBU	XN637 (03)	G-BKOU
XE489	G-JETH	XP242	G-BUCI
XE665 (876/VL)	G-BWGM	XP254	G-ASCC
XE685 (861/VL)	G-GAII	XP279	G-BWKK
XE689 (864/VL)	G-BWGK	XP282	G-BGTC
XE856	G-DUSK	XP355	G-BEBC
XE897	G-DHVV	XP672 (27)	G-RAFI
XE920 (A)	G-VMPR	XP772	G-BUCJ
XE956	G-OBLN	XP907	G-SROE
XF114	G-SWIF	XP924	G-CVIX
XF303 (105-A)	G-BWOU	XR240	G-BDFH
XF515 (R)	G-KAXF	XR241	G-AXRR
XF516 (66.F)	G-BVVC	XR246	G-AZBU
XF597 (AH)	G-BKFW	XR442	G-HRON
XF603	G-KAPW	XR486	G-RWWW
XF690	G-MOOS	XR537 (T)	G-NATY
XF785	G-ALBN	XR538 (69)	G-RORI
XF836 (J-G)	G-AWRY	XR595 (M)	G-BWHU
XF877 (JX)	G-AWVF	XR673 (L)	G-BXLO
XG160 (U)	G-BWAF	XR724	G-BTSY
XG232	G-BWIU	XR944	G-ATTB
XG452	G-BRMB	XR991	G-MOUR
XG547	G-HAPR	XR993	G-BVPP
XF766	G-SPDR	XS101	G-GNAT
XG775	G-DHWW	XS165 (37)	G-ASAZ
XH568	G-BVIC	XS587 (252/V)	G-VIXN
XH558	G-VLCN	XS765	G-BSET
XJ389	G-AJJP	XS770	G-HRHI
XJ615	G-BWGL	XT223	G-XTUN
XJ729	G-BVGE	XT634	G-BYRX
XJ763 (P)	G-BKHA	XT671	G-BYRC
XK416	G-AYUA	XT788 (316)	G-BMIR
XK417	G-AVXY	XV126 (X)	G-SCTA
XK482	G-BJWC	XV130 (R)	G-BWJW
XK895 (19/CU)	G-SDEV	XV134 (P)	G-BWLX
XK896	G-RNAS	XV140 (K)	G-KAXL
XK940	G-AYXT	XV268	G-BVER
XL426	G-VJET	XW289 (73)	G-JPVA
XL502	G-BMYP	XW293	G-BWCS
XL571	G-HNTR	XW324 (U)	G-BWSG
XL573	G-BVGH	XW325 (E)	G-BWGF
XL577	G-BXKF	XW333 (79)	G-BVTC
XL587	G-HPUX	XW423 (14)	G-BWUW
XL602	G-BWFT	XW433 (63)	G-JPRO
XL621	G-BNCX	XW635	G-AWSW
XL714	G-AOGR	XW784	G-BBRN
XL716	G-AOIL	XW866 (E)	G-BXTH
XL809	G-BLIX	XW895 (51/CU)	G-BXZD
XL812	G-SARO	XW910 (K)	G-BXZE
XL929	G-BNPU	XX467	G-TVII

225

Serial carried	Civil identity	Serial carried	Civil identity
XX469	G-BNCL	BU+CK (Luftwaffe)	G-BUCK
XX525 (8)	G-CBJJ	CC+43 (Luftwaffe)	G-CJCI
XX622 (B)	G-CBGX	CF+HF (Luftwaffe)	EI-AUY
XX630 (5)	G-SIJW	LG+01 (Luftwaffe)	G-AYSJ
XX713 (G)	G-CBJK	LG+03 (Luftwaffe)	G-AEZX
ZA250	G-VTOL	KG+EM (Luftwaffe)	G-ETME
ZA634 (C)	G-BUHA	NJ+C11 (Luftwaffe)	G-ATBG
ZB500	G-LYNX	S4+A07 (Luftwaffe)	G-BWHP
2+1 (7334 Luftwaffe)	G-SYFW	S5-B06 (Luftwaffe)	G-BSFB
3+ (Luftwaffe)	G-BAYV	TA+RC (Luftwaffe)	G-BPHZ
4+ (Luftwaffe)	G-BSLX	6J+PR (Luftwaffe)	G-AWHB
07 (Russian AF)	G-BMJY	57-H (USAAC)	G-AKAZ
8+ (Luftwaffe)	G-WULF	97+04 (Luftwaffe)	G-APVF
14+ (Luftwaffe)	G-BBII	+114 (Luftwaffe)	G-BSMD
28-02	G-OTAF	146-11042 (7)	G-BMZX
F+IS (Luftwaffe)	G-BIRW	146-11083 (5)	G-BNAI
BU+CC (Luftwaffe)	G-BUCC		

Toy Balloons

Notes	Reg.	Type	Owner or Operator
	G-FYAN	Williams	M. D. Williams
	G-FYAO	Williams	M. D. Williams
	G-FYAU	Williams MK 2	M. D. Williams
	G-FYAV	Osprey Mk 4E2	C. D. Egan & C. Stiles
	G-FYBR	Osprey Mk 4G2	A. J. Pugh
	G-FYBX	Portswood Mk XVI	I. Chadwick
	G-FYCL	Osprey Mk 4G	P. J. Rogers
	G-FYCV	Osprey Mk 4D	M. Thomson
	G-FYCZ	Osprey Mk 4D2	P. Middleton
	G-FYDF	Osprey Mk 4D	K. A. Jones
	G-FYDI	Williams Westwind Two	M. D. Williams
	G-FYDN	European 8C	P. D. Ridout
	G-FYDO	Osprey Mk 4D	N. L. Scallan
	G-FYDP	Williams Westwind Three	M. D. Williams
	G-FYDS	Osprey Mk 4D	N. L. Scallan
	G-FYEK	Unicorn UE.1C	D. & D. Eaves
	G-FYEO	Eagle Mk 1	M. E. Scallan
	G-FYEV	Osprey Mk 1C	M. E. Scallan
	G-FYEZ	Firefly Mk 1	M. E. & N. L. Scallan
	G-FYFI	European E.84DS	M. Stelling
	G-FYFJ	Williams Westland 2	M. D. Williams
	G-FYFN	Osprey Saturn 2	J. & M. Woods
	G-FYFW	Rango NA-55	Rango Kite & Balloon Co
	G-FYFY	Rango NA-55RC	A. M. Lindsay
	G-FYGC	Rango NA-42B	L. J. Wardle
	G-FYGI	Rango NA-55RC	Advertair Ltd
	G-FYGJ	Airspeed 300	N. Wells
	G-FYGM	Saffrey/Smith Princess	A. Smith

Microlights

Reg.	Type	Notes	Reg.	Type	Notes
G-MBAA	Hiway Skytrike Mk 2		G-MBIY	Ultrasports Tripacer	
G-MBAB	Hovey Whing-Ding II		G-MBIZ	Mainair Tri-Flyer	
G-MBAD	Weedhopper JC-24A		G-MBJD	American Aerolights Eagle	
G-MBAF	R. J. Swift 3		G-MBJE	Airwave Nimrod	
G-MBAN	American Aerolights Eagle		G-MBJF	Hiway Skytrike Mk II	
G-MBAR	Skycraft Scout		G-MBJG	Airwave Nimrod	
G-MBAS	Typhoon Tripacer 250		G-MBJI	Southern Aerosports	
G-MBAU	Hiway Skytrike			Scorpion	
G-MBAW	Pterodactyl Ptraveller		G-MBJK	American Aerolights Eagle	
G-MBAZ	Rotec Rally 2B		G-MBJL	Airwave Nimrod	
G-MBBB	Skycraft Scout 2		G-MBJM	Striplin Lone Ranger	
G-MBBG	Weedhopper JC-24B		G-MBJP	Hiway Skytrike	
G-MBBM	Eipper Quicksilver MX		G-MBJR	American Aerolights Eagle	
G-MBBT	Ultrasports Tripacer 330		G-MBJT	Hiway Skytrike II	
G-MBCA	Chargus Cyclone T.250		G-MBJU	American Eagle 215B	
G-MBCJ	Mainair Sports Tri-Flyer		G-MBJZ	Eurowing Catto CP.16	
G-MBCK	Eipper Quicksilver MX		G-MBKS	Hiway Skytrike 160	
G-MBCL	Hiway Demon Triflyer		G-MBKT	Mitchell Wing B.10	
G-MBCM	Hiway Demon 175		G-MBKU	Hiway Demon Skytrike	
G-MBCO	Flexiform Sealander		G-MBKY	American Aerolight Eagle	
	Buggy		G-MBKZ	Hiway Skytrike	
G-MBCU	American Aerolights Eagle		G-MBLB	Eipper Quicksilver MX	
G-MBCX	Airwave Nimrod 165		G-MBLF	Hiway Demon 195 Tri	
G-MBCZ	Chargus Skytrike 160			Pacer	
G-MBDE	Flexiform Skytrike		G-MBLJ	Eipper Quicksilver MX	
G-MBDF	Rotec Rally 2B		G-MBLU	Southdown Lightning	
G-MBDG	Eurowing Goldwing			L.195	
G-MBDM	Southdown Sigma Trike		G-MBLV	Ultrasports Hybrid	
G-MBDZ	Eipper Quicksilver MX		G-MBLY	Flexiform Sealander Trike	
G-MBEA	Hornet Nimrod		G-MBLZ	Southern Aerosports	
G-MBED	Chargus Titan 38			Scorpion	
G-MBEG	Eipper Quicksilver MX		G-MBME	American Aerolights	
G-MBEJ	Electraflyer Eagle			Eagle Z Drive	
G-MBEN	Eipper Quicksilver MX		G-MBMG	Rotec Rally 2B	
G-MBEP	American Aerolights Eagle		G-MBMJ	Mainair Tri-Flyer	
G-MBES	Skyhook Cutlass		G-MBMO	Hiway Skytrike 160	
G-MBET	MEA Mistral Trainer		G-MBMR	Ultrasports Tripacer	
G-MBEU	Hiway Demon T.250			Typhoon	
G-MBFA	Hiway Skytrike 250		G-MBMS	Hornet	
G-MBFE	American Aerolights Eagle		G-MBMU	Eurowing Goldwing	
G-MBFF	Southern Aerosports		G-MBNA	American Aerolights Eagle	
	Scorpion		G-MBNH	Southern Airsports	
G-MBFK	Hiway Demon			Scorpion	
G-MBFM	Hiway Hang Glider		G-MBNJ	Eipper Quicksilver MX	
G-MBFU	Ultrasports Tripacer		G-MBNK	American Aerolights Eagle	
G-MBFY	Mirage II		G-MBNN	Southern Microlight	
G-MBGA	Solo Sealander			Gazelle P.160N	
G-MBGF	Twamley Trike		G-MBOA	Flexiform Hilander	
G-MBGJ	Hiway Skytrike Mk 2		G-MBOE	Solar Wing Typhoon Trike	
G-MBGK	Electra Flyer Eagle		G-MBOF	Pakes Jackdaw	
G-MBGS	Rotec Rally 2B		G-MBOH	Microlight Engineering	
G-MBGX	Southdown Lightning			Mistral	
G-MBGY	Hiway Demon Skytrike		G-MBOK	Dunstable Microlight	
G-MBHA	Trident Trike		G-MBOM	Hiway Hilander	
G-MBHE	American Aerolights Eagle		G-MBOR	Chotia 460B Weedhopper	
G-MBHK	Flexiform Skytrike		G-MBOT	Hiway 250 Skytrike	
G-MBHP	American Aerolights		G-MBOX	American Aerolights Eagle	
	Eagle II		G-MBPA	Weedhopper Srs 2	
G-MBHT	Chargus T.250		G-MBPD	American Aerolights Eagle	
G-MBHZ	Pterodactyl Ptraveller		G-MBPG	Hunt Skytrike	
G-MBIA	Flexiform Sealander		G-MBPJ	Moto-Delta	
	Skytrike		G-MBPN	American Aerolights Eagle	
G-MBIO	American Aerolights Eagle		G-MBPO	Volnik Arrow	
	Z Drive		G-MBPX	Eurowing Goldwing	
G-MBIT	Hiway Demon Skytrike		G-MBPY	Ultrasports Tripacer 330	
G-MBIV	Flexiform Skytrike		G-MBRB	Electraflyer Eagle 1	
G-MBIW	Hiway Demon Tri-Flyer		G-MBRD	American Aerolights Eagle	
	Skytrike		G-MBRE	Wheeler Scout	

Reg.	Type	Notes	Reg.	Type	Notes
G-MBRH	Ultraflight Mirage Mk II		G-MGFK	Pegasus Quantum 15	
G-MBRM	Hiway Demon		G-MGGG	Pegasus Quantum 15	
G-MBRS	American Aerolights Eagle		G-MGGT	CFM Streak Shadow SAM	
G-MBRV	Eurowing Goldwing		G-MGGV	Pegasus Quantum 15-912	
G-MBSD	Southdown Puma DS		G-MGMC	Pegasus Quantum 15	
G-MBSN	American Aerolights Eagle		G-MGND	Rans S.6-ESD Coyote IIXL	
G-MBSS	Ultrasports Puma 2		G-MGOD	Medway Raven	
G-MBST	Mainair Gemini Sprint		G-MGOM	Medway Hybred 44XLR	
G-MBSX	Ultraflight Mirage II		G-MGOO	Renegade Spirit UK Ltd	
G-MBTA	UAS Storm Buggy 5 Mk 2		G-MGPD	Pegasus XL-R	
G-MBTF	Mainair Tri-Flyer Skytrike		G-MGPH	CFM Streak Shadow	
G-MBTH	Whittaker MW.4			(G-RSPH)	
G-MBTI	Hovey Whing Ding		G-MGRW	Cyclone AX3/503	
G-MBTJ	Solar Wings Microlight		G-MGTG	Pegasus Quantum 15	
G-MBTO	Mainair Tri-Flyer 250			(G-MZIO)	
G-MBTW	Raven Vector 600		G-MGTR	Hunt Wing	
G-MBUA	Hiway Demon		G-MGTW	CFM Shadow Srs DD	
G-MBUB	Horne Sigma Skytrike		G-MGUN	Cyclone AX2000	
G-MBUC	Huntair Pathfinder		G-MGUX	Hunt Wing	
G-MBUH	Hiway Skytrike		G-MGUY	CFM Shadow Srs BD	
G-MBUI	Wheeler Scout Mk I		G-MGWH	Thruster T.300	
G-MBUO	Southern Aerosports				
	Scorpion		G-MJAB	Ultrasports Skytrike	
G-MBUP	Hiway Skytrike		G-MJAD	Eipper Quicksilver MX	
G-MBUZ	Wheeler Scout Mk II		G-MJAE	American Aerolights Eagle	
G-MBVA	Volmer Jensen VJ-23E		G-MJAG	Skyhook TR1	
G-MBVC	American Aerolights Eagle		G-MJAH	American Aerolights Eagle	
G-MBVK	Ultraflight Mirage II		G-MJAI	American Aerolights Eagle	
G-MBVL	Southern Aerosports		G-MJAJ	Eurowing Goldwing	
	Scorpion		G-MJAM	Eipper Quicklsilver MX	
G-MBVW	Skyhook Cutlass TR2		G-MJAN	Hiway Skytrike	
G-MBWA	American Aerolights Eagle		G-MJAY	Eurowing Goldwing	
G-MBWB	Hiway Skytrike		G-MJAZ	Aerodyne Vector 610	
G-MBWG	Huntair Pathfinder		G-MJBK	Swallow B	
G-MBWH	Designability Duet I		G-MJBL	American Aerolights Eagle	
G-MBWL	Huntair Pathfinder		G-MJBS	Ultralight Stormbuggy	
G-MBWP	Ultrasports Trike		G-MJBV	American Aerolights Eagle	
G-MBWT	Huntair Pathfinder		G-MJBZ	Huntair Pathfinder	
G-MBWW	Southern Aerosports		G-MJCB	Hornet 330	
	Scorpion		G-MJCD	Sigma Tetley Skytrike	
G-MBWX	Southern Aerosports		G-MJCE	Ultrasports Tripacer	
	Scorpion		G-MJCI	Kruchek Firefly 440	
G-MBXK	Ultrasports Puma		G-MJCJ	Hiway Spectrum	
G-MBXO	Sheffield Trident		G-MJCK	Southern Aerosports	
G-MBXR	Hiway Skytrike 150			Scorpion	
G-MBXT	Eipper Quicksilver MX2		G-MJCN	S.M.C. Flyer Mk 1	
G-MBXX	Ultraflight Mirage II		G-MJCU	Tarjani	
G-MBYD	American Aerolights Eagle		G-MJCW	Hiway Super Scorpion	
G-MBYI	Ultraflight Lazair		G-MJCX	American Aerolights Eagle	
G-MBYL	Huntair Pathfinder 330		G-MJCZ	Southern Aerosports	
G-MBYM	Eipper Quicksilver MX			Scorpion 2	
G-MBYY	Southern Aerosports		G-MJDE	Huntair Pathfinder	
	Scorpion		G-MJDG	Hornet Supertrike	
G-MBZB	Hiway Skytrike		G-MJDH	Huntair Pathfinder	
G-MBZF	American Aerolights Eagle		G-MJDJ	Hiway Skytrike Demon	
G-MBZG	Twinflight Scorpion 2 seat		G-MJDK	American Aerolights Eagle	
G-MBZH	Eurowing Goldwing		G-MJDO	Southdown Puma 440	
G-MBZJ	Southdown Puma		G-MJDP	Eurowing Goldwing	
G-MBZK	Tri-Pacer 250		G-MJDR	Hiway Demon Skytrike	
G-MBZM	UAS Storm Buggy		G-MJDU	Eipper Quicksilver àMX2	
G-MBZO	Tri-Pacer 330		G-MJDW	Eipper Quicksilver MX	
G-MBZP	Skyhook TR2		G-MJEE	Mainair Triflyer Trike	
G-MBZV	American Aerolights Eagle		G-MJEF	Gryphon 180	
G-MBZZ	Southern Aerosports		G-MJEG	Eurowing Goldwing	
	Scorpion		G-MJEJ	American Aerolights Eagle	
			G-MJEL	GMD-01 Trike	
G-MGAA	BFC Challenger II		G-MJEO	American Aerolights Eagle	
G-MGAG	Aviasud Mistral		G-MJER	Flexiform Striker	
G-MGCA	Jabiru UL		G-MJET	Stratos Prototype 3 Axis 1	
G-MGCB	Pegasus XL-Q		G-MJEX	Eipper Quicksilver MX	
G-MGDL	Pegasus Quantum 15		G-MJEY	Southdown Lightning	
G-MGEC	Rans S.6-ESD Coyote IIXL		G-MJFB	Flexiform Striker	
G-MGEF	Pegasus Quantum 15		G-MJFD	Ultrasports Tripacer	

Reg.	Type	Notes	Reg.	Type	Notes
G-MJFJ	Hiway Skytrike 250		G-MJNO	American Aerolights Double Eagle	
G-MJFM	Huntair Pathfinder				
G-MJFO	Eipper Quicksilver MX		G-MJNR	Ultralight Solar Buggy	
G-MJFV	Ultrasports Tripacer		G-MJNT	Hiway Skytrike	
G-MJFX	Skyhook TR-1		G-MJNU	Skyhook Cutlass	
G-MJGI	Eipper Quicksilver MX		G-MJNY	Skyhook Sabre Trike	
G-MJGN	Greenslade Monotrike		G-MJOC	Huntair Pathfinder	
G-MJGT	Skyhook Cutlass Trike		G-MJOE	Eurowing Goldwing	
G-MJGV	Eipper Quicksilver MX2		G-MJOG	American Aerolights Eagle	
G-MJGW	Solar Wings TrikeB		G-MJOI	Hiway Demon	
G-MJHC	Ultrasports Tripacer 330		G-MJOJ	Flexiform Skytrike	
G-MJHF	Skyhook Sailwing Trike		G-MJOL	Skyhook Cutlass	
G-MJHK	Hiway Demon 195		G-MJOM	Southdown Puma 40F	
G-MJHM	Ultrasports Trike		G-MJOW	Eipper Quicksilver MX	
G-MJHN	American Aerolights Eagle		G-MJPA	Rotec Rally 2B	
G-MJHR	Southdown Lightning		G-MJPE	Hiway Demon Skytrike	
G-MJHU	Eipper Quicksilver MX		G-MJPG	American Aerolights Eagle 430R	
G-MJHV	Hiway Demon 250				
G-MJHW	Ultrasports Puma 1		G-MJPI	Flexiform Striker	
G-MJHX	Eipper Quicksilver MX		G-MJPK	Hiway Vulcan	
G-MJIA	Flexiform Striker		G-MJPO	Eurowing Goldwing	
G-MJIC	Ultrasports Puma 330		G-MJPT	Dragon	
G-MJIF	Mainair Triflyer		G-MJPV	Eipper Quicksilver MX	
G-MJIJ	Ultrasports Tripacer 250		G-MJRE	Hiway Demon	
G-MJIK	Southdown Sailwings Lightning		G-MJRI	American Aerolights Eagle	
			G-MJRK	Flexiform Striker	
G-MJIN	Hiway Skytrike		G-MJRL	Eurowing Goldwing	
G-MJIR	Eipper Quicksilver MX		G-MJRN	Flexiform Striker	
G-MJIY	Striker/Panther		G-MJRO	Eurowing Goldwing	
G-MJIZ	Southdown Lightning		G-MJRR	Striplin Skyranger Srs 1	
G-MJJA	Huntair Pathfinder		G-MJRS	Eurowing Goldwing	
G-MJJB	Eipper Quicksilver MX		G-MJRU	MBA Tiger Cub 440	
G-MJJF	Solar Wings Typhoon		G-MJRX	Ultrasports Puma II	
G-MJJJ	Moyes Knight		G-MJSA	Mainair 2-Seat Trike	
G-MJJK	Eipper Quicksilver MX2		G-MJSE	Skyrider Airsports Phantom	
G-MJJM	Birdman Cherokee Mk 1				
G-MJJO	Flexiform Skytrike Dual		G-MJSF	Skyrider Airsports Phantom	
G-MJJV	Wheeler Scoutá				
G-MJJX	Hiway Skytrike		G-MJSL	Dragon 200	
G-MJJY	Tirith Firefly		G-MJSO	Hiway Skytrike	
G-MJKB	Striplin Skyranger		G-MJSP	Romain Tiger Cub 440	
G-MJKE	Mainair Triflyer 330		G-MJSS	American Aerolights Eagle	
G-MJKF	Hiway Demon		G-MJST	Pterodactyl Ptraveler	
G-MJKG	John Ivor Skytrike		G-MJSV	MBA Tiger Cub	
G-MJKJ	Eipper Quicksilver MX		G-MJSY	Eurowing Goldwing	
G-MJKO	Goldmarque 250 Skytrike		G-MJSZ	DH Wasp	
G-MJKS	Mainair Triflyer		G-MJTC	Ultrasports Tri-Pacer	
G-MJKV	Hornet		G-MJTD	Gardner T-M Scout	
G-MJKX	Ultralight Skyrider Phantom		G-MJTE	Skyrider Phantom	
G-MJLB	Ultrasports Puma 2		G-MJTF	Gryphon Wing	
G-MJLH	American Aerolights Eagle 2		G-MJTM	Aerostructure Pipistrelle 2B	
			G-MJTN	Eipper Quicksilver MX	
G-MJLI	Hiway Demon Skytrike		G-MJTP	Flexiform Striker	
G-MJLL	Hiway Demon Skytrike		G-MJTR	Southdown Puma DS Mk 1	
G-MJLR	Skyhook SK-1		G-MJTW	Eurowing Trike	
G-MJLS	Rotec Rally 2B		G-MJTX	Skyrider Airsports Phantom	
G-MJLT	American Aerolights Eagle		G-MJTZ	Skyrider Airsports Phantom	
G-MJME	Ultrasports Tripacer Mega II		G-MJUC	MBA Tiger Cub 440	
			G-MJUI	Flexiform Striker	
G-MJMM	Chargus Vortex		G-MJUS	MBA Tiger Cub 440	
G-MJMP	Eipper Quicksilver MX		G-MJUT	Eurowing Goldwing	
G-MJMR	Solar Wings Typhoon		G-MJUU	Eurowing Goldwing	
G-MJMS	Hiway Skytrike		G-MJUV	Huntair Pathfinder 1	
G-MJMU	Hiway Demon		G-MJUW	MBA Tiger Cub 440	
G-MJMW	Eipper Quicksilver MX2		G-MJUX	Skyrider Airsports Phantom	
G-MJNB	Hiway Skytrike		G-MJUZ	Dragon Srs 150	
G-MJNE	Hornet Supreme Dual Trike		G-MJVA	Skyrider Airsports Phantom	
			G-MJVE	Hybred Skytrike	
G-MJNK	Hiway Skytrike		G-MJVF	CFM Shadow	
G-MJNL	American Aerolights Eagle		G-MJVG	Hiway Skytrike	
G-MJNM	American Aerolights Double Eagle		G-MJVJ	Flexiform Striker Dual	
			G-MJVM	Dragon 150	
G-MJNN	Ultraflight Mirage II		G-MJVN	Ultrasports Puma 440	

Reg.	Type	Notes	Reg.	Type	Notes
G-MJVP	Eipper Quicksilver MX II		G-MMCF	Solar Wings Panther 330	
G-MJVR	Flexiform Striker		G-MMCI	Southdown Puma Sprint	
G-MJVU	Eipper Quicksilver MX II		G-MMCM	Southdown Puma Sprint	
G-MJVW	Airwave Nimrod		G-MMCS	Southdown Puma Sprint	
G-MJVX	Skyrider Phantom		G-MMCV	Solar Wings Typhoon III	
G-MJVY	Dragon Srs 150		G-MMCX	MBA Super Tiger Cub 440	
G-MJVZ	Hiway Demon Tripacer		G-MMCY	Flexiform Striker	
G-MJWB	Eurowing Goldwing		G-MMCZ	Flexiform Striker	
G-MJWF	Tiger Cub 440		G-MMDC	Eipper Quicksilver MXII	
G-MJWJ	MBA Tiger Cub 440		G-MMDE	Solar Wings Typhoon	
G-MJWK	Huntair Pathfinder		G-MMDF	Southdown Lightning II	
G-MJWN	Flexiform Striker		G-MMDK	Flexiform Striker	
G-MJWR	MBA Tiger Cub 440		G-MMDN	Flexiform Striker	
G-MJWU	Maxair Hummer TX		G-MMDO	Southdown Sprint	
G-MJWZ	Ultrasports Panther XL		G-MMDP	Southdown Sprint	
G-MJXD	MBA Tiger Cub 440		G-MMDR	Huntair Pathfinder II	
G-MJXF	MBA Tiger Cub 440		G-MMDV	Ultrasports Panther	
G-MJXM	Hiway Skytrike		G-MMDW	Pterodactyl Pfledgling	
G-MJXR	Huntair Pathfinder II		G-MMDX	Solar Wings Typhoon	
G-MJXS	Huntair Pathfinder II		G-MMDY	Puma Sprint X	
G-MJXV	Flexiform Striker		G-MMDZ	Flexiform Dual Strike	
G-MJXY	Hiway Demon Skytrike		G-MMEE	American Aerolights Eagle	
G-MJYA	Huntair Pathfinder		G-MMEF	Hiway Super Scorpion	
G-MJYD	MBA Tiger Cub 440		G-MMEJ	Striker/TriFlyer	
G-MJYF	Mainair Gemini Flash		G-MMEK	Medway Hybred 44XL	
G-MJYG	Skyhook Orion Canard		G-MMEN	Solar Wings Typhoon XL2	
G-MJYM	Southdown Puma Sprint		G-MMEP	MBA Tiger Cub 440	
G-·MJYP	Mainair Triflyer 440		G-MMET	Skyhook Sabre TR-1 Mk II	
G-MJYR	Catto CP.16		G-MMEW	MBA Tiger Cub 440	
G-MJYS	Southdown Puma Sprint		G-MMEY	MBA Tiger Cub 440	
G-MJYT	Southdown Puma Sprint		G-MMFD	Flexiform Striker	
G-MJYV	Mainair Triflyer 2 Seat		G-MMFE	Flexiform Striker	
G-MJYW	Wasp Gryphon III		G-MMFG	Flexiform Striker	
G-MJYX	Mainair Triflyer		G-MMFI	Flexiform Striker	
G-MJYY	Hiway Demon		G-MMFL	Flexiform Striker	
G-MJZA	MBA Tiger Cub		G-MMFS	MBA Tiger Cub 440	
G-MJZD	Mainair Gemini Flash		G-MMFT	MBA Tiger Cub 440	
G-MJZE	MBA Tiger Cub 440		G-MMFY	Flexiform Dual Striker	
G-MJZJ	Hiway Cutlass Skytrike		G-MMGA	Bass Gosling	
G-MJZK	Southdown Puma Sprint 440		G-MMGB	Southdown Puma Sprint	
			G-MMGC	Southdown Puma Sprint	
G-MJZL	Eipper Quicksilver MX II		G-MMGD	Southdown Puma Sprint	
G-MJZO	Flexiform Striker		G-MMGE	Hiway Super Scorpion	
G-MJZT	Flexiform Striker		G-MMGF	MBA Tiger Cub 440	
G-MJZU	Flexiform Striker		G-MMGL	MBA Tiger Cub 440	
G-MJZW	Eipper Quicksilver MX II		G-MMGN	Southdown Puma Sprint	
G-MJZX	Hummer TX		G-MMGP	Southdown Puma Sprint	
			G-MMGS	Solar Wings Panther XL	
G-MMAC	Dragon Srs 150		G-MMGT	Solar Wings Typhoon	
G-MMAE	Dragon Srs 150		G-MMGU	Flexiform Sealander	
G-MMAG	MBA Tiger Cub 440		G-MMGV	Whittaker MW-5 Sorcerer	
G-MMAH	Eipper Quicksilver MX II		G-MMGX	Southdown Puma	
G-MMAI	Dragon Srs 2		G-MMHE	Southdown Puma Sprint	
G-MMAN	Flexiform Striker		G-MMHL	Hiway Super Scorpion	
G-MMAP	Hummer TX		G-MMHM	Goldmarque Gyr	
G-MMAR	Southdown Puma Sprint		G-MMHN	MBA Tiger Cub 440	
G-MMAT	Southdown Puma Sprint		G-MMHP	Hiway Demon	
G-MMAW	Mainair 330		G-MMHS	SMD Viper	
G-MMAX	Dual Striker		G-MMHX	Hornet Invader 440	
G-MMAZ	Southdown Puma Sprint		G-MMHY	Hornet Invader 440	
G-MMBD	Spectrum 330		G-MMHZ	Solar Wings Typhoon XL	
G-MMBE	MBA Tiger Cub 440		G-MMIC	Luscombe Vitality	
G-MMBH	MBA Super Tiger Cub 440		G-MMIE	MBA Tiger Cub 440	
G-MMBL	Southdown Puma		G-MMIF	Wasp Gryphon	
G-MMBN	Eurowing Goldwing		G-MMIH	MBA Tiger Cub 440	
G-MMBT	MBA Tiger Cub 440		G-MMIL	Eipper Quicksilver MX II	
G-MMBU	Eipper Quicksilver MX II		G-MMIR	Mainair Tri-Flyer 440	
G-MMBV	Huntair Pathfinder		G-MMIW	Southdown Puma Sprint	
G-MMBX	MBA Tiger Cub 440		G-MMIX	MBA Tiger Cub 440	
G-MMBY	Solar Wings Panther XL		G-MMIY	Eurowing Goldwing	
G-MMBZ	Solar Wings Typhoon P		G-MMJD	Southdown Puma Sprint	
G-MMCD	Southdown Lightning DS		G-MMJE	Southdown Puma Sprint	
G-MMCE	MBA Tiger Cub 440				

Reg.	Type	Notes	Reg.	Type	Notes
G-MMJF	Ultrasports Panther Dual 440		G-MMRH	Hiway Demon	
G-MMJG	Mainair Tri-Flyer 440		G-MMRJ	Solar Wings Panther XL	
G-MMJJ	Solar Wings Typhoon		G-MMRK	Solar Wings Panther XL-S	
G-MMJM	Southdown Puma Sprint		G-MMRL	Solar Wings Panther XL	
G-MMJN	Eipper Quicksilver MX II		G-MMRN	Southdown Puma Sprint	
G-MMJT	Southdown Puma Sprint		G-MMRP	Mainair Gemini	
G-MMJU	Hiway Demon		G-MMRU	Tirith Firebird FB-2	
G-MMJV	MBA Tiger Cub 440		G-MMRW	Flexiform Dual Striker	
G-MMJX	Teman Mono-Fly		G-MMRY	Chargus T.250	
G-MMJY	MBA Tiger Cub 440		G-MMRZ	Ultrasports Panther Dual 440	
G-MMKA	Ultrasports Panther Dual		G-MMSA	Ultrasports Panther XL	
G-MMKE	Birdman Chinook WT-11		G-MMSC	Mainair Gemini	
G-MMKG	Solar Wings Typhoon XL		G-MMSE	Eipper Quicksilver MX	
G-MMKH	Solar Wings Typhoon XL		G-MMSG	Solar Wings Panther XL-S	
G-MMKI	Ultrasports Panther 330		G-MMSH	Solar Wings Panther XL	
G-MMKK	Mainair Flash		G-MMSO	Mainair Tri-Flyer 440	
G-MMKL	Mainair Gemini Flash		G-MMSP	Mainair Gemini Flash	
G-MMKM	Flexiform Dual Striker		G-MMSR	MBA Tiger Cub 440	
G-MMKP	MBA Tiger Cub 440		G-MMSS	Southdown Lightning	
G-MMKR	Southdown Lightning DS		G-MMSW	MBA Tiger Cub 440	
G-MMKU	Southdown Puma Sprint		G-MMSZ	Medway Half Pint	
G-MMKV	Southdown Puma Sprint		G-MMTA	Ultrasports Panther XL	
G-MMKW	Solar Wings Storm		G-MMTC	Ultrasports Panther Dual	
G-MMKX	Skyrider Phantom 330		G-MMTD	Mainair Tri-Flyer 330	
G-MMKZ	Ultrasports Puma 440		G-MMTH	Southdown Puma Sprint	
G-MMLB	MBA Tiger Cub 440		G-MMTI	Southdown Puma Sprint	
G-MMLE	Eurowing Goldwing SP		G-MMTJ	Southdown Puma Sprint	
G-MMLH	Hiway Demon		G-MMTL	Mainair Gemini	
G-MMLM	MBA Tiger Cub 440		G-MMTR	Ultrasports Panther	
G-MMLO	Skyhook Pixie		G-MMTS	Solar Wings Panther XL	
G-MMLP	Southdown Sprint		G-MMTT	Solar Wings Panther XL-S	
G-MMMB	Mainair Tri-Flyer		G-MMTV	American Aerolights Eagle	
G-MMMD	Flexiform Dual Striker		G-MMTX	Mainair Gemini 440	
G-MMMG	Eipper Quicksilver MXL		G-MMTY	Fisher FP.202U	
G-MMMH	Hadland Willow		G-MMTZ	Eurowing Goldwing	
G-MMMJ	Southdown Sprint		G-MMUC	Mainair Gemini 440	
G-MMMK	Hornet Invader		G-MMUG	Mainair Tri-Flyer	
G-MMML	Dragon 150		G-MMUH	Mainair Tri-Flyer	
G-MMMN	Ultrasports Panther Dual 440		G-MMUK	Mainair Tri-Flyer	
			G-MMUL	Ward Elf E.47	
G-MMMP	Flexiform Dual Striker		G-MMUM	MBA Tiger Cub 440	
G-MMNB	Eipper Quicksilver MX		G-MMUO	Mainair Gemini Flash	
G-MMND	Eipper Quicksilver MX II-Q2		G-MMUP	Airwave Nimrod 140	
			G-MMUT	Mainair Gemini Flash	
G-MMNF	Hornet		G-MMUU	ParaPlane PM-1	
G-MMNG	Solar Wings Typhoon XL		G-MMUV	Southdown Puma Sprint	
G-MMNH	Dragon 150		G-MMUW	Mainair Gemini Flash	
G-MMNN	Buzzard		G-MMVA	Southdown Puma Sprint	
G-MMNS	Mitchell U-2 Super Wing		G-MMVC	Ultrasports Panther XL	
G-MMNT	Flexiform Striker		G-MMVH	Southdown Raven	
G-MMOB	Southdown Sprint		G-MMVI	Southdown Puma Sprint	
G-MMOH	Solar Wings Typhoon XL		G-MMVL	Ultrasports Panther XL-S	
G-MMOI	MBA Tiger Cub 440		G-MMVM	Whiteley Orion 1	
G-MMOK	Solar Wings Panther XL		G-MMVP	Mainair Gemini Flash	
G-MMOL	Skycraft Scout R3		G-MMVR	Hiway Skytrike 1	
G-MMOW	Mainair Gemini Flash		G-MMVS	Skyhook Pixie	
G-MMOY	Mainair Gemini Sprint		G-MMVX	Southdown Puma Sprint	
G-MMPG	Southdown Puma		G-MMVZ	Southdown Puma Sprint	
G-MMPH	Southdown Puma Sprint		G-MMWA	Mainair Gemini Flash	
G-MMPI	Pterodactyl Ptraveller		G-MMWC	Eipper Quicksilver MXII	
G-MMPJ	Mainair Tri-Flyer 440		G-MMWF	Hiway Skytrike 250	
G-MMPL	Flexiform Dual Striker		G-MMWG	Greenslade Mono-Trike	
G-MMPN	Chargus T250		G-MMWI	Southdown Lightning	
G-MMPO	Mainair Gemini Flash		G-MMWL	Eurowing Goldwing	
G-MMPT	SMD Gazelle		G-MMWN	Ultrasports Tripacer	
G-MMPU	Ultrasports Tripacer 250		G-MMWS	Mainair Tri-Flyer	
G-MMPW	Airwave Nimrod		G-MMWT	CFM Shadow	
G-MMPX	Ultrasports Panther Dual 440		G-MMWX	Southdown Puma Sprint	
			G-MMXD	Mainair Gemini Flash	
G-MMPZ	Teman Mono-Fly		G-MMXE	Mainair Gemini Flash	
G-MMRA	Mainair Tri-Flyer 250		G-MMXG	Mainair Gemini Flash	
G-MMRF	MBA Tiger Cub 440		G-MMXI	Horizon Prototype	

Reg.	Type	Notes	Reg.	Type	Notes
G-MMXJ	Mainair Gemini Flash		G-MNBT	Mainair Gemini Flash	
G-MMXK	Mainair Gemini Flash		G-MNBV	Mainair Gemini Flash	
G-MMXL	Mainair Gemini Flash		G-MNBW	Mainair Gemini Flash	
G-MMXM	Mainair Gemini Flash		G-MNCA	Hiway Demon 175	
G-MMXN	Southdown Puma Sprint		G-MNCF	Mainair Gemini Flash	
G-MMXO	Southdown Puma Sprint		G-MNCG	Mainair Gemini Flash	
G-MMXU	Mainair Gemini Flash		G-MNCI	Southdown Puma Sprint	
G-MMXV	Mainair Gemini Flash		G-MNCJ	Mainair Gemini Flash	
G-MMXW	Mainair Gemini		G-MNCL	Southdown Puma Sprint	
G-MMXX	Mainair Gemini		G-MNCM	CFM Shadow Srs B	
G-MMYA	Solar Wings Pegasus XL		G-MNCO	Eipper Quicksilver MXII	
G-MMYB	Solar Wings Pegasus XL		G-MNCP	Southdown Puma Sprint	
G-MMYD	CFM Shadow Srs B		G-MNCR	Flexiform Striker	
G-MMYF	Southdown Puma Sprint		G-MNCS	Skyrider Airsports Phantom	
G-MMYI	Cyclone 70		G-MNCU	Medway Hybred 44XL	
G-MMYL	Cyclone 70		G-MNCV	Medway Hybred 44XL	
G-MMYN	Ultrasports Panther XL		G-MNCZ	Solar Wings Pegasus XL	
G-MMYO	Southdown Puma Sprint		G-MNDA	Thruster TST	
G-MMYR	Eipper Quicksilver MXII		G-MNDD	Mainair Scorcher Solo	
G-MMYS	Southdown Puma Sprint		G-MNDE	Medway Half Pint	
G-MMYT	Southdown Puma Sprint		G-MNDF	Mainair Gemini Flash	
G-MMYU	Southdown Puma Sprint		G-MNDG	Southdown Puma Sprint	
G-MMYV	Webb Trike		G-MNDH	Hiway Skytrike	
G-MMYY	Southdown Puma Sprint		G-MNDI	MBA Tiger Cub 440	
G-MMZA	Mainair Gemini Flash		G-MNDO	Mainair Flash	
G-MMZB	Mainair Gemini Flash		G-MNDU	Midland Sirocco 377GB	
G-MMZE	Mainair Gemini Flash		G-MNDV	Midland Sirocco 377GB	
G-MMZF	Mainair Gemini Flash		G-MNDW	Midland Sirocco 377GB	
G-MMZG	Ultrasports Panther XL-S		G-MNDY	Southdown Puma Sprint	
G-MMZI	Medway 130SX		G-MNEF	Mainair Gemini Flash	
G-MMZJ	Mainair Gemini Flash		G-MNEH	Mainair Gemini Flash	
G-MMZK	Mainair Gemini Flash		G-MNEI	Medway Hybred 440	
G-MMZL	Mainair Gemini Flash		G-MNEK	Medway Half Pint	
G-MMZM	Mainair Gemini Flash		G-MNEP	Aerostructure Pipstrelle	
G-MMZN	Mainair Gemini Flash			P.2B	
G-MMZO	Microflight Spectrum		G-MNER	CFM Shadow Srs B	
G-MMZP	Ultrasports Panther XL		G-MNET	Mainair Gemini Flash	
G-MMZR	Southdown Puma Sprint		G-MNEV	Mainair Gemini Flash	
G-MMZS	Eipper Quicksilver MX1		G-MNEY	Mainair Gemini Flash	
G-MMZV	Mainair Gemini Flash		G-MNEZ	Skyhook TR1 Mk 2	
G-MMZW	Southdown Puma Sprint		G-MNFB	Southdown Puma Sprint	
G-MMZX	Southdown Puma Sprint		G-MNFE	Mainair Gemini Flash	
G-MMZY	Ultrasports Tripacer 330		G-MNFF	Mainair Gemini Flash	
			G-MNFG	Southdown Puma Sprint	
G-MNAA	Striplin Sky Ranger		G-MNFH	Mainair Gemini Flash	
G-MNAC	Mainair Gemini Flash		G-MNFL	AMF Chevvron	
G-MNAE	Mainair Gemini Flash		G-MNFM	Mainair Gemini Flash	
G-MNAF	Solar Wings Panther XL-S		G-MNFN	Mainair Gemini Flash	
G-MNAH	Solar Wings Panther XL		G-MNFP	Mainair Gemini Flash	
G-MNAI	Ultrasports Panther XL-S		G-MNFW	Medway Hybred 44XL	
G-MNAJ	Solar Wings Panther XL-S		G-MNFX	Southdown Puma Sprint	
G-MNAK	Solar Wings Panther XL-S		G-MNFY	Hornet 250	
G-MNAM	Solar Wings Panther XL-S		G-MNGA	Aerial Arts Chaser 110SX	
G-MNAO	Solar Wings Panther XL-S		G-MNGD	Quest Air Services	
G-MNAT	Solar Wings Pegasus XL-R		G-MNGF	Solar Wings Pegasus	
G-MNAV	Southdown Puma Sprint		G-MNGG	Solar Wings Pegasus XL-R	
G-MNAW	Solar Wings Pegasus XL-R		G-MNGH	Skyhook Pixie	
G-MNAX	Solar Wings Pegasus XL-R		G-MNGJ	Skyhook Zipper	
G-MNAY	Ultrasports Panther XL-S		G-MNGK	Mainair Gemini Flash	
G-MNAZ	Solar Wings Pegasus XL-R		G-MNGL	Mainair Gemini Flash	
G-MNBA	Solar Wings Pegasus XL-R		G-MNGM	Mainair Gemini Flash	
G-MNBB	Solar Wings Pegasus XL-R		G-MNGN	Mainair Gemini Flash	
G-MNBC	Solar Wings Pegasus XL-R		G-MNGO	Solar Wings Storm	
G-MNBD	Mainair Gemini Flash		G-MNGS	Southdown Puma 330	
G-MNBE	Southdown Puma Sprint		G-MNGT	Mainair Gemini Flash	
G-MNBF	Mainair Gemini Flash		G-MNGU	Mainair Gemini Flash	
G-MNBG	Mainair Gemini Flash		G-MNGW	Mainair Gemini Flash	
G-MNBI	Ultrasports Panther XL		G-MNGX	Southdown Puma Sprint	
G-MNBJ	Skyhook Pixie		G-MNHB	Solar Wings Pegasus XL-R	
G-MNBM	Southdown Puma Sprint		G-MNHC	Solar Wings Pegasus XL-R	
G-MNBN	Mainair Gemini Flash		G-MNHD	Solar Wings Pegasus XL-R	
G-MNBP	Mainair Gemini Flash		G-MNHE	Solar Wings Pegasus XL-R	
G-MNBS	Mainair Gemini Flash		G-MNHH	Solar Wings Panther XL-S	

Reg.	Type	Notes
G-MNHI	Solar Wings Pegasus XL-R	
G-MNHJ	Solar Wings Pegasus XL-R	
G-MNHK	Solar Wings Pegasus XL-R	
G-MNHL	Solar Wings Pegasus XL-R	
G-MNHM	Solar Wings Pegasus XL-R	
G-MNHN	Solar Wings Pegasus XL-R	
G-MNHR	Solar Wings Pegasus XL-R	
G-MNHS	Solar Wings Pegasus XL-R	
G-MNHT	Solar Wings Pegasus XL-R	
G-MNHV	Solar Wings Pegasus XL-R	
G-MNHX	Solar Wings Typhoon S4	
G-MNHZ	Mainair Gemini Flash	
G-MNIA	Mainair Gemini Flash	
G-MNIE	Mainair Gemini Flash	
G-MNIF	Mainair Gemini Flash	
G-MNIG	Mainair Gemini Flash	
G-MNIH	Mainair Gemini Flash	
G-MNII	Mainair Gemini Flash	
G-MNIK	Pegasus Photon	
G-MNIL	Southdown Puma Sprint	
G-MNIM	Maxair Hummer	
G-MNIO	Mainair Gemini Flash	
G-MNIP	Mainair Gemini Flash	
G-MNIS	CFM Shadow Srs B	
G-MNIT	Aerial Arts 130SX	
G-MNIU	Solar Wings Pegasus Photon	
G-MNIV	Solar Wings Typhoon	
G-MNIW	Airwave Nimrod 165	
G-MNIX	Mainair Gemini Flash	
G-MNIY	Skyhook Pixie Zipper	
G-MNIZ	Mainair Gemini Flash	
G-MNJB	Southdown Raven	
G-MNJC	MBA Tiger Cub 440	
G-MNJD	Southdown Puma Sprint	
G-MNJF	Dragon 150	
G-MNJG	Mainair Tri-Flyer	
G-MNJH	SW Pegasus Flash	
G-MNJI	SW Pegasus Flash	
G-MNJJ	SW Pegasus Flash	
G-MNJL	SW Pegasus Flash	
G-MNJM	SW Pegasus Flash	
G-MNJN	SW Pegasus Flash	
G-MNJO	SW Pegasus Flash	
G-MNJR	SW Pegasus Flash	
G-MNJS	Southdown Puma Sprint	
G-MNJT	Southdown Raven	
G-MNJU	Mainair Gemini Flash	
G-MNJV	Medway Half Pint	
G-MNJX	Medway Hybred 44XL	
G-MNKB	SW Pegasus Photon	
G-MNKC	SW Pegasus Photon	
G-MNKD	SW Pegasus Photon	
G-MNKE	SW Pegasus Photon	
G-MNKG	SW Pegasus Photon	
G-MNKK	SW Pegasus Photon	
G-MNKM	MBA Tiger Cub 440	
G-MNKO	SW Pegasus Flash	
G-MNKP	SW Pegasus Flash	
G-MNKS	SW Pegasus Flash	
G-MNKT	Solar Wings Typhoon S4	
G-MNKU	Southdown Puma Sprint	
G-MNKV	SW Pegasus Flash	
G-MNKW	SW Pegasus Flash	
G-MNKX	SW Pegasus Flash	
G-MNKZ	Southdown Raven	
G-MNLB	Southdown Raven X	
G-MNLE	Southdown Raven X	
G-MNLH	Romain Cobra Biplane	
G-MNLI	Mainair Gemini Flash	
G-MNLK	Southdown Raven	
G-MNLM	Southdown Raven	
G-MNLN	Southdown Raven	

Reg.	Type	Notes
G-MNLP	Southdown Raven	
G-MNLT	Southdown Raven	
G-MNLU	Southdown Raven	
G-MNLV	Southdown Raven X	
G-MNLY	Mainair Gemini Flash	
G-MNLZ	Southdown Raven	
G-MNMC	Southdown Puma MS	
G-MNMD	Southdown Raven	
G-MNMG	Mainair Gemini Flash	
G-MNMI	Mainair Gemini Flash	
G-MNMJ	Mainair Gemini Flash	
G-MNMK	Solar Wings Pegasus XL-R	
G-MNML	Southdown Puma Sprint	
G-MNMM	Aerotech MW.5 Sorcerer	
G-MNMN	Medway Hybred 44XLR	
G-MNMR	Solar Wings Typhoon 180	
G-MNMT	Southdown Raven	
G-MNMU	Southdown Raven	
G-MNMV	Mainair Gemini Flash	
G-MNMW	Aerotech MW.6 Merlin	
G-MNMY	Cyclone 70	
G-MNNA	Southdown Raven	
G-MNNB	Southdown Raven	
G-MNNC	Southdown Raven	
G-MNNF	Mainair Gemini Flash	
G-MNNG	Solar Wings Photon	
G-MNNI	Mainair Gemini Flash	
G-MNNK	Mainair Gemini Flash	
G-MNNL	Mainair Gemini Flash	
G-MNNM	Mainair Scorcher Solo	
G-MNNO	Southdown Raven	
G-MNNP	Mainair Gemini Flash	
G-MNNR	Mainair Gemini Flash	
G-MNNS	Eurowing Goldwing	
G-MNNV	Mainair Gemini Flash	
G-MNNY	SW Pegasus Flash	
G-MNNZ	SW Pegasus Flash	
G-MNPA	SW Pegasus Flash	
G-MNPC	Mainair Gemini Flash	
G-MNPF	Mainair Gemini Flash	
G-MNPG	Mainair Gemini Flash	
G-MNPH	Flexiform Dual Striker	
G-MNPL	Ultrasports Panther 330	
G-MNPV	Mainair Scorcher Solo	
G-MNPW	AMF Chevvron	
G-MNPY	Mainair Scorcher Solo	
G-MNPZ	Mainair Scorcher Solo	
G-MNRA	CFM Shadow Srs B	
G-MNRE	Mainair Scorcher Solo	
G-MNRF	Mainair Scorcher Solo	
G-MNRG	Mainair Scorcher Solo	
G-MNRI	Hornet Dual Trainer	
G-MNRK	Hornet Dual Trainer	
G-MNRM	Hornet Dual Trainer	
G-MNRN	Hornet Dual Trainer	
G-MNRP	Southdown Raven	
G-MNRS	Southdown Raven	
G-MNRT	Midland Ultralights Sirocco	
G-MNRW	Mainair Gemini Flash II	
G-MNRX	Mainair Gemini Flash II	
G-MNRY	Mainair Gemini Flash	
G-MNRZ	Mainair Scorcher Solo	
G-MNSA	Mainair Gemini Flash	
G-MNSB	Southdown Puma Sprint	
G-MNSD	Solar Wings Typhoon S4	
G-MNSF	Hornet Dual Trainer	
G-MNSH	SW Pegasus Flash II	
G-MNSI	Mainair Gemini Flash	
G-MNSJ	Mainair Gemini Flash	
G-MNSL	Southdown Raven X	
G-MNSM	Hornet Demon	
G-MNSN	SW Pegasus Flash II	
G-MNSP	Aerial Arts 130SX	

Reg.	Type	Notes	Reg.	Type	Notes
G-MNSR	Mainair Gemini Flash		G-MNXI	Southdown Raven X	
G-MNSS	American Aerolights Eagle		G-MNXM	Medway Hybred 44XLR	
G-MNSV	CFM Shadow Srs B		G-MNXO	Medway Hybred 44XLR	
G-MNSX	Southdown Raven X		G-MNXS	Mainair Gemini Flash II	
G-MNSY	Southdown Raven X		G-MNXU	Mainair Gemini Flash II	
G-MNTC	Southdown Raven X		G-MNXX	CFM Shadow Srs BD	
G-MNTD	Aerial Arts Chaser 110SX		G-MNXZ	Whittaker MW.5 Sorcerer	
G-MNTE	Southdown Raven X		G-MNYA	SW Pegasus Flash II	
G-MNTF	Southdown Raven X		G-MNYB	Solar Wings Pegasus XL-R	
G-MNTH	Mainair Gemini Flash		G-MNYC	Solar Wings Pegasus XL-R	
G-MNTI	Mainair Gemini Flash		G-MNYD	Aerial Arts 110SX Chaser	
G-MNTK	CFM Shadow Srs B		G-MNYE	Aerial Arts 110SX Chaser	
G-MNTM	Southdown Raven X		G-MNYF	Aerial Arts 110SX Chaser	
G-MNTN	Southdown Raven X		G-MNYG	Southdown Raven	
G-MNTP	CFM Shadow Srs B		G-MNYH	Southdown Puma Sprint	
G-MNTS	Mainair Gemini Flash II		G-MNYI	Southdown Raven X	
G-MNTT	Medway Half Pint		G-MNYJ	Mainair Gemini Flash II	
G-MNTU	Mainair Gemini Flash II		G-MNYK	Mainair Gemini Flash II	
G-MNTV	Mainair Gemini Flash II		G-MNYL	Southdown Raven X	
G-MNTW	Mainair Gemini Flash II		G-MNYO	Southdown Raven X	
G-MNTX	Mainair Gemini Flash II		G-MNYP	Southdown Raven X	
G-MNTY	Southdown Raven X		G-MNYS	Southdown Raven X	
G-MNTZ	Mainair Gemini Flash II		G-MNYV	Solar Wings Pegasus XL-R	
G-MNUA	Mainair Gemini Flash II		G-MNYW	Solar Wings Pegasus XL-R	
G-MNUD	SW Pegasus Flash II		G-MNYX	Solar Wings Pegasus XL-R	
G-MNUE	SW Pegasus Flash II		G-MNYZ	SW Pegasus Flash	
G-MNUF	Mainair Gemini Flash II		G-MNZB	Mainair Gemini Flash II	
G-MNUG	Mainair Gemini Flash II		G-MNZC	Mainair Gemini Flash II	
G-MNUI	Skyhook Cutlass Dual		G-MNZD	Mainair Gemini Flash II	
G-MNUM	Southdown Puma Sprint		G-MNZE	Mainair Gemini Flash II	
G-MNUO	Mainair Gemini Flash II		G-MNZF	Mainair Gemini Flash II	
G-MNUR	Mainair Gemini Flash II		G-MNZI	Solar Wings Typhoon	
G-MNUT	Southdown Raven X		G-MNZJ	CFM Shadow Srs BD	
G-MNUU	Southdown Raven X		G-MNZK	Solar Wings Pegasus XL-R	
G-MNUX	Solar Wings Pegasus XL-R		G-MNZM	Solar Wings Pegasus XL-R	
G-MNUY	Mainair Gemini Flash II		G-MNZN	SW Pegasus Flash II	
G-MNVA	Solar Wings Pegasus XL-R		G-MNZO	SW Pegasus Flash II	
G-MNVB	Solar Wings Pegasus XL-R		G-MNZP	CFM Shadow Srs B	
G-MNVC	Solar Wings Pegasus XL-R		G-MNZR	CFM Shadown Srs BD	
G-MNVE	Solar Wings Pegasus XL-R		G-MNZS	Aerial Arts 130SX	
G-MNVG	SW Pegasus Flash II		G-MNZU	Eurowing Goldwing	
G-MNVH	SW Pegasus Flash II		G-MNZW	Southdown Raven X	
G-MNVI	CFM Shadow Srs B		G-MNZX	Southdown Raven X	
G-MNVJ	CFM Shadow Srs CD		G-MNZZ	CFM Shadow Srs B	
G-MNVK	CFM Shadow Srs B				
G-MNVN	Southdown Raven X		G-MTAA	Solar Wings Pegasus XL-R	
G-MNVO	Hovey Whing-Ding II		G-MTAB	Mainair Gemini Flash II	
G-MNVT	Mainair Gemini Flash II		G-MTAC	Mainair Gemini Flash II	
G-MNVU	Mainair Gemini Flash II		G-MTAE	Mainair Gemini Flash II	
G-MNVV	Mainair Gemini Flash II		G-MTAF	Mainair Gemini Flash II	
G-MNVW	Mainair Gemini Flash II		G-MTAG	Mainair Gemini Flash II	
G-MNVZ	SW Pegasus Photon		G-MTAH	Mainair Gemini Flash II	
G-MNWA	Southdown Raven X		G-MTAI	Solar Wings Pegasus XL-R	
G-MNWD	Mainair Gemini Flash		G-MTAJ	Solar Wings Pegasus XL-R	
G-MNWF	Southdown Raven X		G-MTAK	Solar Wings Pegasus XL-R	
G-MNWG	Southdown Raven X		G-MTAL	Solar Wings Photon	
G-MNWI	Mainair Gemini Flash II		G-MTAM	SW Pegasus Flash	
G-MNWJ	Mainair Gemini Flash II		G-MTAO	Solar Wings Pegasus XL-R	
G-MNWK	CFM Shadow Srs B		G-MTAP	Southdown Raven X	
G-MNWL	Aerial Arts 130SX		G-MTAR	Mainair Gemini Flash II	
G-MNWN	Mainair Gemini Flash II		G-MTAS	Whittaker MW.5 Sorcerer	
G-MNWP	SW Pegasus Flash II		G-MTAV	Solar Wings Pegasus XL-R	
G-MNWU	SW Pegasus Flash II		G-MTAW	Solar Wings Pegasus XL-R	
G-MNWV	SW Pegasus Flash II		G-MTAX	Solar Wings Pegasus XL-R	
G-MNWW	Solar Wings Pegasus XL-R		G-MTAY	Solar Wings Pegasus XL-R	
G-MNWY	CFM Shadow Srs B		G-MTAZ	Solar Wings Pegasus XL-R	
G-MNWZ	Mainair Gemini Flash II		G-MTBA	Solar Wings Pegasus XL-R	
G-MNXA	Southdown Raven X		G-MTBB	Southdown Raven X	
G-MNXB	Solar Wings Photon		G-MTBD	Mainair Gemini Flash II	
G-MNXD	Southdown Raven X		G-MTBE	CFM Shadow Srs BD	
G-MNXE	Southdown Raven X		G-MTBF	Mirage Mk II	
G-MNXF	Southdown Raven X		G-MTBH	Mainair Gemini Flash II	
G-MNXG	Southdown Raven X		G-MTBI	Mainair Gemini Flash II	

Reg.	Type	Notes
G-MTBJ	Mainair Gemini Flash II	
G-MTBK	Southdown Raven X	
G-MTBL	Solar Wings Pegasus XL-R	
G-MTBN	Southdown Raven X	
G-MTBO	Southdown Raven X	
G-MTBP	Aerotech MW.5 Sorcerer	
G-MTBR	Aerotech MW.5 Sorcerer	
G-MTBS	Aerotech MW.5 Sorcerer	
G-MTBV	Solar Wings Pegasus XL-R	
G-MTBX	Mainair Gemini Flash II	
G-MTBY	Mainair Gemini Flash II	
G-MTBZ	Southdown Raven X	
G-MTCA	CFM Shadow Srs B	
G-MTCB	Snowbird Mk III	
G-MTCE	Mainair Gemini Flash II	
G-MTCG	Solar Wings Pegasus XL-R	
G-MTCH	Solar Wings Pegasus XL-R	
G-MTCK	SW Pegasus Flash	
G-MTCL	Southdown Raven X	
G-MTCM	Southdown Raven X	
G-MTCN	Solar Wings Pegasus XL-R	
G-MTCO	Solar Wings Pegasus XL-R	
G-MTCP	Aerial Arts Chaser 110SX	
G-MTCR	Solar Wings Pegasus XL-R	
G-MTCT	CFM Shadow Srs BD	
G-MTCU	Mainair Gemini Flash II	
G-MTCV	Microflight Spectrum	
G-MTCW	Mainair Gemini Flash	
G-MTCX	Solar Wings Pegasus XL-R	
G-MTCZ	Ultrasports Tripacer 250	
G-MTDA	Hornet Dual Trainer	
G-MTDD	Aerial Arts Chaser 110SX	
G-MTDE	American Aerolights 110SX	
G-MTDF	Mainair Gemini Flash II	
G-MTDG	Solar Wings Pegasus XL-R	
G-MTDH	Solar Wings Pegasus XL-R	
G-MTDI	Solar Wings Pegasus XL-R	
G-MTDK	Aerotech MW.5 Sorcerer	
G-MTDM	Mainair Gemini Flash II	
G-MTDN	Ultraflight Lazair IIIE	
G-MTDO	Eipper Quicksilver MXII	
G-MTDR	Mainair Gemini Flash II	
G-MTDT	Solar Wings Pegasus XL-R	
G-MTDU	CFM Shadow Srs BD	
G-MTDW	Mainair Gemini Flash II	
G-MTDX	CFM Shadow Srs BD	
G-MTDY	Mainair Gemini Flash II	
G-MTDZ	Eipper Quicksilver MXII	
G-MTEA	Solar Wings Pegasus XL-R	
G-MTEB	Solar Wings Pegasus XL-R	
G-MTEC	Solar Wings Pegasus XL-R	
G-MTED	Solar Wings Pegasus XL-R	
G-MTEE	Solar Wings Pegasus XL-R	
G-MTEG	Mainair Gemini Flash II	
G-MTEJ	Mainair Gemini Flash II	
G-MTEK	Mainair Gemini Flash II	
G-MTEN	Mainair Gemini Flash II	
G-MTEO	Midland Ultralight Sirocco 337	
G-MTER	Solar Wings Pegasus XL-R	
G-MTES	Solar Wings Pegasus XL-R	
G-MTET	Solar Wings Pegasus XL-R	
G-MTEU	Solar Wings Pegasus XL-R	
G-MTEW	Solar Wings Pegasus XL-R	
G-MTEX	Solar Wings Pegasus XL-R	
G-MTEY	Mainair Gemini Flash II	
G-MTFB	Solar Wings Pegasus XL-R	
G-MTFC	Medway Hybred 44XLR	
G-MTFE	Solar Wings Pegasus XL-R	
G-MTFF	Mainair Gemini Flash II	
G-MTFG	AMF Chevvron 232	
G-MTFI	Mainair Gemini Flash II	
G-MTFJ	Mainair Gemini Flash II	

Reg.	Type	Notes
G-MTFL	AMF Lazair IIIE	
G-MTFM	Solar Wings Pegasus XL-R	
G-MTFN	Aerotech MW.5 Sorcerer	
G-MTFO	Solar Wings Pegasus XL-R	
G-MTFP	Solar Wings Pegasus XL-R	
G-MTFR	Solar Wings Pegasus XL-R	
G-MTFS	Solar Wings Pegasus XL-R	
G-MTFT	Solar Wings Pegasus XL-R	
G-MTFU	CFM Shadow Series BD	
G-MTFX	Mainair Gemini Flash	
G-MTFZ	CFM Shadow Srs BD	
G-MTGA	Mainair Gemini Flash	
G-MTGB	Thruster TST Mk 1	
G-MTGC	Thruster TST Mk 1	
G-MTGD	Thruster TST Mk 1	
G-MTGE	Thruster TST Mk 1	
G-MTGF	Thruster TST Mk 1	
G-MTGH	Mainair Gemini Flash IIA	
G-MTGJ	Solar Wings Pegasus XL-R	
G-MTGK	Solar Wings Pegasus XL-R	
G-MTGL	Solar Wings Pegasus XL-R	
G-MTGM	Solar Wings Pegasus XL-R	
G-MTGO	Mainair Gemini Flash	
G-MTGP	Thruster TST Mk 1	
G-MTGR	Thruster TST Mk 1	
G-MTGS	Thruster TST Mk 1	
G-MTGT	Thruster TST Mk 1	
G-MTGU	Thruster TST Mk 1	
G-MTGV	CFM Shadow Srs BD	
G-MTGW	CFM Shadow Srs BD	
G-MTGX	Hornet Dual Trainer	
G-MTGY	Southdown Lightning	
G-MTHB	Aerotech MW.5B Sorcerer	
G-MTHC	Raven X	
G-MTHG	Solar Wings Pegasus XL-R	
G-MTHH	Solar Wings Pegasus XL-R	
G-MTHI	Solar Wings Pegasus XL-R	
G-MTHJ	Solar Wings Pegasus XL-R	
G-MTHK	Solar Wings Pegasus XL-R	
G-MTHN	Solar Wings Pegasus XL-R	
G-MTHT	CFM Shadow Srs BD	
G-MTHU	Hornet Dual Trainer	
G-MTHV	CFM Shadow Srs BD	
G-MTHW	Mainair Gemini Flash II	
G-MTHZ	Mainair Gemini Flash IIA	
G-MTIA	Mainair Gemini Flash IIA	
G-MTIB	Mainair Gemini Flash IIA	
G-MTIE	Solar Wings Pegasus XL-R	
G-MTIH	Solar Wings Pegasus XL-R	
G-MTIJ	Solar Wings Pegasus XL-R	
G-MTIK	Southdown Raven X	
G-MTIL	Mainair Gemini Flash IIA	
G-MTIM	Mainair Gemini Flash IIA	
G-MTIN	Mainair Gemini Flash IIA	
G-MTIO	Solar Wings Pegasus XL-R	
G-MTIP	Solar Wings Pegasus XL-R	
G-MTIR	Solar Wings Pegasus XL-R	
G-MTIS	Solar Wings Pegasus XL-R	
G-MTIT	Solar Wings Pegasus XL-R	
G-MTIU	Solar Wings Pegasus XL-R	
G-MTIV	Solar Wings Pegasus XL-R	
G-MTIW	Solar Wings Pegasus XL-R	
G-MTIX	Solar Wings Pegasus XL-R	
G-MTIY	Solar Wings Pegasus XL-R	
G-MTIZ	Solar Wings Pegasus XL-R	
G-MTJA	Mainair Gemini Flash IIA	
G-MTJB	Mainair Gemini Flash IIA	
G-MTJC	Mainair Gemini Flash IIA	
G-MTJD	Mainair Gemini Flash IIA	
G-MTJE	Mainair Gemini Flash IIA	
G-MTJG	Medway Hybred 44XLR	
G-MTJH	SW Pegasus Flash	
G-MTJK	Mainair Gemini Flash IIA	

Reg.	Type	Notes	Reg.	Type	Notes
G-MTJL	Mainair Gemini Flash IIA		G-MTNR	Thruster TST Mk 1	
G-MTJM	Mainair Gemini Flash IIA		G-MTNS	Thruster TST Mk 1	
G-MTJN	Midland Ultralights Sirocco 377GB		G-MTNT	Thruster TST Mk 1	
			G-MTNU	Thruster TST Mk 1	
G-MTJP	Medway Hybred 44XLR		G-MTNV	Thruster TST Mk 1	
G-MTJS	Solar Wings Pegasus XL-Q		G-MTNX	Mainair Gemini Flash II	
G-MTJT	Mainair Gemini Flash IIA		G-MTNY	Mainair Gemini Flash IIA	
G-MTJV	Mainair Gemini Flash IIA		G-MTOA	Solar Wings Pegasus XL-R	
G-MTJW	Mainair Gemini Flash IIA		G-MTOB	Solar Wings Pegasus XL-R	
G-MTJX	Raven/Dual Trainer		G-MTOD	Solar Wings Pegasus XL-R	
G-MTJZ	Mainair Gemini Flash IIA		G-MTOE	Solar Wings Pegasus XL-R	
G-MTKA	Thruster TST Mk 1		G-MTOG	Solar Wings Pegasus XL-R	
G-MTKB	Thruster TST Mk 1		G-MTOH	Solar Wings Pegasus XL-R	
G-MTKD	Thruster TST Mk 1		G-MTOI	Solar Wings Pegasus XL-R	
G-MTKE	Thruster TST Mk 1		G-MTOJ	Solar Wings Pegasus XL-R	
G-MTKG	Solar Wings Pegasus XL-R		G-MTOK	Solar Wings Pegasus XL-R	
G-MTKH	Solar Wings Pegasus XL-R		G-MTOL	Solar Wings Pegasus XL-R	
G-MTKI	Solar Wings Pegasus XL-R		G-MTOM	Solar Wings Pegasus XL-R	
G-MTKM	Gardner T-M Scout S.2		G-MTON	Solar Wings Pegasus XL-R	
G-MTKN	Mainair Gemini Flash IIA		G-MTOO	Solar Wings Pegasus XL-R	
G-MTKR	CFM Shadow Srs BD		G-MTOP	Solar Wings Pegasus XL-R	
G-MTKS	CFM Shadow Srs BD		G-MTOS	Solar Wings Pegasus XL-R	
G-MTKW	Mainair Gemini Flash IIA		G-MTOT	Solar Wings Pegasus XL-R	
G-MTKX	Mainair Gemini Flash IIA		G-MTOU	Solar Wings Pegasus XL-R	
G-MTKZ	Mainair Gemini Flash IIA		G-MTOV	Solar Wings Pegasus XL-R	
G-MTLB	Mainair Gemini Flash IIA		G-MTOX	Solar Wings Pegasus XL-R	
G-MTLC	Mainair Gemini Flash IIA		G-MTOY	Solar Wings Pegasus XL-R	
G-MTLD	Mainair Gemini Flash IIA		G-MTOZ	Solar Wings Pegasus XL-R	
G-MTLE	See main Register		G-MTPA	Mainair Gemini Flash IIA	
G-MTLG	Solar Wings Pegasus XL-R		G-MTPC	Raven X	
G-MTLI	Solar Wings Pegasus XL-R		G-MTPE	Solar Wings Pegasus XL-R	
G-MTLJ	Solar Wings Pegasus XL-R		G-MTPF	Solar Wings Pegasus XL-R	
G-MTLK	Raven X		G-MTPG	Solar Wings Pegasus XL-R	
G-MTLL	Mainair Gemini Flash IIA		G-MTPH	Solar Wings Pegasus XL-R	
G-MTLM	Thruster TST Mk 1		G-MTPI	Solar Wings Pegasus XL-R	
G-MTLN	Thruster TST Mk 1		G-MTPJ	Solar Wings Pegasus XL-R	
G-MTLR	Thruster TST Mk 1		G-MTPK	Solar Wings Pegasus XL-R	
G-MTLS	Solar Wings Pegasus XL-R		G-MTPL	Solar Wings Pegasus XL-R	
G-MTLT	Solar Wings Pegasus XL-R		G-MTPM	Solar Wings Pegasus XL-R	
G-MTLU	Solar Wings Pegasus XL-R		G-MTPN	Solar Wings Pegasus XL-Q	
G-MTLV	Solar Wings Pegasus XL-R		G-MTPP	Solar Wings Pegasus XL-R	
G-MTLX	Medway Hybred 44XLR		G-MTPR	Solar Wings Pegasus XL-R	
G-MTLY	Solar Wings Pegasus XL-R		G-MTPS	Solar Wings Pegasus XL-Q	
G-MTLZ	Whittaker MW.5 Sorceror		G-MTPT	Thruster TST Mk 1	
G-MTMA	Mainair Gemini Flash IIA		G-MTPU	Thruster TST Mk 1	
G-MTMB	Mainair Gemini Flash IIA		G-MTPV	Thruster TST Mk 1	
G-MTMC	Mainair Gemini Flash IIA		G-MTPW	Thruster TST Mk 1	
G-MTME	Solar Wings Pegasus XL-R		G-MTPX	Thruster TST Mk 1	
G-MTMF	Solar Wings Pegasus XL-R		G-MTPY	Thruster TST Mk 1	
G-MTMG	Solar Wings Pegasus XL-R		G-MTRA	Mainair Gemini Flash IIA	
G-MTMI	Solar Wings Pegasus XL-R		G-MTRC	Midlands Ultralights Sirocco 377GB	
G-MTMK	Raven X				
G-MTML	Mainair Gemini Flash IIA		G-MTRD	Midlands Ultralights Sirocco 377GB	
G-MTMO	Raven X				
G-MTMP	Hornet Dual Trainer/Raven		G-MTRJ	AMF Chevvron 232	
G-MTMR	Hornet Dual Trainer/Raven		G-MTRL	Hornet Dual Trainer	
G-MTMT	Mainair Gemini Flash IIA		G-MTRM	Solar Wings Pegasus XL-R	
G-MTMV	Mainair Gemini Flash IIA		G-MTRN	Solar Wings Pegasus XL-R	
G-MTMW	Mainair Gemini Flash IIA		G-MTRO	Solar Wings Pegasus XL-R	
G-MTMX	CFM Shadow Srs BD		G-MTRP	Solar Wings Pegasus XL-R	
G-MTMY	CFM Shadow Srs BD		G-MTRS	Solar Wings Pegasus XL-R	
G-MTNC	Mainair Gemini Flash IIA		G-MTRT	Raven X	
G-MTND	Medway Hybred 44XLR		G-MTRU	Solar Wings Pegasus XL-Q	
G-MTNE	Medway Hybred 44XLR		G-MTRV	Solar Wings Pegasus XL-Q	
G-MTNF	Medway Hybred 44XLR		G-MTRW	Raven X	
G-MTNG	Mainair Gemini Flash IIA		G-MTRX	Whittaker MW.5 Sorceror	
G-MTNH	Mainair Gemini Flash IIA		G-MTRZ	Mainair Gemini Flash IIA	
G-MTNI	Mainair Gemini Flash IIA		G-MTSB	Mainair Gemini Flash IIA	
G-MTNK	Weedhopper JC-24B		G-MTSC	Mainair Gemini Flash IIA	
G-MTNL	Mainair Gemini Flash IIA		G-MTSD	Raven X	
G-MTNM	Mainair Gemini Flash IIA		G-MTSG	CFM Shadow Srs BD	
G-MTNO	Solar Wings Pegasus XL-Q		G-MTSH	Thruster TST Mk 1	
G-MTNP	Solar Wings Pegasus XL-Q		G-MTSJ	Thruster TST Mk 1	

Reg.	Type	Notes	Reg.	Type	Notes
G-MTSK	Thruster TST Mk 1		G-MTWK	CFM Shadow Srs BD	
G-MTSM	Thruster TST Mk 1		G-MTWL	CFM Shadow Srs BD	
G-MTSN	Solar Wings Pegasus XL-R		G-MTWN	CFM Shadow Srs BD	
G-MTSO	Solar Wings Pegasus XL-R		G-MTWP	CFM Shadow Srs BD	
G-MTSP	Solar Wings Pegasus XL-R		G-MTWR	Mainair Gemini Flash IIA	
G-MTSR	Solar Wings Pegasus XL-R		G-MTWS	Mainair Gemini Flash IIA	
G-MTSS	Solar Wings Pegasus XL-R		G-MTWX	Mainair Gemini Flash IIA	
G-MTST	Thruster TST Mk 1		G-MTWY	Thruster TST Mk 1	
G-MTSU	Solar Wings Pegasus XL-R		G-MTWZ	Thruster TST Mk 1	
G-MTSV	Solar Wings Pegasus XL-R		G-MTXA	Thruster TST Mk 1	
G-MTSX	Solar Wings Pegasus XL-R		G-MTXB	Thruster TST Mk 1	
G-MTSY	Solar Wings Pegasus XL-R		G-MTXC	Thruster TST Mk 1	
G-MTSZ	Solar Wings Pegasus XL-R		G-MTXD	Thruster TST Mk 1	
G-MTTA	Solar Wings Pegasus XL-R		G-MTXE	Hornet Dual Trainer	
G-MTTB	Solar Wings Pegasus XL-R		G-MTXH	Solar Wings Pegasus XL-Q	
G-MTTD	Solar Wings Pegasus XL-R		G-MTXI	Solar Wings Pegasus XL-Q	
G-MTTE	Solar Wings Pegasus XL-R		G-MTXJ	Solar Wings Pegasus XL-Q	
G-MTTF	Aerotech MW.6 Merlin		G-MTXK	Solar Wings Pegasus XL-Q	
G-MTTH	CFM Shadow Srs BD		G-MTXL	Noble Hardman Snowbird	
G-MTTI	Mainair Gemini Flash IIA			Mk IV	
G-MTTL	Hiway Sky-Trike		G-MTXM	Mainair Gemini Flash IIA	
G-MTTM	Mainair Gemini Flash IIA		G-MTXP	Mainair Gemini Flash IIA	
G-MTTN	Ultralight Flight Phantom		G-MTXR	CFM Shadow Srs BD	
G-MTTO	Mainair Gemini Flash IIA		G-MTXT	MBA Tiger Cub 440	
G-MTTP	Mainair Gemini Flash IIA		G-MTXU	Snowbird Mk.IV	
G-MTTR	Mainair Gemini Flash IIA		G-MTXW	Snowbird Mk.IV	
G-MTTS	Mainair Gemini Flash IIA		G-MTXY	Hornet Dual Trainer	
G-MTTU	Solar Wings Pegasus XL-R		G-MTXZ	Mainair Gemini Flash IIA	
G-MTTW	Mainair Gemini Flash IIA		G-MTYA	Solar Wings Pegasus XL-Q	
G-MTTX	Solar Wings Pegasus XL-Q		G-MTYC	Solar Wings Pegasus XL-Q	
G-MTTZ	Solar Wings Pegasus XL-Q		G-MTYD	Solar Wings Pegasus XL-Q	
G-MTUA	Solar Wings Pegasus XL-R		G-MTYE	Solar Wings Pegasus XL-Q	
G-MTUB	Thruster TST Mk 1		G-MTYF	Solar Wings Pegasus XL-Q	
G-MTUC	Thruster TST Mk 1		G-MTYG	Solar Wings Pegasus XL-Q	
G-MTUD	Thruster TST Mk 1		G-MTYI	Solar Wings Pegasus XL-Q	
G-MTUF	Thruster TST Mk 1		G-MTYL	Solar Wings Pegasus XL-Q	
G-MTUH	Solar Wings Pegasus XL-R		G-MTYP	Solar Wings Pegasus XL-Q	
G-MTUI	Solar Wings Pegasus XL-R		G-MTYR	Solar Wings Pegasus XL-Q	
G-MTUJ	Solar Wings Pegasus XL-R		G-MTYS	Solar Wings Pegasus XL-Q	
G-MTUK	Solar Wings Pegasus XL-R		G-MTYU	Solar Wings Pegasus XL-Q	
G-MTUL	Solar Wings Pegasus XL-R		G-MTYV	Raven X	
G-MTUP	Solar Wings Pegasus XL-Q		G-MTYW	Ravan X	
G-MTUR	Solar Wings Pegasus XL-Q		G-MTYX	Raven X	
G-MTUS	Solar Wings Pegasus XL-Q		G-MTYY	Solar Wings Pegasus XL-R	
G-MTUT	Solar Wings Pegasus XL-Q		G-MTZA	Thruster TST Mk 1	
G-MTUU	Mainair Gemini Flash IIA		G-MTZB	Thruster TST Mk 1	
G-MTUV	Mainair Gemini Flash IIA		G-MTZC	Thruster TST Mk 1	
G-MTUX	Medway Hybred 44XLR		G-MTZD	Thruster TST Mk 1	
G-MTUY	Solar Wings Pegasus XL-Q		G-MTZE	Thruster TST Mk 1	
G-MTVA	Solar Wings Pegasus XL-R		G-MTZF	Thruster TST Mk 1	
G-MTVB	Solar Wings Pegasus XL-R		G-MTZG	Mainair Gemini Flash IIA	
G-MTVE	Solar Wings Pegasus XL-R		G-MTZH	Mainair Gemini Flash IIA	
G-MTVF	Solar Wings Pegasus XL-R		G-MTZJ	Solar Wings Pegasus XL-R	
G-MTVH	Mainair Gemini Flash IIA		G-MTZK	Solar Wings Pegasus XL-R	
G-MTVI	Mainair Gemini Flash IIA		G-MTZL	Mainair Gemini Flash IIA	
G-MTVJ	Mainair Gemini Flash IIA		G-MTZK	Solar Wings Pegasus XL-R	
G-MTVK	Solar Wings Pegasus XL-R		G-MTZM	Mainair Gemini Flash IIA	
G-MTVL	Solar Wings Pegasus XL-R		G-MTZN	Mainair Gemini Flash IIA	
G-MTVM	Solar Wings Pegasus XL-R		G-MTZO	Mainair Gemini Flash IIA	
G-MTVN	Solar Wings Pegasus XL-R		G-MTZP	Solar Wings Pegasus XL-Q	
G-MTVO	Solar Wings Pegasus XL-R		G-MTZR	Solar Wings Pegasus XL-Q	
G-MTVP	Thruster TST Mk 1		G-MTZS	Solar Wings Pegasus XL-Q	
G-MTVR	Thruster TST Mk 1		G-MTZT	Solar Wings Pegasus XL-Q	
G-MTVS	Thruster TST Mk 1		G-MTZV	Mainair Gemini Flash IIA	
G-MTVT	Thruster TST Mk 1		G-MTZW	Mainair Gemini Flash IIA	
G-MTVV	Thruster TST Mk 1		G-MTZX	Mainair Gemini Flash IIA	
G-MTVX	Solar Wings Pegasus XL-Q		G-MTZY	Mainair Gemini Flash IIA	
G-MTWA	Solar Wings Pegasus XL-R		G-MTZZ	Mainair Gemini Flash IIA	
G-MTWB	Solar Wings Pegasus XL-R				
G-MTWD	Solar Wings Pegasus XL-R		G-MVAA	Mainair Gemini Flash IIA	
G-MTWF	Mainair Gemini Flash IIA		G-MVAB	Mainair Gemini Flash IIA	
G-MTWG	Mainair Gemini Flash IIA		G-MVAC	CFM Shadow Srs BD	
G-MTWH	CFM Shadow Srs BD		G-MVAD	Mainair Gemini Flash IIA	

Reg.	Type	Notes	Reg.	Type	Notes
G-MVAF	Southdown Puma Sprint		G-MVDU	Solar Wings Pegasus XL-R	
G-MVAG	Thruster TST Mk 1		G-MVDV	Solar Wings Pegasus XL-R	
G-MVAH	Thruster TST Mk 1		G-MVDW	Solar Wings Pegasus XL-R	
G-MVAI	Thruster TST Mk 1		G-MVDX	Solar Wings Pegasus XL-R	
G-MVAJ	Thruster TST Mk 1		G-MVDY	Solar Wings Pegasus XL-R	
G-MVAK	Thruster TST Mk 1		G-MVDZ	Solar Wings Pegasus XL-R	
G-MVAL	Thruster TST Mk 1		G-MVEC	Solar Wings Pegasus XL-R	
G-MVAM	CFM Shadow Srs BD		G-MVED	Solar Wings Pegasus XL-R	
G-MVAN	CFM Shadow Srs BD		G-MVEE	Medway Hybred 44XLR	
G-MVAO	Mainair Gemini Flash IIA		G-MVEF	Solar Wings Pegasus XL-R	
G-MVAP	Mainair Gemini Flash IIA		G-MVEG	Solar Wings Pegasus XL-R	
G-MVAR	Solar Wings Pegasus XL-R		G-MVEH	Mainair Gemini Flash IIA	
G-MVAT	Solar Wings Pegasus XL-R		G-MVEI	CFM Shadow Srs BD	
G-MVAV	Solar Wings Pegasus XL-R		G-MVEJ	Mainair Gemini Flash IIA	
G-MVAW	Solar Wings Pegasus XL-Q		G-MVEK	Mainair Gemini Flash IIA	
G-MVAX	Solar Wings Pegasus XL-Q		G-MVEL	Mainair Gemini Flash IIA	
G-MVAY	Solar Wings Pegasus XL-Q		G-MVEN	CFM Shadow Srs BD	
G-MVAZ	Solar Wings Pegasus XL-Q		G-MVEO	Mainair Gemini Flash IIA	
G-MVBA	Solar Wings Pegasus XL-Q		G-MVER	Mainair Gemini Flash IIA	
G-MVBB	CFM Shadow Srs BD		G-MVES	Mainair Gemini Flash IIA	
G-MVBC	Aerial Arts Tri-Flyer 130SX		G-MVET	Mainair Gemini Flash IIA	
G-MVBD	Mainair Gemini Flash IIA		G-MVEV	Mainair Gemini Flash IIA	
G-MVBF	Mainair Gemini Flash IIA		G-MVEW	Mainair Gemini Flash IIA	
G-MVBG	Mainair Gemini Flash IIA		G-MVEX	Solar Wings Pegasus XL-Q	
G-MVBH	Mainair Gemini Flash IIA		G-MVEZ	Solar Wings Pegasus XL-Q	
G-MVBI	Mainair Gemini Flash IIA		G-MVFA	Solar Wings Pegasus XL-Q	
G-MVBJ	Solar Wings Pegasus XL-R		G-MVFB	Solar Wings Pegasus XL-Q	
G-MVBK	Mainair Gemini Flash IIA		G-MVFC	Solar Wings Pegasus XL-Q	
G-MVBL	Mainair Gemini Flash IIA		G-MVFD	Solar Wings Pegasus XL-Q	
G-MVBM	Mainair Gemini Flash IIA		G-MVFE	Solar Wings Pegasus XL-Q	
G-MVBN	Mainair Gemini Flash IIA		G-MVFF	Solar Wings Pegasus XL-Q	
G-MVBO	Mainair Gemini Flash IIA		G-MVFG	Solar Wings Pegasus XL-Q	
G-MVBP	Thruster TST Mk 1		G-MVFH	CFM Shadow Srs BD	
G-MVBS	Thruster TST Mk 1		G-MVFJ	Thruster TST Mk 1	
G-MVBT	Thruster TST Mk 1		G-MVFK	Thruster TST Mk 1	
G-MVBY	Solar Wings Pegasus XL-R		G-MVFL	Thruster TST Mk 1	
G-MVBZ	Solar Wings Pegasus XL-R		G-MVFM	Thruster TST Mk 1	
G-MVCA	Solar Wings Pegasus XL-R		G-MVFN	Thruster TST Mk 1	
G-MVCB	Solar Wings Pegasus XL-R		G-MVFO	Thruster TST Mk 1	
G-MVCC	CFM Shadow Srs BD		G-MVFP	Solar Wings Pegasus XL-R	
G-MVCD	Medway Hybred 44XLR		G-MVFR	Solar Wings Pegasus XL-R	
G-MVCE	Mainair Gemini Flash IIA		G-MVFS	Solar Wings Pegasus XL-R	
G-MVCF	Mainair Gemini Flash IIA		G-MVFT	Solar Wings Pegasus XL-R	
G-MVCH	Noble Hardman Snowbird Mk IV		G-MVFV	Solar Wings Pegasus XL-R	
			G-MVFW	Solar Wings Pegasus XL-R	
G-MVCI	Noble Hardman Snowbird Mk IV		G-MVFX	Solar Wings Pegasus XL-R	
			G-MVFY	Solar Wings Pegasus XL-R	
G-MVCJ	Noble Hardman Snowbird Mk IV		G-MVFZ	Solar Wings Pegasus XL-R	
			G-MVGA	Aerial Arts Chaser S	
G-MVCL	Solar Wings Pegasus XL-Q		G-MVGB	Medway Hybred 44XLR	
G-MVCM	Solar Wings Pegasus XL-Q		G-MVGC	AMF Chevvron 2-32	
G-MVCN	Solar Wings Pegasus XL-Q		G-MVGD	AMF Chevvron 2-32	
G-MVCP	Solar Wings Pegasus XL-Q		G-MVGE	AMF Chevvron 2-32	
G-MVCR	Solar Wings Pegasus XL-Q		G-MVGF	Aerial Arts Chaser S	
G-MVCS	Solar Wings Pegasus XL-Q		G-MVGG	Aerial Arts Chaser S	
G-MVCT	Solar Wings Pegasus XL-Q		G-MVGH	Aerial Arts Chaser S	
G-MVCV	Solar Wings Pegasus XL-Q		G-MVGI	Aerial Arts Chaser S	
G-MVCW	CFM Shadow Srs BD		G-MVGM	Mainair Gemini Flash IIA	
G-MVCY	Mainair Gemini Flash IIA		G-MVGN	Solar Wings Pegasus XL-R	
G-MVDA	Mainair Gemini Flash IIA		G-MVGO	Solar Wings Pegasus XL-R	
G-MVDB	Medway Hybred 44XLR		G-MVGS	Solar Wings Pegasus XL-R	
G-MVDD	Thruster TST Mk 1		G-MVGU	Solar Wings Pegasus XL-Q	
G-MVDE	Thruster TST Mk 1		G-MVGW	Solar Wings Pegasus XL-Q	
G-MVDF	Thruster TST Mk 1		G-MVGX	Solar Wings Pegasus XL-Q	
G-MVDG	Thruster TST Mk 1		G-MVGY	Medway Hybred 44XL	
G-MVDH	Thruster TST Mk 1		G-MVGZ	Ultraflight Lazair IIIE	
G-MVDJ	Medway Hybred 44XLR		G-MVHA	Aerial Arts Chaser S	
G-MVDK	Aerial Arts Chaser S		G-MVHB	Powerchute Raider	
G-MVDL	Aerial Arts Chaser S		G-MVHC	Powerchute Raider	
G-MVDO	Aerial Arts Chaser S		G-MVHD	CFM Shadow Srs BD	
G-MVDP	Aerial Arts Chaser S		G-MVHE	Mainair Gemini Flash IIA	
G-MVDR	Aerial Arts Chaser S.447		G-MVHF	Mainair Gemini Flash IIA	
G-MVDT	Mainair Gemini Flash IIA		G-MVHG	Mainair Gemini Flash IIA	

Reg.	Type	Notes
G-MVHH	Mainair Gemini Flash IIA	
G-MVHI	Thruster TST Mk 1	
G-MVHJ	Thruster TST Mk 1	
G-MVHK	Thruster TST Mk 1	
G-MVHL	Thruster TST Mk 1	
G-MVHN	Aerial Arts Chaser S	
G-MVHO	Solar Wings Pegasus XL-Q	
G-MVHP	Solar Wings Pegasus XL-Q	
G-MVHR	Solar Wings Pegasus XL-Q	
G-MVHS	Solar Wings Pegasus XL-Q	
G-MVHV	Solar Wings Pegasus XL-Q	
G-MVHW	Solar Wings Pegasus XL-Q	
G-MVHX	Solar Wings Pegasus XL-Q	
G-MVHY	Solar Wings Pegasus XL-Q	
G-MVHZ	Hornet Dual Trainer	
G-MVIA	Solar Wings Pegasus XL-R	
G-MVIB	Mainair Gemini Flash IIA	
G-MVID	Aerial Arts Chaser 5	
G-MVIE	Aerial Arts Chaser S	
G-MVIF	Medway Raven X	
G-MVIG	CFM Shadow Srs B	
G-MVIH	Mainair Gemini Flash IIA	
G-MVIL	Noble Hardman Snowbird Mk IV	
G-MVIN	Noble Hardman Snowbird Mk IV	
G-MVIO	Noble Hardman Snowbird Mk IV	
G-MVIP	AMF Chevvron 232	
G-MVIR	Thruster TST Mk 1	
G-MVIT	Thruster TST Mk 1	
G-MVIU	Thruster TST Mk 1	
G-MVIV	Thruster TST Mk 1	
G-MVIW	Thruster TST Mk 1	
G-MVIX	Mainair Gemini Flash IIA	
G-MVIY	Mainair Gemini Flash IIA	
G-MVIZ	Mainair Gemini Flash IIA	
G-MVJA	Mainair Gemini Flash IIA	
G-MVJC	Mainair Gemini Flash IIA	
G-MVJD	Solar Wings Pegasus XL-R	
G-MVJE	Mainair Gemini Flash IIA	
G-MVJF	Aerial Arts Chaser S	
G-MVJG	Aerial Arts Chaser S	
G-MVJH	Aerial Arts Chaser S	
G-MVJJ	Aerial Arts Chaser S	
G-MVJK	Aerial Arts Chaser S	
G-MVJL	Mainair Gemini Flash IIA	
G-MVJM	Microflight Spectrum	
G-MVJN	Solar Wings Pegasus XL-Q	
G-MVJO	Solar Wings Pegasus XL-Q	
G-MVJP	Solar Wings Pegasus XL-Q	
G-MVJR	Solar Wings Pegasus XL-Q	
G-MVJS	Solar Wings Pegasus XL-Q	
G-MVJT	Solar Wings Pegasus XL-Q	
G-MVJU	Solar Wings Pegasus XL-Q	
G-MVJW	Solar Wings Pegasus XL-Q	
G-MVJZ	Birdman Cherokee	
G-MVKB	Medway Hybred 44XLR	
G-MVKC	Mainair Gemini Flash IIA	
G-MVKF	Solar Wings Pegasus XL-R	
G-M˜VKH	Solar Wings Pegasus XL-R	
G-MVKJ	Solar Wings Pegasus XL-R	
G-MVKK	Solar Wings Pegasus XL-R	
G-MVKL	Solar Wings Pegasus XL-R	
G-MVKM	Solar Wings Pegasus XL-R	
G-MVKN	Solar Wings Pegasus XL-Q	
G-MVKO	Solar Wings Pegasus XL-Q	
G-MVKP	Solar Wings Pegasus XL-Q	
G-MVKR	Solar Wings Pegasus XL-Q	
G-MVKS	Solar Wings Pegasus XL-Q	
G-MVKT	Solar Wings Pegasus XL-Q	
G-MVKU	Solar Wings Pegasus XL-Q	
G-MVKV	Solar Wings Pegasus XL-Q	

Reg.	Type	Notes
G-MVKW	Solar Wings Pegasus XL-Q	
G-MVKY	Aerial Arts Chaser S	
G-MVKZ	Aerial Arts Chaser S	
G-MVLA	Aerial Arts Chaser S	
G-MVLC	Aerial Arts Chaser S	
G-MVLD	Aerial Arts Chaser S	
G-MVLE	Aerial Arts Chaser S	
G-MVLF	Aerial Arts Chaser S	
G-MVLG	Aerial Arts Chaser S	
G-MVLH	Aerial Arts Chaser S	
G-MVLJ	CFM Shadow Srs B	
G-MVLL	Mainair Gemini Flash IIA	
G-MVLP	CFM Shadow Srs BD	
G-MVLR	Mainair Gemini Flash IIA	
G-MVLS	Aerial Arts Chaser S	
G-MVLT	Aerial Arts Chaser S	
G-MVLW	Aerial Arts Chaser S	
G-MVLX	Solar Wings Pegasus XL-Q	
G-MVLY	Solar Wings Pegasus XL-Q	
G-MVMC	Solar Wings Pegasus XL-Q	
G-MVMD	Powerchute Raider	
G-MVME	Thruster TST Mk 1	
G-MVMG	Thruster TST Mk 1	
G-MVMI	Thruster TST Mk 1	
G-MVMK	Medway Hybred 44XLR	
G-MVML	Aerial Arts Chaser S	
G-MVMM	Aerial Arts Chaser S	
G-MVMO	Mainair Gemini Flash IIA	
G-MVMR	Mainair Gemini Flash IIA	
G-MVMT	Mainair Gemini Flash IIA	
G-MVMU	Mainair Gemini Flash IIA	
G-MVMV	Aerotech MW.5 (K) Sorcerer	
G-MVMW	Mainair Gemini Flash IIA	
G-MVMX	Mainair Gemini Flash IIA	
G-MVMY	Mainair Gemini Flash IIA	
G-MVMZ	Mainair Gemini Flash IIA	
G-MVNA	Powerchute Raider	
G-MVNC	Powerchute Raider	
G-MVNF	Powerchute Raider	
G-MVNI	Powerchute Raider	
G-MVNK	Powerchute Raider	
G-MVNL	Powerchute Raider	
G-MVNM	Mainair Gemini Flash IIA	
G-MVNN	Whittaker MW.5 (K) Sorcerer	
G-MVNO	Aerotech MW.5 (K) Sorcerer	
G-MVNP	Aerotech MW.5 (K) Sorcerer	
G-MVNR	Aerotech MW.5 (K) Sorcerer	
G-MVNS	Aerotech MW.5 (K) Sorcerer	
G-MVNT	Whittaker MW.5 (K) Sorcerer	
G-MVNU	Aerotech MW.5 Sorcerer	
G-MVNV	Aerotech MW.5 Sorcerer	
G-MVNW	Mainair Gemini Flash IIA	
G-MVNX	Mainair Gemini Flash IIA	
G-MVNY	Mainair Gemini Flash IIA	
G-MVNZ	Mainair Gemini Flash IIA	
G-MVOA	Aerial Arts Alligator	
G-MVOB	Mainair Gemini Flash IIA	
G-MVOD	Aerial Arts Chaser 110SX	
G-MVOF	Mainair Gemini Flash IIA	
G-MVOH	CFM Shadow Srs B	
G-MVOI	Noble Hardman Snowbird Mk IV	
G-MVOJ	Noble Hardman Snowbird Mk IV	
G-MVOK	Noble Hardman Snowbird Mk IV	

Reg.	Type	Notes
G-MVOL	Noble Hardman Snowbird Mk IV	
G-MVON	Mainair Gemini Flash IIA	
G-MVOO	AMF Chevvron 2-32	
G-MVOP	Aerial Arts Chaser S	
G-MVOR	Mainair Gemini Flash IIA	
G-MVOT	Thruster TST Mk 1	
G-MVOU	Thruster TST Mk 1	
G-MVOV	Thruster TST Mk 1	
G-MVOW	Thruster TST Mk 1	
G-MVOX	Thruster TST Mk 1	
G-MVOY	Thruster TST Mk 1	
G-MVPA	Mainair Gemini Flash IIA	
G-MVPB	Mainair Gemini Flash IIA	
G-MVPD	Mainair Gemini Flash IIA	
G-MVPE	Mainair Gemini Flash IIA	
G-MVPF	Medway Hybred 44XLR	
G-MVPG	Medway Hybred 44XLR	
G-MVPH	Whittaker MW.6 Merlin	
G-MVPI	Mainair Gemini Flash IIA	
G-MVPJ	Rans S.5	
G-MVPK	CFM Shadow Srs B	
G-MVPL	Medway Hybred 44XLR	
G-MVPM	Whittaker MW.6 Merlin	
G-MVPN	Whittaker MW.6 Merlin	
G-MVPO	Mainair Gemini Flash IIA	
G-MVPR	Solar Wings Pegasus XL-Q	
G-MVPS	Solar Wings Pegasus XL-Q	
G-MVPT	Solar Wings Pegasus XL-Q	
G-MVPU	Solar Wings Pegasus XL-Q	
G-MVPW	Solar Wings Pegasus XL-R	
G-MVPX	Solar Wings Pegasus XL-Q	
G-MVPY	Solar Wings Pegasus XL-Q	
G-MVRA	Mainair Gemini Flash IIA	
G-MVRC	Mainair Gemini Flash IIA	
G-MVRD	Mainair Gemini Flash IIA	
G-MVRE	CFM Shadow Srs BD	
G-MVRF	Rotec Rally 2B	
G-MVRG	Aerial Arts Chaser S	
G-MVRH	Solar Wings Pegasus XL-Q	
G-MVRI	Solar Wings Pegasus XL-Q	
G-MVRJ	Solar Wings Pegasus XL-Q	
G-MVRL	Aerial Arts Chaser S	
G-MVRM	Mainair Gemini Flash IIA	
G-MVRO	CFM Shadow Srs BD	
G-MVRP	CFM Shadow Srs BD	
G-MVRR	CFM Shadow Srs BD	
G-MVRT	CFM Shadow Srs BD	
G-MVRU	Solar Wings Pegasus XL-Q	
G-MVRV	Powerchute Kestrel	
G-MVRW	Solar Wings Pegasus XL-Q	
G-MVRX	Solar Wings Pegasus XL-Q	
G-MVRY	Medway Hybred 44XLR	
G-MVRZ	Medway Hybred 44XLR	
G-MVSA	Solar Wings Pegasus XL-Q	
G-MVSB	Solar Wings Pegasus XL-Q	
G-MVSD	Solar Wings Pegasus XL-Q	
G-MVSE	Solar Wings Pegasus XL-Q	
G-MVSG	Aerial Arts Chaser S	
G-MVSI	Medway Hybred 44XLR	
G-MVSJ	Aviasud Mistral 532	
G-MVSK	Aerial Arts Chaser S	
G-MVSM	Midland Ultralights Sirocco	
G-MVSN	Mainair Gemini Flash IIA	
G-MVSO	Mainair Gemini Flash IIA	
G-MVSP	Mainair Gemini Flash IIA	
G-MVSR	Medway Hybred 44XLR	
G-MVSS	Hornet RS-ZA	
G-MVST	Mainair Gemini Flash IIA	
G-MVSU	Microflight Spectrum	
G-MVSV	Mainair Gemini Flash IIA	
G-MVSW	Solar Wings Pegasus XL-Q	
G-MVSX	Solar Wings Pegasus XL-Q	

Reg.	Type	Notes
G-MVSY	Solar Wings Pegasus XL-Q	
G-MVSZ	Solar Wings Pegasus XL-Q	
G-MVTA	Solar Wings Pegasus XL-Q	
G-MVTC	Mainair Gemini Flash IIA	
G-MVTD	Whittaker MW.6 Merlin	
G-MVTI	Solar Wings Pegasus XL-Q	
G-MVTJ	Solar Wings Pegasus XL-Q	
G-MVTK	Solar Wings Pegasus XL-Q	
G-MVTL	Aerial Arts Chaser S	
G-MVTM	Aerial Arts Chaser S	
G-MVUA	Mainair Gemini Flash IIA	
G-MVUB	Thruster T.300	
G-MVUC	Medway Hybred 44XLR	
G-MVUD	Medway Hybred 44XLR	
G-MVUE	Solar Wings Pegasus XL-Q	
G-MVUF	Solar Wings Pegasus XL-Q	
G-MVUG	Solar Wings Pegasus XL-Q	
G-MVUI	Solar Wings Pegasus XL-Q	
G-MVUJ	Solar Wings Pegasus XL-Q	
G-MVUL	Solar Wings Pegasus XL-Q	
G-MVUM	Solar Wings Pegasus XL-Q	
G-MVUN	Solar Wings Pegasus XL-Q	
G-MVUO	AMF Chevvron 2-32	
G-MVUP	Aviasud Mistral	
G-MVUR	Hornet ZA	
G-MVUS	Aerial Arts Chaser S	
G-MVUT	Aerial Arts Chaser S	
G-MVUU	Hornet R-ZA	
G-MVVF	Medway Hybred 44XLR	
G-MVVG	Medway Hybred 44XLR	
G-MVVH	Medway Hybred 44XLR	
G-MVVI	Medway Hybred 44XLR	
G-MVVK	Solar Wings Pegasus XL-R	
G-MVVM	Solar Wings Pegasus XL-R	
G-MVVN	Solar Wings Pegasus XL-Q	
G-MVVP	Solar Wings Pegasus XL-Q	
G-MVVT	CFM Shadow Srs BD	
G-MVVU	Aerial Arts Chaser S	
G-MVVV	AMF Chevvron 2-32	
G-MVVZ	Powerchute Raider	
G-MVWD	Powerchute Raider	
G-MVWE	Powerchute Raider	
G-MVWH	Powerchute Raider	
G-MVWJ	Powerchute Raider	
G-MVWN	Thruster T.300	
G-MVWO	Thruster T.300	
G-MVWR	Thruster T.300	
G-MVWS	Thruster T.300	
G-MVWV	Medway Hybred 44XLR	
G-MVWW	Aviasud Mistral	
G-MVWX	Microflight Spectrum	
G-MVWZ	Aviasud Mistral	
G-MVXA	Whittaker MW.6 Merlin	
G-MVXB	Mainair Gemini Flash IIA	
G-MVXC	Mainair Gemini Flash IIA	
G-MVXD	Medway Hybred 44XLR	
G-MVXE	Medway Hybred 44XLR	
G-MVXH	Spectrum	
G-MVXI	Medway Hybred 44XLR	
G-MVXJ	Medway Hybred 44XLR	
G-MVXL	Thruster TST Mk 1	
G-MVXM	Medway Hybred 44XLR	
G-MVXN	Aviasud Mistral	
G-MVXR	Mainair Gemini Flash IIA	
G-MVXS	Mainair Gemini Flash IIA	
G-MVXT	Mainair Gemini Flash IIA	
G-MVXV	Aviasud Mistral	
G-MVXW	Rans S.4 Coyote	
G-MVXX	AMF Chevvron 232	
G-MVYA	Aerial Arts Chaser S	
G-MVYC	Solar Wings Pegasus XL-Q	
G-MVYD	Solar Wings Pegasus XL-Q	
G-MVYE	Thruster TST Mk 1	

Reg.	Type	Notes	Reg.	Type	Notes
G-MVYG	Hornet R-ZA		G-MWBU	Hornet RS-ZA	
G-MVYI	Hornet R-ZA		G-MWBW	Hornet RS-ZA	
G-MVYJ	Hornet R-ZA		G-MWBX	Hornet RS-ZA	
G-MVYK	Hornet R-ZA		G-MWBY	Hornet RS-ZA	
G-MVYL	Hornet R-ZA		G-MWBZ	Hornet RS-ZA	
G-MVYN	Hornet R-ZA		G-MWCB	Solar Wings Pegasus XL-Q	
G-MVYP	Medway Hybred 44XLR		G-MWCE	Mainair Gemini Flash IIA	
G-MVYR	Medway Hybred 44XLR		G-MWCF	Solar Wings Pegasus XL-R	
G-MVYS	Mainair Gemini Flash IIA		G-MWCG	Microflight Spectrum	
G-MVYT	Noble Hardman Snowbird Mk IV		G-MWCH	Rans S.6 Coyote	
			G-MWCI	Powerchute Kestrel	
G-MVYU	Noble Hardman Snowbird Mk IV		G-MWCJ	Powerchute Kestrel	
			G-MWCK	Powerchute Kestrel	
G-MVYV	Noble Hardman Snowbird Mk IV		G-MWCM	Powerchute Kestrel	
			G-MWCN	Powerchute Kestrel	
G-MVYW	Noble Hardman Snowbird Mk IV		G-MWCO	Powerchute Kestrel	
			G-MWCP	Powerchute Kestrel	
G-MVYX	Noble Hardman Snowbird Mk IV		G-MWCR	Southdown Puma Sprint	
			G-MWCS	Powerchute Kestrel	
G-MVYY	Aerial Arts Chaser S508		G-MWCU	Solar Wings Pegasus XL-R	
G-MVYZ	CFM Shadow Srs BD		G-MWCV	Solar Wings Pegasus XL-Q	
G-MVZA	Thruster T.300		G-MWCW	Mainair Gemini Flash IIA	
G-MVZB	Thruster T.300		G-MWCX	Medway Hybred 44XLR	
G-MVZC	Thruster T.300		G-MWCY	Medway Hybred 44XLR	
G-MVZD	Thruster T.300		G-MWCZ	Medway Hybred 44XLR	
G-MVZE	Thruster T.300		G-MWDB	CFM Shadow Srs BD	
G-MVZG	Thruster T.300		G-MWDC	Solar Wings Pegasus XL-R	
G-MVZI	Thruster T.300		G-MWDD	Solar Wings Pegasus XL-Q	
G-MVZJ	Solar Wings Pegasus XL-Q		G-MWDE	Hornet RS-ZA	
G-MVZK	Challenger II		G-MWDF	Hornet RS-ZA	
G-MVZL	Solar Wings Pegasus XL-Q		G-MWDG	Hornet RS-ZA	
G-MVZM	Aerial Arts Chaser S		G-MWDH	Hornet RS-ZA	
G-MVZN	Aerial Arts Chaser S		G-MWDI	Hornet RS-ZA	
G-MVZO	Medway Hybred 44XLR		G-MWDJ	Mainair Gemini Flash IIA	
G-MVZP	Renegade Spirit UK		G-MWDK	Solar Wings Pegasus XL-R	
G-MVZR	Aviasud Mistral		G-MWDL	Solar Wings Pegasus XL-R	
G-MVZS	Mainair Gemini Flash IIA		G-MWDM	Renegade Spirit UK	
G-MVZT	Solar Wings Pegasus XL-Q		G-MWDN	CFM Shadow Srs BD	
G-MVZU	Solar Wings Pegasus XL-Q		G-MWDP	Thruster TST Mk 1	
G-MVZV	Solar Wings Pegasus XL-Q		G-MWDS	Thruster T.300	
G-MVZW	Hornet R-ZA		G-MWDZ	Eipper Quicksilver MXL II	
G-MVZX	Renegade Spirit UK		G-MWEE	Solar Wings Pegasus XL-Q	
G-MVZY	Aerial Arts Chaser S		G-MWEF	Solar Wings Pegasus XL-Q	
G-MVZZ	AMF Chevvron 232		G-MWEG	Solar Wings Pegasus XL-Q	
			G-MWEH	Solar Wings Pegasus XL-Q	
G-MWAB	Mainair Gemini Flash IIA		G-MWEK	Whittaker MW.5 Sorcerer	
G-MWAC	Solar Wings Pegasus XL-Q		G-MWEL	Mainair Gemini Flash IIA	
G-MWAD	Solar Wings Pegasus XL-Q		G-MWEN	CFM Shadow Srs BD	
G-MWAE	CFM Shadow Srs BD		G-MWEO	Whittaker MW.5 Sorcerer	
G-MWAF	Solar Wings Pegasus XL-R		G-MWEP	Rans S.4 Coyote	
G-MWAG	Solar Wings Pegasus XL-R		G-MWER	Solar Wings Pegasus XL-Q	
G-MWAH	Hornet RS-ZA		G-MWES	Rans S.4 Coyote	
G-MWAI	Solar Wings Pegasus XL-R		G-MWEU	Hornet RS-ZA	
G-MWAJ	Renegade Spirit UK		G-MWEY	Hornet RS-ZA	
G-MWAL	Solar Wings Pegasus XL-Q		G-MWEZ	CFM Shadow Srs CD	
G-MWAM	Thruster T.300		G-MWFA	Solar Wings Pegasus XL-R	
G-MWAN	Thruster T.300		G-MWFB	CFM Shadow Srs BD	
G-MWAP	Thruster T.300		G-MWFC	Team Minimax (G-BTXC)	
G-MWAR	Thruster T.300		G-MWFD	Team Minimax	
G-MWAT	Solar Wings Pegasus XL-Q		G-MWFE	Robin 330/Lightning 195	
G-MWAU	Mainair Gemini Flash IIA		G-MWFF	Rans S.4 Coyote	
G-MWAV	Solar Wings Pegasus XL-R		G-MWFH	Powerchute Kestrel	
G-MWAW	Whittaker MW.6 Merlin		G-MWFI	Powerchute Kestrel	
G-MWBH	Hornet RS-ZA		G-MWFL	Powerchute Kestrel	
G-MWBI	Medway Hybred 44XLR		G-MWFP	Solar Wings Pegasus XL-R	
G-MWBJ	Medway Sprint		G-MWFS	Solar Wings Pegasus XL-Q	
G-MWBK	Solar Wings Pegasus XL-Q		G-MWFT	MBA Tiger Cub 440	
G-MWBL	Solar Wings Pegasus XL-Q		G-MWFU	Quad City Challenger II UK	
G-MWBM	Hornet RS-ZA		G-MWFV	Quad City Challenger II UK	
G-MWBO	Rans S.4 Coyote		G-MWFW	Rans S.4 Coyote	
G-MWBP	Hornet RS-ZA		G-MWFX	Quad City Challenger II UK	
G-MWBR	Hornet RS-ZA		G-MWFY	Quad City Challenger II UK	
G-MWBS	Hornet RS-ZA		G-MWFZ	Quad City Challenger II UK	

Reg.	Type	Notes	Reg.	Type	Notes
G-MWGA	Rans S.5 Coyote		G-MWJV	SW Pegasus Quasar	
G-MWGC	Medway Hybred 44XLR		G-MWJW	Whittaker MW.5 Sorcerer	
G-MWGF	Renegade Spirit UK		G-MWJX	Medway Puma Sprint	
G-MWGG	Mainair Gemini Flash IIA		G-MWJY	Mainair Gemini Flash IIA	
G-MWGI	Whittaker MW.5 (K) Sorcerer		G-MWJZ	CFM Shadow Srs CD	
G-MWGJ	Whittaker MW.5 (K) Sorcerer		G-MWKA	Renegade Spirit UK	
			G-MWKE	Hornet R-ZA	
G-MWGK	Whittaker MW.5 (K) Sorcerer		G-MWKO	Solar Wings Pegasus XL-Q	
			G-MWKP	Solar Wings Pegasus XL-Q	
G-MWGL	Solar Wings Pegasus XL-Q		G-MWKW	Microflight Spectrum	
G-MWGM	Solar Wings Pegasus XL-Q		G-MWKX	Microflight Spectrum	
G-MWGN	Rans S.4 Coyote		G-MWKY	Solar Wings Pegasus XL-Q	
G-MWGO	Aerial Arts Chaser 110SX		G-MWKZ	Solar Wings Pegasus XL-Q	
G-MWGR	Solar Wings Pegasus XL-Q		G-MWLA	Rans S.4 Coyote	
G-MWGT	Powerchute Kestrel		G-MWLB	Medway Hybred 44XLR	
G-MWGU	Powerchute Kestrel		G-MWLC	Medway Hybred 44XLR	
G-MWGW	Powerchute Kestrel		G-MWLD	CFM Shadow Srs BD	
G-MWGY	Powerchute Kestrel		G-MWLE	Solar Wings Pegasus XL-R	
G-MWGZ	Powerchute Kestrel		G-MWLF	Solar Wings Pegasus XL-R	
G-MWHC	Solar Wings Pegasus XL-Q		G-MWLG	Solar Wings Pegasus XL-R	
G-MWHD	Microflight Spectrum		G-MWLH	Solar Wings Pegasus XL-R	
G-MWHE	Microflight Spectrum		G-MWLI	SW Pegasus Quasar	
G-MWHF	Solar Wings Pegasus XL-Q		G-MWLJ	SW Pegasus Quasar	
G-MWHG	Solar Wings Pegasus XL-Q		G-MWLK	SW Pegasus Quasar	
G-MWHH	Team Minimax		G-MWLL	Solar Wings Pegasus XL-Q	
G-MWHL	Solar Wings Pegasus XL-Q		G-MWLM	Solar Wings Pegasus XL-Q	
G-MWHM	Whittaker MW.6 Merlin		G-MWLN	Whittaker MW.6-S Fatboy Flyer	
G-MWHO	Mainair Gemini Flash IIA				
G-MWHP	Rans S.6-ESD Coyote		G-MWLO	Whittaker MW.6 Merlin	
G-MWHR	Mainair Gemini Flash IIA		G-MWLP	Mainair Gemini Flash IIA	
G-MWHT	SW Pegasus Quasar		G-MWLR	Mainair Gemini Flash IIA	
G-MWHU	SW Pegasus Quasar		G-MWLS	Medway Hybred 44XLR	
G-MWHV	SW Pegasus Quasar		G-MWLT	Mainair Gemini Flash IIA	
G-MWHW	Solar Wings Pegasus XL-Q		G-MWLU	Solar Wings Pegasus XL-R	
G-MWHX	Solar Wings Pegasus XL-Q		G-MWLW	Team Minimax	
G-MWHZ	Trion J-1		G-MWLX	Mainair Gemini Flash IIA	
G-MWIA	Mainair Gemini Flash IIA		G-MWLZ	Rans S.4 Coyote	
G-MWIB	Aviasud Mistral		G-MWMA	Powerchute Kestrel	
G-MWIC	Whittaker MW.5 Sorcerer		G-MWMB	Powerchute Kestrel	
G-MWIE	Solar Wings Pegasus XL-Q		G-MWMC	Powerchute Kestrel	
G-MWIF	Rans S.6-ESD Coyote II		G-MWMD	Powerchute Kestrel	
G-MWIG	Mainair Gemini Flash IIA		G-MWMF	Powerchute Kestrel	
G-MWIH	Mainair Gemini Flash IIA		G-MWMG	Powerchute Kestrel	
G-MWIK	Medway Hybred 44XLR		G-MWMH	Powerchute Kestrel	
G-MWIL	Medway Hybred 44XLR		G-MWMI	SW Pegasus Quasar	
G-MWIM	SW Pegasus Quasar		G-MWMJ	SW Pegasus Quasar	
G-MWIO	Rans S.4 Coyote		G-MWMK	SW Pegasus Quasar TC	
G-MWIP	Whittaker MW.6 Merlin		G-MWML	SW Pegasus Quasar	
G-MWIR	Solar Wings Pegasus XL-Q		G-MWMM	Mainair Gemini Flash IIA	
G-MWIS	Solar Wings Pegasus XL-Q		G-MWMN	Solar Wings Pegasus XL-Q	
G-MWIT	Solar Wings Pegasus XL-Q		G-MWMO	Solar Wings Pegasus XL-Q	
G-MWIU	Solar Wings Pegasus XL-Q		G-MWMP	Solar Wings Pegasus XL-Q	
G-MWIV	Mainair Gemini Flash IIA		G-MWMR	Solar Wings Pegasus XL-R	
G-MWIW	SW Pegasus Quasar		G-MWMS	Mainair Gemini Flash	
G-MWIX	SW Pegasus Quasar		G-MWMT	Mainair Gemini Flash IIA	
G-MWIY	SW Pegasus Quasar		G-MWMU	CFM Shadow Srs CD	
G-MWIZ	CFM Shadow Srs BD		G-MWMV	Solar Wings Pegasus XL-R	
G-MWJD	SW Pegasus Quasar		G-MWMW	Renegade Spirit UK	
G-MWJF	CFM Shadow Srs BD		G-MWMX	Mainair Gemini Flash IIA	
G-MWJG	Solar Wings Pegasus XL-R		G-MWMY	Mainair Gemini Flash IIA	
G-MWJH	SW Pegasus Quasar		G-MWMZ	Solar Wings Pegasus XL-Q	
G-MWJI	SW Pegasus Quasar		G-MWNA	Solar Wings Pegasus XL-Q	
G-MWJJ	SW Pegasus Quasar		G-MWNB	Solar Wings Pegasus XL-Q	
G-MWJK	SW Pegasus Quasar		G-MWNC	Solar Wings Pegasus XL-Q	
G-MWJM	AMF Chevvron 232		G-MWND	Tiger Cub Developments RL.5A	
G-MWJN	Solar Wings Pegasus XL-Q				
G-MWJO	Solar Wings Pegasus XL-Q		G-MWNE	Mainair Gemini Flash IIA	
G-MWJP	Medway Hybred 44XLR		G-MWNF	Renegade Spirit UK	
G-MWJR	Medway Hybred 44XLR		G-MWNG	Solar Wings Pegasus XL-Q	
G-MWJS	SW Pegasus Quasar		G-MWNK	SW Pegasus Quasar	
G-MWJT	SW Pegasus Quasar		G-MWNL	SW Pegasus Quasar	
G-MWJU	SW Pegasus Quasar		G-MWNM	SW Pegasus Quasar	
			G-MWNN	SW Pegasus Quasar	

Reg.	Type	Notes	Reg.	Type	Notes
G-MWNO	AMF Chevvron 232		G-MWSD	Solar Wings Pegasus XL-Q	
G-MWNP	AMF Chevvron 232		G-MWSE	Solar Wings Pegasus XL-R	
G-MWNR	Renegade Spirit UK		G-MWSF	Solar Wings Pegasus XL-R	
G-MWNS	Mainair Gemini Flash IIA		G-MWSH	SW Pegasus Quasar TC	
G-MWNT	Mainair Gemini Flash IIA		G-MWSI	SW Pegasus Quasar TC	
G-MWNU	Mainair Gemini Flash IIA		G-MWSJ	Solar Wings Pegasus XL-Q	
G-MWNV	Powerchute Kestrel		G-MWSK	Solar Wings Pegasus XL-Q	
G-MWNX	Powerchute Kestrel		G-MWSL	Mainair Gemini Flash IIA	
G-MWOB	Powerchute Kestrel		G-MWSM	Mainair Gemini Flash IIA	
G-MWOC	Powerchute Kestrel		G-MWSN	SW Pegasus Quasar TC	
G-MWOD	Powerchute Kestrel		G-MWSO	Solar Wings Pegasus XL-R	
G-MWOE	Powerchute Kestrel		G-MWSP	Solar Wings Pegasus XL-R	
G-MWOF	Microflight Spectrum		G-MWSR	Solar Wings Pegasus XL-R	
G-MWOH	Solar Wings Pegasus XL-R		G-MWSS	Medway Hybred 44XLR	
G-MWOI	Solar Wings Pegasus XL-R		G-MWST	Medway Hybred 44XLR	
G-MWOJ	Mainair Gemini Flash IIA		G-MWSU	Medway Hybred 44XLR	
G-MWOK	Mainair Gemini Flash IIA		G-MWSV	SW Pegasus Quasar TC	
G-MWOL	Mainair Gemini Flash IIA		G-MWSW	Whittaker MW.6 Merlin	
G-MWOM	SW Pegasus Quasar TC		G-MWSX	Whittaker MW.5 Sorcerer	
G-MWON	CFM Shadow Srs CD		G-MWSY	Whittaker MW.5 Sorcerer	
G-MWOO	Renegade Spirit UK		G-MWSZ	CFM Shadow Srs CD	
G-MWOP	SW Pegasus Quasar		G-MWTA	Solar Wings Pegasus XL-Q	
G-MWOR	Solar Wings Pegasus XL-Q		G-MWTB	Solar Wings Pegasus XL-Q	
G-MWOS	Cosmos Chronos		G-MWTC	Solar Wings Pegasus XL-Q	
G-MWOV	Whittaker MW.6 Merlin		G-MWTD	Microflight Spectrum	
G-MWOX	Solar Wings Pegasus XL-Q		G-MWTE	Microflight Spectrum	
G-MWOY	Solar Wings Pegasus XL-Q		G-MWTG	Mainair Gemini Flash IIA	
G-MWPA	Mainair Gemini Flash IIA		G-MWTH	Mainair Gemini Flash IIA	
G-MWPB	Mainair Gemini Flash IIA		G-MWTI	Solar Wings Pegasus XL-Q	
G-MWPC	Mainair Gemini Flash IIA		G-MWTJ	CFM Shadow Srs CD	
G-MWPD	Mainair Gemini Flash IIA		G-MWTK	Solar Wings Pegasus XL-R	
G-MWPE	Solar Wings Pegasus XL-Q		G-MWTL	Solar Wings Pegasus XL-R	
G-MWPF	Mainair Gemini Flash IIA		G-MWTM	Solar Wings Pegasus XL-R	
G-MWPG	Microflight Spectrum		G-MWTN	CFM Shadow Srs CD	
G-MWPH	Microflight Spectrum		G-MWTO	Mainair Gemini Flash IIA	
G-MWPJ	Solar Wings Pegasus XL-Q		G-MWTP	CFM Shadow Srs CD	
G-MWPK	Solar Wings Pegasus XL-Q		G-MWTR	Mainair Gemini Flash IIA	
G-MWPL	MBA Tiger Cub 440		G-MWTT	Rans S.6-ESD Coyote II	
G-MWPO	Mainair Gemini Flash IIA		G-MWTU	Solar Wings Pegasus XL-R	
G-MWPP	CFM Streak Shadow		G-MWTY	Mainair Gemini Flash IIA	
	(G-BTEM)		G-MWTZ	Mainair Gemini Flash IIA	
G-MWPR	Whittaker MW.6 Merlin		G-MWUA	CFM Shadow Srs CD	
G-MWPS	Renegade Spirit UK		G-MWUB	Solar Wings Pegasus XL-R	
G-MWPT	Hunt Wing		G-MWUC	Solar Wings Pegasus XL-R	
G-MWPU	SW Pegasus Quasar TC		G-MWUD	Solar Wings Pegasus XL-R	
G-MWPX	Solar Wings Pegasus XL-R		G-MWUF	Solar Wings Pegasus XL-R	
G-MWPZ	Renegade Spirit UK		G-MWUH	Renegade Spirit UK	
G-MWRB	Mainair Gemini Flash IIA		G-MWUI	AMF Chevvron 2-32C	
G-MWRC	Mainair Gemini Flash IIA		G-MWUK	Rans S.6-ESD Coyote II	
G-MWRD	Mainair Gemini Flash IIA		G-MWUL	Rans S.6-ESD Coyote II	
G-MWRE	Mainair Gemini Flash IIA		G-MWUO	Solar Wings Pegasus XL-Q	
G-MWRF	Mainair Gemini Flash IIA		G-MWUP	Solar Wings Pegasus XL-R	
G-MWRG	Mainair Gemini Flash IIA		G-MWUR	Solar Wings Pegasus XL-R	
G-MWRH	Mainair Gemini Flash IIA		G-MWUS	Solar Wings Pegasus XL-R	
G-MWRI	Mainair Gemini Flash IIA		G-MWUU	Solar Wings Pegasus XL-R	
G-MWRJ	Mainair Gemini Flash IIA		G-MWUV	Solar Wings Pegasus XL-R	
G-MWRL	CFM Shadow Srs CD		G-MWUW	Solar Wings Pegasus XL-R	
G-MWRM	Medway Hybred 44XLR		G-MWUX	Solar Wings Pegasus XL-Q	
G-MWRN	Solar Wings Pegasus XL-R		G-MWUY	Solar Wings Pegasus XL-Q	
G-MWRO	Solar Wings Pegasus XL-R		G-MWUZ	Solar Wings Pegasus XL-Q	
G-MWRP	Solar Wings Pegasus XL-R		G-MWVA	Solar Wings Pegasus XL-Q	
G-MWRR	Mainair Gemini Flash IIA		G-MWVB	Solar Wings Pegasus XL-R	
G-MWRS	Ultravia Super Pelican		G-MWVE	Solar Wings Pegasus XL-R	
G-MWRT	Solar Wings Pegasus XL-R		G-MWVF	Solar Wings Pegasus XL-R	
G-MWRU	Solar Wings Pegasus XL-R		G-MWVG	CFM Shadow Srs CD	
G-MWRV	Solar Wings Pegasus XL-R		G-MWVH	CFM Shadow Srs CD	
G-MWRW	Solar Wings Pegasus XL-Q		G-MWVK	Mainair Mercury	
G-MWRX	Solar Wings Pegasus XL-Q		G-MWVL	Rans S.6-ESD Coyote II	
G-MWRY	CFM Shadow Srs CD		G-MWVM	SW Pegasus Quasar II	
G-MWRZ	AMF Chevvron 232		G-MWVN	Mainair Gemini Flash IIA	
G-MWSA	Team Minimax		G-MWVO	Mainair Gemini Flash IIA	
G-MWSB	Mainair Gemini Flash IIA		G-MWVP	Renegade Spirit UK	
G-MWSC	Rans S.6-ESD Coyote II		G-MWVS	Mainair Gemini Flash IIA	

Reg.	Type	Notes	Reg.	Type	Notes
G-MWVT	Mainair Gemini Flash IIA		G-MWZI	Solar Wings Pegasus XL-R	
G-MWVU	Medway Hybred 44XLR		G-MWZJ	Solar Wings Pegasus XL-R	
G-MWVW	Mainair Gemini Flash IIA		G-MWZK	Solar Wings Pegasus XL-R	
G-MWVY	Mainair Gemini Flash IIA		G-MWZL	Mainair Gemini Flash IIA	
G-MWVZ	Mainair Gemini Flash IIA		G-MWZM	Team Minimax 91	
G-MWWB	Mainair Gemini Flash IIA		G-MWZN	Mainair Gemini Flash IIA	
G-MWWC	Mainair Gemini Flash IIA		G-MWZO	SW Pegasus Quasar IITC	
G-MWWD	Renegade Spirit		G-MWZP	SW Pegasus Quasar IITC	
G-MWWE	Team Minimax		G-MWZR	SW Pegasus Quasar IITC	
G-MWWF	Kolb Twinstar Mk 3		G-MWZS	SW Pegasus Quasar IITC	
G-MWWG	Solar Wings Pegasus XL-Q		G-MWZT	Solar Wings Pegasus XL-R	
G-MWWH	Solar Wings Pegasus XL-Q		G-MWZU	Solar Wings Pegasus XL-R	
G-MWWI	Mainair Gemini Flash IIA		G-MWZV	Solar Wings Pegasus XL-R	
G-MWWJ	Mainair Gemini Flash IIA		G-MWZX	Solar Wings Pegasus XL-R	
G-MWWK	Mainair Gemini Flash IIA		G-MWZY	Solar Wings Pegasus XL-R	
G-MWWL	Rans S.6-ESD Coyote II		G-MWZZ	Solar Wings Pegasus XL-R	
G-MWWM	Kolb Twinstar Mk 2				
G-MWWN	Mainair Gemini Flash IIA		G-MYAB	Solar Wings Pegasus XL-R	
G-MWWP	Rans S.4 Coyote		G-MYAC	Solar Wings Pegasus XL-Q	
G-MWVR	Mainair Gemini Flash IIA		G-MYAD	Solar Wings Pegasus XL-Q	
G-MWWR	Microflight Spectrum		G-MYAE	Solar Wings Pegasus XL-Q	
G-MWWS	Thruster T.300		G-MYAF	Solar Wings Pegasus XL-Q	
G-MWWU	Air Creation Fun 18 GTBI		G-MYAG	Quad City Challenger II	
G-MWWV	Solar Wings Pegasus XL-Q		G-MYAH	Whittaker MW.5 Sorcerer	
G-MWWW	Whittaker MW.6-S Fatboy Flyer		G-MYAI	Mainair Mercury	
			G-MYAJ	Rans S.6-ESD Coyote II	
G-MWWZ	Cyclone Chaser S		G-MYAK	SW Pegasus Quasar IITC	
G-MWXB	Mainair Gemini Flash IIA		G-MYAM	Renegade Spirit UK	
G-MWXC	Mainair Gemini Flash IIA		G-MYAN	Whittaker MW.5 (K) Sorcerer	
G-MWXE	Flexiform Skytrike				
G-MWXF	Mainair Mercury		G-MYAO	Mainair Gemini Flash IIA	
G-MWXG	SW Pegasus Quasar IITC		G-MYAP	Thruster T.300	
G-MWXH	SW Pegasus Quasar IITC		G-MYAR	Thruster T.300	
G-MWXJ	Mainair Mercury		G-MYAS	Mainair Gemini Flash IIA	
G-MWXK	Mainair Mercury		G-MYAT	Team Minimax	
G-MWXL	Mainair Gemini Flash IIA		G-MYAU	Mainair Gemini Flash IIA	
G-MWXN	Mainair Gemini Flash IIA		G-MYAV	Mainair Mercury	
G-MWXO	Mainair Gemini Flash IIA		G-MYAY	Microflight Spectrum	
G-MWXP	Solar Wings Pegasus XL-Q		G-MYAZ	Renegade Spirit UK	
G-MWXR	Solar Wings Pegasus XL-Q		G-MYBA	Rans S.6-ESD Coyote II	
G-MWXU	Mainair Gemini Flash IIA		G-MYBB	Maxair Drifter	
G-MWXV	Mainair Gemini Flash IIA		G-MYBC	CFM Shadow Srs CD	
G-MWXW	Cyclone Chaser S		G-MYBD	SW Pegasus Quaser IITC	
G-MWXX	Cyclone Chaser S 447		G-MYBE	SW Pegasus Quasar IITC	
G-MWXY	Cyclone Chaser S 447		G-MYBF	Solar Wings Pegasus XL-Q	
G-MWXZ	Cyclone Chaser S 508		G-MYBG	Solar Wings Pegasus XL-Q	
G-MWYA	Mainair Gemini Flash IIA		G-MYBI	Rans S.6-ESD Coyote II	
G-MWYB	Solar Wings Pegasus XL-Q		G-MYBJ	Mainair Gemini Flash IIA	
G-MWYC	Solar Wings Pegasus XL-Q		G-MYBK	SW Pegasus Quasar IITC	
G-MWYD	CFM Shadow Srs C		G-MYBL	CFM Shadow Srs C	
G-MWYE	Rans S.6 Coyote II		G-MYBM	Team Minimax	
G-MWYF	Rans S.6 Coyote II		G-MYBN	Hiway Demon 175	
G-MWYG	Mainair Gemini Flash IIA		G-MYBO	Solar Wings Pegasus XL-R	
G-MWYH	Mainair Gemini Flash IIA		G-MYBP	Solar Wings Pegasus XL-R	
G-MWYI	SW Pegasus Quasar II		G-MYBR	Solar Wings Pegasus XL-Q	
G-MWYJ	SW Pegasus Quasar IITC		G-MYBS	Solar Wings Pegasus XL-Q	
G-MWYL	Mainair Gemini Flash IIA		G-MYBT	SW Pegasus Quasar IITC	
G-MWYM	Cyclone Chaser S 1000		G-MYBU	Cyclone Chaser S447	
G-MWYS	CGS Hawk 1 Arrow		G-MYBV	Solar Wings Pegasus XL-Q	
G-MWYT	Mainair Gemini Flash IIA		G-MYBW	Solar Wings Pegasus XL-Q	
G-MWYU	Solar Wings Pegasus XL-Q		G-MYBY	Solar Wings Pegasus XL-Q	
G-MWYV	Mainair Gemini Flash IIA		G-MYBZ	Solar Wings Pegasus XL-Q	
G-MWYX	Mainair Gemini Flash IIA		G-MYCA	Whittaker MW.6 Merlin	
G-MWYY	Mainair Gemini Flash IIA		G-MYCB	Cyclone Chaser S 447	
G-MWYZ	Solar Wings Pegasus XL-Q		G-MYCE	SW Pegasus Quasar IITC	
G-MWZA	Mainair Mercury		G-MYCF	SW Pegasus Quasar IITC	
G-MWZB	AMF Chevvron 2-32C		G-MYCJ	Mainair Mercury	
G-MWZC	Mainair Gemini Flash IIA		G-MYCK	Mainair Gemini Flash IIA	
G-MWZD	SW Pegasus Quasar IITC		G-MYCL	Mainair Mercury	
G-MWZE	SW Pegasus Quasar IITC		G-MYCM	CFM Shadow Srs CD	
G-MWZF	SW Pegasus Quasar IITC		G-MYCN	Mainair Mercury	
G-MWZG	Mainair Gemini Flash IIA		G-MYCO	Renegade Spirit UK	
G-MWZH	Solar Wings Pegasus XL-R		G-MYCP	Whittaker MW.6 Merlin	

Reg.	Type	Notes	Reg.	Type	Notes
G-MYCR	Mainair Gemini Flash IIA		G-MYGG	Mainair Mercury	
G-MYCS	Mainair Gemini Flash IIA		G-MYGH	Rans S.6-ESD Coyote II	
G-MYCT	Team Minimax		G-MYGI	Cyclone Chaser S 447	
G-MYCV	Mainair Mercury		G-MYGJ	Mainair Mercury	
G-MYCW	Powerchute Kestrel		G-MYGK	Cyclone Chaser S 508	
G-MYCX	Powerchute Kestrel		G-MYGL	Team Minimax	
G-MYCY	Powerchute Kestrel		G-MYGM	Quad City Challenger II	
G-MYDA	Powerchute Kestrel		G-MYGO	CFM Shadow Srs CD	
G-MYDB	Powerchute Kestrel		G-MYGP	Rans S.6-ESD Coyote II	
G-MYDC	Mainair Mercury		G-MYGR	Rans S.6-ESD Coyote II	
G-MYDD	CFM Shadow Srs CD		G-MYGS	Whittaker MW.5 (K)	
G-MYDE	CFM Shadow Srs CD			Sorcerer	
G-MYDF	Team Minimax		G-MYGT	Solar Wings Pegasus XL-R	
G-MYDG	Solar Wings Pegasus XL-R		G-MYGU	Solar Wings Pegasus XL-R	
G-MYDI	Solar Wings Pegasus XL-R		G-MYGV	Solar Wings Pegasus XL-R	
G-MYDJ	Solar Wings Pegasus XL-R		G-MYGZ	Mainair Gemini Flash IIA	
G-MYDK	Rans S.6-ESD Coyote II		G-MYHF	Mainair Gemini Flash IIA	
G-MYDL	Whittaker MW.5 (K)		G-MYHG	Cyclone AX/503	
	Sorcerer		G-MYHH	Cyclone AX/503	
G-MYDM	Whittaker MW.6-S Fatboy		G-MYHI	Rans S.6-ESD Coyote II	
	Flyer		G-MYHK	Rans S.6-ESD Coyote II	
G-MYDN	Quad City Challenger II		G-MYHL	Mainair Gemini Flash IIA	
G-MYDO	Rans S.5 Coyote		G-MYHM	Cyclone AX3/503	
G-MYDP	Kolb Twinstar Mk 3		G-MYHN	Mainair Gemini Flash IIA	
G-MYDR	Thruster Tn.300		G-MYHP	Rans S.6-ESD Coyote II	
G-MYDS	Quad City Challenger II		G-MYHR	Cyclone AX3/503	
G-MYDU	Thruster T.300		G-MYHS	Powerchute Kestrel	
G-MYDV	Thruster T.300		G-MYHX	Mainair Gemini Flash IIA	
G-MYDW	Whittaker MW.6 Merlin		G-MYIA	Quad City Challenger II	
G-MYDX	Rans S.6-ESD Coyote II		G-MYIE	Whittaker MW.6 Merlin	
G-MYDZ	Mignet HM.1000 Balerit		G-MYIF	CFM Shadow Srs CD	
G-MYEA	Solar Wings Pegasus XL-Q		G-MYIH	Mainair Gemini Flash IIA	
G-MYEC	Solar Wings Pegasus XL-Q		G-MYII	Team Minimax	
G-MYED	Solar Wings Pegasus XL-R		G-MYIJ	Cyclone AX3/503	
G-MYEG	Solar Wings Pegasus XL-R		G-MYIK	Kolb Twinstar Mk 3	
G-MYEH	Solar Wings Pegasus XL-R		G-MYIL	Cyclone Chaser S 508	
G-MYEI	Cyclone Chaser S447		G-MYIN	SW Pegasus Quasar IITC	
G-MYEJ	Cyclone Chaser S447		G-MYIO	SW Pegasus Quasar IITC	
G-MYEK	SW Pegasus Quasar IITC		G-MYIP	CFM Shadow Srs CD	
G-MYEL	SW Pegasus Quasar IITC		G-MYIR	Rans S.6-ESD Coyote II	
G-MYEM	SW Pegasus Quasar IITC		G-MYIS	Rans S.6-ESD Coyote II	
G-MYEN	SW Pegasus Quasar IITC		G-MYIT	Cyclone Chaser S 508	
G-MYEO	SW Pegasus Quasar IITC		G-MYIU	Cyclone AX3/503	
G-MYEP	CFM Shadow Srs CD		G-MYIV	Mainair Gemini Flash IIA	
G-MYER	Cyclone AX3/503		G-MYIW	Mainair Mercury	
G-MYES	Rans S.6-ESD Coyote II		G-MYIX	Quad City Challenger II	
G-MYET	Whittaker MW.6 Merlin		G-MYIY	Mainair Gemini Flash IIA	
G-MYEU	Mainair Gemini Flash IIA		G-MYIZ	Team Minimax 2	
G-MYEV	Whittaker MW.6 Merlin		G-MYJA	—	
G-MYEW	Powerchute Kestrel		G-MYJB	Mainair Gemini Flash IIA	
G-MYEX	Powerchute Kestrel		G-MYJC	Mainair Gemini Flash IIA	
G-MYFA	Powerchute Kestrel		G-MYJD	Rans S.6-ESD Coyote II	
G-MYFE	Rans S.6-ESD Coyote II		G-MYJF	Thruster T.300	
G-MYFG	Hunt Avon Skytrike		G-MYJG	Thruster Super T.300	
G-MYFH	Quad City Challenger II		G-MYJH	Thruster Super T.300	
G-MYFI	Cyclone AX3/503		G-MYJJ	SW Pegasus Quasar IITC	
G-MYFL	SW Pegasus Quasar IITC		G-MYJK	SW Pegasus Quasar IITC	
G-MYFM	Renegade Spirit UK		G-MYJL	Rans S.6-ESD Coyote II	
G-MYFN	Rans S.5 Coyote		G-MYJM	Mainair Gemini Flash IIA	
G-MYFO	Cyclone Chaser S		G-MYJN	Mainair Mercury	
G-MYFP	Mainair Gemini Flash IIA		G-MYJO	Cyclone Chaser S 508	
G-MYFR	Mainair Gemini Flash IIA		G-MYJP	Renegade Spirit UK	
G-MYFT	Mainair Scorcher		G-MYJR	Mainair Mercury	
G-MYFU	Mainair Gemini Flash IIA		G-MYJS	SW Pegasus Quasar IITC	
G-MYFV	Cyclone AX3/503		G-MYJT	SW Pegasus Quasar IITC	
G-MYFW	Cyclone AX3/503		G-MYJU	SW Pegasus Quasar IITC	
G-MYFX	Solar Wings Pegasus XL-Q		G-MYJW	Cyclone Chaser S 508	
G-MYFY	Cyclone AX3/503		G-MYJY	Rans S.6-ESD Coyote II	
G-MYFZ	Cyclone AX3/503		G-MYJZ	Whittaker MW.5D Sorcerer	
			G-MYKA	Cyclone AX3/503	
G-MYGD	Cyclone AX3/503		G-MYKB	Kōlb Twinstar Mk 3	
G-MYGE	Whittaker MW.6 Merlin		G-MYKC	Mainair Gemini Flash IIA	
G-MYGF	Team Minimax		G-MYKD	Cyclone Chaser S 447	

MICROLIGHTS

Reg.	Type	Notes	Reg.	Type	Notes
G-MYKE	CFM Shadow Srs BD		G-MYNI	Team Minimax	
G-MYKF	Cyclone AX3/503		G-MYNJ	Mainair Mercury	
G-MYKG	Mainair Gemini Flash IIA		G-MYNK	SW Pegasus Quantum 15	
G-MYKH	Mainair Gemini Flash IIA		G-MYNL	SW Pegasus Quantum 15	
G-MYKI	Mainair Mercury		G-MYNN	SW Pegasus Quantum 15	
G-MYKJ	Team Minimax		G-MYNO	SW Pegasus Quantum 15	
G-MYKL	Medway Raven		G-MYNP	SW Pegasus Quantum 15	
G-MYKN	Rans S.6-ESD Coyote II		G-MYNR	SW Pegasus Quantum 15	
G-MYKO	Whittaker MW.6-S Fat Boy Flyer		G-MYNS	SW Pegasus Quantum 15	
			G-MYNT	SW Pegasus Quantum 15	
G-MYKP	SW Pegasus Quasar IITC		G-MYNV	SW Pegasus Quantum 15	
G-MYKR	SW Pegasus Quasar IITC		G-MYNX	CFM Streak Shadow Srs S-A1	
G-MYKS	SW Pegasus Quasar IITC				
G-MYKT	Cyclone AX3/503		G-MYNY	Kölb Twinstar Mk 3	
G-MYKV	Mainair Gemini Flash IIA		G-MYNZ	SW Pegasus Quantum 15	
G-MYKW	Mainair Mercury		G-MYOA	Rans S.6-ESD Coyote II	
G-MYKX	Mainair Mercury		G-MYOB	Mainair Mercury	
G-MYKY	Mainair Mercury		G-MYOF	Mainair Mercury	
G-MYKZ	Team Minimax (G-BVAV)		G-MYOG	Kölb Twinstar Mk 3	
G-MYLB	Team Minimax		G-MYOH	CFM Shadow Srs CD	
G-MYLC	SW Pegasus Quantum 15		G-MYOI	Rans S.6-ESD Coyote II	
G-MYLD	Rans S.6-ESD Coyote II		G-MYOL	Air Creation Fun 18S GTBIS	
G-MYLE	SW Pegasus Quantum 15				
G-MYLF	Rans S.6-ESD Coyote II		G-MYOM	Mainair Gemini Flash IIA	
G-MYLG	Mainair Gemini Flash IIA		G-MYON	CFM Shadow Srs CD	
G-MYLH	SW Pegasus Quantum 15		G-MYOO	Kölb Twinstar Mk 3	
G-MYLI	SW Pegasus Quantum 15		G-MYOR	Kölb Twinstar Mk 3	
G-MYLJ	Cyclone Chaser S 447		G-MYOT	Rans S.6-ESD Coyote II	
G-MYLK	SW Pegasus Quantum 15		G-MYOU	SW Pegasus Quantum 15	
G-MYLL	SW Pegasus Quantum 15		G-MYOV	Mainair Mercury	
G-MYLM	SW Pegasus Quasar IITC		G-MYOW	Mainair Gemini Flash IIA	
G-MYLN	Kölb Twinstar Mk 3		G-MYOX	Mainair Mercury	
G-MYLO	Rans S.6-ESD Coyote II		G-MYOY	Cyclone AX3/503	
G-MYLP	Kölb Twinstar Mk 3 (G-BVCR)		G-MYOZ	Quad City Challenger II UK	
			G-MYPA	Rans S.6-ESD Coyote II	
G-MYLR	Mainair Gemini Flash IIA		G-MYPB	Cyclone Chaser S 447	
G-MYLS	Mainair Mercury		G-MYPC	Kölb Twinstar Mk 3	
G-MYLT	Mainair Blade		G-MYPD	Mainair Mercury	
G-MYLU	Experience/Hunt Wing		G-MYPE	Mainair Gemini Flash IIA	
G-MYLV	CFM Shadow Srs CD		G-MYPG	SW Pegasus XL-Q	
G-MYLW	Rans S.6-ESD Coyote II		G-MYPH	SW Pegasus Quantum 15	
G-MYLX	Medway Raven		G-MYPI	SW Pegasus Quantum 15	
G-MYLY	Medway Raven		G-MYPJ	Rans S.6-ESD Coyote II	
G-MYLZ	SW Pegasus Quantum 15		G-MYPK	Rans S.6-ESD Coyote II	
G-MYMB	SW Pegasus Quantum 15		G-MYPL	CFM Shadow Srs CD	
G-MYMC	SW Pegasus Quantum 15		G-MYPM	Cyclone AX3/503	
G-MYME	Cyclone AX3/503		G-MYPN	SW Pegasus Quantum 15	
G-MYMF	Cyclone AX3/503		G-MYPO	Hunt Wing/Experience	
G-MYMH	Rans S.6-ESD Coyote II		G-MYPR	Cyclone AX3/503	
G-MYMI	Kölb Twinstar Mk 3		G-MYPS	Whittaker MW.6 Merlin	
G-MYMJ	Medway Raven		G-MYPT	CFM Shadow Srs CD	
G-MYMK	Mainair Gemini Flash IIA		G-MYPV	Mainair Mercury	
G-MYML	Mainair Mercury		G-MYPW	Mainair Gemini Flash IIA	
G-MYMM	Ultraflight Fun 18S		G-MYPX	SW Pegasus Quantum 15	
G-MYMN	Whittaker MW.6 Merlin		G-MYPY	SW Pegasus Quantum 15	
G-MYMO	Mainair Gemini Flash IIA		G-MYPZ	Quad City Challenger II	
G-MYMP	Rans S.6-ESD Coyote II (G-CHAZ)		G-MYRA	Kölb Twinstar Mk 3	
			G-MYRB	Whittaker MW.5 Sorcerer	
G-MYMR	Rans S.6-ESD Coyote II		G-MYRC	Mainair Blade	
G-MYMS	Rans S.6-ESD Coyote II		G-MYRD	Mainair Blade	
G-MYMT	Mainair Mercury		G-MYRE	Cyclone Chaser S	
G-MYMV	Mainair Gemini Flash IIA		G-MYRF	SW Pegasus Quantum 15	
G-MYMW	Cyclone AX3/503		G-MYRG	Team Minimax	
G-MYMX	SW Pegasus Quantum 15		G-MYRH	Quad City Challenger II	
G-MYMY	Cyclone Chaser S 508		G-MYRI	Medway 44XLR	
G-MYMZ	Cyclone AX3/503		G-MYRJ	Quad City Challenger II	
G-MYNA	CFM Shadow Srs BD		G-MYRK	Renegade Spirit UK	
G-MYNB	SW Pegasus Quantum 15		G-MYRL	Team Minimax	
G-MYNC	Mainair Mercury		G-MYRM	SW Pegasus Quantum 15	
G-MYND	Mainair Gemini Flash IIA		G-MYRN	SW Pegasus Quantum 15	
G-MYNE	Rans S.6-ESD Coyote II		G-MYRO	Cyclone AX3/503	
G-MYNF	Mainair Mercury		G-MYRP	Letov LK-2M Sluka	
G-MYNH	Rans S.6-ESD Coyote II		G-MYRR	Letov LK-2M Sluka	

Reg.	Type	Notes	Reg.	Type	Notes
G-MYRS	SW Pegasus Quantum 15		G-MYVB	Mainair Blade	
G-MYRT	SW Pegasus Quantum 15		G-MYVC	Pegasus Quantum 15	
G-MYRU	Cyclone AX3/503		G-MYVE	Mainair Blade	
G-MYRV	Cyclone AX3/503		G-MYVF	Pegasus Quantum 15	
G-MYRW	Mainair Mercury		G-MYVG	Letov LK-2M Sluka	
G-MYRY	SW Pegasus Quantum 15		G-MYVH	Mainair Mercury	
G-MYRZ	SW Pegasus Quantum 15		G-MYVI	Air Creation Fun 18S	
G-MYSA	Cyclone Chaser S 508			GTBIS	
G-MYSB	SW Pegasus Quantum 15		G-MYVJ	Pegasus Quantum 15	
G-MYSC	SW Pegasus Quantum 15		G-MYVK	Pegasus Quantum 15	
G-MYSD	Quad City Challenger II		G-MYVM	Pegasus Quantum 15	
G-MYSG	Mainair Mercury		G-MYVN	Cyclone AX3/503	
G-MYSI	HM14/93		G-MYVO	Mainair Blade	
G-MYSJ	Mainair Gemini Flash IIA		G-MYVP	Rans S.6-ESD Coyote II	
G-MYSK	Team Minimax		G-MYVR	Pegasus Quantum 15	
G-MYSL	Aviasud Mistral		G-MYVS	Mainair Mercury	
G-MYSM	CFM Shadow Srs CD		G-MYVT	Letov LK-2M Sluka	
G-MYSN	Whittaker MW.6 Merlin		G-MYVU	Medway Raven	
G-MYSO	Cyclone AX3/503		G-MYVV	Medway Hybred 44XLR	
G-MYSP	Rans S.6-ESD Coyote II		G-MYVW	Medway Raven	
G-MYSR	SW Pegasus Quatum 15		G-MYVX	Medway Hybred 44XLR	
G-MYSU	Rans S.6-ESD Coyote II		G-MYVY	Mainair Blade	
G-MYSV	Aerial Arts Chaser		G-MYVZ	Mainair Blade	
G-MYSW	SW Pegasus Quantum 15		G-MYWA	Mainair Mercury	
G-MYSX	SW Pegasus Quantum 15		G-MYWC	Hunt Wing	
G-MYSY	SW Pegasus Quantum 15		G-MYWD	Thruster T.600	
G-MYSZ	Mainair Mercury		G-MYWE	Thruster T.600	
G-MYTA	Team Minimax		G-MYWF	CFM Shadow Srs CD	
G-MYTB	Mainair Mercury		G-MYWG	Pegasus Quantum 15	
G-MYTC	SW Pegasus XL-Q		G-MYWH	Hunt Wing/Experience	
G-MYTD	Mainair Blade		G-MYWI	Pegasus Quantum 15	
G-MYTE	Rans S.6-ESD Coyote II		G-MYWJ	Pegasus Quantum 15	
G-MYTG	Mainair Blade		G-MYWK	Pegasus Quantum 15	
G-MYTH	CFM Shadow Srs CD		G-MYWL	Pegasus Quantum 15	
G-MYTI	Pegasus Quantum 15		G-MYWM	CFM Shadow Srs CD	
G-MYTJ	SW Pegasus Quantum 15		G-MYWN	Cyclone Chaser S 508	
G-MYTK	Mainair Mercury		G-MYWO	Pegasus Quantum 15	
G-MYTL	Mainair Blade		G-MYWP	Kolb Twinstar Mk 3	
G-MYTM	Cyclone AX3/503		G-MYWR	Pegasus Quantum 15	
G-MYTN	SW Pegasus Quantum 15		G-MYWS	Cyclone Chaser S 447	
G-MYTO	Quad City Challenger II		G-MYWT	Pegasus Quantum 15	
G-MYTP	Arrowflight Hawk II		G-MYWU	Pegasus Quantum 15	
G-MYTR	Pegasus Quantum 15		G-MYWV	Rans S.4 Coyote	
G-MYTT	Quad City Challenger II		G-MYWW	Pegasus Quantum 15	
G-MYTU	Mainair Blade		G-MYWX	Pegasus Quantum 15	
G-MYTV	Hunt Avon Skytrike		G-MYWY	Pegasus Quantum 15	
G-MYTW	Mainair Blade		G-MYWZ	Thruster TST Mk 1	
G-MYTX	Mainair Mercury		G-MYXA	Team Minimax 91	
G-MYTY	CFM Streak Shadow Srs M		G-MYXB	Rans S.6-ESD Coyote II	
G-MYTZ	Air Creation Fun 18S		G-MYXC	Quad City Challenger II	
	GTBIS		G-MYXD	Pegasus Quasar IITC	
G-MYUA	Air Creation Fun 18S		G-MYXE	Pegasus Quantum 15	
	GTBIS		G-MYXF	Air Creation Fun GT503	
G-MYUB	Mainair Mercury		G-MYXG	Rans S.6-ESD Coyote II	
G-MYUC	Mainair Blade		G-MYXH	Cyclone AX3/503	
G-MYUD	Mainair Mercury		G-MYXI	Aries 1	
G-MYUE	Mainair Mercury		G-MYXJ	Mainair Blade	
G-MYUF	Renegade Spirit		G-MYXK	Quad City Challenger II	
G-MYUH	SW Pegasus XL-Q		G-MYXL	Mignet HM.1000 Balerit	
G-MYUK	Mainair Mercury		G-MYXM	Mainair Blade	
G-MYUL	Quad City Challenger II		G-MYXN	Mainair Blade	
G-MYUM	Mainair Blade		G-MYXO	Letov LK-2M Sluka	
G-MYUN	Mainair Blade		G-MYXP	Rans S.6-ESD Coyote II	
G-MYUO	Pegasus Quantum 15		G-MYXR	Renegade Spirit UK	
G-MYUP	Letov LK-2M Sluka		G-MYXS	Kolb Twinstar Mk 3	
G-MYUR	Hunt Wing		G-MYXT	Pegasus Quantum 15	
G-MYUS	CFM Shadow Srs CD		G-MYXU	Thruster T.300	
G-MYUT	Hunt Wing		G-MYXV	Quad City Challenger II	
G-MYUU	Pegasus Quantum 15		G-MYXW	Pegasus Quantum 15	
G-MYUV	Pegasus Quantum 15		G-MYXX	Pegasus Quantum 15	
G-MYUW	Mainair Mercury		G-MYXY	CFM Shadow Srs CD	
G-MYUZ	Rans S.6-ESD Coyote II		G-MYXZ	Pegasus Quantum 15	
G-MYVA	Kolb Twinstar Mk 3		G-MYYA	Mainair Blade	

Reg.	Type	Notes	Reg.	Type	Notes
G-MYYB	Pegasus Quantum 15		G-MZBH	Rans S.6-ESD Coyote II	
G-MYYC	Pegasus Quantum 15		G-MZBI	Pegasus Quantum 15	
G-MYYD	Cyclone Chaser S 447		G-MZBK	Letov LK-2M Sluka	
G-MYYF	Quad City Challenger II		G-MZBL	Mainair Blade	
G-MYYG	Mainair Blade		G-MZBM	Pegasus Quantum 15	
G-MYYH	Mainair Blade		G-MZBN	CFM Shadow Srs BD	
G-MYYI	Pegasus Quantum 15		G-MZBO	Pegasus Quantum 15	
G-MYYJ	Hunt Wing		G-MZBR	Southdown Raven	
G-MYYK	Pegasus Quantum 15		G-MZBS	CFM Shadow Srs D	
G-MYYL	Cyclone AX3/503		G-MZBT	Pegasus Quantum 15	
G-MYYM	Microchute Motor 27		G-MZBU	Rans S.6-ESD Coyote II	
G-MYYN	Pegasus Quantum 15		G-MZBV	Rans S.6-ESD Coyote II	
G-MYYO	Medway Raven X		G-MZBW	Quad City Challenger II UK	
G-MYYP	AMF Chevvron 2-45CS		G-MZBX	Whittaker MW.6-S Fatboy Flyer	
G-MYYR	Team Minimax 91		G-MZBY	Pegasus Quantum 15	
G-MYYS	Team Minimax		G-MZBZ	Quad City Challenger II UK	
G-MYYU	Mainair Mercury		G-MZCA	Rans S.6-ESD Coyote II	
G-MYYV	Rans S.6-ESD Coyote IIXL		G-MZCB	Cyclone Chaser S 447	
G-MYYW	Mainair Blade		G-MZCC	Mainair Blade 912	
G-MYYX	Pegasus Quantum 15		G-MZCD	Mainair Blade	
G-MYYY	Mainair Blade		G-MZCE	Mainair Blade	
G-MYYZ	Medway Raven X		G-MZCG	Mainair Blade	
G-MYZA	Whittaker MW.6 Merlin		G-MZCH	Whittaker MW.6-S Fatboy Flyer	
G-MYZB	Pegasus Quantum 15				
G-MYZC	Cyclone AX3/503		G-MZCI	Pegasus Quantum 15	
G-MYZD	Pegasus Quantum 15		G-MZCJ	Pegasus Quantum 15	
G-MYZE	Team Minimax		G-MZCM	Pegasus Quantum 15	
G-MYZF	Cyclone AX3/503		G-MZCN	Mainair Blade	
G-MYZH	Chargus Titan 38		G-MZCO	Mainair Mercury	
G-MYZJ	Pegasus Quantum 15		G-MZCP	SW Pegasus XL-Q	
G-MYZK	Pegasus Quantum 15		G-MZCR	Rans S.6-ESD Coyote II	
G-MYZL	Pegasus Quantum 15		G-MZCS	Team Minimax	
G-MYZM	Pegasus Quantum 15		G-MZCT	CFM Shadow Srs CD	
G-MYZN	Whittaker MW.6-S Fatboy Flyer		G-MZCU	Mainair Blade	
			G-MZCV	Pegasus Quantum 15	
G-MYZO	Medway Raven X		G-MZCW	Pegasus Quantum 15	
G-MYZP	CFM Shadow Srs DD		G-MZCX	Hunt Wing	
G-MYZR	Rans S.6-ESD Coyote II		G-MZCY	Pegasus Quantum 15	
G-MYZV	Rans S.6-ESD Coyote II		G-MZDA	Rans S.6-ESD Coyote IIXL	
G-MYZW	Cyclone Chaser S 508		G-MZDB	Pegasus Quantum 15	
G-MYZY	Pegasus Quantum 15		G-MZDC	Pegasus Quantum 15	
G-MYZZ	Pegasus Quantum 15		G-MZDD	Pegasus Quantum 15	
			G-MZDE	Pegasus Quantum 15	
G-MZAA	Mainair Blade		G-MZDF	Mainair Blade	
G-MZAC	Quad City Challenger II		G-MZDG	Rans S.6-ESD Coyote IIXL	
G-MZAE	Mainair Blade		G-MZDH	Pegasus Quantum 15	
G-MZAF	Mainair Blade		G-MZDI	Whittaker MW.6-S Fatboy Flyer (G-BUNN)	
G-MZAG	Mainair Blade				
G-MZAH	Rans S.6-ESD Coyote II		G-MZDJ	Medway Raven X	
G-MZAI	Mainair Blade		G-MZDK	Mainair Blade	
G-MZAJ	Mainair Blade		G-MZDL	Whittaker MW.6-S Fatboy Flyer	
G-MZAK	Mainair Mercury				
G-MZAL	Mainair Blade		G-MZDM	Rans S.6-ESD Coyote II	
G-MZAM	Mainair Blade		G-MZDN	Pegasus Quantum 15	
G-MZAN	Pegasus Quantum 15		G-MZDO	Cyclone AX3/503	
G-MZAO	Mainair Blade 912		G-MZDP	AMF Chevvron 2-32	
G-MZAP	Mainair Blade		G-MZDR	Rans S.6-ESD Coyote IIXL	
G-MZAR	Mainair Blade		G-MZDS	Cyclone AX3/503	
G-MZAS	Mainair Blade		G-MZDT	Mainair Blade	
G-MZAT	Mainair Blade		G-MZDU	Pegasus Quantum 15	
G-MZAV	Mainair Blade		G-MZDV	Pegasus Quantum 15	
G-MZAW	Pegasus Quantum 15		G-MZDX	Letov LK-2M Sluka	
G-MZAY	Mainair Blade		G-MZDY	Pegasus Quantum 15	
G-MZAZ	Mainair Blade		G-MZDZ	Hunt Wing	
G-MZBA	Mainair Blade 912		G-MZEA	Quad City Challenger II UK	
G-MZBB	Pegasus Quantum 15		G-MZEB	Mainair Blade	
G-MZBC	Pegasus Quantum 15		G-MZEC	Pegasus Quantum 15	
G-MZBD	Rans S.6-ESD Coyote II		G-MZED	Mainair Blade	
G-MZBE	CFM Streak Shadow Srs SA-M		G-MZEE	Pegasus Quantum 15	
			G-MZEG	Mainair Blade	
G-MZBF	Letov LK-2M Sluka		G-MZEH	Pegasus Quantum 15	
G-MZBG	Whittaker MW.6-S Fatboy Flyer		G-MZEI	Whittaker MW.5-D Sorcerer	

Reg.	Type	Notes	Reg.	Type	Notes
G-MZEJ	Mainair Blade		G-MZHM	Team Himax 1700R	
G-MZEK	Mainair Mercury		G-MZHN	Pegasus Quantum 15	
G-MZEL	Cyclone AX3/503		G-MZHO	Quad City Challenger II	
G-MZEM	Pegasus Quantum 15		G-MZHP	Pegasus Quantum 15	
G-MZEN	Rans S.6-ESD Coyote II		G-MZHR	Cyclone AX2000	
G-MZEO	Rans S.6-ESD Coyote IIXL		G-MZHS	Thruster T.600T	
G-MZEP	Mainair Rapier		G-MZHT	Whittaker MW.6 Merlin	
G-MZER	Cyclone AX2000		G-MZHU	Thruster T.600T	
G-MZES	Letov LK-2N Sluka		G-MZHV	Thruster T.600T	
G-MZET	Pegasus Quantum 15		G-MZHW	Thruster T.600N	
G-MZEU	Rans S.6-ESD Coyote IIXL		G-MZHX	Thruster T.600N	
G-MZEV	Mainair Rapier		G-MZHY	Thruster T.600N	
G-MZEW	Mainair Blade		G-MZHZ	Thruster T.600N	
G-MZEX	Pegasus Quantum 15		G-MZIA	Team Himax 1700R	
G-MZEY	Micro Bantam B.22		G-MZIB	Pegasus Quantum 15	
G-MZEZ	Pegasus Quantum 15		G-MZIC	Pegasus Quantum 15	
G-MZFA	Cyclone AX2000		G-MZID	Whittaker MW-6 Merlin	
G-MZFB	Mainair Blade		G-MZIE	Pegasus Quantum 15	
G-MZFC	Letov LK-2M Sluka		G-MZIF	Pegasus Quantum 15	
G-MZFD	Mainair Rapier		G-MZIH	Mainair Blade	
G-MZFE	Hunt Wing		G-MZII	Team Minimax	
G-MZFF	Hunt Wing		G-MZIJ	Pegasus Quantum 15	
G-MZFG	Pegasus Quantum 15		G-MZIK	Pegasus Quantum 15	
G-MZFI	Iolaire		G-MZIL	Mainair Rapier	
G-MZFK	Whittaker MW.6 Merlin		G-MZIM	Mainair Rapier	
G-MZFL	Rans S.6-ESD Coyote IIXL		G-MZIN	Whittaker MW-6 Merlin	
G-MZFM	Pegasus Quantum 15		G-MZIP	Renegade Spirit UK	
G-MZFN	Rans S.6.ESD Coyote IIXL		G-MZIR	Mainair Blade	
G-MZFO	Thruster T.600N		G-MZIS	Mainair Blade	
G-MZFP	Thruster T.600N		G-MZIT	Mainair Blade 912	
G-MZFR	Thruster T.600N		G-MZIU	Pegasus Quantum 15	
G-MZFS	Mainair Blade		G-MZIV	Cyclone AX2000	
G-MZFT	Pegasus Quantum 15		G-MZIW	Mainair Blade	
G-MZFU	Thruster T.600N		G-MZIX	Mignet HM.1000 Balerit	
G-MZFV	Pegasus Quantum 15		G-MZIY	Rans S.6-ESD Coyote II	
G-MZFX	Cyclone AX2000		G-MZIZ	Renegade Spirit UK	
G-MZFY	Rans S.6-ESD Coyote IIXL			(G-MWGP)	
G-MZFZ	Mainair Blade		G-MZJA	Mainair Blade	
G-MZGA	Cyclone AX2000		G-MZJB	Aviasud Mistral	
G-MZGB	Cyclone AX2000		G-MZJC	Micro Bantam B22-S	
G-MZGC	Cyclone AX2000		G-MZJD	Mainair Blade	
G-MZGD	Rans S.6 Coyote II		G-MZJE	Mainair Rapier	
G-MZGF	Letov LK-2M Sluka		G-MZJF	Cyclone AX2000	
G-MZGG	Pegasus Quantum 15		G-MZJG	Pegasus Quantum 15	
G-MZGH	Hunt Wing/Avon 462		G-MZJH	Pegasus Quantum 15	
G-MZGI	Mainair Blade 912		G-MZJI	Rans S.6-ESD Coyote II	
G-MZGJ	Kolb Twinstar Mk 1		G-MZJJ	Maverick	
G-MZGK	Pegasus Quantum 15		G-MZJK	Mainair Blade	
G-MZGL	Mainair Rapier		G-MZJL	Cyclone AX2000	
G-MZGM	Cyclone AX2000		G-MZJM	Rans S.6-ESD Coyote IIXL	
G-MZGN	Pegasus Quantum 15		G-MZJN	Pegasus Quantum 15	
G-MZGO	Pegasus Quantum 15		G-MZJO	Pegasus Quantum 15	
G-MZGP	Cyclone AX2000		G-MZJP	Whittaker MW.6-S Fatboy	
G-MZGR	Team Minimax			Flyer	
G-MZGS	CFM Shadow Srs BD		G-MZJR	Cyclone AX2000	
G-MZGT	RH78 Tiger Light		G-MZJS	Meridian Maverick	
G-MZGU	Arrowflight Hawk II (UK)		G-MZJT	Pegasus Quantum 15	
G-MZGV	Pegasus Quantum 15		G-MZJV	Mainair Blade 912	
G-MZGW	Mainair Blade		G-MZJW	Pegasus Quantum 15	
G-MZGX	Thruster T.600N		G-MZJX	Mainair Blade	
G-MZGY	Thruster T.600N		G-MZJY	Pegasus Quantum 15	
G-MZGZ	Thruster T.600N		G-MZJZ	Mainair Blade	
G-MZHA	Thruster T.600N		G-MZKA	Pegasus Quantum 15	
G-MZHB	Mainair Blade		G-MZKC	Cyclone AX2000	
G-MZHC	Thruster T.600N		G-MZKD	Pegasus Quantum 15	
G-MZHD	Thruster T.600N		G-MZKE	Rans S.6-ESD Coyote IIXL	
G-MZHE	Thruster T.600N		G-MZKF	Pegasus Quantum 15	
G-MZHF	Thruster T.600N		G-MZKG	Mainair Blade	
G-MZHG	Whittaker MW.6-T		G-MZKH	CFM Shadow Srs DD	
G-MZHI	Pegasus Quantum 15		G-MZKI	Mainair Blade	
G-MZHJ	Mainair Rapier		G-MZKJ	Mainair Blade	
G-MZHK	Pegasus Quantum 15		G-MZKK	Mainair Blade 912	
G-MZHL	Mainair Rapier		G-MZKL	Pegasus Quantum 15	

Reg.	Type	Notes	Reg.	Type	Notes
G-MZKM	Mainair Blade 912		G-MZNB	Pegasus Quantum 15	
G-MZKN	Mainair Rapier		G-MZNC	Mainair Blade 912	
G-MZKO	Mainair Blade		G-MZND	Mainair Rapier	
G-MZKP	Thruster T.600N		G-MZNE	Whittaker MW.6-S Fatboy	
G-MZKR	Thruster T.600N			Flyer	
G-MZKS	Thruster T.600N		G-MZNG	Pegasus Quantum 15	
G-MZKT	Thruster T.600N		G-MZNH	CFM Shadow Srs DD	
G-MZKU	Thruster T.600N		G-MZNI	Mainair Blade 912	
G-MZKV	Mainair Blade 912		G-MZNJ	Mainair Blade	
G-MZKW	Quad City Challenger II		G-MZNK	Mainair Blade 912	
G-MZKX	Pegasus Quantum 15		G-MZNL	Mainair Blade 912	
G-MZKY	Pegasus Quantum 15		G-MZNM	Team Minimax	
G-MZKZ	Mainair Blade		G-MZNN	Team Minimax	
G-MZLA	Pegasus Quantum 15		G-MZNO	Mainair Blade	
G-MZLB	Hunt Wing		G-MZNP	Pegasus Quantum 15	
G-MZLC	Mainair Blade 912		G-MZNR	Pegasus Quantum 15	
G-MZLD	Pegasus Quantum 15		G-MZNS	Pegasus Quantum 15	
G-MZLE	Maverick (G-BXSZ)		G-MZNT	Pegasus Quantum 15-912	
G-MZLF	Pegasus Quantum 15		G-MZNU	Mainair Rapier	
G-MZLG	Rans S.6-ESD Coyote IIXL		G-MZNV	Rans S.6-ESD Coyote II	
G-MZLH	Pegasus Quantum 15		G-MZNW	Thruster T.600N HKS	
G-MZLI	Mignet HM.1000 Balerit		G-MZNX	Thruster T.600N	
G-MZLJ	Pegasus Quantum 15		G-MZNY	Thruster T.600N	
G-MZLL	Rans S.6-ESD Coyote II		G-MZOC	Mainair Blade	
G-MZLM	Cyclone AX2000		G-MZOD	Pegasus Quantum 15	
G-MZLN	Pegasus Quantum 15		G-MZOE	Cyclone AX2000	
G-MZLO	CFM Shadow Srs O		G-MZOF	Mainair Blade	
G-MZLP	CFM Shadow Srs O		G-MZOG	Pegasus Quantum 15-912	
G-MZLR	SW Pegasus XL-Q		G-MZOH	Whittaker MW.5D Sorcerer	
G-MZLS	Cyclone AX2000		G-MZOI	Letov LK-2M Sluka	
G-MZLT	Pegasus Quantum 15		G-MZOJ	Pegasus Quantum 15	
G-MZLU	Cyclone AX2000		G-MZOK	Whittaker MW.6 Merlin	
G-MZLV	Pegasus Quantum 15		G-MZOM	CFM Shadow Srs DD	
G-MZLW	Pegasus Quantum 15		G-MZON	Mainair Rapier	
G-MZLX	Micro Bantam B.22-5		G-MZOP	Mainair Blade 912	
G-MZLY	Letov LK-2M Sluka		G-MZOR	Mainair Blade 912	
G-MZLZ	Mainair Blade 912		G-MZOS	Pegasus Quantum 15-912	
G-MZMA	SW Pegasus Quasar IITC		G-MZOT	Letov LK-2M Sluka	
G-MZMB	Mainair Blade		G-MZOV	Pegasus Quantum 15	
G-MZMC	Pegasus Quantum 15		G-MZOW	Pegasus Quantum 15-912	
G-MZMD	Mainair Blade 912		G-MZOX	Letov LK-2M Sluka	
G-MZMG	Pegasus Quantum 15		G-MZOZ	Rans S.6-ESD Coyote IIXL	
G-MZMH	Pegasus Quantum 15		G-MZPB	Mignet HM.1000 Balerit	
G-MZMJ	Mainair Blade		G-MZPD	Pegasus Quantum 15	
G-MZMK	Chevvron 2-32C		G-MZPH	Mainair Blade	
G-MZML	Mainair Blade 912		G-MZPJ	Team Minimax	
G-MZMM	Mainair Blade 912		G-MZPW	Pegasus Quantum 15	
G-MZMN	Pegasus Quantum 912		G-MZRC	Pegasus Quantum 15	
G-MZMO	Team Minimax 91		G-MZRH	Pegasus Quantum 15	
G-MZMP	Mainair Blade		G-MZRM	Pegasus Quantum 15	
G-MZMR	Rans S.6-ESA Coyote II		G-MZRS	CFM Shadow Srs CD	
G-MZMS	Rans S.6-ESD Coyote II		G-MZSC	Pegasus Quantum 15	
G-MZMT	Pegasus Quantum 15		G-MZSD	Mainair Blade 912	
G-MZMU	Rans S.6-ESD Coyote II		G-MZSM	Mainair Blade	
G-MZMV	Mainair Blade		G-MZTA	Mignet HM.1000 Balerit	
G-MZMW	Mignet HM.1000 Balerit		G-MZTS	Aerial Arts Chaser S	
G-MZMX	Cyclone AX2000			(G-MVDM)	
G-MZMY	Mainair Blade		G-MZUB	Rans S.6-ESD Coyote IIXL	
G-MZMZ	Mainair Blade		G-MZZT	Kolb Twinstar Mk 3	
G-MZNA	Quad City Challenger II UK		G-MZZY	Mainair Blade 912	

D-ABAX Boeing 737-86J (winglets) of Air-Berlin. *A.S.Wright*

251

OE-LFL Fokker 70 of Tyrolean Airways. *A.S.Wright*

OK-TVA Boeing 737-86N of Travel Service Airlines. *A.S.Wright*

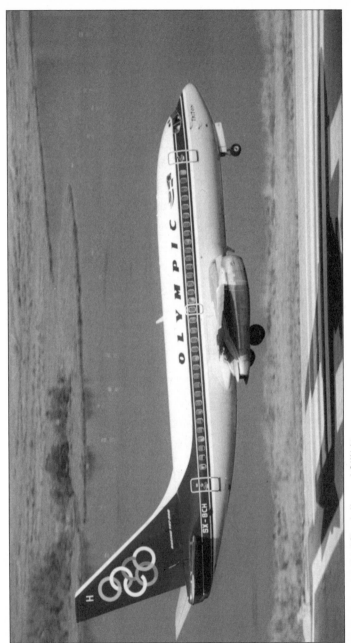

SX-BCH Boeing 737-284 of Olympic Airways. *A.S.Wright*

Overseas Airliner Registrations

(Aircraft included in this section are those most likely to be seen at UK and major European airports on scheduled or charter services.)

Reg.	Type	Owner or Operator	Notes

A4O (Oman)

Reg.	Type	Owner or Operator
A4O-GI	Boeing 767-3P6ER (604)	Gulf Air *Alkhor*
A4O-GJ	Boeing 767-3P6ER (605)	Gulf Air *Al Muharraq*
A4O-GK	Boeing 767-3P6ER (606)	Gulf Air *Al Burami*
A4O-GS	Boeing 767-3P6ER (613)	Gulf Air *Al -Ain*
A4O-GT	Boeing 767-3P6ER (614)	Gulf Air *Auwakrah*
A4O-GU	Boeing 767-3P6ER (615)	Gulf Air
A4O-GV	Boeing 767-3P6ER (616)	Gulf Air *Dukhan*
A4O-GY	Boeing 767-3P6ER (619)	Gulf Air
A4O-GZ	Boeing 767-3P6ER (620)	Gulf Air
A4O-KA	Airbus A.330-243 (501)	Gulf Air
A4O-KB	Airbus A.330-243 (502)	Gulf Air
A4O-KC	Airbus A.330-243 (503)	Gulf Air
A4O-KD	Airbus A.330-243 (504)	Gulf Air
A4O-KE	Airbus A.330-243 (505)	Gulf Air
A4O-KF	Airbus A.330-243 (506)	Gulf Air
A4O-LB	Airbus A.340-312 (402)	Gulf Air *Al Fateh*
A4O-LC	Airbus A.340-312 (403)	Gulf Air *Doha*
A4O-LD	Airbus A.340-312 (404)	Gulf Air *Abu Dhabi*
A4O-LE	Airbus A.340-312 (405)	Gulf Air
A4O-LF	Airbus A.340-312 (406)	Gulf Air
A4O-SO	Boeing 747SP-27	Oman Royal Flight
A4O-SP	Boeing 747SP-27	Oman Government

A6 (United Arab Emirates)

Reg.	Type	Owner or Operator
A6-EAA	Airbus A.330-243	Emirate Airlines
A6-EAB	Airbus A.330-243	Emirate Airlines
A6-EAC	Airbus A.330-243	Emirate Airlines
A6-EAD	Airbus A.330-243	Emirate Airlines
A6-EAE	Airbus A.330-243	Emirate Airlines
A6-EAF	Airbus A.330-243	Emirate Airlines
A6-EAG	Airbus A.330-243	Emirate Airlines
A6-EAH	Airbus A.330-243	Emirate Airlines
A6-EAI	Airbus A.330-243	Emirate Airlines
A6-EAJ	Airbus A.330-243	Emirate Airlines
A6-EAK	Airbus A.330-243	Emirate Airlines
A6-EHQ	Boeing 777-31HER	Emirate Airlines
A6-EKK	Airbus A.310-308	Emirate Airlines
A6-EKL	Airbus A.310-308	Emirate Airlines
A6-EKM	Airbus A.300-605R	Emirate Airlines
A6-EKP	Airbus A.310-308	Emirate Airlines
A6-EKQ	Airbus A.330-243	Emirate Airlines
A6-EKR	Airbus A.330-243	Emirate Airlines
A6-EKS	Airbus A.330-243	Emirate Airlines
A6-EKT	Airbus A.330-243	Emirate Airlines
A6-EKU	Airbus A.330-243	Emirate Airlines
A6-EKV	Airbus A.330-243	Emirate Airlines
A6-EKW	Airbus A.330-243	Emirate Airlines
A6-EKX	Airbus A.330-243	Emirate Airlines
A6-EKY	Airbus A.330-243	Emirate Airlines
A6-EKZ	Airbus A.330-243	Emirate Airlines
A6-EMD	Boeing 777-21HER	Emirate Airlines
A6-EME	Boeing 777-21HER	Emirate Airlines
A6-EMF	Boeing 777-21HER	Emirate Airlines
A6-EMG	Boeing 777-21HER	Emirate Airlines
A6-EMH	Boeing 777-21HER	Emirate Airlines
A6-EMI	Boeing 777-21HER	Emirate Airlines
A6-EMJ	Boeing 777-21HER	Emirate Airlines
A6-EMK	Boeing 777-21HER	Emirate Airlines
A6-EML	Boeing 777-21HER	Emirate Airlines
A6-EMM	Boeing 777-31H	Emirate Airlines
A6-EMN	Boeing 777-31H	Emirate Airlines

Notes	Reg.	Type	Owner or Operator
	A6-EMO	Boeing 777-31H	Emirate Airlines
	A6-EMP	Boeing 777-31H	Emirate Airlines
	A6-EMQ	Boeing 777-31H	Emirate Airlines
	A6-EMR	Boeing 777-31H	Emirate Airlines
	A6-EMS	Boeing 777-31H	Emirate Airlines
	A6-EMU	Boeing 777-31H	Emirate Airlines
	A6-LIW	Boeing 737-7Z5	Government of Abu Dhabi
	A6-SMM	Boeing 747SP-31	United Arab Emirates
	A6-SMR	Boeing 747SP-31	United Arab Emirates
	A6-	Airbus A.340-541	Emirate Airlines
	A6-	Airbus A.340-541	Emirate Airlines
	A6-	Airbus A.340-541	Emirate Airlines

A7 (Qatar)

	A7-AAF	Airbus A.310-304	Qatar Government
	A7-AAG	Airbus A.320-232	Qatar Government
	A7-ABN	Airbus A.300B4-622R	Qatar Airways
	A7-ABO	Airbus A.300B4-622R	Qatar Airways
	A7-ABV	Airbus A.300B4-622R	Qatar Airways
	A7-ABW	Airbus A.300B4-622R	Qatar Airways
	A7-ABX	Airbus A.300B4-622R	Qatar Airways
	A7-ABY	Airbus A.300B4-622R	Qatar Airways
	A7-	Airbus A.330-203	Qatar Airways
	A7-	Airbus A.330-203	Qatar Airways
	A7-HHK	Airbus A.340-211	Qatar Government

AP (Pakistan)

	AP-AYV	Boeing 747-282B	Pakistan International Airlines
	AP-AYW	Boeing 747-282B	Pakistan International Airlines
	AP-BAK	Boeing 747-240B (SCD)	Pakistan International Airlines
	AP-BAT	Boeing 747-240B (SCD)	Pakistan International Airlines
	AP-BCL	Boeing 747-217B	Pakistan International Airlines
	AP-BCM	Boeing 747-217B	Pakistan International Airlines
	AP-BCN	Boeing 747-217B	Pakistan International Airlines
	AP-BCO	Boeing 747-217B	Pakistan International Airlines
	AP-BDZ	Airbus A.310-308	Pakistan International Airlines
	AP-BEB	Airbus A.310-308	Pakistan International Airlines
	AP-BEC	Airbus A.310-308	Pakistan International Airlines
	AP-BEG	Airbus A.310-308	Pakistan International Airlines
	AP-BEQ	Airbus A.310-308	Pakistan International Airlines
	AP-BEU	Airbus A.310-308	Pakistan International Airlines
	AP-BFU	Boeing 747-367	Pakistan International Airlines
	AP-BFV	Boeing 747-367	Pakistan International Airlines
	AP-BFW	Boeing 747-367	Pakistan International Airlines
	AP-BFX	Boeing 747-367	Pakistan International Airlines
	AP-BFY	Boeing 747-367	Pakistan International Airlines

B (China/Taiwan/Hong Kong)

	B-HIA	Boeing 747-267B	Cathay Pacific Airways
	B-HIB	Boeing 747-267B	Cathay Pacific Airways
	B-HIH	Boeing 747-267F (SCD)	Cathay Pacific Airways
	B-HMD	Boeing 747-2L5F (SCD)	Air Hong Kong
	B-HME	Boeing 747-2L5F (SCD)	Air Hong Kong
	B-HMF	Boeing 747-2L5F (SCD)	Air Hong Kong
	B-HOO	Boeing 747-467	Cathay Pacific Airways
	B-HOP	Boeing 747-467	Cathay Pacific Airways
	B-HOR	Boeing 747-467	Cathay Pacific Airways
	B-HOS	Boeing 747-467	Cathay Pacific Airways
	B-HOT	Boeing 747-467	Cathay Pacific Airways
	B-HOU	Boeing 747-467	Cathay Pacific Airways
	B-HOV	Boeing 747-467	Cathay Pacific Airways
	B-HOW	Boeing 747-467	Cathay Pacific Airways
	B-HOX	Boeing 747-467	Cathay Pacific Airways
	B-HOY	Boeing 747-467	Cathay Pacific Airways
	B-HOZ	Boeing 747-467	Cathay Pacific Airways
	B-HUA	Boeing 747-467	Cathay Pacific Airways
	B-HUB	Boeing 747-467	Cathay Pacific Airways

Reg.	Type	Owner or Operator	Notes
B-HUD	Boeing 747-467	Cathay Pacific Airways	
B-HUE	Boeing 747-467	Cathay Pacific Airways	
B-HUF	Boeing 747-467	Cathay Pacific Airways	
B-HUG	Boeing 747-467	Cathay Pacific Airways	
B-HUH	Boeing 747-467F	Cathay Pacific Airways	
B-HUI	Boeing 747-467	Cathay Pacific Airways	
B-HUJ	Boeing 747-467	Cathay Pacific Airways	
B-HUK	Boeing 747-467F	Cathay Pacific Airways	
B-HUL	Boeing 747-467F	Cathay Pacific Airways	
B-HUO	Boeing 747-467F	Cathay Pacific Airways	
B-HUP	Boeing 747-467F	Cathay Pacific Airways	
B-HVX	Boeing 747-267F (SCD)	Cathay Pacific Airways	
B-HVY	Boeing 747-236F (SCD)	Cathay Pacific Airways	
B-HVZ	Boeing 747-267F (SCD)	Cathay Pacific Airways	
B-HXA	Airbus A.340-313X	Cathay Pacific Airways	
B-HXB	Airbus A.340-313X	Cathay Pacific Airways	
B-HXC	Airbus A.340-313X	Cathay Pacific Airways	
B-HXD	Airbus A.340-313X	Cathay Pacific Airways	
B-HXE	Airbus A.340-313X	Cathay Pacific Airways	
B-HXF	Airbus A.340-313X	Cathay Pacific Airways	
B-HXG	Airbus A.340-313X	Cathay Pacific Airways	
B-HXH	Airbus A.340-313X	Cathay Pacific Airways	
B-HXI	Airbus A.340-313X	Cathay Pacific Airways	
B-HXJ	Airbus A.340-313X	Cathay Pacific Airways	
B-HXK	Airbus A.340-313X	Cathay Pacific Airways	
B-HXL	Airbus A.340-313X	Cathay Pacific Airways	
B-HXM	Airbus A.340-313X	Cathay Pacific Airways	
B-HXN	Airbus A.340-313X	Cathay Pacific Airways	
B-HXO	Airbus A.340-313X	Cathay Pacific Airways	
B-KAA	Boeing 747-312F (SCD)	Dragonair Cargo	
B-KAB	Boeing 747-312F (SCD)	Dragonair Cargo	
B-160	Boeing 747-209F (SCD)	China Airlines	
B-162	Boeing 747-409	China Airlines	
B-163	Boeing 747-409	China Airlines	
B-164	Boeing 747-409	China Airlines	
B-2059	Boeing 777-2J6ER	Air China	
B-2060	Boeing 777-2J6ER	Air China	
B-2061	Boeing 777-2J6ER	Air China	
B-2063	Boeing 777-2J6ER	Air China	
B-2064	Boeing 777-2J6ER	Air China	
B-2065	Boeing 777-2J6ER	Air China	
B-2066	Boeing 777-2J6ER	Air China	
B-2067	Boeing 777-2J6ER	Air China	
B-2068	Boeing 777-2J6ER	Air China	
B-2069	Boeing 777-2J6ER	Air China	
B-2438	Boeing 747SP-J6	Air China	
B-2442	Boeing 747SP-J6	Air China	
B-2443	Boeing 747-4J6	Air China	
B-2445	Boeing 747-4J6	Air China	
B-2446	Boeing 747-2J6B (SCD)	Air China	
B-2447	Boeing 747-4J6	Air China	
B-2448	Boeing 747-2J6B (SCD)	Air China	
B-2450	Boeing 747-2J6B (SCD)	Air China	
B-2456	Boeing 747-4J6 (SCD)	Air China	
B-2458	Boeing 747-4J6 (SCD)	Air China	
B-2460	Boeing 747-4J6 (SCD)	Air China	
B-2462	Boeing 747-2J6F (SCD)	Air China	
B-2467	Boeing 747-4J6	Air China	
B-2468	Boeing 747-4J6	Air China	
B-2469	Boeing 747-4J6	Air China	
B-2470	Boeing 747-4J6	Air China	
B-2471	Boeing 747-4J6	Air China	
B-2472	Boeing 747-4J6	Air China	
B-16101	McD Douglas MD-11	EVA Airways	
B-16102	McD Douglas MD-11	EVA Airways	
B-16103	McD Douglas MD-11	EVA Airways	
B-16106	McD Douglas MD-11F	EVA Airways	
B-16107	McD Douglas MD-11F	EVA Airways	
B-16108	McD Douglas MD-11F	EVA Airways	
B-16109	McD Douglas MD-11F	EVA Airways	
B-16110	McD Douglas MD-11F	EVA Airways	
B-16111	McD Douglas MD-11F	EVA Airways	
B-16112	McD Douglas MD-11F	EVA Airways	

Notes	Reg.	Type	Owner or Operator
	B-16113	McD Douglas MD-11F	EVA Airways
	B-16401	Boeing 747-45E	EVA Airways
	B-16402	Boeing 747-45E	EVA Airways
	B-16403	Boeing 747-45E	EVA Airways
	B-16405	Boeing 747-45E	EVA Airways
	B-16406	Boeing 747-45E	EVA Airways
	B-16407	Boeing 747-45E	EVA Airways
	B-16408	Boeing 747-45E	EVA Airways
	B-16409	Boeing 747-45E	EVA Airways
	B-16410	Boeing 747-45E	EVA Airways
	B-16411	Boeing 747-45E	EVA Airways
	B-16412	Boeing 747-45E	EVA Airways
	B-16461	Boeing 747-45E (SCD)	EVA Airways
	B-16462	Boeing 747-45E (SCD)	EVA Airways
	B-16463	Boeing 747-45E (SCD)	EVA Airways
	B-16465	Boeing 747-45E (SCD)	EVA Airways
	B-16481	Boeing 747-45E	EVA Airways
	B-16482	Boeing 747-45EF	EVA Airways
	B-18202	Boeing 747-409	China Airlines
	B-18203	Boeing 747-409	China Airlines
	B-18205	Boeing 747-409	China Airlines
	B-18206	Boeing 747-409	China Airlines
	B-18207	Boeing 747-409	China Airlines
	B-18208	Boeing 747-409	China Airlines
	B-18209	Boeing 747-409	China Airlines
	B-18255	Boeing 747-209B	China Airlines
	B-18271	Boeing 747-409	China Airlines
	B-18701	Boeing 747-409F	China Airlines
	B-18702	Boeing 747-409F	China Airlines
	B-18703	Boeing 747-409F	China Airlines
	B-18705	Boeing 747-409F	China Airlines
	B-18706	Boeing 747-409F	China Airlines
	B-18707	Boeing 747-409F	China Airlines
	B-18751	Boeing 747-209F	China Airlines
	B-18752	Boeing 747-209F (SCD)	China Airlines
	B-18753	Boeing 747-209B	China Airlines
	B-18755	Boeing 747-209B	China Airlines

Note: China Airlines also operates N4508H and N4522V, both Boeing 747SP-09s. EVA Airways operates the MD-11F N105EV together with Boeing 767-3T7ERs N601EV and N602EV.

C-F and C-G (Canada)

C-FBCA	Boeing 747-475 (384)	Air Canada *Grant McConachie*
C-FBEF	Boeing 767-233ER (617)	Air Canada
C-FBEG	Boeing 767-233ER (618)	Air Canada
C-FBEM	Boeing 767-233ER (619)	Air Canada
C-FBUS	Airbus A.330-322	Skyservice
C-FCAB	Boeing 767-375ER (681)	Air Canada
C-FCAE	Boeing 767-375ER (682)	Air Canada
C-FCAF	Boeing 767-375ER (683)	Air Canada
C-FCAG	Boeing 767-375ER (684)	Air Canada
C-FCRA	Boeing 747-475 (382)	Air Canada *T.Russ Baker*
C-FGHZ	Boeing 747-4F6 (385)	Air Canada *Rhys T.Eyton*
C-FICA	Airbus A.300B4-203F	ICC Air Cargo
C-FICB	Airbus A.300B4-203F	ICC Air Cargo
C-FICR	Airbus A.300B4-203F	ICC Air Cargo
C-FMWP	Boeing 767-333ER (631)	Air Canada
C-FMWQ	Boeing 767-333ER (632)	Air Canada
C-FMWU	Boeing 767-333ER (633)	Air Canada
C-FMWV	Boeing 767-333ER (634)	Air Canada
C-FMWY	Boeing 767-333ER (635)	Air Canada
C-FMXC	Boeing 767-333ER (636)	Air Canada
C-FOCA	Boeing 767-375ER (640)	Air Canada
C-FPCA	Boeing 767-375ER (637)	Air Canada
C-FRAE	Airbus A.330-322	Skyservice Airlines
C-FRAV	Airbus A.330-322	Skyservice Airlines
C-FTCA	Boeing 767-375ER (638)	Air Canada
C-FTNA	L.1011-385 TriStar 150 (501)	Air Transat
C-FTNC	L.1011-385 TriStar 150 (503)	Air Transat
C-FTNG	L.1011-385 TriStar 150 (507)	Air Transat
C-FTNH	L.1011-385 TriStar 150 (508)	Air Transat

Reg.	Type	Owner or Operator	Notes
C-FTNL	L.1011-385 TriStar 100 (512)	Air Transat	
C-FTNP	Airbus A.340-313 (982)	Air Canada	
C-FTNQ	Airbus A.340-313 (981)	Air Canada	
C-FTSW	L.1011-385 TriStar 500	Air Transat	
C-FUCL	Boeing 767-209ER (622)	Air Canada	
C-FVNM	Boeing 767-209ER (621)	Air Canada	
C-FXCA	Boeing 767-375ER (639)	Air Canada	
C-FYKX	Airbus A.340-313 (901)	Air Canada	
C-FYKZ	Airbus A.340-313 (902)	Air Canada	
C-FYLC	Airbus A.340-313 (903)	Air Canada	
C-FYLD	Airbus A.340-313 (904)	Air Canada	
C-FYLG	Airbus A.340-313 (905)	Air Canada	
C-FYLU	Airbus A.340-313 (906)	Air Canada	
C-GAGA	Boeing 747-233B (SCD) (306)	Air Canada	
C-GAGB	Boeing 747-233B (SCD) (307)	Air Canada	
C-GAGC	Boeing 747-238B (SCD) (308)	Air Canada	
C-GAGL	Boeing 747-433 (SCD) (341)	Air Canada	
C-GAGM	Boeing 747-433 (SCD) (342)	Air Canada	
C-GAGN	Boeing 747-433 (SCD) (343)	Air Canada	
C-GATH	L.1011-385 TriStar 500 (235)	Air Transat	
C-GATI	L.1011-385 TriStar 500	Air Transat	
C-GATM	L.1011-385 TriStar 500 (236)	Air Transat	
C-GAUY	Boeing 767-233ER (609)	Air Canada	
C-GAVA	Boeing 767-233ER (610)	Air Canada	
C-GAVC	Boeing 767-233ER (611)	Air Canada	
C-GAVF	Boeing 767-233ER (612)	Air Canada	
C-GBBS	L.1011-385 TriStar 100	Air Transat	
C-GBQM	Airbus A.340-313 (907)	Air Canada	
C-GBZR	Boeing 767-38EER (645)	Air Canada	
C-GDSP	Boeing 767-233ER (613)	Air Canada	
C-GDSS	Boeing 767-233ER (614)	Air Canada	
C-GDSU	Boeing 767-233ER (615)	Air Canada	
C-GDSY	Boeing 767-233ER (616)	Air Canada	
C-GDUZ	Boeing 767-38EER (646)	Air Canada	
C-GDVV	Airbus A.340-313X (908)	Air Canada	
C-GDVW	Airbus A.340-313X (909)	Air Canada	
C-GDVZ	Airbus A.340-313X (910)	Air Canada	
C-GEOQ	Boeing 767-375ER (647)	Air Canada	
C-GEOU	Boeing 767-375ER (648)	Air Canada	
C-GFAF	Airbus A.330-343X (931)	Air Canada	
C-GFAH	Airbus A.330-343X (932)	Air Canada	
C-GFAJ	Airbus A.330-343X (933)	Air Canada	
C-GFAT	Airbus A.310-304	Air Transat	
C-GFUR	Airbus A.330-343X (934)	Air Canada	
C-GGBI	Boeing 767-3S1ER (650)	Air Canada	
C-GGBK	Boeing 767-35HER	Air Canada	
C-GGBK	Boeing 767-3S1ER (649)	Air Canada	
C-GGFJ	Boeing 767-3Y0ER (652)	Air Canada	
C-GGMX	Boeing 767-3Y0ER (653)	Air Canada	
C-GGOH	Boeing 767-3Y0ER (654)	Air Canada	
C-GGTS	Airbus A.330-243	Air Transat	
C-GHKR	Airbus A.330-343X (935)	Air Canada	
C-GHKW	Airbus A.330-343X (936)	Air Canada	
C-GHKX	Airbus A.330-343X (937)	Air Canada	
C-GHLA	Boeing 767-35HER	Air Canada	
C-GHLK	Boeing 767-35HER	Air Canada	
C-GHLM	Airbus A.330-343X (938)	Air Canada	
C-GHLQ	Boeing 767-36NER (658)	Air Canada	
C-GHLT	Boeing 767-36NER (659)	Air Canada	
C-GHLU	Boeing 767-36NER (660)	Air Canada	
C-GHLV	Boeing 767-36NER (661)	Air Canada	
C-GHML	Boeing 767-3Y0ER (655)	Air Canada	
C-GITS	Airbus A.330-243	Air Transat	
C-GKTS	Airbus A.330-342	Air Transat	
C-GLAT	Airbus A.310-308	Air Transat	
C-GLCA	Boeing 767-375ER (641)	Air Canada	
C-GMWW	Boeing 747-475 (381)	Air Canada *Maxwell W.Ward*	
C-GPAT	Airbus A.310-308	Air Transat	
C-GSAT	Airbus A.310-308	Air Transat	
C-GSCA	Boeing 767-375ER (642)	Air Canada	
C-GTSB	L.1011-385 TriStar 100 (122)	Air Transat	
C-GTSE	Boeing 757-23A	Air Transat	
C-GTSJ	Boeing 757-236	Air Transat	

Notes	Reg.	Type	Owner or Operator
	C-GTSK	L.1011-385 TriStar 1 (502)	Air Transat
	C-GTSN	Boeing 757-28A	Air Transat
	C-GTSP	L.1011-385 TriStar 500 (242)	Air Transat
	C-GTSQ	L.1011-385 TriStar 500 (243)	Air Transat
	C-GTSR	L.1011-385 TriStar 500 (239)	Air Transat
	C-GTSV	Boeing 757-28A (622)	Air Transat
	C-GTSX	L.1011-385 TriStar 1 (547)	Air Transat
	C-GTSZ	L.1011-385 TriStar 100 (548)	Air Transat
	C-G	Airbus A.330-242	Air Transat
	C-G	Airbus A.330-242	Air Transat

Note: Airline fleet number when carried on aircraft is shown in parentheses.

CC (Chile)

	CC-CQA	Airbus A.340-313X	LAN-Chile
	CC-CQC	Airbus A.340-313X	LAN-Chile
	CC-CQE	Airbus A.340-313X	LAN-Chile
	CC-CQF	Airbus A.340-313X	LAN-Chile

CN (Morocco)

	CN-RGA	Boeing 747-428	Royal Air Maroc
	CN-RME	Boeing 747-2B6B (SCD)	Royal Air Maroc
	CN-RMF	Boeing 737-4B6	Royal Air Maroc
	CN-RMG	Boeing 737-4B6	Royal Air Maroc
	CN-RMI	Boeing 737-2B6	Royal Air Maroc *El Ayounne*
	CN-RMJ	Boeing 737-2B6	Royal Air Maroc *Oujda*
	CN-RMK	Boeing 737-2B6	Royal Air Maroc *Smara*
	CN-RMM	Boeing 737-2B6C	Royal Air Maroc
	CN-RMN	Boeing 737-2B6C	Royal Air Maroc
	CN-RMT	Boeing 757-2B6	Royal Air Maroc
	CN-RMV	Boeing 737-5B6	Royal Air Maroc
	CN-RMW	Boeing 737-5B6	Royal Air Maroc
	CN-RMX	Boeing 737-4B6	Royal Air Maroc
	CN-RMY	Boeing 737-5B6	Royal Air Maroc
	CN-RMZ	Boeing 757-2B6	Royal Air Maroc
	CN-RNA	Boeing 737-4B6	Royal Air Maroc
	CN-RNB	Boeing 737-5B6	Royal Air Maroc
	CN-RNC	Boeing 737-4B6	Royal Air Maroc
	CN-RND	Boeing 737-4B6	Royal Air Maroc
	CN-RNF	Boeing 737-4B6	Royal Air Maroc
	CN-RNG	Boeing 737-5B6	Royal Air Maroc
	CN-RNH	Boeing 737-5B6	Royal Air Maroc
	CN-RNJ	Boeing 737-8B6	Royal Air Maroc
	CN-RNK	Boeing 737-8B6	Royal Air Maroc
	CN-RNL	Boeing 737-7B6	Royal Air Maroc
	CN-RNM	Boeing 737-7B6	Royal Air Maroc
	CN-RNN	Boeing 737-86N	Royal Air Maroc
	CN-RNO	Boeing 737-86N	Royal Air Maroc
	CN-RNP	Boeing 737-8B6	Royal Air Maroc
	CN-RNQ	Boeing 737-7B6	Royal Air Maroc
	CN-RNR	Boeing 737-7B6	Royal Air Maroc
	CN-RNS	Boeing 767-3B6ER	Royal Air Maroc
	CN-RNT	Boeing 767-3B6ER	Royal Air Maroc

CS (Portugal)

	CS-TEB	L.1011-385 TriStar 500	Euro Atlantic Airways *Naughton Simao*
	CS-TEH	Airbus A.310-304	TAP - Air Portugal *Bartolomeu Dias*
	CS-TEI	Airbus A.310-304	TAP - Air Portugal *Fernao de Magalhaes*
	CS-TEJ	Airbus A.310-304	TAP - Air Portugal *Pedro Nunes*
	CS-TEW	Airbus A.310-304	TAP - Air Portugal *Vasco da Gama*
	CS-TEX	Airbus A.310-304	TAP - Air Portugal *Joao XXI*
	CS-TGP	Boeing 737-3Q8	SATA International
	CS-TGQ	Boeing 737-36N	SATA International
	CS-TGU	Airbus A.310-304	SATA International *Terceira*
	CS-TGV	Airbus A.310-304	SATA International *St. Miguel*
	CS-TGW	Boeing 737-4Y0	SATA International
	CS-TIF	Boeing 737-3K9	TAP - Air Portugal *Costa Verde*
	CS-TIG	Boeing 737-3K9	Euro Atlantic Airways

Reg.	Type	Owner or Operator	Notes
CS-TIO	Boeing 737-33A	Euro Atlantic Airways	
CS-TJE	Airbus A.321-211	TAP - Air Portugal *Pero Vaz de Caminha*	
CS-TJF	Airbus A.321-211	TAP - Air Portugal	
CS-TJG	Airbus A.321-211	TAP - Air Portugal	
CS-TMP	L.1011-385 TriStar 500	Air Luxor	
CS-TMR	L.1011-385 TriStar 500	Air Luxor/Yestours	
CS-TMT	Airbus A.330-223	Air Luxor	
CS-TMU	Beech 1900D	PGA Express *Castor*	
CS-TMV	Beech 1900D	PGA Express *Esquillo*	
CS-TNC	L.1011-385 TriStar 500	Yestours	
CS-TNA	Airbus A.320-211	TAP - Air Portugal *Grao Vasco*	
CS-TNB	Airbus A.320-211	Air Luxor	
CS-TNC	Airbus A.320-211	Yestours	
CS-TNE	Airbus A.320-212	Air Luxor *Sa de Miranda*	
CS-TNG	Airbus A.320-214	TAP - Air Portugal *Mouzinhp de Silveria*	
CS-TNH	Airbus A.320-214	TAP - Air Portugal *Almada Negreiros*	
CS-TNI	Airbus A.320-214	TAP - Air Portugal	
CS-TNJ	Airbus A.320-214	TAP - Air Portugal *Florbela Espanca*	
CS-TNK	Airbus A.320-214	TAP - Air Portugal *Teofilo Braga*	
CS-TNL	Airbus A.320-214	TAP - Air Portugal *Vitorino Nermesio*	
CS-TNM	Airbus A.320-214	TAP - Air Portugal	
CS-TOA	Airbus A.340-312	TAP - Air Portugal *Ferrei Mendes Pinto*	
CS-TOB	Airbus A.340-312	TAP - Air Portugal *D. Joao de Castro*	
CS-TOC	Airbus A.340-312	TAP - Air Portugal *Wenceslau de Moraes*	
CS-TOD	Airbus A.340-312	TAP - Air Portugal *D. Francisco de Almeida*	
CS-TPA	Fokker 100	Portugalia *Albatroz*	
CS-TPB	Fokker 100	Portugalia *Pelican*	
CS-TPC	Fokker 100	Portugalia *Flamingo*	
CS-TPD	Fokker 100	Portugalia *Condor*	
CS-TPE	Fokker 100	Portugalia *Gaviao*	
CS-TPF	Fokker 100	Portugalia *Grifo*	
CS-TPG	Embraer RJ145EP	Portugalia *Melro*	
CS-TPH	Embraer RJ145EP	Portugalia *Pardal*	
CS-TPI	Embraer RJ145EP	Portugalia *Cuca*	
CS-TPJ	Embraer RJ145EP	Portugalia *Chapim*	
CS-TPK	Embraer RJ145EP	Portugalia *Gaio*	
CS-TPL	Embraer RJ145EP	Portugalia *Pisco*	
CS-TPM	Embraer RJ145EP	Portugalia *Rola*	
CS-TPN	Embraer RJ145EP	Portugalia *Brigao*	
CS-TTA	Airbus A.319-111	TAP - Air Portugal *Vieira da Silva*	
CS-TTB	Airbus A.319-111	TAP - Air Portugal *Gago Coutinho*	
CS-TTC	Airbus A.319-111	TAP - Air Portugal *Fernando Pessoa*	
CS-TTD	Airbus A.319-111	TAP - Air Portugal *Amadeo de Souza Cardoso*	
CS-TTE	Airbus A.319-111	TAP - Air Portugal *Francisco d'Ollanda*	
CS-TTF	Airbus A.319-111	TAP - Air Portugal *Calouste Gulbenkian*	
CS-TTG	Airbus A.319-111	TAP - Air Portugal *Humberto Delgado*	
CS-TTH	Airbus A.319-111	TAP - Air Portugal *Antonio Sergio*	
CS-TTI	Airbus A.319-111	TAP - Air Portugal *Eca de Queiros*	
CS-TTJ	Airbus A.319-111	TAP - Air Portugal *Viana da Mota*	
CS-TTK	Airbus A.319-111	TAP - Air Portugal *Miguel Torga*	
CS-TTL	Airbus A.319-111	TAP - Air Portugal *Almeida Garrett*	
CS-TTM	Airbus A.319-111	TAP - Air Portugal *Alexandre Herculano*	
CS-TTN	Airbus A.319-111	TAP - Air Portugal *Camilo Castelo Branco*	
CS-TTO	Airbus A.319-111	TAP - Air Portugal *Antero de Quental*	
CS-TTP	Airbus A.319-111	TAP - Air Portugal *Josefa d'Obidos*	

CU (Cuba)

CU-T1209	Ilyushin IL-62M	Cubana	
CU-T1215	Ilyushin IL-62M	Cubana	
CU-T1280	Ilyushin IL-62M	Cubana	
CU-T1282	Ilyushin IL-62M	Cubana	
CU-T1283	Ilyushin IL-62M	Cubana	
CU-T1284	Iluushin IL-62M	Cubana	

Note: British Airways operate European flights for Cubana using Boeing 777-200s.

D (Germany)

D-AAAC	F.27 Friendship Mk 500	Express Airways	

D

Notes	Reg.	Type	Owner or Operator
	D-AAAF	F.27 Friendship Mk 500	Express Airways
	D-ABAC	Boeing 737-86J	Air Berlin
	D-ABAD	Boeing 737-86J	Air Berlin
	D-ABAE	Boeing 737-86J	Air Berlin
	D-ABAF	Boeing 737-86J	Air Berlin
	D-ABAG	Boeing 737-86J	Air Berlin
	D-ABAH	Boeing 737-46J	Air Berlin
	D-ABAI	Boeing 737-46J	Air Berlin
	D-ABAK	Boeing 737-46J	Air Berlin
	D-ABAL	Boeing 737-46J	Air Berlin
	D-ABAM	Boeing 737-46J	Air Berlin
	D-ABAN	Boeing 737-86J	Air Berlin
	D-ABAO	Boeing 737-86J	Air Berlin
	D-ABAP	Boeing 737-86J	Air Berlin
	D-ABAQ	Boeing 737-86J	Air Berlin
	D-ABAR	Boeing 737-86J	Air Berlin
	D-ABAS	Boeing 737-86J	Air Berlin
	D-ABAT	Boeing 737-86J	Air Berlin
	D-ABAU	Boeing 737-86J	Air Berlin
	D-ABAV	Boeing 737-86J	Air Berlin
	D-ABAW	Boeing 737-86J	Air Berlin
	D-ABAX	Boeing 737-86J	Air Berlin
	D-ABAY	Boeing 737-86J	Air Berlin
	D-ABAZ	Boeing 737-86J	Air Berlin
	D-ABBA	Boeing 737-86J	Air Berlin
	D-ABBB	Boeing 737-86J	Air Berlin
	D-ABBC	Boeing 737-86J	Air Berlin
	D-ABBD	Boeing 737-86J	Air Berlin
	D-ABBE	Boeing 737-86J	Air Berlin
	D-ABEA	Boeing 737-330	Lufthansa *Saarbrücken*
	D-ABEB	Boeing 737-330	Lufthansa *Xanten*
	D-ABEC	Boeing 737-330	Lufthansa *Karlsrühe*
	D-ABED	Boeing 737-330	Lufthansa *Hagen*
	D-ABEE	Boeing 737-330	Lufthansa *Ulm*
	D-ABEF	Boeing 737-330	Lufthansa *Weiden i.d.Obf.*
	D-ABEH	Boeing 737-330	Lufthansa *Bad Kissingen*
	D-ABEI	Boeing 737-330	Lufthansa *Bamberg*
	D-ABEK	Boeing 737-330	Lufthansa *Wuppertal*
	D-ABEL	Boeing 737-330	Lufthansa *Pforzheim*
	D-ABEM	Boeing 737-330	Lufthansa *Eberswalde*
	D-ABEN	Boeing 737-330	Lufthansa *Neubrandenburg*
	D-ABEO	Boeing 737-330	Lufthansa *Plauen*
	D-ABEP	Boeing 737-330	Lufthansa *Naumburg (Saale)*
	D-ABER	Boeing 737-330	Lufthansa *Merseburg*
	D-ABES	Boeing 737-330	Lufthansa *Koethen/Anhalt*
	D-ABET	Boeing 737-330	Lufthansa *Gelsenkirchen*
	D-ABEU	Boeing 737-330	Lufthansa *Goslar*
	D-ABEW	Boeing 737-330	Lufthansa *Detmold*
	D-ABIA	Boeing 737-530	Lufthansa *Greifswald*
	D-ABIB	Boeing 737-530	Lufthansa *Esslingen*
	D-ABIC	Boeing 737-530	Lufthansa *Krefeld*
	D-ABID	Boeing 737-530	Lufthansa *Aachen*
	D-ABIE	Boeing 737-530	Lufthansa *Hildesheim*
	D-ABIF	Boeing 737-530	Lufthansa *Landau*
	D-ABIH	Boeing 737-530	Lufthansa *Bruchsal*
	D-ABII	Boeing 737-530	Lufthansa *Lörrach*
	D-ABIK	Boeing 737-530	Lufthansa *Rastatt*
	D-ABIL	Boeing 737-530	Lufthansa *Memmingen*
	D-ABIM	Boeing 737-530	Lufthansa *Salzgitter*
	D-ABIN	Boeing 737-530	Lufthansa *Langenhagen*
	D-ABIO	Boeing 737-530	Lufthansa *Wesel*
	D-ABIP	Boeing 737-530	Lufthansa *Oberhausen*
	D-ABIR	Boeing 737-530	Lufthansa *Anklam*
	D-ABIS	Boeing 737-530	Lufthansa *Rendsburg*
	D-ABIT	Boeing 737-530	Lufthansa *Neumünster*
	D-ABIU	Boeing 737-530	Lufthansa *Limburg a.d. Lahn*
	D-ABIW	Boeing 737-530	Lufthansa *Bad Nauheim*
	D-ABIX	Boeing 737-530	Lufthansa *Iserlohn*
	D-ABIY	Boeing 737-530	Lufthansa *Lingen*
	D-ABIZ	Boeing 737-530	Lufthansa *Kirchheim unter Teck*
	D-ABJA	Boeing 737-530	Lufthansa *Bad Segeberg*
	D-ABJB	Boeing 737-530	Lufthansa *Rheine*
	D-ABJC	Boeing 737-530	Lufthansa *Erding*

OVERSEAS AIRLINERS

D

Reg.	Type	Owner or Operator	Notes
D-ABJD	Boeing 737-530	Lufthansa *Freising*	
D-ABJE	Boeing 737-530	Lufthansa *Ingelheim am Rhein*	
D-ABJF	Boeing 737-530	Lufthansa *Aalen*	
D-ABJH	Boeing 737-530	Lufthansa *Heppenheim/Bergstrasse*	
D-ABJI	Boeing 737-530	Lufthansa *Siegburg*	
D-ABNE	Boeing 757-230	Condor Flugdienst	
D-ABNF	Boeing 757-230	Condor Flugdienst	
D-ABNH	Boeing 757-230	Condor Flugdienst	
D-ABNI	Boeing 757-230	Condor Flugdienst	
D-ABNK	Boeing 757-230	Condor Flugdienst	
D-ABNL	Boeing 757-230	Condor Flugdienst	
D-ABNM	Boeing 757-230	Condor Flugdienst	
D-ABNN	Boeing 757-230	Condor Flugdienst	
D-ABNO	Boeing 757-230	Condor Flugdienst	
D-ABNP	Boeing 757-230	Condor Flugdienst	
D-ABNR	Boeing 757-230	Condor Flugdienst	
D-ABNS	Boeing 757-230	Condor Flugdienst	
D-ABNT	Boeing 757-230	Condor Flugdienst	
D-ABOA	Boeing 757-330	Condor Flugdienst	
D-ABOB	Boeing 757-330	Condor Flugdienst	
D-ABOC	Boeing 757-330	Condor Flugdienst	
D-ABOE	Boeing 757-330	Condor Flugdienst	
D-ABOF	Boeing 757-330	Condor Flugdienst	
D-ABOG	Boeing 757-330	Condor Flugdienst	
D-ABOH	Boeing 757-330	Condor Flugdienst	
D-ABOI	Boeing 757-330	Condor Flugdienst	
D-ABOJ	Boeing 757-330	Condor Flugdienst	
D-ABOK	Boeing 757-330	Condor Flugdienst	
D-ABOL	Boeing 757-330	Condor Flugdienst	
D-ABOM	Boeing 757-330	Condor Flugdienst	
D-ABON	Boeing 757-330	Condor Flugdienst	
D-ABTA	Boeing 747-430 (SCD)	Lufthansa *Sachsen*	
D-ABTB	Boeing 747-430 (SCD)	Lufthansa *Brandenburg*	
D-ABTC	Boeing 747-430 (SCD)	Lufthansa *Mecklenburg-Verpommern*	
D-ABTD	Boeing 747-430 (SCD)	Lufthansa *Hamburg*	
D-ABTE	Boeing 747-430 (SCD)	Lufthansa *Sachsen-Anhalt*	
D-ABTF	Boeing 747-430 (SCD)	Lufthansa *Thüringen*	
D-ABTH	Boeing 747-430 (SCD)	Lufthansa *Duisburg*	
D-ABTK	Boeing 747-430 (SCD)	Lufthansa	
D-ABTL	Boeing 747-430 (SCD)	Lufthansa	
D-ABUA	Boeing 767-330ER	Condor Flugdienst	
D-ABUB	Boeing 767-330ER	Condor Flugdienst	
D-ABUC	Boeing 767-330ER	Condor Flugdienst	
D-ABUD	Boeing 767-330ER	Condor Flugdienst	
D-ABUE	Boeing 767-330ER	Condor Flugdienst	
D-ABUF	Boeing 767-330ER	Condor Flugdienst	
D-ABUH	Boeing 767-330ER	Condor Flugdienst	
D-ABUI	Boeing 767-330ER	Condor Flugdienst	
D-ABUZ	Boeing 767-330ER	Condor Flugdienst	
D-ABVA	Boeing 747-430	Lufthansa *Berlin*	
D-ABVB	Boeing 747-430	Lufthansa *Bonn*	
D-ABVC	Boeing 747-430	Lufthansa *Baden-Württemberg*	
D-ABVD	Boeing 747-430	Lufthansa *Bochum*	
D-ABVE	Boeing 747-430	Lufthansa *Potsdam*	
D-ABVF	Boeing 747-430	Lufthansa *Frankfurt am Main*	
D-ABVH	Boeing 747-430	Lufthansa *Düsseldorf*	
D-ABVK	Boeing 747-430	Lufthansa *Hannover*	
D-ABVL	Boeing 747-430	Lufthansa *Muenchen*	
D-ABVM	Boeing 747-430	Lufthansa	
D-ABVN	Boeing 747-430	Lufthansa *Dortmund*	
D-ABVO	Boeing 747-430	Lufthansa *Mulheim a.d.Ruhr*	
D-ABVP	Boeing 747-430	Lufthansa	
D-ABVR	Boeing 747-430	Lufthansa	
D-ABVS	Boeing 747-430	Lufthansa	
D-ABVT	Boeing 747-430	Lufthansa	
D-ABVU	Boeing 747-430	Lufthansa *Bayern*	
D-ABVW	Boeing 747-430	Lufthansa *Wolfsburg*	
D-ABVX	Boeing 747-430	Lufthansa	
D-ABVY	Boeing 747-430	Lufthansa	
D-ABVZ	Boeing 747-430	Lufthansa	
D-ABWC	Boeing 737-330QC	Lufthansa	
D-ABWD	Boeing 737-330QC	Lufthansa *Westerland/Sylt*	
D-ABWE	Boeing 737-330QC	Lufthansa *Goerlitz*	

Notes	Reg.	Type	Owner or Operator
	D-ABWF	Boeing 737-330F	Lufthansa *Rüdesheim am Rhein*
	D-ABWH	Boeing 737-330	Lufthansa *Rothenburg*
	D-ABXE	Boeing 737-330	Lufthansa *Hamm*
	D-ABXF	Boeing 737-330	Lufthansa *Minden*
	D-ABXH	Boeing 737-330	Lufthansa *Cuxhaven*
	D-ABXI	Boeing 737-330	Lufthansa *Berchtesgaden*
	D-ABXK	Boeing 737-330	Lufthansa *Ludwigsburg*
	D-ABXL	Boeing 737-330	Lufthansa *Neuss*
	D-ABXM	Boeing 737-330	Lufthansa *Herford*
	D-ABXN	Boeing 737-330	Lufthansa *Böblingen*
	D-ABXO	Boeing 737-330	Lufthansa *Schwäbisch-Gmünd*
	D-ABXP	Boeing 737-330	Lufthansa *Fulda*
	D-ABXR	Boeing 737-330	Lufthansa *Celle*
	D-ABXS	Boeing 737-330	Lufthansa *Sindelfingen*
	D-ABXT	Boeing 737-330	Lufthansa *Reutlingen*
	D-ABXU	Boeing 737-330	Lufthansa *Seeheim-Jugenheim*
	D-ABXW	Boeing 737-330	Lufthansa *Hanau*
	D-ABXX	Boeing 737-330	Lufthansa *Bad Homburg v.d. Höhe*
	D-ABXY	Boeing 737-330	Lufthansa *Hof*
	D-ABXZ	Boeing 737-330	Lufthansa *Bad Mergentheim*
	D-ABYO	Boeing 747-230F (SCD)	Lufthansa Cargo *America*
	D-ABYP	Boeing 747-230B	Lufthansa *Niedersachen*
	D-ABYR	Boeing 747-230B (SCD)	Lufthansa *Nordrhein-Westfalen*
	D-ABYU	Boeing 747-230F (SCD)	Lufthansa Cargo *Asia*
	D-ABYZ	Boeing 747-230F (SCD)	Lufthansa Cargo
	D-ABZB	Boeing 747-230F (SCD)	Lufthansa Cargo *New York*
	D-ABZC	Boeing 747-230F (SCD)	Lufthansa Cargo
	D-ABZD	Boeing 747-230B	Lufthansa *Kiel*
	D-ABZE	Boeing 747-230B (SCD)	Lufthansa *Stuttgart*
	D-ABZF	Boeing 747-230F (SCD)	Lufthansa Cargo *Africa*
	D-ABZH	Boeing 747-230B	Lufthansa *Bonn*
	D-ABZI	Boeing 747-230F (SCD)	Lufthansa Cargo *Australia*
	D-ACCC	Aérospatiale ATR-72-212	European Air Express
	D-ACCS	F.27 Friendship Mk 500	ECCS Air Cargo Service
	D-ACCT	F.27 Friendship Mk 500	ECCS Air Cargo Service
	D-ACFA	BAe 146-200	Eurowings
	D-ACHA	Canadair CL.600-2B19 RJ	Lufthansa CityLine *Murrhardi*
	D-ACHB	Canadair CL.600-2B19 RJ	Lufthansa CityLine *Meersburg*
	D-ACHC	Canadair CL.600-2B19 RJ	Lyfthansa CityLine *Füssen*
	D-ACHD	Canadair CL.600-2B19 RJ	Lufthansa CityLine
	D-ACHE	Canadair CL.600-2B19 RJ	Lufthansa CityLine *Mei Ben*
	D-ACHF	Canadair CL.600-2B19 RJ	Lufthansa CityLine *Montabaur*
	D-ACHG	Canadair CL.600-2B19 RJ	Lufthansa CityLine *Weil am Rhein*
	D-ACHH	Canadair CL.600-2B19 RJ	Lufthansa CityLine
	D-ACHI	Canadair CL.600-2B19 RJ	Lufthansa CityLine
	D-ACHK	Canadair CL.600-2B19 RJ	Lufthansa CityLine
	D-ACIR	Embraer RJ145MP	Cirrus Air/Team Lufthansa
	D-ACJA	Canadair CL.600-2B19 RJ	Lufthansa CityLine
	D-ACJB	Canadair CL.600-2B19 RJ	Lufthansa CityLine
	D-ACJC	Canadair CL.600-2B19 RJ	Lufthansa CityLine
	D-ACJD	Canadair CL.600-2B19 RJ	Lufthansa CityLine
	D-ACJE	Canadair CL.600-2B19 RJ	Lufthansa CityLine
	D-ACJF	Canadair CL.600-2B19 RJ	Lufthansa CityLine
	D-ACJG	Canadair CL.600-2B19 RJ	Lufthansa CityLine
	D-ACJH	Canadair CL.600-2B19 RJ	Lufthansa CityLine
	D-ACJI	Canadair CL.600-2B19 RJ	Lufthansa CityLine
	D-ACJJ	Canadair CL.600-2B19 RJ	Lufthansa CityLine
	D-ACLA	Canadair CL.600-2B19 RJ	Lufthansa CityLine
	D-ACLB	Canadair CL.600-2B19 RJ	Lufthansa CityLine
	D-ACLC	Canadair CL.600-2B19 RJ	Lufthansa CityLine
	D-ACLD	Canadair CL.600-2B19 RJ	Lufthansa CityLine
	D-ACLE	Canadair CL.600-2B19 RJ	Lufthansa CityLine
	D-ACLF	Canadair CL.600-2B19 RJ	Lufthansa CityLine
	D-ACLG	Canadair CL.600-2B19 RJ	Lufthansa CityLine
	D-ACLH	Canadair CL.600-2B19 RJ	Lufthansa CityLine
	D-ACLI	Canadair CL.600-2B19 RJ	Lufthansa CityLine
	D-ACLJ	Canadair CL.600-2B19 RJ	Lufthansa CityLine
	D-ACLK	Canadair CL.600-2B19 RJ	Lufthansa CityLine
	D-ACLL	Canadair CL.600-2B19 RJ	Lufthansa CityLine
	D-ACLM	Canadair CL.600-2B19 RJ	Lufthansa CityLine
	D-ACLP	Canadair CL.600-2B19 RJ	Lufthansa CityLine
	D-ACLQ	Canadair CL.600-2B19 RJ	Lufthansa CityLine
	D-ACLR	Canadair CL.600-2B19 RJ	Lufthansa CityLine

Reg.	Type	Owner or Operator	Notes
D-ACLS	Canadair CL.600-2B19 RJ	Lufthansa CityLine	
D-ACLT	Canadair CL.600-2B19 RJ	Lufthansa CityLine	
D-ACLU	Canadair CL.600-2B19 RJ	Lufthansa CityLine	
D-ACLV	Canadair CL.600-2B19 RJ	Lufthansa CityLine	
D-ACLW	Canadair CL.600-2B19 RJ	Lufthansa CityLine	
D-ACLY	Canadair CL.600-2B19 RJ	Lufthansa CityLine	
D-ACLZ	Canadair CL.600-2B19 RJ	Lufthansa CityLine	
D-ACPA	Canadair CL.600-2C10 RJ	Lufthansa CityLine	
D-ACPB	Canadair CL.600-2C10 RJ	Lufthansa CityLine	
D-ACPC	Canadair CL.600-2C10 RJ	Lufthansa CityLine	
D-ACPD	Canadair CL.600-2C10 RJ	Lufthansa CityLine	
D-ACPE	Canadair CL.600-2C10 RJ	Lufthansa CityLine	
D-ACPF	Canadair CL.600-2C10 RJ	Lufthansa CityLine	
D-ACPG	Canadair CL.600-2C10 RJ	Lufthansa CityLine	
D-ACPH	Canadair CL.600-2C10 RJ	Lufthansa CityLine	
D-ACPI	Canadair CL.600-2C10 RJ	Lufthansa CityLine	
D-ACPJ	Canadair CL.600-2C10 RJ	Lufthansa CityLine	
D-ACPK	Canadair CL.600-2C10 RJ	Lufthansa CityLine	
D-ACPL	Canadair CL.600-2C10 RJ	Lufthansa CityLine	
D-ACPM	Canadair CL.600-2C10 RJ	Lufthansa CityLine	
D-ACPN	Canadair CL.600-2C10 RJ	Lufthansa CityLine	
D-ACPO	Canadair CL.600-2C10 RJ	Lufthansa CityLine	
D-ACPP	Canadair CL.600-2C10 RJ	Lufthansa CityLine	
D-ACRA	Canadair CL.600-2B19 RJ	Eurowings	
D-ACRB	Canadair CL.600-2B19 RJ	Eurowings	
D-ACRC	Canadair CL.600-2B19 RJ	Eurowings	
D-ACRD	Canadair CL.600-2B19 RJ	Eurowings	
D-ADBK	Boeing 737-31S	Deutsche BA	
D-ADBL	Boeing 737-31S	Deutsche BA	
D-ADBM	Boeing 737-31S	Deutsche BA	
D-ADBN	Boeing 737-31S	Deutsche BA	
D-ADBO	Boeing 737-31S	Deutsche BA	
D-ADBP	Boeing 737-31S	Deutsche BA	
D-ADBQ	Boeing 737-31S	Deutsche BA	
D-ADBR	Boeing 737-31S	Deutsche BA	
D-ADBS	Boeing 737-31S	Deutsche BA	
D-ADBT	Boeing 737-31S	Deutsche BA	
D-ADBU	Boeing 737-31S	Deutsche BA	
D-ADBV	Boeing 737-31S	Deutsche BA	
D-ADBW	Boeing 737-31S	Deutsche BA	
D-ADEP	F.27 Friendship Mk 600	WDL	
D-ADHA	D.H.C.8Q-402 Dash Eight	Augsburg Airways/Team Lufthansa	
D-ADHB	D.H.C.8Q-402 Dash Eight	Augsburg Airways/Team Lufthansa	
D-ADHC	D.H.C.8Q-402 Dash Eight	Augsburg Airways/Team Lufthansa	
D-ADHD	D.H.C.8Q-402 Dash Eight	Augsburg Airways/Team Lufthansa	
D-ADHE	D.H.C.8Q-402 Dash Eight	Augsburg Airways/Team Lufthansa	
D-ADIA	Boeing 737-36Q	Deutsche BA	
D-ADIB	Boeing 737-36Q	Deutsche BA *Enzian*	
D-ADIC	Boeing 737-36Q	Deutsche BA *Alpenrose*	
D-ADOP	F.27 Friendship Mk 600	WDL	
D-ADUP	F.27 Friendship Mk 500	Sky Team	
D-AELC	F.27 Friendship Mk 600	WDL	
D-AELD	F.27 Friendship Mk 600	WDL	
D-AELE	F.27 Friendship Mk 600	WDL	
D-AELF	F.27 Friendship Mk 600	WDL	
D-AELG	F.27 Friendship Mk 600	WDL	
D-AELH	F.27 Friendship Mk 600	WDL	
D-AELI	F.27 Friendship Mk 600	WDL	
D-AELJ	F.27 Friendship Mk 600	WDL	
D-AELK	F.27 Friendship Mk 600	WDL	
D-AELM	F.27 Friendship Mk 600	WDL	
D-AERF	Airbus A.330-322	LTU	
D-AERG	Airbus A.330-322	LTU	
D-AERK	Airbus A.330-322	LTU	
D-AERQ	Airbus A.330-322	LTU	
D-AEWA	BAe 146-300	Eurowings	
D-AEWB	BAe 146-300	Eurowings	
D-AEWD	BAe 146-200	Eurowings	
D-AEWE	BAe 146-200	Eurowings	
D-AEWG	Aérospatiale ATR-72-212	Eurowings	
D-AEWH	Aérospatiale ATR-72-212	Eurowings	
D-AEWI	Aérospatiale ATR-72-212	Eurowings	
D-AEWK	Aérospatiale ATR-72-212	Eurowings	

D

Notes	Reg.	Type	Owner or Operator
	D-AFFI	Fokker 50	Contactair/Team Lufthansa
	D-AFFX	Fokker 50	Contactair/Team Lufthansa
	D-AFFY	Fokker 50	Contactair/Team Lufthansa
	D-AFFZ	Fokker 50	Contactair/Team Lufthansa
	D-AFKK	Fokker 50	Contactair/Team Lufthansa
	D-AFKL	Fokker 50	Contactair/Team Lufthansa
	D-AFKM	Fokker 50	Contactair/Team Lufthansa
	D-AFKN	Fokker 50	Contactair/Team Lufthansa
	D-AFKO	Fokker 50	Contactair/Team Lufthansa
	D-AFKP	Fokker 50	Contactair/Team Lufthansa
	D-AFKU	Fokker 50	Contactair/Team Lufthansa
	D-AGEL	Boeing 737-75B	Germania
	D-AGEN	Boeing 737-75B	Germania
	D-AGEP	Boeing 737-75B	Germania
	D-AGEQ	Boeing 737-75B	Germania
	D-AGER	Boeing 737-75B	Germania
	D-AGES	Boeing 737-75B	Germania
	D-AGET	Boeing 737-75B	Germania
	D-AGEY	Boeing 737-73S	Germania
	D-AGEZ	Boeing 737-73S	Germania
	D-AGMR	Boeing 737-430	Air One
	D-AGWB	McD Douglas MD-83	Aero Lloyd
	D-AHFA	Boeing 737-8K5	Hapag-Lloyd
	D-AHFB	Boeing 737-8K5	Hapag-Lloyd
	D-AHFC	Boeing 737-8K5	Hapag-Lloyd
	D-AHFD	Boeing 737-8K5	Hapag-Lloyd
	D-AHFE	Boeing 737-8K5	Hapag-Lloyd
	D-AHFF	Boeing 737-8K5	Hapag-Lloyd
	D-AHFG	Boeing 737-8K5	Hapag-Lloyd
	D-AHFH	Boeing 737-8K5	Hapag-Lloyd
	D-AHFI	Boeing 737-8K5	Hapag-Lloyd
	D-AHFJ	Boeing 737-8K5	Hapag-Lloyd
	D-AHFK	Boeing 737-8K5	Hapag-Lloyd
	D-AHFL	Boeing 737-8K5	Hapag-Lloyd
	D-AHFM	Boeing 737-8K5	Hapag-Lloyd
	D-AHFN	Boeing 737-8K5	Hapag-Lloyd
	D-AHFO	Boeing 737-8K5	Hapag-Lloyd
	D-AHFP	Boeing 737-8K5	Hapag-Lloyd
	D-AHFQ	Boeing 737-8K5	Hapag-Lloyd
	D-AHFR	Boeing 737-8K5	Hapag-Lloyd
	D-AHFS	Boeing 737-8K5	Hapag-Lloyd
	D-AHFT	Boeing 737-8K5	Hapag-Lloyd
	D-AHFU	Boeing 737-8K5	Hapag-Lloyd
	D-AHFV	Boeing 737-8K5	Hapag-Lloyd
	D-AHFW	Boeing 737-8K5	Hapag-Lloyd
	D-AHFX	Boeing 737-8K5	Hapag-Lloyd
	D-AHFY	Boeing 737-8K5	Hapag-Lloyd
	D-AHFZ	Boeing 737-8K5	Hapag-Lloyd
	D-AHIA	Boeing 737-73S	Hamburg International Airlines
	D-AHIB	Boeing 737-73S	Hamburg International Airlines
	D-AHIC	Boeing 737-7BK	Hamburg International Airlines
	D-AHLA	Airbus A.310-304	Hapag-Lloyd
	D-AHLC	Airbus A.310-308	Hapag-Lloyd
	D-AHLH	Boeing 737-8K5	Hapag-Lloyd
	D-AHLJ	Boeing 737-4K5	Hapag-Lloyd
	D-AHLN	Boeing 737-4K5	Hapag-Lloyd
	D-AHLO	Boeing 737-4K5	Hapag-Lloyd
	D-AHLP	Boeing 737-8K5	Hapag-Lloyd
	D-AHLQ	Boeing 737-8K5	Hapag Lloyd
	D-AHLR	Boeing 737-8K5	Hapag Lloyd
	D-AHLV	Airbus A.310-204	Hapag-Lloyd
	D-AHLW	Airbus A.310-204	Hapag-Lloyd
	D-AHLX	Airbus A.310-204	Hapag-Lloyd
	D-AHLZ	Airbus A.310-204	Hapag-Lloyd
	D-AHOI	BAe 146-300	Eurowings
	D-AIAH	Airbus A.300B4-603	Lufthansa *Lindau/Bodensee*
	D-AIAI	Airbus A.300B4-603	Lufthansa *Erbach/Odenwald*
	D-AIAK	Airbus A.300B4-603	Lufthansa *Kronberg/Taunus*
	D-AIAL	Airbus A.300B4-603	Lufthansa *Stade*
	D-AIAM	Airbus A.300B4-603	Lufthansa *Rosenheim*
	D-AIAN	Airbus A.300B4-603	Lufthansa *Nördlingen*
	D-AIAP	Airbus A.300B4-603	Lufthansa *Donauwörth*
	D-AIAR	Airbus A.300B4-603	Lufthansa *Bingen am Rhein*

Reg.	Type	Owner or Operator	Notes
D-AIAS	Airbus A.300B4-603	Lufthansa *Mönchengladbach*	
D-AIAT	Airbus A.300B4-603	Lufthansa *Bottrop*	
D-AIAU	Airbus A.300B4-603	Lufthansa *Bocholt*	
D-AIAW	Airbus A.300B4-605R	Lufthansa *Witten*	
D-AIAX	Airbus A.300B4-605R	Lufthansa *Fürth*	
D-AIAY	Airbus A.300B4-606R	Lufthansa	
D-AIBA	Airbus A.340-211	Lufthansa *Neurnberg*	
D-AIBC	Airbus A.340-211	Lufthansa *Leverkusen*	
D-AIBD	Airbus A.340-211	Lufthansa *Essen*	
D-AIBE	Airbus A.340-211	Lufthansa *Stuttgart*	
D-AIBF	Airbus A.340-211	Lufthansa *Luebeck*	
D-AIBH	Airbus A.340-211	Lufthansa *Bremerhaven*	
D-AICA	Airbus A.320-212	Condor Berlin	
D-AICB	Airbus A.320-212	Condor Berlin	
D-AICC	Airbus A.320-212	Condor Berlin	
D-AICD	Airbus A.320-212	Condor Berlin	
D-AICE	Airbus A.320-212	Condor Berlin	
D-AICF	Airbus A.320-212	Condor Berlin	
D-AICG	Airbus A.320-212	Condor Berlin	
D-AICH	Airbus A.320-212	Condor Berlin	
D-AICI	Airbus A.320-212	Condor Berlin	
D-AICJ	Airbus A.320-212	Condor Berlin	
D-AICK	Airbus A.320-212	Condor Berlin	
D-AICL	Airbus A.320-212	Condor Berlin	
D-AIDD	Airbus A.310-304	Lufthansa *Emden*	
D-AIDF	Airbus A.310-304	Lufthansa *Aschaffenburg*	
D-AIDH	Airbus A.310-304	Lufthansa *Wetzlar*	
D-AIDL	Airbus A.310-304	Lufthansa *Obersdorf*	
D-AIDN	Airbus A.310-304	Lufthansa *Gütersloh*	
D-AIFA	Airbus A.340-313X	Lufthansa	
D-AIFB	Airbus A.340-313X	Lufthansa	
D-AIFC	Airbus A.340-313X	Lufthansa	
D-AIFD	Airbus A.340-313X	Lufthansa	
D-AIFE	Airbus A.340-313X	Lufthansa	
D-AIFF	Airbus A.340-313X	Lufthansa	
D-AIGA	Airbus A.340-311	Lufthansa *Oldenburg*	
D-AIGB	Airbus A.340-311	Lufthansa *Recklinghausen*	
D-AIGC	Airbus A.340-311	Lufthansa *Wilhelmshaven*	
D-AIGD	Airbus A.340-311	Lufthansa *Remscheid*	
D-AIGE	Airbus A.340-313	Lufthansa	
D-AIGF	Airbus A.340-311	Lufthansa *Gottingen*	
D-AIGG	Airbus A.340-313	Lufthansa	
D-AIGH	Airbus A.340-311	Lufthansa *Koblenz*	
D-AIGI	Airbus A.340-311	Lufthansa *Worms*	
D-AIGK	Airbus A.340-311	Lufthansa *Bayreuth*	
D-AIGL	Airbus A.340-313X	Lufthansa *Herne*	
D-AIGM	Airbus A.340-313X	Lufthansa *Wolfsburg*	
D-AIGN	Airbus A.340-313X	Lufthansa	
D-AIGO	Airbus A.340-313X	Lufthansa	
D-AIGP	Airbus A.340-313X	Lufthansa	
D-AIGR	Airbus A.340-313X	Lufthansa *Leipzig*	
D-AIGS	Airbus A.340-313X	Lufthansa *Bergisch-Gladbach*	
D-AIGT	Airbus A.340-313X	Lufthansa *Viersen*	
D-AIGU	Airbus A.340-313X	Lufthansa *Castrop-Rauxei*	
D-AIGV	Airbus A.340-313X	Lufthansa	
D-AIGW	Airbus A.340-313X	Lufthansa	
D-AIGX	Airbus A.340-313X	Lufthansa	
D-AIGY	Airbus A.340-313X	Lufthansa *Lünen*	
D-AIGZ	Airbus A.340-313X	Lufthansa *Villingen-Schwenningen*	
D-AIKA	Airbus A.319-133	Lufthansa	
D-AILA	Airbus A.319-114	Lufthansa *Frankfurt (Oder)*	
D-AILB	Airbus A.319-114	Lufthansa *Lutherstadt Wittenburg*	
D-AILC	Airbus A.319-114	Lufthansa *Russelsheim*	
D-AILD	Airbus A.319-114	Lufthansa *Dinkelsbühl*	
D-AILE	Airbus A.319-114	Lufthansa *Kelsterbach*	
D-AILF	Airbus A.319-114	Lufthansa *Trier*	
D-AILH	Airbus A.319-114	Lufthansa *Norderstedt*/Khalifa Airways	
D-AILI	Airbus A.319-114	Lufthansa *Ingolstadt*/Khalifa Airways	
D-AILK	Airbus A.319-114	Lufthansa *Landshut*/Khalifa Airways	
D-AILL	Airbus A.319-114	Lufthansa *Marburg*	
D-AILM	Airbus A.319-114	Lufthansa *Friedrichshafen*	
D-AILN	Airbus A.319-114	Lufthansa *Idar-Oberstein*	
D-AILP	Airbus A.319-114	Lufthansa *Tubingen*	

Notes	Reg.	Type	Owner or Operator
	D-AILR	Airbus A.319-114	Lufthansa *Tegernsee*
	D-AILS	Airbus A.319-114	Lufthansa *Heide*
	D-AILT	Airbus A.319-114	Lufthansa *Straubing*
	D-AILU	Airbus A.319-114	Lufthansa *Verden*
	D-AILW	Airbus A.319-114	Lufthansa *Donaueschingen*
	D-AILX	Airbus A.319-114	Lufthansa *Fellbach*
	D-AILY	Airbus A.319-114	Lufthansa *Schweinfurt*
	D-AIPA	Airbus A.320-211	Lufthansa *Buxtehude*
	D-AIPB	Airbus A.320-211	Lufthansa *Heidelberg*
	D-AIPC	Airbus A.320-211	Lufthansa *Braunschweig*
	D-AIPD	Airbus A.320-211	Lufthansa *Freiburg*
	D-AIPE	Airbus A.320-211	Lufthansa *Kassel*
	D-AIPF	Airbus A.320-211	Lufthansa *Leipzig*
	D-AIPH	Airbus A.320-211	Lufthansa *Münster*
	D-AIPK	Airbus A.320-211	Lufthansa *Wiesbaden*
	D-AIPL	Airbus A.320-211	Lufthansa *Ludwigshafen am Rhein*
	D-AIPM	Airbus A.320-211	Lufthansa *Troisdorf*
	D-AIPP	Airbus A.320-211	Lufthansa *Starnberg*
	D-AIPR	Airbus A.320-211	Lufthansa *Kaufbeuren*
	D-AIPS	Airbus A.320-211	Lufthansa *Augsburg*
	D-AIPT	Airbus A.320-211	Lufthansa *Cottbus*
	D-AIPU	Airbus A.320-211	Lufthansa *Dresden*
	D-AIPW	Airbus A.320-211	Lufthansa *Schwerin*
	D-AIPX	Airbus A.320-211	Lufthansa *Mannheim*
	D-AIPY	Airbus A.320-211	Lufthansa *Magdeburg*
	D-AIPZ	Airbus A.320-211	Lufthansa *Erfurt*
	D-AIQA	Airbus A.320-211	Lufthansa *Mainz*
	D-AIQB	Airbus A.320-211	Lufthansa *Bielefeld*
	D-AIQC	Airbus A.320-211	Lufthansa *Zwickau*
	D-AIQD	Airbus A.320-211	Lufthansa *Jena*
	D-AIQE	Airbus A.320-211	Lufthansa *Gera*
	D-AIQF	Airbus A.320-211	Lufthansa *Halle a.d. Saale*
	D-AIQH	Airbus A.320-211	Lufthansa *Dessau*
	D-AIQK	Airbus A.320-211	Lufthansa *Rostock*
	D-AIQL	Airbus A.320-211	Lufthansa *Stralsund*
	D-AIQM	Airbus A.320-211	Lufthansa *Nordenham*
	D-AIQN	Airbus A.320-211	Lufthansa *Laupheim*
	D-AIQP	Airbus A.320-211	Lufthansa *Suhl*
	D-AIQR	Airbus A.320-211	Lufthansa *Lahr/Schwarzwald*
	D-AIQS	Airbus A.320-211	Lufthansa *Eisenach*
	D-AIQT	Airbus A.320-211	Lufthansa *Gotha*
	D-AIQU	Airbus A.320-211	Lufthansa
	D-AIQW	Airbus A.320-211	Lufthansa *Kleve*
	D-AIRA	Airbus A.321-131	Lufthansa *Finkenwerder*
	D-AIRB	Airbus A.321-131	Lufthansa *Baden-Baden*
	D-AIRC	Airbus A.321-131	Lufthansa *Erlangen*
	D-AIRD	Airbus A.321-131	Lufthansa *Coburg*
	D-AIRE	Airbus A.321-131	Lufthansa *Osnabrueck*
	D-AIRF	Airbus A.321-131	Lufthansa *Kempten*
	D-AIRH	Airbus A.321-131	Lufthansa *Garmisch-Partenkirchen*
	D-AIRK	Airbus A.321-131	Lufthansa *Freudenstadt/Schwarzwald*
	D-AIRL	Airbus A.321-131	Lufthansa *Kulmbach*
	D-AIRM	Airbus A.321-131	Lufthansa *Darmstadt*
	D-AIRN	Airbus A.321-131	Lufthansa *Kaiserslautern*
	D-AIRO	Airbus A.321-131	Lufthansa *Konstanz*
	D-AIRP	Airbus A.321-131	Lufthansa *Lüneburg*
	D-AIRR	Airbus A.321-131	Lufthansa *Wismar*
	D-AIRS	Airbus A.321-131	Lufthansa *Husum*
	D-AIRT	Airbus A.321-131	Lufthansa *Regensburg*
	D-AIRU	Airbus A.321-131	Lufthansa *Würzburg*
	D-AIRW	Airbus A.321-131	Lufthansa *Heilbronn*
	D-AIRX	Airbus A.321-131	Lufthansa *Weimar*
	D-AIRY	Airbus A.321-131	Lufthansa *Flensburg*
	D-AISB	Airbus A.321-231	Lufthansa *Hameln*
	D-AISC	Airbus A.321-231	Lufthansa *Speyer*
	D-AISD	Airbus A.321-231	Lufthansa *Chemnitz*
	D-AISE	Airbus A.321-231	Lufthansa *Neustadt an der Weinstrasse*
	D-AISF	Airbus A.321-231	Lufthansa
	D-AISG	Airbus A.321-231	Lufthansa *Lippstadt*
	D-AISY	F.27 Friendship Mk 600	WDL
	D-AJET	BAe 146-200	Eurowings
	D-AKEN	Canadair CL.600-2B19 RJ	Eurowings
	D-AKNF	Airbus A.319-112	Eurowings *Albrecht Durer*

OVERSEAS AIRLINERS

Reg.	Type	Owner or Operator
D-AKNG	Airbus A.319-112	Eurowings *Johan Wolfgang von Goethe*
D-AKNH	Airbus A.319-112	Eurowings *Heinrich Heine*
D-AKNI	Airbus A.319-112	Eurowings *Johannes Gutenburg*
D-AKNJ	Airbus A.319-112	Eurowings
D-AKNK	Airbus A.319-112	Eurowings
D-AK	Airbus A.319-112	Eurowings
D-ALAA	Airbus A.320-232	Aero Lloyd
D-ALAB	Airbus A.320-232	Aero Lloyd
D-ALAC	Airbus A.320-232	Aero Lloyd
D-ALAD	Airbus A.320-232	Aero Lloyd
D-ALAE	Airbus A.320-232	Aero Lloyd
D-ALAF	Airbus A.320-232	Aero Lloyd
D-ALAG	Airbus A.321-231	Aero Lloyd *Stadt Linz*
D-ALAH	Airbus A.321-231	Aero Lloyd
D-ALAI	Airbus A.321-231	Aero Lloyd
D-ALAJ	Airbus A.320-232	Aero Lloyd
D-ALAK	Airbus A.321-231	Aero Lloyd
D-ALAL	Airbus A.321-231	Aero Lloyd
D-ALAM	Airbus A.321-231	Aero Lloyd *FC Bayern Munchen*
D-ALAN	Airbus A.321-231	Aero Lloyd
D-ALAO	Airbus A.321-231	Aero Lloyd
D-ALAP	Airbus A.321-231	Aero Lloyd
D-ALAQ	Airbus A.321-231	Aero Lloyd
D-ALAR	Airbus A.321-231	Aero Lloyd
D-ALAS	Airbus A.321-231	Aero Lloyd
D-ALAT	Airbus A.321-231	Aero Lloyd
D-ALCA	McD Douglas MD-11F	Lufthansa Cargo
D-ALCB	McD Douglas MD-11F	Lufthansa Cargo
D-ALCC	McD Douglas MD-11F	Lufthansa Cargo
D-ALCD	McD Douglas MD-11F	Lufthansa Cargo
D-ALCE	McD Douglas MD-11F	Lufthansa Cargo
D-ALCF	McD Douglas MD-11F	Lufthansa Cargo
D-ALCG	McD Douglas MD-11F	Lufthansa Cargo
D-ALCH	McD Douglas MD-11F	Lufthansa Cargo
D-ALCI	McD Douglas MD-11F	Lufthansa Cargo
D-ALCJ	McD Douglas MD-11F	Lufthansa Cargo
D-ALCK	McD Douglas MD-11F	Lufthansa Cargo
D-ALCL	McD Douglas MD-11F	Lufthansa Cargo
D-ALCM	McD Douglas MD-11F	Lufthansa Cargo
D-ALCN	McD Douglas MD-11F	Lufthansa Cargo
D-ALIT	Canadair CL.600-2B19 RJ	Eurowings
D-ALIV	Canadair CL.600-2B19 RJ	Eurowings
D-ALLF	McD Douglas MD-83	Aero Lloyd
D-ALOA	BAe 146-200	Eurowings
D-ALPA	Airbus A.330-223	LTU
D-ALPB	Airbus A.330-223	LTU
D-ALPC	Airbus A.330-223	LTU
D-ALPD	Airbus A.330-223	LTU
D-ALPE	Airbus A.330-223	LTU
D-ALPF	Airbus A.330-223	LTU
D-ALPG	Airbus A.330-223	LTU
D-ALPH	Airbus A.330-223	LTU
D-ALPI	Airbus A.330-223	LTU
D-ALSA	Airbus A.321-211	LTU
D-ALSB	Airbus A.321-211	LTU
D-ALSC	Airbus A.321-211	LTU
D-ALSD	Airbus A.321-211	LTU
D-ALSE	Airbus A.321-211	LTU
D-ALTA	Airbus A.320-232	LTU
D-ALTB	Airbus A.320-214	LTU
D-ALTC	Airbus A.320-214	LTU
D-ALTD	Airbus A.320-214	LTU
D-ALTE	Airbus A.320-214	LTU
D-ALTF	Airbus A.320-214	LTU
D-ALTG	Airbus A.320-214	LTU
D-ALTH	Airbus A.320-214	LTU
D-ALTI	Airbus A.320-214	LTU
D-ALTJ	Airbus A.320-214	LTU
D-ALTK	Airbus A.320-214	LTU
D-ALTL	Airbus A.320-214	LTU
D-ALTM	Airbus A.320-214	LTU
D-AMAJ	BAe 146-200	WDL
D-AMUA	Boeing 757-2G5	LTU

	Type	Owner or Operator
	Boeing 757-2G5	LTU
	Boeing 757-2G5	LTU
	Boeing 757-2G5	LTU
	Boeing 767-3G5ER	LTU
JM	Boeing 757-2G5	LTU
UN	Boeing 767-3G5ER	LTU
MUO	Boeing 767-3G5ER	LTU
AMUP	Boeing 767-33AER	LTU
AMUR	Boeing 767-3G5ER	LTU
D-AMUS	Boeing 767-3G5ER	LTU
D-AMUV	Boeing 757-2G5	LTU
D-AMUW	Boeing 757-2G5	LTU
D-AMUY	Boeing 757-2G5	LTU
D-AMUZ	Boeing 757-2G5	LTU
D-ANFA	Aérospatiale ATR-72-202	Eurowings
D-ANFB	Aérospatiale ATR-72-202	Eurowings/Team Lufthansa
D-ANFC	Aérospatiale ATR-72-202	Eurowings
D-ANFD	Aérospatiale ATR-72-202	Eurowings/Team Lufthansa
D-ANFE	Aérospatiale ATR-72-202	Eurowings
D-ANFF	Aérospatiale ATR-72-202	Eurowings
D-ANFG	Aérospatiale ATR-72-212A	Eurowings
D-ANFH	Aérospatiale ATR-72-212A	Eurowings
D-ANFI	Aérospatiale ATR-72-212A	Eurowings
D-ANFJ	Aérospatiale ATR-72-212A	Eurowings
D-ANFK	Aérospatiale ATR-72-212A	Eurowings
D-ANFL	Aérospatiale ATR-72-212A	Eurowings
D-ANIK	Canadair CL.600-2B19 RJ	Eurowings
D-AQUA	BAe 146-300	Eurowings
D-AQUI	Junkers Ju.52/3m	Lufthansa Traditionsflug
D-ASKH	Boeing 737-73S	Hamburg International
D-ASKY	F.27 Friendship Mk 200	ECCS Air Cargo Service
D-AVRA	Avro RJ85	Lufthansa CityLine
D-AVRB	Avro RJ85	Lufthansa CityLine
D-AVRC	Avro RJ85	Lufthansa CityLine
D-AVRD	Avro RJ85	Lufthansa CityLine
D-AVRE	Avro RJ85	Lufthansa CityLine
D-AVRF	Avro RJ85	Lufthansa CityLine
D-AVRG	Avro RJ85	Lufthansa CityLine
D-AVRH	Avro RJ85	Lufthansa CityLine
D-AVRI	Avro RJ85	Lufthansa CityLine
D-AVRJ	Avro RJ85	Lufthansa CityLine
D-AVRK	Avro RJ85	Lufthansa CityLine
D-AVRL	Avro RJ85	Lufthansa CityLine
D-AVRM	Avro RJ85	Lufthansa CityLine
D-AVRN	Avro RJ85	Lufthansa CityLine
D-AVRO	Avro RJ85	Lufthansa CityLine
D-AVRP	Avro RJ85	Lufthansa CityLine
D-AVRQ	Avro RJ85	Lufthansa CityLine
D-AVRR	Avro RJ85	Lufthansa CityLine
D-AWBA	BAe 146-300	WDL
D-AWDL	BAe 146-100	WDL
D-AWUE	BAe 146-200	WDL
D-AZUR	BAe 146-200	Eurowings
D-BAAA	Aérospatiale ATR-42-300	European Air Express
D-BACH	D.H.C.8-311 Dash Eight	Augsburg Airways/Team Lufthansa
D-BAKB	F.27 Friendship Mk 600	WDL
D-BAKC	F.27 Friendship Mk 600	WDL
D-BBBB	Aérospatiale ATR-42-300	European Air Express
D-BCRO	Aérospatiale ATR-42-300QC	Eurowings
D-BCRP	Aérospatiale ATR-42-300QC	Eurowings
D-BCRQ	Aérospatiale ATR-42-320	European Air Express
D-BCRR	Aérospatiale ATR-42-320	European Air Express
D-BCRS	Aérospatiale ATR-42-320	European Air Express
D-BCRT	Aérospatiale ATR-42-320	European Air Express
D-BDTM	D.H.C.8Q-314 Dash Eight	Augsburg Airways/Team Lufthansa
D-BEBA	D.H.C.8Q-314 Dash Eight	Augsburg Airways/Team Lufthansa
D-BGAB	Dornier Do.328JET	Gandalf Airlines
D-BGAD	Dornier Do.328JET	Gandalf Airlines
D-BGAE	Dornier Do.328JET	Gandalf Airlines
D-BGAF	Dornier Do.328JET	Gandalf Airlines
D-BGAG	Dornier Do.328JET	Gandalf Airlines
D-BGAL	Dornier Do.328JET	Gandalf Airlines
D-BGAQ	Dornier Do.328JET	Gandalf Airlines

Reg.	Type	Owner or Operator	Notes
D-BGAR	Dornier Do.328JET	Gandalf Airlines	
D-BGAS	Dornier Do.328JET	Gandalf Airlines	
D-BHAL	D.H.C.8Q-202 Dash Eight	Augsburg Airways/Team Lufthansa	
D-BHAM	D.H.C.8-311 Dash Eight	Augsburg Airways/Team Lufthansa	
D-BHAS	D.H.C.8Q-311 Dash Eight	Augsburg Airways/Team Lufthansa	
D-BHAT	D.H.C.8Q-311 Dash Eight	Augsburg Airways/Team Lufthansa	
D-BHOQ	D.H.C.8Q-314 Dash Eight	Augsburg Airways/Team Lufthansa	
D-BIER	D.H.C.8-102 Dash Eight	Augsburg Airways/Team Lufthansa	
D-BJJJ	Aérospatiale ATR-42-300	European Air Express	
D-BKIM	D.H.C.8-311 Dash Eight	Augsburg Airways/Team Lufthansa	
D-BKKK	Aérospatiale ATR-42-512	Eurowings	
D-BLEJ	D.H.C.8Q-314 Dash Eight	Augsburg Airways/Team Lufthansa	
D-BLLL	Aérospatiale ATR-42-512	Eurowings	
D-BMMM	Aérospatiale ATR-42-512	Eurowings	
D-BMUC	D.H.C.8-314 Dash Eight	Augsburg Airways	
D-BNNN	Aérospatiale ATR-42-512	Eurowings	
D-BOBL	D.H.C.8-102A Dash Eight	Cirrus Airlines/Team Lufthansa	
D-BOBO	D.H.C.8-102 Dash Eight	Baden Air (Cirrus)/Team Lufthansa	
D-BOBU	D.H.C.8-311 Dash Eight	Cirrus Airlines/Team Lufthansa	
D-BOBY	D.H.C.8-102 Dash Eight	Cirrus Airlines	
D-BOOO	Aérospatiale ATR-42-512	Eurowings	
D-BPAD	D.H.C.8Q-314 Dash Eight	Augsburg Airways/Team Lufthansa	
D-BPPP	Aérospatiale ATR-42-512	Eurowings	
D-BQQQ	Aérospatiale ATR-42-512	Eurowings	
D-BRRR	Aérospatiale ATR-42-512	Eurowings	
D-BSSS	Aérospatiale ATR-42-512	Eurowings	
D-BTHF	D.H.C.8-202 Dash Eight	Augsburg Airways/Team Lufthansa	
D-BTTT	Aérospatiale ATR-42-512	Eurowings	
D-CCIR	Dornier Do.328-130	Cirrus Air	
D-CFAO	Short SD3-60 Variant 100	Farnair Europe/Federal Express	
D-CFDX	Short SD3-60 Variant 100	Farnair Europe/Federal Express	
D-CFXA	Short SD3-60 Variant 100	Farnair Europe/Federal Express	
D-CFXB	Short SD3-60 Variant 100	Farnair Europe/Federal Express	
D-CFXC	Short SD3-60 Variant 100	Farnair Europe/Federal Express	
D-CFXD	Short SD3-60 Variant 100	Farnair Europe/Federal Express	
D-CFXE	Short SD3-60 Variant 100	Farnair Europe/Federal Express	
D-CFXF	Short SD3-60 Variant 100	Farnair Europe/Federal Express	
D-CFXG	Short SD3-60 Variant 100	Farnair Europe/Federal Express	
D-CFXH	Short SD3-60 Variant 100	Farnair Europe/Federal Express	
D-CGAN	Dornier Do.328-110	Gandalf Airlines	
D-CGAO	Dornier Do.328-110	Gandalf Airlines	
D-CGAP	Dornier Do.328-110	Gandalf Airlines	
D-CGEP	Dornier Do.328-110	Gandalf Airlines	
D-CNAC	Swearingen SA227DC Metro 23	Northern Air Freight	
D-CNAF	Swearingen SA227AC Metro III	Northern Air Freight	
D-CNRX	BAe Jetstream 3102	European Air Express	
D-CNRY	BAe Jetstream 3103	European Air Express	
D-CNRZ	BAe Jetstream 3107	European Air Express	
D-COLB	Swearingen SA227AC Metro III	OLT/Roland Air	
D-COLC	Swearingen SA227AC Metro III	OLT/Roland Air	
D-COLD	Swearingen SA227AC Metro III	OLT/Roland Air	
D-COLE	SAAB SF.340A	OLT/Roland Air	
D-COLT	Swearingen SA226AC Metro III	OLT/Roland Air	
D-CRAS	Short SD3-60 Variant 100	Farnair Europe/Federal Express	
D-IHCW	Swearingen SA226TC Metro II	OLT/Roland Air	

EC (Spain)

EC-DIA	Boeing 747-256B	Iberia *Tirso de Molina*	
EC-DIB	Boeing 747-256B	Iberia *Cervantes*	
EC-DLD	Boeing 747-256B (SCD)	Iberia *Lupe de Vega*	
EC-DLF	Airbus A.300B4-120	Iberia *Canadas del Teide*	
EC-DLG	Airbus A.300B4-120	Iberia *Las Tablas de Daimiel*	
EC-DLH	Airbus A.300B4-120	Iberia *Aigues Tortes*	
EC-DNP	Boeing 747-256B	Iberia *Juan Ramon Jimenez*	
EC-DNQ	Airbus A.300B4-120	Iberia *Islas Cies*	
EC-DNR	Airbus A.300B4-120	Iberia *Ordesa*	
EC-EMD	Douglas DC-8-62F	Cygnus Air	
EC-EMX	Douglas DC-8-62F	Cygnus Air	
EC-EON	Airbus A.300B4-203	Iberia *Penalara*	
EC-EXF	McD Douglas MD-87	Iberia *Ciudad de Pamplona*	
EC-EXG	McD Douglas MD-87	Iberia *Ciudad de Almeria*	

Notes	Reg.	Type	Owner or Operator
	EC-EXM	McD Douglas MD-87	Iberia *Ciudad de Zaragoza*
	EC-EXN	McD Douglas MD-87	Iberia *Ciudad de Badajoz*
	EC-EXR	McD Douglas MD-87	Iberia *Ciudad de Oviedo*
	EC-EXT	McD Douglas MD-87	Iberia *Ciudad de Albacete*
	EC-EYB	McD Douglas MD-87	Iberia *Cangas de Onis*
	EC-EYX	McD Douglas MD-87	Iberia *Ciudad de Caceres*
	EC-EYY	McD Douglas MD-87	Iberia *Ciudad de Barcelona*
	EC-EYZ	McD Douglas MD-87	Iberia *Ciudad de Las Palmas*
	EC-EZA	McD Douglas MD-87	Iberia *Ciudad de Segovia*
	EC-EZS	McD Douglas MD-87	Iberia *Ciudad de Mahon*
	EC-FCB	Airbus A.320-211	Iberia *Montana de Covadonga*
	EC-FCU	Boeing 767-3Y0ER	Spanair *Baleares*
	EC-FDA	Airbus A.320-211	Iberia *Lagunas de Ruidera*
	EC-FDB	Airbus A.320-211	Iberia *Lago de Sanabria*
	EC-FEE	Boeing 757-236	Iberia *Catalunya*
	EC-FEY	McD Douglas MD-87	Iberia *Ciudad de Jaen*
	EC-FEZ	McD Douglas MD-87	Iberia *Ciudad de Malaga*
	EC-FFA	McD Douglas MD-87	Iberia *Ciudad de Avila*
	EC-FFH	McD Douglas MD-87	Iberia *Ciudad de Logrono*
	EC-FFI	McD Douglas MD-87	Iberia *Ciudad de Cuenca*
	EC-FFK	Boeing 757-236	Air Europa *Galicia*
	EC-FGH	Airbus A.320-211	Iberia *Caldera de Taburiente*
	EC-FGM	McD Douglas MD-88	Iberia *Torre de Hercules*
	EC-FGR	Airbus A.320-211	Iberia *Dehesa de Moncayo*
	EC-FGU	Airbus A.320-211	Iberia *Sierra Espuna*
	EC-FGV	Airbus A.320-211	Iberia *Monfrague*
	EC-FHA	Boeing 767-3Y0ER	Spanair *Canarias*
	EC-FHD	McD Douglas MD-87	Iberia *Ciudad de Leon*
	EC-FHG	McD Douglas MD-88	Iberia *La Almudiana*
	EC-FHK	McD Douglas MD-87	Iberia *Ciudad de Tarragona*
	EC-FIA	Airbus A.320-211	Iberia *Isla de la Cartuja*
	EC-FIC	Airbus A.320-211	Iberia *Sierra de Grazalema*
	EC-FIG	McD Douglas MD-88	Iberia *Penon de Ifach*
	EC-FIH	McD Douglas MD-88	Iberia *Albaicin*
	EC-FJE	McD Douglas MD-88	Iberia *Gibralfaro*
	EC-FKD	Airbus A.320-211	Iberia *Monte Alhoya*
	EC-FLK	McD Douglas MD-88	Iberia *Palacio de la Magdalena*
	EC-FLN	McD Douglas MD-88	Iberia *Puerta de Tierra*
	EC-FLP	Airbus A.320-211	Iberia *Torcal de Antequera*
	EC-FLQ	Airbus A.320-211	Iberia *Dunas de Liencres*
	EC-FML	Airbus A.320-211	Iberia *Hayedo de Tejera Negra*
	EC-FMN	Airbus A.320-211	Iberia *Cadi Moixero*
	EC-FND	McD Douglas MD-88	Iberia *Playa de la Concha*
	EC-FNR	Airbus A.320-211	Iberia *Monte del Valle*
	EC-FOF	McD Douglas MD-88	Iberia *Puerta de Alcala*
	EC-FOG	McD Douglas MD-88	Iberia *La Giralda*
	EC-FOZ	McD Douglas MD-88	Iberia *Montjuic*
	EC-FPD	McD Douglas MD-88	Iberia *Lagos de Coradonga*
	EC-FPJ	McD Douglas MD-88	Iberia *Ria de Vigo*
	EC-FQY	Airbus A.320-211	Iberia *Joan Miro*
	EC-FTR	Boeing 757-256	Iberia *Sierra de Guadarrama*
	EC-FTS	McD Douglas MD-83	Spanair *Sunbird*
	EC-FXA	McD Douglas MD-83	Spanair *Sunstar*
	EC-FXI	McD Douglas MD-83	Spanair *Sunseeker*
	EC-FXP	Boeing 737-4Q8	Air Europa *Villanueva del Conde*
	EC-FXQ	Boeing 737-4Q8	Air Europa *Salamanca*
	EC-FXV	Boeing 757-256	Iberia *Argentina*
	EC-FXY	McD Douglas MD-83	Spanair *Sunbeam*
	EC-FYJ	Boeing 757-256	Air Europa
	EC-FYK	Boeing 757-256	Air Europa
	EC-FYN	Boeing 757-256	Iberia *Costa Rica*
	EC-FZC	McD Douglas MD-83	Spanair *Sunflower*
	EC-FZE	BAe 146-200QT	TNT Airways
	EC-FZZ	Boeing 737-4Y0	Air Europa *Baleares*
	EC-GAG	Boeing 747-256B	Iberia *Calderon de la Barca*
	EC-GAT	McD Douglas MD-83	Spanair *Sunmyth*
	EC-GBA	McD Douglas MD-83	Spanair *Sungod*
	EC-GBX	Boeing 757-236	Air Europa
	EC-GCV	McD Douglas MD-82	Spanair *Sunburst*
	EC-GDD	Fokker 50	Air Nostrum
	EC-GDV	Swearingen SA.226AT Merlin IVA	Flightline (Spain) Ltd
	EC-GEU	Boeing 737-375	Air Europa Lugo
	EC-GFK	Swearingen SA.226AT Merlin IVA	Flightline (Spain) Ltd

Reg.	Type	Owner or Operator	Notes
EC-GFP	Fokker 50	Air Nostrum/Iberia	
EC-GGO	Boeing 737-3M8	Air Europa	
EC-GGS	Airbus A.340-313	Iberia Concha Espina	
EC-GGV	McD Douglas MD-83	Spanair Sunbow	
EC-GHC	Fokker 50	Air Nostrum/Iberia	
EC-GHD	Boeing 737-3M8	Air Europa	
EC-GHE	McD Douglas MD-83	Spanair Sunset	
EC-GHH	McD Douglas MD-83	Spanair Sundance	
EC-GHM	Boeing 767-204ER	Air Europa/Air Atlanta Iceland (TF-ATR)	
EC-GHX	Airbus A.340-313	Iberia Rosalia de Castro	
EC-GJI	Fokker 50	Air Nostrum/Iberia	
EC-GJT	Airbus A.340-313	Iberia Rosa Chacel	
EC-GJY	Fokker 50	Air Nostrum/Iberia	
EC-GKE	Fokker 50	Air Nostrum/Iberia	
EC-GKF	McD Douglas MD-87	Spanair Sundream	
EC-GKG	McD Douglas MD-83	Spanair Sunshine	
EC-GKU	Fokker 50	Air Nostrum/Iberia	
EC-GKV	Fokker 50	Air Nostrum/Iberia	
EC-GKX	Fokker 50	Air Nostrum/Iberia	
EC-GLE	Airbus A.340-313	Iberia Concepcion Arenal	
EC-GLT	Airbus A.320-231	Iberworld	
EC-GMU	Airbus A.310-324	Air Plus Comet	
EC-GMY	Boeing 737-36Q	Air Europa CanariasCamnini de Santiago	
EC-GNY	McD Douglas MD-83	Spanair Sunflash	
EC-GNZ	Boeing 737-4Y0	Futura International Airways	
EC-GOJ	Boeing 767-204ER	Air Europa	
EC-GOM	McD Douglas MD-83	Spanair Sunlight	
EC-GOT	Airbus A.310-324	Air Plus Comet	
EC-GOU	McD Douglas MD-83	Spanair Sunlover	
EC-GPB	Airbus A.340-313X	Iberia	
EC-GPI	Boeing 737-46Q	Air Europa/Iberia	
EC-GPS	Swearingen SA227AC Metro III	Euro Continental Air	
EC-GQG	McD Douglas MD-83	Spanair Sunrise	
EC-GQI	Fokker 50	Air Nostrum/Iberia	
EC-GQK	Airbus A.340-313X	Iberia	
EC-GQU	Aérospatiale ATR-72-201	Air Nostrum/Iberia	
EC-GQV	Aérospatiale ATR-72-201	Air Nostrum/Iberia	
EC-GQZ	McD Douglas MD-82	Spanair Sunbear	
EC-GRE	Airbus A.320-211	Iberia Sierra de Cazorla	
EC-GRF	Airbus A.320-211	Iberia Montseny	
EC-GRG	Airbus A.320-211	Iberia Timanfaya	
EC-GRH	Airbus A.320-211	Iberia Sierra de Segura	
EC-GRI	Airbus A.320-211	Iberia Delta del Ebro	
EC-GRJ	Airbus A.320-211	Iberia Canon del Rio Lobos	
EC-GRK	McD Douglas MD-87	Iberia Ciudad de Savilla	
EC-GRL	McD Douglas MD-87	Iberia Ciudad de Toledo	
EC-GRM	McD Douglas MD-87	Iberia Ciudad de Burgos	
EC-GRN	McD Douglas MD-87	Iberia Ciudad de Cadiz	
EC-GRO	McD Douglas MD-87	Iberia Arrecife de Lanzarote	
EC-GRX	Boeing 737-46B	Futura International Airways	
EC-GRY	Fokker 50	Air Nostrum/Iberia	
EC-GRZ	Fokker 50	Air Nostrum/Iberia	
EC-GSJ	Convair 580	Swiftair	
EC-GSU	Boeing 767-3Y0ER	Iberia/Air Europa	
EC-GTE	Fokker 50	Air Nostrum	
EC-GTG	Canadair CL.600-2B19 RJ	Air Nostrum/Iberia Regional	
EC-GTI	Boeing 767-3Y0ER	Iberia/Air Europa	
EC-GTO	McD Douglas MD-82	Spanair Sunjet	
EC-GUG	Boeing 737-4S3	Futura International Airways	
EC-GUL	Aérospatiale ATR-72-212	Air Nostrum/Iberia	
EC-GUO	Boeing 737-4Q8	Air Europa	
EC-GUP	Airbus A.340-313X	Iberia Agustina De Aragon	
EC-GUQ	Airbus A.340-313X	Iberia Beatriz Galindo	
EC-GUR	Airbus A.320-231	Iberworld	
EC-GVB	Boeing 737-4Y0	Futura International Airways	
EC-GVI	McD Douglas MD-83	Spanair Sunup	
EC-GVO	McD Douglas MD-83	Spanair Sunspot	
EC-GXU	McD Douglas MD-83	Spanair Sunray	
EC-GYI	Canadair CL.600-2B19 RJ	Air Nostrum/Iberia Pinazo	
EC-GZA	Canadair CL.600-2B19 RJ	Air Nostrum/Iberia	
EC-GZD	Airbus A.320-214	Iberworld	
EC-GZE	Airbus A.320-214	Iberworld	
EC-GZI	Embraer RJ145EU	European Regions Airlines	

Notes	Reg.	Type	Owner or Operator
	EC-GZY	Boeing 757-256	Iberia
	EC-GZZ	Boeing 757-256	Iberia
	EC-HAA	Boeing 757-256	Iberia
	EC-HAB	Airbus A.320-214	Iberia Cabaneros
	EC-HAD	Airbus A.320-214	Iberia Garajonay
	EC-HAF	Airbus A.320-214	Iberia
	EC-HAG	Airbus A.320-214	Iberia Senorio de Bertiz
	EC-HAH	Boeing 727-223F	Swiftair/DHL
	EC-HAL	Airbus A.310-324	Iberworld
	EC-HBF	Swearingen SA.226AT Merlin IVA	Flightline Ltd (Spain) Ltd/Ibertrans
	EC-HBH	Boeing 727-224F	Swiftair/DHL
	EC-HBL	Boeing 737-85P	Air Europa
	EC-HBM	Boeing 737-85P	Air Europa
	EC-HBN	Boeing 737-85P	Air Europa Lluchmajor
	EC-HBP	McD Douglas MD-83	Spanair
	EC-HBR	Boeing 727-224F	Swiftair/DHL
	EC-HBY	Aérospatiale ATR-72-212A	Air Nostrum/Iberia
	EC-HBZ	Boeing 737-4Y0	Futura International Airways
	EC-HCG	Aérospatiale ATR-72-212A	Air Nostrum/Iberia
	EC-HCP	Boeing 737-46B	Futura International Airways
	EC-HCR	Airbus A.320-231	Iberworld
	EC-HDH	BAe 146-200QT	TNT Airways
	EC-HDK	Airbus A.320-214	Iberia Mar Ortigola
	EC-HDL	Airbus A.320-214	Iberia Corredor del Duero
	EC-HDM	Boeing 757-256	Iberia Brasil
	EC-HDN	Airbus A.320-214	Iberia Parque National de Omiedo
	EC-HDO	Airbus A.320-214	Iberia Formentera
	EC-HDP	Airbus A.320-214	Iberia Parque de Cabarceno
	EC-HDQ	Airbus A.340-313X	Iberia Sor Juana Ines de la Cruz
	EC-HDR	Boeing 757-256	Iberia
	EC-HDS	Boeing 757-256	Iberia
	EC-HDT	Airbus A.320-214	Iberia Museo Guggenheim Bilbao
	EC-HDU	Boeing 757-256	Iberia Uruguay
	EC-HDV	Boeing 757-256	Iberia
	EC-HEI	Aérospatiale ATR-72-212A	Air Nostrum/Iberia Eucalipto
	EC-HEJ	Aérospatiale ATR-72-212A	Air Nostrum/Iberia
	EC-HEK	Canadair CL.600-2B19 RJ	Air Nostrum/Iberia Cecilio Pla
	EC-HFB	Airbus A.310-324	Air Plus Comet
	EC-HFP	McD Douglas MD-83	Spanair Sunbreeze
	EC-HFQ	Airbus A.310-324	Air Plus Comet
	EC-HFS	McD Douglas MD-82	Spanair Sunbeach
	EC-HFT	McD Douglas MD-82	Spanair Sunspirit
	EC-HFZ	EMB-120RT Brasilia	Regional Airlines
	EC-HGA	McD Douglas MD-83	Spanair Sunisland
	EC-HGJ	McD Douglas MD-82	Spanair Sunworld
	EC-HGO	Boeing 737-85P	Air Europa
	EC-HGP	Boeing 737-85P	Air Europa
	EC-HGQ	Boeing 737-85P	Air Europa
	EC-HGR	Airbus A.319-112	Iberia Ribeira Sacra
	EC-HGS	Airbus A.319-112	Iberia
	EC-HGT	Airbus A.319-112	Iberia
	EC-HGU	Airbus A.340-313X	Iberia Maria de Molina
	EC-HGV	Airbus A.340-313X	Iberia Maria Guerrero
	EC-HGX	Airbus A.340-313X	Iberia
	EC-HGY	Airbus A.320-214	Iberia Albarracin
	EC-HGZ	Airbus A.320-214	Iberia Boi Taull
	EC-HHA	Airbus A.320-214	Iberia Serrania de Ronda
	EC-HHB	Airbus A.320-214	Iberia Hoces de Cabriel
	EC-HHC	Airbus A.320-214	Iberia Mar Menor
	EC-HHF	McD Douglas MD-82	Spanair
	EC-HHG	Boeing 737-86N	Futura International Airways
	EC-HHH	Boeing 737-86N	Futura International Airways
	EC-HHI	Canadair CL.600-2B19 RJ	Air Nostrum/Iberia
	EC-HHP	McD Douglas MD-82	Spanair
	EC-HHU	Boeing 727-277F	Swiftair/DHL
	EC-HHV	Canadair CL.600-2B19 RJ	Air Nostrum/Iberia
	EC-HIF	Airbus A.310-325	Air Plus Comet
	EC-HIG	Boeing 727-277F	Swiftair/DHL
	EC-HIP	Boeing 757-256	Iberia
	EC-HIQ	Boeing 757-256	Iberia Honduras
	EC-HIR	Boeing 757-256	Iberia El Salvador
	EC-HIS	Boeing 757-256	Iberia Bolivia
	EC-HIT	Boeing 757-256	Iberia Guatemala

Reg.	Type	Owner or Operator	Notes
EC-HIU	Boeing 757-256	Iberia	
EC-HIV	Boeing 757-256	Iberia *Villa de Bilbao*	
EC-HIX	Boeing 757-256	Iberia	
EC-HJB	McD Douglas MD-82	Spanair	
EC-HJH	BAe 146-200QT	TNT Airways	
EC-HJI	Aérospatiale ATR-72-212A	Air Nostrum/Iberia	
EC-HJJ	Boeing 737-86N	Futura International Airways	
EC-HJP	Boeing 737-85P	Air Europa	
EC-HJQ	Boeing 737-85P	Air Europa	
EC-HJU	Convair Cv.580	Swiftair	
EC-HJV	Boeing 727-264F	Swiftair/DHL	
EC-HKA	Fokker 50	Air Nostrum/Iberia	
EC-HKO	Airbus A.319-111	Iberia	
EC-HKP	McD Douglas MD-83	Spanair *Sunshine*	
EC-HKQ	Boeing 737-85P	Air Europa	
EC-HKR	Boeing 737-85P	Air Europa	
EC-HKS	Boeing 767-3Q8ER	Air Europa	
EC-HLA	Airbus A.310-324	Air Plus *Comet*	
EC-HLC	Fokker 50	Air Nostrum/Iberia	
EC-HLD	Convair Cv.580	Swiftair (DHL)	
EC-HLM	Boeing 737-3K9	Seven Air	
EC-HLN	Boeing 737-86N	Futura International Airways	
EC-HLP	Boeing 727-264F	Swiftair/DHL	
EC-HME	Boeing 737-46B	Futura International Airways	
EC-HMI	McD Douglas MD-87	Spanair	
EC-HMJ	Boeing 737-86N	Futura International Airways	
EC-HMK	Boeing 737-86N	Futura International Airways	
EC-HNB	Boeing 737-4Q8	Air Europa	
EC-HNC	McD Douglas MD-83	Spanair *Sunplace*	
EC-HNO	Boeing 737-3K9	Seven Air/Andalucio Directo	
EC-HNS	Fokker 50	Air Nostrum/Iberia	
EC-HNY	Boeing 717-2CM	Air Balear	
EC-HNZ	Boeing 717-2CM	Air Balear	
EC-HOA	Boeing 717-2CM	Air Balear *Macarella*	
EC-HOV	McD Douglas MD-82	Spanair	
EC-HPM	Airbus A.321-231	Spanair *Camillo Jose Cela*	
EC-HPR	Canadair CL.600-2B19 RJ	Air Nostrum/Iberia	
EC-HPU	Boeing 767-3Q8ER	Air Europa	
EC-HQF	Airbus A.340-313X	Iberia	
EC-HQG	Airbus A.320-214	Iberia	
EC-HQH	Airbus A.340-313X	Iberia *Mariana de Silva*	
EC-HQJ	Airbus A.320-214	Iberia	
EC-HQK	Airbus A.320-214	Iberia *Cararella*	
EC-HQL	Airbus A.320-214	Iberia *Liebana*	
EC-HQM	Airbus A.320-214	Iberia	
EC-HQN	Airbus A.340-313X	Iberia *Luisa Carvajal y Mendoza*	
EC-HQT	Airbus A.300B4-203F	TNT Airways	
EC-HQV	Boeing 757-2G5	LTE International Airways	
EC-HQX	Boeing 757-2G5	LTE International Airways	
EC-HQZ	Airbus A.321-231	Spanair *Placido Domingo*	
EC-HRB	Boeing 757-2G5	LTE International Airways	
EC-HRG	Airbus A.321-231	Spanair	
EC-HRP	Airbus A.320-232	Spanair	
EC-HSH	Canadair CL.600-2B19 RJ	Air Nostrum/Iberia	
EC-HSV	Boeing 767-3Q8ER	Air Europa	
EC-HTA	Airbus A.320-214	Iberia	
EC-HTB	Airbus A.320-214	Iberia	
EC-HTC	Airbus A.320-214	Iberia	
EC-HTD	Airbus A.320-214	Iberia *Calblanque*	
EC-HTE	Airbus A.320-214	Iberia	
EC-HTF	Airbus A.320-214	Iberia *Costa Calida*	
EC-HTZ	Canadair CL.600-2B19 RJ	Air Nostrum/Iberia	
EC-HUH	Airbus A.321-211	Iberia *Benidorm*	
EC-HUI	Airbus A.321-211	Iberia *Comunidad Autonoma de la Rioja*	
EC-HUJ	Airbus A.320-214	Iberia *Getaria*	
EC-HUK	Airbus A.320-214	Iberia *Laguna Negra*	
EC-HUL	Airbus A.320-214	Iberia *Monasterio de Rueda*	
EC-HUZ	Boeing 717-23S	Aerolineas Baleares	
EC-HVB	Airbus A.310-324	Air Plus Comet	
EC-HVC	McD Douglas MD-83	Spanair	
EC-HVD	Boeing 747-256B (SCD)	Iberia *Francisco de Quevedo*	
EC-HVG	Boeing 767-3Z9ER	Spanair	
EC-HVX	McD Douglas MD-83	Spanair	

Notes	Reg.	Type	Owner or Operator
	EC-HVY	Boeing 737-4Y0	Futura International Airways
	EC-HVZ	Airbus A.300B4-203F	TNT Airways
	EC-HXA	Airbus A.320-232	Spanair
	EC-HXM	Canadair CL.600-2B19 RJ	Air Nostrum/Iberia
	EC-HXT	Boeing 737-4K5	Air Europa
	EC-HYC	Airbus A.320-214	Iberia
	EC-HYD	Airbus A.320-214	Iberia Maspalomas
	EC-HYJ	Fokker 50	Air Nostrum/Iberia
	EC-HZA	Fokker 50	Air Nostrum/Iberia
	EC-HZR	Canadair CL.600-2B19 RJ	Air Nostrum/Iberia
	EC-HZS	Boeing 737-86Q	Air Europa
	EC-HZU	Airbus A.320-214	Iberworld
	EC-IAF	Boeing 747-256B	Iberia
	EC-IAG	Airbus A.320-214	Iberworld
	EC-IAZ	Airbus A.320-232	Spanair
	EC-IBM	Canadair CL.600-2B19 R3	Air Nostrum
	EC-IBR	D.H.C.8-315 Dash Eight	Air Nostrum
	EC-IBS	D.H.C.8-315 Dash Eight	Air Nostrum

Note: Iberia also employs Boeing 747s TF-ATH, TF-ATI and TF-ATJ on lease from Air Atlanta

EI (Republic of Ireland)

Including complete current Irish Civil Register.

Reg.	Type	Owner or Operator
EI-ABI	D.H.84 Dragon	Aer Lingus Teo *Iolar* (EI-AFK)
EI-ADV	PA-12 Super Cruiser	R. E. Levis
EI-AFE	Piper J3C-65 Cub	J. Conlon
EI-AFF	B.A. Swallow 2	J. J. Sullivan & ptnrs
EI-AFN	B.A. Swallow 2 ★	J. McCarthy
EI-AGB	Miles M.38 Messenger 4 ★	J. McLoughlin
EI-AGD	Taylorcraft Plus D	B. & K. O'Sullivan
EI-AGJ	J/1 Autocrat	W. G. Rafter
EI-AHA	D.H.82A Tiger Moth ★	J. H. Maher
EI-AHI	D.H.82A Tiger Moth	High Fidelity Flyers
EI-AHR	D.H.C.1 Chipmunk 22 ★	C. Lane
EI-AKM	Piper J-3C-65 Cub	Setanta Flying Group
EI-ALH	Taylorcraft Plus D	N. Reilly
EI-ALP	Avro 643 Cadet	J. C. O'Loughlin
EI-ALU	Avro 631 Cadet	M. P. Cahill *(stored)*
EI-AMK	J/1 Autocrat	Irish Aero Club
EI-ANT	Champion 7ECA Citabria	T. Croke & ptnrs
EI-ANY	PA-18 Super Cub 95	Bogavia Group
EI-AOB	PA-28 Cherokee 140	J. Surdival & ptnrs
EI-AOP	D.H.82A Tiger Moth ★	Institute of Technology/Dublin
EI-AOS	Cessna 310B	Joyce Aviation Ltd
EI-APF	Cessna F.150F	Sligo Aero Club
EI-APS	Schleicher ASK.14	SLG Group
EI-ARH	Currie Wot/S.E.5 Replica	L. Garrison
EI-ARM	Currie Wot/S.E.5 Replica	L. Garrison
EI-ARW	Jodel D.R.1050	P. Walsh & P. Ryan
EI-AST	Cessna F.150H	S. Coughlan
EI-ATJ	B.121 Pup 1	L. O'Leary
EI-ATS	M.S.880B Rallye Club	ATS Group
EI-AUC	Cessna FA.150K	D. Bruton
EI-AUE	M.S.880B Rallye Club	Kilkenny Flying Club Ltd
EI-AUG	M.S.894 Rallye Minerva 220	K. O'Leary
EI-AUJ	M.S.880B Rallye Club	Ormond Flying Club Ltd
EI-AUM	J/1 Autocrat	J. G. Rafter
EI-AUO	Cessna FA.150K Aerobat	Kerry Aero Club
EI-AUS	J/5F Aiglet Trainer	T. Stephens & T. Lennon
EI-AUT	Forney F-1A Aircoupe	*(stored)*
EI-AUV	PA-23 Aztec 250C	Shannon Executive Aviation
EI-AUY	Morane-Saulnier M.S.502 (CF+HF)	G. Warner/Duxford
EI-AVB	Aeronca 7AC Champion	T. Brett
EI-AVM	Cessna F.150L	T. Carter & ptnrs
EI-AWE	Cessna F.150M	D. Bruton
EI-AWH	Cessna 210J	Rathcode Flying Club Ltd
EI-AWP	D.H.82A Tiger Moth	A. P. Bruton
EI-AWR	Malmö MFI-9 Junior	M. Whyte & J. Brennen
EI-AWU	M.S.880B Rallye Club	Longford Aviation Ltd
EI-AYA	M.S.880B Rallye Club	Limerick Flying Club Ltd

Reg.	Type	Owner or Operator	Notes
EI-AYB	GY-80 Horizon 180	J. B. Smith	
EI-AYD	AA-5 Traveler	P. Howick & ptnrs	
EI-AYF	Cessna FRA.150L	Limerick Flying Club (Coonagh) Ltd	
EI-AYI	M.S.880B Rallye Club	J. McNamara	
EI-AYK	Cessna F.172M	D. Gallagher	
EI-AYN	BN-2A-8 Islander	Galway Aviation Services Ltd	
EI-AYO	Douglas DC-3A ★	Science Museum, Wroughton	
EI-AYR	Schleicher ASK-16	B. O'Broin & ptnrs	
EI-AYV	M.S.892A Rallye Commodore 150	P. Murtagh	
EI-AYY	Evans VP-1	M. Donoghue	
EI-BAO	Cessna F.172G	D. Bruton	
EI-BAR	Thunder Ax8-105 balloon	J. Burke & V. Hourihane	
EI-BAS	Cessna F.172M	Falcon Aviation Ltd	
EI-BAT	Cessna F.150M	K. A. O'Connor	
EI-BAV	PA-22 Colt 108	J. Davy	
EI-BBC	PA-28 Cherokee 180C	Piper Aero Club Ltd	
EI-BBD	Evans VP-1	Volksplane Group	
EI-BBE	Champion 7FC Tri-Traveler (tailwheel)	P. Forde & D. Connaire	
EI-BBG	M.S.880B Rallye Club ★	Weston Ltd (stored)	
EI-BBI	M.S.892 Rallye Commodore	Kilkenny Airport Ltd	
EI-BBJ	M.S.880B Rallye Club	Weston Ltd	
EI-BBM	Cameron O-65 balloon	Dublin Ballooning Club	
EI-BBO	M.S.893E Rallye 180GT	G. P. Moorhead	
EI-BBV	Piper J-3C-65 Cub	F. Cronin	
EI-BCE	BN-2A-26 Islander	Galway Aviation Services Ltd	
EI-BCF	Bensen B.8M	P. Flanagan	
EI-BCH	M.S.892A Rallye Commodore 150	Limerick Flying Club	
EI-BCJ	Aeromere F.8L Falco 1 Srs 3	D. Kelly	
EI-BCK	Cessna F.172N II	K. A. O'Connor	
EI-BCL	Cessna 182P	L. Burke	
EI-BCM	Piper J-3C-65 Cub	Kilmoon Flying Group	
EI-BCN	Piper J-3C-65 Cub	Snowflake Flying Group	
EI-BCO	Piper J-3C-65 Cub	J. Molloy	
EI-BCP	D.628 Condor	A. Delaney	
EI-BCS	M.S.880B Rallye Club	Organic Fruit & Vegetables of Ireland Ltd	
EI-BCW	M.S.880B Rallye Club	Kilkenny Flying Club	
EI-BDH	M.S.880B Rallye Club	Munster Wings Ltd	
EI-BDK	M.S.880B Rallye Club	Limerick Flying Club Ltd	
EI-BDL	Evans VP-2	P. Buggle	
EI-BDM	PA-23 Aztec 250D ★	Industrial Training School	
EI-BDR	PA-28 Cherokee 180	Cherokee Group	
EI-BEA	M.S.880B Rallye 100ST ★	Weston Ltd (stored)	
EI-BEN	Piper J-3C-65 Cub	J. J. Sullivan	
EI-BEY	Naval N3N-3 ★	Huntley & Huntley Ltd	
EI-BFF	Beech A.23 Musketeer	P. McCoole	
EI-BFO	Piper J-3C-90 Cub	D. Gordon	
EI-BFP	M.S.800B Rallye 100ST	Weston Ltd	
EI-BFR	M.S.880B Rallye 100ST	J. Power	
EI-BFV	M.S.880B Rallye 100T	Ormond Flying Club	
EI-BGA	SOCATA Rallye 100ST	J. J. Frew	
EI-BGB	M.S.880B Rallye Club	Limerick Flying Club Ltd	
EI-BGD	M.S.880B Rallye Club	N. Kavanagh	
EI-BGJ	Cessna F.152	Sligo Aero Club Ltd	
EI-BGT	Colt 77A balloon	M. J. Mills	
EI-BGU	M.S.880B Rallye Club	M. F. Neary	
EI-BHC	Cessna F.177RG	B. Palfrey & ptnrs	
EI-BHF	M.S.892A Rallye Commodore 150	B. Mullen	
EI-BHI	Bell 206B JetRanger 2	H. S. S. Ltd	
EI-BHM	Cessna F.337E ★	Dublin Institute of Technology	
EI-BHN	M.S.893A Rallye Commodore 180T	T. Garvan	
EI-BHP	M.S.893A Rallye Commodore 180T	Spanish Point Flying Club	
EI-BHT	Beech 77 Skipper	Waterford Aero Club	
EI-BHV	Champion 7EC Traveler	E. P. O'Donnell	
EI-BHW	Cessna F.150F	R. Sharpe	
EI-BHY	SOCATA Rallye 150ST	Limerick Flying Club	
EI-BIB	Cessna F.152	Galway Flying Club	
EI-BIC	Cessna F.172N	Oriel Flying Group Ltd	

Notes	Reg.	Type	Owner or Operator
	EI-BID	PA-18 Super Cub 95	D. MacCarthy
	EI-BIG	Zlin 526	P. von Lonkhuyzen
	EI-BIJ	AB-206B JetRanger 2	Medavia Properties Ltd
	EI-BIK	PA-18 Super Cub 180	Dublin Gliding Club
	EI-BIM	M.S.880B Rallye Club	D. Millar
	EI-BIO	Piper J-3C-65 Cub	Monasterevin Flying Club
	EI-BIR	Cessna F.172M	B. Harrison & ptnrs
	EI-BIS	Robin R.1180TD	Robin Aiglon Group
	EI-BIT	M.S.887 Rallye 125	Spanish Point Flying Club
	EI-BIV	Bellanca 8KCAB Citabria	Aerocrats Flying Group
	EI-BIW	M.S.880B Rallye Club	E. J. Barr
	EI-BJA	Cessna FRA.150L	Blackwater Flying Group
	EI-BJB	Aeronca 7DC Champion	W. Kennedy
	EI-BJC	Aeronca 7AC Champion	E. Griffin
	EI-BJG	Robin R.1180	N. Hanley
	EI-BJJ	Aeronca 15AC Sedan	O. Bruton
	EI-BJK	M.S.880B Rallye 110ST	M. Keenen
	EI-BJM	Cessna A.152	Leinster Aero Club
	EI-BJO	Cessna R.172K	P. Hogan & G. Ryder
	EI-BJS	AA-5B Tiger	P. Morrisey
	EI-BJT	PA-38-112 Tomahawk	S. Corrigan & W. Lennon
	EI-BKC	Aeronca 15AC Sedan	G. Hendrick & ptnrs
	EI-BKF	Cessna F.172H	E. McEllim
	EI-BKK	Taylor JT.1 Monoplane	Waterford Aero Club
	EI-BKN	M.S.880B Rallye 100ST	Weston Ltd
	EI-BKS	Eipper Quicksilver	Irish Microlight Ltd
	EI-BKT	AB-206B JetRanger 3	Irish Helicopters Ltd
	EI-BKU	M.S.892A Rallye Commodore 150	Limerick Flying Club Ltd
	EI-BLB	SNCAN Stampe SV-4C	J. E. Hutchinson & R. A. Stafford
	EI-BLD	Bolkow Bo 105C	Irish Helicopters Ltd
	EI-BLE	Eipper Microlight	R. P. St George-Smith
	EI-BLN	Eipper Quicksilver MX	O. J. Conway & B. Daffy
	EI-BLO	Catto CP.16	R. W. Hall
	EI-BLU	Evans VP-1	S. Pallister
	EI-BLW	PA-23 Aztec 250C	— (stored)
	EI-BMA	M.S.880B Rallye Club	W. Rankin & M. Kelleher
	EI-BMB	M.S.880B Rallye 100T	Clyde Court Development Ltd
	EI-BMC	Hiway Demon Skytrike	S. Pallister
	EI-BMF	Laverda F.8L Falco	M. Slazenger & H. McCann
	EI-BMH	M.S.880B Rallye Club	N. J. Bracken
	EI-BMI	SOCATA TB.9 Tampico	Ashford Flying Group
	EI-BMJ	M.S.880B Rallye 100T	Weston Ltd
	EI-BML	PA-23 Aztec 250	Bruton Aircraft Engineering Ltd
	EI-BMM	Cessna F.152 II	P. Redmond
	EI-BMN	Cessna F.152 II	Iona National Airways Ltd
	EI-BMU	Monnet Sonerai IIL	A. Fenton
	EI-BMW	Vulcan Air Trike	L. Maddock
	EI-BNF	Goldwing Canard	T. Morelli
	EI-BNG	M.S.892A Rallye Commodore 150	Shannon Executive Aviation
	EI-BNH	Hiway Skytrike	M. Martin
	EI-BNJ	Evans VP-2	G. A. Cashman
	EI-BNK	Cessna U.206F	Irish Parachute Club Ltd
	EI-BNL	Rand KR-2	K. Hayes
	EI-BNP	Rotorway 133	R. L. Renfroe
	EI-BNT	Cvjetkovic CA-65	B. Tobin & P. G. Ryan
	EI-BNU	M.S.880B Rallye Club	P. A. Doyle
	EI-BOA	Pterodactyl Ptraveller	A. Murphy
	EI-BOE	SOCATA TB.10 Tobago	P. Byron & ptnrs
	EI-BOH	Eipper Quicksilver	J. Leech
	EI-BOV	Rand KR-2	G. O'Hara & G. Callan
	EI-BOX	Duet	K. Riccius
	EI-BPE	Viking Dragonfly	G. Bracken
	EI-BPJ	Cessna 182A	Falcon Parachute Club Ltd
	EI-BPL	Cessna F.172K	Phoenix Flying
	EI-BPO	Southdown Sailwings	A. Channing
	EI-BPP	Quicksilver MX	J. A. Smith
	EI-BPT	Skyhook Sabre	T. McGrath
	EI-BPU	Hiway Demon	A. Channing
	EI-BRK	Flexiform Trike	L. Maddock
	EI-BRS	Cessna P.172D	D. & M. Hillery
	EI-BRU	Evans VP-1	R. Smith & T. Coughlan

Reg.	Type	Owner or Operator	Notes
EI-BRV	Hiway Demon	M. Garvey & C. Tully	
EI-BRW	Ultralight Deltabird	A. & E. Aerosports	
EI-BRX	Cessna FRA.150L	Auburn Air Ltd	
EI-BSB	Jodel D.112	Estartit Ltd	
EI-BSC	Cessna F.172N	S. Phelan	
EI-BSF	Avro 748 Srs 1 ★	Ryanair *cabin trainer*/Dublin	
EI-BSG	Bensen B.80	J. Todd	
EI-BSK	SOCATA TB.9 Tampico	Weston Ltd	
EI-BSL	PA-34-220T Seneca	E. L. Symmons	
EI-BSN	Cameron O-65 balloon	C. O'Neill & T. Hooper	
EI-BSO	PA-28 Cherokee 140B	H. M. Hanley	
EI-BST	Bell 206B JetRanger	Celtic Helicopters Ltd	
EI-BSV	SOCATA TB.20 Trinidad	J. Condron	
EI-BSW	Solar Wings Pegasus XL-R	E. Fitzgerald	
EI-BSX	Piper J-3C-65 Cub	J. & T. O'Dwyer	
EI-BTX	McD Douglas MD-82	Airplanes Holdings Ltd *(leased to AeroMexico)*	
EI-BTY	McD Douglas MD-82	Airplanes Holdings Ltd *(leased to AeroMexico)*	
EI-BUA	Cessna 172M	Skyhawks Flying Club	
EI-BUC	Jodel D.9 Bebe	D. Lyons	
EI-BUF	Cessna 210N	210 Group	
EI-BUG	SOCATA ST.10 Diplomate	J. Cooke	
EI-BUH	Lake LA.4-200 Buccaneer	T. Henderson	
EI-BUJ	M.S.892A Rallye Commodore 150	T. Cunniffe	
EI-BUL	Whittaker MW-5 Sorcerer	J. Conlon	
EI-BUN	Beech 76 Duchess	K. A. O'Connor & ptnrs	
EI-BUO	Quickkit Glass S.005E	C. J. Lavery & A. C. Donaldson	
EI-BUR	PA-38-112 Tomahawk	Westair Aviation Ltd	
EI-BUS	PA-38-112 Tomahawk	Westair Aviation Ltd	
EI-BUT	M.S.893A Commodore 180	T. Keating	
EI-BUU	Solar Wings Pegasus XL-R	R. L. T. Hudson	
EI-BUV	Cessna 172RG	J. J. Spollen	
EI-BUW	Noble Hardman Snowbird IIIA	T.I.F.C. & I.S. Ltd	
EI-BUX	Agusta A.109A	Orring Ltd	
EI-BVB	Whittaker MW.6 Merlin	R. England	
EI-BVJ	AMF Chevvron 232	S. J. Dunn	
EI-BVK	PA-38-112 Tomahawk	Pegasus Flying Group Ltd	
EI-BVN	Bell 206B JetRanger 3	Helicopter Hire (Ireland) Ltd	
EI-BVT	Evans VP-2	P. Morrison	
EI-BVY	Zenith 200AA-RW	J. Matthews & ptnrs	
EI-BWH	Partenavia P.68C	K. Buckley	
EI-BXB	Boeing 737-448	Aer Lingus Teo *St Gall*	
EI-BXC	Boeing 737-448	Aer Lingus Teo *St Brendan*	
EI-BXD	Boeing 737-448	Aer Lingus Teo *St Colman*	
EI-BXI	Boeing 737-448	Aer Lingus Teo *St Finnian*	
EI-BXK	Boeing 737-448	Aer Lingus Teo *St Caimin*	
EI-BXL	Polaris F1B-OK350	M. McKeon	
EI-BXM	Boeing 737-2T4	Air Tara Ltd	
EI-BXO	Fouga CM.170 Magister	G. W. Connolly	
EI-BXT	D.62B Condor	S. Bruton	
EI-BXX	AB-206B JetRanger 3	Westair Aviation Ltd	
EI-BYA	Thruster TST Mk 1	E. Fagan	
EI-BYD	Cessna 150J	Kestrel Flying Group	
EI-BYF	Cessna 150M	Twentieth Air Training Group	
EI-BYG	SOCATA TB.9 Tampico	Weston Ltd	
EI-BYJ	Bell 206B JetRanger	Medeva Properties Ltd	
EI-BYL	Zenith CH.250	M. McLoughlin	
EI-BYR	Bell 206L-3 LongRanger 3	H. S. S. Ltd	
EI-BYV	Hughes 369D	Irish Helicopters Ltd	
EI-BYX	Champion 7GCAA	P. J. Gallagher	
EI-BYY	Piper J-3C-85 Cub	V. Murphy	
EI-BZE	Boeing 737-3Y0	GPA Group Ltd	
EI-BZF	Boeing 737-3Y0	Pergola Ltd	
EI-BZJ	Boeing 737-3Y0	Pergola Ltd	
EI-BZL	Boeing 737-3Y0	GECAS Ltd	
EI-BZM	Boeing 737-3Y0	GECAS Ltd	
EI-BZN	Boeing 737-3Y0	Airplanes Finance Ltd	
EI-CAC	Grob G.115A	G. Tracey	
EI-CAE	Grob G.115A	D. Kehoe	
EI-CAN	Aerotech MW.5 Sorcerer	V. Vaughan	
EI-CAP	Cessna R.182RG	M. J. Hanlon	

Notes	Reg.	Type	Owner or Operator
	EI-CAU	AMF Chevvron 232	J. Farrant
	EI-CAW	Bell 206B JetRanger	Celtic Helicopters Ltd
	EI-CAX	Cessna P.210N	J. Rafter
	EI-CAY	Mooney M.20C	Ranger Flights Ltd
	EI-CBB	Douglas DC-9-15	GPA Finance Ltd *(stored)*
	EI-CBJ	D.H.C. 8-102 Dash Eight	Debis Airfinance Jetprop Ltd
			(leased to Allegheny Commuter)
	EI-CBK	Aérospatiale ATR-42-310	GPA-ATR Ltd
			(leased to Aer Arann Express)
	EI-CBO	McD Douglas MD-83	Irish Aerospace Ltd *(leased to Nouvelair)*
	EI-CBR	McD Douglas MD-83	Airplanes 111 Ltd *(leased to Avianca)*
	EI-CBS	McD Douglas MD-83	GECAS Ltd *(leased to Avianca)*
	EI-CBY	McD Douglas MD-83	GECAS Ltd *(leased to Avianca)*
	EI-CBZ	McD Douglas MD-83	GECAS Ltd *(leased to Avianca)*
	EI-CCC	McD Douglas MD-83	Airplanes 111 Ltd *(leased to Avianca)*
	EI-CCD	Grob G.115A	M.O.D. Aviation Ltd
	EI-CCE	McD Douglas MD-83	GECAS Ltd *(leased to Avianca)*
	EI-CCF	Aeronca 11AC Chief	L. Murray & ptnrs
	EI-CCH	Piper J-3C-65 Cub	J. Matthews & ptnrs
	EI-CCJ	Cessna 152 II	Irish Aero Club
	EI-CCK	Cessna 152 II	Irish Aero Club
	EI-CCM	Cessna 152 II	E. Hopkins
	EI-CCV	Cessna R.172K-XP	Kerry Aero Club
	EI-CCY	AA-1B Trainer	N. & C. Whisler
	EI-CDA	Boeing 737-548	Aer Lingus Teo
	EI-CDB	Boeing 737-548	Aer Lingus Teo *St Albert*
	EI-CDC	Boeing 737-548	Aer Lingus Teo *St Munchin*
	EI-CDD	Boeing 737-548	Aer Lingus Teo *St Macartan*
	EI-CDE	Boeing 737-548	Aer Lingus Teo *St Jarlath*
	EI-CDF	Boeing 737-548	Aer Lingus Teo *St Cronan*
	EI-CDG	Boeing 737-548	Aer Lingus Teo *St Moling*
	EI-CDH	Boeing 737-548	Aer Lingus Teo *St Ronan*
	EI-CDP	Cessna 182L	Irish Parachute Club Ltd
	EI-CDV	Cessna 150G	K. A. O'Connor
	EI-CDX	Cessna 210K	Falcon Aviation Ltd
	EI-CDY	McD Douglas MD-83	GECAS Ltd *(leased to Avianca)*
	EI-CEG	M.S.893A Rallye 180GT	M. Farrelly
	EI-CEK	McD Douglas MD-83	Airplanes IAL Ltd
	EI-CEL	Rans S.6 Coyote	D. J. O'Gorman
	EI-CEN	Thruster T.300	P. J. Murphy
	EI-CEP	McD Douglas MD-83	GECAS Ltd *(leased to Avianca)*
	EI-CEQ	McD Douglas MD-83	GECAS Ltd *(leased to Avianca)*
	EI-CER	McD Douglas MD-83	Airplanes 111 Ltd *(leased to Avianca)*
	EI-CES	Taylorcraft BC-65	N. O'Brien
	EI-CEX	Lake LA-4-200	Derg Developments Ltd
	EI-CEY	Boeing 757-2Y0	Pergola Ltd *(leased to Avianca)*
	EI-CEZ	Boeing 757-2Y0	GPA 11 Ltd *(leased to Avianca)*
	EI-CFE	Robinson R-22B	Premier Aviation Services Ltd
	EI-CFF	PA-12 Super Cruiser	J. O'Dwyer & J. Molloy
	EI-CFG	CP.301B Emeraude	Southlink Ltd
	EI-CFH	PA-12 Super Cruiser	G. Treacy
	EI-CFL	Airbus A.300B4	Air Tara Ltd
	EI-CFN	Cessna 172P	B. Fitzmaurice & G. O'Connell
	EI-CFO	Piper J-3C-65 Cub	J. Mathews & ptnrs
	EI-CFP	Cessna 172P (floatplane)	K. A. O'Connor
	EI-CFX	Robinson R-22B	Helicopter Aviation Sales Ltd
	EI-CFY	Cessna 172N	K. A. O'Connor
	EI-CFZ	McD Douglas MD-83	Airplanes 111 Ltd *(leased to Avianca)*
	EI-CGB	Team Minimax	M. Garvey
	EI-CGC	Stinson 108-3	A. P. Bruton
	EI-CGD	Cessna 172M	J. Murray
	EI-CGE	Hiway Demon	T. E. Carr
	EI-CGF	Luton LA-5 Major	F. Doyle & J. Duggan
	EI-CGH	Cessna 210N	J. J. Spollen
	EI-CGJ	Solar Wings Pegasus XL-R	P. Heraty
	EI-CGK	Robinson R-22B	Skyfare Ltd
	EI-CGM	Solar Wings Pegasus XL-R	Microflight Ltd
	EI-CGN	Solar Wings Pegasus XL-R	V. Power
	EI-CGO	Douglas DC-8-63AF	Aer Turas Teo
	EI-CGP	PA-28 Cherokee 140C	G. Cashman
	EI-CGQ	AS.350B Ecureuil	Caulstown Air Ltd
	EI-CGT	Cessna 152 II	J. Rafter
	EI-CGV	Piper J-5A Cub Cruiser	J5 Group

Reg.	Type	Owner or Operator	Notes
EI-CGW	Powerchute Kestrel	C. Kiernan	
EI-CHH	Boeing 737-317	Airplanes Finance Ltd (leased to Frontier Airlines)	
EI-CHK	Piper J-3C-65 Cub	N. Higgins	
EI-CHM	Cessna 150M	K. A. O'Connor	
EI-CHN	M.S.880B Rallye Club	Limerick Flying Club (Coonagh) Ltd	
EI-CHP	D.H.C.8-103 Dash Eight	Airplanes Jetprop Finance Ltd (leased to US Airways Express)	
EI-CHR	CFM Shadow Srs BD	J. Smith	
EI-CHS	Cessna 172M	Kerry Aero Club Ltd	
EI-CHV	Agusta A.109A-II	Celtic Helicopters Ltd	
EI-CIA	M.S.880B Rallye Club	G. Hackett & C. Mason	
EI-CIF	PA-28 Cherokee 180C	AA Flying Group	
EI-CIG	PA-18 Super Cub 150	K. A. O'Connor	
EI-CIJ	Cessna 340	Airlink Airways Ltd	
EI-CIK	Mooney M.20C	T. G. Gordon	
EI-CIM	Light Aero Avid Speedwing Mk IV	P. Swan	
EI-CIN	Cessna 150K	K. O'Connor	
EI-CIR	Cessna 551 Citation II	Air Group Finance Ltd	
EI-CIV	PA-28 Cherokee 140	G. Cashman & E. Callanan	
EI-CIW	McD Douglas MD-83	Carotene Ltd (leased to Meridiana)	
EI-CJC	Boeing 737-204ADV	Ryanair Ltd (Hertz)	
EI-CJD	Boeing 737-204ADV	Ryanair Ltd (Ercell)	
EI-CJE	Boeing 737-204ADV	Ryanair Ltd (Jaguar)	
EI-CJF	Boeing 737-204ADV	Ryanair Ltd	
EI-CJG	Boeing 737-204ADV	Ryanair Ltd	
EI-CJH	Boeing 737-204ADV	Ryanair Ltd	
EI-CJI	Boeing 737-2E7ADV	Ryanair Ltd	
EI-CJR	SNCAN Stampe SV-4A	C. Scully & ptnrs	
EI-CJS	Jodel D.120A	K. Houlihan	
EI-CJT	Slingsby Motor Cadet III	J. Tarrant	
EI-CJV	Moskito 2	M. Peril & ptnrs	
EI-CJZ	Whittaker MW.6 Merlin	M. McCarthy	
EI-CKG	Avon Hunt Weightlift	B. Kelly	
EI-CKH	PA-18 Super Cub 95	G. Brady & C. Keenan	
EI-CKI	Thruster TST Mk 1	S. Pallister	
EI-CKJ	Cameron N-77 balloon	F. Meldon	
EI-CKM	McD Douglas MD-83	Airplanes IAL Finance Ltd (leased to Meridiana)	
EI-CKN	Whittaker MW.6-S Fatboy Flyer	F. Byrne & M. D.'Carroll	
EI-CKP	Boeing 737-2K2	Ryanair Ltd	
EI-CKQ	Boeing 737-2K2	Ryanair Ltd	
EI-CKR	Boeing 737-2K2	Ryanair Ltd	
EI-CKS	Boeing 737-2T5	Ryanair Ltd	
EI-CKT	Mainair Gemini Flash	C. Burke	
EI-CKU	Solar Wings Pegasus SLR	M. O'Regan	
EI-CKX	Jodel D.112	W. R. Prescott	
EI-CKZ	Jodel D.18	J. O'Brien	
EI-CLA	HOAC Katana DV.20	Weston Ltd	
EI-CLB	Aérospatiale ATR-72-212	Tarquin Ltd (leased to Alitalia Express)	
EI-CLC	Aérospatiale ATR-72-212	Tarquin Ltd (leased to Alitalia Express)	
EI-CLD	Aérospatiale ATR-72-212	Tarquin Ltd (leased to Alitalia Express)	
EI-CLG	BAe 146-300	Aer Lingus Commuter St Finbarr	
EI-CLH	BAe 146-300	Aer Lingus Commuter St Aoife	
EI-CLI	BAe 146-300	Aer Lingus Commuter St Eithne	
EI-CLL	Whittaker MW.6-S Fat Boy Flyer	F. Stack	
EI-CLQ	Cessna F.172N	K. Dardis & ptnrs	
EI-CLW	Boeing 737-3Y0	Airplanes Finance Ltd (leased to Air One)	
EI-CLY	BAe 146-300	Aer Lingus Commuter St Eugene	
EI-CLZ	Boeing 737-3Y0	Airplanes Finance Ltd (leased to Air One)	
EI-CMB	PA-28 Cherokee 140	Kestrel Flying Group Ltd	
EI-CMF	CFM Streak Shadow	O. Williams	
EI-CMI	Robinson R-22B	Toriamos Ltd	
EI-CMJ	Aérospatiale ATR-72-212	Tarquin Ltd (leased to Alitalia Express)	
EI-CMK	Goldwing ST	M. Gavigan	
EI-CML	Cessna 150M	K. A. O'Connor	
EI-CMM	McD Douglas MD-83	Irish Aerospace Ltd (leased to Eurofly)	
EI-CMN	PA-12 Super Cruiser	D. Graham & ptnrs	
EI-CMR	Rutan LongEz	F. & C. O'Caoimh	
EI-CMS	BAe 146-200	CityJet Ltd	
EI-CMT	PA-34-200T Seneca II	Atlantic Flight Training Ltd	
EI-CMU	Mainair Mercury	L. Langan & L. Laffan	
EI-CMV	Cessna 150L	K. A. O'Connor	

Notes	Reg.	Type	Owner or Operator
	EI-CMW	Rotorway Executive	B. McNamee
	EI-CMY	BAe 146-200	CityJet Ltd/Air France
	EI-CMZ	McD Douglas MD-83	Airplanes Finance Ltd (leased to Eurofly)
	EI-CNA	Letov LK-2M Sluka	G. H. Doody
	EI-CNB	BAe 146-200	CityJet Ltd
	EI-CNC	Team Minimax	A. M. S. Allen
	EI-CNG	Air & Space 18A gyroplane	P. Joyce
	EI-CNH	—	—
	EI-CNI	Avro RJ85	Azzurra Air
	EI-CNJ	Avro RJ85	Azzurra Air
	EI-CNK	Avro RJ85	Azzurra Air
	EI-CNL	Sikorsky S-61N	CHC (Ireland) Ltd
	EI-CNM	PA-31-350 Navajo Chieftain	M. Goss
	EI-CNN	L.1011-385 TriStar 1	Aer Turas Teo
	EI-CNO	McD Douglas MD-83	Airplanes Finance Ltd (leased to Nouvelair)
	EI-CNQ	BAe 146-200	CityJet Ltd/Air France Express
	EI-CNR	McD Douglas MD-83	Aircraft Finance Trust Ltd (leased to Eurofly)
	EI-CNT	Boeing 737-230ADV	Ryanair Ltd (The Sun/News of the World)
	EI-CNU	Pegasus Quantum 15-912	M. Ffrench
	EI-CNV	Boeing 737-230ADV	Ryanair Ltd
	EI-CNW	Boeing 737-230ADV	Ryanair Ltd
	EI-CNX	Boeing 737-230ADV	Ryanair Ltd (Tipperary Crystal)
	EI-CNY	Boeing 737-230ADV	Ryanair Ltd (Kilkenny)
	EI-CNZ	Boeing 737-230ADV	Ryanair Ltd
	EI-COA	Boeing 737-230ADV	Ryanair Ltd
	EI-COB	Boeing 737-230ADV	Ryanair Ltd
	EI-COE	Shaw Europa	F. Flynn
	EI-COG	Gyroscopic Rotorcraft gyroplane	R. C. Fidler & D. Bracken
	EI-COH	Boeing 737-430	Maike Ltd (leased to Air One)
	EI-COI	Boeing 737-430	Challey Ltd (leased to Air One)
	EI-COJ	Boeing 737-430	Challey Ltd (leased to Air One)
	EI-COM	Whittaker MW.6-S Fatboy Flyer	M. Watson
	EI-CON	Boeing 737-2T5	Ryanair Ltd
	EI-COO	Carlson Sparrow II	D. Logue
	EI-COP	Cessna F.150L	High Kings Flying Group Ltd
	EI-COQ	Avro RJ70	Azzurra Air
	EI-COT	Cessna F.172N	Kawasaki Distributors (Ireland) Ltd
	EI-COV	H.S.125 Srs 700B	Wilton Bridge Ltd
	EI-COX	Boeing 737-230	Ryanair Ltd
	EI-COY	Piper J-3C-65 Cub	P. McWade
	EI-COZ	PA-28 Cherokee 140C	G. Cashman
	EI-CPB	McD Douglas MD-83	Irish Aerospace Ltd (leased to Eurofly)
	EI-CPC	Airbus A.321-211	Aer Lingus Teo St Fergus
	EI-CPD	Airbus A.321-211	Aer Lingus Teo St Davnet
	EI-CPE	Airbus A.321-211	Aer Lingus Teo St Enda
	EI-CPF	Airbus A.321-211	Aer Lingus Teo St Ide
	EI-CPG	Airbus A.321-211	Aer Lingus Teo St. Aidan
	EI-CPH	Airbus A.321-211	Aer Lingus Teo St Dervilla
	EI-CPI	Rutan LongEz	D. J. Ryan
	EI-CPJ	Avro RJ70	Azzurra Air
	EI-CPK	Avro RJ70	Azzurra Air
	EI-CPL	Avro RJ70	Azzurra Air
	EI-CPN	Auster J/4	E. Fagan
	EI-CPO	Robinson R-22B-2	Santail Ltd
	EI-CPP	Piper J-3C-65 Cub	E. Fitzgerald
	EI-CPS	Beech 95-58 Baron	F. Doherty
	EI-CPT	Aérospatiale ATR-42-320	GPA-ATR Ltd (leased to Aer Arran Express)
	EI-CPU	Boeing 737-430	Flightlease (Ireland) Ltd
	EI-CPX	Sky Arrow 650T	N. Irwin
	EI-CRC	Boeing 737-46B	-
	EI-CRB	Lindstrand LBL-90A balloon	J. & C. Concannon
	EI-CRD	Boeing 767-31BER	ILFC Ireland Ltd (leased to Alitalia)
	EI-CRE	McD Douglas MD-83	AAR Ireland Ltd (leased to Meridiana)
	EI-CRF	Boeing 767-31BER	ILFC Ireland Ltd (leased to Eurofly)
	EI-CRG	Robin DR.400/180R	D. & B. Lodge
	EI-CRH	McD Douglas MD-83	Airplanes 111 Ltd (leased to Meridiana)
	EI-CRJ	McD Douglas MD-83	C. A. Aviation Ltd (leased to Meridiana)
	EI-CRK	Airbus A.330-301	Aer Lingus Teo
	EI-CRL	Boeing 767-343ER	GECAS Ltd (leased to Alitalia)
	EI-CRM	Boeing 767-343ER	GECAS Ltd (leased to Alitalia)

Reg.	Type	Owner or Operator	Notes
EI-CRO	Boeing 767-3Q8ER	ILFC Ireland Ltd (leased to Alitalia)	
EI-CRP	Boeing 737-73S	Pembroke Capital (leased to Azzurra Air)	
EI-CRQ	Boeing 737-73S	Pembroke Capital (leased to Azzurra Air)	
EI-CRR	Aeronca 11AC Chief	L. Maddock & ptnrs	
EI-CRS	Boeing 777-2Q8	ILFC Ireland Ltd (leased to Air Europe SpA)	
EI-CRT	Boeing 777-2Q8	ILFC Ireland Ltd (leased to Air Europe SpA)	
EI-CRU	Cessna 152	W. Reilly	
EI-CRV	Hoffmann H-36 Dimona	Falcon Aviation Ltd	
EI-CRW	McD Douglas MD-83	Airplanes IAL Ltd (leased to Meridiana)	
EI-CRX	SOCATA TB-9 Tampico	Hotel Bravo Flying Club Ltd	
EI-CRY	Medway Eclipse	G. A. Murphy	
EI-CRZ	Boeing 737-36E	ILFC Ireland Ltd (leased to Air One)	
EI-CSA	Boeing 737-8AS	Ryanair Ltd	
EI-CSB	Boeing 737-8AS	Ryanair Ltd	
EI-CSC	Boeing 737-8AS	Ryanair Ltd	
EI-CSD	Boeing 737-8AS	Ryanair Ltd	
EI-CSE	Boeing 737-8AS	Ryanair Ltd	
EI-CSF	Boeing 737-8AS	Ryanair Ltd	
EI-CSG	Boeing 737-8AS	Ryanair Ltd	
EI-CSH	Boeing 737-8AS	Ryanair Ltd	
EI-CSI	Boeing 737-8AS	Ryanair Ltd	
EI-CSJ	Boeing 737-8AS	Ryanair Ltd	
EI-CSK	BAe 146-200	CityJet Ltd/Air France	
EI-CSL	BAe 146-200	CityJet Ltd/Air France	
EI-CSM	Boeing 737-8AS	Ryanair Ltd	
EI-CSN	Boeing 737-8AS	Ryanair Ltd	
EI-CSO	Boeing 737-8AS	Ryanair Ltd	
EI-CSP	Boeing 737-8AS	Ryanair Ltd	
EI-CSQ	Boeing 737-8AS	Ryanair Ltd	
EI-CSR	Boeing 737-8AS	Ryanair Ltd	
EI-CSS	Boeing 737-8AS	Ryanair Ltd	
EI-CST	Boeing 737-8AS	Ryanair Ltd	
EI-CSU	Boeing 737-36E	ILFC Ireland Ltd (leased to Air One)	
EI-CSV	Boeing 737-8AS	Ryanair Ltd	
EI-CSW	Boeing 737-8AS	Ryanair Ltd	
EI-CSX	Boeing 737-8AS	Ryanair Ltd	
EI-CSY	Boeing 737-8AS	Ryanair Ltd	
EI-CSZ	Boeing 737-8AS	Ryanair Ltd	
EI-CTA	Boeing 737-8AS	Ryanair Ltd	
EI-CTB	Boeing 737-8AS	Ryanair Ltd	
EI-CTC	Medway Eclipse	C. Brogan	
EI-CTD	Airbus A.320-211	Aerco Ireland Ltd (leased to Air Europe Italy)	
EI-CTG	Stoddard-Hamilton Glasair RG	K. Higgins	
EI-CTI	Cessna FRA.150L	O. Bruton	
EI-CTJ	McD Douglas MD-82	Lift Ireland Leasing Ltd (leased to Nouvelair	
EI-CTL	Aerotech MW-5B Sorcerer	M. Wade	
EI-CTM	BAe 146-300	Aer Lingus Commuter St. Fiacre	
EI-CTN	BAe 146-300	Aer Lingus Commuter	
EI-CTO	BAe 146-300	Aer Lingus Commuter	
EI-CTT	PA-28-161 Warrior II	M. Farrell	
EI-CTW	Boeing 767-341ER	GECAS Ltd (leased to Eurofly)	
EI-CUA	Boeing 737-4K5	Gustav Leasing Ltd (leased to Blue Panorama)	
EI-CUB	Piper J-3C-65 Cub	J. Connelly & ptnrs	
EI-CUC	Airbus A.320-214	Lift Ireland Leasing Ltd (leased to Volare Airlines Ltd)	
EI-CUD	Boeing 737-4Q8	ILFC Ireland Ltd (leased to Blue Panorama)	
EI-CUE	Cameron balloon	Bord Telecom Eireann	
EI-CUG	Bell 206B Jet Ranger	J. O'Reilly & B. McNamara	
EI-CUI	Robinson R-44	Santail Ltd	
EI-CUK	Airbus A.320-214	GECAS Ltd (leased to Volare Airlines)	
EI-CUL	Boeing 737-36N	Virgin Express (Ireland) Ltd	
EI-CUN	Boeing 737-4K5	Gustav Leasing Ltd (leased to Blue Panorama)	
EI-CUP	Cessna 335	J. Greany	
EI-CUQ	Airbus A.320-214	Flightlease Ltd (leased to Volare Airlines)	
EI-CUS	AB-206B JetRanger 3	Emerald Helicopter Consultants	
EI-CUT	Maule MX-7-180A	Cosair Ltd	

Notes	Reg.	Type	Owner or Operator
	EI-CUU	Cessna 172N	M. Casey
	EI-CUW	BN-2B-20 Islander	Aer Arann
	EI-CVA	Airbus A.320-214	Aer Lingus Teo *St.Schira*
	EI-CVB	Airbus A.320-214	Aer Lingus Teo *St. Mobhi*
	EI-CVC	Airbus A.320-214	Aer Lingus Teo
	EI-CVD	Airbus A.320-214	Aer Lingus Teo *St. Kevin*
	EI-CVE	Airbus A.320-214	Aer Lingus Teo
	EI-CVF	Airbus A.320-214	Aer Lingus Teo
	EI-CVL	Ercoupe 415CD	D. Lyons
	EI-CVM	Schweizer S.269C	B. Moloney
	EI-CVN	Boeing 737-4Y0	GECAS Ltd *(leased to Philippine Airlines)*
	EI-CVO	Boeing 737-4S3	Aerco Ireland Ltd *(leased to Philippine Airlines)*
	EI-CVP	Boeing 737-4Y0	Airplanes Finance Ltd *(leased to Philippine A/L)*
	EI-CVR	Aérospatiale ATR-42-300	Aer Arann Express
	EI-CVS	Aérospatiale ATR-42-300	Aer Arann Express
	EI-CVT	G.1159C Gulfstream 4	AC Executive Aircraft Leasing
	EI-CVW	Bensen B.8M	F. Kavanagh
	EI-CVX	Bensen B.8M	C. Condell
	EI-CWA	BAe 146-200	CityJet Ltd
	EI-CWB	BAe 146-200	CityJet Ltd
	EI-CWC	BAe 146-200	CityJet Ltd
	EI-CWD	BAe 146-200	CityJet Ltd
	EI-CWE	Boeing 737-42C	Rockshaw Ltd *(leased to Air One)*
	EI-CWF	Boeing 737-42C	Rockshaw Ltd *(leased to Air One)*
	EI-CWH	Agusta A.109E	Lochbrea Aircraft Ltd
	EI-CWL	Robinson R-22B	J. McLoughlin
	EI-CWP	Robinson R-22B	Santail Ltd
	EI-CWR	Robinson R-22B	Inflight Aviation
	EI-CWS	Schweizer 269C	European Helicopter Academy
	EI-CWT	Airbus A.320-214	Singapore Aircraft Leasing
	EI-CWU	Airbus A.320-214	Singapore Aircraft Leasing
	EI-CWV	Airbus A.320-214	Caladborg Lease Ltd
	EI-CWY	Airbus A.319-112	Beuevue Aircraft Leasing Ltd
	EI-CWZ	Airbus A.319-112	Singapore Aircraft Leasing
	EI-CXA	Airbus A.319-112	Singapore Aircraft Leasing
	EI-DAA	Airbus A.330-202	Aer Lingus Teo
	EI-DAB	Cessna 550 Citation II	D. Colgan
	EI-DHL	Airbus A.300B4-203F	Air Contractors (Ireland) Ltd
	EI-DLA	Douglas DC-10-30 (076)	GECAS Ltd *(leased to Continental)*
	EI-DLP	Agusta A.109	-
	EI-DMG	Cessna 441	Dawn Meats Group Ltd
	EI-DUB	Airbus A.330-301	Aer Lingus Teo St Patrick
	EI-EAA	Airbus A.300B4-203F	Air Contractors (Ireland) Ltd/DHL
	EI-EAB	Airbus A.300B4-203F	Air Contractors (Ireland) Ltd/DHL
	EI-EAC	Airbus A.300B4-203F	Air Contractors (Ireland) Ltd/DHL
	EI-EAD	Airbus A.300B4-203F	Air Contractors (Ireland) Ltd/DHL
	EI-EAE	Airbus A.300B4-203F	Air Contractors (Ireland) Ltd/DHL
	EI-EAT	Airbus A.300B4-203F	Air Contractors (Ireland) Ltd/DHL
	EI-ECA	Agusta A.109A-II	Backdrive Ltd
	EI-EDR	PA-28R Cherokee Arrow 200	Kestrel Flying Group Ltd
	EI-EEC	PA-23 Aztec 250	Westair Ltd
	EI-EIO	PA-34-200T Seneca II	K. A. O'Connor
	EI-ELL	Medway Eclipse	Microflex Ltd
	EI-EUR	Eurocopter EC.120B	Atlantic Helicopters Ltd
	EI-EWR	Airbus A.330-202	Aer Lingus Teo Laurence O'Toole
	EI-FBG	Cessna F.182Q	Messs Tunney, Helly & Spelman
	EI-GER	Maule MX7-180A	P. J. Lanigan Ryan
	EI-GFC	SOCATA TB.9 Tampico	B. McGrath & ptnrs
	EI-GSM	Cessna 182S	Westpoint Flying Group Ltd
	EI-GWY	Cessna 172R	Galway Flying Club Ltd
	EI-HAM	Light Aero Avid Flyer	H. Goulding
	EI-HCA	Boeing 727-225F	Air Contractors (Ireland) Ltd
	EI-HCB	Boeing 727-223F	Air Contractors (Ireland) Ltd
	EI-HCC	Boeing 727-223F	Air Contractors (Ireland) Ltd
	EI-HCD	Boeing 727-223F	Air Contractors (Ireland) Ltd
	EI-HCI	Boeing 727-225F	Air Contractors (Ireland) Ltd
	EI-HCS	Grob G.109B	H. Sydner
	EI-HER	Bell 206B JetRanger 3	SELC Ireland Ltd & ptnrs
	EI-HXM	Bell 206B JetRanger	Euprepia Enterprises Ltd
	EI-IAU	Learjet 60	Irish Air Transport
	EI-IAW	Learjet 60	Irish Air Transport

Reg.	Type	Owner or Operator	Notes
EI-IRV	AS.350B Ecureuil	Rathalope Ltd	
EI-IZO	Eurocopter EC.120B	Cloud Nine Helicopters Ltd	
EI-JBC	Agusta A.109A	Medeva Properties Ltd	
EI-JFD	Robinson R-44	New World Plant Ltd	
EI-JFK	Airbus A.330-301	Aer Lingus Teo Colmcille	
EI-JWM	Robinson R-22B	C. Shiel	
EI-LAX	Airbus A.330-202	Aer Lingus Teo	
EI-LCH	Boeing 727-281F	Air Contractors (Ireland) Ltd	
EI-LIT	MBB Bo 105S	Irish Helicopters Ltd	
EI-LJR	Dassault Falcon 2000	EAT Executive Air Transport (Management) Ltd	
EI-LRS	Hughes 269C	Lynch Roofing Systems Ltd	
EI-MAG	Robinson R-22B-2	Airo Helicopters Ltd	
EI-MCF	Cessna 172R	Galway Flying Club Ltd	
EI-MEL	Agusta A.109C	Mercury Engineering Ltd	
EI-MER	Bell 206B JetRanger	Gaelic Helicopters Ltd	
EI-MES	Sikorsky S-61N	CHC (Ireland) Ltd	
EI-MIK	Eurocopter EC.120B	Bachir Ltd	
EI-MIP	SA.365N Dauphin 2	CHC (Ireland) Ltd	
EI-MLA	F.27 Friendship Mk 600	-	
EI-MUL	Robinson R-44	Cotton Box Design Group Ltd	
EI-ONE	Bell 206B JetRanger	TCI Aircraft Ltd	
EI-OPM	Cessna 525A CitationJet	Atron	
EI-ORD	Airbus A.330-301	Aer Lingus Teo	
EI-PAL	Cessna 550 Citation II	Eurojet Aviation	
EI-PAM	Boeing 737-4Q8	IAI Marichan Ltd *(leased to Panair)*	
EI-PAR	Boeing 737-3Q8	IAI Bailey Ltd *(leased to Panair)*	
EI-PAT	BAe 146-200	CityJet Ltd/Air France Express	
EI-PAX	Cessna 560 Citation V XL	Eurojet Ireland Ltd	
EI-PMI	AB-206B JetRanger 3	Ping Golf Equipment Ltd	
EI-POD	Cessna 177B	Trim Flying Club Ltd	
EI-PRI	Bell 206B JetRanger	Brentwood Properties Ltd	
EI-RCG	Sikorsky S-61N	CHC (Ireland) Ltd	
EI-RRR	H.S.125 Srs 700A	Starair Inc	
EI-RYR	Boeing Stearman N2S-5	Ryanair Ltd	
EI-SAC	Cessna 172P	Sligo Aero Club Ltd	
EI-SAF	Airbus A.300B4-203F	Air Contractors (Ireland) Ltd/DHL	
EI-SAM	Extra EA.300/200	D. Bruton	
EI-SAR	Sikorsky S-61N	CHC (Ireland) Ltd	
EI-SAT	Steen Skybolt	B. O'Sullivan	
EI-SBP	Cessna T.206H	P. Morrissey	
EI-SKT	PA-44-180 Seminole	Skytrace	
EI-SQG	Agusta A.109E	Quinn Group Ltd	
EI-STR	Bell 407	S. Ryan	
EI-STT	Cessna 172M	Garda Aviation Club Ltd	
EI-TAA	Airbus A.320-233	Rockshaw Ltd *(leased to TACA International)*	
EI-TAI	Airbus A.320-233	Rockshaw Ltd *(leased to TACA International)*	
EI-TKI	Robinson R-22B	J. McDaid	
EI-UFO	PA-22 Tri-Pacer 150 (tailwheel)	W. Treacy	
EI-WAC	PA-23 Aztec 250E	Westair Aviation Ltd	
EI-WAV	Bell 430	Westair Aviation Ltd	
EI-WBC	Bell 222A	Westair Aviation Ltd	
EI-WDC	H.S.125 Srs 3B	Westair Aviation Ltd	
EI-WGV	G.1159 Gulfstream 5	Westair Aviation Ltd	
EI-WHE	Beech B200 Super King Air	Westair Aviation Ltd	
EI-WJN	H.S.125 Srs 700A	Westair Aviation Ltd	
EI-WMN	PA-23 Aztec 250F	Westair Aviation Ltd	
EI-WRC	Bell 222A	Westair Aviation Ltd	
EI-WRN	PA-28-151 Warrior	Westair Aviation Ltd	
EI-WSH	Bell 430	Westair Aviation Ltd	
EI-WSN	Bell 206B JetRanger 2	Westair Aviation Ltd	
EI-WYO	PA-31-350 Navajo Chieftain	Westair Aviation Ltd	

EK (Armenia)

The following are operated by Armenian Airlines with the registrations prefixed by EK.

Reg.	Type	Notes	Reg.	Type	Notes
65044	Tu-134A-3		65831	Tu-134A	
65072	Tu-134A		65848	Tu-134A	
65822	Tu-134A		65975	Tu-134A-3	

Notes	Reg.	Type	Notes	Reg.	Type
	85166	Tu-154B-1		85536	Tu-154B-2
	85200	Tu-154B-1		85566	Tu-154B-2
	85279	Tu-154B-2		86117	IL-86
	85442	Tu-154B-2		86118	IL-86

Note: Armenian Airlines also operates the A310-222 registered F-OGYW.

EL (Liberia)

Notes	Reg.	Type	Owner or Operator
	EL-AJB	Boeing 707-351C	Scibe Airlift Zaïre
	EL-AKL	Boeing 707-351C	Liberia World Airlines
	EL-ALG	Boeing 707-369C	Shuttle Air Cargo
	EL-JNS	Boeing 707-323C	Transway Air International

EP (Iran)

	EP-IAA	Boeing 747SP-86	Iran Air Kurdistan
	EP-IAB	Boeing 747SP-86	Iran Air
	EP-IAC	Boeing 747SP-86	Iran Air Fars
	EP-IAD	Boeing 747SP-86	Iran Air
	EP-IAG	Boeing 747-286B (SCD)	Iran Air Azarabadegan
	EP-IAH	Boeing 747-286B (SCD)	Iran Air Khuzestan
	EP-IAM	Boeing 747-186B	Iran Air
	EP-IBA	Airbus A.300B4-605R	Iran Air
	EP-IBB	Airbus A.300B4-605R	Iran Air
	EP-IBN	Airbus A.310-203	Iran Air
	EP-IBO	Airbus A.310-203	Iran Air
	EP-IBQ	Airbus A.310-203	Iran Air
	EP-IBX	Airbus A.310-203	Iran Air
	EP-ICC	Boeing 747-2J9F	Iran Air
	EP-SHA	Boeing 747-2J9F	Saha Air Cargo
	EP-SHB	Boeing 747-2J9F	Saha Air Cargo
	EP-SHH	Boeing 747-2J9F	Saha Air Cargo

ER (Moldova)

The following are operated by Air Moldova (MLD) and Moldavian Airlines (MDV) with the registrations prefixed by ER.

Notes	Reg.	Type	Notes	Reg.	Type
	SGB	SAAB SF.340B (MDV)		65791	Tu-134A-3 (MLD)
	TCF	Tu-134A (MDV)		65897	Tu-134A-3 (MLD)
	65036	Tu-134A-3 (MLD)		65971	Tu-134A-3 (MLD)
	65050	Tu-134A-3 (MLD)		85044	Tu-154B (MLD)
	65051	Tu-134A-3 (MLD)		85090	Tu-154A (MLD)
	65071	Tu-134A-3 (MLD)		85285	Tu-154B-1 (MLD)
	65094	Tu-134A-3 (MLD)		85324	Tu-154B-2 (MLD)
	65140	Tu-134A-3 (MLD)		85332	Tu-154B-2 (MLD)
	65707	Tu-134A-3 (MLD)		85384	Tu-154B-2 (MLD)
	65736	Tu-134A-3 (MLD)		85405	Tu-154B-2 (MLD)
	65741	Tu-134A-3 (MLD)		85565	Tu-154B-2 (MLD)

ES (Estonia)

Notes	Reg.	Type	Owner or Operator
	ES-ABC	Boeing 737-5Q8	Estonian Air Koit
	ES-ABD	Boeing 737-5Q8	Estonian Air Hamarik
	ES-AFM	Fokker 50	Estonian Air
	ES-AFN	Fokker 50	Estonian Air
	ES-LJD	BAe Jetstream 3102	ELK Airways
	ES-LTC	Tupolev Tu-154M	ELK Airways
	ES-LTP	Tupolev Tu-154M	ELK Airways
	ES-NOB	Antonov An-72	Enimex
	ES-NOC	Antonov An-72	Enimex
	ES-NOG	Antonov An-72	Enimex
	ES-NOK	Antonov An-72	Enimex

ET (Ethiopia)

Reg.	Type	Owner or Operator
ET-AIE	Boeing 767-260ER	Ethiopian Airlines
ET-AIF	Boeing 767-260ER	Ethiopian Airlines
ET-AJS	Boeing 757-260PF	Ethiopian Airlines
ET-AJX	Boeing 757-260	Ethiopian Airlines
ET-AKC	Boeing 757-260	Ethiopian Airlines
ET-AKE	Boeing 757-260	Ethiopian Airlines
ET-AKF	Boeing 757-260	Ethiopian Airlines
ET-AKW	Boeing 767-33AER	Ethiopian Airlines
ET-ALC	Boeing 767-33AER	Ethiopian Airlines

EW (Belarus)

The following are operated by Belavia with the registrations prefixed by EW.

Reg.	Type	Notes	Reg.	Type	Notes
65082	Tu-134A		85509	Tu-154B-2	
65085	Tu-134A		85538	Tu-154B-2	
65106	Tu-134A		85545	Tu-154B-2	
65108	Tu-134A		85580	Tu-154B-2	
65133	Tu-134A-3		85581	Tu-154B-2	
65145	Tu-134A		85591	Tu-154B-2	
65149	Tu-134A		85593	Tu-154B-2	
65754	Tu-134A		85703	Tu-154M	
65772	Tu-134A-3		85706	Tu-154M	
85411	Tu-154B-2		85741	Tu-154M	
85419	Tu-154B-2		85748	Tu-154M	
85465	Tu-154B-2		85815	Tu-154M	

EX (Kyrgyzstan)

The following are operated by Kyrgyzstan Airlines with the registrations prefixed by EX.

Reg.	Type	Reg.	Type
65111	Tu-134A-3	85294	Tu-154B-1
65119	Tu-134A-3	85313	Tu-154B-2
65125	Tu-134A-3	85369	Tu-154B-2
65778	Tu-134A-3	85444	Tu-154B-2
65779	Tu-134A-3	85491	Tu-154B-2
65789	Tu-134A-3	85497	Tu-154B-2
76815	IL-76TD	85519	Tu-154B-2
85252	Tu-154B-1	85590	Tu-154B-2
85257	Tu-154B-1	85718	Tu-154M
85259	Tu-154B-1	85762	Tu-154M

EY (Tajikistan)

The following are operated by Tajikistan Airlines with the registrations prefixd by EY.

Reg.	Type	Reg.	Type
65003	Tu-134A-3	85466	Tu-154B-2
65022	Tu-134A	85469	Tu-154B-2
65763	Tu-134A-3	85475	Tu-154B-2
65788	Tu-134A-3	85487	Tu-154B-2
65820	Tu-134A-3	85511	Tu-154B-2
65835	Tu-134A-3	85691	Tu-154M
65876	Tu-134A-3	85692	Tu-154M
85385	Tu-154B-2	85717	Tu-154M

EZ (Turkmenistan)

Turkmenistan Airlines operates the following with the registrations prefixed by EZ.

Reg.	Type	Reg.	Type
A001	Boeing 737-341	A102	Boeing 717-22K
A002	Boeing 737-332	A103	Boeing 717-22K
A003	Boeing 737-332	F423	IL-76TD
A010	Boeing 757-23A	F426	IL-76TD
A011	Boeing 757-22K	F427	IL-76TD
A012	Boeing 757-22K	F428	IL-76TD
A014	Boeing 757-22K	85507	Tu-154B-2
A101	Boeing 717-22K	85549	Tu-154B-2

F (France)

	Reg.	Type	Owner or Operator
	F-BPVR	Boeing 747-228F (SCD)	Air France
	F-BPVS	Boeing 747-228B (SCD)	Air France
	F-BPVT	Boeing 747-228B (SCD)	Air France
	F-BPVX	Boeing 747-228B (SCD)	Air France
	F-BPVY	Boeing 747-228B	Air France
	F-BPVZ	Boeing 747-228F (SCD)	Air France
	F-BTDD	Douglas DC-10-30	Aero Lyon
	F-BTDE	Douglas DC-10-30	Air Lib
	F-BTDG	Boeing 747-2B3B (SCD)	Air France
	F-BTDH	Boeing 747-2B3B (SCD)	Air France
	F-BTSD	Concorde 101	Air France
	F-BVFA	Concorde 101	Air France
	F-BVFB	Concorde 101	Air France
	F-BVFC	Concorde 101	Air France
	F-BVFF	Concorde 101	Air France
	F-GBOX	Boeing 747-2B3F (SCD)	Air France Cargo
	F-GCBA	Boeing 747-228B	Air France
	F-GCBB	Boeing 747-228B	Air France
	F-GCBD	Boeing 747-228B (SF)	Air France
	F-GCBE	Boeing 747-228F (SCD)	Air France
	F-GCBF	Boeing 747-228F (SCD)	Air France
	F-GCBG	Boeing 747-228F (SCD)	Air France Cargo
	F-GCBH	Boeing 747-228F (SCD)	Air France Asia Cargo
	F-GCBI	Boeing 747-228B (SCD)	Air France
	F-GCBJ	Boeing 747-228B (SCD)	Air France
	F-GCBK	Boeing 747-228F (SCD)	Air France Cargo
	F-GCBL	Boeing 747-228F (SCD)	Air France Cargo
	F-GCBM	Boeing 747-228F	Air France Asia Cargo
	F-GCJL	Boeing 737-222	Air Mediterranée
	F-GCSL	Boeing 737-222	Air Mediterranée
	F-GDFD	F.28 Fellowship 4000	Air Lib
	F-GDPP	Douglas DC-3C	SA Publi-Air (France)
	F-GDUS	F.28 Fellowship 2000	Air Lib
	F-GDUT	F.28 Fellowship 2000	Air Lib
	F-GDXL	Aérospatiale ATR-42-300	Brit Air/Air France
	F-GEGD	Aérospatiale ATR-42-300	Air Littoral
	F-GEGE	Aérospatiale ATR-42-300	Air Littoral
	F-GEMN	Airbus A.310-304	Air France
	F-GEMO	Airbus A.310-304	Air France
	F-GEMP	Airbus A.310-304	Air France
	F-GEMQ	Airbus A.310-304	Air France
	F-GETA	Boeing 747-3B3 (SCD)	Air France
	F-GETB	Boeing 747-3B3 (SCD)	Air France
	F-GEXA	Boeing 747-4B3	Air France
	F-GEXB	Boeing 747-4B3	Air France
	F-GFEO	EMB-120RT Brasilia	Regional Airlines/Air France
	F-GFKA	Airbus A.320-111	Air France *Ville de Paris*
	F-GFKB	Airbus A.320-111	Air France *Ville de Rome*
	F-GFKD	Airbus A.320-111	Air France *Ville de Londres*
	F-GFKE	Airbus A.320-111	Air France *Ville de Bonn*
	F-GFKF	Airbus A.320-111	Air France *Ville de Madrid*
	F-GFKG	Airbus A.320-111	Air France *Ville d'Amsterdam*
	F-GFKH	Airbus A.320-211	Air France *Ville de Bruxelles*
	F-GFKI	Airbus A.320-211	Air France *Ville de Lisbonne*
	F-GFKJ	Airbus A.320-211	Air France *Ville de Copenhague*
	F-GFKK	Airbus A.320-211	Air France *Ville d'Athenes*
	F-GFKL	Airbus A.320-211	Air France/Air Charter *Ville de Dublin*
	F-GFKM	Airbus A.320-211	Air France *Ville de Luxembourg*
	F-GFKN	Airbus A.320-211	Air France *Ville de Strasbourg*
	F-GFKO	Airbus A.320-211	Air France *Ville de Milan*
	F-GFKP	Airbus A.320-211	Air France *Ville de Nice*
	F-GFKQ	Airbus A.320-111	Air France *Ville de Berlin*
	F-GFKR	Airbus A.320-211	Air France *Ville de Barcelona*
	F-GFKS	Airbus A.320-211	Air France *Ville de Marseilles*
	F-GFKT	Airbus A.320-211	Air France *Ville de Lyon*
	F-GFKU	Airbus A.320-211	Air France *Ville de Manchester*
	F-GFKV	Airbus A.320-211	Air France *Ville de Bordeaux*
	F-GFKX	Airbus A.320-211	Air France/Air Charter *Ville de Francfurt*
	F-GFKY	Airbus A.320-211	Air France *Ville de Toulouse*

Reg.	Type	Owner or Operator	Notes
F-GFKZ	Airbus A.320-211	Air France *Ville de Turin*	
F-GFPR	Swearingen SA226AT Merlin IVA	Regional Airlines	
F-GFUA	Boeing 737-33A	Air France	
F-GFUD	Boeing 737-33A	Air France	
F-GFUE	Boeing 737-3B3QC	Europe Air Post	
F-GFUF	Boeing 737-3B3QC	Europe Air Post	
F-GFUG	Boeing 737-4B3	Corsair	
F-GFUH	Boeing 737-4B3	Corsair	
F-GFUI	Boeing 737-3M8	Corsair	
F-GFUJ	Boeing 737-33A	Air France	
F-GFVI	Boeing 737-230C	Europe Air Post	
F-GFYL	Boeing 737-2A9C	Euralair International	
F-GGEA	Airbus A.320-111	Air France	
F-GGEB	Airbus A.320-111	Air France	
F-GGEC	Airbus A.320-111	Air France	
F-GGEE	Airbus A.320-111	Air France	
F-GGEF	Airbus A.320-111	Air France	
F-GGEG	Airbus A.320-111	Air France	
F-GGLK	Aérospatiale ATR-42-300	T.A.T. European	
F-GGMF	McD Douglas MD-83	Air Lib	
F-GGTD	EMB-120ER Brasilia	Regional Airlines	
F-GGVP	Boeing 737-2K2C	Europe Air Post	
F-GGVQ	Boeing 737-2K2C	Europe Air Post	
F-GHEC	McD Douglas MD-83	Air Lib	
F-GHED	McD Douglas MD-83	Air Lib	
F-GHEI	McD Douglas MD-83	Air Lib	
F-GHEK	McD Douglas MD-83	Air Lib	
F-GHEY	EMB-120ER Brasilia	Regional Airlines	
F-GHGF	Boeing 767-3Q8ER	Air France	
F-GHGG	Boeing 767-3Q8ER	Air France	
F-GHGH	Boeing 767-37EER	Air France	
F-GHGI	Boeing 767-328ER	Air France	
F-GHGJ	Boeing 767-328ER	Air France	
F-GHHO	McD Douglas MD-83	Air Lib	
F-GHHP	McD Douglas MD-83	Air Lib	
F-GHIA	EMB-120ER Brasilia	Proteus Airlines	
F-GHIB	EMB-120ER Brasilia	Proteus Airlines	
F-GHMJ	SAAB SF.340A	Brit Air/Air France Express	
F-GHOI	Douglas DC-10-30	Air Lib	
F-GHPI	Aérospatiale ATR-42-300	Brit Air/Air France Express	
F-GHPK	Aérospatiale ATR-42-300	Brit Air/Air France Express	
F-GHPS	Aérospatiale ATR-42-300	Brit Air/Air France Express	
F-GHPU	Aérospatiale ATR-72-101	Brit Air/Air France Express	
F-GHPV	Aérospatiale ATR-72-101	Brit Air/Air France Express	
F-GHPY	Aérospatiale ATR-42-300	Brit Air/Air France	
F-GHPZ	Aérospatiale ATR-42-300	Brit Air/Air France	
F-GHQA	Airbus A.320-211	Air France	
F-GHQB	Airbus A.320-211	Air France	
F-GHQC	Airbus A.320-211	Air France	
F-GHQD	Airbus A.320-211	Air France	
F-GHQE	Airbus A.320-211	Air France	
F-GHQF	Airbus A.320-211	Air France	
F-GHQG	Airbus A.320-211	Air France	
F-GHQH	Airbus A.320-211	Air France	
F-GHQI	Airbus A.320-211	Air France	
F-GHQJ	Airbus A.320-211	Air France	
F-GHQK	Airbus A.320-211	Air France	
F-GHQL	Airbus A.320-211	Air France	
F-GHQM	Airbus A.320-211	Air France	
F-GHQO	Airbus A.320-211	Air France	
F-GHQP	Airbus A.320-211	Air France	
F-GHQQ	Airbus A.320-211	Air France	
F-GHQR	Airbus A.320-211	Air France	
F-GHSE	Beech 1900C-1	Regional Airlines	
F-GHSI	Beech 1900C-1	Regional Airlines	
F-GHVA	Swearingen SA227AC Metro III	Regional Airlines	
F-GHVG	Swearingen SA227AC Metro III	Regional Airlines	
F-GHVM	Boeing 737-33A	Air France	
F-GHVN	Boeing 737-33A	Air France	
F-GHVO	Boeing 737-33A	Air France	
F-GHXM	Boeing 737-53A	Air France	
F-GIAH	F.28 Fellowship 1000	Air Lib	
F-GIAI	F.28 Fellowship 1000	Air Lib	

Notes	Reg.	Type	Owner or Operator
	F-GIDK	Douglas DC-3C	Dakota Air
	F-GIIA	Aérospatiale ATR-42-300	Air Atlantique
	F-GIJS	Airbus A.300B4-203	Air France
	F-GIMJ	Boeing 747-121	Corsair
	F-GIOA	Fokker 100	Air Lib
	F-GIOG	Fokker 100	Air Lib
	F-GIOH	Fokker 100	Air Lib
	F-GIOI	Fokker 100	Air Lib
	F-GIOJ	Fokker 100	Air Lib
	F-GIOK	Fokker 100	Air Lib
	F-GISA	Boeing 747-428 (SCD)	Air France
	F-GISB	Boeing 747-428 (SCD)	Air France
	F-GISC	Boeing 747-428 (SCD)	Air France
	F-GISD	Boeing 747-428 (SCD)	Air France
	F-GISE	Boeing 747-428 (SCD)	Air France
	F-GITA	Boeing 747-428	Air France
	F-GITB	Boeing 747-428	Air France
	F-GITC	Boeing 747-428	Air France
	F-GITD	Boeing 747-428	Air France
	F-GITE	Boeing 747-428	Air France
	F-GITF	Boeing 747-428	Air France
	F-GIVK	EMB-120ER Brasilia	Regional Airlines
	F-GIXA	Boeing 737-2K2C	Europe Air Post
	F-GIXB	Boeing 737-33AQC	Europe Air Post
	F-GIXC	Boeing 737-38BQC	Europe Air Post
	F-GIXD	Boeing 737-33AQC	Europe Air Post
	F-GIXE	Boeing 737-3B3QC	Europe Air Post
	F-GIXF	Boeing 737-3B3QC	Europe Air Post
	F-GIXG	Boeing 737-382QC	Europe Air Post
	F-GIXH	Boeing 737-3S3QC	Europe Air Post
	F-GIXI	Boeing 737-348QC	Europe Air Post
	F-GIXJ	Boeing 737-3Y0QC	Europe Air Post
	F-GIXK	Boeing 737-33AQC	Air France/Europe Air Post
	F-GIXL	Boeing 737-348QC	Europe Air Post
	F-GIXO	Boeing 737-3Q8QC	Europe Air Post
	F-GIXP	Boeing 737-3M8F	Europe Air Post
	F-GIXR	Boeing 737-3H6F	Europe Air Post
	F-GIXS	Boeing 737-3H6F	Europe Air Post
	F-GIYH	EMB-120ER Brasilia	Regional Airlines
	F-GIYI	EMB-120RT Brasilia	Regional Airlines
	F-GJAK	EMB-120ER Brasilia	Regional Airlines
	F-GJHQ	McD Douglas MD-83	Air Lib
	F-GJNA	Boeing 737-528	Air France
	F-GJNB	Boeing 737-528	Air France
	F-GJNC	Boeing 737-528	Air France
	F-GJND	Boeing 737-528	Air France
	F-GJNE	Boeing 737-528	Air France
	F-GJNF	Boeing 737-528	Air France
	F-GJNG	Boeing 737-528	Air France
	F-GJNH	Boeing 737-528	Air France
	F-GJNI	Boeing 737-528	Air France
	F-GJNJ	Boeing 737-528	Air France
	F-GJNK	Boeing 737-528	Air France
	F-GJNL	Boeing 737-5H6	Air France
	F-GJNM	Boeing 737-528	Air France
	F-GJNN	Boeing 737-528	Air France
	F-GJNO	Boeing 737-528	Air France
	F-GJNP	Boeing 737-5H6	Air France
	F-GJNQ	Boeing 737-5H6	Air France
	F-GJNR	Boeing 737-5H6	Air France
	F-GJNS	Boeing 737-53S	Air France
	F-GJNT	Boeing 737-53S	Air France
	F-GJNU	Boeing 737-53S	Air France
	F-GJNV	Boeing 737-548	Air France
	F-GJNX	Boeing 737-5H6	Air France
	F-GJNY	Boeing 737-5H6	Air France
	F-GJNZ	Boeing 737-5H6	Air France
	F-GJUA	Boeing 737-548	Air France
	F-GJVA	Airbus A.320-211	Air France
	F-GJVB	Airbus A.320-211	Air France
	F-GJVC	Airbus A.320-211	Air France
	F-GJVD	Airbus A.320-211	Air France
	F-GJVE	Airbus A.320-211	Air France

Reg.	Type	Owner or Operator	Notes
F-GJVF	Airbus A.320-211	Air France	
F-GJVG	Airbus A.320-211	Air France	
F-GJVU	Airbus A.320-211	Volare Airlines	
F-GJVW	Airbus A.320-211	Air France	
F-GJVX	Airbus A.320-211	Volare Airlines	
F-GKHD	Fokker 100	Air Lib	
F-GKHE	Fokker 100	Air Lib	
F-GKLJ	Boeing 747-121	Corsair	
F-GKMY	Douglas DC-10-30	Air Lib	
F-GKNC	Aérospatiale ATR-42-300	Air Lib/Airlinair	
F-GKND	Aérospatiale ATR-42-300	Air Lib/Airlinair	
F-GKOA	Aérospatiale ATR-72-202	Air Lib/Airlinair	
F-GKOB	Aérospatiale ATR-72-202	Air Lib/Airlinair	
F-GKOC	Aérospatiale ATR-72-202	Air Lib/Airlinair	
F-GKPC	Aérospatiale ATR-72-102	Corse Mediterranée/Air France	
F-GKPD	Aéropspatiale ATR-72-102	Corse Mediterranée/Air France	
F-GKPE	Aérospatiale ATR-72-102	Compagnie Corse Mediterranée	
F-GKPF	Aérospatiale ATR-72-102	Compagnie Corse Mediterranée	
F-GKPH	Aérospatiale ATR-72-202	Compagnie Corse Mediterranée	
F-GKST	Beech 1900C-1	Proteus Airlines	
F-GKTA	Boeing 737-3M8	Air One	
F-GKTB	Boeing 737-3M8	Air One	
F-GKXA	Airbus A.320-211	Air France *Ville de Nantes*	
F-GKXB	Airbus A.320-211	Air France	
F-GKXC	Airbus A.320-211	Air France	
F-GLGG	Airbus A.320-212	Air France	
F-GLGH	Airbus A.320-212	Air France	
F-GLIA	Aérospatiale ATR-42-300	Brit Air/Air France	
F-GLIB	Aérospatiale ATR-42-300	Brit Air/Air France	
F-GLIJ	Canadair CL.600-2B19 RJ	Air Littoral/Team Lufthansa	
F-GLIK	Canadair CL.600-2B19 RJ	Air Littoral/Team Lufthansa	
F-GLIR	Fokker 100	Air Littoral/Air France	
F-GLIS	Fokker 70	Air Littoral/Air France	
F-GLIT	Fokker 70	Air Littoral/Air France	
F-GLIU	Fokker 70	Air Littoral/Air France	
F-GLIV	Fokker 70	Air Littoral/Air France	
F-GLIX	Fokker 70	Air Littoral/Air France	
F-GLIY	Canadair CL.600-2B19 RJ	Air Littoral/Air France	
F-GLIZ	Canadair CL.600-2B19 RJ	Air Littoral/Air France	
F-GLMX	Douglas DC-10-30	Air Lib	
F-GLNA	Boeing 747-206B	Corsair	
F-GLND	Beech 1900D	Regional Airlines	
F-GLNE	Beech 1900D	Regional Airlines	
F-GLNF	Beech 1900D	Air Lib	
F-GLNI	BAe 146-200QC	Air Jet	
F-GLNJ	Beech 1900D	Regional Airlines	
F-GLNK	Beech 1900D	Regional Airlines	
F-GLPJ	Beech 1900C-1	Regional Airlines	
F-GLPL	Beech 1900C-1	Regional Airlines	
F-GLRG	EMB-120RT Brasilia	Regional Airlines	
F-GLXF	Boeing 737-219	Aeris International	
F-GLYS	Douglas DC-10-30	Aero Lyon	
F-GLZA	Airbus A.340-312	Air France	
F-GLZB	Airbus A.340-312	Air France	
F-GLZC	Airbus A.340-312	Air France	
F-GLZE	Airbus A.340-211	Air Lib	
F-GLZF	Airbus A.340-211	Air Lib	
F-GLZG	Airbus A.340-312	Air France	
F-GLZH	Airbus A.340-312	Air France	
F-GLZI	Airbus A.340-312	Air France	
F-GLZJ	Airbus A.340-313X	Air France	
F-GLZK	Airbus A.340-313X	Air France	
F-GLZL	Airbus A.340-313X	Air France	
F-GLZM	Airbus A.340-313X	Air France	
F-GLZN	Airbus A.340-313X	Air France	
F-GLZO	Airbus A.340-313X	Air France	
F-GLZP	Airbus A.340-313X	Air France	
F-GLZQ	Airbus A.340-313X	Air France	
F-GLZR	Airbus A.340-313X	Air France	
F-GLZS	Airbus A.340-313X	Air France	
F-GLZT	Airbus A.340-313X	Air France	
F-GLZU	Airbus A.340-313X	Air France	
F-GMAD	Beech 1900D	Proteus Airlines *Ville de Rodez*	

Notes	Reg.	Type	Owner or Operator
	F-GMJD	Boeing 737-2K5	Corsair
	F-GMMU	EMB-120ER Brasilia	Air Littoral
	F-GMPG	Fokker 100	Compagnie Corse Mediterranée
	F-GMSU	EMB-120RT Brasilia	Regional Airlines
	F-GMVB	SAAB 2000	Regional Airlines
	F-GMVC	SAAB 2000	Regional Airlines
	F-GMVD	SAAB 2000	Regional Airlines/Air France Express
	F-GMVE	SAAB 2000	Regional Airlines
	F-GMVG	SAAB 2000	Regional Airlines
	F-GMVL	BAe Jetstream 3206	Regional Airlines
	F-GMVO	BAe Jetstream 3206	Regional Airlines
	F-GMVU	SAAB 2000	Regional Airlines
	F-GMVY	SAAB SF.340B	Regional Airlines
	F-GMZA	Airbus A.321-111	Air France
	F-GMZB	Airbus A.321-111	Air France
	F-GMZC	Airbus A.321-111	Air France
	F-GMZD	Airbus A.321-111	Air France
	F-GMZE	Airbus A.321-111	Air France
	F-GNAD	Beech 1900C-1	Proteus Airlines
	F-GNAH	Beech 1900C-1	Proteus Airlines
	F-GNDC	Douglas DC-10-30	Air Lib
	F-GNEH	SAAB 2000	Regional Airlines/Air France
	F-GNEI	SAAB 2000	Regional Alrlines/Air France
	F-GNEM	Douglas DC-10-30	Air Lib
	F-GNFC	Boeing 737-36E	Aeris SA
	F-GNFD	Boeing 737-36E	Aeris SA
	F-GNFH	Boeing 737-382	Aeris SA
	F-GNFT	Boeing 737-3Y0	Aeris SA
	F-GNFU	Boeing 737-3Y0	Aeris SA
	F-GNIF	Airbus A.340-313X	Air France
	F-GNIG	Airbus A.340-313X	Air France
	F-GNIH	Airbus A.340-313X	Air France
	F-GNII	Airbus A.340-313X	Air France
	F-GNLG	Fokker 100	Air Lib
	F-GNLH	Fokker 100	Air Lib
	F-GNLI	Fokker 100	Air Lib
	F-GNLJ	Fokker 100	Air Lib
	F-GNLK	Fokker 100	Air Lib
	F-GNMN	Canadair CL.600-2B19	Air Littoral/Air France Express
	F-GNPA	Dornier Do.328-110	Proteus Airlines
	F-GNPL	Aérospatiale ATR-42-310	Chalair
	F-GNPM	Beech 1900C-1	Proteus Airlines
	F-GOAF	Boeing 737-242C	Air Mediterranée
	F-GOAJ	SAAB 2000	Air Jet
	F-GOHA	Embraer RJ135ER	Proteus Airlines
	F-GOHB	Embraer RJ135ER	Proteus Airlines
	F-GOHC	Embraer RJ135ER	Proteus Airlines/Air France
	F-GOHD	Embraer RJ135ER	Proteus Airlines/Air France
	F-GOHE	Embraer RJ135ER	Proteus Airlines/Air France
	F-GOHF	Embraer RJ135ER	Proteus Airlines/Air France
	F-GOMA	BAe 146-200QC	Air Jet/Air France Express
	F-GOZA	Airbus A.300B4-103F	L'Aéropostale
	F-GOZB	Airbus A.300B4-103F	L'Aéropostale
	F-GOZC	Airbus A.300B4-103F	L'Aéropostale
	F-GPAN	Boeing 747-2B3F (SCD)	Air France Cargo
	F-GPBM	Beech 1900D	Proteus Airlines
	F-GPJM	Boeing 747-206B	Corsair
	F-GPMA	Airbus A.319-113	Air France
	F-GPMB	Airbus A.319-113	Air France
	F-GPMC	Airbus A.319-113	Air France
	F-GPMD	Airbus A.319-113	Air France
	F-GPME	Airbus A.319-113	Air France
	F-GPMF	Airbus A.319-113	Air France
	F-GPMG	Airbus A.319-113	Air France
	F-GPMH	Airbus A.319-113	Air France
	F-GPMI	Airbus A.319-113	Air France
	F-GPNK	Fokker 100	Proteus Airlines/Air France
	F-GPNL	Fokker 100	Proteus Airlines/Air France
	F-GPOA	Aérospatiale ATR-72-202	Europe Air Post
	F-GPOB	Aérospatiale ATR-72-202	Europe Air Post
	F-GPOC	Aérospatiale ATR-72-212	Europe Air Post
	F-GPOD	Aérospatiale ATR-72-212	Europe Air Post
	F-GPSD	Beech 1900D	Proteus Airlines *Ville de Dijon*

Reg.	Type	Owner or Operator	Notes
F-GPTB	Canadair CL.600-2B19 RJ	Air Littoral	
F-GPTC	Canadair CL.600-2B19 RJ	Air Littoral	
F-GPTD	Canadair CL.600-2B19 RJ	Air Littoral	
F-GPTE	Canadair CL.600-2B19 RJ	Air Littoral	
F-GPTF	Canadair CL.600-2B19 RJ	Air Littoral/Team Lufthansa	
F-GPTG	Canadair CL.600-2B19 RJ	Air Littoral	
F-GPTH	Canadair CL.600-2B19 RJ	Air Littoral/Team Lufthansa	
F-GPTI	Canadair CL.600-2B19 RJ	Air Littoral	
F-GPTJ	Canadair CL.600-2B19 RJ	Air Littoral	
F-GPTK	Canadair CL.600-2B19 RJ	Air Littoral	
F-GPTM	Canadair CL.600-2B19 RJ	Air Littoral	
F-GPVA	Douglas DC-10-30	Air Lib	
F-GPVC	Douglas DC-10-30	Air Lib	
F-GPVD	Douglas DC-10-30	Air Lib	
F-GPVV	Boeing 747-228F (SCD)	Air France	
F-GPXA	Fokker 100	Brit Air/Air France	
F-GPXB	Fokker 100	Brit Air/Air France	
F-GPXC	Fokker 100	Brit Air/Air France	
F-GPXD	Fokker 100	Brit Air/Air France	
F-GPXE	Fokker 100	Brit Air/Air France	
F-GPXG	Fokker 100	Brit Air/Air France	
F-GPXH	Fokker 100	Brit Air/Air France	
F-GPYA	Aérospatiale ATR-42-512	Air Littoral	
F-GPYB	Aérospatiale ATR-42-512	Air Littoral	
F-GPYC	Aérospatiale ATR-42-512	Air Littoral	
F-GPYD	Aérospatiale ATR-42-512	Air Littoral	
F-GPYF	Aérospatiale ATR 42-512	Air Littoral *Marie Sara*	
F-GPYG	Aérospatiale ATR-42-512	Air Littoral	
F-GPYH	Aérospatiale ATR-42-512	Air Littoral	
F-GPYI	Aérospatiale ATR-42-512	Air Littoral	
F-GPYJ	Aérospatiale ATR-42-512	Air Littoral	
F-GPYK	Aérospatiale ATR-42-512	Air Littoral	
F-GPYL	Aérospatiale ATR-42-512	Air Littoral	
F-GPYM	Aérospatiale ATR-42-512	Air Littoral	
F-GPYN	Aérospatiale ATR-42-512	Air Littoral	
F-GPYO	Aérospatiale ATR-42-512	Air Littoral	
F-GPYP	Canadair CL.600-2B19 RJ	Air Littoral	
F-GPYQ	Canadair CL.600-2B19 RJ	Air Littoral	
F-GPYR	Canadair CL.600-2B19 RJ	Air Littoral	
F-GPYS	Beech 1900C-1	Air Littoral/UPS	
F-GPYT	Beech 1900C-1	Air Littoral/UPS	
F-GPYU	Beech 1900C-1	Air Littoral/UPS	
F-GPYV	Beech 1900C-1	Air Littoral/UPS	
F-GPYX	Beech 1900C-1	Air Littoral/UPS	
F-GPYY	Beech 1900C-1	Air Littoral/UPS	
F-GPZA	McD Douglas MD-83	Air Lib	
F-GPZC	McD Douglas MD-82	Air Lib	
F-GPZD	McD Douglas MD-82	Air Lib	
F-GPZE	McD Douglas MD-82	Air Lib	
F-GPZF	McD Douglas MD-83	Air Lib	
F-GRCD	Beech 1900D	Proteus Airlines	
F-GREA	Beech 1900D	Proteus Airlines	
F-GRFA	Boeing 737-36N	Air France	
F-GRFB	Boeing 737-36N	Air France	
F-GRFC	Boeing 737-36N	Air France	
F-GRGA	Embraer RJ145EU	Regional Airlines	
F-GRGB	Embraer RJ145EU	Regional Airlines	
F-GRGC	Embraer RJ145EU	Regional Airlines/Air France	
F-GRGD	Embraer RJ145EU	Regional Airlines	
F-GRGE	Embraer RJ145EU	Regional Airlines	
F-GRGF	Embraer RJ145EU	Regional Airlines	
F-GRGG	Embraer RJ145EU	Regional Airlines	
F-GRGH	Embraer RJ145EU	Regional Airlines	
F-GRGI	Embraer RJ145EU	Regional Airlines	
F-GRGJ	Embraer RJ145EU	Regional Airlines/Air France	
F-GRGK	Embraer RJ145EU	Regional Airlines/Air France	
F-GRGL	Embraer RJ145EU	Regional Airlines	
F-GRGM	Embraer RJ145EU	Regional Airlines	
F-GRGN	Embraer RJ145EU	Regional Airlines	
F-GRGO	Embraer RJ145EU	Regional Airlines	
F-GRGP	Embraer RJ135ER	Regional Airlines	
F-GRGQ	Embraer RJ135ER	Regional Airlines	
F-GRGR	Embraer RJ135ER	Regional Airlines	

Notes	Reg.	Type	Owner or Operator
	F-GRGS	Embraer RJ135ER	Regional Airlines
	F-GRGT	Embraer RJ135ER	Regional Airlines
	F-GRHA	Airbus A.319-111	Air France
	F-GRHB	Airbus A.319-111	Air France
	F-GRHC	Airbus A.319-111	Air France
	F-GRHD	Airbus A.319-111	Air France
	F-GRHE	Airbus A.319-111	Air France
	F-GRHF	Airbus A.319-111	Air France
	F-GRHG	Airbus A.319-111	Air France
	F-GRHH	Airbus A.319-111	Air France
	F-GRHI	Airbus A.319-111	Air France
	F-GRHJ	Airbus A.319-111	Air France
	F-GRHK	Airbus A.319-111	Air France
	F-GRHL	Airbus A.319-111	Air France
	F-GRHM	Airbus A.319-111	Air France
	F-GRHN	Airbus A.319-111	Air France
	F-GRHO	Airbus A.319-111	Air France
	F-GRHP	Airbus A.319-111	Air France
	F-GRHQ	Airbus A.319-111	Air France
	F-GRHR	Airbus A.319-111	Air France
	F-GRHS	Airbus A.319-111	Air France
	F-GRHT	Airbus A.319-111	Air France
	F-GRHU	Airbus A.319-111	Air France
	F-GRHV	Airbus A.319-111	Air France
	F-GRHX	Airbus A.319-111	Air France
	F-GRHY	Airbus A.319-111	Air France
	F-GRHZ	Airbus A.319-111	Air France
	F-GRJA	Canadair CL.600-2B19 RJ	Brit Air/Air France Express
	F-GRJB	Canadair CL.600-2B19 RJ	Brit Air/Air France Express
	F-GRJC	Canadair CL.600-2B19 RJ	Brit Air/Air France Express
	F-GRJD	Canadair CL.600-2B19 RJ	Brit Air/Air France Express
	F-GRJE	Canadair CL.600-2B19 RJ	Brit Air/Air France Express
	F-GRJF	Canadair CL.600-2B19 RJ	Brit Air/Air France Express
	F-GRJG	Canadair CL.600-2B19 RJ	Brit Air/Air France Express
	F-GRJH	Canadair CL.600-2B19 RJ	Brit Air/Air France Express
	F-GRJI	Canadair CL.600-2B19 RJ	Brit Air/Air France Express
	F-GRJJ	Canadair CL.600-2B19 RJ	Brit Air/Air France Express
	F-GRJK	Canadair CL.600-2B19 RJ	Brit Air/Air France Express
	F-GRJL	Canadair CL.600-2B19 RJ	Brit Air/Air France Express
	F-GRJM	Canadair CL.600-2B19 RJ	Brit Air/Air France Express
	F-GRJN	Canadair CL.600-2B19 RJ	Brit Air/Air France Express
	F-GRJO	Canadair CL.600-2B19 RJ	Brit Air/Air France Express
	F-GRJP	Canadair CL.600-2B19 RJ	Brit Air/Air France Express
	F-GRJQ	Canadair CL.600-2B19 RJ	Brit Air/Air France Express
	F-GRJR	Canadair CL.600-2B19 RJ	Brit Air/Air France Express
	F-GRJS	Canadair CL.600-2B19 RJ	Brit Air/Air France Express
	F-GRJT	Canadair CL.600-2B19 RJ	Brit Air/Air France Express
	F-GRMC	McD Douglas MD-83	Air Lib
	F-GRMD	Beech 1900D	Proteus Airlines
	F-GRMG	McD Douglas MD-83	Air Lib
	F-GRMH	McD Douglas MD-83	Air Lib
	F-GRMI	McD Douglas MD-83	Air Lib
	F-GRMJ	McD Douglas MD-83	Air Lib
	F-GRML	McD Douglas MD-83	Air Lib
	F-GRNA	Boeing 737-85F	Euralair
	F-GRNB	Boeing 737-85F	Euralair
	F-GRNC	Boeing 737-85F	Euralair
	F-GRND	Boeing 737-85F	Euralair
	F-GRNE	Boeing 737-86J	Euralair
	F-GRNZ	Boeing 737-430	Euralair
	F-GRPM	Beech 1900D	Proteus Airlines
	F-GRSD	Airbus A.320-214	Star Airlines
	F-GRSE	Airbus A.320-214	Star Airlines
	F-GRSG	Airbus A.320-214	Star Airlines
	F-GRSH	Airbus A.320-214	Star Airlines
	F-GRSI	Airbus A.320-214	Star Airlines
	F-GRXA	Airbus A.319-111	Air France
	F-GRXB	Airbus A.319-111	Air France
	F-GRXC	Airbus A.319-111	Air France
	F-GRXD	Airbus A.319-111	Air France
	F-GRXE	Airbus A.319-111	Air France
	F-GRYL	Beech 1900D	Proteus Airlines
	F-GRZA	Canadair CL.600-2C10 RJ	Brit Air/Air France Express

Reg.	Type	Owner or Operator	Notes
F-GRZB	Canadair CL.600-2C10 RJ	Brit Air/Air France Express	
F-GRZC	Canadair CL.600-2C10 RJ	Brit Air/Air France Express	
F-GRZD	Canadair CL.600-2C10 RJ	Brit Air/Air France Express	
F-GRZE	Canadair CL.600-2C10 RJ	Brit Air/Air France Express	
F-GRZF	Canadair CL.600-2C10 RJ	Brit Air/Air France Express	
F-GRZG	Canadair CL.600-2C10 RJ	Brit Air/Air France Express	
F-GRZH	Canadair CL.600-2C10 RJ	Brit Air/Air France Express	
F-GRZI	Canadair CL.600-2C10 RJ	Brit Air/Air France Express	
F-GRZJ	Canadair CL.600-2C10 RJ	Brit Air/Air France Express	
F-GRZK	Canadair CL.600-2C10 RJ	Brit Air/Air France Express	
F-GRZL	Canadair CL.600-2C10 RJ	Brit Air/Air France Express	
F-GSEA	Boeing 747-312	Corsair	
F-GSEX	Boeing 747-312	Corsair	
F-GSPA	Boeing 777-228ER	Air France	
F-GSPB	Boeing 777-228ER	Air France	
F-GSPC	Boeing 777-228ER	Air France	
F-GSPD	Boeing 777-228ER	Air France	
F-GSPE	Boeing 777-228ER	Air France	
F-GSPF	Boeing 777-228ER	Air France	
F-GSPG	Boeing 777-228ER	Air France	
F-GSPH	Boeing 777-228ER	Air France	
F-GSPI	Boeing 777-228ER	Air France	
F-GSPJ	Boeing 777-228ER	Air France	
F-GSPK	Boeing 777-228ER	Air France	
F-GSPL	Boeing 777-228ER	Air France	
F-GSPM	Boeing 777-228ER	Air France	
F-GSPN	Boeing 777-228ER	Air France	
F-GSPO	Boeing 777-228ER	Air France	
F-GSPP	Boeing 777-228ER	Air France	
F-GSPQ	Boeing 777-228ER	Air France	
F-GSPR	Boeing 777-228ER	Air France	
F-GSPS	Boeing 777-228ER	Air France	
F-GSPT	Boeing 777-228ER	Air France	
F-GSPU	Boeing 777-228ER	Air France	
F-GSPV	Boeing 777-228ER	Air France	
F-GSPX	Boeing 777-228ER	Air France	
F-GSPZ	Boeing 777-228ER	Air France	
F-GSTA	Airbus A.300-608ST Beluga (1)	Airbus Inter Transport	
F-GSTB	Airbus A.300-608ST Beluga (2)	Airbus Inter Transport	
F-GSTC	Airbus A.300-608ST Beluga (3)	Airbus Inter Transport	
F-GSTD	Airbus A.300-608ST Beluga (4)	Airbus Inter Transport	
F-GSTF	Airbus A.300-608ST Beluga (5)	Airbus Inter Transport	
F-GSUN	Boeing 747-312	Corsair	
F-GTAA	Airbus A.321-211	Air France	
F-GTAB	Airbus A.321-211	Air France	
F-GTAC	Airbus A.321-211	Air France	
F-GTAD	Airbus A.321-211	Air France	
F-GTAE	Airbus A.321-211	Air France	
F-GTAF	Airbus A.321-211	Air France	
F-GTAG	Airbus A.321-211	Air France	
F-GTAH	Airbus A.321-211	Air France	
F-GTAI	Airbus A.321-211	Air France	
F-GTAJ	Airbus A.321-211	Air France	
F-GTAK	Airbus A.321-211	Air France	
F-GTDF	Douglas DC-10-30	Air Lib	
F-GTDG	Douglas DC-10-30	Air Lib	
F-GTDH	Douglas DC-10-30	Air Lib	
F-GTLY	Douglas DC-10-30	Air Lib	
F-GTOM	Boeing 747SP-44	Corsair	
F-GTSB	SAAB 2000	Regional Airlines	
F-GTSG	EMB-120ER Brasilia	Regional Airlines	
F-GTSH	EMB-120ER Brasilia	Regional Airlines	
F-GTSI	EMB-120ER Brasilia	Regional Airlines	
F-GTSJ	EMB-120ER Brasilia	Regional Airlines	
F-GTSK	EMB-120ER Brasilia	Regional Airlines	
F-GTSL	SAAB 2000	Regional Airlines	
F-GTSN	EMB-120ER Brasilia	Regional Airlines	
F-GTSP	EMB-120ER Brasilia	Regional Airlines	
F-GTSO	EMB-120RT Brasilia	Regional Airlines	
F-GTSU	EMB-120ER Brasilia	Regional Airlines	
F-GTUA	Airbus A.340-313X	Air Lib	
F-GTUB	Airbus A.340-313X	Air Lib	
F-GUAM	Embraer RJ145MP	Proteus Airlines/Air France	

Notes	Reg.	Type	Owner or Operator
	F-GUBA	Embraer RJ145MP	Proteus Airlines/Air France
	F-GUBB	Embraer RJ145MP	Proteus/Air France Airlines
	F-GUBD	Embraer RJ145MP	Proteus Airlines/Air France
	F-GUCB	Beech 1900D	Proteus Airlines/Air France
	F-GUEA	Embraer RJ145MP	Proteus Airlines/Air France
	F-GUFD	Embraer RJ145EU	Proteus Airlines/Air France
	F-GUPT	Embraer RJ145MP	Proteus Airlines/Air France.
	F-GVAC	Boeing 737-229	Aigle Azur Transports Aeriens
	F-GVBR	Embraer EMB-120RT Brasilia	Octavia Airlines
	F-GVHD	Embraer RJ145EU	Proteus Airlines
	F-GYAB	Beech 1900D	Air Bretagne
	F-GYAL	Boeing 737-222	Air Mediterranée
	F-GZCA	Airbus A.330-203	Air France
	F-GZCB	Airbus A.330-203	Air France
	F-GZCC	Airbus A.330-203	Air France
	F-GZCD	Airbus A.330-203	Air France
	F-GZCE	Airbus A.330-203	Air France
	F-GZCF	Airbus A.330-203	Air France
	F-GZCG	Airbus A.330-203	Air France
	F-GZCH	Airbus A.330-203	Air France
	F-HBIL	Airbus A.330-243	Corsair
	F-HCAT	Airbus A.330-243	Corsair
	F-ODJG	Boeing 747-2Q2B	Air Gabon *President Leon Mba*
	F-ODLZ	Douglas DC-10-30	AOM French Airlines *Saphir*
	F-ODTK	Airbus A.300-622R	Sudan Airways
	F-ODVF	Airbus A.310-304	Royal Jordanian
	F-ODVG	Airbus A.310-304	Royal Jordanian *Prince Faisal*
	F-ODVH	Airbus A.310-304	Royal Jordanian *Prince Hamzeh*
	F-ODVI	Airbus A.310-304	Royal Jordanian *Princess Haya*
	F-OGQQ	Airbus A.310-308	Aeroflot Russian International *Tchaikovsky*
	F-OGQR	Airbus A.310-308	Aeroflot Russian International *Rachmaninov*
	F-OGQT	Airbus A.310-308	Aeroflot Russian International *Moussorgski*
	F-OGQU	Airbus A.310-308	Aeroflot Russian International *Skriabin*
	F-OGYA	Airbus A.320-211	Royal Jordanian *Cairo*
	F-OGYB	Airbus A.320-211	Royal Jordanian *Baghdad*
	F-OGYC	Airbus A.320-212	Royal Jordanian
	F-OGYM	Airbus A.310-324	Khalifa Airways
	F-OGYN	Airbus A.310-324	Khalifa Airways
	F-OGYO	Airbus A.310-324	Yemenia
	F-OGYP	Airbus A.310-324	Aeroflot Russian International *Rymsky Korsakov*
	F-OGYQ	Airbus A.310-324	Aeroflot Russian International
	F-OGYR	Airbus A.310-324	Transaero
	F-OGYS	Airbus A.310-324	Khalifa Airways
	F-OGYT	Airbus A.310-324	Aeroflot Russian International
	F-OGYU	Airbus A.310-324	Aeroflot Russian International *Alyabiev*
	F-OGYV	Airbus A.310-324	Aeroflot Russian International *Igor Stravinsky*
	F-OGYW	Airbus A.310-222	Armenian Airlines
	F-OHFR	Airbus A.320-212	Volare Airlines
	F-OHFT	Airbus A.320-212	Volare Airlines
	F-OHFU	Airbus A.320-212	Volare Airlines
	F-OHGB	Airbus A.320-211	Royal Jordanian
	F-OHGC	Airbus A.320-211	Royal Jordanian
	F-OHLN	Airbus A.300B4-605R	Middle East Airlines
	F-OHLO	Airbus A.320-232	Middle East Airlines
	F-OHMO	Airbus A.320-232	Middle East Airlines
	F-OHMP	Airbus A.321-231	Middle East Airlines
	F-OHMQ	Airbus A.321-231	Middle East Airlines
	F-OHMR	Airbus A.320-232	Middle East Airlines
	F-OHPR	Airbus A.310-325	Yemenia
	F-OHPS	Airbus A.310-325	Yemenia
	F-OHPU	Airbus A.310-324	Khalifa Airways
	F-OHPV	Airbus A.310-324	Khalifa Airways
	F-OHPY	Airbus A.310-324	Khalifa Airways
	F-OIHA	Airbus A.300B4-622R	Sudan Airways
	F-OIHS	Airbus A.310-324	Khalifa Airways

Reg.	Type	Owner or Operator	Notes

HA (Hungary)

HA-FAB	F.27 Friendship Mk 500	Farnair Air Transport Hungary	
HA-LCO	Tupolev Tu-154B-2	Malev	
HA-LCP	Tupolev Tu-154B-2	Malev	
HA-LCU	Tupolev Tu-154B-2	Malev	
HA-LCV	Tupolev Tu-154B-2	Malev	
HA-LCX	Tupolev Tu-154	Pannon Air	
HA-LCY	Tupolev Tu-154	Pannon Air	
HA-LED	Boeing 737-3Y0	Malev	
HA-LEF	Boeing 737-3Y0	Malev	
HA-LEG	Boeing 737-3Y0	Malev *Szent Istvan-Sanctus Stephanus*	
HA-LEJ	Boeing 737-3Q8	Malev	
HA-LEN	Boeing 737-4Y0	Malev	
HA-LEO	Boeing 737-4Y0	Malev	
HA-LEP	Boeing 737-5K5	Malev	
HA-LER	Boeing 737-5K5	Malev	
HA-LES	Boeing 737-3Y0	Malev	
HA-LET	Boeing 737-3Y0	Malev	
HA-LEU	Boeing 737-4Y0	Malev	
HA-LHA	Boeing 767-27GER	Malev	
HA-LHB	Boeing 767-27GER	Malev	
HA-LHD	Boeing 767-3P6ER	Malev	
HA-LMA	Fokker 70	Malev	
HA-LMB	Fokker 70	Malev	
HA-LMC	Fokker 70	Malev	
HA-LMD	Fokker 70	Malev	
HA-LME	Fokker 70	Malev	
HA-LMF	Fokker 70	Malev	

HB (Switzerland)

HB-AEE	Dornier Do.328-110	Swisswings	
HB-AEF	Dornier Do.328-110	Swisswings	
HB-AEG	Dornier Do.328-110	Swisswings	
HB-AEH	Dornier Do.328-110	Swisswings	
HB-AEI	Dornier Do.328-110	Swisswings	
HB-AEJ	Dornier Do.328-110	Swisswings	
HB-AFC	Aérospatiale ATR-42-320	Falcon Air/Federal Express	
HB-AKA	SAAB SF.340B	swiss	
HB-AKB	SAAB SF.340B	swiss	
HB-AKC	SAAB SF.340B	swiss	
HB-AKE	SAAB SF.340B	swiss	
HB-AKM	SAAB SF.340B	swiss	
HB-AKN	SAAB SF.340B	swiss	
HB-AKO	SAAB SF.340B	swiss	
HB-IEE	Boeing 757-23A	PrivatAir	
HB-IHR	Boeing 757-2G5	Belair	
HB-IHS	Boeing 757-2G5	Belair	
HB-IHV	Boeing 767-3G5ER	Belair	
HB-IHW	Boeing 767-3G5ER	Belair	
HB-IHX	Airbus A.320-214	Edelweiss Air *Calvaro*	
HB-IHY	Airbus A.320-214	Edelweiss Air *Upali*	
HB-IHZ	Airbus A.320-214	Edelweiss Air *Viktoria*	
HB-III	Boeing 737-33V	easyJet Switzerland	
HB-IIJ	Boeing 737-33V	easyJet Switzerland	
HB-IIK	Boeing 737-33V	easyJet Switzerland	
HB-IIM	Boeing 737-33V	easyJet Switzerland	
HB-IIN	Boeing 737-3L9	PrivatAir	
HB-IIO	Boeing 737-7AK	PrivatAir	
HB-IIP	Boeing 737-7AK	PrivatAir	
HB-IIQ	Boeing 737-7CN	PrivatAir	
HB-IJA	Airbus A.320-214	swiss *Opfikon*	
HB-IJB	Airbus A.320-214	swiss *Embrach*	
HB-IJC	Airbus A.320-214	swiss *Winkle*	
HB-IJD	Airbus A.320-214	swiss *Regensdorf*	
HB-IJE	Airbus A.320-214	swiss *Dubendorf*	
HB-IJF	Airbus A.320-214	swiss *Bellevue*	
HB-IJG	Airbus A.320-214	swiss *Illnau-Effretikon*	
HB-IJH	Airbus A.320-214	swiss *Wangen-Bruttisellen*	
HB-IJI	Airbus A.320-214	swiss *Binningen*	

Notes	Reg.	Type	Owner or Operator
	HB-IJJ	Airbus A.320-214	swiss *Dietlikon*
	HB-IJK	Airbus A.320-214	swiss *Genthod*
	HB-IJL	Airbus A.320-214	swiss *Bassersdorf*
	HB-IJM	Airbus A.320-214	swiss *Wallisellen*
	HB-IJN	Airbus A.320-214	swiss *Meyrin*
	HB-IJO	Airbus A.320-214	swiss *Grand-Saconnex*
	HB-IJP	Airbus A.320-214	swiss *Vernier*
	HB-IJQ	Airbus A.320-214	swiss *Niederhasli*
	HB-IJR	Airbus A.320-214	swiss
	HB-IJT	Airbus A.320-214	swiss
	HB-IJU	Airbus A.320-214	swiss
	HB-ILJ	F.27 Friendship Mk 500	Farner Europe
	HB-ILQ	F.27 Friendship Mk 500	Farner Europe
	HB-INR	McD Douglas MD-82	Nordic Airlink
	HB-INV	McD Douglas MD-83	swiss
	HB-INW	McD Douglas MD-83	swiss
	HB-INZ	McD Douglas MD-83	swiss
	HB-IOA	Airbus A.321-111	swiss *Neuchâtel*
	HB-IOB	Airbus A.321-111	swiss *Aargau*
	HB-IOC	Airbus A.321-111	swiss *Lausanne*
	HB-IOD	Airbus A.321-111	swiss *Kloten*
	HB-IOF	Airbus A.321-111	swiss *Winterthur*
	HB-IOG	Airbus A.321-111	swiss *Bülach*
	HB-IOH	Airbus A.321-111	swiss *Würenlos*
	HB-IOI	Airbus A.321-111	swiss
	HB-IOK	Airbus A.321-111	swiss
	HB-IOL	Airbus A.321-111	swiss *Lugano*
	HB-IPR	Airbus A.319-111	swiss *Commune de Champagne*
	HB-IPS	Airbus A.319-112	swiss *Weiach*
	HB-IPT	Airbus A.319-112	swiss *Stadel*
	HB-IPU	Airbus A.319-112	swiss *Hochfelden*
	HB-IPV	Airbus A.319-112	swiss *Rumlang*
	HB-IPW	Airbus A.319-112	swiss *Bachenbulach*
	HB-IPX	Airbus A.319-112	swiss *Steinmaur*
	HB-IPY	Airbus A.319-112	swiss *Hori*
	HB-IPZ	Airbus A.319-112	swiss *Oberglatt*
	HB-IQA	Airbus A.330-223	swiss
	HB-IQB	Airbus A.330-223	swiss
	HB-IQC	Airbus A.330-223	swiss
	HB-IQD	Airbus A.330-223	swiss
	HB-IQE	Airbus A.330-222	swiss
	HB-IQF	Airbus A.330-223	swiss
	HB-IQG	Airbus A.330-223	swiss
	HB-IQH	Airbus A.330-223	swiss
	HB-IQI	Airbus A.330-223	swiss
	HB-IQJ	Airbus A.330-223	swiss
	HB-IQK	Airbus A.330-223	swiss
	HB-IQL	Airbus A.330-223	swiss
	HB-IQM	Airbus A.330-223	swiss
	HB-IQN	Airbus A.330-223	swiss
	HB-IQO	Airbus A.330-223	swiss
	HB-IQP	Airbus A.330-223	swiss
	HB-IQQ	Airbus A.330-223	swiss
	HB-IQR	Airbus A.330-223	swiss
	HB-IQZ	Airbus A.330-243	Edelweiss Air
	HB-ISB	Douglas DC-3C	Classic Air
	HB-ISC	Douglas DC-3C	Classic Air
	HB-ISQ	F.27 Friendship Mk 500	Farnair Europe
	HB-ISX	McD Douglas MD-83	swiss
	HB-ISZ	McD Douglas MD-83	swiss
	HB-ITQ	F.27 Friendship Mk 400	Farnair Europe
	HB-IUG	McD Douglas MD-83	swiss
	HB-IUH	McD Douglas MD-83	swiss
	HB-IUM	McD Douglas MD-83	swiss
	HB-IUN	McD Douglas MD-83	swiss
	HB-IUO	McD Douglas MD-83	swiss
	HB-IUP	McD Douglas MD-83	swiss
	HB-IWA	McD Douglas MD-11	swiss *Obwalden*
	HB-IWB	McD Douglas MD-11	swiss *Graubünden*
	HB-IWC	McD Douglas MD-11	swiss *Schaffhausen*
	HB-IWD	McD Douglas MD-11	swiss *Thurgau*
	HB-IWE	McD Douglas MD-11	swiss *Nidwalden*
	HB-IWG	McD Douglas MD-11	swiss *Asia Valais/Wallis*

Reg.	Type	Owner or Operator	Notes
HB-IWH	McD Douglas MD-11	swiss *St Gallen*	
HB-IWI	McD Douglas MD-11	swiss *Uri*	
HB-IWK	McD Douglas MD-11	swiss *Fribourg*	
HB-IWL	McD Douglas MD-11	swiss *Appenzell a.Rh*	
HB-IWM	McD Douglas MD-11	swiss *Jura*	
HB-IWN	McD Douglas MD-11	swiss *Basel-Land*	
HB-IWO	McD Douglas MD-11	swiss *Schwyz*	
HB-IWP	McD Douglas MD-11	swiss	
HB-IWQ	McD Douglas MD-11	swiss	
HB-IWR	McD Douglas MD-11	swiss	
HB-IWS	McD Douglas MD-11	swiss	
HB-IWT	McD Douglas MD-11	swiss	
HB-IWU	McD Douglas MD-11	swiss	
HB-IXF	Avro RJ85	swiss	
HB-IXG	Avro RJ85	swiss	
HB-IXH	Avro RJ85	swiss	
HB-IXK	Avro RJ85	swiss	
HB-IXN	Avro RJ100	swiss	
HB-IXO	Avro RJ100	swiss	
HB-IXP	Avro RJ100	swiss	
HB-IXQ	Avro RJ100	swiss	
HB-IXR	Avro RJ100	swiss	
HB-IXS	Avro RJ100	swiss	
HB-IXT	Avro RJ100	swiss	
HB-IXU	Avro RJ100	swiss	
HB-IXV	Avro RJ100	swiss	
HB-IXW	Avro RJ100	swiss	
HB-IXX	Avro RJ100	swiss	
HB-IYA	SAAB 2000	swiss	
HB-IYB	SAAB 2000	swiss	
HB-IYC	SAAB 2000	swiss	
HB-IYD	SAAB 2000	swiss	
HB-IYE	SAAB 2000	swiss	
HB-IYF	SAAB 2000	swiss	
HB-IYG	SAAB 2000	swiss	
HB-IYH	SAAB 2000	swiss	
HB-IYW	Avro RJ100	swiss	
HB-IYX	Avro RJ100	swiss	
HB-IYY	Avro RJ100	swiss/Eurocross	
HB-IYZ	Avro RJ100	swiss	
HB-IZA	SAAB 2000	swiss	
HB-IZB	SAAB 2000	swiss	
HB-IZC	SAAB 2000	swiss	
HB-IZD	SAAB 2000	swiss	
HB-IZE	SAAB 2000	swiss	
HB-IZF	SAAB 2000	swiss	
HB-IZG	SAAB 2000	swiss	
HB-IZH	SAAB 2000	swiss	
HB-IZI	SAAB 2000	swiss	
HB-IZJ	SAAB 2000	swiss	
HB-IZK	SAAB 2000	swiss	
HB-IZL	SAAB 2000	swiss	
HB-IZM	SAAB 2000	swiss	
HB-IZN	SAAB 2000	swiss	
HB-IZO	SAAB 2000	swiss	
HB-IZQ	SAAB 2000	swiss	
HB-IZR	SAAB 2000	swiss	
HB-IZS	SAAB 2000	swiss	
HB-IZT	SAAB 2000	swiss	
HB-IZU	SAAB 2000	swiss	
HB-IZV	SAAB 2000	swiss	
HB-IZW	SAAB 2000	swiss	
HB-IZX	SAAB 2000	swiss	
HB-IZY	SAAB 2000	swiss	
HB-IZZ	SAAB 2000	swiss	
HB-JAA	Embraer RJ145LU	swiss	
HB-JAB	Embraer RJ145LU	swiss	
HB-JAC	Embraer RJ145LU	swiss	
HB-JAD	Embraer RJ145LU	swiss	
HB-JAE	Embraer RJ145LU	swiss	
HB-JAF	Embraer RJ145LU	swiss	
HB-JAG	Embraer RJ145LU	swiss	
HB-JAH	Embraer RJ145LU	swiss	

Notes	Reg.	Type	Owner or Operator
	HB-JAI	Embraer RJ145LU	swiss
	HB-JAJ	Embraer RJ145LU	swiss
	HB-JAK	Embraer RJ145LU	swiss
	HB-JAL	Embraer RJ145LU	swiss
	HB-JAM	Embraer RJ145LU	swiss
	HB-JAN	Embraer RJ145LU	swiss
	HB-JAO	Embraer RJ145LU	swiss

HK (Colombia)

Note: Avianca operates Boeing 767s registered N984AN, N985AN, N986AN and N988AN.

HL (Korea)

HL7371	McD Douglas MD-11F	Korean Air Cargo
HL7372	McD Douglas MD-11F	Korean Air Cargo
HL7374	McD Douglas MD-11F	Korean Air Cargo
HL7375	McD Douglas MD-11F	Korean Air Cargo
HL7400	Boeing 747-4B5F	Korean Air Cargo
HL7402	Boeing 747-4B5	Korean Air
HL7403	Boeing 747-4B5F	Korean Air Cargo
HL7404	Boeing 747-4B5	Korean Air
HL7405	Boeing 747-2B5F (SCD)	Korean Air Cargo
HL7407	Boeing 747-4B5	Korean Air
HL7408	Boeing 747-2B5F (SCD)	Korean Air Cargo
HL7409	Boeing 747-4B5	Korean Air
HL7412	Boeing 747-4B5	Korean Air
HL7419	Boeing 747-48EF (SCD)	Asiana Airlines
HL7420	Boeing 747-48EF (SCD)	Asiana Airlines
HL7422	Boeing 747-48EF (SCD)	Asiana Airlines
HL7424	Boeing 747-2S4F (SCD)	Korean Air Cargo
HL7426	Boeing 747-48EF (SCD)	Asiana Airlines
HL7428	Boeing 747-48EF (SCD)	Asiana Airlines
HL7434	Boeing 747-4B5F	Korean Air
HL7436	Boeing 747-48EF (SCD)	Asiana Airlines
HL7443	Boeing 747-2B5B	Korean Air
HL7448	Boeing 747-4B5F (SCD)	Korean Air Cargo
HL7449	Boeing 747-4B5F (SCD)	Korean Air Cargo
HL7452	Boeing 747-2B5F (SCD)	Korean Air Cargo
HL7454	Boeing 747-2B5F (SCD)	Korean Air Cargo
HL7458	Boeing 747-2B5F (SCD)	Korean Air Cargo
HL7459	Boeing 747-2B5F (SCD)	Korean Air Cargo
HL7460	Boeing 747-4B5	Korean Air
HL7461	Boeing 747-4B5	Korean Air
HL7462	Boeing 747-4B5F	Korean Air Cargo
HL7463	Boeing 747-2B5B	Korean Air
HL7464	Boeing 747-2B5B	Korean Air
HL7469	Boeing 747-3B5	Korean Air
HL7470	Boeing 747-3B5 (SCD)	Korean Air
HL7472	Boeing 747-4B5	Korean Air
HL7473	Boeing 747-4B5	Korean Air
HL7480	Boeing 747-4B5 (SCD)	Korean Air
HL7481	Boeing 747-4B5	Korean Air
HL7482	Boeing 747-4B5	Korean Air
HL7483	Boeing 747-4B5	Korean Air
HL7484	Boeing 747-4B5	Korean Air
HL7485	Boeing 747-4B5	Korean Air
HL7486	Boeing 747-4B5	Korean Air
HL7487	Boeing 747-4B5	Korean Air
HL7488	Boeing 747-4B5	Korean Air
HL7489	Boeing 747-4B5	Korean Air
HL7490	Boeing 747-4B5	Korean Air
HL7491	Boeing 747-4B5	Korean Air
HL7492	Boeing 747-4B5	Korean Air
HL7493	Boeing 747-4B5	Korean Air
HL7494	Boeing 747-4B5	Korean Air
HL7495	Boeing 747-4B5	Korean Air
HL7496	Boeing 747-4B5	Korean Air
HL7497	Boeing 747-4B5	Korean Air
HL7498	Boeing 747-4B5	Korean Air

Reg.	Type	Owner or Operator	Notes

HS (Thailand)

HS-TGD	Boeing 747-3D7	Thai Airways International *Suchada*	
HS-TGE	Boeing 747-3D7	Thai Airways International *Chutamat*	
HS-TGH	Boeing 747-4D7	Thai Airways International *Chaiprakarn*	
HS-TGJ	Boeing 747-4D7	Thai Airways International *Hariphunchai*	
HS-TGK	Boeing 747-4D7	Thai Airways International *Alongkorn*	
HS-TGL	Boeing 747-4D7	Thai Airways International *Theparat*	
HS-TGM	Boeing 747-4D7	Thai Airways International *Chao Phraya*	
HS-TGN	Boeing 747-4D7	Thai Airways International *Simongkhon*	
HS-TGO	Boeing 747-4D7	Thai Airways International *Bowonrangsi*	
HS-TGP	Boeing 747-4D7	Thai Airways International *Thepprasit*	
HS-TGR	Boeing 747-4D7	Thai Airways International *Siriwatthana*	
HS-TGT	Boeing 747-4D7	Thai Airways International *Watthanothai*	
HS-TGW	Boeing 747-4D7	Thai Airways International *Visuthakasatriya*	
HS-TGX	Boeing 747-4D7	Thai Airways International *Sirisobhakya*	
HS-TGY	Boeing 747-4D7	Thai Airways International *Dararasmi*	
HS-TGZ	Boeing 747-4D7	Thai Airways International	
HS-TJA	Boeing 777-2D7	Thai Airways International	
HS-TJB	Boeing 777-2D7	Thai Airways International	
HS-TJC	Boeing 777-2D7	Thai Airways International	
HS-TJD	Boeing 777-2D7	Thai Airways International	
HS-TJE	Boeing 777-2D7	Thai Airways International	
HS-TJF	Boeing 777-2D7	Thai Airways International	
HS-TJG	Boeing 777-2D7	Thai Airways International	
HS-TJH	Boeing 777-2D7	Thai Airways International	
HS-TKA	Boeing 777-3D7	Thai Airways International	
HS-TKB	Boeing 777-3D7	Thai Airways International	
HS-TKC	Boeing 777-3D7	Thai Airways International	
HS-TKD	Boeing 777-3D7	Thai Airways International	
HS-TKE	Boeing 777-3D7	Thai Airways International	
HS-TKF	Boeing 777-3D7	Thai Airways International	
HS-TMD	McD Douglas MD-11	Thai Airways International *Phra Nakhon*	
HS-TME	McD Douglas MD-11	Thai Airways International *Pathumwan*	
HS-TMF	McD Douglas MD-11	Thai Airways International *Phichit*	
HS-TMG	McD Douglas MD-11	Thai Airways International *Nakhon Sawan*	

HZ (Saudi Arabia)

HZ-AIA	Boeing 747-168B	Saudia - Saudi Arabian Airlines	
HZ-AIB	Boeing 747-168B	Saudia - Saudi Arabian Airlines	
HZ-AIC	Boeing 747-168B	Saudia - Saudi Arabian Airlines	
HZ-AID	Boeing 747-168B	Saudia - Saudi Arabian Airlines	
HZ-AIE	Boeing 747-168B	Saudia - Saudi Arabian Airlines	
HZ-AIF	Boeing 747SP-68	Saudia - Saudi Arabian Airlines	
HZ-AIG	Boeing 747-168B	Saudia - Saudi Arabian Airlines	
HZ-AII	Boeing 747-168B	Saudia - Saudi Arabian Airlines	
HZ-AIJ	Boeing 747SP-68	Saudi Royal Flight	
HZ-AIK	Boeing 747-368	Saudia - Saudi Arabian Airlines	
HZ-AIL	Boeing 747-368	Saudia - Saudi Arabian Airlines	
HZ-AIM	Boeing 747-368	Saudia - Saudi Arabian Airlines	
HZ-AIN	Boeing 747-368	Saudia - Saudi Arabian Airlines	
HZ-AIO	Boeing 747-368	Saudia - Saudi Arabian Airlines	
HZ-AIP	Boeing 747-368	Saudia - Saudi Arabian Airlines	
HZ-AIQ	Boeing 747-368	Saudia - Saudi Arabian Airlines	
HZ-AIR	Boeing 747-368	Saudia - Saudi Arabian Airlines	
HZ-AIS	Boeing 747-368	Saudia - Saudi Arabian Airlines	
HZ-AIT	Boeing 747-368	Saudia - Saudi Arabian Airlines	
HZ-AIU	Boeing 747-268F (SCD)	Saudia -Saudi Arabian Airlines	
HZ-AIV	Boeing 747-468	Saudia - Saudi Arabian Airlines	
HZ-AIW	Boeing 747-468	Saudia - Saudi Arabian Airlines	
HZ-AIX	Boeing 747-468	Saudia - Saudi Arabian Airlines	
HZ-AIY	Boeing 747-468	Saudia - Saudi Arabian Airlines	
HZ-AIZ	Boeing 747-468	Saudia - Saudi Arabian Airlines	
HZ-AKA	Boeing 777-268ER	Saudia - Saudi Arabian Airlines	
HZ-AKB	Boeing 777-268ER	Saudia - Saudi Arabian Airlines	
HZ-AKC	Boeing 777-268ER	Saudia - Saudi Arabian Airlines	
HZ-AKD	Boeing 777-268ER	Saudia - Saudi Arabian Airlines	
HZ-AKE	Boeing 777-268ER	Saudia - Saudi Arabian Airlines	
HZ-AKF	Boeing 777-268ER	Saudia - Saudi Arabian Airlines	

Notes	Reg.	Type	Owner or Operator
	HZ-AKG	Boeing 777-268ER	Saudia - Saudi Arabian Airlines
	HZ-AKH	Boeing 777-268ER	Saudia - Saudi Arabian Airlines
	HZ-AKI	Boeing 777-268ER	Saudia - Saudi Arabian Airlines
	HZ-AKJ	Boeing 777-268ER	Saudia - Saudi Arabian Airlines
	HZ-AKK	Boeing 777-268ER	Saudia - Saudi Arabian Airlines
	HZ-AKL	Boeing 777-268ER	Saudia - Saudi Arabian Airlines
	HZ-AKM	Boeing 777-268ER	Saudia - Saudi Arabian Airlines
	HZ-AKN	Boeing 777-268ER	Saudia - Saudi Arabian Airlines
	HZ-AKO	Boeing 777-268ER	Saudia - Saudi Arabian Airlines
	HZ-AKP	Boeing 777-268ER	Saudia - Saudi Arabian Airlines
	HZ-AKQ	Boeing 777-268ER	Saudia - Saudi Arabian Airlines
	HZ-AKR	Boeing 777-268ER	Saudia - Saudi Arabian Airlines
	HZ-AKS	Boeing 777-268ER	Saudia - Saudi Arabian Airlines
	HZ-AKT	Boeing 777-268ER	Saudia - Saudi Arabian Airlines
	HZ-ANA	McD Douglas MD-11F	Saudia - Saudi Arabian Airlines
	HZ-ANB	McD Douglas MD-11F	Saudia - Saudi Arabian Airlines
	HZ-ANC	McD Douglas MD-11F	Saudia - Saudi Arabian Airlines
	HZ-AND	McD Douglas MD-11F	Saudia - Saudi Arabian Airlines
	HZ-HM5	L.1011-385 TriStar 500	Saudia VIP
	HZ-HM6	L.1011-385 TriStar 500	Saudia VIP

I (Italy)

	I-AEIY	Boeing 767-330ER	Air Europe Italy
	I-ALPK	Fokker 100	Alpi Eagles *San Antonio*
	I-ALPL	Fokker 100	Alpi Eagles *San Marco*
	I-ALPQ	Fokker 100	Alpi Eagles
	I-ALPS	Fokker 100	Alpi Eagles *San Zeno*
	I-ALPW	Fokker 100	Alpi Eagles
	I-ALPX	Fokker 100	Alpi Eagles
	I-ALPZ	Fokker 100	Alpi Eagles *San Pietro*
	I-ATMC	Aérospatiale ATR-72-212A	Alitalia Express *Fiume Arno*
	I-ATPA	Aérospatiale ATR-72-212A	Alitalia Express *Lago Trasimeno*
	I-ATSL	Aérospatiale ATR-72-212A	Alitalia Express *Lago di Garda*
	I-BIKA	Airbus A.320-214	Alitalia Team
	I-BIKB	Airbus A.320-214	Alitalia Team *Wolfgang Amadeus Mozart*
	I-BIKC	Airbus A.320-214	Eurofly
	I-BIKD	Airbus A.320-214	Eurofly
	I-BIKE	Airbus A.320-214	Alitalia Team *Franz Liszt*
	I-BIKF	Airbus A.320-214	Eurofly
	I-BIKG	Airbus A.320-214	Eurofly
	I-BIKI	Airbus A.320-214	Alitalia Team *Girolamo Frescobaldi*
	I-BIKL	Airbus A.320-214	Eurofly
	I-BIKO	Airbus A.320-214	Alitalia Team
	I-BIKU	Airbus A.320-214	Alitalia Team *Frederyk Chopin*
	I-BIXA	Airbus A.321-112	Alitalia Team *Piazza del Duomo Milano*
	I-BIXB	Airbus A.321-112	Alitalia Team *Piazza Castello Torino*
	I-BIXC	Airbus A.321-112	Alitalia Team *Piazza del Campo Siena*
	I-BIXD	Airbus A.321-112	Alitalia Team *Piazza Pretoria Palermo*
	I-BIXE	Airbus A.321-112	Alitalia Team *Piazza di Spagna Roma*
	I-BIXF	Airbus A.321-112	Alitalia Team *Piazza Maggiore Bologna*
	I-BIXG	Airbus A.321-112	Alitalia Team *Piazza dei Miracoli Pisa*
	I-BIXH	Airbus A.321-112	Alitalia Team
	I-BIXI	Airbus A.321-112	Alitalia Team *Piazza San Marco-Venezia*
	I-BIXJ	Airbus A.321-112	Alitalia Team
	I-BIXK	Airbus A.321-112	Alitalia Team *Piazza Ducale Vigevano*
	I-BIXL	Airbus A.321-112	Alitalia Team *Piazza del Duomo Lecce*
	I-BIXM	Airbus A.321-112	Alitalia Team *Piazza di San Franceso Assisi*
	I-BIXN	Airbus A.321-112	Alitalia Team *Piazza del Duomo Catania*
	I-BIXO	Airbus A.321-112	Alitalia Team *Piazza Plebiscito Napoli*
	I-BIXP	Airbus A.321-112	Alitalia Team *Carlo Morelli*
	I-BIXQ	Airbus A.321-112	Alitalia Team *Domenico Colapietro*
	I-BIXR	Airbus A.321-112	Alitalia Team *Piazza del Campidoglio-Roma*
	I-BIXS	Airbus A.321-112	Alitalia Team *Piazza San Martino-Lucca*
	I-BIXT	Airbus A.321-112	Alitalia *Piazza dei Miracoli Pisa*
	I-BIXU	Airbus A.321-112	Alitalia *Piazza dell Signori Firenze*
	I-BIXV	Airbus A.321-112	Alitalia *Piazza dell Rinaccimento-Urbino*
	I-BIXZ	Airbus A.321-112	Alitalia *Piazza dell Duomo Orvieto*

Reg.	Type	Owner or Operator	Notes
I-DACM	McD Douglas MD-82	Alitalia *La Spezia*	
I-DACN	McD Douglas MD-82	Alitalia *Rieti*	
I-DACP	McD Douglas MD-82	Alitalia *Padova*	
I-DACQ	McD Douglas MD-82	Alitalia *Taranto*	
I-DACR	McD Douglas MD-82	Alitalia *Carrara*	
I-DACS	McD Douglas MD-82	Alitalia *Maratea*	
I-DACT	McD Douglas MD-82	Alitalia *Valtellina*	
I-DACU	McD Douglas MD-82	Alitalia *Fabriano*	
I-DACV	McD Douglas MD-82	Alitalia *Riccione*	
I-DACW	McD Douglas MD-82	Alitalia *Vieste*	
I-DACX	McD Douglas MD-82	Alitalia *Piacenza*	
I-DACY	McD Douglas MD-82	Alitalia Team *Novara*	
I-DACZ	McD Douglas MD-82	Alitalia *Castelfidardo*	
I-DAND	McD Douglas MD-82	Alitalia *Bolzano*	
I-DANF	McD Douglas MD-82	Alitalia *Vicenza*	
I-DANG	McD Douglas MD-82	Alitalia *Benevento*	
I-DANH	McD Douglas MD-82	Alitalia *Messina*	
I-DANL	McD Douglas MD-82	Alitalia *Cosenza*	
I-DANM	McD Douglas MD-82	Alitalia *Vicenza*	
I-DANP	McD Douglas MD-82	Alitalia *Fabriano*	
I-DANQ	McD Douglas MD-82	Alitalia *Lecce*	
I-DANR	McD Douglas MD-82	Alitalia *Matera*	
I-DANU	McD Douglas MD-82	Alitalia *Trapani*	
I-DANV	McD Douglas MD-82	Alitalia *Forte dei Marmi*	
I-DANW	McD Douglas MD-82	Alitalia *Siena*	
I-DATA	McD Douglas MD-82	Alitalia *Gubbio*	
I-DATB	McD Douglas MD-82	Alitalia *Bergamo*	
I-DATC	McD Douglas MD-82	Alitalia *Foggia*	
I-DATD	McD Douglas MD-82	Alitalia *Savona*	
I-DATE	McD Douglas MD-82	Alitalia *Grosseto*	
I-DATF	McD Douglas MD-82	Alitalia *Vittorio Veneto*	
I-DATG	McD Douglas MD-82	Alitalia *Arezzo*	
I-DATH	McD Douglas MD-82	Alitalia *Pescara*	
I-DATI	McD Douglas MD-82	Alitalia *Siracusa*	
I-DATJ	McD Douglas MD-82	Alitalia *Lunigiana*	
I-DATK	McD Douglas MD-82	Alitalia *Ravenna*	
I-DATL	McD Douglas MD-82	Alitalia *Alghero*	
I-DATM	McD Douglas MD-82	Alitalia Team *Cividale del Friuli*	
I-DATN	McD Douglas MD-82	Alitalia *Sondrio*	
I-DATO	McD Douglas MD-82	Alitalia Team *Reggio Emilia*	
I-DATP	McD Douglas MD-82	Alitalia Team *Latina*	
I-DATQ	McD Douglas MD-82	Alitalia Team *Modena*	
I-DATR	McD Douglas MD-82	Alitalia Team *Livorno*	
I-DATS	McD Douglas MD-82	Alitalia *Foligno*	
I-DATU	McD Douglas MD-82	Alitalia *Verona*	
I-DAVA	McD Douglas MD-82	Alitalia *Cuneo*	
I-DAVB	McD Douglas MD-82	Alitalia *Ferrara*	
I-DAVC	McD Douglas MD-82	Alitalia *Lucca*	
I-DAVD	McD Douglas MD-82	Alitalia *Mantova*	
I-DAVF	McD Douglas MD-82	Alitalia *Oristano*	
I-DAVG	McD Douglas MD-82	Alitalia *Pesaro*	
I-DAVH	McD Douglas MD-82	Alitalia *Salerno*	
I-DAVI	McD Douglas MD-82	Alitalia *Assisi*	
I-DAVJ	McD Douglas MD-82	Alitalia *Parma*	
I-DAVK	McD Douglas MD-82	Alitalia *Pompei*	
I-DAVL	McD Douglas MD-82	Alitalia *Reggio Calabria*	
I-DAVM	McD Douglas MD-82	Alitalia *Caserta*	
I-DAVN	McD Douglas MD-82	Alitalia *Volterra*	
I-DAVP	McD Douglas MD-82	Alitalia *Gorizia*	
I-DAVR	McD Douglas MD-82	Alitalia *Pisa*	
I-DAVS	McD Douglas MD-82	Alitalia *Catania*	
I-DAVT	McD Douglas MD-82	Alitalia *Como*	
I-DAVU	McD Douglas MD-82	Alitalia *Udine*	
I-DAVV	McD Douglas MD-82	Alitalia *Pavia*	
I-DAVW	McD Douglas MD-82	Alitalia *Camerino*	
I-DAVX	McD Douglas MD-82	Alitalia *Asti*	
I-DAVZ	McD Douglas MD-82	Alitalia *Brescia*	
I-DAWA	McD Douglas MD-82	Alitalia *Roma*	
I-DAWB	McD Douglas MD-82	Alitalia *Cagliari*	
I-DAWC	McD Douglas MD-82	Alitalia *Campobasso*	
I-DAWD	McD Douglas MD-82	Alitalia *Catanzaro*	
I-DAWE	McD Douglas MD-82	Alitalia *Milano*	
I-DAWF	McD Douglas MD-82	Alitalia *Firenze*	

Notes	Reg.	Type	Owner or Operator
	I-DAWG	McD Douglas MD-82	Alitalia L'Aquila
	I-DAWH	McD Douglas MD-82	Alitalia Palermo
	I-DAWI	McD Douglas MD-82	Alitalia Ancona
	I-DAWJ	McD Douglas MD-82	Alitalia Genova
	I-DAWL	McD Douglas MD-82	Alitalia Perugia
	I-DAWM	McD Douglas MD-82	Alitalia Potenza
	I-DAWO	McD Douglas MD-82	Alitalia Bari
	I-DAWP	McD Douglas MD-82	Alitalia Torino
	I-DAWQ	McD Douglas MD-82	Alitalia Trieste
	I-DAWR	McD Douglas MD-82	Alitalia Venezia
	I-DAWS	McD Douglas MD-82	Alitalia Aosta
	I-DAWT	McD Douglas MD-82	Alitalia Napoli
	I-DAWU	McD Douglas MD-82	Alitalia Bologna
	I-DAWV	McD Douglas MD-82	Alitalia Trento
	I-DAWW	McD Douglas MD-82	Alitalia Riace
	I-DAWY	McD Douglas MD-82	Alitalia Agrigento
	I-DAWZ	McD Douglas MD-82	Alitalia Avellino
	I-DEIB	Boeing 767-33AER	Alitalia Team Pier Paolo Racchetti
	I-DEIC	Boeing 767-33AER	Alitalia Team Alberto Nassetti
	I-DEID	Boeing 767-33AER	Alitalia Team Marco Polo
	I-DEIF	Boeing 767-33AER	Alitalia Team Cristoforo Colombo
	I-DEIG	Boeing 767-33AER	Alitalia Team Francesco Agello
	I-DEIL	Boeing 767-33AER	Alitalia Team Arturo Ferrarin
	I-DEMC	Boeing 747-243B (SCD)	Alitalia Taormina
	I-DEMG	Boeing 747-243B	Alitalia Cervinia
	I-DEML	Boeing 747-243B	Alitalia Sorrento
	I-DEMN	Boeing 747-243B	Alitalia Portocervo
	I-DEMP	Boeing 747-243B	Alitalia Capri
	I-DEMR	Boeing 747-243F (SCD)	Alitalia Titano
	I-DEMS	Boeing 747-243B	Alitalia Monte Argentario
	I-DEMV	Boeing 747-243B	Alitalia Sestriere
	I-DEMY	Boeing 747-230B	Alitalia Asolo
	I-DIKR	Douglas DC-9-32	Alitalia Piemonte
	I-DIZE	Douglas DC-9-32	Alitalia Isola della Meloria
	I-DUPA	McD Douglas MD-11C	Alitalia Gioacchino Rossini
	I-DUPB	McD Douglas MD-11	Alitalia Pietro Mascagni
	I-DUPC	McD Douglas MD-11	Alitalia V. Bellini
	I-DUPD	McD Douglas MD-11	Alitalia G. Donizetti
	I-DUPE	McD Douglas MD-11C	Alitalia Giuseppe Verdi
	I-DUPI	McD Douglas MD-11C	Alitalia Gioacomo Puccini
	I-DUPO	McD Douglas MD-11C	Alitalia Nicolo Paganini
	I-DUPU	McD Douglas MD-11C	Alitalia Antonio Vivaldi
	I-EXMA	Embraer RJ145LR	Alitalia Express Giosue Carducci
	I-EXMB	Embraer RJ145LR	Alitalia Express Salvatori Quasidomo
	I-EXMC	Embraer RJ145LR	Alitalia Express
	I-EXMD	Embraer RJ145LR	Alitalia Express
	I-EXME	Embraer RJ145LR	Alitalia Express Guglialmo Marconi
	I-EXMF	Embraer RJ145LR	Alitalia Express
	I-EXMG	Embraer RJ145LR	Alitalia Express
	I-EXMH	Embraer RJ145LR	Alitalia Express
	I-EXMI	Embraer RJ145LR	Alitalia Express Grazia Deledda
	I-EXML	Embraer RJ145LR	Alitalia Express
	I-EXMO	Embraer RJ145LR	Alitalia Express Luigi Pirandello
	I-EXMU	Embraer RJ145LR	Alitalia Express Enrico Fermi
	I-FLRE	BAe 146-200	Meridiana
	I-FLRI	BAe 146-200	Meridiana
	I-FLRO	BAe 146-200	Meridiana
	I-FLRU	BAe 146-200	Meridiana
	I-FLYY	Douglas DC-9-51	Eurofly
	I-FLYZ	Douglas DC-9-51	Eurofly
	I-GANL	Dornier Do.328JET	Gandalf Airlines
	I-	Dornier Do.328JET	Gandalf Airlines
	I-	Dornier Do.328JET	Gandalf Airlines
	I-	Dornier Do.328JET	Gandalf Airlines
	I-JETA	Boeing 737-229	Air Sicilia
	I-JETC	Boeing 737-230	Air One
	I-JETD	Boeing 737-230	Air One
	I-PEKA	Airbus A.320-214	Air Europe

Reg.	Type	Owner or Operator	Notes
I-PEKC	Airbus A.320-214	Air Europe	
I-PEKD	Airbus A.320-214	Air Europe	
I-PEKE	Airbus A.320-214	Air Europe	
I-PEKF	Airbus A.320-214	Air Europe	
I-PEKZ	Airbus A.320-214	Air Europe	
I-RIML	Aérospatiale ATR-42-300	Italy First	
I-RIMS	Aérospatiale ATR-42-300	Italy First	
I-SMEB	McD Douglas MD-82	Meridiana	
I-SMEC	McD Douglas MD-83	Meridiana	
I-SMED	McD Douglas MD-83	Meridiana	
I-SMEL	McD Douglas MD-82	Meridiana	
I-SMEM	McD Douglas MD-82	Meridiana	
I-SMEP	McD Douglas MD-82	Meridiana	
I-SMER	McD Douglas MD-82	Meridiana	
I-SMES	McD Douglas MD-82	Meridiana	
I-SMET	McD Douglas MD-82	Meridiana	
I-SMEV	McD Douglas MD-82	Meridiana	
I-SMEZ	McD Douglas MD-83	Meridiana	
I-TNTC	BAe 146-200QT	Mistral Air/TNT	
I-VEIY	Boeing 767-330ER	Volare Airlines	
I-VIMQ	Boeing 767-3Q8ER	Air Europe Italy	
I-VLEB	Boeing 767-3Q8ER	Air Europe Italy	
I-VLEO	Airbus A.320-214	Volare Airlines	

Note: Meridiana also operates MD-83s which retain the registrations EI-CIW, EI-CKM, EI-CRE, EI-CRH, EI-CRJ and EI-CRW. Air Europe Italy also operates Boeing 767s registered EI-CJA, EI-CJB and EI-CLS, plus Boeing 777s EI-CRS and EI-CRT. Air One also operates Boeing 737s D-AGMR, EI-CLW, EI-CLZ, EI-COH, EI-COI, EI-COJ, EI-CRZ, EI-CSU, F-GKTA and F-GKTB, while Eurofly leases the MD-83s EI-CEK, EI-CMM, EI-CMZ and EI-CNR. Azzurra Air employs Avro RJs which retain the Irish marks EI-CNI, EI-CNJ, EI-CNK, EI-COQ and EI-CUO. The Boeing 767s EI-CRL EI-CRM and EI-CRO are operated by Alitalia. The A.320s F-GJVU, F-GJVX, F-OHFR, F-OHFT, F-OHFU, F-OHPX, EI-CUC, EI-CUK and EI-CUQ are operated by Volare Airlines. Gandalf Airlines employs the Dornier Do.328-110s D-CGAC, D-CGAN, D-CGAO, D-CGAP and D-CGEP. The ATR-72s EI-CLB, EI-CLC, EI-CLD and EI-CMJ fly for Alitalia Express carrying Irish registrations. Rome-based Blue Panorama operates leased Boeing 737-400s registered EI-CUA, EI-CUD and EI-CUN.

JA (Japan)

JA401A	Boeing 747-481	All Nippon Airways
JA402A	Boeing 747-481	All Nippon Airways
JA403A	Boeing 747-481	All Nippon Airways
JA404A	Boeing 747-481	All Nippon Airways
JA405A	Boeing 747-481	All Nippon Airways
JA811J	Boeing 747-246F	Japan Airlines
JA812J	Boeing 747-346	Japan Airlines
JA813J	Boeing 747-346	Japan Airlines
JA892D	Boeing 747-446	Japan Airlines
JA8071	Boeing 747-446	Japan Airlines
JA8072	Boeing 747-446	Japan Airlines
JA8073	Boeing 747-446	Japan Airlines
JA8074	Boeing 747-446	Japan Airlines
JA8075	Boeing 747-446	Japan Airlines
JA8076	Boeing 747-446	Japan Airlines
JA8077	Boeing 747-446	Japan Airlines
JA8078	Boeing 747-446	Japan Airlines
JA8079	Boeing 747-446	Japan Airlines
JA8080	Boeing 747-446	Japan Airlines
JA8081	Boeing 747-446	Japan Airlines
JA8082	Boeing 747-446	Japan Airlines
JA8085	Boeing 747-446	Japan Airlines
JA8086	Boeing 747-446	Japan Airlines
JA8087	Boeing 747-446	Japan Airlines
JA8088	Boeing 747-446	Japan Airlines
JA8089	Boeing 747-446	Japan Airlines
JA8094	Boeing 747-481	All Nippon Airways
JA8095	Boeing 747-481	All Nippon Airways

Notes	Reg.	Type	Owner or Operator
	JA8096	Boeing 747-481	All Nippon Airways
	JA8097	Boeing 747-481	All Nippon Airways
	JA8098	Boeing 747-481	All Nippon Airways
	JA8122	Boeing 747-246B	Japan Airlines
	JA8123	Boeing 747-246F (SCD)	Japan Airlines
	JA8130	Boeing 747-246B	Japan Airlines
	JA8131	Boeing 747-246B	Japan Airlines
	JA8132	Boeing 747-246F	Japan Airlines
	JA8140	Boeing 747-246B	Japan Airlines
	JA8141	Boeing 747-246B	Japan Airlines
	JA8151	Boeing 747-246F	Japan Airlines
	JA8154	Boeing 747-246B	Japan Airlines
	JA8158	Boeing 747SR-81	Nippon Cargo Airlines
	JA8160	Boeing 747-221F (SCD)	Japan Airlines
	JA8161	Boeing 747-246B	Japan Airlines
	JA8162	Boeing 747-246B	Japan Airlines
	JA8163	Boeing 747-346	Japan Airlines
	JA8165	Boeing 747-221F (SCD)	Japan Airlines
	JA8166	Boeing 747-346	Japan Airlines
	JA8167	Boeing 747-281F (SCD)	Nippon Cargo Airlines
	JA8168	Boeing 747-281F (SCD)	Nippon Cargo Airlines
	JA8169	Boeing 747-246B	Japan Airlines
	JA8171	Boeing 747-246F (SCD)	Japan Airlines
	JA8172	Boeing 747-281F (SCD)	Nippon Cargo Airlines
	JA8173	Boeing 747-346	Japan Airlines
	JA8174	Boeing 747-281B	All Nippon Airways
	JA8175	Boeing 747-281B	All Nippon Airways
	JA8177	Boeing 747-346	Japan Airlines
	JA8178	Boeing 747-346	Japan Airlines
	JA8179	Boeing 747-346	Japan Airlines
	JA8180	Boeing 747-246F (SCD)	Japan Airlines
	JA8181	Boeing 747-281F	All Nippon Airways
	JA8182	Boeing 747-281B	All Nippon Airways
	JA8184	Boeing 747-346	Japan Airlines
	JA8185	Boeing 747-346	Japan Airlines
	JA8186	Boeing 747-346	Japan Airlines
	JA8188	Boeing 747-281F (SCD)	Nippon Cargo Airlines
	JA8190	Boeing 747-281B	All Nippon Airways
	JA8191	Boeing 747-281F (SCD)	Nippon Cargo Airlines
	JA8192	Boeing 747-2D3F(SCD)	Nippon Cargo Airlines
	JA8193	Boeing 747-212F (SCD)	Japan Airlines
	JA8194	Boeing 747-281F (SCD)	Nippon Cargo Airlines
	JA8580	McD Douglas MD-11	Japan Airlines
	JA8581	McD Douglas MD-11	Japan Airlines
	JA8582	McD Douglas MD-11	Japan Airlines
	JA8583	McD Douglas MD-11	Japan Airlines
	JA8584	McD Douglas MD-11	Japan Airlines
	JA8585	McD Douglas MD-11	Japan Airlines
	JA8586	McD Douglas MD-11	Japan Airlines
	JA8587	McD Douglas MD-11	Japan Airlines
	JA8588	McD Douglas MD-11	Japan Airlines
	JA8589	McD Douglas MD-11	Japan Airlines
	JA8901	Boeing 747-446	Japan Airlines
	JA8902	Boeing 747-446	Japan Airlines
	JA8906	Boeing 747-446	Japan Airlines
	JA8909	Boeing 747-446	Japan Airlines
	JA8910	Boeing 747-446	Japan Airlines
	JA8911	Boeing 747-446	Japan Airlines
	JA8912	Boeing 747-446	Japan Airlines
	JA8913	Boeing 747-446	Japan Airlines
	JA8914	Boeing 747-446	Japan Airlines
	JA8915	Boeing 747-446	Japan Airlines
	JA8916	Boeing 747-446	Japan Airlines
	JA8917	Boeing 747-446	Japan Airlines
	JA8918	Boeing 747-446	Japan Airlines
	JA8919	Boeing 747-446	Japan Airlines
	JA8920	Boeing 747-446	Japan Airlines
	JA8921	Boeing 747-446	Japan Airlines
	JA8922	Boeing 747-446	Japan Airlines
	JA8937	Boeing 747-246F	Japan Airlines
	JA8957	Boeing 747-481F	All Nippon Airways
	JA8958	Boeing 747-481	All Nippon Airways
	JA8962	Boeing 747-481	All Nippon Airways

Reg.	Type	Owner or Operator	Notes

JY (Jordan)

JY-ABH	Airbus A.340-211	Jordanian Government	
JY-AGK	Airbus A.310-308	Royal Jordanian	
JY-AGL	Airbus A.310-304	Royal Jordanian	
JY-AGS	Airbus A.310-304	Royal Jordanian	
JY-AGT	Airbus A.310-308	Royal Jordanian	
JY-AGV	Airbus A.310-203	Royal Jordanian/Libyan Arab	
JY-AJN	Boeing 707-3J6C	Royal Jordanian Cargo	
JY-AJO	Boeing 707-3J6C	Royal Jordanian Cargo	
JY-GAX	Airbus A.300B4-622R	Royal Jordanian/Libyan Arab	
JY-GAZ	Airbus A.300B4-622R	Royal Jordanian/Libyan Arab	

Note: Royal Jordanian also operates A.310s registered F-ODVF, F-ODVG, F-ODVH, F-ODVI and F-OIHS. Similarly A.320s retain the registrations F-OGYA, F-OGYB, F-OGYC, F-OHGB and F-OHGC.

LN (Norway)

LN-BBA	Fokker 50	Norwegian Air Shuttle	
LN-BBB	Fokker 50	Norwegian Air Shuttle	
LN-BBC	Fokker 50	Norwegian Air Shuttle	
LN-BRD	Boeing 737-505	Braathens	
LN-BRE	Boeing 737-405	Braathens *Haakon V Magnusson*	
LN-BRF	Boeing 737-505	Braathens *Magnus Lagaboeter*	
LN-BRH	Boeing 737-505	Braathens *Haakon den Gode*	
LN-BRI	Boeing 737-405	Braathens *Harald Haarfagre*	
LN-BRJ	Boeing 737-505	Braathens *Magnus Barfot*	
LN-BRK	Boeing 737-505	Braathens *Olav Tryggvason*	
LN-BRM	Boeing 737-505	Braathens *Olav den Hellige*	
LN-BRN	Boeing 737-505	Braathens *Haakon Herdebrei*	
LN-BRO	Boeing 737-505	Braathens *Magnus Haraldsson*	
LN-BRP	Boeing 737-405	Braathens *Harald Hardraade*	
LN-BRQ	Boeing 737-405	Braathens *Harald Graafell*	
LN-BRR	Boeing 737-505	Braathens *Halvdan Svarte*	
LN-BRS	Boeing 737-505	Braathens *Olav Kyrre*	
LN-BRU	Boeing 737-505	Braathens *Eirik Magnusson*	
LN-BRV	Boeing 737-505	Braathens *Haakon Sverresson*	
LN-BRX	Boeing 737-505	Braathens *Sigurd Munn*	
LN-BUC	Boeing 737-505	Braathens *Magnus Erlingsson*	
LN-BUD	Boeing 737-505	Braathens *Inge Krokrygg*	
LN-BUE	Boeing 737-505	Braathens *Erling Skjalgsson*	
LN-BUF	Boeing 737-405	Braathens	
LN-BUG	Boeing 737-505	Braathens *Oystein Haraldsson*	
LN-FAJ	BAe Jetstream 3100	Coast Air	
LN-FAL	BAe Jetstream 3100	Coast Air	
LN-FAM	BAe Jetstream 3100	Coast Air	
LN-FAO	Aérospatiale ATR-42-300	Coast Air	
LN-FAP	Aérospatiale ATR-42-300	Coast Air	
LN-FAV	BAe Jetstream 3100	Coast Air	
LN-FAZ	BAe Jetstream 3100	Coast Air	
LN-KKA	Fokker 50	Norwegian Air Shuttle	
LN-KKD	Fokker 50	Norwegian Air Shuttle	
LN-KKE	Fokker 50	Norwegian Air Shuttle	
LN-RCD	Boeing 767-383ER	Scandinavian Airlines System (S.A.S.) *Gyda Viking*	
LN-RCE	Boeing 767-383ER	S.A.S. *Aase Viking*	
LN-RCF	Boeing 767-383ER	S.A.S. *Svea Viking*	
LN-RCG	Boeing 767-383ER	S.A.S. *Yrsa Viking*	
LN-RCH	Boeing 767-383ER	S.A.S. *Ingegerd Viking*	
LN-RCK	Boeing 767-383ER	S.A.S. *Tor Viking*	
LN-RCL	Boeing 767-383ER	S.A.S. *Sven Viking*	
LN-RCM	Boeing 767-383ER	S.A.S. *Gudrun Viking*	
LN-RCN	Boeing 737-883	S.A.S. *Hedrun Viking*	
LN-RCO	Boeing 737-883	S.A.S. *Gunn Viking*	
LN-RCP	Boeing 737-883	S.A.S.	
LN-RCR	Boeing 737-883	S.A.S.	
LN-RCS	Boeing 737-883	S.A.S.	
LN-RCT	Boeing 737-683	S.A.S.	
LN-RCU	Boeing 737-683	S.A.S. *Sigfrid Viking*	
LN-RCW	Boeing 737-683	S.A.S. *Yngvar Viking*	
LN-RCX	Boeing 737-883	S.A.S.	

Notes	Reg.	Type	Owner or Operator
	LN-RCY	Boeing 737-883	S.A.S.
	LN-RCZ	Boeing 737-883	S.A.S.
	LN-RDA	D.H.C.8Q-402 Dash Eight	S.A.S. Commuter *Frej Viking*
	LN-RDB	D.H.C.8Q-402 Dash Eight	S.A.S. Commuter *Kari Viking*
	LN-RDC	D.H.C.8Q-402 Dash Eight	S.A.S. Commuter *Hader Viking*
	LN-RDD	D.H.C.8Q-402 Dash Eight	S.A.S. Commuter *Loge Viking*
	LN-RDE	D.H.C.8Q-402 Dash Eight	S.A.S. Commuter *Dore Viking*
	LN-RDF	D.H.C.8Q-402 Dash Eight	S.A.S. Commuter *Fenja Viking*
	LN-RDG	D.H.C.8Q-402 Dash Eight	S.A.S. Commuter *Greip Viking*
	LN-RDH	D.H.C.8Q-402 Dash Eight	S.A.S. Commuter *Gloe Viking*
	LN-RDI	D.H.C.8Q-402 Dash Eight	S.A.S. Commuter *Asta Viking*
	LN-RDJ	D.H.C.8Q-402 Dash Eight	S.A.S. Commuter *Toke Viking*
	LN-RDK	D.H.C.8Q-402 Dash Eight	S.A.S. Commuter *Ingrid Viking*
	LN-RDL	D.H.C.8Q-402 Dash Eight	S.A.S. Commuter *Ulv Viking*
	LN-RDM	D.H.C.8Q-402 Dash Eight	S.A.S. Commuter *Banke Viking*
	LN-RDN	D.H.C.8Q-402 Dash Eight	S.A.S. Commuter *Gnupa Viking*
	LN-RDO	D.H.C.8Q-402 Dash Eight	S.A.S. Commuter *Frid Viking*
	LN-RDP	D.H.C.8Q-402 Dash Eight	S.A.S. Commuter *Huge Viking*
	LN-RDQ	D.H.C.8Q-402 Dash Eight	S.A.S. Commuter *Herta Viking*
	LN-RDS	D.H.C.8Q-402 Dash Eight	S.A.S. Commuter *Gote Viking*
	LN-RDT	D.H.C.8Q-402 Dash Eight	S.A.S. Commuter *Kile Viking*
	LN-RDU	D.H.C.8Q-402 Dash Eight	S.A.S. Commuter *Eide Viking*
	LN-RDW	D.H.C.8Q-402 Dash Eight	S.A.S. Commuter *Floke Viking*
	LN-RDX	D.H.C.8Q-402 Dash Eight	S.A.S. Commuter *Humle Viking*
	LN-RKF	Airbus A.340-313X	S.A.S. *Godfred Viking*
	LN-RKG	Airbus A.340-313X	S.A.S. *Gudrod Viking*
	LN-RKH	Airbus A.321-231	S.A.S. *Ragnvald Viking*
	LN-RKI	Airbus A.321-231	S.A.S. *Gunnhild Viking*
	LN-RLE	McD Douglas MD-82	S.A.S. *Ketill Viking*
	LN-RLF	McD Douglas MD-82	S.A.S. *Finn Viking*
	LN-RLG	McD Douglas MD-82	S.A.S. *Trond Viking*
	LN-RLR	McD Douglas MD-82	S.A.S. *Vegard Viking*
	LN-RMA	McD Douglas MD-82	S.A.S. *Hasting Viking*
	LN-RMD	McD Douglas MD-82	S.A.S. *Fenge Viking*
	LN-RMF	McD Douglas MD-83	S.A.S. *Torgny Viking*
	LN-RMG	McD Douglas MD-87	S.A.S. *Snorre Viking*
	LN-RMH	McD Douglas MD-87	S.A.S. *Solmund Viking*
	LN-RMJ	McD Douglas MD-82	S.A.S. *Rand Viking*
	LN-RMK	McD Douglas MD-87	S.A.S. *Ragnhild Viking*
	LN-RML	McD Douglas MD-82	S.A.S. *Aud Viking*
	LN-RMM	McD Douglas MD-81	S.A.S. *Blenda Viking*
	LN-RMN	McD Douglas MD-82	S.A.S. *Ivar Viking*
	LN-RMO	McD Douglas MD-81	S.A.S. *Bergljot Viking*
	LN-RMP	McD Douglas MD-87	S.A.S. *Reidun Viking*
	LN-RMR	McD Douglas MD-81	S.A.S. *Olav Viking*
	LN-RMS	McD Douglas MD-81	S.A.S. *Nial Viking*
	LN-RMT	McD Douglas MD-81	S.A.S. *Jarl Viking*
	LN-RMU	McD Douglas MD-87	S.A.S. *Grim Viking*
	LN-RMX	McD Douglas MD-87	S.A.S. *Vidar Viking*
	LN-RMY	McD Douglas MD-87	S.A.S. *Ingolf Viking*
	LN-RNB	Fokker 50	S.A.S. Commuter *Brae Viking*
	LN-RNC	Fokker 50	S.A.S. Commuter *Elvink Viking*
	LN-RND	Fokker 50	S.A.S. Commuter *Inge Viking*
	LN-RNE	Fokker 50	S.A.S. Commuter *Ebbe Viking*
	LN-RNF	Fokker 50	S.A.S. Commuter *Leif Viking*
	LN-RNG	Fokker 50	S.A.S. Commuter *Gudrid Viking*
	LN-RNH	Fokker 50	S.A.S. Commuter *Harald Viking*
	LN-ROA	McD Douglas MD-90-30	S.A.S. *Sigurd Viking*
	LN-ROB	McD Douglas MD-90-30	S.A.S. *Isrid Viking*
	LN-ROM	McD Douglas MD-81	S.A.S. *Albin Viking*
	LN-RON	McD Douglas MD-81	S.A.S. *Holmfrid Viking*
	LN-ROO	McD Douglas MD-81	S.A.S. *Kristin Viking*
	LN-ROP	McD Douglas MD-82	S.A.S. *Bjoern Viking*
	LN-ROR	McD Douglas MD-82	S.A.S. *Assur Viking*
	LN-ROS	McD Douglas MD-82	S.A.S. *Isulv Viking*
	LN-ROT	McD Douglas MD-82	S.A.S. *Ingjaid Viking*
	LN-ROU	McD Douglas MD-82	S.A.S. *Ring Viking*
	LN-ROW	McD Douglas MD-82	S.A.S. *Ottar Viking*
	LN-ROX	McD Douglas MD-82	S.A.S. *Ulvrik Viking*
	LN-ROY	McD Douglas MD-82	S.A.S. *Spjute Viking*
	LN-ROZ	McD Douglas MD-87	S.A.S. *Slagfinn Viking*
	LN-RPA	Boeing 737-683	S.A.S. *Arnljot Viking*
	LN-RPB	Boeing 737-683	S.A.S. *Bure Viking*

Reg.	Type	Owner or Operator	Notes
LN-RPC	Boeing 737-683	S.A.S. *Gyrd Viking*	
LN-RPD	Boeing 737-883	S.A.S. *Ramveig Viking*	
LN-RPE	Boeing 737-683	S.A.S. *Edla Viking*	
LN-RPF	Boeing 737-683	S.A.S. *Freda Viking*	
LN-RPG	Boeing 737-683	S.A.S. *Geinnund Viking*	
LN-RPH	Boeing 737-683	S.A.S. *Hamder Viking*	
LN-RPJ	Boeing 737-783	S.A.S. *Grimhild Viking*	
LN-RPK	Boeing 737-783	S.A.S. *Heimer Viking*	
LN-RPL	Boeing 737-883	S.A.S. *Svanevit Viking*	
LN-RPM	Boeing 737-883	S.A.S. *Fritt Viking*	
LN-RPN	Boeing 737-883	S.A.S. *Bergfora Viking*	
LN-RPO	Boeing 737-883	S.A.S.	
LN-RPP	Boeing 737-883	S.A.S. *Gerda Viking*	
LN-RPS	Boeing 737-683	S.A.S.	
LN-RPT	Boeing 737-683	S.A.S.	
LN-RPU	Boeing 737-683	S.A.S. *Ragne Viking*	
LN-RPW	Boeing 737-683	S.A.S. *Alvid Viking*	
LN-RPX	Boeing 737-683	S.A.S. *Nanna Viking*	
LN-RPY	Boeing 737-683	S.A.S. *Olov Viking*	
LN-RPZ	Boeing 737-683	S.A.S. *Bera Viking*	
LN-RRS	Boeing 737-883	S.A.S.	
LN-RRT	Boeing 737-883	S.A.S.	
LN-RRX	Boeing 737-683	S.A.S. *Ragnfast Viking*	
LN-RRY	Boeing 737-683	S.A.S. *Signer Viking*	
LN-RRZ	Boeing 737-683	S.A.S. *Gisela Viking*	
LN-TUA	Boeing 737-705	Braathens *Ingeborg Eriksdatter*	
LN-TUB	Boeing 737-705	Braathens	
LN-TUC	Boeing 737-705	Braathens	
LN-TUD	Boeing 737-705	Braathens *Margrete Skulesdatter*	
LN-TUE	Boeing 737-705	Braathens	
LN-TUF	Boeing 737-705	Braathens	
LN-TUG	Boeing 737-705	Braathens *Ingrid Svensdatter*	
LN-TUH	Boeing 737-705	Braathens	
LN-TUI	Boeing 737-705	Braathens *Kristin Knudsdatter*	
LN-TUJ	Boeing 737-705	Braathens	
LN-TUK	Boeing 737-705	Braathens	
LN-WFA	D.H.C.8-311 Dash Eight	Wideroe's Flyveselskap	
LN-WFB	D.H.C.8-311 Dash Eight	Wideroe's Flyveselskap	
LN-WFC	D.H.C.8-311 Dash Eight	Wideroe's Flyveselskap	
LN-WFE	D.H.C.8Q-311 Dash Eight	Wideroe's Flyveselskap	
LN-WFH	D.H.C.8-311 Dash Eight	Wideroe's Flyveselskap	
LN-WFO	D.H.C.8Q-311 Dash Eight	Wideroe's Flyveselskap	
LN-WFP	D.H.C.8Q-311 Dash Eight	Wideroe's Flyveselskap	
LN-WFR	D.H.C.8-311 Dash Eight	Wideroe's Flyveselskap	
LN-WFS	D.H.C.8Q-311 Dash Eight	Wideroe's Flyveselskap	
LN-WND	Douglas DC-3C	Dakota Norway	

LV (Argentina)

LV-MLO	Boeing 747-287B	Aerolineas Argentinas	
LV-MLP	Boeing 747-287B	Aerolineas Argentinas	
LV-MLR	Boeing 747-287B	Aerolineas Argentinas	
LV-OEP	Boeing 747-287B	Aerolineas Argentinas	
LV-OOZ	Boeing 747-287B	Aerolineas Argentinas	
LV-OPA	Boeing 747-287B	Aerolineas Argentinas	
LV-YPC	Boeing 747-212B	Aerolineas Argentinas	
LV-ZPJ	Airbus A.340-211	Aerolineas Argentinas	
LV-ZPO	Airbus A.340-211	Aerolineas Argentinas	
LV-ZPX	Airbus A.340-211	Aerolineas Argentinas	
LV-ZRA	Airbus A.340-211	Aerolineas Argentinas	

LX (Luxembourg)

LX-FCV	Boeing 747-4R7F (SCD)	Cargolux *City of Luxembourg*	
LX-GCV	Boeing 747-4R7F (SCD)	Cargolux *City of Esch/Alzette*	
LX-ICV	Boeing 747-428F (SCD)	Cargolux *City of Ettelbruck*	
LX-KCV	Boeing 747-4R7F (SCD)	Cargolux *City of Dudelange*	
LX-LCV	Boeing 747-4R7F (SCD)	Cargolux *City of Grevenmacher*	
LX-LGB	Fokker 50	Luxair	
LX-LGC	Fokker 50	Luxair *Prince Guillaume*	
LX-LGD	Fokker 50	Luxair *Prince Felix*	

Notes	Reg.	Type	Owner or Operator
	LX-LGE	Fokker 50	Luxair *Prince Louis*
	LX-LGF	Boeing 737-4C9	Luxair *Chateau de Vianden*
	LX-LGG	Boeing 737-4C9	Luxair *Château de Bourscheid*
	LX-LGI	Embraer RJ145LU	Luxair
	LX-LGJ	Embraer RJ145LU	Luxair
	LX-LGK	Embraer RJ145LU	Luxair
	LX-LGN	Boeing 737-59D	Luxair
	LX-LGO	Boeing 737-5C9	Luxair *Château de Clervaux*
	LX-LGP	Boeing 737-5C9	Luxair *Château de Bourglinster*
	LX-LGU	Embraer RJ145EP	Luxair *Prince Sebastien*
	LX-LGV	Embraer RJ145LU	Luxair
	LX-LGW	Embraer RJ145LU	Luxair
	LX-LGX	Embraer RJ145LU	Luxair
	LX-LGY	Embraer RJ145LU	Luxair
	LX-LGZ	Embraer RJ145LU	Luxair
	LX-MCV	Boeing 747-4R7F (SCD)	Cargolux *City of Echternach*
	LX-NCV	Boeing 747-4R7F (SCD)	Cargolux *City of Vianden*
	LX-OCV	Boeing 747-4R7F (SCD)	Cargolux *City of Differdange*
	LX-PCV	Boeing 747-4R7F (SCD)	Cargolux *City of Diekirch*
	LX-PTU	EMB-120RT Brasilia	Europe Air Charter
	LX-RCT	EMB-120ER Brasilia	Europe Air Charter
	LX-RCV	Boeing 747-4R7F (SCD)	Cargolux *City of Schengen*
	LX-RGI	EMB-120ER Brasilia	Europe Air Charter
	LX-SCV	Boeing 747-4R7F	Cargolux *City of Niederanven*
	LX-VDV	EMB-120RT Brasilia	Europe Air Charter

Note: The Boeing 747-271Cs N537MC and N538MC are operated by Atlas Air on behalf of Cargolux

LY (Lithuania)

	LY-AAO	Yakovlev Yak-42	Lithuanian Airlines
	LY-AAQ	Yakovlev Yak-42	Lithuanian Airlines
	LY-AAR	Yakovlev Yak-42	Lithuanian Airlines
	LY-AAT	Yakovlev Yak-42	Lithuanian Airlines
	LY-AAV	Yakovlev Yak-42D	Lithuanian Airlines
	LY-AAW	Yakovlev Yak-42D	Lithuanian Airlines
	LY-BAG	Boeing 737-382	Lithuanian Airlines
	LY-BFV	Boeing 737-59D	Lithuanian Airlines
	LY-BSD	Boeing 737-2T4	Lithuanian Airlines
	LY-BSG	Boeing 737-2T2	Lithuanian Airlines
	LY-SBC	SAAB 2000	Lithuanian Airlines
	LY-SBD	SAAB 2000	Lithuanian Airlines

LZ (Bulgaria)

	LZ-BAC	Antonov An-12B	Balkan Bulgarian Airlines/HeavyLift
	LZ-BAE	Antonov An-12BP	Balkan Bulgarian Airlines
	LZ-BAF	Antonov An-12B	Balkan Bulgarian Airlines
	LZ-BTH	Tupolev Tu-154M	Balkan Bulgarian Airlines
	LZ-BOC	Boeing 737-53A	Balkan Bulgarian Airlines
	LZ-BTQ	Tupolev Tu-154M	Hemus Air
	LZ-BTW	Tupolev Tu-154M	Balkan Bulgarian Airlines
	LZ-BTY	Tupolev Tu-154M	Balkan Bulgarian Airlines
	LZ-HMI	Tupolev Tu-154M	Hemus Air/Bulgarian Holidays
	LZ-HMN	Tupolev Tu-154M	Hemus Air
	LZ-HMP	Tupolev Tu-154M	Hemus Air
	LZ-HMS	Tupolev Tu-154M	Hemus Air
	LZ-HMW	Tupolev Tu-154M	Hemus Air
	LZ-ITA	Antonov An-12	Inter Trans Air
	LZ-ITB	Antonov An-12	Inter Trans Air
	LZ-ITS	Antonov An-12	Inter Trans Air
	LZ-LCA	Tupolev Tu-154M	Bulgarian Air Charter
	LZ-LCB	Tupolev Tu-154M	Bulgarian Air Charter
	LZ-LCO	Tupolev Tu-154M	Bulgarian Air Charter
	LZ-LCX	Tupolev Tu-154M	Bulgarian Air Charter
	LZ-LTV	Tupolev Tu-154M	Balkan Bulgarian Airlines
	LZ-MIG	Tupolev Tu-154M	Air VIA Bulgarian Airways
	LZ-MIK	Tupolev Tu-154M	Air VIA Bulgarian Airways
	LZ-MIL	Tupolev Tu-154M	Air VIA Bulgarian Airways
	LZ-MIR	Tupolev Tu-154M	Air VIA Bulgarian Airways
	LZ-MIS	Tupolev Tu-154M	Air VIA Bulgarian Airways

Reg.	Type	Owner or Operator	Notes
LZ-MIV	Tupolev Tu-154M	Air VIA Bulgarian Airways	
LZ-NHA	Antonov An-26	Air Nove	
LZ-SFA	Antonov An-12BP	Air Sofia	
LZ-SFH	Antonov An-26	Air Sofia	
LZ-SFK	Antonov An-12BP	Air Sofia	
LZ-SFL	Antonov An-12BP	Air Sofia	
LZ-SFN	Antonov An-12BP	Air Sofia	
LZ-SFS	Antonov An-12BP	Air Sofia	
LZ-TUH	Tupolev Tu-134A-3	Hemus Air	
LZ-TUJ	Tupolev Tu-134A-3	Hemus Air/Albanian Airlines	
LZ-TUL	Tupolev Tu-134A-3	Hemus Air	
LZ-TUN	Tupolev Tu-134A-3	Hemus Air/Albanian Airlines	
LZ-TUP	Tupolev Tu-134A	Hemus Air	
LZ-TUT	Tupolev Tu-134B-3	Hemus Air/Albanian Airlines	

N (USA)

Reg.	Type	Owner or Operator	Notes
N100UN	Boeing 737-7K9	Transaero	
N101UN	Boeing 737-7K9	Transaero *Seattle I*	
N104TR	Boeing 747-237BF	Tower Air	
N104UA	Boeing 747-422	United Airlines	
N105EV	McD Douglas MD-11F	EVA Airways	
N105UA	Boeing 747-451	United Airlines	
N106UA	Boeing 747-451	United Airlines	
N107UA	Boeing 747-422	United Airlines	
N107WA	Douglas DC-10-30CF	World Airways/Federal Express	
N108UA	Boeing 747-422	United Airlines	
N109UA	Boeing 747-422	United Airlines	
N116UA	Boeing 747-422	United Airlines	
N117UA	Boeing 747-422	United Airlines	
N117WA	Douglas DC-10-30	World Airways	
N118UA	Boeing 747-422	United Airlines	
N119UA	Boeing 747-422	United Airlines	
N120UA	Boeing 747-422	United Airlines	
N120UP	Airbus A.300F4-622R	United Parcel Service	
N121UA	Boeing 747-422	United Airlines	
N121UP	Airbus A.300F4-622R	United Parcel Service	
N122UA	Boeing 747-422	United Airlines	
N122UP	Airbus A.300F4-622R	United Parcel Service	
N123UP	Airbus A.300F4-622R	United Parcel Service	
N124UP	Airbus A.300F4-622R	United Parcel Service	
N125UP	Airbus A.300F4-622R	United Parcel Service	
N126UP	Airbus A.300F4-622R	United Parcel Service	
N127UA	Boeing 747-422	United Airlines	
N127UP	Airbus A.300F4-622R	United Parcel Service	
N128UA	Boeing 747-422	United Airlines	
N128UP	Airbus A.300F4-622R	United Parcel Service	
N129UP	Airbus A.300F4-622R	United Parcel Service	
N130UP	Airbus A.300F4-622R	United Parcel Service	
N131UP	Airbus A.300F4-622R	United Parcel Service	
N132UP	Airbus A.300F4-622R	United Parcel Service	
N133JC	Douglas DC-10-40	Northwest Airlines	
N133UP	Airbus A.300F4-622R	United Parcel Service	
N134UP	Airbus A.300F4-622R	United Parcel Service	
N135UP	Airbus A.300F4-622R	United Parcel Service	
N136UP	Airbus A.300F4-622R	United Parcel Service	
N137UP	Airbus A.300F4-622R	United Parcel Service	
N138UP	Airbus A.300F4-622R	United Parcel Service	
N139UP	Airbus A.300F4-622R	United Parcel Service	
N140UP	Airbus A.300F4-622R	United Parcel Service	
N141UP	Airbus A.300F4-622R	United Parcel Service	
N141US	Douglas DC-10-40	Northwest Airlines	
N144JC	Douglas DC-10-40	Northwest Airlines	
N145US	Douglas DC-10-40	Northwest Airlines	
N146US	Douglas DC-10-40	Northwest Airlines	
N147US	Douglas DC-10-40	Northwest Airlines	
N148US	Douglas DC-10-40	Northwest Airlines	
N149US	Douglas DC-10-40	Northwest Airlines	
N150US	Douglas DC-10-40	Northwest Airlines	
N151US	Douglas DC-10-40	Northwest Airlines	
N152US	Douglas DC-10-40	Northwest Airlines	
N153US	Douglas DC-10-40	Northwest Airlines	

Notes	Reg.	Type	Owner or Operator
	N154DL	Boeing 767-3P6ER	Delta Air Lines
	N154US	Douglas DC-10-40	Northwest Airlines
	N155DL	Boeing 767-3P6ER	Delta Air Lines
	N155US	Douglas DC-10-40	Northwest Airlines
	N156DL	Boeing 767-3P6ER	Delta Air Lines
	N156US	Douglas DC-10-40	Northwest Airlines
	N157US	Douglas DC-10-40	Northwest Airlines
	N158UA	Boeing 747-238B	United Airlines
	N158US	Douglas DC-10-40	Northwest Airlines
	N159UA	Boeing 747-238B	United Airlines
	N159US	Douglas DC-10-40	Northwest Airlines
	N160AT	L.1011-385 TriStar 500	American Trans Air
	N160UA	Boeing 747-238B	United Airlines
	N160US	Douglas DC-10-40	Northwest Airlines
	N161AT	L.1011-385 TriStar 500	American Trans Air
	N161UA	Boeing 747-238B	United Airlines
	N161US	Douglas DC-10-40	Northwest Airlines
	N162AT	L.1011-385 TriStar 500	American Trans Air
	N162US	Douglas DC-10-40	Northwest Airlines
	N163AT	L.1011-385 TriStar 500	American Trans Air
	N163UA	Boeing 747-238B	United Airlines
	N164AT	L.1011-385 TriStar 500	American Trans Air
	N164UA	Boeing 747-238B	United Airlines
	N165UA	Boeing 747-238B	United Airlines
	N169DZ	Boeing 767-332ER	Delta Air Lines
	N171DN	Boeing 767-332ER	Delta Air Lines
	N171DZ	Boeing 767-332ER	Delta Air Lines
	N171UA	Boeing 747-422	United Airlines *Spirit of Seattle II*
	N172DN	Boeing 767-332ER	Delta Air Lines
	N172DZ	Boeing 767-332ER	Delta Air Lines
	N172UA	Boeing 747-422	United Airlines
	N173DN	Boeing 767-332ER	Delta Air Lines
	N173DZ	Boeing 767-332ER	Delta Air Lines
	N173UA	Boeing 747-422	United Airlines
	N174DN	Boeing 767-332ER	Delta Air Lines
	N174DZ	Boeing 767-332ER	Delta Air Lines
	N174UA	Boeing 747-422	United Airlines
	N175DN	Boeing 767-332ER	Delta Air Lines
	N175DZ	Boeing 767-332ER	Delta Air Lines
	N175UA	Boeing 747-422	United Airlines
	N176DN	Boeing 767-332ER	Delta Air Lines
	N176DZ	Boeing 767-332ER	Delta Air Lines
	N176UA	Boeing 747-422	United Airlines
	N177DN	Boeing 767-332ER	Delta Air Lines
	N177DZ	Boeing 767-332ER	Delta Air Lines
	N177UA	Boeing 747-422	United Airlines
	N178DN	Boeing 767-332ER	Delta Air Lines
	N178DZ	Boeing 767-332ER	Delta Air Lines
	N178UA	Boeing 747-422	United Airlines
	N179DN	Boeing 767-332ER	Delta Air Lines
	N179DZ	Boeing 767-332ER	Delta Air Lines
	N179UA	Boeing 747-422	United Airlines
	N180DN	Boeing 767-332ER	Delta Air Lines
	N180UA	Boeing 747-422	United Airlines
	N181DN	Boeing 767-332ER	Delta Air Lines
	N181UA	Boeing 747-422	United Airlines
	N182DN	Boeing 767-332ER	Delta Air Lines
	N182UA	Boeing 747-422	United Airlines
	N183DN	Boeing 767-332ER	Delta Air Lines
	N183UA	Boeing 747-422	United Airlines
	N184DN	Boeing 767-332ER	Delta Air Lines
	N184UA	Boeing 747-422	United Airlines
	N185AT	L.1011-385 TriStar 50	American Trans Air
	N185DN	Boeing 767-332ER	Delta Air Lines
	N185UA	Boeing 747-422	United Airlines
	N186AT	L.1011-385 TriStar 50	American Trans Air
	N186DN	Boeing 767-332ER	Delta Air Lines
	N186UA	Boeing 747-422	United Airlines
	N187AT	L.1011-385 TriStar 50	American Trans Air
	N187DN	Boeing 767-332ER	Delta Air Lines
	N187UA	Boeing 747-422	United Airlines
	N188AT	L.1011-385 TriStar 50	American Trans Air
	N188DN	Boeing 767-332ER	Delta Air Lines

Reg.	Type	Owner or Operator	Notes
N188UA	Boeing 747-422	United Airlines	
N189AT	L.1011-385 TriStar 50	American Trans Air	
N189DN	Boeing 767-332ER	Delta Air Lines	
N189UA	Boeing 747-422	United Airlines	
N190AT	L.1011-385 TriStar 50	American Trans Air	
N190DN	Boeing 767-332ER	Delta Air Lines	
N190UA	Boeing 747-422	United Airlines	
N191AT	L.1011-385 TriStar 50	American Trans Air	
N191DN	Boeing 767-332ER	Delta Air Lines	
N191UA	Boeing 747-422	United Airlines	
N192AT	L.1011-385 TriStar 50	American Trans Air	
N192DN	Boeing 767-332ER	Delta Air Lines	
N192UA	Boeing 747-422	United Airlines	
N193AT	L.1011-385 TriStar 50	American Trans Air	
N193DN	Boeing 767-332ER	Delta Air Lines	
N193UA	Boeing 747-422	United Airlines	
N194AT	L.1011-385 TriStar 100	American Trans Air	
N194DN	Boeing 767-332ER	Delta Air Lines	
N194UA	Boeing 747-422	United Airlines	
N195AT	L.1011-385 TriStar 150	American Trans Air	
N195DN	Boeing 767-332ER	Delta Air Lines	
N195UA	Boeing 747-422	United Airlines	
N196AT	L.1011-385 TriStar 50	American Trans Air	
N196DN	Boeing 767-332ER	Delta Air Lines	
N196UA	Boeing 747-422	United Airlines	
N197AT	L.1011-385 TriStar 50	American Trans Air	
N197DN	Boeing 767-332ER	Delta Air Lines	
N197UA	Boeing 747-422	United Airlines	
N198AT	L.1011-385 TriStar 100	American Trans Air	
N198DN	Boeing 767-332ER	Delta Air Lines	
N198UA	Boeing 747-422	United Airlines	
N199DN	Boeing 767-332ER	Delta Air Lines	
N199UA	Boeing 747-422	United Airlines	
N204UA	Boeing 777-222ER	United Airlines	
N205UA	Boeing 777-222ER	United Airlines	
N206UA	Boeing 777-222ER	United Airlines	
N207UA	Boeing 777-222ER	United Airlines	
N208UA	Boeing 777-222ER	United Airlines	
N209UA	Boeing 777-222ER	United Airlines	
N210UA	Boeing 777-222ER	United Airlines	
N211NW	Douglas DC-10-30	Northwest Airlines	
N211UA	Boeing 777-222ER	United Airlines	
N212UA	Boeing 777-222ER	United Airlines	
N213UA	Boeing 777-222ER	United Airlines	
N214UA	Boeing 777-222ER	United Airlines	
N215UA	Boeing 777-222ER	United Airlines	
N216UA	Boeing 777-222ER	United Airlines	
N217UA	Boeing 777-222ER	United Airlines	
N218UA	Boeing 777-222ER	United Airlines	
N219UA	Boeing 777-222ER	United Airlines	
N220AU	Douglas DC-10-10	Orbis	
N220NW	Douglas DC-10-30	Northwest Airlines	
N220UA	Boeing 777-222ER	United Airlines	
N221NW	Douglas DC-10-30	Northwest Airlines	
N221UA	Boeing 777-222ER	United Airlines	
N222UA	Boeing 777-222ER	United Airlines	
N223NW	Douglas DC-10-30	Northwest Airlines	
N223UA	Boeing 777-222ER	United Airlines	
N224NW	Douglas DC-10-30	Northwest Airlines	
N224UA	Boeing 777-222ER	United Airlines	
N225NW	Douglas DC-10-30	Northwest Airlines	
N226NW	Douglas DC-10-30	Northwest Airlines	
N227NW	Douglas DC-10-30	Northwest Airlines	
N228NW	Douglas DC-10-30	Northwest Airlines	
N229NW	Douglas DC-10-30	Northwest Airlines	
N230NW	Douglas DC-10-30	Northwest Airlines	
N232NW	Douglas DC-10-30	Northwest Airlines	
N234NW	Douglas DC-10-30	Northwest Airlines	
N235NW	Douglas DC-10-30	Northwest Airlines	
N236NW	Douglas DC-10-30	Northwest Airlines	
N237NW	Douglas DC-10-30	Northwest Airlines	
N238NW	Douglas DC-10-30	Northwest Airlines	
N239NW	Douglas DC-10-30	Northwest Airlines	

Notes	Reg.	Type	Owner or Operator
	N240NW	Douglas DC-10-30	Northwest Airlines
	N241NW	Douglas DC-10-30	Northwest Airlines
	N242NW	Douglas DC-10-30	Northwest Airlines
	N243NW	Douglas DC-10-30	Northwest Airlines
	N244NW	Douglas DC-10-30	Northwest Airlines
	N250UP	McD Douglas MD-11	United Parcel Service
	N271WA	McD Douglas MD-11	World Airways
	N272WA	McD Douglas MD-11	World Airways
	N273WA	McD Douglas MD-11	World Airways
	N274WA	McD Douglas MD-11F	World Airways
	N275WA	McD Douglas MD-11CF	World Airways
	N276WA	McD Douglas MD-11CF	World Airways
	N277WA	McD Douglas MD-11	World Airways
	N278WA	McD Douglas MD-11	World Airways
	N301FE	Douglas DC-10-30AF	Federal Express
	N301UP	Boeing 767-34AFER	United Parcel Service
	N302FE	Douglas DC-10-30AF	Federal Express
	N302UP	Boeing 767-34AFER	United Parcel Service
	N303FE	Douglas DC-10-30AF	Federal Express
	N303UP	Boeing 767-34AFER	United Parcel Service
	N304FE	Douglas DC-10-30AF	Federal Express
	N304UP	Boeing 767-34AFER	United Parcel Service
	N305FE	Douglas DC-10-30AF	Federal Express *John David*
	N305UP	Boeing 767-34AFER	United Parcel Service
	N306FE	Douglas DC-10-30AF	Federal Express *John Peter Jr*
	N306GB	L.1011-385 TriStar 200F	Arrow Air
	N306UP	Boeing 767-34AFER	United Parcel Service
	N307FE	Douglas DC-10-30AF	Federal Express *Erin Lee*
	N307GB	L.1011-385 TriStar 200F	Arrow Air *San Juan*
	N307UP	Boeing 767-34AFER	United Parcel Service
	N308FE	Douglas DC-10-30AF	Federal Express *Ann*
	N308GB	L.1011-385 TriStar 200F	Arrow Air
	N308UP	Boeing 767-34AFER	United Parcel Service
	N309FE	Douglas DC-10-30AF	Federal Express *Stacey*
	N309UP	Boeing 767-34AFER	United Parcel Service
	N310FE	Douglas DC-10-30AF	Federal Express *John Shelby*
	N310UP	Boeing 767-34AFER	United Parcel Service
	N311FE	Douglas DC-10-30AF	Federal Express *Abe*
	N311UP	Boeing 767-34AFER	United Parcel Service
	N312AA	Boeing 767-223ER	American Airlines
	N312FE	Douglas DC-10-30AF	Federal Express *Angela*
	N312UP	Boeing 767-34AFER	United Parcel Service
	N313AA	Boeing 767-223ER	American Airlines
	N313FE	Douglas DC-10-30AF	Federal Express *Brandon Parks*
	N313UP	Boeing 767-34AFER	United Parcel Service
	N314FE	Douglas DC-10-30AF	Federal Express *Caitlin-Ann*
	N314UP	Boeing 767-34AFER	United Parcel Service
	N315AA	Boeing 767-223ER	American Airlines
	N315FE	Douglas DC-10-30AF	Federal Express *Kevin*
	N315UP	Boeing 767-34AFER	United Parcel Service
	N316AA	Boeing 767-223ER	American Airlines
	N316FE	Douglas MD-10-30AF	Federal Express *Brandon*
	N317AA	Boeing 767-223ER	American Airlines
	N317FE	Douglas DC-10-30CF	Federal Express
	N317UP	Boeing 767-34AFER	United Parcel Service
	N318FE	Douglas DC-10-30CF	Federal Express
	N318UP	Boeing 767-34AFER	United Parcel Service
	N319AA	Boeing 767-223ER	American Airlines
	N319FE	Douglas DC-10-30CF	Federal Express
	N319UP	Boeing 767-34AFER	United Parcel Service
	N320AA	Boeing 767-223ER	American Airlines
	N320FE	Douglas DC-10-30CF	Federal Express
	N320UP	Boeing 767-34AFER	United Parcel Service
	N321AA	Boeing 767-223ER	American Airlines
	N321FE	Douglas DC-10-30CF	Federal Express
	N322AA	Boeing 767-223ER	American Airlines
	N322FE	Douglas DC-10-30CF	Federal Express *King Frank*
	N322UP	Boeing 767-34AFER	United Parcel Service
	N323AA	Boeing 767-223ER	American Airlines
	N323MC	Boeing 747-2D7B	Atlas Air
	N323UP	Boeing 767-34AFER	United Parcel Service
	N324AA	Boeing 767-223ER	American Airlines
	N324UP	Boeing 767-34AFER	United Parcel Service

Reg.	Type	Owner or Operator	Notes
N325AA	Boeing 767-223ER	American Airlines	
N325UP	Boeing 767-34AFER	United Parcel Service	
N326FE	Douglas DC-10-30F	Federal Express	
N326UP	Boeing 767-34AFER	United Parcel Service	
N327AA	Boeing 767-223ER	American Airlines	
N327UP	Boeing 767-34AFER	United Parcel Service	
N328AA	Boeing 767-223ER	American Airlines	
N328UP	Boeing 767-34AFER	United Parcel Service	
N329AA	Boeing 767-223ER	American Airlines	
N329UP	Boeing 767-34AER	United Parcel Service	
N330AA	Boeing 767-223ER	American Airlines	
N330UP	Boeing 767-34AER	United Parcel Service	
N331UP	Boeing 767-34AER	United Parcel Service	
N332AA	Boeing 767-223ER	American Airlines	
N332UP	Boeing 767-34AER	United Parcel Service	
N334UP	Boeing 767-34AER	United Parcel Service	
N335AA	Boeing 767-223ER	American Airlines	
N336AA	Boeing 767-223ER	American Airlines	
N338AA	Boeing 767-223ER	American Airlines	
N339AA	Boeing 767-223ER	American Airlines	
N341HA	L.188AF Electra	Channel Express (Air Services) Ltd	
N343HA	L.188AF Electra	Channel Express (Air Services) Ltd	
N344HA	L.188AF Electra	Channel Express (Air Services) Ltd	
N345JW	Douglas DC-8-63AF	Arrow Air	
N351AA	Boeing 767-323ER	American Airlines	
N352AA	Boeing 767-323ER	American Airlines	
N353AA	Boeing 767-323ER	American Airlines	
N354AA	Boeing 767-323ER	American Airlines	
N354MC	Boeing 747-341F	Atlas Air	
N355AA	Boeing 767-323ER	American Airlines	
N355MC	Boeing 747-341F	Atlas Air	
N357AA	Boeing 767-323ER	American Airlines	
N358AA	Boeing 767-323ER	American Airlines	
N359AA	Boeing 767-323ER	American Airlines	
N360AA	Boeing 767-323ER	American Airlines	
N360Q	L.188F Electra	Channel Express (Air Services) Ltd	
N361AA	Boeing 767-323ER	American Airlines	
N361DH	Airbus A.300B4-103F	DHL Airways	
N362AA	Boeing 767-323ER	American Airlines	
N362DH	Airbus A.300B4-103F	DHL Airways	
N363AA	Boeing 767-323ER	American Airlines	
N363DH	Airbus A.300B4-103F	DHL Airways	
N364DH	Airbus A.300B4-203F	DHL Airways	
N365DH	Airbus A.300B4-203F	DHL Airways	
N366AA	Boeing 767-323ER	American Airlines	
N366DH	Airbus A.300B4-203F	DHL Airways	
N367DH	Airbus A.300B4-203F	DHL Airways	
N368AA	Boeing 767-323ER	American Airlines	
N369AA	Boeing 767-323ER	American Airlines	
N370AA	Boeing 767-323ER	American Airlines	
N371AA	Boeing 767-323ER	American Airlines	
N372AA	Boeing 767-323ER	American Airlines	
N373AA	Boeing 767-323ER	American Airlines	
N374AA	Boeing 767-323ER	American Airlines	
N376AN	Boeing 767-323ER	American Airlines	
N377AN	Boeing 767-323ER	American Airlines	
N378AN	Boeing 767-323ER	American Airlines	
N379AA	Boeing 767-323ER	American Airlines	
N380AN	Boeing 767-323ER	American Airlines	
N381AN	Boeing 767-323ER	American Airlines	
N382AN	Boeing 767-323ER	American Airlines	
N383AN	Boeing 767-323ER	American Airlines	
N384AA	Boeing 767-323ER	American Airlines	
N385AM	Boeing 767-323ER	American Airlines	
N386AA	Boeing 767-323ER	American Airlines	
N387AM	Boeing 767-323ER	American Airlines	
N388AA	Boeing 767-323ER	American Airlines	
N389AA	Boeing 767-323ER	American Airlines	
N390AA	Boeing 767-323ER	American Airlines	
N391AA	Boeing 767-323ER	American Airlines	
N392AN	Boeing 767-323ER	American Airlines	
N393AN	Boeing 767-323ER	American Airlines	
N394AN	Boeing 767-323ER	American Airlines	

Notes	Reg.	Type	Owner or Operator
	N394DL	Boeing 767-324ER	Delta Air Lines
	N395AN	Boeing 767-323ER	American Airlines
	N396AN	Boeing 767-323ER	American Airlines
	N397AN	Boeing 767-323ER	American Airlines
	N398AN	Boeing 767-323ER	American Airlines
	N399AN	Boeing 767-323ER	American Airlines
	N400JR	Douglas DC-10-30F	DAS Air Cargo
	N401FE	Airbus A.310-203F	Federal Express
	N401JR	Douglas DC-10-30F	DAS Air Cargo
	N402FE	Airbus A.310-203F	Federal Express
	N402JR	Douglas DC-10-30F	DAS Air Cargo
	N403FE	Airbus A.310-203F	Federal Express
	N404FE	Airbus A.310-203F	Federal Express
	N405FE	Airbus A.310-203F	Federal Express
	N407FE	Airbus A.310-203F	Federal Express
	N408FE	Airbus A.310-203F	Federal Express
	N408MC	Boeing 747-47UF	Atlas Air
	N409FE	Airbus A.310-203F	Federal Express
	N409MC	Boeing 747-47UF	Atlas Air
	N410FE	Airbus A.310-203F	Federal Express
	N411FE	Airbus A.310-203F	Federal Express
	N412FE	Airbus A.310-203F	Federal Express
	N412MC	Boeing 747-47UF	Atlas Air
	N413FE	Airbus A.310-203F	Federal Express
	N414FE	Airbus A.310-203F	Federal Express
	N415MC	Boeing 747-47UF	Atlas Air
	N416FE	Airbus A.310-222F	Federal Express
	N416MC	Boeing 747-47UF	Atlas Air
	N417FE	Airbus A.310-222F	Federal Express
	N418FE	Airbus A.310-222F	Federal Express
	N419FE	Airbus A.310-222F	Federal Express
	N420FE	Airbus A.310-222F	Federal Express
	N421AV	Boeing 767-2B1ER	Avianca
	N421FE	Airbus A.310-222F	Federal Express
	N422FE	Airbus A.310-222F	Federal Express
	N427UP	Boeing 757-24APF	United Parcel Service
	N431FE	Airbus A.310-203F	Federal Express
	N432FE	Airbus A.310-203F	Federal Express
	N433FE	Airbus A.310-203F	Federal Express
	N434FE	Airbus A.310-203F	Federal Express
	N435FE	Airbus A.310-203F	Federal Express
	N436FE	Airbus A.310-203F	Federal Express
	N441J	Douglas DC-8-63CF	Arrow Air
	N446FE	Airbus A.310-221F	Federal Express
	N450PA	Boeing 747-46NF	Polar Air Cargo
	N451FE	Airbus A.310-221F	Federal Express
	N451PA	Boeing 747-46NF	Polar Air Cargo
	N452FE	Airbus A.310-221F	Federal Express
	N452PA	Boeing 747-46NF	Polar Air Cargo
	N453FE	Airbus A.310-221F	Federal Express
	N453PA	Boeing 747-46NF	Polar Air Cargo
	N454FE	Airbus A.310-221F	Federal Express
	N454PA	Boeing 747-46NF	Polar Air Cargo
	N455FE	Airbus A.310-222F	Federal Express
	N456FE	Airbus A.310-222F	Federal Express
	N470EV	Boeing 747-273C	Evergreen International Airlines
	N471EV	Boeing 747-273C	Evergreen International Airlines
	N472EV	Boeing 747-131	Evergreen International Airlines
	N474EV	Boeing 747-121	Evergreen International Airlines
	N477EV	Boeing SR-46 (SCD)	Evergreen International Airlines
	N479EV	Boeing 747-132 (SCD)	Evergreen International Airlines
	N480EV	Boeing 747-121F	Evergreen International Airlines
	N481EV	Boeing 747-132 (SCD)	Evergreen International Airlines
	N482EV	Boeing 747-212B (SCD)	Evergreen International Airlines
	N483EV	Boeing 747-121	Evergreen International Airlines
	N484EV	Boeing 747-121	Evergreen International Airlines
	N485EV	Boeing 747-212B (SCD)	Evergreen International Airlines
	N486EV	Boeing 747-212B	Evergreen International Airlines
	N491MC	Boeing 747-47UF	Atlas Air
	N492MC	Boeing 747-47UF	Atlas Air *Spirit of Panalpina*
	N493MC	Boeing 747-47UF	Atlas Air
	N494MC	Boeing 747-47UF	Atlas Air
	N495MC	Boeing 747-47UF	Atlas Air

Reg.	Type	Owner or Operator	Notes
N496MC	Boeing 747-47UF	Arlas Air	
N497MC	Boeing 747-47UF	Atlas Air	
N498MC	Boeing 747-47UF	Atlas Air	
N499MC	Boeing 747-47UF	Atlas Air	
N505MC	Boeing 747-2D3B (SCD)	Atlas Air	
N506MC	Boeing 747-2D3B (SCD)	Atlas Air	
N507MC	Boeing 747-230B (SCD)	Atlas Air	
N508MC	Boeing 747-230B (SCD)	Atlas Air	
N509MC	Boeing 747-230B (SCD)	Atlas Air	
N512MC	Boeing 747-230B (SCD)	Atlas Air	
N513AT	Boeing 757-28A	American Trans Air	
N514AT	Boeing 757-23N	American Trans Air	
N515AT	Boeing 757-23N	American Trans Air	
N516AT	Boeing 757-23N	American Trans Air	
N516MC	Boeing 747-243F (SCD)	Atlas Air	
N517AT	Boeing 757-23N	American Trans Air	
N517MC	Boeing 747-243F (SCD)	Atlas Air	
N518AT	Boeing 767-23N	American Trans Air	
N518MC	Boeing 747-243F (SCD)	Atlas Air	
N519AT	Boeing 757-23N	American Trans Air	
N520AT	Boeing 757-23N	American Trans Air	
N520UP	Boeing 747-212BF	United Parcel Service	
N521AT	Boeing 757-28A	American Trans Air	
N521UP	Boeing 747-212BF	United Parcel Service	
N522AT	Boeing 757-23N	American Trans Air	
N522MC	Boeing 747-2D7B (SCD)	Atlas Air	
N522SJ	L.100-20 Hercules	Southern Air Transport	
N522UP	Boeing 747-212F	United Parcel Service	
N523AT	Boeing 757-23N	American Trans Air	
N523MC	Boeing 747-2D7BF	Atlas Air	
N523UP	Boeing 747-283F	United Parcel Service	
N524AT	Boeing 757-23N	American Trans Air	
N524MC	Boeing 747-2D7BF	Atlas Air	
N524MD	Douglas DC-10-30	Aeroflot Russian International	
N525AT	Boeing 757-23N	American Trans Air	
N525UP	Boeing 747-212BF	United Parcel Service	
N526AT	Boeing 757-23N	American Trans Air	
N526MC	Boeing 747-2D7BF	Atlas Air	
N526UP	Boeing 747-212B	United Parcel Service	
N527AT	Boeing 757-23N	American Trans Air	
N527MC	Boeing 747-2D7BF	Atlas Air	
N528AT	Boeing 757-23N	American Trans Air	
N528MC	Boeing 747-2D7B	Atlas Air	
N528UP	Boeing 747-256B	United Parcel Service	
N534MC	Boeing 747-2F6B	Atlas Air	
N535AW	Boeing 767-33AER	Avianca	
N535MC	Boeing 747-2F6B	Atlas Air	
N537MC	Boeing 747-271C (SCD)	Atlas Air	
N538MC	Boeing 747-271C (SCD)	Atlas Air	
N539MC	Boeing 747-271C (SCD)	Atlas Air	
N540MC	Boeing 747-243B (SCD)	Atlas Air	
N550TZ	Boeing 757-33N	American Trans Air	
N551TZ	Boeing 757-33N	American Trans Air	
N552TZ	Boeing 757-33N	American Trans Air	
N553TZ	Boeing 757-33N	American Trans Air	
N554TZ	Boeing 757-33N	American Trans Air	
N555TZ	Boeing 757-33N	American Trans Air	
N556TZ	Boeing 757-33N	American Trans Air	
N557TZ	Boeing 757-33N	American Trans Air	
N558TZ	Boeing 757-33N	American Trans Air	
N559TZ	Boeing 757-33N	American Trans Air	
N578FE	McD Douglas MD-11F	Federal Express	
N579FE	McD Douglas MD-11F	Federal Express	
N580FE	McD Douglas MD-11F	Federal Express	
N582FE	McD Douglas MD-11F	Federal Express *Jamie*	
N583FE	McD Douglas MD-11F	Federal Express *Nancy*	
N584FE	McD Douglas MD-11F	Federal Express *Jeffrey Wellington*	
N585FE	McD Douglas MD-11F	Federal Express	
N586FE	McD Douglas MD-11F	Federal Express *Dylan*	
N587FE	McD Douglas MD-11F	Federal Express *Jeanna*	
N588FE	McD Douglas MD-11F	Federal Express	
N589FE	McD Douglas MD-11F	Federal Express	
N590FE	McD Douglas MD-11F	Federal Express	

Notes	Reg.	Type	Owner or Operator
	N591FE	McD Douglas MD-11F	Federal Express
	N592FE	McD Douglas MD-11F	Federal Express
	N593FE	McD Douglas MD-11F	Federal Express
	N595FE	McD Douglas MD-11F	Federal Express
	N596FE	McD Douglas MD-11F	Federal Express
	N600GC	Douglas DC-10-30F	Gemini Air Cargo
	N601EV	Boeing 767-3T7ER	EVA Airways
	N601FE	McD Douglas MD-11F	Federal Express *Jim Riedmeyer*
	N601GC	Douglas DC-10-30F	Gemini Air Cargo
	N602AA	Boeing 747SP-31	American Airlines
	N602EV	Boeing 767-3T7ER	EVA Airways
	N602FE	McDouglas MD-11F	Federal Express *Malcolm Baldrige 1990*
	N602GC	Douglas DC-10-30F	Gemini Air Cargo
	N602UA	Boeing 767-222ER	United Airlines
	N603FE	McD Douglas MD-11F	Federal Express *Elizabeth*
	N603GC	Douglas DC-10-30F	Gemini Air Cargo
	N604FE	McD Douglas MD-11F	Federal Express *Hollis*
	N604GC	Douglas DC-10-30F	Gemini Air Cargo
	N605FE	McD Douglas MD-11F	Federal Express *April Star*
	N605GC	Douglas DC-10-30F	Gemini Air Cargo
	N605UA	Boeing 767-222ER	United Airlines
	N606FE	McD Douglas MD-11F	Federal Express *Charles & Theresa*
	N606GC	Douglas DC-10-30F	Gemini Air Cargo
	N606UA	Boeing 767-222ER	United Airlines *City of Chicago*
	N607FE	McD Douglas MD-11F	Federal Express *Christina*
	N607GC	Douglas DC-10-30F	Gemini Air Cargo
	N607UA	Boeing 767-222ER	United Airlines *City of Denver*
	N608FE	McD Douglas MD-11F	Federal Express *Dana Elena*
	N608FF	Boeing 747-131	Tower Air
	N608GC	Douglas DC-10-30F	Gemini Air Cargo
	N608UA	Boeing 767-222ER	United Airlines
	N609FE	McD Douglas MD-11F	Federal Express *Scott*
	N609FF	Boeing 747-121	Tower Air
	N609GC	Douglas DC-10-30	Gemini Air Cargo
	N609UA	Boeing 767-222ER	United Airlines
	N610FE	McD Douglas MD-11F	Federal Express *Marisa*
	N610FF	Boeing 747-282B	Tower Air
	N610UA	Boeing 767-222ER	United Airlines
	N611FF	Boeing 747-282B	Tower Air
	N611UA	Boeing 767-222ER	United Airlines
	N612FE	McD Douglas MD-11F	Federal Express *Alyssa*
	N612GC	Douglas DC-10-30F	Gemini Air Cargo
	N612US	Boeing 747-251B	Northwest Airlines
	N613FE	McD Douglas MD-11F	Federal Express *Krista*
	N613US	Boeing 747-251B	Northwest Airlines
	N614FE	McD Douglas MD-11F	Federal Express *Christy Allison*
	N614US	Boeing 747-251B	Northwest Airlines
	N615FE	McD Douglas MD-11F	Federal Express *Max*
	N615US	Boeing 747-251B	Northwest Airlines
	N616FE	McD Douglas MD-11F	Federal Express *Shanita*
	N616US	Boeing 747-251F (SCD)	Northwest Airlines
	N617FE	McD Douglas MD-11F	Federal Express *Travis*
	N617FF	Boeing 747-121F (SCD)	Tower Air
	N617US	Boeing 747-251F (SCD)	Northwest Airlines
	N618FE	McD Douglas MD-11F	Federal Express *Justin*
	N618US	Boeing 747-251F (SCD)	Northwest Airlines
	N619FE	McD Douglas MD-11F	Federal Express *Tara Lynn*
	N619US	Boeing 747-251F (SCD)	Northwest Airlines
	N620FE	McD Douglas MD-11F	Federal Express
	N621FE	McD Douglas MD-11F	Federal Express
	N622US	Boeing 747-251B	Northwest Airlines
	N623FE	McD Douglas MD-11F	Federal Express
	N623FF	Boeing 747-2F6B	Tower Air
	N623US	Boeing 747-251B	Northwest Airlines
	N624US	Boeing 747-251B	Northwest Airlines
	N625US	Boeing 747-251B	Northwest Airlines
	N626US	Boeing 747-251B	Northwest Airlines
	N627US	Boeing 747-251B	Northwest Airlines
	N628US	Boeing 747-251B	Northwest Airlines
	N629US	Boeing 747-251F (SCD)	Northwest Airlines
	N630US	Boeing 747-2J9F	Northwest Airlines
	N631US	Boeing 747-251B	Northwest Airlines
	N632TW	Boeing 767-3Y0ER	TWA/American Airlines

Reg.	Type	Owner or Operator	Notes
N632US	Boeing 747-251B	Northwest Airlines	
N633US	Boeing 747-227B	Northwest Airlines	
N634TW	Boeing 767-3Q8ER	TWA/American Airlines	
N634US	Boeing 747-227B	Northwest Airlines	
N635TW	Boeing 767-3Q8ER	TWA/American Airlines	
N635US	Boeing 747-227B	Northwest Airlines	
N636FE	Boeing 747-245F (SCD)	Federal Express	
N636TW	Boeing 767-3Q8ER	TWA/American Airlines	
N636US	Boeing 747-251B	Northwest Airlines	
N637TW	Boeing 767-33AER	TWA/American Airlines	
N637US	Boeing 747-251B	Northwest Airlines	
N638US	Boeing 747-251B	Northwest Airlines	
N639FE	Boeing 747-2R7F (SCD)	Federal Express	
N639TW	Boeing 767-3Y0ER	TWA/American Airlines	
N639US	Boeing 747-251F (SCD)	Northwest Airlines	
N640TW	Boeing 767-3Y0ER	TWA/American Airlines	
N640US	Boeing 747-251F (SCD)	Northwest Airlines	
N641NW	Boeing 747-212B	Northwest Airlines	
N641UA	Boeing 767-322ER	United Airlines	
N642NW	Boeing 747-212B	Northwest Airlines	
N642UA	Boeing 767-322ER	United Airlines	
N643NW	Boeing 747-249F	Northwest Airlines	
N643UA	Boeing 767-322ER	United Airlines	
N644NW	Boeing 747-212F	Northwest Airlines	
N644UA	Boeing 767-322ER	United Airlines	
N645NW	Boeing 747-222F	Northwest Cargo	
N645UA	Boeing 767-322ER	United Airlines	
N645US	Boeing 767-201ER	US Airways	
N646NW	Boeing 747-222F	Northwest Cargo	
N646UA	Boeing 767-322ER	United Airlines	
N646US	Boeing 767-201ER	US Airways	
N647UA	Boeing 767-322ER	United Airlines	
N647US	Boeing 767-201ER	US Airways	
N648UA	Boeing 767-322ER	United Airlines	
N648US	Boeing 767-201ER	US Airways	
N649UA	Boeing 767-322ER	United Airlines	
N649US	Boeing 767-201ER	US Airways	
N650UA	Boeing 767-322ER	United Airlines	
N650US	Boeing 767-201ER	US Airways	
N651FE	Airbus A.300-605R	Federal Express	
N651UA	Boeing 767-322ER	United Airlines	
N651US	Boeing 767-2B7ER	US Airways	
N652UA	Boeing 767-322ER	United Airlines	
N652US	Boeing 767-2B7ER	US Airways	
N653UA	Boeing 767-322ER	United Airlines	
N653US	Boeing 767-2B7ER	US Airways	
N654UA	Boeing 767-322ER	United Airlines	
N655UA	Boeing 767-322ER	United Airlines	
N655US	Boeing 767-2B7ER	US Airways	
N656FE	Airbus A.300-605R	Federal Express	
N656UA	Boeing 767-322ER	United Airlines	
N656US	Boeing 767-2B7ER	US Airways	
N657FE	Airbus A.300-605R	Federal Express	
N657UA	Boeing 767-322ER	United Airlines	
N658FE	Airbus A.300-605R	Federal Express	
N658UA	Boeing 767-322ER	United Airlines	
N659FE	Airbus A.300-605R	Federal Express	
N659UA	Boeing 767-322ER	United Airlines	
N660UA	Boeing 767-322ER	United Airlines	
N661AV	Douglas DC-8-63AF	Arrow Air	
N661UA	Boeing 767-322ER	United Airlines	
N661US	Boeing 747-451	Northwest Airlines	
N662FE	Airbus A.300-605R	Federal Express	
N662UA	Boeing 767-322ER	United Airlines	
N662US	Boeing 747-451	Northwest Airlines	
N663UA	Boeing 767-322ER	United Airlines	
N663US	Boeing 747-451	Northwest Airlines	
N664FE	Airbus A.300-605R	Federal Express	
N664UA	Boeing 767-322ER	United Airlines	
N664US	Boeing 747-451	Northwest Airlines	
N665FE	Airbus A.300-605R	Federal Express	
N665UA	Boeing 767-322ER	United Airlines	
N665US	Boeing 747-451	Northwest Airlines	

Notes	Reg.	Type	Owner or Operator
	N666UA	Boeing 767-322ER	United Airlines
	N666US	Boeing 747-451	Northwest Airlines
	N667FE	Airbus A.300-605R	Federal Express
	N667UA	Boeing 767-322ER	United Airlines
	N667US	Boeing 747-451	Northwest Airlines
	N668FE	Airbus A.300-605R	Federal Express
	N668UA	Boeing 767-322ER	United Airlines
	N668US	Boeing 747-451	Northwest Airlines
	N669FE	Airbus A.300-605R	Federal Express
	N669UA	Boeing 767-322ER	United Airlines
	N669US	Boeing 747-451	Northwest Airlines
	N670UA	Boeing 767-322ER	United Airlines
	N670US	Boeing 747-451	Northwest Airlines
	N670UW	Airbus A.330-323X	US Airways
	N671UA	Boeing 767-322ER	United Airlines
	N671US	Boeing 747-451	Northwest Airlines
	N671UW	Airbus A.330-323X	US Airways
	N672UA	Boeing 767-322ER	United Airlines
	N672UP	Boeing 747-123F (SCD)	United Parcel Service
	N672US	Boeing 747-451	Northwest Airlines
	N672UW	Airbus A.330-323X	US Airways
	N673UA	Boeing 767-322ER	United Airlines
	N673UP	Boeing 747-123F (SCD)	United Parcel Service
	N673US	Boeing 747-451	Northwest Airlines
	N673UW	Airbus A.330-323X	US Airways
	N674UA	Boeing 767-322ER	United Airlines
	N674UP	Boeing 747-123F (SCD)	United Parcel Service
	N674US	Boeing 747-451	Northwest Airlines
	N674UW	Airbus A.330-323X	US Airways
	N675UA	Boeing 767-322ER	United Airlines
	N675UP	Boeing 747-123F (SCD)	United Parcel Service
	N675US	Airbus A.330-323X	US Airways
	N676UA	Boeing 767-322ER	United Airlines
	N676UP	Boeing 747-123F (SCD)	United Parcel Service
	N676UW	Airbus A.330-323X	US Airways
	N677UA	Boeing 767-322ER	United Airlines
	N677UP	Boeing 747-123F (SCD)	United Parcel Service
	N677UW	Airbus A.330-323X	US Airways
	N678US	Airbus A.330-323X	US Airways
	N679US	Airbus A.330-323X	US Airways
	N681UP	Boeing 747-121F (SCD)	United Parcel Service
	N682UP	Boeing 747-121F (SCD)	United Parcel Service
	N683UP	Boeing 747-121F (SCD)	United Parcel Service
	N687AA	Boeing 757-223ER	American Airlines
	N688AA	Boeing 757-223ER	American Airlines
	N689AA	Boeing 757-223ER	American Airlines
	N690AA	Boeing 757-223ER	American Airlines
	N691AA	Boeing 757-223ER	American Airlines
	N692AA	Boeing 757-223ER	American Airlines
	N701GC	McD Douglas MD-11F	Gemini Air Cargo
	N701TW	Boeing 757-2Q8	TWA/American Airlines
	N702GC	McD Douglas MD-11F	Gemini Air Cargo
	N702TW	Boeing 757-2Q8	TWA/American Airlines
	N703GC	McD Douglas MD-11F	Gemini Air Cargo
	N703TW	Boeing 757-2Q8	TWA/American Airlines
	N705GC	McD Douglas MD-11F	Gemini Air Cargo
	N707TW	Boeing 757-2Q8	TWA/American Airlines
	N708TW	Boeing 757-231	TWA/American Airlines
	N709TW	Boeing 757-2Q8	TWA/American Airlines
	N718TW	Boeing 757-231	TWA/American Airlines
	N719TW	Boeing 757-231	TWA/American Airlines
	N720TW	Boeing 757-231	TWA/American Airlines
	N721TW	Boeing 757-231	TWA/American Airlines
	N722TW	Boeing 757-231	TWA/American Airlines
	N723TW	Boeing 757-231	TWA/American Airlines
	N724TW	Boeing 757-231	TWA/American Airlines
	N725TW	Boeing 757-231	TWA/American Airlines
	N726TW	Boeing 757-231	TWA/American Airlines
	N727TW	Boeing 757-231	TWA/American Airlines
	N742SA	Boeing 747-230F (SCD)	Southern Air
	N743SA	Boeing 747-230F (SCD)	Southern Air
	N744SA	Boeing 747-230BF (SCD)	Southern Air
	N750AN	Boeing 777-223ER	American Airlines

Reg.	Type	Owner or Operator	Notes
N750NA	Boeing 757-28A	North American Airlines	
N751AN	Boeing 777-223ER	American Airlines	
N752AN	Boeing 777-223ER	American Airlines	
N752NA	Boeing 757-28A	North American Airlines	
N753AN	Boeing 777-223ER	American Airlines	
N754AN	Boeing 777-223ER	American Airlines	
N755AN	Boeing 777-223ER	American Airlines	
N756AM	Boeing 777-223ER	American Airlines	
N756NA	Boeing 757-28A	North American Airlines	
N757AN	Boeing 777-223ER	American Airlines	
N758AN	Boeing 777-223ER	American Airlines	
N759AN	Boeing 777-223ER	American Airlines	
N760AN	Boeing 777-223ER	American Airlines	
N766UA	Boeing 777-222	United Airlines	
N767UA	Boeing 777-222	United Airlines	
N768UA	Boeing 777-222	United Airlines	
N769UA	Boeing 777-222	United Airlines	
N770AN	Boeing 777-223ER	American Airlines	
N770UA	Boeing 777-222	United Airlines	
N771AN	Boeing 777-223ER	American Airlines	
N771UA	Boeing 777-222	United Airlines	
N772AN	Boeing 777-223ER	American Airlines	
N772UA	Boeing 777-222	United Airlines	
N773AN	Boeing 777-223ER	American Airlines	
N773UA	Boeing 777-222	United Airlines	
N774AN	Boeing 777-223ER	American Airlines	
N774UA	Boeing 777-222	United Airlines	
N775AN	Boeing 777-223ER	American Airlines	
N775UA	Boeing 777-222	United Airlines	
N776AN	Boeing 777-223ER	American Airlines	
N776UA	Boeing 777-222	United Airlines	
N777AN	Boeing 777-223ER	American Airlines	
N777UA	Boeing 777-222	United Airlines	
N778AN	Boeing 777-223ER	American Airlines	
N778UA	Boeing 777-222	United Airlines	
N779AN	Boeing 777-223ER	American Airlines	
N779UA	Boeing 777-222	United Airlines	
N780AN	Boeing 777-223ER	American Airlines	
N780UA	Boeing 777-222	United Airlines	
N781AN	Boeing 777-223ER	American Airlines	
N781UA	Boeing 777-222	United Airlines	
N782AN	Boeing 777-223ER	American Airlines	
N782UA	Boeing 777-222ER	United Airlines	
N783AN	Boeing 777-223ER	American Airlines	
N783UA	Boeing 777-222ER	United Airlines	
N784AN	Boeing 777-223ER	American Airlines	
N784UA	Boeing 777-222ER	United Airlines	
N785AN	Boeing 777-223ER	American Airlines	
N785UA	Boeing 777-222ER	United Airlines	
N786AN	Boeing 777-223ER	American Airlines	
N786UA	Boeing 777-222ER	United Airlines	
N787AL	Boeing 777-223ER	American Airlines	
N787M	L.1011-385 TriStar 100	Operation Blessing International Relief	
N787UA	Boeing 777-222ER	United Airlines	
N788AN	Boeing 777-223ER	American Airlines	
N788UA	Boeing 777-222ER	United Airlines	
N789AN	Boeing 777-223ER	American Airlines	
N789UA	Boeing 777-222ER	United Airlines	
N790AN	Boeing 777-223ER	American Airlines	
N790UA	Boeing 777-222ER	United Airlines	
N791AL	Douglas DC-8-62AF	Arrow Air	
N791AN	Boeing 777-223ER	American Airlines	
N791UA	Boeing 777-222ER	United Airlines	
N792AN	Boeing 777-223ER	American Airlines	
N792UA	Boeing 777-222ER	United Airlines	
N793AN	Boeing 777-223ER	American Airlines	
N793UA	Boeing 777-222ER	United Airlines	
N794AN	Boeing 777-223ER	American Airlines	
N794UA	Boeing 777-222ER	United Airlines	
N795AN	Boeing 777-223ER	American Airlines	
N795UA	Boeing 777-222ER	United Airlines	
N796AN	Boeing 777-223ER	American Airlines	
N796UA	Boeing 777-222ER	United Airlines	

Notes	Reg.	Type	Owner or Operator
	N797AN	Boeing 777-223ER	American Airlines
	N797UA	Boeing 777-222ER	United Airlines
	N798AN	Boeing 777-223ER	American Airlines
	N798UA	Boeing 777-222ER	United Airlines
	N799AN	Boeing 777-223ER	American Airlines
	N799UA	Boeing 777-222ER	United Airlines
	N801DH	Douglas DC-8-73AF	DHL Worldwide
	N801FD	Airbus A.310-324F	Federal Express
	N801UP	Douglas DC-8-73AF	United Parcel Service
	N802BN	Douglas DC-8-62AF	Arrow Air
	N802DE	McD Douglas MD-11 (802)	Delta Air Lines
	N802DH	Douglas DC-8-73AF	DHL Worldwide
	N802FD	Airbus A.310-324F	Federal Express
	N802UP	Douglas DC-8-73AF	United Parcel Service
	N803DE	McD Douglas MD-11 (803)	Delta Air Lines
	N803DH	Douglas DC-8-73AF	DHL Worldwide
	N803UP	Douglas DC-8-63AF	United Parcel Service
	N804DE	McD Douglas MD-11 (804)	Delta Air Lines
	N804DH	Douglas DC-8-73AF	DHL Worldwide
	N804UP	Douglas DC-8-73AF	United Parcel Service
	N805DE	McD Douglas MD-11 (805)	Delta Air Lines
	N805DH	Douglas DC-8-73AF	DHL Worldwide
	N805UP	Douglas DC-8-73CF	United Parcel Service
	N806DE	McD Douglas MD-11 (806)	Delta Air Lines
	N806DH	Douglas DC-8-73CF	DHL Worldwide
	N806FT	Boeing 747-249F (SCD)	Polar Air Cargo
	N806UP	Douglas DC-8-73AF	United Parcel Service
	N807DE	McD Douglas MD-11 (807)	Delta Air Lines
	N807DH	Douglas DC-8-73CF	DHL Worldwide
	N807UP	Douglas DC-8-73AF	United Parcel Service
	N808DE	McD Douglas MD-11 (808)	Delta Air Lines
	N808MC	Boeing 747-212B (SCD)	Atlas Air
	N808UP	Douglas DC-8-73AF	United Parcel Service
	N809DE	McD Douglas MD-11 (809)	Delta Air Lines
	N809MC	Boeing 747-228F (SCD)	Atlas Air
	N809UP	Douglas DC-8-73AF	United Parcel Service
	N810DE	McD Douglas MD-11 (810)	Delta Air Lines
	N810UP	Douglas DC-8-71AF	United Parcel Service
	N811DE	McD Douglas MD-11 (811)	Delta Air Lines
	N811UP	Douglas DC-8-73AF	United Parcel Service
	N812DE	McD Douglas MD-11 (812)	Delta Air Lines
	N812UP	Douglas DC-8-73AF	United Parcel Service
	N813DE	McD Douglas MD-11 (813)	Delta Air Lines
	N813UP	Douglas DC-8-73AF	United Parcel Service
	N814DE	McD Douglas MD-11 (814)	Delta Air Lines
	N814UP	Douglas DC-8-73AF	United Parcel Service
	N815DE	McD Douglas MD-11 (815)	Delta Air Lines
	N818UP	Douglas DC-8-73AF	United Parcel Service
	N819UP	Douglas DC-8-73AF	United Parcel Service
	N820BX	Douglas DC-8-71AF	BAX Global
	N821BX	Douglas DC-8-71AF	BAX Global
	N822BX	Douglas DC-8-71AF	BAX Global
	N823BX	Douglas DC-8-71AF	BAX Global
	N824BX	Douglas DC-8-71AF	BAX Global
	N825MH	Boeing 767-432ER (1801)	Delta Air Lines
	N826MH	Boeing 767-432ER (1802)	Delta Air Lines
	N827MH	Boeing 767-432ER (1803)	Delta Air Lines
	N828MH	Boeing 767-432ER (1804)	Delta Air Lines
	N829MH	Boeing 767-432ER (1805)	Delta Air Lines
	N830FT	Boeing 747-121F (SCD)	Polar Air Cargo
	N830MH	Boeing 767-432ER (1806)	Delta Air Lines
	N831MH	Boeing 767-432ER (1807)	Delta Air Lines
	N832FT	Boeing 747-121F (SCD)	Polar Air Cargo
	N832MH	Boeing 767-432ER (1808)	Delta Air Lines
	N833MH	Boeing 767-432ER (1809)	Delta Air Lines
	N834MH	Boeing 767-432ER (1810)	Delta Air Lines
	N835MH	Boeing 767-432ER (1811)	Delta Air Lines
	N836MH	Boeing 767-432ER (1812)	Delta Air Lines
	N836UP	Douglas DC-8-73AF	United Parcel Service
	N837MH	Boeing 767-432ER (1813)	Delta Air Lines
	N838MH	Boeing 767-432ER (1814)	Delta Air Lines
	N839MH	Boeing 767-432ER (1815)	Delta Air Lines
	N840MH	Boeing 767-432ER (1816)	Delta Air Lines

Reg.	Type	Owner or Operator	Notes
N840UP	Douglas DC-8-73AF	United Parcel Service	
N841MH	Boeing 767-432ER (1817)	Delta Air Lines	
N842MH	Boeing 767-432ER (1818)	Delta Air Lines	
N843MH	Boeing 767-432ER (1819)	Delta Air Lines	
N844MH	Boeing 767-432ER (1820)	Delta Air Lines	
N845MH	Boeing 767-432ER (1821)	Delta Air Lines	
N850FT	Boeing 747-122F	Polar Air Cargo	
N851FT	Boeing 747-122F	Polar Air Cargo *Sandy Moore*	
N851UP	Douglas DC-8-73AF	United Parcel Service	
N852FT	Boeing 747-122F	Polar Air Cargo *Martin Moore*	
N852UP	Douglas DC-8-73AF	United Parcel Service	
N853FT	Boeing 747-122F	Polar Air Cargo	
N854FT	Boeing 747-122F	Polar Air Cargo *Sunny Lam*	
N857FT	Boeing 747-132F	Polar Air Cargo	
N858FT	Boeing 747-123F	Polar Air Cargo	
N859FT	Boeing 747-123F	Polar Air Cargo	
N860DA	Boeing 777-232ER (7001)	Delta Air Lines	
N861DA	Boeing 777-232ER (7002)	Delta Air Lines	
N862DA	Boeing 777-232ER (7003)	Delta Air Lines	
N863BX	Boeing 707-321C	BAX Global	
N863DA	Boeing 777-232ER (7004)	Delta Air Lines	
N864DA	Boeing 777-232ER (7005)	Delta Air Lines	
N865DA	Boeing 777-232ER (7006)	Delta Air Lines	
N866DA	Boeing 777-232ER (7007)	Delta Air Lines	
N866UP	Douglas DC-8-73AF	United Parcel Service	
N867BX	Douglas DC-8-63AF	BAX Global	
N867DA	Boeing 777-232ER (7008)	Delta Air Lines	
N867UP	Douglas DC-8-73AF	United Parcel Service	
N868BX	Douglas DC-8-63AF	BAX Global	
N868DA	Boeing 777-232ER (7009)	Delta Air Lines	
N868UP	Douglas DC-8-73AF	United Parcel Service	
N869BX	Douglas DC-8-63AF	BAX Global	
N869DA	Boeing 777-232ER (7010)	Delta Air Lines	
N870BX	Douglas DC-8-63AF	BAX Global	
N870DA	Boeing 777-232ER (7011)	Delta Air Lines	
N871DA	Boeing 777-232ER (7012)	Delta Air Lines	
N872DA	Boeing 777-232ER (7013)	Delta Air Lines	
N874UP	Douglas DC-8-73AF	United Parcel Service	
N880UP	Douglas DC-8-73AF	United Parcel Service	
N894UP	Douglas DC-8-73AF	United Parcel Service	
N920FT	Boeing 747-249F (SCD)	Polar Air Cargo	
N921FT	Boeing 747-283F	Polar Air Cargo	
N921UP	Boeing 727-180C	United Parcel Service	
N922FT	Boeing 747-2U3BF	Polar Air Cargo	
N923FT	Boeing 747-2U3BF	Polar Air Cargo	
N924FT	Boeing 747-259BF	Polar Air Cargo	
N925FT	Boeing 747-245F	Polar Air Cargo	
N926FT	Boeing 747-2R7F	Polar Air Cargo	
N984AN	Boeing 767-383ER	Avianca	
N985AN	Boeing 767-259ER	Avianca *Cristobal Colon*	
N986AN	Boeing 767-259ER	Avianca	
N988AN	Boeing 767-284ER	Avianca	
N1200K	Boeing 767-332ER (200)	Delta Air Lines	
N1201P	Boeing 767-332ER (201)	Delta Air Lines	
N1501P	Boeing 767-3P6ER (1501)	Delta Air Lines	
N1602	Boeing 767-332ER (1602)	Delta Air Lines	
N1603	Boeing 767-332ER (1603)	Delta Air Lines	
N1604R	Boeing 767-332ER (1604)	Delta Air Lines	
N1605	Boeing 767-332ER (1605)	Delta Air Lines	
N1606P	Boeing 767-332ER (1606)	Delta Air Lines	
N1607B	Boeing 767-332ER (1607)	Delta Air Lines	
N1608B	Boeing 767-332ER (1608)	Delta Air Lines	
N1609B	Boeing 767-332ER (1609)	Delta Air Lines	
N1610D	Boeing 767-332ER (1610)	Delta Air Lines	
N1611B	Boeing 767-332ER (1611)	Delta Air Lines	
N1612T	Boeing 767-332ER (1612)	Delta Air Lines	
N1613B	Boeing 767-332ER (1613)	Delta Air Lines	
N1808E	Douglas DC-8-62AF	Arrow Air	
N3140D	L.1011-385 TriStar 500 (598)	B.W.I.A. *Sunjet St. Lucia*	
N4508H	Boeing 747SP-09	China Airlines	
N4522V	Boeing 747SP-09	China Airlines	
N7375A	Boeing 767-323ER	American Airlines	
N8067A	Airbus A.300B4-605R (067)	American Airlines	

Notes	Reg.	Type	Owner or Operator
	N8968U	Douglas DC-8-62AF	Arrow Air
	N12109	Boeing 757-224 (109)	Continental Airlines
	N12114	Boeing 757-224 (114)	Continental Airlines
	N12116	Boeing 757-224 (116)	Continental Airlines
	N12125	Boeing 757-224 (125)	Continental Airlines
	N13110	Boeing 757-224 (110)	Continental Airlines
	N13113	Boeing 757-224 (113)	Continental Airlines
	N13138	Boeing 757-224 (138)	Continental Airlines
	N14065	Airbus A.300B4-605R (065)	American Airlines
	N14068	Airbus A.300B4-605R (068)	American Airlines
	N14102	Boeing 757-224 (102)	Continental Airlines
	N14106	Boeing 757-224 (106)	Continental Airlines
	N14107	Boeing 757-224 (107)	Continental Airlines
	N14115	Boeing 757-224 (115)	Continental Airlines
	N14118	Boeing 757-224 (118)	Continental Airlines
	N14120	Boeing 757-224 (120	Continental Airlines
	N14121	Boeing 757-224 (121)	Continental Airlines
	N16065	Boeing 767-332ER	Delta Air Lines
	N16078	Boeing 767-332ER	Delta Air Lines
	N17104	Boeing 757-224 (104)	Continental Airlines
	N17105	Boeing 757-224 (105)	Continental Airlines
	N17122	Boeing 757-224 (122)	Continental Airlines
	N17126	Boeing 757-224 (126)	Continental Airlines
	N17128	Boeing 757-224 (128)	Continental Airlines
	N17133	Boeing 757-224 (133)	Continental Airlines
	N17139	Boeing 757-224 (139)	Continental Airlines
	N18066	Airbus A.300B4-605R (066)	American Airlines
	N18112	Boeing 757-224 (112)	Continental Airlines
	N18119	Boeing 757-224 (119)	Continental Airlines
	N19117	Boeing 757-224 (117)	Continental Airlines
	N19130	Boeing 757-224 (130)	Continental Airlines
	N19136	Boeing 757-224 (136)	Continental Airlines
	N19141	Boeing 757-224 (141)	Continental Airlines
	N21108	Boeing 757-224 (108)	Continental Airlines
	N25071	Airbus A.300B4-605R (071)	American Airlines
	N26123	Boeing 757-224 (123)	Continental Airlines
	N27015	Boeing 777-224ER (015)	Continental Airlines
	N29124	Boeing 757-224 (124)	Continental Airlines
	N29129	Boeing 757-224 (129)	Continental Airlines
	N33069	Airbus A.300B4-605R (069)	American Airlines
	N33103	Boeing 757-224 (103)	Continental Airlines
	N33132	Boeing 757-224 (132)	Continental Airlines
	N34131	Boeing 757-224 (131	Continental Airlines
	N34137	Boeing 757-224 (137)	Continental Airlines
	N39356	Boeing 767-323ER	American Airlines
	N39364	Boeing 767-323ER	American Airlines
	N39365	Boeing 767-323ER	American Airlines
	N39367	Boeing 767-323ER	American Airlines
	N41135	Boeing 757-224 (135)	Continental Airlines
	N41140	Boeing 757-224 (140)	Continental Airlines
	N42086	Douglas DC-8-62AF	Arrow Air
	N48127	Boeing 757-224 (127)	Continental Airlines
	N57016	Boeing 777-224ER	Continental Airlines
	N57111	Boeing 757-224	Continental Airlines
	N58101	Boeing 757-224 (101)	Continental Airlines
	N59053	Boeing 767-424ER (053)	Continental Airlines
	N66051	Boeing 767-424ER (051)	Continental Airlines
	N66056	Boeing 767-424ER (056)	Continental Airlines
	N67052	Boeing 767-424ER (052)	Continental Airlines
	N67134	Boeing 757-224 (134)	Continental Airlines
	N67157	Boeing 767-224ER (157)	Continental Airlines
	N67158	Boeing 767-224ER (158)	Continental Airlines
	N68155	Boeing 767-224ER (155)	Continental Airlines
	N68159	Boeing 767-224ER (159)	Continental Airlines
	N68160	Boeing 767-224ER (160)	Continental Airlines
	N69154	Boeing 767-224ER (154)	Continental Airlines
	N70072	Airbus A.300B4-605R (072)	American Airlines
	N70073	Airbus A.300B4-605R (073)	American Airlines
	N70074	Airbus A.300B4-605R (074)	American Airlines
	N73152	Boeing 767-224ER (152)	Continental Airlines
	N74007	Boeing 777-224ER (007)	Continental Airlines
	N75851	Boeing 757-324ER (151)	Continental Airlines
	N76010	Boeing 777-224ER (010)	Continental Airlines

Reg.	Type	Owner or Operator	Notes
N76054	Boeing 767-424ER (054)	Continental Airlines	
N76055	Boeing 767-424ER (055)	Continental Airlines	
N76151	Boeing 767-224ER (151)	Continental Airlines	
N76153	Boeing 767-224ER (153)	Continental Airlines	
N76156	Boeing 767-224ER (156)	Continental Airlines	
N76401	Boeing 767-424ER	Continental Airlines	
N76851	Boeing 757-324ER	Continental Airlines	
N77006	Boeing 777-224ER (006)	Continental Airlines	
N77012	Boeing 777-224ER (012)	Continental Airlines	
N77014	Boeing 777-224ER (014))	Continental Airlines	
N78001	Boeing 777-224ER (001)	Continental Airlines	
N78002	Boeing 777-224ER (002)	Continental Airlines	
N78003	Boeing 777-224ER (003)	Continental Airlines	
N78004	Boeing 777-224ER (004)	Continental Airlines	
N78005	Boeing 777-224ER (005)	Continental Airlines	
N78008	Boeing 777-224ER (008)	Continental Airlines	
N78009	Boeing 777-224ER (009)	Continental Airlines	
N78013	Boeing 777-224ER (013)	Continental Airlines	
N79011	Boeing 777-224ER (011)	Continental Airlines	
N83071	Douglas DC-10-30ER (071)	Continental Airlines	
N87070	Douglas DC-10-30ER (070)	Continental Airlines	
N90070	Airbus A.300B4-605R (070)	American Airlines	

OD (Lebanon)

OD-AGD	Boeing 707-323C	TMA of Lebanon	
OD-AGO	Boeing 707-321C	TMA of Lebanon	
OD-AGP	Boeing 707-321C	TMA of Lebanon	
OD-AGS	Boeing 707-331C	TMA of Lebanon	
OD-AHC	Boeing 707-323C	Middle East Airlines	
OD-AHD	Boeing 707-323C	Middle East Airlines	
OD-AHF	Boeing 707-323B	Middle East Airlines	

Note: MEA also operates A.300 F-OHLN, A.310s registered 3B-STI, 3B-STJ and 3B-STK, two A.320s registered F-OHMO and F-OHMR and a pair of A.321s which carry the identities F-OHMP and F-OHMQ.

OE (Austria)

OE-ILA	L.188AF Electra	Amerer Air	
OE-ILB	L.188AF Electra	Amerer Air	
OE-ILF	Boeing 737-3Z9	Lauda Air *Bob Marley*	
OE-ILG	Boeing 737-3Z9	Lauda Air *John Lennon*	
OE-ILW	F.27 Friendship Mk.500	Amerer Air	
OE-LAE	Boeing 767-3Z9ER	Lauda Air	
OE-LAG	Airbus A.340-212	Austrian Airlines *Europe*	
OE-LAH	Airbus A.340-212	Austrian Airlines *Asia*	
OE-LAK	Airbus A.340-313	Austrian Airlines *Afrika*	
OE-LAL	Airbus A.340-313	Austrian Airlines *America*	
OE-LAM	Airbus A.330-223	Austrian Airlines *Daschstein*	
OE-LAN	Airbus A.330-223	Austrian Airlines *Arlberg*	
OE-LAO	Airbus A.330-223	Austrian Airlines *Grossglockner*	
OE-LAP	Airbus A.330-223	Austrian Airlines *Semmering*	
OE-LAT	Boeing 767-31AER	Lauda Air *Enzo Ferrari*	
OE-LAU	Boeing 767-3Z9ER	Lauda Air Italy *Marilyn Monroe*	
OE-LAW	Boeing 767-3Z9ER	Lauda Air *Franz Schubert*	
OE-LAX	Boeing 767-3Z9ER	Lauda Air *James Dean*	
OE-LAY	Boeing 767-3Z9ER	Lauda Air	
OE-LAZ	Boeing 767-3Z9ER	Lauda Air	
OE-LBA	Airbus A.321-111	Austrian Airlines *Salzkammergut*	
OE-LBB	Airbus A.321-111	Austrian Airlines *Pinzgau*	
OE-LBC	Airbus A.321-111	Austrian Airlines *Sudtirol*	
OE-LBD	Airbus A.321-111	Austrian Airlines	
OE-LBE	Airbus A.321-111	Austrian Airlines	
OE-LBF	Airbus A.321-111	Austrian Airlines *Wien*	
OE-LBN	Airbus A.320-214	Austrian Airlines *Osttirol*	
OE-LBO	Airbus A.320-214	Austrian Airlines *Pyhrn-Eisenwurzen*	
OE-LBP	Airbus A.320-214	Austrian Airlines *Neusiedler See*	
OE-LBQ	Airbus A.320-214	Austrian Airlines	
OE-LBR	Airbus A.320-214	Austrian Airlines *Bregenzer Wald*	
OE-LBS	Airbus A.320-214	Austrian Airlines *Waldviertel*	
OE-LBT	Airbus A.320-214	Austrian Airlines *Worthersee*	

Notes	Reg.	Type	Owner or Operator
	OE-LBU	Airbus A.320-214	Austrian Airlines *Weinerwald*
	OE-LBV	Airbus A.320-214	Austrian Airlines
	OE-LCF	Canadair CL.600-2B19 RJ	Tyrolean Airways *Stadt Dusseldorf*
	OE-LCG	Canadair CL.600-2B19 RJ	Tyrolean Airways *Stadt Köln*
	OE-LCH	Canadair CL.600-2B19 RJ	Tyrolean Airways *Stadt Amsterdam*
	OE-LCI	Canadair CL.600-2B19 RJ	Tyrolean Airways *Stadt Zürich*
	OE-LCJ	Canadair CL.600-2B19 RJ	Tyrolean Airways *Stadt Hannover*
	OE-LCK	Canadair CL.600-2B19 RJ	Tyrolean Airways *Stadt Brussel*
	OE-LCL	Canadair CL.600-2B19 RJ	Tyrolean Airways *Stadt Oslo*
	OE-LCM	Canadair CL.600-2B19 RJ	Tyrolean Airways *Stadt Bologna*
	OE-LCN	Canadair CL.600-2B19 RJ	Tyrolean Airways
	OE-LCO	Canadair CL.600-2B19 RJ	Tyrolean Airways
	OE-LCP	Canadair CL.600-2B19 RJ	Tyrolean Airways
	OE-LCQ	Canadair CL.600-2B19 RJ	Tyrolean Airways
	OE-LCR	Canadair CL.600-2B19 RJ	Tyrolean Airways
	OE-LCS	Canadair CL.600-2B19 RJ	Tyrolean Airways
	OE-LCT	Canadair CL.600-2B19 RJ	Tyrolean Airways
	OE-LCU	Canadair CL.600-2B19 RJ	Tyrolean Airways
	OE-LDX	McD Douglas MD-82	Austrian Airlines *Tirol*
	OE-LFG	Fokker 70	Tyrolean Airways *Stadt Innsbruck*
	OE-LFH	Fokker 70	Tyrolean Airways *Stadt Salzburg*
	OE-LFI	Fokker 70	Tyrolean Airways *Stadt Klagenfurt*
	OE-LFJ	Fokker 70	Tyrolean Airways *Stadt Graz*
	OE-LFK	Fokker 70	Tyrolean Airways *Stadt Wien*
	OE-LFL	Fokker 70	Tyrolean Airways *Stadt Linz*
	OE-LFO	Fokker 70	Austrian Airlines *Wiener Neustadt*
	OE-LFP	Fokker 70	Austrian Airlines *Wels*
	OE-LFQ	Fokker 70	Austrian Airlines *Dornbirn*
	OE-LFR	Fokker 70	Austrian Airlines *Steyr*
	OE-LFS	Fokker 70	Austrian Airlines *Schwechat*
	OE-LFT	Fokker 70	Austrian Airlines *Tullin*
	OE-LGA	D.H.C.8Q-402 Dash Eight	Tyrolean Airways
	OE-LGB	D.H.C.8Q-402 Dash Eight	Tyrolean Airways
	OE-LGC	D.H.C.8Q-402 Dash Eight	Turolean Airways
	OE-LGD	D.H.C.8Q-402 Dash Eight	Tyrolean Airways
	OE-LGE	D.H.C.8Q-402 Dash Eight	Tyrolean Airways
	OE-LGF	D.H.C.8Q-402 Dash Eight	Tyrolean Airways
	OE-LKB	Dornier Do.328-100	Air Alps Aviation/K.L.M. alps
	OE-LKC	Dornier Do.328-100	Air Alps Aviation/K.L.M. alps
	OE-LKD	Dornier Do.328-100	Air Alps Aviation/K.L.M. alps
	OE-LKE	Dornier Do.328-100	Air Alps Aviation/K.L.M. alps
	OE-LLE	D.H.C.8-106 Dash Eight	Tyrolean Airways *Zillertal*
	OE-LLF	D.H.C.8-106 Dash Eight	Tyrolean Airways *Seefeld*
	OE-LLG	D.H.C.8-106 Dash Eight	Tyrolean Airways *Kufstein*
	OE-LLU	D.H.C.7-102 Dash Seven	Tyrolean Airways
	OE-LLZ	D.H.C.8-314 Dash Eight	Tyrolean Airways *Land Burgenland*
	OE-LMA	McD Douglas MD-82	Austrian Airlines *Linz*
	OE-LMB	McD Douglas MD-82	Austrian Airlines *Eisenstadt*
	OE-LMC	McD Douglas MD-82	Austrian Airlines *Baden*
	OE-LMD	McD Douglas MD-83	Austrian Airlines *Villach*
	OE-LME	McD Douglas MD-83	Austrian Airlines *Krems*
	OE-LMK	McD Douglas MD-87	Austrian Airlines *St Pölten*
	OE-LML	McD Douglas MD-87	Austrian Airlines *Salzburg*
	OE-LMN	McD Douglas MD-87	Austrian Airlines *Klagenfurt*
	OE-LMO	McD Douglas MD-87	Austrian Airlines *Bregenz*
	OE-LNH	Boeing 737-4Z9	Lauda Air *Elvis Presley*
	OE-LNI	Boeing 737-4Z9	Lauda Air *Janise Joplin*
	OE-LNJ	Boeing 737-8Z9	Lauda Air *Falco*
	OE-LNK	Boeing 737-8Z9	Lauda Air
	OE-LNL	Boeing 737-6Z9	Lauda Air *Romy Schneider*
	OE-LNM	Boeing 737-6Z9	Lauda Air
	OE-LNN	Boeing 737-7Z9	Lauda Air
	OE-LNO	Boeing 737-7Z9	Lauda Air
	OE-LPA	Boeing 777-2Z9	Lauda Air
	OE-LPB	Boeing 777-2Z9	Lauda Air
	OE-LRA	Canadair CL.600-2B19 RJ	Lauda Air
	OE-LRB	Canadair CL.600-2B19 RJ	Lauda Air
	OE-LRC	Canadair CL.600-2B19 RJ	Lauda Air
	OE-LRE	Canadair CL.600-2B19 RJ	Lauda Air
	OE-LRF	Canadair CL.600-2B19 RJ	Lauda Air
	OE-LRG	Canadair CL.600-2B19 RJ	Lauda Air
	OE-LRH	Canadair CL.600-2B19 RJ	Lauda Air *Jochen Rindt*
	OE-LSA	D.H.C.8Q-314 Dash Eight	Rheintalflug/Team Lufthansa

Reg.	Type	Owner or Operator	Notes
OE-LSB	D.H.C.8Q-314 Dash Eight	Rheintalflug/Team Lufthansa	
OE-LSM	Embraer RJ145MP	Rheintalflug *Stadt Wien*	
OE-LSP	Embraer RJ145MP	Rheintalflug	
OE-LSR	Embraer RJ145MP	Rheintalflug	
OE-	D.H.C.8Q-314 Dash Eight	Rheintalflug/Team Lufthansa	
OE-	D.H.C.8Q-401 Dash Eight	Rheintalflug	
OE-LTD	D.H.C.8-314 Dash Eight	Tyrolean Airways *Land Oberösterreich*	
OE-LTF	D.H.C.8-314 Dash Eight	Tyrolean Airways *Land Niederösterreich*	
OE-LTG	D.H.C.8-314 Dash Eight	Tyrolean Airways *Land Tirol*	
OE-LTH	D.H.C.8-314 Dash Eight	Tyrolean Airways	
OE-LTI	D.H.C.8-314 Dash Eight	Tyrolean Airways	
OE-LTJ	D.H.C.8-314 Dash Eight	Tyrolean Airways	
OE-LTK	D.H.C.8-314 Dash Eight	Tyrolean Airways	
OE-LTL	D.H.C.8-314 Dash Eight	Tyrolean Airways	
OE-LTM	D.H.C.8-314 Dash Eight	Tyrolean Airways	
OE-LTN	D.H.C.8-314 Dash Eight	Tyrolean Airways	
OE-LTO	D.H.C.8-314 Dash Eight	Tyrolean Airways	

OH (Finland)

OH-LBO	Boeing 757-2Q8	Finnair	
OH-LBR	Boeing 757-2Q8	Finnair	
OH-LBS	Boeing 757-2Q8	Finnair	
OH-LBT	Boeing 757-2Q8	Finnair	
OH-LBU	Boeing 757-2Q8	Finnair	
OH-LBV	Boeing 757-2Q8	Finnair	
OH-LBX	Boeing 757-2Q8	Finnair	
OH-	Boeing 757-330	Finnair/Condor	
OH-	Boeing 757-330	Finnair/Condor	
OH-LGA	McD Douglas MD-11	Finnair	
OH-LGB	McD Douglas MD-11	Finnair	
OH-LGC	McD Douglas MD-11	Finnair	
OH-LGD	McD Douglas MD-11	Finnair	
OH-LMG	McD Douglas MD-83	Finnair	
OH-LMH	McD Douglas MD-82	Finnair	
OH-LMP	McD Douglas MD-82	Finnair	
OH-LMR	McD Douglas MD-83	Finnair	
OH-LMS	McD Douglas MD-83	Finnair	
OH-LMT	McD Douglas MD-82	Finnair	
OH-LMV	McD Douglas MD-83	Finnair	
OH-LMW	McD Douglas MD-82	Finnair	
OH-LMX	McD Douglas MD-82	Finnair	
OH-LMY	McD Douglas MD-82	Finnair	
OH-LMZ	McD Douglas MD-82	Finnair	
OH-LPA	McD Douglas MD-82	Finnair	
OH-LPB	McD Douglas MD-83	Finnair	
OH-LPC	McD Douglas MD-83	Finnair	
OH-LPD	McD Douglas MD-83	Finnair	
OH-LPE	McD Douglas MD-83	Finnair	
OH-LPF	McD Douglas MD-83	Finnair	
OH-LPG	McD Douglas MD-83	Finnair	
OH-LPH	McD Douglas MD-83	Finnair	
OH-LVA	Airbus A.319-112	Finnair	
OH-LVB	Airbus A.319-112	Finnair	
OH-LVC	Airbus A.319-112	Finnair	
OH-LVD	Airbus A.319-112	Finnair	
OH-LVE	Airbus A.319-112	Finnair	
OH-LVF	Airbus A.319-112	Finnair	
OH-LXA	Airbus A.320-214	Finnair	
OH-LXB	Airbus A.320-214	Finnair	
OH-LXC	Airbus A.320-214	Finnair	
OH-LXD	Airbus A.320-214	Finnair	
OH-LXE	Airbus A.320-214	Finnair	
OH-LXF	Airbus A.320-214	Finnair	
OH-LXG	Airbus A.320-214	Finnair	
OH-LXH	Airbus A.320-214	Finnair	
OH-LXI	Airbus A.320-214	Finnair	
OH-LYP	Douglas DC-9-51	Finnair	
OH-LYR	Douglas DC-9-51	Finnair	
OH-LYS	Douglas DC-9-51	Finnair	
OH-LYU	Douglas DC-9-51	Finnair	
OH-LYV	Douglas DC-9-51	Finnair	

Notes	Reg.	Type	Owner or Operator
	OH-LYW	Douglas DC-9-51	Finnair
	OH-LYX	Douglas DC-9-51	Finnair
	OH-LYY	Douglas DC-9-51	Finnair
	OH-LYZ	Douglas DC-9-51	Finnair
	OH-LZA	Airbus A,321-211	Finnair
	OH-LZB	Airbus A.321-211	Finnair
	OH-LZC	Airbus A.321-211	Finnair
	OH-LZD	Airbus A.321-211	Finnair
	OH-SAH	Avro RJ85	Air Botnia
	OH-SAI	Avro RJ85	Air Botnia
	OH-SAJ	Avro RJ85	Air Botnia
	OH-SAK	Avro RJ85	Air Botnia
	OH-SAL	Avro RJ85	Air Botnia

OK (Czech Republic)

	OK-AFE	Aérospatiale ATR42-400	CSA Czech Airlines
	OK-AFF	Aérospatiale ATR-42-400	CSA Czech Airlines
	OK-BFG	Aérospatiale ATR-42-320	CSA Czech Airlines
	OK-BGQ	Boeing 737-43Q	CSA Czech Airlines
	OK-BFH	Aérospatiale ATR-42-320	CSA Czech Airlines
	OK-CGH	Boeing 737-55S	CSA Czech Airlines *Usti n. Labem*
	OK-CGI	Boeing 737-49R	CSA Czech Airlines
	OK-CGJ	Boeing 737-55S	CSA Czech Airlines *Hradec Kralove*
	OK-CGK	Boeing 737-55S	CSA Czech Airlines *Pardubice*
	OK-DGL	Boeing 737-55S	CSA Czech Airlines *Tabor*
	OK-DGM	Boeing 737-45S	CSA Czech Airlines
	OK-DGN	Boeing 737-45S	CSA Czech Airlines *Trebic*
	OK-EGO	Boeing 737-55S	CSA Czech Airlines
	OK-EGP	Boeing 737-45S	CSA Czech Airlines
	OK-FAN	Boeing 737-33A	Fischer Air
	OK-FGR	Boeing 737-45S	CSA Czech Airlines
	OK-FGS	Boeing 737-45S	CSA Czech Airlines
	OK-FIT	Boeing 737-36N	Fischer Air
	OK-FUN	Boeing 737-33A	Fischer Air
	OK-TVA	Boeing 737-86N	Travel Service Airlines
	OK-TVB	Boeing 737-8CX	Travel Service Airlines
	OK-TVQ	Boeing 737-86N	Travel Service Airlines
	OK-TVR	Boeing 737-4Y0	Travel Service Airlines
	OK-TVS	Boeing 737-4Y0	Travel Service Airlines
	OK-VCG	Tupolev Tu-154M	CSA Czech Airlines *Luhacovice*
	OK-VCP	Tupolev Tu-154M	Travel Service Airlines
	OK-VFI	Aérospatiale ATR-42-300	CSA Czech Airlines
	OK-WAA	Airbus A.310-304	CSA Czech Airlines *Praha*
	OK-WAB	Airbus A.310-304	CSA Czech Airlines *Bratislava*
	OK-WGF	Boeing 737-4Y0	CSA Czech Airlines *Jihlava*
	OK-XFA	Aérospatiale ATR-72-202	CSA Czech Airlines
	OK-XFB	Aérospatiale ATR-72-202	CSA Czech Airlines
	OK-XFC	Aérospatiale ATR-72-202	CSA Czech Airlines
	OK-XFD	Aérospatiale ATR-72-202	CSA Czech Airlines
	OK-XGA	Boeing 737-55S	CSA Czech Airlines *Pizen*
	OK-XGB	Boeing 737-55S	CSA Czech Airlines *Olomouc*
	OK-XGC	Boeing 737-55S	CSA Czech Airlines *Ceske Budejovice*
	OK-XGD	Boeing 737-55S	CSA Czech Airlines *Poprad*
	OK-XGE	Boeing 737-55S	CSA Czech Airlines *Kosice*

OM (Slovakia)

	OM-AAA	Tupolev Tu-154M	Slovak Airlines
	OM-AAB	Tupolev Tu-154M	Slovak Airlines
	OM-AAC	Tupolev Tu-154M	Slovak Airlines
	OM-BAA	SAAB SF.340A	Slovak Airlines
	OM-BYO	Tupolev Tu-154M	Slovak Government.
	OM-BYR	Tupolev Tu-154M	Slovak Government
	OM-ERA	Boeing 737-2H4	Air Slovakia.
	OM-GAT	Tupolev Tu-134A-3	Air Transport Europe
	OM-NKD	BAe Jetstream 3102	SK Air

OO (Belgium)

	OO-DHK	Boeing 727-277F	European Air Transport (DHL)

Reg.	Type	Owner or Operator	Notes
OO-DHM	Boeing 727-31F	European Air Transport (DHL)	
OO-DHN	Boeing 727-31F	European Air Transport (DHL)	
OO-DHO	Boeing 727-31F	European Air Transport (DHL)	
OO-DHR	Boeing 727-35F	European Air Transport (DHL)	
OO-DHS	Boeing 727-223F	European Air Transport (DHL)	
OO-DHT	Boeing 727-223F	European Air Transport (DHL)	
OO-DHU	Boeing 727-223F	European Air Transport (DHL)	
OO-DHV	Boeing 727-223F	European Air Transport (DHL)	
OO-DHW	Boeing 727-223F	European Air Transport (DHL)	
OO-DHX	Boeing 727-223F	European Air Transport (DHL)	
OO-DHY	Boeing 727-230F	European Air Transport (DHL)	
OO-DHZ	Boeing 727-2Q4F	European Air Transport (DHL)	
OO-DJE	BAe 146-200	SN Brussels Airlines	
OO-DJF	BAe 146-200	SN Brussels Airlines	
OO-DJG	BAe 146-200	SN Brussels Airlines	
OO-DJH	BAe 146-200	SN Brussels Airlines	
OO-DJJ	BAe 146-200	SN Brussels Airlines	
OO-DJK	Avro RJ85	SN Brussels Airlines	
OO-DJL	Avro RJ85	SN Brussels Airlines	
OO-DJN	Avro RJ85	SN Brussels Airlines	
OO-DJO	Avro RJ85	SN Brussels Airlines	
OO-DJP	Avro RJ85	SN Brussels Airlines	
OO-DJQ	Avro RJ85	SN Brussels Airlines	
OO-DJR	Avro RJ85	SN Brussels Airlines	
OO-DJS	Avro RJ85	SN Brussels Airlines	
OO-DJT	Avro RJ85	SN Brussels Airlines	
OO-DJV	Avro RJ85	SN Brussels Airlines	
OO-DJW	Avro RJ85	SN Brussels Airlines	
OO-DJX	Avro RJ85	SN Brussels Airlines	
OO-DJY	Avro RJ85	SN Brussels Airlines	
OO-DJZ	Avro RJ85	SN Brussels Airlines	
OO-DLB	Boeing 727-277F	European Air Transport (DHL)	
OO-DLC	Airbus A.300B4-203F	European Air Transport (DHL)	
OO-DLD	Airbus A.300B4-203F	European Air Transport (DHL)	
OO-DLE	Airbus A.300B4-203F	European Air Transport (DHL)	
OO-DLG	Airbus A.300B4-203F	European Air Transport (DHL)	
OO-DLI	Airbus A.300B4-203F	European Air Transport (DHL)	
OO-DLJ	Boeing 757-23APF	European Air Transport (DHL)	
OO-DLK	Boeing 757-23APF	European Air Transport (DHL)	
OO-DLL	Airbus A.300B4-203F	European Air Transport (DHL)	
OO-DLN	Boeing 757-236F	European Air Transport (DHL)	
OO-DLO	Boeing 757-236F	European Air Transport (DHL)	
OO-D	Boeing 757-236F	European Air Transport (DHL)	
OO-D	Boeing 757-236F	European Air Transport (DHL)	
OO-D	Boeing 757-236F	European Air Transport (DHL)	
OO-D	Boeing 757-236F	European Air Transport (DHL)	
OO-D	Boeing 757-236F	European Air Transport (DHL)	
OO-D	Boeing 757-236F	European Air Transport (DHL)	
OO-DWA	Avro RJ100	SN Brussels Airlines	
OO-DWB	Avro RJ100	SN Brussels Airlines	
OO-DWC	Avro RJ100	SN Brussels Airlines	
OO-DWD	Avro RJ100	SN Brussels Airlines	
OO-DWE	Avro RJ100	SN Brussels Airlines	
OO-DWF	Avro RJ100	SN Brussels Airlines	
OO-DWG	Avro RJ100	SN Brussels Airlines	
OO-DWH	Avro RJ100	SN Brussels Airlines	
OO-DWI	Avro RJ100	SN Brussels Airlines	
OO-DWJ	Avro RJ100	SN Brussels Airlines	
OO-DWK	Avro RJ100	SN Brussels Airlines	
OO-DWL	Avro RJ100	SN Brussels Airlines	
OO-LTL	Boeing 737-3M8	Virgin Express	
OO-LTM	Boeing 737-3M8	Virgin Express	
OO-LTP	Boeing 737-33A	Virgin Express	
OO-LTU	Boeing 737-33A	Virgin Express	
OO-LTW	Boeing 737-33A	Virgin Express	
OO-MJE	BAe 146-200	SN Brussels Airlines	
OO-SBJ	Boeing 737-46B	Sobelair *Juliette*	
OO-SBM	Boeing 737-429	Sobelair	
OO-SBX	Boeing 737-3M8	Sobelair	
OO-SBZ	Boeing 737-329	Sobelair	
OO-SCW	Airbus A.340-211	-	
OO-SCX	Airbus A.340-211	-	
OO-SCY	Airbus A.340-311	-	

Notes	Reg.	Type	Owner or Operator
	OO-SCZ	Airbus A.340-311	-
	OO-SDV	Boeing 737-329	-
	OO-SDW	Boeing 737-329	-
	OO-SDX	Boeing 737-329	-
	OO-SDY	Boeing 737-329	-
	OO-SFM	Airbus A.330-301	-
	OO-SFN	Airbus A.330-301	-
	OO-SFO	Airbus A.330-301	-
	OO-SFP	Airbus A.330-223	-
	OO-SFQ	Airbus A.330-223	-
	OO-SFR	Airbus A.330-223	-
	OO-SFS	Airbus A.330-223	-
	OO-SFT	Airbus A.330-223	-
	OO-SFU	Airbus A.330-223	-
	OO-SFX	Airbus A.330-322	-
	OO-SKU	Embraer EMB-110P1 Bandeirante	Sky Service
	OO-SKW	Embraer EMB-110P1 Bandeirante	Sky Service
	OO-SLK	Boeing 737-33S	Sobelair
	OO-SLR	Boeing 767-3BGER	Sobelair
	OO-SLS	Boeing 767-3BGER	Sobelair
	OO-SLW	Boeing 737-448	Sobelair
	OO-SNE	Airbus A.320-214	-
	OO-SNF	Airbus A.320-214	-
	OO-SNG	Airbus A.320-214	-
	OO-SSA	Airbus A.319-112	-
	OO-SSB	Airbus A.319-112	-
	OO-SSC	Airbus A.319-112	-
	OO-SSD	Airbus A.319-112	-
	OO-SSE	Airbus A.319-112	-
	OO-SSF	Airbus A.319-112	-
	OO-SSG	Airbus A.319-112	-
	OO-SSH	Airbus A.319-112	-
	OO-SSI	Airbus A.319-112	-
	OO-SSJ	Airbus A.319-112	-
	OO-SSK	Airbus A.319-112	-
	OO-SSL	Airbus A.319-112	-
	OO-SSM	Airbus A.319-112	-
	OO-SSR	Airbus A.319-112	-
	OO-SSS	Airbus A.319-112	-
	OO-SST	Airbus A.319-112	-
	OO-SSU	Airbus A.319-112	-
	OO-SSV	Airbus A.319-112	-
	OO-SUA	Airbus A.321-211	-
	OO-SUB	Airbus A.321-211	-
	OO-SUC	Airbus A.321-211	-
	OO-SYA	Boeing 737-329	-
	OO-SYB	Boeing 737-329	-
	OO-SYF	Boeing 737-429	-
	OO-SYG	Boeing 737-529	-
	OO-SYH	Boeing 737-529	-
	OO-SYJ	Boeing 737-529	-
	OO-SYK	Boeing 737-529	
	OO-TAA	BAe 145-300QT	TNT Airways (G-TNTR)
	OO-TAD	BAe 146-300QT	TNT Airways (G-TNTM)
	OO-TAE	BAe 146-300QT	TNT Airways (G-TNTG)
	OO-TAF	BAe 146-300QT	TNT Airways (G-TNTK)
	OO-TAH	BAe 146-300QT	TNT Airways (G-TNTL)
	OO-TAJ	BAe 146-300QT	TNT Airways (G-TNTE)
	OO-TAK	BAe 146-300QT	TNT Airways (G-TJPM)
	OO-TAQ	BAe 146-200QT	TNT Airways (EC-ELT)
	OO-TAR	BAe 146-200QT	TNT Airways (G-TNTB)
	OO-TAS	BAe 146-300QT	TNT Airways (EC-FFY)
	OO-TAU	BAe 146-200QT	TNT Airways (EC-GQP)
	OO-TAW	BAe 146-200QT	TNT Airways (EC-EPA)
	OO-TAY	BAe 146-200QT	TNT Airways (EC-FVY)
	OO-TZA	Airbus A.300B4-203F	TNT Airways
	OO-TZB	Airbus A.300B4-203F	TNT Airways
	OO-TZC	Airbus A.300B4-203F	TNT Airways
	OO-TZD	Airbus A.300B4-203F	TNT Airways
	OO-VBR	Boeing 737-4Y0	Virgin Express
	OO-VEF	Boeing 737-430	Virgin Express
	OO-VEG	Boeing 737-36N	Virgin Express
	OO-VEH	Boeing 737-36N	Virgin Express

Reg.	Type	Owner or Operator	Notes
OO-VEJ	Boeing 737-405	Virgin Express	
OO-VEK	Boeing 737-405	Virgin Express	
OO-VEN	Boeing 737-36N	Virgin Express	
OO-VEX	Boeing 737-36N	Virgin Express	
OO-VLE	Fokker 50	V.L.M. Airlines *City of Dusseldorf*	
OO-VLG	Fokker 50	V.L.M. Airlines *Royal Jersey*	
OO-VLJ	Fokker 50	V.L.M. Airlines *Diana Princess of Wales*	
OO-VLK	Fokker 50	V.L.M. Airlines *City of Monchengladbach*	
OO-VLO	Fokker 50	V.L.M. Airlines *City of Geneva*	
OO-VLQ	Fokker 50	V.L.M.	
OO-VLR	Fokker 50	V.L.M. Airlines *City of Luxembourg*	
OO-VLS	Fokker 50	V.L.M. Airlines	
OO-VLV	Fokker 50	V.L.M. Airlines	

OY (Denmark)

Reg.	Type	Owner or Operator	Notes
OY-APB	Boeing 737-5L9	Maersk Air	
OY-APC	Boeing 737-5L9	Maersk Air	
OY-APH	Boeing 737-5L9	Maersk Air	
OY-API	Boeing 737-5L9	Maersk Air	
OY-APK	Boeing 737-5L9	Maersk Air	
OY-APN	Boeing 737-5L9	Maersk Air	
OY-APP	Boeing 737-5L9	Maersk Air	
OY-APR	Boeing 737-5L9	Maersk Air	
OY-ASY	EMB-110P1 Bandeirante	Scan Con Airways	
OY-BHT	EMB-110P2 Bandeirante	Scan Con Airways	
OY-BPB	Douglas DC-3C (K-682)	Flyvende Museumsfly	
OY-CHA	Swearingen SA226AT Merlin IV	Jetair	
OY-CIA	Aérospatiale ATR-42-300	Danish Air Transport	
OY-CIB	Aérospatiale ATR-42-300	Cimber Air	
OY-CID	Aérospatiale ATR-42-300	Cimber Air	
OY-CIE	Aérospatiale ATR-42-300	Cimber Air/Team Lufthansa	
OY-CIG	Aérospatiale ATR-42-300	Cimber Air	
OY-CIH	Aérospatiale ATR-42-300	Cimber Air	
OY-CIJ	Aérospatiale ATR-42-512	Cimber Air	
OY-CIK	Aérospatiale ATR-42-512	Cimber Air	
OY-CIL	Aérospatiale ATR-42-512	Cimber Air	
OY-CIM	Aérospatiale ATR-72-212A	Cimber Air	
OY-CIN	Aérospatiale ATR-72-212A	Cimber Air	
OY-CIO	Aérospatiale ATR-72-212A	Cimber Air/Team Lufthansa	
OY-CIR	Aérospatiale ATR-42-310	Danish Air Transport	
OY-CIS	Aérospatiale ATR-42-300	Cimber Air	
OY-CIT	Aérospatiale ATR-42-300	Cimber Air	
OY-CIU	Aérospatiale ATR-42-320	Danish Air Transport	
OY-CNA	Airbus A.300B4-120	My Travel Airways (Premiair)	
OY-CNB	Airbus A.320-212	My Travel Airways (Premiair)	
OY-CNC	Airbus A.320-212	My Travel Airways (Premiair)	
OY-CNK	Airbus A.300B4-120	My Travel Airways (Premiair)	
OY-CNL	Airbus A.300B4-120	My Travel Airways (Premiair)	
OY-CNM	Airbus A.320-212	My Travel Airways (Premiair)	
OY-CNN	Airbus A.320-212	My Travel Airways (Premiair)	
OY-CNP	Airbus A.320-212	My Travel Airways (Premiair)	
OY-CNR	Airbus A.320-212	My Travel Airways (Premiair)	
OY-CNW	Airbus A.320-212	My Travel Airways (Premiair)	
OY-EBB	Fokker 50	Newair	
OY-EBC	F.27 Friendship Mk.200	Newair	
OY-EBD	Fokker 50	Newair	
OY-EBG	Fokker 50	Newair	
OY-GEP	Beech 1900D	Trans Travel Airline	
OY-GRL	Boeing 757-236	Greenlandair	
OY-JEO	Swearingen SA226TC Metro II	Jetair	
OY-JRF	Beech 1900C	Danish Air Transport	
OY-JRI	Beech 1900C-1	Danish Air Transport	
OY-JRJ	Aérospatiale ATR-42-320	Danish Air Transport	
OY-JRK	SC.7 Skyvan	Danish Air Transport	
OY-JRV	Beech 1900D	Danish Air Transport	
OY-JRY	Aérospatiale ATR-42-320	Danish Air Transport	
OY-KBA	Airbus A.340-313X	S.A.S. *Adalstein Viking*	
OY-KBB	Airbus A.321-231	S.A.S. *Hjorulf Viking*	

Notes	Reg.	Type	Owner or Operator
	OY-KBE	Airbus A.321-231	S.A.S.
	OY-KBF	Airbus A.321-231	S.A.S.
	OY-KBH	Airbus A.321-231	S.A.S. *Sulke Viking*
	OY-KBI	Airbus A.340-313X	S.A.S. *Rurik Viking*
	OY-KBK	Airbus A.321-231	S.A.S. *Arne Viking*
	OY-KBL	Airbus A.321-231	S.A.S. *Gynnbjorn Viking*
	OY-KBM	Airbus A.340-313X	S.A.S.
	OY-KCC	D.H.C.8Q-402 Dash Eight	S.A.S. Commuter
	OY-KCD	D.H.C.8Q-402 Dash Eight	S.A.S. Commuter *Bjarke Viking*
	OY-KCE	D.H.C.8Q-402 Dash Eight	S.A.S. Commuter *Alf Viking*
	OY-KCF	D.H.C.8Q-402 Dash Eight	S.A.S. Commuter
	OY-KCG	D.H.C.8Q-402 Dash Eight	S.A.S. Commuter
	OY-KCH	D.H.C.8Q-402 Dash Eight	S.A.S. Commuter
	OY-KDH	Boeing 767-383ER	S.A.S. *Tyra Viking*
	OY-KDL	Boeing 767-383ER	S.A.S. *Tjodhild Viking*
	OY-KDM	Boeing 767-383ER	S.A.S. *Ingvar Viking*
	OY-KDN	Boeing 767-383ER	S.A.S. *Ulf Viking*
	OY-KGM	Douglas DC-9-41	S.A.S. *Arnfinn Viking*
	OY-KGO	Douglas DC-9-41	S.A.S. *Holte Viking*
	OY-KGR	Douglas DC-9-41	S.A.S. *Holger Viking*
	OY-KGS	Douglas DC-9-41	S.A.S. *Hall Viking*
	OY-KGT	McD Douglas MD-81	S.A.S. *Hake Viking*
	OY-KGY	McD Douglas MD-81	S.A.S. *Rollo Viking*
	OY-KGZ	McD Douglas MD-81	S.A.S. *Hagbard Viking*
	OY-KHC	McD Douglas MD-82	S.A.S. *Faste Viking*
	OY-KHE	McD Douglas MD-82	S.A.S.
	OY-KHF	McD Douglas MD-87	S.A.S. *Ragnar Viking*
	OY-KHG	McD Douglas MD-82	S.A.S. *Alle Viking*
	OY-KHI	McD Douglas MD-87	S.A.S. *Torkel Viking*
	OY-KHK	McD Douglas MD-81	S.A.S. *Roald Viking*
	OY-KHL	McD Douglas MD-81	S.A.S. *Knud Viking*
	OY-KHM	McD Douglas MD-81	S.A.S. *Mette Viking*
	OY-KHN	McD Douglas MD-81	S.A.S. *Dan Viking*
	OY-KHP	McD Douglas MD-81	S.A.S. *Arild Viking*
	OY-KHR	McD Douglas MD-81	S.A.S. *Torkild Viking*
	OY-KHT	McD Douglas MD-82	S.A.S. *Gorm Viking*
	OY-KHU	McD Douglas MD-87	S.A.S. *Ravn Viking*
	OY-KHW	McD Douglas MD-87	S.A.S. *Ingemund Viking*
	OY-KIL	McD Douglas MD-90-30	S.A.S. *Kaare Viking*
	OY-KIM	McD Douglas MD-90-30	S.A.S. *Jon Viking*
	OY-KIN	McD Douglas MD-90-30	S.A.S. *Tormod Viking*
	OY-KKE	Boeing 737-683	S.A.S. *Elisabeth Viking*
	OY-KKG	Boeing 737-683	S.A.S.
	OY-KKH	Boeing 737-683	S.A.S *Sindre Viking*
	OY-KKI	Boeing 737-783	S.A.S.
	OY-KKK	Boeing 737-683	S.A.S. *Borgny Viking*
	OY-KKN	Boeing 737-683	S.A.S.
	OY-KKR	Boeing 737-783	S.A.S. *Gjuke Viking*
	OY-KKT	Boeing 737-883	S.A.S.
	OY-MAA	Boeing 737-5L9	Maersk Air
	OY-MAC	Boeing 737-5L9	Maersk Air
	OY-MAE	Boeing 737-5L9	Maersk Air
	OY-MAH	Boeing 737-5L9	Maersk Air
	OY-MBO	Canadair CL.600-2B19 RJ	Maersk Air
	OY-MBP	Canadair CL.600-2B19 RJ	Maersk Air
	OY-MBR	Canadair CL.600-2B19 RJ	Maersk Air
	OY-MBS	Canadair CL.600-2B19 RJ	Maersk Air
	OY-MMA	Boeing 737-5L9	Maersk Air
	OY-MMG	Fokker 50	Maersk Air
	OY-MMH	Fokker 50	Maersk Air
	OY-MMS	Fokker 50	Newair
	OY-MRC	Boeing 737-7L9	Maersk Air
	OY-MRD	Boeing 737-7L9	Maersk Air
	OY-MRE	Boeing 737-7L9	Maersk Air
	OY-MRF	Boeing 737-7L9	Maersk Air
	OY-MRG	Boeing 737-7L9	Maersk Air
	OY-MRH	Boeing 737-7L9	Maersk Air
	OY-MRI	Boeing 737-7L9	Maersk Air
	OY-MRJ	Boeing 737-7L9	Maersk Air
	OY-MUE	BAe Jetstream 3100	Sun Air/British Airways
	OY-MUF	Fairchild F.27	Newair
	OY-MUH	Aérospatiale ATR-42-300	Danish Air Transport
	OY-MUK	Aérospatiale ATR-42-300	Danish Air Transport

Reg.	Type	Owner or Operator	Notes
OY-RJA	Canadair CL.600-2B19 RJ	Cimber Air/Team Lufthansa	
OY-RJB	Canadair CL.600-2B19 RJ	Cimber Air/Team Lufthansa	
OY-RUA	Aérospatiale ATR-72-201	Danish Air Transport	
OY-RUB	Aérospatiale ATR-72-201	Danish Air Transport	
OY-SEA	Boeing 737-8Q8	Sterling European Airlines	
OY-SEB	Boeing 737-8Q8	Sterling European Airlines	
OY-SEC	Boeing 737-8Q8	Sterling European Airlines	
OY-SED	Boeing 737-8Q8	Sterling European Airlines.	
OY-SEH	Boeing 737-85H	Sterling European Airlines	
OY-SEI	Boeing 737-85H	Sterling European Airlines	
OY-SER	Boeing 727-232F	Sterling European Airlines/TNT	
OY-SES	Boeing 727-251F	Sterling European Airlines/TNT	
OY-SET	Boeing 727-227F	Sterling European Airlines/TNT	
OY-SEW	Boeing 727-287F	Sterling European Airlines/TNT	
OY-SEY	Boeing 727-224F	Sterling European Airlines/TNT	
OY-SVF	BAe Jetstream 3102	Sun-Air/British Airways	
OY-SVI	BAe ATP	Sun-Air/British Airways	
OY-SVJ	BAe Jetstream 3102	Sun-Air/British Airways	
OY-SVS	BAe Jetstream 4102	Sun-Air/British Airways	
OY-SVT	BAe ATP	Sun-Air/British Airways	
OY-SVU	BAe ATP	Sun-Air/British Airways	
OY-SVW	BAe Jetstream 4102	Sun-Air/British Airways	
OY-UPA	Boeing 727-31C	Starair/UPS	
OY-UPC	Boeing 727-31C	Starair/UPS *Gynnbjorn Viking*	
OY-UPD	Boeing 727-22C	Starair/UPS	
OY-UPJ	Boeing 727-22C	Starair/UPS	
OY-UPM	Boeing 727-31C	Starair/UPS	
OY-UPS	Boeing 727-31C	Starair/UPS	
OY-UPT	Boeing 727-22C	Starair/UPS	
OY-USA	Boeing 757-24APF	Starair/UPS	
OY-VKF	Airbus A.330-343X	Premiair	
OY-VKG	Airbus A.330-343X	Premiair	
OY-VKH	Airbus A.330-343X	Premiair	
OY-VKI	Airbus A.330-343X	Premiair	
OY-VKL	Airbus A.321-	My Travel Airways (Premiair)	
OY-VKM	Airbus A.321-	My Travel Airways (Premiair)	
OY-VKN	Airbus A.321-	My Travel Airways (Premiair)	
OY-VKO	Airbus A.321-	My Travel Airways (Premiair)	
OY-VKT	Airbus A.321-	My Travel Airways (Premiair)	
OY-VKU	Airbus A.321-	My Travel Airways (Premiair)	

PH (Netherlands)

PH-ABF	Airbus A.300B4-103F	Tulip Air	
PH-ACY	Beech 1900D	Ace Air Charters	
PH-AHE	Boeing 757-27B	Air Holland	
PH-AHF	Boeing 757-27B	Air Holland	
PH-AHI	Boeing 757-27B	Martinair	
PH-AJU	Douglas DC-2	Dutch Dakota Association	
PH-BDA	Boeing 737-306	Koninklijke Luchtvaart Maatschappij (K.L.M.) *Willem Barentsz*	
PH-BDB	Boeing 737-306	K.L.M. *Olivier van Noort*	
PH-BDC	Boeing 737-306	K.L.M. *Cornelis De Houteman*	
PH-BDD	Boeing 737-306	K.L.M. *Anthony van Diemen*	
PH-BDE	Boeing 737-306	K.L.M. *Abel J. Tasman*	
PH-BDG	Boeing 737-306	K.L.M. *Michiel A. de Ruyter*	
PH-BDI	Boeing 737-306	K.L.M. *Maarten H. Tromp*	
PH-BDK	Boeing 737-306	K.L.M. *Jan H. van Linschoten*	
PH-BDN	Boeing 737-306	K.L.M. *Willem van Ruysbroeck*	
PH-BDO	Boeing 737-306	K.L.M. *Jacob van Heemskerck*	
PH-BDP	Boeing 737-306	K.L.M. *Jacob Roggeveen*	
PH-BDR	Boeing 737-406	K.L.M. *Willem C. Schouten*	
PH-BDS	Boeing 737-406	K.L.M. *Jorris van Spilbergen*	
PH-BDT	Boeing 737-406	K.L.M. *Gerrit de Veer*	
PH-BDU	Boeing 737-406	K.L.M. *Marco Polo*	
PH-BDW	Boeing 737-406	K.L.M. *Leifur Eiriksson*	
PH-BDY	Boeing 737-406	K.L.M. *Vasco da Gama*	
PH-BDZ	Boeing 737-406	K.L.M. *Christophorus Columbus*	
PH-BFA	Boeing 747-406	K.L.M. *City of Atlanta*	
PH-BFB	Boeing 747-406	K.L.M. *City of Bangkok*	
PH-BFC	Boeing 747-406 (SCD)	K.L.M. Asia *City of Calgary*	
PH-BFD	Boeing 747-406 (SCD)	K.L.M. Asia *City of Dubai*	

Notes	Reg.	Type	Owner or Operator
	PH-BFE	Boeing 747-406 (SCD)	K.L.M. *City of Melbourne*
	PH-BFF	Boeing 747-406 (SCD)	K.L.M. *City of Freetown*
	PH-BFG	Boeing 747-406	K.L.M. *City of Guayaquil*
	PH-BFH	Boeing 747-406 (SCD)	K.L.M. Asia *City of Hong Kong*
	PH-BFI	Boeing 747-406 (SCD)	K.L.M. *City of Jakarta*
	PH-BFK	Boeing 747-406 (SCD)	K.L.M. *City of Karachi*
	PH-BFL	Boeing 747-406	K.L.M. *City of Lima*
	PH-BFM	Boeing 747-406 (SCD)	K.L.M. Asia *City of Mexico*
	PH-BFN	Boeing 747-406	K.L.M. *City of Nairobi*
	PH-BFO	Boeing 747-406 (SCD)	K.L.M. *City of Orlando*
	PH-BFP	Boeing 747-406 (SCD)	K.L.M. *City of Paramaribo*
	PH-BFR	Boeing 747-406 (SCD)	K.L.M. *City of Rio de Janiero*
	PH-BFS	Boeing 747-406 (SCD)	K.L.M. *City of Seoul*
	PH-BFT	Boeing 747-406 (SCD)	K.L.M. *City of Tokyo*
	PH-BFU	Boeing 747-406 (SCD)	K.L.M. *City of Beijing*
	PH-BFV	Boeing 747-406	K.L.M.
	PH-BFW	Boeing 747-406	K.L.M.
	PH-BFX	Boeing 747-406	K.L.M.
	PH-BFY	Boeing 747-406	K.L.M.
	PH-BPB	Boeing 737-4Y0	K.L.M.
	PH-BPC	Boeing 737-4Y0	K.L.M.
	PH-BPE	Boeing 737-42C	K.L.M.
	PH-BRL	EMB-120RT Brasilia	Metropolis Airlines
	PH-BRM	EMB-120RT Brasilia	Metropolis Airlines
	PH-BRP	EMB-120RT Brasilia	Metropolis Airlines
	PH-BTA	Boeing 737-406	K.L.M. *Fernao Magalhaes*
	PH-BTB	Boeing 737-406	K.L.M. *Henry Hudson*
	PH-BTC	Boeing 737-406	K.L.M. *David Livingstone*
	PH-BTD	Boeing 737-306	K.L.M. *James Cook*
	PH-BTE	Boeing 737-306	K.L.M. *Roald Amundsen*
	PH-BTF	Boeing 737-406	K.L.M. *Alexander von Humboldt*
	PH-BTG	Boeing 737-406	K.L.M. *Henry Morton Stanley*
	PH-BTH	Boeing 737-306	K.L.M.
	PH-BTI	Boeing 737-306	K.L.M.
	PH-BUH	Boeing 747-206F (SCD)	K.L.M. *Dr Albert Plesman*
	PH-BUI	Boeing 747-206F (SCD)	K.L.M. *Wilbur Wright*
	PH-BUK	Boeing 747-306 (SCD)	K.L.M. *Louis Blériot*
	PH-BUL	Boeing 747-306 (SCD)	K.L.M. *Charles A. Lindbergh*
	PH-BUM	Boeing 747-306 (SCD)	K.L.M. *Charles E. Kingsford-Smith*
	PH-BUN	Boeing 747-306 (SCD)	K.L.M. *Anthony H. G. Fokker*
	PH-BUO	Boeing 747-306	K.L.M. *Missouri*
	PH-BUP	Boeing 747-306	K.L.M. *The Ganges*
	PH-BUR	Boeing 747-306	K.L.M. *The Indus*
	PH-BUT	Boeing 747-306	K.L.M. *Admiral Richard E. Byrd*
	PH-BUU	Boeing 747-306 (SCD)	K.L.M. *Sir Frank Whittle*
	PH-BUV	Boeing 747-306 (SCD)	K.L.M. *Sir Geoffrey de Havilland*
	PH-BUW	Boeing 747-306 (SCD)	K.L.M. *Leonardo da Vinci*
	PH-BXA	Boeing 737-8K2	K.L.M.
	PH-BXB	Boeing 737-8K2	K.L.M.
	PH-BXC	Boeing 737-8K2	K.L.M.
	PH-BXD	Boeing 737-8K2	K.L.M.
	PH-BXE	Boeing 737-8K2	K.L.M.
	PH-BXF	Boeing 737-8K2	K.L.M. *Zwallou*
	PH-BXG	Boeing 737-8K2	K.L.M. *Crane*
	PH-BXH	Boeing 737-8K2	K.L.M.
	PH-BXI	Boeing 737-8K2	K.L.M.
	PH-BXK	Boeing 737-8K2	K.L.M.
	PH-BXL	Boeing 737-8K2	K.L.M.
	PH-BXM	Boeing 737-8K2	K.L.M.
	PH-BXN	Boeing 737-8K2	K.L.M.
	PH-BXO	Boeing 737-9K2	K.L.M. *Plevier*
	PH-BXP	Boeing 737-9K2	K.L.M.
	PH-BXR	Boeing 737-9K2	K.L.M.
	PH-BXS	Boeing 737-9K2	K.L.M.
	PH-BZA	Boeing 767-306ER	K.L.M. *Blue Bridge*
	PH-BZB	Boeing 767-306ER	K.L.M. *Pont Neuf*
	PH-BZC	Boeing 767-306ER	K.L.M. *Brooklyn Bridge*
	PH-BZD	Boeing 767-306ER	K.L.M. *King Hussain Bridge*
	PH-BZE	Boeing 767-306ER	K.L.M. *Ponte Rialto*
	PH-BZF	Boeing 767-306ER	K.L.M. *Golden Gate Bridge*
	PH-BZG	Boeing 767-306ER	K.L.M. *Erasmus Bridge*
	PH-BZH	Boeing 767-306ER	K.L.M. *Tower Bridge*
	PH-BZI	Boeing 767-306ER	K.L.M. *Bosporus Bridge*

Reg.	Type	Owner or Operator	Notes
PH-BZK	Boeing 767-306ER	K.L.M. *Zeeland Bridge*	
PH-BZM	Boeing 767-306ER	K.L.M. *Garibaldi Bridge*	
PH-BZO	Boeing 767-306ER	K.L.M. *Karmsund Bridge*	
PH-CLA	Airbus A.300B4-203F	Farnair Europe/DHL	
PH-DBA	Boeing 757-230	DutchBird	
PH-DBB	Boeing 757-230	DutchBird	
PH-DBH	Boeing 757-230	DutchBird	
PH-DDS	Douglas DC-4	Dutch Dakota Association	
PH-DDZ	Douglas DC-3	Dutch Dakota Association	
PH-DMB	Fokker 50	Denim Air	
PH-DMO	Fokker 50	Denim Air	
PH-DMR	D.H.C.8Q-315 Dash Eight	Denim Air	
PH-DMV	D.H.C.8Q-315 Dash Eight	Denim Air	
PH-DMW	D.H.C.8Q-315 Dash Eight	Denim Air	
PH-DMX	D.H.C.8Q-315 Dash Eight	Denim Air	
PH-DMY	D.H.C.8Q-315 Dash Eight	Denim Air/Air Nostrum/Iberia	
PH-DMZ	D.H.C.8Q-315 Dash Eight	Denim Air	
PH-DYM	Swearingen SA.227AC Metro III	Rijnmond Air Services	
PH-EAN	Airbus A.300B4-103F	Farnair Europe/DHL	
PH-FHL	F.27 Friendship Mk.500	Farnair Europe	
PH-FNV	F.27 Friendship Mk 500	Farnair Europe	
PH-FNW	F.27 Friendship Mk 500	Farnair Europe	
PH-FYC	F.27 Friendship Mk.500	Farnair Europe	
PH-FZE	Fokker 50	Denim Air	
PH-GIR	Airbus A.300B4-103F	Farnair Europe	
PH-HVN	Boeing 737-3K2	Transavia	
PH-HVT	Boeing 737-3K2	Transavia	
PH-HVV	Boeing 737-3K2	Transavia	
PH-HZA	Boeing 737-8K2	Transavia	
PH-HZB	Boeing 737-8K2	Transavia	
PH-HZC	Boeing 737-8K2	Transavia	
PH-HZD	Boeing 737-8K2	Transavia	
PH-HZE	Boeing 737-8K2	Transavia *City of Rhodos*	
PH-HZF	Boeing 737-8K2	Transavia	
PH-HZG	Boeing 737-8K2	Transavia	
PH-HZI	Boeing 737-8K2	Transavia	
PH-HZJ	Boeing 737-8K2	Transavia	
PH-HZK	Boeing 737-8K2	Transavia	
PH-HZL	Boeing 737-8K2	Transavia	
PH-HZM	Boeing 737-8K2	Transavia	
PH-HZN	Boeing 737-8K2	Transavia	
PH-HZO	Boeing 737-8K2	Transavia	
PH-HZP	Boeing 737-8K2	Transavia	
PH-HZW	Boeing 737-8K2	Transavia	
PH-HZX	Boeing 737-7K2	Transavia	
PH-JLH	Airbus A.300B4-203F	Jet Link Holland	
PH-JLI	Airbus A.300B4-203F	Jet Link Holland	
PH-JXJ	Fokker 50	K.L.M. CityHopper	
PH-JXK	Fokker 50	K.L.M. CityHopper	
PH-KCA	McD Douglas MD-11	K.L.M. *Amy Johnson*	
PH-KCB	McD Douglas MD-11	K.L.M. *Maria Montessori*	
PH-KCC	McD Douglas MD-11	K.L.M. *Marie Curie*	
PH-KCD	McD Douglas MD-11	K.L.M. *Florence Nightingale*	
PH-KCE	McD Douglas MD-11	K.L.M. *Audrey Hepburn*	
PH-KCF	McD Douglas MD-11	K.L.M. *Annie Romein*	
PH-KCG	McD Douglas MD-11	K.L.M. *Maria Callas*	
PH-KCH	McD Douglas MD-11	K.L.M. *Anna Pavlova*	
PH-KCI	McD Douglas MD-11	K.L.M. *Ingrid Bergman*	
PH-KCK	McD Douglas MD-11	K.L.M. *Marie Servaes*	
PH-KJB	BAe Jetstream 3108	BASE Airlines/BA Express	
PH-KJG	BAe Jetstream 3108	BASE Airlines/BA Express	
PH-KVA	Fokker 50	K.L.M. CityHopper *Bremen*	
PH-KVB	Fokker 50	K.L.M. CityHopper *Brussels*	
PH-KVC	Fokker 50	K.L.M. CityHopper *Stavanger*	
PH-KVD	Fokker 50	K.L.M. CityHopper *Dusseldorf*	
PH-KVE	Fokker 50	K.L.M. CityHopper *Amsterdam*	
PH-KVF	Fokker 50	K.L.M. CityHopper *Paris/Paris*	
PH-KVG	Fokker 50	K.L.M. CityHopper *Stuttgart*	
PH-KVH	Fokker 50	K.L.M. CityHopper *Hannover*	
PH-KVI	Fokker 50	K.L.M. CityHopper *Bordeaux*	
PH-KVK	Fokker 50	K.L.M. CityHopper *London*	
PH-KXM	Fokker 50	K.L.M. CityHopper	
PH-KZA	Fokker 70	K.L.M. CityHopper	

Notes	Reg.	Type	Owner or Operator
	PH-KZB	Fokker 70	K.L.M. CityHopper
	PH-KZC	Fokker 70	K.L.M. CityHopper
	PH-KZD	Fokker 70	K.L.M. CityHopper
	PH-KZE	Fokker 70	K.L.M. CityHopper
	PH-KZF	Fokker 70	K.L.M. CityHopper
	PH-KZG	Fokker 70	K.L.M. CityHopper
	PH-KZH	Fokker 70	K.L.M. CityHopper
	PH-KZI	Fokker 70	K.L.M. CityHopper
	PH-KZK	Fokker 70	K.L.M. CityHopper
	PH-KZL	Fokker 70	K.L.M. CityHopper
	PH-KZM	Fokker 70	K.L.M. CityHopper
	PH-MCE	Boeing 747-21AC (SCD)	Martinair *Prins van Oranje*
	PH-MCF	Boeing 747-21AC (SCD)	Martinair *Prins Claus*
	PH-MCG	Boeing 767-31AER	Martinair *Prins Johan Friso*
	PH-MCH	Boeing 767-31AER	Martinair *Prins Constantijn*
	PH-MCI	Boeing 767-31AER	Martinair *Prins Pieter-Christiaan*
	PH-MCL	Boeing 767-31AER	Martinair *Koningin Beatrix*
	PH-MCM	Boeing 767-31AER	Martinair *Prins Floris*
	PH-MCN	Boeing 747-228F	Martinair *Prins Bernhard*
	PH-MCP	McD Douglas MD-11CF	Martinair
	PH-MCR	McD Douglas MD-11CF	Martinair
	PH-MCS	McD Douglas MD-11CF	Martinair
	PH-MCT	McD Douglas MD-11CF	Martinair
	PH-MCU	McD Douglas MD-11F	Martinair
	PH-MCV	Boeing 767-31AER	Martinair
	PH-MCW	McD Douglas MD-11CF	Martinair
	PH-PBA	Douglas DC-3C	Dutch Dakota Association
	PH-PRG	Fokker 50	Denim Air
	PH-PRH	Fokker 50	Denim Air
	PH-PRI	Fokker 50	Denim Air
	PH-PRJ	Fokker 50	Trans Travel Airlines
	PH-RXA	Embraer RJ145MP	Air Exel Netherlands
	PH-RXB	Embraer RJ145MP	Air Exel Netherlands
	PH-RXC	Embraer RJ145LR	Air Exel Netherlands
	PH-RXD	Embraer RJ145MP	Air Exel Netherlands
	PH-SCY	Aérospatiale ATR-72-211	Schreiner Airways
	PH-SCZ	Aérospatiale ATR-72-211	Schreiner Airways
	PH-SDM	D.H.C.8-311 Dash Eight	Schreiner Airways
	PH-SDP	D.H.C.8-311 Dash Eight	Schreiner Airways
	PH-SDR	D.H.C.8-311 Dash Eight	Schreiner Airways
	PH-SDT	D.H.C.8-311 Dash Eight	Schreiner Airways
	PH-SDU	D.H.C.8-311 Dash Eight	Schreiner Airways
	PH-TKA	Boeing 757-2K2	Transavia
	PH-TKB	Boeing 757-2K2	Transavia
	PH-TKC	Boeing 757-2K2	Transavia
	PH-TKD	Boeing 757-2K2	Transavia
	PH-TTA	D.H.C. 8-102 Dash Eight	Schreiner Airways
	PH-TTB	D.H. C.8-102 Dash Eight	Schreiner Airways
	PH-VLM	Fokker 50	V.L.M. *City of Rotterdam*
	PH-VLN	Fokker 50	V.L.M. *City of Antwerp*
	PH-WXA	Fokker 70	K.L.M. CityHopper
	PH-WXC	Fokker 70	K.L.M. CityHopper
	PH-XLA	EMB-120RT Brasilia	Air Exel Netherlands
	PH-XLB	EMB-120RT Brasilia	Air Exel Netherlands
	PH-XLC	Aérospatiale ATR-42-320	Air Exel Netherlands
	PH-XLD	Aérospatiale ATR-42-320	Air Exel Netherlands
	PH-XLE	Aérospatiale ATR-42-320	Air Exel Netherlands
	PH-XLF	EMB-120ER Brasilia	Air Exel Netherlands
	PH-XLG	EMB-120ER Brasilia	Air Exel Netherlands
	PH-XLH	Aérospatiale ATR-72-200	Air Exel Netherlands
	PH-XLI	Aérospatiale ATR-42-320	Air Exel Netherlands
	PH-XLK	Aérospatiale ATR-42-320	Air Exel Netherlands
	PH-XLL	Aérospatiale ATR-42-320	Air Exel Netherlands
	PH-XLM	Aérospatiale ATR-42-320	Air Exel Netherlands
	PH-XRA	Boeing 737-7K2	Transavia
	PH-XRB	Boeing 737-7K2	Transavia
	PH-XRC	Boeing 737-7K2	Transavia
	PH-XRD	Boeing 737-7K2	Transavia
	PH-XRE	Boeing 737-7K2	Transavia
	PH-XRF	Boeing 737-7K2	Transavia

Reg.	Type	Owner or Operator	Notes

PK (Indonesia)

PK-GSA	Boeing 747-2U3B	Garuda Indonesian Airways	
PK-GSB	Boeing 747-2U3B	Garuda Indonesian Airways	
PK-GSC	Boeing 747-2U3B	Garuda Indonesian Airways	
PK-GSD	Boeing 747-2U3B	Garuda Indonesian Airways	
PK-GSE	Boeing 747-2U3B	Garuda Indonesian Airways	
PK-GSG	Boeing 747-4U3	Garuda Indonesian Airways	
PK-GSH	Boeing 747-4U3	Garuda Indonesian Airways	
PK-GSI	Boeing 747-441	Garuda Indonesian Airways	

PP/PT (Brazil)

PP-VMA	Douglas DC-10-30	Viacao Aerea Rio Grandense (VARIG)	
PP-VMB	Douglas DC-10-30	VARIG	
PP-VMT	Douglas DC-10-30F	VARIG Cargo	
PP-VMU	Douglas DC-10-30F	VARIG Cargo	
PP-VOI	Boeing 767-341ER	VARIG	
PP-VOJ	Boeing 767-341ER	VARIG	
PP-VOK	Boeing 767-341ER	VARIG	
PP-VOL	Boeing 767-341ER	VARIG	
PP-VPJ	McD Douglas MD-11	VARIG	
PP-VPK	McD Douglas MD-11	VARIG	
PP-VPL	McD Douglas MD-11	VARIG	
PP-VPM	McD Douglas MD-11	VARIG	
PP-VPN	McD Douglas MD-11	VARIG	
PP-VPO	McD Douglas MD-11	VARIG	
PP-VPP	McD Douglas MD-11	VARIG	
PP-VPV	Boeing 767-375ER	VARIG	
PP-VPW	Boeing 767-375ER	VARIG	
PP-VQF	McD Douglas MD-11	VARIG	
PP-VQG	McD Douglas MD-11	VARIG	
PP-VQH	McD Douglas MD-11	VARIG	
PP-VQI	McD Douglas MD-11	VARIG	
PP-VQJ	McD Douglas MD-11	VARIG	
PP-VQK	McD Douglas MD-11	VARIG	
PP-VQL	McD Douglas MD-11	VARIG	
PP-VQM	McD Douglas MD-11	VARIG	
PP-VQX	McD Douglas MD-11	VARIG	
PP-VRA	Boeing 777-2Q8ER	VARIG	
PP-VRB	Boeing 777-2Q8ER	VARIG	
PT-MSD	Airbus A.330-243	TAM-Brasil	
PT-MSE	Airbus A.330-243	TAM-Brasil	
PT-MVA	Airbus A.330-223	TAM-Brasil	
PT-MVB	Airbus A.330-223	TAM-Brasil	
PT-MVC	Airbus A.330-223	TAM-Brasil	
PT-MVD	Airbus A.330-223	TAM-Brasil	
PT-MVE	Airbus A.330-223	TAM-Brasil	

RA (Russia)

Although many of the aircraft used previously by Aeroflot have been transferred to one of the numerous airlines that have been created in recent years, a large proportion still retain the familiar livery. The following registrations are prefixed by RA and are shown with the operators' code in parenthesis after the type. Those used are AFL (Aeroflot Russian International Airlines), AIS (AIS Airlines), DCA (Dacono Air), EFR (Elf Air), HLA (HeavyLift), IKT (Sakhaavia), JSC (Airstan), LSV (Alak Airlines), MSC (Moscow Airlines), PAR (Spair), PLK (Pulkovo Aviation), PVV (Continental Airways), SDM (Russia State Transport), SVR (Ural Airlines), TEP (Transeuropean), TRJ (AJT Air), TSO (Transaero), UPA (Air Foyle), VDA (Volga Dnepr) and VKO (Vnukovo Airlines).

Reg.	Type	Notes	Reg.	Type	Notes
11003	An-12B (PAR)		65042	Tu-134A-3 (PLK)	
11049	An-12 (PAR)		65068	Tu-134A-3 (PLK)	
11356	An-12 (PAR)		65088	Tu-134A-3 (PLK)	
11415	An-12 (PAR)		65093	Tu-134A-3 (PLK)	
			65097	Tu-134A (EFR)	
65004	Tu-134A-3 (PLK)		65099	Tu-134A (EFR)	
65020	Tu-134A-3 (PLK)		65109	Tu-134A (PLK)	

Notes	Reg.	Type	Notes	Reg.	Type
	65112	Tu-134A (AFL)		85299	Tu-154B-2 (VKO)
	65113	Tu-134A (PLK)		85301	Tu-154B-2 (VKO)
	65128	Tu-134A (PLK)		85310	Tu-154B-2 (SVR)
	65559	Tu-134A (AFL)		85319	Tu-154B-2 (SVR)
	65566	Tu-134A (AFL)		85323	Tu-154B-2 (IKT)
	65567	Tu-134A-3 (AFL)		85328	Tu-154B-2 (SVR)
	65568	Tu-134A (AFL)		85337	Tu-154B-2 (SVR)
	65604	Tu-134A (EFR)		85348	Tu-154B-2 (IKT)
	65623	Tu-134A (AFL)		85354	Tu-154B-2 (IKT)
	65626	Tu-134A (AIS)		85357	Tu-154B-2 (SVR)
	65697	Tu-134A-3 (AFL)		85363	Tu-154B-2 (AFL)
	65717	Tu-134A-3 (AFL)		85367	Tu-154B-2 (IKT)
	65759	Tu-134A (PLK)		85374	Tu-154B-2 (SVR)
	65769	Tu-134A-3 (AFL)		85375	Tu-154B-2 (SVR)
	65770	Tu-134A-3 (AFL)		85376	Tu-154B-2 (IKT)
	65781	Tu-134A-3 (AFL)		85377	Tu-154B-2 (PLK)
	65783	Tu-134A-3 (AFL)		85381	Tu-154B-2 (PLK)
	65784	Tu-134A-3 (AFL)		85390	Tu-154B-2 (PLK)
	65785	Tu-134A-3 (AFL)		85432	Tu-154B-2 (SVR)
	65830	Tu-134A-3 (TSO)		85439	Tu-154B-2 (SVR)
	65837	Tu-134A-3 (PLK)		85441	Tu-154B-2 (PLK)
	65855	Tu-134A-3 (AIS)		85459	Tu-154B-2 (SVR)
	65862	Tu-134A-3 (PLK)		85486	Tu-154B-2 (IKT)
	65872	Tu-134A-3 (PLK)		85508	Tu-154B-2 (SVR)
				85520	Tu-154B-2 (IKT)
	73001	Boeing 737 (TSO)		85530	Tu-154B-2 (PLK)
	73002	Boeing 737 (TSO)		85542	Tu-154B-2 (PLK)
				85552	Tu-154B-2 (PLK)
	76355	IL-76TD (MSC)		85553	Tu-154B-2 (PLK)
	76369	IL-76TD (JSC)		85564	Tu-154B-2 (AFL)
	76421	IL-76TD (DCA)		85568	Tu-154B-2 (IKT)
	76467	IL-76TD (AFL)		85570	Tu-154B-2 (AFL)
	76468	IL-76TD (AFL)		85577	Tu-154B-2 (IKT)
	76469	IL-76TD (AFL)		85579	Tu-154B-2 (PLK)
	76470	IL-76TD (AFL)		85592	Tu-154B-2 (AFL)
	76476	IL-76TD (AFL)		85597	Tu-154B-2 (IKT)
	76478	IL-76TD (AFL)		85610	Tu-154M (VKO)
	76479	IL-76TD (AFL)		85611	Tu-154M (VKO)
	76482	IL-76TD (AFL)		85612	Tu-154M (VKO)
	76485	IL-76TD (IKT)		85615	Tu-154M (VKO)
	76486	IL-76TD (IKT)		85618	Tu-154M (VKO)
	76487	IL-76TD (IKT)		85619	Tu-154M (VKO)
	76488	IL-76TD (AFL)		85620	Tu-154M (VKO)
	76498	IL-76TD (MSC)		85622	Tu-154M (VKO)
	76527	IL-76T (PAR)		85623	Tu-154M (VKO)
	76750	IL-76TD (AFL)		85624	Tu-154M (VKO)
	76785	IL-76TD (AFL)		85625	Tu-154M (AFL)
	76790	IL-76TD (PAR)		85626	Tu-154M (AFL)
	76795	IL-76TD (AFL)		85628	Tu-154M (VKO)
	76797	IL-76TD (IKT)		85629	Tu-154M (SDM)
	76814	IL-76TD (LSV)		85630	Tu-154M (SDM)
	76842	IL-76TD (JSC)		85631	Tu-154M (SDM)
				85632	Tu-154M (VKO)
	82042	An-124 (VDA/HLA)		85633	Tu-154M (VKO)
	82043	An-124 (VDA/HLA)		85635	Tu-154M (VKO)
	82044	An-124 (VDA/HLA)		85637	Tu-154M (AFL)
	82045	An-124 (VDA/HLA)		85638	Tu-154M (AFL)
	82046	An-124 (VDA/HLA)		85639	Tu-154M (AFL)
	82047	An-124 (VDA/HLA)		85640	Tu-154M (AFL)
	82072	An-124 (SDM)		85641	Tu-154M (AFL)
	82073	An-124 (SDM)		85642	Tu-154M (AFL)
	82078	An-124 (VDA)		85643	Tu-154M (AFL)
				85644	Tu-154M (AFL)
	85075	Tu-154B (AIS)		85645	Tu-154M (SDM)
	85084	Tu-154S (VKO)		85646	Tu-154M (AFL)
	85099	Tu-154B (VKO)		85647	Tu-154M (AFL)
	85141	Tu-154B-1 (SVR)		85648	Tu-154M (AFL)
	85156	Tu-154B-1 (VKO)		85649	Tu-154M (AFL)
	85182	Tu-154B-1 (VKO)		85651	Tu-154M (SDM)
	85193	Tu-154B (SVR)		85653	Tu-154M (SDM)
	85215	Tu-154B-1 (VKO)		85658	Tu-154M (PLK)
	85217	Tu-154B-2 (IKT)		85659	Tu-154M (SDM)
	85219	Tu-154B-1 (SVR)		85661	Tu-154M (AFL)

Reg.	Type	Notes	Reg.	Type	Notes
85662	Tu-154M (AFL)		86084	IL-86 (VKO)	
85663	Tu-154M (AFL)		86085	IL-86 (VKO)	
85665	Tu-154M (AFL)		86087	IL-86 (AFL)	
85666	Tu-154M (SDM)		86088	IL-86 (AFL)	
85668	Tu-154M (AFL)		86089	IL-86 (VKO)	
85669	Tu-154M (AFL)		86091	IL-86 (VKO)	
85670	Tu-154M (AFL)		86092	IL-86 (PLK)	
85673	Tu-154M (VKO)		86093	IL-86 (SVR)	
85674	Tu-154M (VKO)		86094	IL-86 (PLK)	
85675	Tu-154M (SDM)		86095	IL-86 (AFL)	
85676	Tu-154M (AFL)		86096	IL-86 (AFL)	
85686	Tu-154M (SDM)		86097	IL-86 (VKO)	
85688	Tu-154M (AFL)		86103	IL-86 (AFL)	
85695	Tu-154M (PLK)		86104	IL-86 (VKO)	
85712	Tu-154M (LSV)		86106	IL-86 (PLK)	
85713	Tu-154M (LSV)		86108	IL-86 (AFL)	
85736	Tu-154M (VKO)		86110	IL-86 (AFL)	
85743	Tu-154M (VKO)		86111	IL-86 (VKO)	
85754	Tu-154M (AFL)		86113	IL-86 (AFL)	
85767	Tu-154M (PLK)		86114	IL-86 (SVR)	
85769	Tu-154M (PLK)		86115	IL-86 (TRJ)	
85770	Tu-154M (PLK)		86123	IL-86 (TSO)	
85771	Tu-154M (PLK)		86124	IL-86 (AFL)	
85779	Tu-154M (PLK)		86136	IL-86 (PVV)	
85785	Tu-154M (PLK)		86138	IL-86 (PVV)	
85791	Tu-154M (IKT)		86140	IL-86 (TRJ)	
85793	Tu-154M (IKT)		86141	IL-86 (TRJ)	
85794	Tu-154M (IKT)				
85799	Tu-154M (TEP)		86466	IL-62M (SDM)	
85800	Tu-154M (PLK)		86467	IL-62M (SDM)	
85807	Tu-154M (SVR)		86468	IL-62M (SDM)	
85810	Tu-154M (AFL)		86489	IL-62M (AFL)	
85811	Tu-154M (AFL)		86497	IL-62M (AFL)	
85812	Tu-154M (IKT)		86502	IL-62M (AFL)	
85814	Tu-154M (SVR)		86506	IL-62M (AFL)	
			86510	IL-62M (AFL)	
86002	IL-86 (AFL)		86512	IL-62M (AFL)	
86004	IL-86 (VKO)		86514	IL-62M (AFL)	
86005	IL-86 (VKO)		86515	IL-62M (MSC)	
86006	IL-86 (VKO)		86517	IL-62M (AFL)	
86007	IL-86 (VKO)		86518	IL-62M (AFL)	
86008	IL-86 (VKO)		86520	IL-62M (AFL)	
86009	IL-86 (VKO)		86522	IL-62M (AFL)	
86010	IL-86 (VKO)		86523	IL-62M (AFL)	
86011	IL-86 (VKO)		86524	IL-62M (AFL)	
86013	IL-86 (VKO)		86531	IL-62M (AFL)	
86014	IL-86 (VKO)		86532	IL-62M (AFL)	
86015	IL-86 (AFL)		86533	IL-62M (AFL)	
86017	IL-86 (VKO)		86534	IL-62M (AFL)	
86018	IL-86 (VKO)		86536	IL-62M (SDM)	
86050	IL-86 (PLK)		86537	IL-62M (SDM)	
86051	IL-86 (SVR)		86540	IL-62M (SDM)	
86054	IL-86 (AFL)		86553	IL-62M (SDM)	
86055	IL-86 (VKO)		86558	IL-62M (AFL)	
86058	IL-86 (AFL)		86559	IL-62M (SDM)	
86059	IL-86 (AFL)		86561	IL-62M (SDM)	
86060	IL-86 (PLK)		86562	IL-62M (AFL)	
86061	IL-86 (PLK)		86564	IL-62M (AFL)	
86063	IL-86 (PLK)		86565	IL-62M (AFL)	
86065	IL-86 (AFL)		86566	IL-62M (AFL)	
86066	IL-86 (AFL)		86710	IL-62M (SDM)	
86067	IL-86 (AFL)		86711	IL-62M (SDM)	
86070	IL-86 (PLK)		86712	IL-62M (SDM)	
86073	IL-86 (PLK)				
86074	IL-86 (AFL)		96005	IL-96 (AFL)	
86075	IL-86 (AFL)		96007	IL-96 (AFL)	
86078	IL-86 (SVR)		96008	IL-96 (AFL)	
86079	IL-86 (AFL)		96010	IL-96 (AFL)	
86080	IL-86 (AFL)		96011	IL-96 (AFL)	
86081	IL-86 (VKO)		96015	IL-96 (AFL)	
86082	IL-86 (VKO)				

Notes	Reg.	Type	Owner or Operator

Note: Aeroflot Russian International also operates the DC-10-30 N524MD, Airbus A.310s F-OGQQ, F-OGQR, F-OGQT, F-OGQU, F-OGYP, F-OGYT, F-OGYU, F-OGYV, VP-BAF and VP-BAG. The airline also employs Boeing 737-4M0s registered VP-BAH, VP-BAI, VP-BAJ, VP-BAL, VP-BAM, VP-BAN, VP-BAO, VP-BAP, VP-BAQ, VP-BAR and Boeing 767-300s VP-BAV, VP-BAX, VP-BAY and VP-BAZ, plus Boeing 777s VP-BAS and VP-BAU. Transaero employs Boeing 737-200s VP-BTA, VP-BTB, YL-BAA, YL-BAB and YL-BAC, Boeing 737-700s N100UN and N101UN, plus Airbus A.310 F-OGYR.

S2 (Bangladesh)

S2-ACO	Douglas DC-10-30	Bangladesh Biman *The City of Hazrat-Shah Makhdoom (R.A.)*
S2-ACP	Douglas DC-10-30	Bangladesh Biman *The City of Dhaka*
S2-ACQ	Douglas DC-10-30	Bangladesh Biman *The City of Hazrat-Shah Jalal (R.A.)*
S2-ACR	Douglas DC-10-30	Bangladesh Biman *The New Era*
S2-ACS	Douglas DC-10-30	Bangladesh Biman
S2-ADE	Airbus A.310-325	Bangladesh Biman *City of Hazrat Khan Jahan Ali*
S2-ADF	Airbus A.310-325	Bangladesh Biman *City of Chittagong*
S2-ADG	Airbus A.310-324	Bangladesh Biman
S2-ADN	Douglas DC-10-30	Bangladesh Biman

S5 (Slovenia)

S5-AAA	Airbus A.320-231	Adria Airways
S5-AAB	Airbus A.320-231	Adria Airways
S5-AAC	Airbus A.320-231	Adria Airways
S5-AAD	Canadair CL.600-2B19 RJ	Adria Airways
S5-AAE	Canadair CL.600-2B19 RJ	Adria Airways
S5-AAF	Canadair CL.600-2B19 RJ	Adria Airways
S5-AAG	Canadair CL.600-2B19 RJ	Adria Airways

S7 (Seychelles)

S7-AHM	Boeing 767-37DER	Air Seychelles *Vailee de Mai*
S7-ASY	Boeing 767-3Q8ER	Air Seychelles

SE (Sweden)

SE-CFP	Douglas DC-3	Flygande Veteraner *Fridtjof Viking*
SE-DAS	Douglas DC-9-41	S.A.S. *Garder Viking*
SE-DAU	Douglas DC-9-41	S.A.S. *Hadding Viking*
SE-DAW	Douglas DC-9-41	S.A.S. *Gotrik Viking*
SE-DDR	Douglas DC-9-41	S.A.S. *Atle Viking*
SE-DDT	Douglas DC-9-41	S.A.S. *Amund Viking*
SE-DGG	F.28 Fellowship 4000	S.A.S. *Gunnhild Viking*
SE-DGI	F.28 Fellowship 4000	S.A.S. *Ingeborg Viking*
SE-DGL	F.28 Fellowship 4000	S.A.S. *Loke Viking*
SE-DGP	F.28 Fellowship 4000	S.A.S. *Steinar Viking*
SE-DGR	F.28 Fellowship 4000	S.A.S. *Randver Viking*
SE-DGT	F.28 Fellowship 4000	S.A.S. *Tola Viking*
SE-DGU	F.28 Fellowship 4000	S.A.S. *Ulfljot Viking*
SE-DIB	McD Douglas MD-87	S.A.S. *Varin Viking*
SE-DIC	McD Douglas MD-87	S.A.S. *Grane Viking*
SE-DIF	McD Douglas MD-87	S.A.S. *Hjorulv Viking*
SE-DII	McD Douglas MD-82	S.A.S. *Sigtrygg Viking*
SE-DIK	McD Douglas MD-82	S.A.S. *Stenkil Viking*
SE-DIL	McD Douglas MD-82	S.A.S. *Tord Viking*
SE-DIN	McD Douglas MD-82	S.A.S. *Eskil Viking*
SE-DIP	McD Douglas MD-87	S.A.S. *Jarl Viking*
SE-DIR	McD Douglas MD-81	S.A.S. *Nora Viking*
SE-DIS	McD Douglas MD-81	S.A.S. *Sigmund Viking*
SE-DIU	McD Douglas MD-87	S.A.S. *Torsten Viking*
SE-DIX	McD Douglas MD-82	S.A.S. *Adils Viking*
SE-DIZ	McD Douglas MD-82	S.A.S. *Sigyn Viking*
SE-DMA	McD Douglas MD-87	S.A.S. *Lage Viking*
SE-DMB	McD Douglas MD-81	S.A.S. *Bjarne Viking*
SE-DMF	McD Douglas MD-90-30	S.A.S. *Heidrek Viking*

Reg.	Type	Owner or Operator	Notes
SE-DMG	McD Douglas MD-90-30	S.A.S. *Hervor Viking*	
SE-DMH	McD Douglas MD-90-30	S.A.S. *Torolf Viking*	
SE-DNM	Boeing 737-683	S.A.S. *Bernt Viking*	
SE-DNT	Boeing 737-683	S.A.S. *Sneifrid Viking*	
SE-DNU	Boeing 737-683	S.A.S. *Unn Viking*	
SE-DNX	Boeing 737-683	S.A.S. *Torvald Vikingi*	
SE-DOK	Douglas DC-9-41	S.A.S. *Audun Viking*	
SE-DOL	Douglas DC-9-41	S.A.S. *Halldor Viking*	
SE-DOM	Douglas DC-9-41	S.A.S. *Bodvar Viking*	
SE-DOO	Douglas DC-9-41	S.A.S. *Froste Viking*	
SE-DPA	Boeing 737-33AQC	Falcon Aviation *Aftonfalken*	
SE-DPB	Boeing 737-33AQC	Falcon Aviation *Pilgrimsfalken*	
SE-DPC	Boeing 737-33AQC	Falcon Aviation *Tornfalken*	
SE-DPI	McD Douglas MD-83	S.A.S. *Erik Viking*	
SE-DRA	BAe 146-200	Braathens Malmö Aviation	
SE-DRB	BAe 146-200	Braathens Malmö Aviation	
SE-DRF	BAe 146-200	Braathens Malmö Aviation	
SE-DSO	Avro RJ100	Braathens Malmo Aviation	
SE-DSP	Avro RJ100	Braathens Malmo Aviation	
SE-DSR	Avro RJ100	Braathens Malmo Aviation	
SE-DSS	Avro RJ100	Braathens Malmö Aviation	
SE-DST	Avro RJ100	Braathens Malmö Aviation	
SE-DSU	Avro RJ100	Braathens Malmö Aviation	
SE-DSV	Avro RJ100	Braathens Malmö Aviation	
SE-DSX	Avro RJ100	Braathens Malmö Aviation	
SE-DSY	Avro RL100	Braathens Malmo Aviation	
SE-DTF	Boeing 737-683	S.A.S. *Torbjorn Viking*	
SE-DTG	Boeing 737-783	S.A.S. *Solveig Viking*	
SE-DTH	Boeing 737-683	S.A.S. *Vile Viking*	
SE-DTI	Boeing 737-783	S.A.S. *Erland Viking*	
SE-DTR	Boeing 737-683	S.A.S.	
SE-DTU	Boeing 737-683	S.A.S.	
SE-DUK	Boeing 757-236	Britannia Airways AB	
SE-DUO	Boeing 757-236	Britannia Airways AB (G-CDUO)	
SE-DUP	Boeing 757-236	Britannia Airways AB (G-CDUP)	
SE-DUT	Boeing 737-548	Braathens Malmö Aviation	
SE-DVO	Boeing 737-85F	Novair Airlines	
SE-DVR	Boeing 737-85F	Novair Airlines	
SE-DVU	Boeing 737-85F	Novair Airlines	
SE-DYC	Boeing 737-883	S.A.S.	
SE-DYD	Boeing 737-883	S.A.S.	
SE-DYG	Boeing 737-883	S.A.S.	
SE-DYP	Boeing 737-883	S.A.S.	
SE-DYR	Boeing 737-883	S.A.S.	
SE-DZA	Embraer RJ145EP	Skyways	
SE-DZB	Embraer RJ145EP	Skyways	
SE-DZC	Embraer RJ145EP	Skyways	
SE-DZD	Embraer RJ145EP	Skyways	
SE-DZG	Boeing 767-304ER	Britannia Airways AB (G-OBYD)	
SE-DZH	Boeing 737-804	Britannia Airways AB	
SE-DZI	Boeing 737-804	Britannia Airways AB	
SE-DZK	Boeing 737-804	Britannia Airways AB	
SE-DZL	Boeing 737-804	Britannia Airways AB	
SE-DZM	Boeing 737-804	Britannia Airways AB	
SE-DZN	Boeing 737-804	Britannia Airways AB	
SE-DZO	Boeing 767-304ER	Britannia Airways AB (G-OBYH)	
SE-DZV	Boeing 737-804	Britannia Airways AB	
SE-LEA	Fokker 50	Skyways	
SE-LEB	Fokker 50	Skyways	
SE-LEC	Fokker 50	Skyways	
SE-LED	Fokker 50	Skyways	
SE-LEG	H.S.748 Srs 2A	West Air Sweden	
SE-LEH	Fokker 50	Skyways	
SE-LEK	H.S.748 Srs 2A	West Air Sweden	
SE-LEL	Fokker 50	Skyways	
SE-LEO	H.S.748 Srs 2A	West Air Sweden	
SE-LEU	Fokker 50	Skyways	
SE-LEX	H.S.748 Srs 2A	West Air Sweden	
SE-LEZ	Fokker 50	Skyways	
SE-LGC	BAe Jetstream 31	European Executive Express	
SE-LGU	BAe ATP	West Air Sweden	
SE-LGV	BAe ATP	West Air Sweden	
SE-LGX	BAe ATP	West Air Sweden	

Notes	Reg.	Type	Owner or Operator
	SE-LGY	BAe ATP	West Air Sweden
	SE-LGZ	BAe ATP	West Air Sweden
	SE-LIA	H.S.748 Srs 2A	West Air Sweden
	SE-LID	H.S.748 Srs 2A	West Air Sweden
	SE-LIE	H.S.748 Srs 2	West Air Sweden
	SE-LIN	Fokker 50	Skyways
	SE-LIO	Fokker 50	Skyways
	SE-LIP	Fokker 50	Skyways
	SE-LIT	Fokker 50	Skyways
	SE-LOG	SAAB 2000	Golden Air
	SE-LRA	D.H.C.8Q-402 Dash Eight	S.A.S. Commuter *Toke Viking*
	SE-LRB	D.H.C.8Q-402 Dash Eight	S.A.S. Commuter *Ulv Viking*
	SE-LRC	D.H.C.8Q-402 Dash Eight	S.A.S. Commuter *Ingrid Viking*
	SE-LRD	D.H.C.8Q-402 Dash Eight	S.A.S. Commuter
	SE-LRE	D.H.C.8Q-402 Dash Eight	S.A.S. Commuter
	SE-LRF	D.H.C.8Q-402 Dash Eight	S.A.S. Commuter
	SE-LRG	D.H.C.8Q-402 Dash Eight	S.A.S. Commuter
	SE-LRH	D.H.C.8Q-402 Dash Eight	S.A.S. Commuter
	SE-RAA	Embraer RJ135ER	City Airlines/Eastern Airways Ltd
	SE-RAB	Embraer RJ135ER	City Airlines/Eastern Airways Ltd
	SE-RAC	Embraer RJ135ER	City Airlines/Eastern Airways Ltd
	SE-RBF	Airbus A.330-223	Novair Airlines
	SE-RBG	Airbus A.330-223	Novair Airlines
	SE-RBH	Boeing 747-212B	Transjet Airways
	SE-RBI	McD Douglas MD-83	Transjet Airways
	SE-RBL	McD Douglas MD-83	Transjet Airways
	SE-RBN	Boeing 747-212B	Transjet Airways
	SE-	McD Douglas MD-83	Transjet Airways
	SE-	McD Douglas MD-83	Transjet Airways
	SE-	McD Douglas MD-83	Transjet Airways
	SE-	McD Douglas MD-83	Transjet Airways
	SE-REE	Airbus A.340-313X	S.A.S. *Freydis Viking*
	SE-REF	Airbus A.340-313X	S.A.S. *Toste Viking*
	SE-REG	Airbus A.321-231	S.A.S.
	SE-REH	Airbus A.321-231	S.A.S.
	SE-REI	Airbus A.321-231	S.A.S. *Arne Viking*
	SE-REK	Airbus A.321-231	S.A.S. *Gynnbjörn Viking*
	SE-REL	Airbus A.321-231	S.A.S. *Emma Viking*
	SE-REM	Airbus A.321-231	S.A.S.
	SE-REN	Airbus A.321-231	S.A.S.
	SE-REO	Airbus A.321-231	S.A.S.
	SE-REP	Airbus A.321-231	S.A.S.
	SE-REQ	Airbus A.321-231	S.A.S.

SP (Poland)

	SP-EEA	Aérospatiale ATR-42-310	Eurolot
	SP-EEB	Aérospatiale ATR-42-310	Eurolot
	SP-EEC	Aérospatiale ATR-42-310	Eurolot
	SP-EED	Aérospatiale ATR-42-310	Eurolot
	SP-EEE	Aérospatiale ATR-42-310	Eurolot
	SP-FNF	F.27 Friendship Mk 600	White Eagle Aviation/UPS *Blue Eyes*
	SP-KEK	Boeing 737-4K5	White Eagle Aviation
	SP-KEI	Boeing 737-4K5	White Eagle Aviation
	SP-LGA	Embraer RJ145MP	Polskie Linie Lotnicze (LOT)
	SP-LGB	Embraer RJ145MP	LOT
	SP-LGC	Embraer RJ145MP	LOT
	SP-LGD	Embraer RJ145MP	LOT
	SP-LGE	Embraer RJ145MP	LOT
	SP-LGF	Embraer RJ145MP	LOT
	SP-LGG	Embraer RJ145MP	LOT
	SP-LGH	Embraer RJ145MP	LOT
	SP-LGI	Embraer RJ145MP	LOT
	SP-LGK	Embraer RJ145MP	LOT
	SP-LKA	Boeing 737-55D	LOT
	SP-LKB	Boeing 737-55D	LOT
	SP-LKC	Boeing 737-55D	LOT
	SP-LKD	Boeing 737-55D	LOT
	SP-LKE	Boeing 737-55D	LOT
	SP-LKF	Boeing 737-55D	LOT
	SP-LKG	Boeing 737-53C	LOT
	SP-LKH	Boeing 737-53C	LOT

Reg.	Type	Owner or Operator	Notes
SP-LKI	Boeing 737-53C	LOT	
SP-LKK	Boeing 737-5L9	LOT	
SP-LLA	Boeing 737-45D	LOT	
SP-LLB	Boeing 737-45D	LOT	
SP-LLC	Boeing 737-45D	LOT	
SP-LLD	Boeing 737-45D	LOT	
SP-LLE	Boeing 737-45D	LOT	
SP-LLF	Boeing 737-45D	LOT	
SP-LLG	Boeing 737-45D	LOT	
SP-LMC	Boeing 737-36N	LOT	
SP-LMD	Boeing 737-36N	LOT	
SP-LOA	Boeing 767-25DER	LOT *Gneizao*	
SP-LOB	Boeing 767-25DER	LOT *Kracow*	
SP-LPA	Boeing 767-35DER	LOT *Warszawa*	
SP-LPB	Boeing 767-35DER	LOT *Gdansk*	
SP-LPC	Boeing 767-35DER	LOT	

ST (Sudan)

ST-AFA	Boeing 707-3J8C	Sudan Airways	
ST-AFB	Boeing 707-3J8C	Sudan Cargo	
ST-AIX	Boeing 707-369C	Sudan Airways	
ST-AMF	Boeing 707-321C	Trans Arabian Air Transport	

Note: Sudan Airways also operates the A.300-622Rs F-ODTK & F-OIHA.

SU (Egypt)

SU-AVZ	Boeing 707-366C	Air Memphis	
SU-BDG	Airbus A.300B4-203F	EgyptAir Cargo *Toshki*	
SU-BMM	Airbus A.300B4-203	AMC Aviation	
SU-BMR	McD Douglas MD-90-30	AMC Aviation	
SU-BMS	McD Douglas MD-90-30	AMC Aviation	
SU-BMT	McD Douglas MD-90-30	AMC Aviation	
SU-BMV	Boeing 707-3B4C	Luxor Air	
SU-BMZ	Airbus A.300B4-203F	Khalifa Airways	
SU-BNN	McD Douglas MD-90-30	AMC Aviation	
SU-EAF	Tupolev Tu-204-120	Air Cairo Cargo	
SU-EAG	Tupolev Tu-204-120	Air Cairo/TNT	
SU-EAH	Tupolev Tu-204-120	Air Cairo	
SU-EAJ	Tupolev Tu-204-120	HC Airlines/TNT	
SU-EAK	Tupolev Tu-204-120	HC Airlines/TNT	
SU-GAC	Airbus A.300B4-203F	EgyptAir Cargo *New Valley*	
SU-GAJ	Boeing 767-266ER	EgyptAir *Tiye*	
SU-GAL	Boeing 747-366 (SCD)	EgyptAir *Hatshepsut*	
SU-GAM	Boeing 747-366 (SCD)	EgyptAir *Cleopatra*	
SU-GAR	Airbus A.300B4-622R	EgyptAir *Zoser*	
SU-GAS	Airbus A.300B4-622R	EgyptAir *Cheops*	
SU-GAT	Airbus A.300B4-622R	EgyptAir *Chephren*	
SU-GAU	Airbus A.300B4-622R	EgyptAir *Mycerinus*	
SU-GAV	Airbus A.300B4-622R	EgyptAir *Menes*	
SU-GAW	Airbus A.300B4-622R	EgyptAir *Ahmuse*	
SU-GAY	Airbus A.300B4-622R	EgyptAir *Seti I*	
SU-GAZ	Airbus A.300B4-622R	EgyptAir	
SU-GBA	Airbus A.320-231	EgyptAir *Aswan*	
SU-GBB	Airbus A.320-231	EgyptAir *Luxor*	
SU-GBC	Airbus A.320-231	EgyptAir *Hurghada*	
SU-GBD	Airbus A.320-231	EgyptAir *Taba*	
SU-GBE	Airbus A.320-231	EgyptAir *El Alamein*	
SU-GBF	Airbus A.320-231	EgyptAir *Sharm El Sheikh*	
SU-GBG	Airbus A.320-231	EgyptAir *Saint Catherine*	
SU-GBM	Airbus A.340-212	EgyptAir *Osiris Express*	
SU-GBN	Airbus A.340-212	EgyptAir *Cleo Express*	
SU-GBO	Airbus A.340-212	EgyptAir *Hathor Express*	
SU-GBP	Boeing 777-266	EgyptAir *Nefertiti*	
SU-GBR	Boeing 777-266	EgyptAir *Nefertari*	
SU-GBS	Boeing 777-266	EgyptAir *Tyie*	
SU-GBT	Airbus A.321-231	EgyptAir *Red Sea*	
SU-GBU	Airbus A.321-231	EgyptAir *Sinai*	
SU-GBV	Airbus A.321-231	EgyptAir *Mediterranean*	
SU-GBW	Airbus A.321-231	EgyptAir *The Nile*	
SU-GBX	Boeing 777-266ER	EgyptAir	

Reg.	Type	Owner or Operator
SU-GBY	Boeing 777-266ER	EgyptAir
SU-LBA	Airbus A.320-211	Lotus Air *The Spirit of Egypt*
SU-LBB	Airbus A.320-212	Lotus Air
SU-LBA	Airbus A.320-211	Lotus Air
SU-LBB	Airbus A.320-212	Lotus Air
SU-LBC	Airbus A.320-214	Lotus Air
SU-LBD	Airbus A.320-214	Lotus Air/Air 2000 Ltd
SU-MWA	Airbus A.310-304	Midwest Airlines *Almahrousa*
SU-MWB	Airbus A.310-304	Midwest Airlines *Oasis of Heliopolis*
SU-PBB	Boeing 707-328C	Air Memphis
SU-PMA	Boeing 737-222	Pharaoh Airlines *Akhnaton*
SU-RAA	Airbus A.320-231	Shorouk Air
SU-RAB	Airbus A.320-231	Shorouk Air
SU-RAC	Airbus A.320-231	Shorouk Air
SU-RAD	Airbus A.320-231	Shorouk Air
SU-YAK	Boeing 727-230	Palestinian Airlines
SU-ZCC	Boeing 737-3Q8	Heliopolis Airlines
SU-ZCD	Boeing 737-3Q8	Heliopolis Airlines
SU-ZCF	Boeing 737-3Q8	Heliopolis Airlines

SX (Greece)

SX-BBT	Boeing 737-33A	Cronus Airlines *Kastalia*
SX-BBU	Boeing 737-33A	Aegean Cronus Airlines
SX-BCA	Boeing 737-284	Olympic Airways *Apollo*
SX-BCB	Boeing 737-284	Olympic Airways *Hermes*
SX-BCC	Boeing 737-284	Olympic Airways *Hercules*
SX-BCD	Boeing 737-284	Olympic Airways *Hephaestus*
SX-BCE	Boeing 737-284	Olympic Airways *Dionysus*
SX-BCF	Boeing 737-284	Olympic Airways *Poseidon*
SX-BCG	Boeing 737-284	Olympic Airways *Phoebus*
SX-BCH	Boeing 737-284	Olympic Airways *Triton*
SX-BCI	Boeing 737-284	Olympic Airways *Proteus*
SX-BCK	Boeing 737-284	Olympic Airways *Nereus*
SX-BCL	Boeing 737-284	Olympic Airways *Isle of Thassos*
SX-BEK	Airbus A.300B4-605R	Olympic Airways *Macedonia*
SX-BEL	Airbus A.300B4-605R	Olympic Airways *Athena*
SX-BEM	Airbus A.300B4-605R	Olympic Airways *Creta*
SX-BFP	Boeing 737-5K5	Galaxy Airways *City of Thessaloniki*
SX-BGH	Boeing 737-4Y0	Aegean Cronus Airlines *Iniochos*
SX-BGI	Boeing 737-3L9	Aegean Cronus Airlines
SX-BGJ	Boeing 737-4S3	Aegean Cronus Airlines
SX-BGK	Boeing 737-3Y0	Aegean Cronus Airlines
SX-BKA	Boeing 737-484	Olympic Airways *Vergina*
SX-BKB	Boeing 737-484	Olympic Airways *Olynthos*
SX-BKC	Boeing 737-484	Olympic Airways *Philipoli*
SX-BKD	Boeing 737-484	Olympic Airways *Amphipoli*
SX-BKE	Boeing 737-484	Olympic Airways *Stagira*
SX-BKF	Boeing 737-484	Olympic Airways *Dion*
SX-BKG	Boeing 737-484	Olympic Airways
SX-BKH	Boeing 737-4Q8	Olympic Airways
SX-BKI	Boeing 737-4Q8	Olympic Airways
SX-BKK	Boeing 737-4Q8	Olympic Airways
SX-BKL	Boeing 737-4Y0	Olympic Airways
SX-BKM	Boeing 737-4Q8	Olympic Airways
SX-BKN	Boeing 737-4Q8	Olympic Airways
SX-BLA	Boeing 737-33R	Olympic Airways
SX-BMA	Boeing 737-46J	Macedonian Airlines
SX-BMB	Boeing 737-46J	Macedonian Airlines
SX-BMC	Boeing 737-42J	Macedonian Airlines *City of Alexandroupoli*
SX-BOA	Boeing 717-2K9	Olympic Aviation
SX-BOB	Boeing 717-2K9	Olympic Aviation
SX-BOC	Boeing 717-23S	Olympic Aviation
SX-CBG	Boeing 727-230	Macedonian Airlines
SX-CBH	Boeing 727-230	Macedonian Airlines
SX-CVH	Douglas DC-10-15	Electra Airlines
SX-CVP	Douglas DC-10-15	Electra Airlines
SX-DFA	Airbus A.340-313X	Olympic Airways *Olympia*
SX-DFB	Airbus A.340-313X	Olympic Airways *Delphi*
SX-DFC	Airbus A.340-313X	Olympic Airways *Marathon*
SX-DFD	Airbus A.340-313X	Olympic Airways

Reg.	Type	Owner or Operator	Notes
SX-OAB	Boeing 747-284B	Olympic Airways *Olympic Eagle*	
SX-OAE	Boeing 747-212B	Olympic Airways *Olympic Peace*	

TC (Turkey)

TC-ABB	Airbus A.321-131	Alfa Airlines	
TC-ABD	Airbus A.300B4-622R	Alfa Airlines	
TC-ABE	Airbus A.300B4-622R	Alfa Airlines	
TC-ABF	Airbus A.300B4-622R	Alfa Airlines	
TC-AEA	Boeing 737-268C	An Express Hava Yollari	
TC-AEB	Boeing 737-268	An Express Hava Yollari	
TC-AEC	Boeing 737-268	An Express Hava Yollari	
TC-AFA	Boeing 737-4Q8	Pegasus Airlines	
TC-AFJ	Boeing 737-4Y0	Pegasus Airlines	
TC-AFM	Boeing 737-4Q8	Pegasus Airlines	
TC-AFV	Boeing 727-230F	Istanbul Cargo	
TC-ALS	Airbus A.300B4-103	Alfa Airlines	
TC-ANH	Boeing 737-4Q8	Air Anatolia	
TC-ANI	Airbus A.300B4-203	Air Anatolia	
TC-ANL	Boeing 737-4Q8	Air Anatolia	
TC-APC	Boeing 737-4Y0	Pegasus Airlines	
TC-APD	Boeing 737-42R	Pegasus Airlines *Khalifa*	
TC-APF	Boeing 737-86N	Pegasus Airlines	
TC-APG	Boeing 737-82R	Pegasus Airlines	
TC-APH	Boeing 737-8S3	Pegasus Airlines	
TC-API	Boeing 737-86N	Pegasus Airlines	
TC-APJ	Boeing 737-86N	Pegasus Airlines	
TC-APK	Boeing 737-86N	Pegasus Airlines	
TC-APL	Boeing 737-86N	Pegasus Airlines	
TC-APM	Boeing 737-809	Khalifa Airways	
TC-APN	Boeing 737-86N	Pegasus Airlines	
TC-APP	Boeing 737-4Q8	Pegasus Airlines	
TC-APR	Boeing 737-4Y0	Pegasus Airlines	
TC-APT	Boeing 737-4Y0	Pegasus Airlines	
TC-APU	Boeing 737-82R	Pegasus Airlines	
TC-APV	Boeing 737-86N	Pegasus Airlines	
TC-APY	Boeing 737-86N	Pegasus Airlines/Khalifa Airways	
TC-ESA	Boeing 737-3K2	EuroSun	
TC-ESB	Boeing 737-3K2	Air Anatolia	
TC-ESC	Boeing 737-236	EuroSun *Side*	
TC-GTA	Airbus A.300B4-103	Air Anatolia *Dila*	
TC-GTB	Airbus A.300B4-203	Air Anatolia *Ferit Torosluoglu*	
TC-IYA	Boeing 727-2F2	Top Air *Hezarfen*	
TC-IYB	Boeing 727-243	Top Air	
TC-IYC	Boeing 727-2F2	Top Air *Merve*	
TC-JBG	Boeing 727-2F2	Kibris Turkish Airlines *Besparmak*	
TC-JCM	Airbus A.310-203	Turkish Airlines *Ceyhan*	
TC-JCO	Airbus A.310-203	Kibris Turkish Airlines *Firat*	
TC-JCR	Airbus A.310-203	Turkish Airlines *Kizilirmak*	
TC-JCV	Airbus A.310-304	Turkish Airlines *Aras*	
TC-JCY	Airbus A.310-304	Turkish Airlines *Coruh*	
TC-JCZ	Airbus A.310-304	Turkish Airlines *Ergene*	
TC-JDA	Airbus A.310-304	Turkish Airlines *Aksu*	
TC-JDB	Airbus A.310-304ET	Turkish Airlines *Göksu*	
TC-JDC	Airbus A.310-304ET	Turkish Airlines *Meric*	
TC-JDD	Airbus A.310-304ET	Turkish Airlines *Dalaman*	
TC-JDF	Boeing 737-4Y0	Turkish Airlines *Ayvalik*	
TC-JDG	Boeing 737-4Y0	Turkish Airlines *Marmaris*	
TC-JDH	Boeing 737-4Y0	Turkish Airlines *Amasra*	
TC-JDI	Boeing 737-4Q8	Turkish Airlines *Urgup*	
TC-JDJ	Airbus A.340-311	Turkish Airlines *Istanbul*	
TC-JDK	Airbus A.340-311	Turkish Airlines *Isparta*	
TC-JDL	Airbus A.340-311	Turkish Airlines *Ankara*	
TC-JDM	Airbus A.340-311	Turkish Airlines *Izmir*	
TC-JDN	Airbus A.340-313	Turkish Airlines *Adana*	
TC-JDO	Airbus A.340-313	Turkish Airlines	
TC-JDP	Airbus A.340-313	Turkish Airlines	
TC-JDT	Boeing 737-4Y0	Turkish Airlines *Alanya*	
TC-JDU	Boeing 737-5Y0	Turkish Airlines *Trabzon*	
TC-JDV	Boeing 737-5Y0	Turkish Airlines *Bursa*	
TC-JDY	Boeing 737-4Y0	Turkish Airlines *Antalya*	
TC-JDZ	Boeing 737-4Y0	Turkish Airlines *Fethiye*	

Notes	Reg.	Type	Owner or Operator
	TC-JEC	Boeing 727-228	Kibris Turkish Airlines *Yesilada*
	TC-JEE	Boeing 737-4Q8	Turkish Airlines *Cesme*
	TC-JEN	Boeing 737-4Q8	Turkish Airlines *Gelibolu*
	TC-JEO	Boeing 737-4Q8	Turkish Airlines *Anadolu*
	TC-JER	Boeing 737-4Y0	Turkish Airlines *Mugla*
	TC-JET	Boeing 737-4Y0	Turkish Airlines *Canakkale*
	TC-JEU	Boeing 737-4Y0	Turkish Airlines *Kayseri*
	TC-JEV	Boeing 737-4Y0	Turkish Airlines *Efes*
	TC-JEY	Boeing 737-4Y0	Turkish Airlines *Side*
	TC-JEZ	Boeing 737-4Y0	Turkish Airlines *Bergama*
	TC-JFC	Boeing 737-8F2	Turkish Airlines *Diyarbakir*
	TC-JFD	Boeing 737-8F2	Turkish Airlines *Rize*
	TC-JFE	Boeing 737-8F2	Turkish Airlines *Hatay*
	TC-JFF	Boeing 737-8F2	Turkish Airlines *Afyon*
	TC-JFG	Boeing 737-8F2	Turkish Airlines *Mardi*
	TC-JFH	Boeing 737-8F2	Turkish Airlines *Igdir*
	TC-JFI	Boeing 737-8F2	Turkish Airlines
	TC-JFJ	Boeing 737-8F2	Turkish Airlines
	TC-JFK	Boeing 737-8F2	Turkish Airlines
	TC-JFL	Boeing 737-8F2	Turkish Airlines
	TC-JFM	Boeing 737-8F2	Turkish Airlines
	TC-JFN	Boeing 737-8F2	Turkish Airlines *Bitlis*
	TC-JFO	Boeing 737-8F2	Turkish Airlines *Batman*
	TC-JFP	Boeing 737-8F2	Turkish Airlines
	TC-JFR	Boeing 737-8F2	Turkish Airlines
	TC-JFT	Boeing 737-8F2	Turkish Airlines *Kastamonu*
	TC-JFU	Boeing 737-8F2	Turkish Airlines
	TC-JFV	Boeing 737-8F2	Turkish Airlines
	TC-JFY	Boeing 737-8F2	Turkish Airlines *Manisa*
	TC-JFZ	Boeing 737-8F2	Turkish Airlines
	TC-JGA	Boeing 737-8F2	Turkish Airlines
	TC-JGB	Boeing 737-8F2	Turkish Airlines
	TC-JGC	Boeing 737-8F2	Turkish Airlines
	TC-JGD	Boeing 737-8F2	Turkish Airlines
	TC-JGE	Boeing 737-8F2	Turkish Airlines
	TC-JGF	Boeing 737-8F2	Turkish Airlines
	TC-JGG	Boeing 737-8F2	Turkish Airlines
	TC-JGH	Boeing 737-8F2	Turkish Airlines
	TC-JIH	Airbus A.340-313X	Turkish Airlines
	TC-JII	Airbus A.340-313X	Turkish Airlines *Aydin*
	TC-JKA	Boeing 737-4Q8	Turkish Airlines *Kars*
	TC-JYK	Airbus A.310-203	Kibris Turkish Airlines *Erenkoy*
	TC-JHA	McD Douglas MD-90-30	Turkish Airlines
	TC-JHB	McD Douglas MD-90-30	Turkish Airlines
	TC-MAO	Boeing 737-86N	Kibris Turkish Airlines
	TC-MNA	Airbus A.300B4-203F	MNG Cargo Airlines
	TC-MNB	Airbus A.300B4-203F	MNG Cargo Airlines
	TC-MNC	Airbus A.300B4-203F	MNG Cargo Airlines
	TC-MND	Airbus A.300B4-203F	MNG Cargo Airlines
	TC-MNE	Airbus A.300B4-203F	MNG Cargo Airlines
	TC-MNG	Airbus A. 300C4-203	MNG Cargo Airlines *Hayal*
	TC-MSO	Boeing 737-8S3	Kibris Turkish Airlines
	TC-MZZ	Boeing 737-8S3	Kibris Turkish Airlines
	TC-OGA	Boeing 757-225	Atlas International
	TC-OGB	Boeing 757-225	Atlas International *Perihant*
	TC-OGC	Boeing 757-2G5	Atlas International
	TC-OGZ	Boeing 737-46B	Atlas International
	TC-ONJ	Airbus A.321-131	Onur Air *Kaptan Soray Sahin*
	TC-ONK	Airbus A.300B4-103	Onur Air *Pinar*
	TC-ONL	Airbus A.300B4-103	Onur Air *Selin*
	TC-ONM	McD Douglas MD-88	Onur Air *Yasemin*
	TC-ONN	McD Douglas MD-88	Onur Air *Ece*
	TC-ONO	McD Douglas MD-88	Onur Air *Yonca*
	TC-ONP	McD Douglas MD-88	Onur Air *Esra*
	TC-ONR	McD Douglas MD-88	Onur Air *Evren*
	TC-ONS	Airbus A.321-131	Onur Air *Funda*
	TC-ONT	Airbus A.300B4-203	Onur Air
	TC-ONU	Airbus A.300B4-203	Onur Air
	TC-SKA	Boeing 737-4Y0	Sky Airlines *Sun*
	TC-SKB	Boeing 737-430	Sky Airlines
	TC-SKC	Boeing 737-85F	Excelairways-Cyprus
	TC-SUA	Boeing 737-86N	Sun Express
	TC-SUB	Boeing 737-86N	Sun Express

Reg.	Type	Owner or Operator	Notes
TC-SUC	Boeing 737-86N	Sun Express	
TC-SUD	Boeing 737-86N	Sun Express	
TC-SUE	Boeing 737-73S	Sun Express	
TC-SUF	Boeing 737-73S	Sun Express	

TF (Iceland)

TF-ABA	Boeing 747-267B	Air Atlanta Iceland	
TF-ABE	L.1011-385 TriStar 1	Air Atlanta Iceland	
TF-ABO	Boeing 747-1D1	Air Atlanta Iceland	
TF-ABP	Boeing 747-267B	Air Atlanta Iceland/Air Asia	
TF-ABQ	Boeing 747-246B	Air Atlanta Iceland *(stored)*	
TF-ABT	L.1011-385 TriStar 100	Air Atlanta Iceland	
TF-ADF	Boeing 747-236B	Air Atlanta Iceland	
TF-ADI	Boeing 747-236B	Air Atlanta Iceland	
TF-ADJ	Boeing 747-236B	Air Atlanta Iceland	
TF-ADK	Boeing 747-236B	Air Atlanta Iceland	
TF-ADL	Boeing 747-236B	Air Atlanta Iceland	
TF-ADO	Boeing 747-236B	Air Atlanta Iceland/Bangladesh Biman	
TF-ATA	Boeing 747-230B	Air Atlanta Iceland	
TF-ATB	Boeing 747-246B	Air Atlanta Iceland *(stored)*	
TF-ATC	Boeing 747-267B	Air Atlanta Iceland	
TF-ATD	Boeing 747-267B	Air Atlanta Iceland/Saudia	
TF-ATE	Boeing 747-146	Air Atlanta Iceland *(stored)*	
TF-ATH	Boeing 747-341	Air Atlanta Iceland/Iberia	
TF-ATI	Boeing 747-341	Air Atlanta Iceland/Iberia	
TF-ATJ	Boeing 747-341	Air Atlanta Iceland/Iberia	
TF-ATK	Boeing 747-367	Air Atlanta iceland	
TF-ATN	Boeing 747-219B	Air Atlanta Iceland	
TF-ATO	Boeing 767-204ER	Air Atlanta Iceland	
TF-ATP	Boeing 767-204ER	Air Atlanta Iceland	
TF-ATR	Boeing 767-204ER	Air Atlanta Iceland	
TF-ATS	Boeing 747-312	Air Atlanta Iceland/Nigeria Airways	
TF-ATU	Boeing 767-204	Air Atlanta Iceland	
TF-ATV	Boeing 747-267B	Air Atlanta Iceland	
TF-ATX	Boeing 747-236BF	Air Atlanta Iceland	
TF-ATZ	Boeing 747-236	Air Atlanta Iceland *(stored)*	
TF-BBD	Boeing 737-3Y0	Bluebird Cargo	
TF-BBG	Swearingen SA.227AC Metro III	Islandsflug	
TF-ELJ	Aérospatiale ATR-42-310	Islandsflug	
TF-ELK	Aérospatiale ATR-42-310	Islandsflug	
TF-ELL	Boeing 737-210C	Islandsflug	
TF-ELM	Boeing 737-2M8	Islandsflug	
TF-ELN	Boeing 737-3Q8QC	Islandsflug/DHL	
TF-ELP	Boeing 737-330QC	Islandsflug/Channel Express	
TF-ELR	Boeing 737-330QC	Islandsflug/Channel Express	
TF-FDA	Boeing 737-3Q8	Islandsflug/Sunbird	
TF-FIA	Boeing 737-408	Icelandair	
TF-FID	Boeing 737-408	Icelandair *Heiddis*	
TF-FIE	Boeing 737-3S3F	Icelandair	
TF-FIG	Boeing 757-23APF	Icelandair	
TF-FIH	Boeing 757-208	Icelandair *Hafdis*	
TF-FII	Boeing 757-208	Icelandair *Fanndis*	
TF-FIJ	Boeing 757-208	Icelandair *Svandis*	
TF-FIK	Boeing 757-28A	Icelandair *Soldis*	
TF-FIN	Boeing 757-208	Icelandair *Bryndis*	
TF-FIO	Boeing 757-208	Icelandair *Valdis*	
TF-FIP	Boeing 757-208	Icelandair	
TF-FIV	Boeing 757-208	Icelandair	
TF-FIW	Boeing 757-27B	Icelandair	
TF-FIX	Boeing 757-308	Icelandair	
TF-JME	Swearingen SA.227DC Metro 23	Flugfelag Islands	
TF-JMG	Fokker 50	Air Iceland	
TF-JMK	Swearingen SA.227AC Metro III	Flugfelag Islands	
TF-JML	Swearingen SA.227DC Metro 23	Flugfelag Islands	
TF-JMR	Fokker 50	Air Iceland *Asdis*	
TF-JMS	Fokker 50	Air Iceland *Sigdis*	
TF-JMT	Fokker 50	Air Iceland *Freydis*	
TF-JMU	Fokker 50	Air Iceland	
TF-MDA	McD Douglas MD-81	MD Icelandic Airlines	
TF-MDB	McD Douglas MD-83	MD Icelandic Airlines	
TF-MDC	McD Douglas MD-83	MD Icelandic Airlines	

Notes	Reg.	Type	Owner or Operator
	TF-SUN	Boeing 737-3Q8	Islandsflug

TJ (Cameroon)

	TJ-CAC	Boeing 767-33AER	Cameroon Airlines
	TJ-CAD	Boeing 767-231ER	Cameroon Airlines

TR (Gabon)

	TR-LFH	Boeing 767-266ER	Air Gabon

Note: Air Gabon operates Boeing 747-2Q2B F-ODJG *President Leon Mba*

TS (Tunisia)

	TS-IEB	Boeing 737-3Y0	Tuninter
	TS-IMA	Airbus A.300B4-203	Tunis Air *Amilcar*
	TS-IMB	Airbus A.320-211	Tunis Air *Fahrat Hached*
	TS-IMC	Airbus A.320-211	Tunis Air *7 Novembre*
	TS-IMD	Airbus A.320-211	Tunis Air *Khereddine*
	TS-IME	Airbus A.320-211	Tunis Air *Tabarka*
	TS-IMF	Airbus A.320-211	Tunis Air *Jerba*
	TS-IMG	Airbus A.320-211	Tunis Air *Abou el Kacem Chebbi*
	TS-IMH	Airbus A.320-211	Tunis Air *Ali Belhaouane*
	TS-IMI	Airbus A.320-211	Tunis Air *Jughurta*
	TS-IMJ	Airbus A.319-114	Tunis Air *El Kantaoui*
	TS-IMK	Airbus A.319-114	Tunis Air *Kerkenah*
	TS-IML	Airbus A.320-211	Tunis Air *Gafsa del Ksar*
	TS-IMM	Airbus A.320-211	Tunis Air
	TS-IMN	Airbus A.320-211	Tunis Air *Khaldoun*
	TS-IMO	Airbus A.319-114	Tunis Air
	TS-IMP	Airbus A.320-211	Tunis Air
	TS-INA	Airbus A.320-214	Nouvelair
	TS-INB	Airbus A.320-214	Nouvelair
	TS-IOC	Boeing 737-2H3	Tunis Air *Salammbo*
	TS-IOD	Boeing 737-2H3C	Mediterranean Air Service
	TS-IOE	Boeing 737-2H3	Tunis Air *Zarzis*
	TS-IOF	Boeing 737-2H3	Tunis Air *Sousse*
	TS-IOG	Boeing 737-5H3	Tunis Air *Sfax*
	TS-IOH	Boeing 737-5H3	Tunis Air *Hammamet*
	TS-IOI	Boeing 737-5H3	Tunis Air *Mahida*
	TS-IOJ	Boeing 737-5H3	Tunis Air *Monastir*
	TS-IOK	Boeing 737-6H3	Tunis Air
	TS-IOL	Boeing 737-6H3	Tunis Air
	TS-IOM	Boeing 737-6H3	Tunis Air
	TS-ION	Boeing 737-6H3	Tunis Air *Utioue*
	TS-IOP	Boeing 737-6H3	Tunis Air *El Jem*
	TS-IOQ	Boeing 737-6H3	Tunis Air *Bizerte*
	TS-IOR	Boeing 737-6H3	Tunis Air *Tahar Haddad*
	TS-IPA	Airbus A.300B4-605R	Tunis Air *Sidi Bou Said*
	TS-IPB	Airbus A.300B4-605R	Tunis Air *Tunis*
	TS-IPC	Airbus A.300B4-605R	Tunis Air
	TS-JHR	Boeing 727-2H3	Tunis Air
	TS-JHT	Boeing 727-2H3	Tunis Air *Sidi Bousaid*
	TS-JHU	Boeing 727-2H3	Tunis Air *Hannibal*
	TS-JHW	Boeing 727-2H3	Tunis Air *Ibn Khaldoun*

Note: Nouvelair also operates MD-83s EI-CBO, EI-CNO and EI-CTJ.

TU (Ivory Coast)

	TU-TAO	Airbus A.300B4-203	Air Afrique *Nouackchott*
	TU-TAQ	Airbus A.300B4-203	Air Afrique
	TU-TAS	Airbus A.300B4-203	Air Afrique *Bangui*
	TU-TAY	Airbus A.330-223	Air Afrique
	TU-TAZ	Airbus A.310-304	Air Afrique

UK (Uzbekistan)

The following are operated by Uzbekistan Airways with registrations prefixed by UK.

Reg.	Type		Reg.	Type
31001	Airbus A.310-324		85398	Tu-154B-2
31002	Airbus A.310-324		85401	Tu-154B-2
31003	Airbus A.310-324		85416	Tu-154B-2
			85438	Tu-154B-2
75700	Boeing 757-23P		85449	Tu-154B-2
75702	Boeing 757-23P		85575	Tu-154B-2
			85578	Tu-154B-2
76351	IL-76TD		85711	Tu-154M
76353	IL-76TD		85764	Tu-154M
76358	IL-76TD		85776	Tu-154M
76359	IL-76TD		86012	IL-86
76426	IL-76TD		86016	IL-86
76428	IL-76TD		86052	IL-86
76448	IL-76TD		86053	IL-86
76449	IL-76TD		86056	IL-86
76782	IL-76TD		86057	IL-86
76793	IL-76TD		86064	IL-86
76794	IL-76TD		86072	IL-86
76805	IL-76TD		86083	IL-86
76811	IL-76TD		86090	IL-86
76813	IL-76TD		86569	IL-62M
76824	IL-76TD		86573	IL-62M
85189	Tu-154B		86574	IL-62M
85272	Tu-154B-1		86575	IL-62M
85286	Tu-154B-1		86576	IL-62M
85344	Tu-154B-2		86577	IL-62M
85356	Tu-154B-2		86578	IL-62M
85370	Tu-154B-2		86579	IL-62M
85397	Tu-154B-2			

Reg.

Note: Uzbekistan Airways also operates Boeing 767-33PERs VP-BUA and VP-BUZ plus the Boeing 757-23P VP-BUB and VP-BUD.

UN (Kazakstan)

Reg.	Type	Notes
UN-A3101	Airbus A.310-322	Air Kazakstan
UN-A3102	Airbus A.310-322	Air Kazakstan
UN-B3705	Boeing 737-2Q8	Air Kazakstan
UN-B3706	Boeing 737-2M8	Air Kazakstan

The following are operated by Air Kazakstan with the registrations prefixed by UN

Reg.	Type		Reg.	Type
65115	Tu-134A-3		85271	Tu-154B-1
65121	Tu-134A-3		85276	Tu-154B-1
65130	Tu-134A-3		85290	Tu-154B-1
65138	Tu-134A		85387	Tu-154B-2
65147	Tu-134A-3		85396	Tu-154B-2
65551	Tu-134A-3		85431	Tu-154B-2
65683	Tu-134A		85455	Tu-154B-2
65767	Tu-134A-3		85464	Tu-154B-2
65776	Tu-134A-3		85478	Tu-154B-2
65787	Tu-134A		85521	Tu-154B-2
65900	Tu-134A-3		85537	Tu-154B-2
76371	IL-76TD		85589	Tu-154B-2
76374	IL-76TD		85719	Tu-154M
76810	IL-76TD		85775	Tu-154M
85076	Tu-154B-1		85780	Tu-154M
85111	Tu-154B-1		85781	Tu-154M
85113	Tu-154B		86068	IL-86
85151	Tu-154B-1		86069	IL-86
85173	Tu-154B		86071	IL-86
85194	Tu-154B		86077	IL-86
85221	Tu-154B-1		86086	IL-86
85230	Tu-154B-1		86101	IL-86
85231	Tu-154B-1		86116	IL-86
85240	Tu-154B-1			

UR (Ukraine)

Reg.	Type	Owner or Operator
UR-BFA	Boeing 737-2L9	Aerosweet Airlines
UR-BVY	Boeing 737-2Q8	Aerosweet Airlines
UR-BYH	Antonov An-74	Khorlv Avia
UR-GAC	Boeing 737-247	Ukraine International
UR-GAD	Boeing 737-2T4	Ukraine International
UR-GAF	Boeing 737-35B	Ukraine International
UR-GAG	Boeing 737-35B	Aerosweet Airlines
UR-GAH	Boeing 737-32Q	Ukraine International *Maymi*
UR-GAI	Boeing 737-529	Ukraine International
UR-PAS	Antonov An-12	Veteran Airlines
UR-UCA	Iluyshin IL-76MD	Ukraine Cargo Airways
UR-UCB	Ilyushin IL-76MD	Ukraine Cargo Airways
UR-UCC	Iluyshin IL-76MD	Ukraine Cargo Airways
UR-UCD	Iluyshin IL-76MD	Ukraine Cargo Airways
UR-UCE	Ilyushin IL-76MD	Ukraine Cargo Airways
UR-UCF	Ilyushin IL-76MD	Ukraine Cargo Airways
UR-UCG	Iluyshin IL-76MDF	Ukraine Cargo Airways
UR-UCH	Ilyushin IL-76MD	Ukraine Cargo Airways
UR-UCJ	Ilyushin IL-76MD	Ukraine Cargo Airways
UR-UCL	Ilyushin IL-76MD	Ukraine Cargo Airways
UR-UCR	Ilyushin IL-76MD	Ukraine Cargo Airways
UR-UCS	Ilyushin IL-76MD	Ukraine Cargo Airways
UR-UCT	Ilyushin IL-76MD	Ukraine Cargo Airways
UR-UCV	Ilyushin IL-76MD	Ukraine Cargo Airways
UR-UCX	Ilyushin IL-76MD	Ukraine Cargo Airways
UR-UDB	Ilyushin IL-76MD	Ukraine Cargo Airways
UR-VAA	Boeing 737-3Q8	Aerosweet Airlines

Note: The following registrations are prefixed by UR and are shown with the operators' code in parenthesis after the type. ADB - Antonov Airlines, AKO - Transago, BSL - BSL Airlines, KHO - Khors Air, UKC - Air Ukraine Cargo, UKR - Air Ukraine, TII - ATI Airlines, VPB - Veteran Airlines.

Notes	Reg.	Type		Notes	Reg.	Type
	65037	Tu-134A-3 (UKR)			76705	IL-76MD (UKR)
	65073	Tu-134A (UKR)			76707	IL-76MD (VPB)
	65076	Tu-134A-3 (UKR)			76717	IL-76MD (VPB)
	65077	Tu-134A-3 (AKO)			76728	IL-76MD (VPB)
	65081	Tu-134A-3 (AKO)			76729	IL-76MD (VPB)
	65089	Tu-134A (UKR)			76748	IL-76MD (UKR)
	65107	Tu-134A (UKR)			76749	IL-76MD (UKR)
	65114	Tu-134A-3 (UKR)			76778	IL-76MD (UKR)
	65123	Tu-134A-3 (UKR)			76758	IL-76MD (UKC)
	65135	Tu-134A-3 (UKR)			78772	IL-76MD (UKC)
	65746	Tu-134A-3 (UKR)			78775	IL-76MD (KHO)
	65752	Tu-134A-3 (UKR)			82007	An-124 (ADB)
	65757	Tu-134A (UKR)			82008	An-124 (ADB)
	65761	Tu-134A (UKR)			82009	An-124 (ADB)
	65764	Tu-134A-3 (UKR)			82027	An-124 (ADB)
	65765	Tu-134A (UKR)			82029	An-124 (ADB)
	65773	Tu-134A-3 (UKR)			82060	An-225 (ADB)
	65790	Tu-134A-3 (UKR)			82066	An-124 (ADB)
	65877	Tu-134A-3 (UKR)			82070	An-124 (ADB)
	76395	IL-76MD (KHO)			82072	An-124 (ADB)
	76396	IL-76MD (KHO)			82073	An-124 (ADB)
	76399	IL-76MD (KHO)			85316	Tu-154B-2 (UKR)
	76561	IL-76MD (UKC)			85362	Tu-154B-2 (UKR)
	76581	IL-76MD (UKR)			85368	Tu-154B-2 (UKR)
	76583	IL-76MD (UKR)			85379	Tu-154B-2 (UKR)
	76628	IL-76MD (UKC)			85395	Tu-154B-2 (UKR)
	76647	IL-76MD (VPB)			85445	Tu-154B-2 (BSL)
	76651	IL-76MD (KHO)			85460	Tu-154B-2 (UKR)
	76664	IL-76MD (KHO)			85482	Tu-154B-2 (UKR)
	76667	IL-76MD (VPB)			85490	Tu-154B-2 (UKR)
	76671	IL-76MD (VPB)			85526	Tu-154B-2 (UKR)
	76677	IL-76MD (VPB)			85535	Tu-154B-2 (UKR)
	76683	IL-76MD (VPB)			85561	Tu-154B-2 (BSL)
	76684	IL-76MD (VPB)			85707	Tu-154M (UKR)
	76694	IL-76MD (VPB)			86132	IL-62M (UKR)
	76697	IL-76MD (VPB)			86133	IL-62M (UKR)
	76698	IL-76MD (VPB)			86134	IL-62M (UKR)

Reg.	Type	Notes	Reg.	Type	Notes
86135	IL-62M (UKR)		86581	IL-62M (UKR)	
86580	IL-62M (UKR)		86582	IL-62M (UKR)	

Reg.	Type	Owner or Operator	Notes

V2 (Antigua)

V2-CVH	Douglas DC-10-15	Skyjet
V2-SKY	Douglas DC-10-15	Skyjet

Note: Skyjet also operates a DC-10-30 registered 9G-PHN

V5 (Namibia)

V5-NMA	Boeing 747-48E	Air Namibia

Note: Air Namibia also leases the Boeing 747SP ZS-SPC from South African Airways.

V8 (Brunei)

V8-AM1	Airbus A.340-211	Brunei Government
V8-BKH	Airbus A.340-212	Brunei Government
V8-DPD	Airbus A.310-304	Brunei Royal Flight (Government/VIP)
V8-JBB	Airbus A.340-213	Brunei Government
V8-MHB	Boeing 767-27GER	Royal Brunei Airlines (Government/VIP)
V8-RBA	Boeing 757-2M6	Royal Brunei Airlines
V8-RBB	Boeing 757-2M6	Royal Brunei Airlines
V8-RBF	Boeing 767-33AER	Royal Brunei Airlines
V8-RBG	Boeing 767-33AER	Royal Brunei Airlines
V8-RBH	Boeing 767-33AER	Royal Brunei Airlines
V8-RBJ	Boeing 767-33AER	Royal Brunei Airlines
V8-RBK	Boeing 767-33AER	Royal Brunei Airlines
V8-RBL	Boeing 767-33AER	Royal Brunei Airlines
V8-RBM	Boeing 767-328ER	Royal Brunei Airlines
V8-RBN	Boeing 767-328ER	Royal Brunei Airlines

VH (Australia)

VH-NOA	Boeing 767-33AER	Kenya Airways
VH-NOF	Boeing 757-23A	Guyana Air 2000
VH-OEB	Boeing 747-48E	Queensland and Northern Territory Aerial Service (QANTAS)
VH-OEC	Boeing 747-4H6	QANTAS
VH-OED	Boeing 747-4H6	QANTAS
VH-OJA	Boeing 747-438	QANTAS *City of Canberra*
VH-OJB	Boeing 747-438	QANTAS *City of Sydney*
VH-OJC	Boeing 747-438	QANTAS *City of Melbourne*
VH-OJD	Boeing 747-438	QANTAS *City of Brisbane*
VH-OJE	Boeing 747-438	QANTAS *City of Adelaide*
VH-OJF	Boeing 747-438	QANTAS *City of Perth*
VH-OJG	Boeing 747-438	QANTAS *City of Hobart*
VH-OJH	Boeing 747-438	QANTAS *City of Darwin*
VH-OJI	Boeing 747-438	QANTAS *Longreach*
VH-OJJ	Boeing 747-438	QANTAS *Winton*
VH-OJK	Boeing 747-438	QANTAS *City of Newcastle*
VH-OJL	Boeing 747-438	QANTAS *City of Ballaarat*
VH-OJM	Boeing 747-438	QANTAS *City of Gosford*
VH-OJN	Boeing 747-438	QANTAS *City of Dubbo*
VH-OJO	Boeing 747-438	QANTAS *City of Toowoomba*
VH-OJP	Boeing 747-438	QANTAS *City of Albury*
VH-OJQ	Boeing 747-438	QANTAS *City of Mandurah*
VH-OJR	Boeing 747-438	QANTAS *City of Bathurst*
VH-OJS	Boeing 747-438	QANTAS
VH-OJT	Boeing 747-438	QANTAS
VH-OJU	Boeing 747-438	QANTAS

VP-B (Bermuda)

VP-BAF	Airbus A.310-304	Aeroflot Russian International

Notes	Reg.	Type	Owner or Operator
	VP-BAG	Airbus A.310-304	Aeroflot Russian International
	VP-BAH	Boeing 737-4M0	Aeroflot Russian International
	VP-BAI	Boeing 737-4M0	Aeroflot Russian International
	VP-BAJ	Boeing 737-4M0	Aeroflot Russian International
	VP-BAL	Boeing 737-4M0	Aeroflot Russian International
	VP-BAM	Boeing 737-4M0	Aeroflot Russian International
	VP-BAN	Boeing 737-4M0	Aeroflot Russian International
	VP-BAO	Boeing 737-4M0	Aeroflot Russian International
	VP-BAP	Boeing 737-4M0	Aeroflot Russian International
	VP-BAQ	Boeing 737-4M0	Aeroflot Russian International
	VP-BAR	Boeing 737-4M0	Aeroflot Russian International
	VP-BAS	Boeing 777-2Q8ER	Aeroflot Russian International
	VP-BAU	Boeing 777-2Q8ER	Aeroflot Russian International
	VP-BAV	Boeing 767-36NER	Aeroflot Russian International
	VP-BAX	Boeing 767-36NER	Aeroflot Russian International
	VP-BAY	Boeing 767-36NER	Aeroflot Russian International
	VP-BAZ	Boeing 767-36NER	Aeroflot Russian International
	VP-BBR	Boeing 757-22L	Azerbaijan Airlines
	VP-BBS	Boeing 757-22L	Azerbaijan Airlines
	VP-BKS	Boeing 767-3P6ER	Kalair
	VP-BTA	Boeing 737-2C9	Transaero
	VP-BTB	Boeing 737-2C9	Transaero
	VP-BUA	Boeing 767-33PER	Uzbekistan Airlines *Samarkand*
	VP-BUB	Boeing 757-23P	Uzbekistan Airlines
	VP-BUD	Boeing 757-23P	Uzbekistan Airlines
	VP-BUZ	Boeing 767-33PER	Uzbekistan Airlines *Khiva*

VT (India)

	VT-EDU	Boeing 747-237B	Air-India *Akbar*
	VT-EFU	Boeing 747-237B	Air-India *Krishna Deva Raya*
	VT-EGA	Boeing 747-237B	Air-India *Samudra Gupta*
	VT-EGB	Boeing 747-237B	Air-India *Mahendra Varman*
	VT-EGC	Boeing 747-237B	Air-India *Harsha Vardhana*
	VT-EJG	Airbus A.310-304	Air-India *Vamuna*
	VT-EJH	Airbus A.310-304	Air-India *Tista*
	VT-EJI	Airbus A.310-304	Air-India *Saraswati*
	VT-EJJ	Airbus A.310-304	Air-India *Beas*
	VT-EJK	Airbus A.310-304	Air-India *Gomti*
	VT-EJL	Airbus A.310-304	Air-India *Sabarmati*
	VT-EPW	Boeing 747-337 (SCD)	Air-India *Shivaji*
	VT-EPX	Boeing 747-337 (SCD)	Air-India *Narasimha Varman*
	VT-EQS	Airbus A.310-304	Air-India *Krishna*
	VT-EQT	Airbus A.310-304	Air-India *Narmada*
	VT-ESM	Boeing 747-437	Air-India *Konark*
	VT-ESN	Boeing 747-437	Air-India *Tanjore*
	VT-ESO	Boeing 747-437	Air-India *Khajuraho*
	VT-ESP	Boeing 747-437	Air-India *Ajanta*
	VT-EVA	Boeing 747-437	Air-India *Agra*
	VT-EVB	Boeing 747-437	Air-India *Velha Goa*

YA (Afghanistan)

	YA-FAY	Boeing 727-228	Ariana Afghan Airlines
	YA-GAA	Boeing 727-51	Balkh Air

YI (Iraq)

Note: All aircraft were grounded after the Gulf conflict in the early 1990s with commercial flights suspended until 2001. Limited operations by Iraqi Airways were then resumed, initially using an IL-76 and an An-26 for domestic flights. A former Qatar Boeing 747SP-27 is also to be employed for similar duties and pilgrim flights.

YK (Syria)

	YK-AGA	Boeing 727-294	Syrianair *October 6*
	YK-AGB	Boeing 727-294	Syrianair *Damascus*
	YK-AGC	Boeing 727-294	Syrianair *Palmyra*
	YK-AGD	Boeing 727-269	Syrianair

Reg.	Type	Owner or Operator	Notes
YK-AGE	Boeing 727-269	Syrianair	
YK-AGF	Boeing 727-269	Syrianair	
YK-AHA	Boeing 747SP-94	Syrianair *November 16*	
YK-AHB	Boeing 747SP-94	Syrianair *Arab Solidarity*	
YK-AIA	Tupolev Tu-154M	Syrianair	
YK-AIB	Tupolev Tu-154M	Syrianair	
YK-AIC	Tupolev Tu-154M	Syrianair	
YK-AKA	Airbus A.320-232	Syrianair *Ugarit*	
YK-AKB	Airbus A.320-232	Syrianair *Ebla*	
YK-AKC	Airbus A.320-232	Syrianair	
YK-AKD	Airbus A.320-232	Syrianair *Mari*	
YK-AKE	Airbus A.320-232	Syrianair *Bosra*	
YK-AKF	Airbus A.320-232	Syrianair	
YK-ATA	Ilyushin IL-76M	Syrianair	
YK-ATB	Ilyushin IL-76M	Syrianair	
YK-ATC	Ilyushin IL-76M	Syrianair	
YK-ATD	Ilyushin IL-76M	Syrianair	
YK-AYA	Tupolev Tu-134B-3	Syrianair	
YK-AYB	Tupolev Tu-134B-3	Syrianair	
YK-AYC	Tupolev Tu-134B-3	Syrianair	
YK-AYD	Tupolev Tu-134B-3	Syrianair	
YK-AYE	Tupolev Tu-134B-3	Syrianair	
YK-AYF	Tupolev Tu-134B-3	Syrianair	

YL (Latvia)

YL-BAA	Boeing 737-236	Transaero	
YL-BAB	Boeing 737-236	Transaero	
YL-BAC	Boeing 737-236	Transaero	
YL-BAG	SAAB SF.340A	Air Baltic	
YL-BAL	Avro RJ70	Air Baltic	
YL-BAN	Avro RJ70	Air Baltic	
YL-BAP	SAAB SF.340A	Air Baltic	
YL-BAR	Fokker 50	Air Baltic	
YL-LAB	Tupolev Tu-154B-2	Latpass Airlines	
YL-LAJ	Ilyushin IL-76T	Inversia	
YL-LAK	Ilyushin IL-76T	Inversia	
YL-LAL	Ilyushin IL-76T	Inversia	
YL-LBA	Tupolev Tu-134A	Latavio	
YL-LBE	Tupolev Tu-134B-3	LAT Charter	
YL-LBG	Tupolev Tu-134B-3	LAT Charter	
YL-LBI	Tupolev Tu-134B-3	Baltic Express Line	
YL-RAA	Antonov An-26	RAF-Avia	
YL-RAB	Antonov An-26	RAF-Avia	
YL-RAC	Antonov An-26	RAF-Avia	

YR (Romania)

YR-ABC	Boeing 707-3K1C	TAROM	
YR-BGA	Boeing 737-38J	TAROM *Alba Lulia*	
YR-BGB	Boeing 737-38J	TAROM *Bucuresti*	
YR-BGC	Boeing 737-38J	TAROM *Constanta*	
YR-BGD	Boeing 737-38J	TAROM *Deva*	
YR-BGE	Boeing 737-38J	TAROM *Timisoara*	
YR-BGF	Boeing 737-78J	TAROM	
YR-BGG	Boeing 737-78J	TAROM	
YR-BGX	Boeing 737-36Q	TAROM *Galati*	
YR-BGY	Boeing 737-36M	TAROM	
YR-BRC	RomBac One-Eleven 561RC	TAROM	
YR-JBA	BAC One-Eleven 528FL	Jaro International	
YR-JBB	BAC One-Eleven 528FL	Jaro International	
YR-JCB	Boeing 707-321B	Jaro International	
YR-LCA	Airbus A.310-325	TAROM *Transilvania*	
YR-LCB	Airbus A.310-325	TAROM *Moldova*	
YR-TPB	Tupolev Tu-154B-1	TAROM	
YR-TPG	Tupolev Tu-154B-1	TAROM	

YU (Yugoslavia)

YU-AHN	Douglas DC-9-32	Jugoslovenski Aerotransport (JAT)	

Notes	Reg.	Type	Owner or Operator
	YU-AHU	Douglas DC-9-32	JAT
	YU-AHV	Douglas DC-9-32	JAT
	YU-AJH	Douglas DC-9-32	JAT/Bellview Airlines
	YU-AJI	Douglas DC-9-32	JAT/Bellview Airlines
	YU-AJJ	Douglas DC-9-32	JAT/Bellview Airlines
	YU-AJK	Douglas DC-9-32	JAT/Bellview Airlines
	YU-AJL	Douglas DC-9-32	JAT/Macedonian Air Transport
	YU-AJM	Douglas DC-9-32	JAT/Bellview Airlines
	YU-AKB	Boeing 727-2H9	JAT
	YU-AKD	Boeing 727-2L8	Aviogenex *Split*
	YU-AKE	Boeing 727-2H9	JAT
	YU-AKF	Boeing 727-2H9	JAT
	YU-AKG	Boeing 727-2H9	JAT
	YU-AKH	Boeing 727-2L8	Aviogenex *Dubrovnik*
	YU-AKI	Boeing 727-2H9	JAT
	YU-AKJ	Boeing 727-2H9	JAT
	YU-AKK	Boeing 727-2H9	JAT
	YU-AKL	Boeing 727-2H9	JAT
	YU-AKM	Boeing 727-243	Aviogenex *Pula*
	YU-ALN	Aérospatiale ATR-72-201	JAT
	YU-ALO	Aérospatiale ATR-72-201	JAT
	YU-ALP	Aérospatiale ATR-72-201	JAT
	YU-AMB	Douglas DC-10-30	JAT *Edvard Rusijan*
	YU-AND	Boeing 737-3H9	JAT
	YU-ANF	Boeing 737-3H9	JAT
	YU-ANJ	Boeing 737-3H9	JAT
	YU-ANK	Boeing 737-3H9	JAT
	YU-ANP	Boeing 737-2K3	Aviogenex *Zadar*
	YU-ANV	Boeing 737-3H9	JAT
	YU-ANW	Boeing 737-3H9	JAT
	YU-AOK	Fokker 100	Montenegro Airlines
	YU-AOL	Fokker 100	Montenegro Airlines

YV (Venezuela)

YV-50C	Douglas DC-10-30	Avensa

Z (Zimbabwe)

Z-WPE	Boeing 767-2N0ER	Air Zimbabwe *Victoria Falls*
Z-WPF	Boeing 767-2N0ER	Air Zimbabwe *Chimanimani*

ZA (Albania)

Note: Albanian Airlines operates the Tupolov Tu-134s LZ-TUJ, LZ-TUN and LZ-TUT on lease from Hemus Air.

Z3 (Macedonia)

Z3-AAA	Boeing 737-3H9	Macedonian Airlines
Z3-AAB	Douglas DC-9-32	Macedonian Airlines
Z3-ARE	Douglas DC-9-32	Macedonian Airlines
Z3-ARF	Boeing 737-3H9	Macedonian Airlines

Note: Macedonian Airlines also operates Boeing 737-400s SX-BMA, SX-BMB and SX-BMC together with the Boeing 727s SX-CBG and SX-CBH.

ZK (New Zealand)

ZK-NBS	Boeing 747-419	Air New Zealand
ZK-NBT	Boeing 747-419	Air New Zealand
ZK-NBU	Boeing 747-419	Air New Zealand
ZK-NBV	Boeing 747-419	Air New Zealand
ZK-NBW	Boeing 747-419	Air New Zealand
ZK-SUH	Boeing 747-475	Air New Zealand
ZK-SUI	Boeing 747-441	Air New Zealand
ZK-SUJ	Boeing 747-4F6	Air New Zealand

Reg.	Type	Owner or Operator	Notes

ZS (South Africa)

ZS-JIV	L.100-30 Hercules	Safair
ZS-JIX	L.100-30 Hercules	Safair
ZS-JIY	L.100-30 Hercules	Safair
ZS-JIZ	L.100-30 Hercules	Safair
ZS-JVL	L.100-30 Hercules	Safair
ZS-OKK	Boeing 747-312 (SCD)	African Star Airways
ZS-	Boeing 747-312	African Star Airways
ZS-RSC	L.100-30 Hercules	Safair
ZS-RSI	L.100-30 Hercules	Safair
ZS-SAC	Boeing 747-312	South African Airways *Shosholoza*
ZS-SAJ	Boeing 747-312	South African Airways
ZS-SAK	Boeing 747-444	South African Airways *Ebhayi*
ZS-SAL	Boeing 747-244B	South African Airways *Tafelberg*
ZS-SAM	Boeing 747-244B	South African Airways *Drakensberg*
ZS-SAN	Boeing 747-244B	South African Airways *Lebombo*
ZS-SAO	Boeing 747-244B	South African Airways *Magaliesberg*
ZS-SAP	Boeing 747-244B	South African Airways *Swartberg*
ZS-SAT	Boeing 747-344	South African Airways
ZS-SAU	Boeing 747-344	South African Airways *Cape Town*
ZS-SAV	Boeing 747-444	South African Airways *Durban*
ZS-SAW	Boeing 747-444	South African Airways *Bloemfontein*
ZS-SAX	Boeing 747-444	South African Airways
ZS-SAY	Boeing 747-444	South African Airways *Vulindlela*
ZS-SAZ	Boeing 747-444	South African Airways
ZS-SBK	Boeing 747-4F6	South African Airways
ZS-SBS	Boeing 747-4F6	South African Airways
ZS-SKA	Boeing 747-357	South African Airways
ZS-SKB	Boeing 747-357	South African Airways
ZS-SPA	Boeing 747SP-44	South African Airways
ZS-SPC	Boeing 747SP-44	South African Airways/Air Namibia
ZS-SPE	Boeing 747SP-44	South African Airways *Hantarn*
ZS-SRA	Boeing 767-266ER	South African Airways
ZS-SRB	Boeing 767-266ER	South African Airways
ZS-SRC	Boeing 767-266ER	South African Airways

3B (Mauritius)

3B-NAK	Boeing 767-23BER	Air Mauritius *City of Curepipe*
3B-NAL	Boeing 767-23BER	Air Mauritius *City of Port Louis*
3B-NAU	Airbus A.340-312	Air Mauritius *Pink Pigeon*
3B-NAV	Airbus A.340-312	Air Mauritius *Kestrel*
3B-NAY	Airbus A.340-313	Air Mauritius *Cardinal*
3B-NBD	Airbus A.340-313X	Air Mauritius
3B-NBE	Airbus A.340-313X	Air Mauritius
3B-STI	Airbus A.310-222	Middle East Airlines
3B-STJ	Airbus A.310-222	Middle East Airlines
3B-STK	Airbus A.310-222	Middle East Airlines

3D (Swaziland)

3D-ADV	Douglas DC-8-54F	African International Airways
3D-AFR	Douglas DC-8-54F	African International Airways
3D-CSB	Boeing 707-373C	Tradewinds Cargo

Reg.	Type	Notes	Reg.	Type	Notes

4K (Azerbaijan)

The following are operated by Azerbaijan Airlines with the registrations prefixed by 4K.

Reg.	Type		Reg.	Type	
AZ1	Boeing 727-235		65709	Tu-134B-3	
AZ8	Boeing 727-230		65710	Tu-134B-3	
AZ10	Tu-154M		65711	Tu-134B-3	
AZ12	Boeing 757-22L		65712	Tu-134B-3	
AZ14	IL-76TD		65713	Tu-134B-3	
65702	Tu-134B-3		65714	Tu-134B-3	
65705	Tu-134B-3		85147	Tu-154B-1	
65708	Tu-134B-3		85158	Tu-154B-1	

Notes	Reg.	Type	Notes	Reg.	Type
	85177	Tu-154B-1		85364	Tu-154B-2
	85192	Tu-154B-1		85391	Tu-154B-2
	85199	Tu-154B-1		85538	Tu-154B-2
	85211	Tu-154B-1		85548	Tu-154B-2
	85214	Tu-154B-1		85698	Tu-154M
	85250	Tu-154B-1		85729	Tu-154M
	85274	Tu-154B-1		85734	Tu-154M
	85329	Tu-154B-2			

Note: Azerbaijan Airways also operates the Boeing 757s VP-BBR & VP-BBS.

4L (Georgia)

The following registrations are prefixed by 4L with the aircraft operated by Adjarian Airlines (ADJ), Air Georgia (GEO), Air Zena (TGZ) or Orbi Georgia (DVU).

AAB	Tu-134B-3 (ADJ)		65857	Tu-134A-3 (DVU)
AAD	Tu-134B-3 (ADJ)		85168	Tu-154B (TGZ)
AAF	Tu-154M (DVU)		85430	Tu-154B-2 (DVU)
AAG	Tu-154B-2 (GEO)		85496	Tu-154B-2 (DVU)
AAH	Tu-154B-2 (GEO)		85518	Tu-154B-2 (DVU)
65750	Tu-134A-3 (DVU)		85547	Tu-154B-2 (GEO)
65774	Tu-134A-3 (DVU)		85558	Tu-154B-2 (GEO)
65798	Tu-134A-3 (DVU)			

Notes	Reg.	Type	Owner or Operator

4R (Sri Lanka)

4R-ADA	Airbus A.340-311	SriLankan Airlines
4R-ADB	Airbus A.340-311	SriLankan Airlines
4R-ADC	Airbus A.340-311	SriLankan Airlines
4R-ALA	Airbus A.330-243	SriLankan Airlines
4R-ALB	Airbus A.330-243	SriLankan Airlines
4R-ALC	Airbus A.330-243	SriLankan Airlines
4R-ALD	Airbus A.330-243	SriLankan Airlines
4R-ALG	Airbus A.330-243	SriLankan Airlines
4R-ALH	Airbus A.330-243	SriLankan Airlines
4R-ALI	Airbus A.330-243	SriLankan Airlines

4X (Israel)

4X-AVX	Aérospatiale ATR-72-212A	Arkia
4X-AXC	Boeing 747-258B	El Al
4X-AXD	Boeing 747-258C	Hydro Air Cargo
4X-AXF	Boeing 747-258C	El Al
4X-AXH	Boeing 747-258B (SCD)	El Al
4X-AXK	Boeing 747-245F (SCD)	Cargo Air lines
4X-AXL	Boeing 747-245F (SCD)	Cargo Air lines
4X-AXQ	Boeing 747-238B	El Al
4X-BAU	Boeing 757-3E7	Arkia
4X-BAW	Boeing 757-3E7	Arkia
4X-BAY	Boeing 757-2Y0	Arkia
4X-BAZ	Boeing 757-236	Arkia
4X-EAA	Boeing 767-258	El Al
4X-EAB	Boeing 767-258	El Al
4X-EAC	Boeing 767-258ER	El Al
4X-EAD	Boeing 767-258ER	El Al
4X-EAE	Boeing 767-27EER	El Al
4X-EAF	Boeing 767-27EER	El Al
4X-EBI	Boeing 757-258	El Al
4X-EBM	Boeing 757-258	El Al/Arkia
4X-EBS	Boeing 757-258	El Al
4X-EBT	Boeing 757-258	El Al
4X-EBU	Boeing 757-258	El Al
4X-EBV	Boeing 757-258	El Al
4X-ECA	Boeing 777-258	El Al
4X-ECB	Boeing 777-258	El Al
4X-ECC	Boeing 777-258	El Al
4X-EKA	Boeing 737-858	El Al
4X-EKB	Boeing 737-858	El Al
4X-EKC	Boeing 737-858	El Al

Reg.	Type	Owner or Operator	Notes
4X-EKD	Boeing 737-758	El Al	
4X-EKE	Boeing 737-758	El Al	
4X-ELA	Boeing 747-458	El Al	
4X-ELB	Boeing 747-458	El Al	
4X-ELC	Boeing 747-458	El Al	
4X-ELD	Boeing 747-458	El Al	
4X-ICL	Boeing 747-271C	Cargo Air Lines	

5A (Libya)

5A-AGU	Airbus A.310-203	Libyan Arab Airlines	
5A-DIB	Boeing 727-2L5	Libyan Arab Airlines	
5A-DIC	Boeing 727-2L5	Libyan Arab Airlines	
5A-DID	Boeing 727-2L5	Libyan Arab Airlines	
5A-DIE	Boeing 727-2L5	Libyan Arab Airlines	
5A-DIF	Boeing 727-2L5	Libyan Arab Airlines	
5A-DIG	Boeing 727-2L5	Libyan Aran Airlines	
5A-DIH	Boeing 727-2L5	Libyan Arab Airlines	
5A-DII	Boeing 727-2L5	Libyan Arab Airlines	
5A-DKR	Ilyushin IL-62M	Libyan Arab Airlines	
5A-DNK	Ilyushin IL-76T	Libyan Arab Air Cargo	
5A-DNU	Ilyushin IL-76T	Libyan Arab Air Cargo	
5A-	Airbus A.320-	Libyan Arab Airlines	
5A-DTG	F.28 Fellowship 4000	Libyan Arab Airlines	
5A-DTH	F.28 Fellowship 4000	Libyan Arab Airlines	
5A-DTI	F.28 Fellowship 4000	Libyan Arab Airlines	

Note: Libyan Arab also operates Airbus A.310s F-OHPQ, F-OHPU, JY-AGU and JY-AGV. Two A300-622R (JY-GAX and JY-GAZ) are also operated by Royal Jordanian on behalf of Libyan Arab.

5B (Cyprus)

5B-DAQ	Airbus A.310-203	Cyprus Airways *Soli*	
5B-DAR	Airbus A.310-203	Cyprus Airways *Aepia*	
5B-DAS	Airbus A.310-203	Cyprus Airways *Salamis*	
5B-DAT	Airbus A.320-231	Cyprus Airways *Praxandros*	
5B-DAU	Airbus A.320-231	Cyprus Airways *Evelthon*	
5B-DAV	Airbus A.320-231	Cyprus Airways *Kinyras*	
5B-DAW	Airbus A.320-231	Cyprus Airways *Agapinor*	
5B-DAX	Airbus A.310-204	Cyprus Airways *Engomi*	
5B-DAZ	Boeing 707-328C	Avistar	
5B-DBA	Airbus A.320-231	Cyprus Airways *Evagoras*	
5B-DBB	Airbus A.320-231	Eurocypria Airways *Akamas*	
5B-DBC	Airbus A.320-231	Eurocypria Airways *Tefkros*	
5B-DBD	Airbus A.320-231	Eurocypria Airways *Onosilos*	
5B-DBG	Boeing 737-86N	Helios Airways	
5B-DBH	Boeing 737-86N	Helios Airways	
5B-DBI	Boeing 737-86N	Helios Airways	
5B-DBJ	Airbus A.320-231	Eurocypria Airways	
5B-DBK	Airbus A.320-231	Eurocypria Airways	

5N (Nigeria)

5N-AAA	Boeing 747-148	Kabo Air	
5N-ANN	Douglas DC-10-30	Nigeria Airways *Yunkari*	
5N-AOO	Boeing 707-351C	Air Atlantic Cargo	
5N-BBF	Boeing 727-231	ADC Airlines	
5N-BDU	BAC One-Eleven 523FJ	Savannah Airlines	
5N-BDV	BAC One-Eleven 530FX	Savannah Airlines	
5N-BVU	Airbus A.300-600R	Bellview Airlines	
5N-EDO	Boeing 747-146	Okada Air *Lady Cherry*	
5N-EEE	Boeing 747-243B	Kabo Air	
5N-EEO	Boeing 707-321C	Air Atlantic Cargo	
5N-JJJ	Boeing 747-136	Kabo Air	
5N-NNN	Boeing 747-287B	Kabo Air	
5N-OOO	Boeing 747-136	Kabo Air	
5N-PDP	Boeing 747-238B	Kabo Air	
5N-PPP	Boeing 747-238B	Kabo Air	
5N-RRR	Boeing 747-136	Kabo Air	
5N-TKE	Boeing 727-82	Triax Airlines *Eze-Ukpo*	

Notes	Reg.	Type	Owner or Operator
	5N-TKT	Boeing 727-22	Triax Airlines
	5N-TNO	Boeing 707-369C	Air Atlantic Cargo
	5N-TTK	Boeing 727-264	Triax Airlines *Chinweze*

Note: Nigeria Airways also operates the Boeing 747-312 TF-ATS on lease from Air Atlanta Iceland

5R (Madagascar)

	5R-MFD	Boeing 767-33AER	Air Madagascar
	5R-MFT	Boeing 747-2B2B (SCD)	Air Madagascar *Ankoay*

5X (Uganda)

	5X-JET	Boeing 707-351C	DAS Air Cargo
	5X-JOE	Douglas DC-10-30F	DAS Air Cargo

Note: DAS Air Cargo also operates Douglas DC-10-30Fs registered N335SJ, N400JR, N401JR and N402JR.

5Y (Kenya)

	5Y-AXI	Boeing 707-330B	African Airlines International
	5Y-BEL	Airbus A.310-304	Kenya Airways *Nyayo Star*
	5Y-BFT	Airbus A.310-304	Kenya Airways *Uhuru Star*
	5Y-BOR	Boeing 707-399C	First International Airlines
	5Y-KQL	Airbus A.310-304	Kenya Airways
	5Y-KQX	Boeing 767-36NER	Kenya Airways
	5Y-KQY	Boeing 767-36NER	Kenya Airways
	5Y-KQZ	Boeing 767-36NER	Kenya Airways
	5Y-MBA	Douglas DC-10-30	African Safari Airways
	5Y-SIM	Boeing 707-336C	Simba Air Cargo
	VH-NOA	Boeing 767-33AER	Kenya Airways

6Y (Jamaica)

	6Y-JAB	Airbus A.310-324	Air Jamaica
	6Y-JAC	Airbus A.310-324	Air Jamaica
	6Y-JAD	Airbus A.310-324	Air Jamaica
	6Y-JAE	Airbus A.310-324	Air Jamaica
	6Y-JMC	Airbus A.340-312	Air Jamaica

7O (Yemen)

	7O-ACV	Boeing 727-2N8	Yemenia
	7O-ACW	Boeing 727-2N8	Yemenia
	7O-ACX	Boeing 727-2N8	Yemenia
	7O-ACY	Boeing 727-2N8	Yemenia
	7O-ADA	Boeing 727-2N8	Yemenia
	7O-ADF	Iluyshin IL-76TD	Yemenia
	7O-ADJ	Airbus A.310-324	Yemenia

Note: Yemenia also operates Airbus A.310s registered F-OGYO, F-OHPR and F-OHPS.

7T (Algeria)

	7T-VEA	Boeing 727-2D6	Air Algerie *Tassili*
	7T-VEB	Boeing 727-2D6	Air Algerie *Hoggar*
	7T-VED	Boeing 737-2D6C	Air Algerie *Atlas Saharien*
	7T-VEF	Boeing 737-2D6	Air Algerie *Saoura*
	7T-VEG	Boeing 737-2D6	Air Algerie *Monts des Ouleds Neils*
	7T-VEH	Boeing 727-2D6	Air Algerie *Lalla Khadidja*
	7T-VEI	Boeing 727-2D6	Air Algerie *Djebel Amour*
	7T-VEJ	Boeing 737-2D6	Air Algerie *Chrea*
	7T-VEK	Boeing 737-2D6	Air Algerie *Edough*
	7T-VEL	Boeing 737-2D6	Air Algerie *Akfadou*
	7T-VEM	Boeing 727-2D6	Air Algerie *Mont du Ksall*
	7T-VEN	Boeing 737-2D6	Air Algerie *La Soummam*
	7T-VEO	Boeing 737-2D6	Air Algerie *La Titteri*
	7T-VEP	Boeing 727-2D6	Air Algerie *Mont du Tessala*

Reg.	Type	Owner or Operator	Notes
7T-VEQ	Boeing 737-2D6	Air Algerie *Le Zaccar*	
7T-VER	Boeing 737-2D6	Air Algerie *Le Souf*	
7T-VES	Boeing 737-2D6C	Air Algerie *Le Tadmaït*	
7T-VET	Boeing 727-2D6	Air Algerie *Georges du Rhumel*	
7T-VEU	Boeing 727-2D6	Air Algerie *Djurdjura*	
7T-VEV	Boeing 727-2D6	Air Algerie	
7T-VEW	Boeing 727-2D6	Air Algerie *Monts de Tlemcen*	
7T-VEX	Boeing 727-2D6	Air Algerie *Djemila*	
7T-VEY	Boeing 737-2D6	Air Algerie *Rhoufi*	
7T-VEZ	Boeing 737-2T4	Air Algerie *Monts du Daia*	
7T-VHG	L.100-30 Hercules	Air Algerie	
7T-VHL	L.100-30 Hercules	Air Algerie	
7T-VJB	Boeing 737-2T4	Air Algerie *Monts des Bibans*	
7T-VJC	Airbus A.310-203	Air Algerie	
7T-VJD	Airbus A.310-203	Air Algerie	
7T-VJG	Boeing 767-3D6	Air Algerie	
7T-VJH	Boeing 767-3D6	Air Algerie	
7T-VJI	Boeing 767-3D6	Air Algerie	
7T-VJJ	Boeing 737-8D6	Air Algerie *Jugurtha*	
7T-VJK	Boeing 737-8D6	Air Algerie *Mansourah*	
7T-VJL	Boeing 737-200	Air Algerie	
7T-VJM	Boeing 737-8D6	Air Algerie	
7T-VJN	Boeing 737-8D6	Air Algerie	
7T-VJO	Boeing 737-8D6	Air Algerie	
7T-VJP	Boeing 737-8D6	Air Algerie	
7T-VJQ	Boeing 737-6D6	Air Algerie	
7T-VJR	Boeing 737-6D6	Air Algerie	
7T-VJS	Boeing 737-6D6	Air Algerie	
7T-VJT	Boeing 737-6D6	Air Algerie	
7T-VJU	Boeing 737-6D6	Air Algerie	
7T-VVA	Boeing 737-200	Antinea Airline	

Note: Khalifa Airways operates a large fleet of aircraft most of which are at present registered in the lessors' country. These include Airbus A310s F-OGYM, F-OGYN, F-OGYS, F-OHPU, F-OHPV, F-OHPY and F-OIHS. The Airbus A300 SU-BMZ is employed as a freighter, while short-haul work is handled by Boeing 737s TC-APD, TC-APT and TC-APY. The airline has a number of Airbus A319s, A320s, A330s and A340s on order. Three a319s are leased from Lufthansa (D-AILH, D-AILI and D-AILK) until mid 2002.

9A (Croatia)

9A-CTF	Airbus A.320-211	Croatia Airlines *Rijeka*	
9A-CTG	Airbus A.319-112	Croatia Airlines *Zadar*	
9A-CTH	Airbus A.319-112	Croatia Airlines	
9A-CTI	Airbus A.319-112	Croatia Airlines *Vukovar*	
9A-CTJ	Airbus A.320-214	Croatia Airlines *Dubrovnik*	
9A-CTK	Airbus A.320-214	Croatia Airlines *Split*	
9A-CTL	Airbus A.319-112	Croatia Airlines	

9G (Ghana)

9G-ADM	Boeing 707-321C	Continental Cargo Airlines	
9G-ADS	Boeing 707-323C	Continental Cargo Airlines	
9G-ANA	Douglas DC-10-30	Ghana Airways	
9G-ANB	Douglas DC-10-30	Ghana Airways	
9G-ANC	Douglas DC-10-30	Ghana Airways	
9G-CDG	Douglas DC-8-55F	Continental Cargo Airlines	
9G-LAD	Boeing 707-323C	Johnsons Air/First International Airlines	
9G-LCA	Canadair CL-44-0	Johnsons Air/First International Airlines	
9G-MKA	Douglas DC-8-55F	MK Airlines	
9G-MKC	Douglas DC-8-55F	MK Airlines	
9G-MKE	Douglas DC-8-55F	MK Airlines	
9G-MKF	Douglas DC-8-55F	MK Airlines	
9G-MKG	Douglas DC-8-62F	MK Airlines	
9G-MKH	Douglas DC-8-62AF	MK Airlines	
9G-MKJ	Boeing 747-244B (SCD)	MK Airlines	
9G-MKK	Douglas DC-8-62AF	MK Airlines	
9G-MKL	Boeing 747-212F	MK Airlines	
9G-OLD	Boeing 707-324C	Johnsons Air/First International Airways	
9G-PHN	Douglas DC-10-30	Ghana Airways/Skyjet	

Notes	Reg.	Type	Owner or Operator

9H (Malta)

	Reg.	Type	Owner or Operator
	9H-ABE	Boeing 737-2Y5	Air Malta *Alof de Wignacourt*
	9H-ABF	Boeing 737-2Y5	Air Malta *Manuel Pinto*
	9H-ABP	Airbus A.320-211	Air Malta *Nicholas de Cottoner*
	9H-ABQ	Airbus A.320-211	Air Malta *Hughes Loubenx de Verdelle*
	9H-ABR	Boeing 737-3Y5	Air Malta *Juan de Homedes*
	9H-ABS	Boeing 737-3Y5	Air Malta *Antoines de Paule*
	9H-ABT	Boeing 737-3Y5	Air Malta *Ferdinand von Hompesch*
	9H-ADH	Boeing 737-33A	Air Malta
	9H-ADI	Boeing 737-33A	Air Malta
	9H-ADM	Boeing 737-382	Air Malta
	9H-ADN	Boeing 737-382	Air Malta
	9H-ADO	Boeing 737-430	Air Malta

Note: Air Malta usually leases-in one or two aircraft for the summer season.

9K (Kuwait)

	Reg.	Type	Owner or Operator
	9K-ADB	Boeing 747-269B (SCD)	Kuwait Airways
	9K-ADD	Boeing 747-269B (SCD)	Kuwait Airways *Al-Salmiya*
	9K-ADE	Boeing 747-469 (SCD)	Kuwait Airways *Al-Jabariya*
	9K-AGC	McD Douglas MD-83	Kuwait Government
	9K-AHI	Airbus A.300C4-620	Kuwait Airways
	9K-ALA	Airbus A.310-308	Kuwait Airways *Al-Jahra*
	9K-ALB	Airbus A.310-308	Kuwait Airways *Gharnada*
	9K-ALD	Airbus A.310-308	Kuwait Government *Al-Salmiya*
	9K-AMA	Airbus A.300B4-605R	Kuwait Airways *Failaka*
	9K-AMB	Airbus A.300B4-605R	Kuwait Airways *Burghan*
	9K-AMC	Airbus A.300B4-605R	Kuwait Airways *Wafra*
	9K-AMD	Airbus A.300B4-605R	Kuwait Airways *Wara*
	9K-AME	Airbus A.300B4-605R	Kuwait Airways *Al-Rawdhatain*
	9K-ANA	Airbus A.340-313	Kuwait Airways *Warba*
	9K-ANB	Airbus A.340-313	Kuwait Airways *Al-Sabahiya*
	9K-ANC	Airbus A.340-313	Kuwait Airways *Al-Mobarakiya*
	9K-AND	Airbus A.340-313	Kuwait Airways *Al-Riggah*
	9K-AOA	Boeing 777-269ER	Kuwait Airways
	9K-AOB	Boeing 777-269ER	Kuwait Airways

9M (Malaysia)

	Reg.	Type	Owner or Operator
	9M-MHI	Boeing 747-236F (SCD)	Malaysian Airlines Cargo *Kuching*
	9M-MHJ	Boeing 747-236F (SCD)	Malaysian Airlines Cargo *Johor Bahru*
	9M-MHL	Boeing 747-4H6 (SCD)	Malaysian Airlines *Kuala Lumpur*
	9M-MHM	Boeing 747-4H6 (SCD)	Malaysian Airlines *Penang*
	9M-MHN	Boeing 747-4H6	Malaysian Airlines *Mallaca*
	9M-MPA	Boeing 747-4H6	Malaysian Airlines *Ipoh*
	9M-MPB	Boeing 747-4H6	Malaysian Airlines *Shah Alam*
	9M-MPC	Boeing 747-4H6	Malaysian Airlines *Kuantan*
	9M-MPD	Boeing 747-4H6	Malaysian Airlines *Serembam*
	9M-MPE	Boeing 747-4H6	Malaysian Airlines *Kangar*
	9M-MPF	Boeing 747-4H6	Malaysian Airlines *Kota Bharu*
	9M-MPG	Boeing 747-4H6	Malaysian Airlines *Kuala Terengganu*
	9M-MPH	Boeing 747-4H6	Malaysian Airlines *Langkawi*
	9M-MPI	Boeing 747-4H6	Malaysian Airlines
	9M-MPJ	Boeing 747-4H6	Malaysian Airlines
	9M-MPK	Boeing 747-4H6	Malaysian Airlines
	9M-MPL	Boeing 747-4H6	Malaysian Airlines
	9M-MPM	Boeing 747-4H6	Malaysian Airlines
	9M-MPN	Boeing 747-4H6	Malaysian Airlines
	9M-MPO	Boeing 747-4H6	Malaysian Airlines
	9M-MPP	Boeing 747-4H6	Malaysian Airlines
	9M-MPQ	Boeing 747-4H6	Malaysian Airlines
	9M-MPR	Boeing 747-4H6	Malaysian Airlines
	9M-MPS	Boeing 747-4H6	Malaysian Airlines
	9M-MPT	Boeing 747-4H6	Malaysian Airlines
	9M-MRA	Boeing 777-2H6ER	Malaysian Airlines
	9M-MRB	Boeing 777-2H6ER	Malaysian Airlines
	9M-MRC	Boeing 777-2H6ER	Malaysian Airlines
	9M-MRD	Boeing 777-2H6ER	Malaysian Airlines
	9M-MRE	Boeing 777-2H6ER	Malaysian Airlines

Reg.	Type	Owner or Operator	Notes
9M-MRF	Boeing 777-2H6ER	Malaysian Airlines	
9M-MRG	Boeing 777-2H6ER	Malaysian Airlines	
9M-MRH	Boeing 777-2H6ER	Malaysian Airlines	
9M-MRI	Boeing 777-2H6ER	Malaysian Airlines	
9M-MRJ	Boeing 777-2H6ER	Malaysian Airlines	
9M-MRK	Boeing 777-2H6ER	Malaysian Airlines	
9M-MRL	Boeing 777-2H6ER	Malaysian Airlines	
9M-MRM	Boeing 777-2H6ER	Malaysian Airlines	
9M-MRN	Boeing 777-2H6ER	Malaysian Airlines	
9M-MRO	Boeing 777-2H6ER	Malaysian Airlines	
9M-MRP	Boeing 777-2H6ER	Malaysian Airlines	
9M-MRQ	Boeing 777-2H6ER	Malaysian Airlines	

9N (Nepal)

9N-ACA	Boeing 757-2F8	Royal Nepal Airlines
9N-ACB	Boeing 757-2F8C	Royal Nepal Airlines

9Q (Congo)

9Q-BAN	Douglas DC-8-62CF	Air Cargo Chartering
9Q-CKB	Boeing 707-366C	Congo Airlines
9Q-CLK	Boeing 707-138B	Government of Congo
9Q-CQC	Boeing 707-323C	Government of Congo

9V (Singapore)

9V-SFA	Boeing 747-412F (SCD)	Singapore Airlines
9V-SFB	Boeing 747-412F (SCD)	Singapore Airlines
9V-SFC	Boeing 747-412F (SCD)	Singapore Airlines
9V-SFD	Boeing 747-412F (SCD)	Singapore Airlines
9V-SFE	Boeing 747-412F (SCD)	Singapore Airlines
9V-SFF	Boeing 747-412F (SCD)	Singapore Airlines
9V-SFG	Boeing 747-412F (SCD)	Singapore Airlines
9V-SFH	Boeing 747-412F (SCD)	Singapore Airlines
9V-SFI	Boeing 747-412F (SCD)	Singapore Airlines
9V-SFJ	Boeing 747-412F (SCD)	Singapore Airlines
9V-SKJ	Boeing 747-312 (SCD)	Singapore Airlines
9V-SJD	Airbus A.340-313X	Singapore Airlines
9V-SJE	Airbus A.340-313X	Singapore Airlines
9V-SJF	Airbus A.340-313X	Singapore Airlines
9V-SJG	Airbus A.340-313X	Singapore Airlines
9V-SJH	Airbus A.340-313X	Singapore Airlines
9V-SJI	Airbus A.340-313X	Singapore Airlines
9V-SJJ	Airbus A.340-313X	Singapore Airlines
9V-SJK	Airbus A.340-313X	Singapore Airlines
9V-SJL	Airbus A.340-313X	Singapore Airlines
9V-SJM	Airbus A.340-313X	Singapore Airlines
9V-SJN	Airbus A.340-313X	Singapore Airlines
9V-SJO	Airbus A.340-313X	Singapore Airlines
9V-SJP	Airbus A.340-313X	Singapore Airlines
9V-SJQ	Airbus A.340-313X	Singapore Airlines
9V-SMA	Boeing 747-412	Singapore Airlines
9V-SMB	Boeing 747-412	Singapore Airlines
9V-SMC	Boeing 747-412	Singapore Airlines
9V-SME	Boeing 747-412	Singapore Airlines
9V-SMF	Boeing 747-412	Singapore Airlines
9V-SMG	Boeing 747-412	Singapore Airlines
9V-SMH	Boeing 747-412	Singapore Airlines
9V-SMI	Boeing 747-412	Singapore Airlines
9V-SMJ	Boeing 747-412	Singapore Airlines
9V-SMK	Boeing 747-412	Singapore Airlines
9V-SML	Boeing 747-412	Singapore Airlines
9V-SMM	Boeing 747-412	Singapore Airlines
9V-SMN	Boeing 747-412	Singapore Airlines
9V-SMO	Boeing 747-412	Singapore Airlines
9V-SMP	Boeing 747-412	Singapore Airlines
9V-SMQ	Boeing 747-412	Singapore Airlines
9V-SMR	Boeing 747-412	Singapore Airlines
9V-SMS	Boeing 747-412	Singapore Airlines

Notes	Reg.	Type	Owner or Operator
	9V-SMT	Boeing 747-412	Singapore Airlines
	9V-SMU	Boeing 747-412	Singapore Airlines
	9V-SMV	Boeing 747-412	Singapore Airlines
	9V-SMW	Boeing 747-412	Singapore Airlines
	9V-SMY	Boeing 747-412	Singapore Airlines
	9V-SMZ	Boeing 747-412	Singapore Airlines
	9V-SPA	Boeing 747-412	Singapore Airlines
	9V-SPB	Boeing 747-412	Singapore Airlines
	9V-SPC	Boeing 747-412	Singapore Airlines
	9V-SPD	Boeing 747-412	Singapore Airlines
	9V-SPE	Boeing 747-412	Singapore Airlines
	9V-SPF	Boeing 747-412	Singapore Airlines
	9V-SPG	Boeing 747-412	Singapore Airlines
	9V-SPH	Boeing 747-412	Singapore Airlines
	9V-SPI	Boeing 747-412	Singapore Airlines
	9V-SPJ	Boeing 747-412	Singapore Airlines
	9V-SPL	Boeing 747-412	Singapore Airlines
	9V-SPM	Boeing 747-412	Singapore Airlines
	9V-SPN	Boeing 747-412	Singapore Airlines
	9V-SPO	Boeing 747-412	Singapore Airlines
	9V-SPP	Boeing 747-412	Singapore Airlines
	9V-SPQ	Boeing 747-412	Singapore Airlines
	9V-SRA	Boeing 777-212ER	Singapore Airlines
	9V-SRB	Boeing 777-212ER	Singapore Airlines
	9V-SRC	Boeing 777-212ER	Singapore Airlines
	9V-SRD	Boeing 777-212ER	Singapore Airlines
	9V-SRE	Boeing 777-212ER	Singapore Airlines
	9V-SRF	Boeing 777-212ER	Singapore Airlines
	9V-SRG	Boeing 777-212ER	Singapore Airlines
	9V-SRH	Boeing 777-212ER	Singapore Airlines
	9V-SRI	Boeing 777-212ER	Singapore Airlines
	9V-SRJ	Boeing 777-212ER	Singapore Airlines
	9V-SRL	Boeing 777-212ER	Singapore Ailrines
	9V-SVA	Boeing 777-212ER	Singapore Airlines
	9V-SVB	Boeing 777-212ER	Singapore Airlines
	9V-SVC	Boeing 777-212ER	Singapore Airlines
	9V-SVD	Boeing 777-212ER	Singapore Airlines
	9V-SVE	Boeing 777-212ER	Singapore Airlines
	9V-SVH	Boeing 777-212ER	Singapore Airlines
	9V-SVI	Boeing 777-212ER	Singapore Airlines
	9V-SVJ	Boeing 777-212ER	Singapore Airlines
	9V-SVK	Boeing 777-212ER	Singapore Airlines

9Y (Trinidad and Tobago)

9Y-TGJ	L.1011-385 TriStar 500 (595)	B.W.I.A. West Indies Airways
9Y-TGN	L.1011-385 TriStar 500 (596)	B.W.I.A. West Indies Airways
9Y-THA	L.1011-385 TriStar 500 (597)	B.W.I.A. West Indies Airways

Note: B.W.I.A. West Indies Airways also operates a TriStar 500 which retains the registration N3140D (598).

Overseas Registrations

Aircraft included in this section are those based in the UK but which retain their non-British identities.

A4O-AB	V.1103 VC10 ★	Brooklands Museum of Aviation (G-ASIX)
CF-EQS	Boeing-Stearman PT-17 (217786) ★	Imperial War Museum/Duxford
CF-KCG	Grumman TBM-3E Avenger AS.3 ★	Imperial War Museum/Duxford
D-HMQV	Bolkow Bo 102 ★	IHM/Weston-s-Mare
D-IFSB	D.H.104 Dove 6 ★	De Havilland Heritage Museum
EL-WXA	B.175 Britannia 253F ★	Britannia Aircraft Preservation Trust/ Kemble
F-AZFV	NA T-28 Fennec	Old Flying Machine Co/Duxford
F-BDRS	Boeing B-17G (231983) ★	Imperial War Museum/Duxford
F-BGNR	V.708 Viscount ★	Skysport Engineering Ltd
F-BGNX	D.H.106 Comet 1 (G-AOJT) ★	De Havilland Heritage Museum *(fuselage only)*

Reg.	Type	Owner or Operator	Notes
F-BMCY	Potez 840 ★	Sumburgh Fire Service	
F-BTGV	Aero Spacelines Super Guppy 201 (1) ★	British Aviation Heritage/Bruntingthorpe	
HA-ABP	Antonov An-2R	- -	
HA-ACL	Dornier Do.28D Turbo	Target Skysports Parachute Centre/Hibaldstow	
HA-ACO	Dornier Do.28D Turbo	-/Hibaldstow	
HA-LAK	Letovlev LET L-410UVP		
HA-MEP	WSK-PZL Antonov An-2R	AeroSuperBatics Ltd/Rendcomb	
HA-MKA	WSK-PZL Antonov An-2R	-/White Waltham	
HA-MKE	WSK-PZL Antonov An-2R	Air Foyle/White Waltham	
HA-MKF	WSK-PZL Antonov An-2TP	Transair Pilot Shop/White Waltham	
HZ-DG1	Boeing 727-51	Dallah Avco/Stansted	
LN-AMY	AT-6D Harvard	Old Flying Machine Co/Duxford	
LY-ABW	Antonov An-2TP	-	
LY-ABZ	Yakovlev Yak-52		
LY-AFA	Yakovlev Yak-52 (110)	-/Barton	
LY-AFB	Yakovlev Yak-52 (112)	Termikas Co Ltd/Little Gransden	
LY-AFV	Yakovlev Yak-52 (102)	A. Fraser	
LY-AFX	Yakovlev Yak-52 (25)	D. Hawkins	
LY-AFZ	Yakovlev Yak-50 (24)	-	
LY-AHB	Yakovlev Yak-52	-/North Weald	
LY-AHE	Yakovlev Yak-52 (10)	-	
LY-AKW	Yakovlev Yak-52 (56)	A. Harris	
LY-ALJ	Yakovlev Yak-52 (132)	D. Hawkins	
LY-ALO	Yakovlev Yak-52 (135)	Sky Associates (UK) Ltd/Little Gransden	
LY-ALS	Yakovlev Yak-52 (69)	M. Jefferies/Little Gransden	
LY-ALU	Yakovlev Yak-52 (124)	S. Goodridge	
LY-AMJ	Yakovlev Yak-18T	-/Earls Colne	
LY-AMP	Yakovlev Yak-52 (52)	B. Brown/Breighton	
LY-AMS	Yakovlev Yak-52 (51)	Willow Air Ltd/Southend	
LY-AMU	Yakovlev Yak-52 (42)	G. Sharpe/North Weald	
LY-ANI	Yakovlev Yak-52	-/Little Gransden	
LY-AOB	Yakovlev Yak-52	M. Schwarz	
LY-AOC	Yakovlev Yak-52 (30)	T. Boxhall	
LY-AOK	Yakovlev Yak-52 (16)	I. Vaughan	
LY-AOX	Yakovlev Yak-52 (122)	J. & J. Van der Luit/Biggin Hill	
LY-AOZ	Yakovlev Yak-52	-	
LY-APP	Yakovlev Yak-18P	A. Hyatt	
LY-ASA	Antonov An-2	-	
N2FU	Learjet 31A	Motor Racing Development Corpn	
N7SY	P.57 Sea Prince T.1 ★	Bournemouth Aviation Museum	
N18E	Boeing 247D ★	Science Museum/Wroughton	
N18V	Beech D.17S Traveler (PB1)	R. Lamplough	
N36SF	Hawker Sea Fury FB.10 (361)	J. Bradshaw/Kemble	
N43SV	Boeing Stearman E.75N-1 (796)	V. S. E. Norman/Rendcomb	
N46EA	P.66 Pembroke C.1 ★	P. G. Vallance Ltd/Charlwood	
N47DD	Republic P-47D Thunderbolt (226413) ★	American Air Museum/Duxford	
N47DG	Republic P-47D Thunderbolt	Flying A Services/Earls Colne	
N47FK	Douglas C-47A (292912)	European Flyers/Blackbushe	
N75TL	Boeing-Stearman N2S-4 Kaydet (669)	-/Headcorn	
N93GS	Grumman G.21C Goose	T. Friedrich/Elstree	
N111LM	Beech 95-58 Baron	Swift Air Ltd/Cranfield	
N112WG	Westland WG-30-100 ★	IHM/Weston-s-Mare	
N114WG	Westland WG-30-100 ★	IHM/Weston-s-Mare	
N116WG	Westland WG-30-100 ★	IHM/Weston-s-Mare	
N118WG	Westland WG-30-100 ★	IHM/Weston-s-Mare	
N139DP	Bell P-39Q-5-BE Airacobra (219993)	The Fighter Collection/Duxford	
N147DC	Douglas C-47A (TS423)	Aces High USA Inc/North Weald	
N179PT	Vought F4U-5N Corsair (122179)	Wizzard Investments Ltd	
N196B	NA F-86A Sabre (80242) ★	American Air Museum/Duxford	
N260QB	Pitts S-2S Special	D. Baker	
N285RA	Consolidated PBY-6A Catalina	Randsburg Corpn/North Weald	
N314BG	NA P-51D-20A Mustang (414151)	Flying A Services/Earls Colne	
N423RS	Consolidated PBY-5A Catalina	Super Catalina Restoration	
N500LN	Howard 500	Western Aviation Leasing Inc/Exeter	
N707KS	Boeing 707-321B	Kalair Corpn/Stansted	
N707TJ	Boeing Stearman A.75N1	V. S. E. Norman/Rendcomb	
N747SY	Mitsubishi Mu.2B-6	Smith Young Partnership	
N768WM	Boeing Stearman B.75N	V. S. E. Norman/Rendcomb	

Notes	Reg.	Type	Owner or Operator
	N909WJ	Grumman FM-2 Wildcat (46867)	Wizzard Investments Ltd
	N999PJ	M.S.760 Paris 2	R. J. Lamplough/North Weald
	N1024L	Beech 60 Duke	R. Ogden/Barton
	N1344	Ryan PT-22	H. Mitchell
	N1364V	Boeing Stearman N2S-5 (43578)	D. Milne
	N1944A	Douglas C-47A (315211)	Wings Venture
	N2138J	EE Canberra T.18 (WK126) ★	Gloucestershire Aviation Collection
	N2929W	PA-28-151 Warrior	R. Lobell
	N3922B	Boeing Stearman E.75N1	Eastern Stearman Ltd/Swanton Morley
	N3929B	Boeing Stearman E.75N1	Eastern Stearman Ltd/Swanton Morley
	N4565L	Douglas DC-3 ★	USAF Museum/Framlingham
	N4596N	Boeing Stearman PT-13D	Intrepid Aviation Co/North Weald
	N4647J	PA-28R Cherokee Arrow 180	R. Breckell/Bourn
	N4712V	Boeing Stearman PT-13D	Wessex Aviation & Transport Ltd
	N4806E	Douglas A-26C Invader ★	R. & R. Cadman (stored)/Manston
	N5057V	Boeing Stearman PT-13D	V. S. E. Norman/Rendcomb
	N5237V	Boeing B-17G (483868) ★	RAF Museum/Hendon
	N5345N	Boeing Stearman PT-13D	Eastern Stearman Ltd/Swanton Morley
	N5419	Bristol Scout D (replica) ★	Bristol Aero Collection
	N5824H	PA-38-112 Tomahawk	Lakenheath Aero Club
	N6268	Travel Air Model 2000 (626/8) ★	Personal Plane Services Ltd/Booker
	N6526D	NA P-51D Mustang (413573) ★	RAF Museum/Hendon
	N7027E	Hawker Tempest V (EJ693)	K Weeks/Andover
	N7374A	Cessna A.150M (tailwheel)	J. Thomas
	N7564J	PA-28R Cherokee Arrow 180	-/Barton
	N7614C	NA B-25J Mitchell (31171) ★	Imperial War Museum/Duxford
	N7777G	L.749A Constellation ★	Science Museum (G-CONI)/Wroughton
	N8162G	Boeing Stearman PT-17 (28)	Eastern Stearman Ltd/Swanton Morley
	N9050T	Douglas C-47A (parts only) ★	Dakota's American Bistro/Fleet
	N9089Z	NA TB-25J Mitchell (30861) ★	Aces High Ltd (G-BKXW)/North Weald
	N9115Z	NA TB-25N Mitchell (34037) ★	RAF Museum/Hendon
	N9521C	Consolidated PBY-5A Catalina	Weavair Inc/North Weald
	N9606H	Fairchild M.62A Cornell ★	Rebel Air Museum/Earls Colne
	N14113	NA T-28A Trojan (51-7545)	Radial Revelations/Duxford
	N23840	Beech C24R Sierra 200	A. Hall/Liverpool
	N26634	PA-24 Comanche 250	P. Biggs (G-BFKR)
	N33600	Cessna L-19A Bird Dog (111989) ★	Museum of Army Flying/Middle Wallop
	N33870	Fairchild M.62A Cornell (02538)	R. Lamplough/North Weald
	N38940	Boeing Stearman PT-17 (18263)	R. W. Sage
	N43069	PA-28-161 Warrior II	D. Wards
	N49272	Fairchild PT-23 (23)	PT Flight/Cosford
	N50755	Boeing Stearman PT-27 (211672)	Eastern Stearman Ltd/Swanton Morley
	N53091	Boeing Stearman PT-17	Eastern Stearman Ltd/Swanton Morley
	N54922	Boeing Stearman N2S-4 (3)	V. S. E. Norman/Rendcomb
	N56421	Ryan PT-22 (855)	PT Flight/Cosford
	N56643	Maule M.5-180C	-/Langar
	N58566	BT-13 Valiant	PT Flight/Cosford
	N63590	Boeing Stearman N2S-3 (07539)	R. W. Sage/Tibenham
	N65200	Boeing Stearman D75N1	Eastern Stearman Ltd/Swanton Morley
	N68427	Boeing Stearman N2S-4 ★	Black Barn Aviation/Tibenham
	N73410	Boeing Stearman N2S-3 ★	Black Barn Aviation/Tibenham
	N75664	Boeing Stearman E.75N1 (208)	—
	N91342	PA-28-112 Tomahawk	Lakenheath Aero Club
	N91384	R. Commander 690A	Cooper Aerial Surveys Ltd/Sandtoft
	N91457	PA-38-112 Tomahawk	Lakenheath Aero Club
	N91590	PA-38-112 Tomahawk	Lakenheath Aero Club
	N96240	Beech D.18S	Edward Bros Aviation (G-AYAH)/ North Weald
	N99153	NA T-28C Trojan (146289) ★	Norfolk & Suffolk Aviation Museum/Flixton
	NC5171N	Lockheed 10A Electra ★	Science Museum (G-LIOA)/Wroughton
	NC16403	Cessna C.34 Airmaster	Sylmar Aviation (G-BSEB)
	NC18028	Beech D.17S	P. H. McConnell/Popham
	NL51EA	NA P-51D Mustang (44-63507)	Old Flying Machine Co Ltd/Duxford
	NX71MY	Vickers Vimy (replica)(G-EAOU)	Greenco (UK) Ltd
	OY-JRR	DHC.2 Turbo Beaver III	Ipswich Parachute Centre/Windrush
	P4-SKI	Boeing 727-212	ARAVCO
	RA-01277	Sukhoi Su-29	-/White Waltham
	RA-01378	Yakovlev Yak-52	T. Evans
	RA-01607	Sukhoi Su-29	-
	RA-01609	Sukhoi Su-29	R. N. Goode/White Waltham
	RA-01610	Sukhoi Su-29	P. Williams/White Waltham
	RA-02209	Yakovlev Yak-52 (31)	P. Scandrett

Reg.	Type	Owner or Operator	Notes
RA-02293	Yakovlev Yak-52 (115)	A. Tyler	
RA-22521	Yakovlev Yak-52 (04)	D. Squires/Wellesbourne	
RA-44470	Yakovlev Yak-18T	B. Austen	
RA-44480	Yakovlev Yak-18T	R. N. Goode/White Waltham	
RA-44506	Yakovlev Yak-18T	-/White Waltham	
TF-ABP	L.1011-385 TriStar 1 ★	British Aviation Heritage/Bruntingthorpe	
UR-67477	LET L-410UVP	-/Sibson	
VH-BRC	S.24 Sandringham ★	Southampton Hall of Aviation	
VH-SNB	D.H.84 Dragon ★	Museum of Flight/E. Fortune	
VH-UQB	D.H.80A Puss Moth ★	Museum of Flight (G-ABDW)/E. Fortune	
VH-UTH	GAL Monospar ST-12 ★	Newark Air Museum (stored)	
VP-BAT	Boeing 747SP-21	Worldwide Aircraft Holding Co	
VP-BET	WS.55 Whirlwind 3 ★	IHM (G-ANJV)/Weston-s-Mare	
VP-BEU	WS.55 Whirlwind 3 ★	IHM (G-ATKV)/Weston-s-Mare	
VP-BFE	Boeing 737-7CP (BBJ)	Fordair/Stansted	
VP-BFO	Boeing 737-7CP (BBJ)	Fordair/Stansted	
VP-BIF	Boeing 727-1H2RE	SP Transport Ltd	
VP-BKQ	Bell 430	USAL Inc	
VP-BKY	H.S.125 Srs F.3B	Corporate Jet Services Inc	
VP-BLK	Gulfstream Commander 840	Control Techniques (Bermuda) Ltd/ Welshpool	
VP-BMF	Dassault Falcon 50	Sally Navigation	
VP-BMZ	Gulfstream Commander 690D	Marlborough Fine Art (London) Ltd	
VP-BNJ	Dassault Falcon 900B	Sliver Sand Ltd	
VP-BNM	Cessna 425	Rig Design Services Ltd	
VP-BNZ	G.1159A Gulfstream 3	Dennis Vanguard (International) Ltd	
VP-BPS	Consolidated PBY-5A Catalina	K. Cousins & ptnrs (G-BLSC)	
VP-BPW	Dassault Falcon 900B	Tower House Consultants Ltd	
VP-BSA	Dassault Falcon 50	Shell Aircraft Ltd/Heathrow	
VP-BSL	Dassault Falcon 50	Shell Aircraft Ltd/Stansted	
VP-CBW	G.1159C Gulfstream 4	Rolls-Royce PLC	
VP-CCK	Agusta A.109A-II	Tarmac PLC/E. Midlands	
VP-CCT	Beech C90-1 King Air	Corgi Investments Ltd	
VP-CEZ	Dassault Falcon 50	IIR Aviation/Biggin Hill	
VP-CIC	Canadair CL.601 Challenger	TGC Aviation Ltd/Stansted	
VP-CJB	Cessna 501 Citation	Brown Prestell Ltd/Biggin Hill	
VP-CJR	Cessna 550 Citation II	Broome & Wellington Aviation Ltd	
VP-CLL	Cessna 421C	Channel Aviation Ltd	
VP-CMF	G.1159C Gulfstream 4	Aravco Ltd/Heathrow	
VP-CMM	Boeing 727-30	MME Farms Maintenance	
VP-COM	Cessna 500 Citation	Robinson Publications Ltd/Leeds	
VP-CPR	Cessna 421C	Fifty North Ltd	
VP-CPT	BAe 125-1000B	Reno Investments Inc/Biggin Hill	
VP-CSP	Cessna 500 Citation	SP Metal Ltd/Biggin Hill	
VP-CYM	G.1159C Gulfstream 4	Jet Fly Aviation Ltd	
VP-FAZ	D.H.C.6-310 Twin Otter	British Antarctic Survey	
VP-FBB	D.H.C.6-310 Twin Otter	British Antarctic Survey	
VP-FBC	D.H.C.6-310 Twin Otter	British Antarctic Survey	
VP-FBL	D.H.C.6-310 Twin Otter	British Antarctic Survey	
VP-FBQ	D.H.C.7-110 Dash Seven	British Antarctic Survey (G-BOAX)	
VR-BEU	W.S.55 Whirlwind 3	East Midlands Aeropark	
YL-CBI	Yakovlev Yak-52 (09)	Computaplane Ltd	
YL-CBJ	Yakovlev Yak-52 (20)	Computaplane Ltd	
5N-ABW	Westland Widgeon 2 ★	IHM (G-AOZE)/Weston-s-Mare	
5N-AOK	BAC One-Eleven 320AZ ★	Fuselage stored/Chorley	

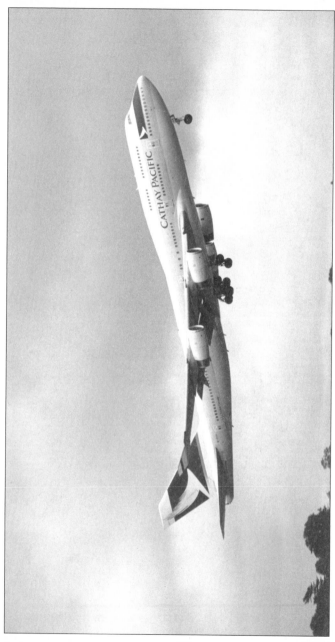

B-HUA Boeing 747-467 of Cathay Pacific Airways.

D-ANFF Aerospatiale ATR-72-202 of Eurowings.

C-GTSJ Boeing 757 of AirTransat.

EC-HJQ Boeing 737-85P of Air Europa.

F-GNFH Boeing 737-382 of Aeris. *A.S.Wright*

OH-SAH Avro RJ85 of Air Botnia.

SX-CVH Douglas DC-10-15 of Electra Airlines. *A.S.Wright*

Radio Frequencies

The frequencies used by the larger airfields/airports are listed below. Abbreviations used: TWR — Tower, APP - Approach, A/G - Air-Ground advisory. It is possible that changes will be made from time to time with the frequencies allocated, all of which are quoted in Megahertz (MHz)

Airfield	TWR	APP	A/G
Aberdeen	118.1	120.4	
Alderney	125.35		
Andrewsfield			130.55
Audley End			122.35
Barton			122.7
Barrow			123.2
Beccles	134.6		
Belfast Intl	118.3	120.9	
Belfast City	130.75	130.85	
Bembridge			123.25
Biggin Hill	134.8	129.4	
Birmingham	118.3	118.05	
Blackbushe			122.3
Blackpool	118.4	119.95	
Bodmin			122.7
Booker			126.55
Bourn			129.8
Bournemouth	125.6	119.625	
Breighton	129.80		
Bristol/Filton	132.35	122.72	
Bristol/Lulsgate	133.85	128.55	
Bruntingthorpe	122.825		
Caernarfon	122.25		
Cambridge	122.2	123.6	
Cardiff	125.0	125.85	
Carlisle		123.6	
Clacton	135.40		
Compton Abbas			122.7
Conington			129.725
Cosford	128.825		
Coventry	124.8	119.25	
Cranfield	134.925	122.85	
Denham			130.725
Dundee	122.9		
Dunkeswell			123.475
Duxford			122.075
Earls Colne			122.425
East Midlands	124.0	119.65	
Edinburgh	118.7	121.2	
Elstree			122.4
Exeter	119.8	128.15	
Fairoaks			123.425
Fenland			122.925
Fowlmere			120.925
Gamston			130.475
Gatwick	124.225	126.825	
Glasgow	118.8	119.1	
Gloucester/ Staverton	122.9	125.65	
Goodwood	122.45		
Guernsey	119.95	128.65	
Haverfordwest			122.2
Hawarden	124.95	123.35	
Headcorn			122.0
Heathrow	118.7	119.725	
	118.5	134.975	
Hethel			122.35
Hucknall			130.8
Humberside	118.55	124.675	
Inverness	122.60	119.35	

Airfield	TWR	APP	A/G
Jersey	119.45	120.3	
Kemble	118.9		
Kidlington	118.875	125.325	
Land's End	130.7		
Leeds Bradford	120.3	123.75	
Leicester	122.125		
Liverpool	118.1	119.85	
London City	118.075	132.7	
Luton	132.55	129.55	
Lydd	120.7		
Manchester	118.625	119.4	
Manston	119.275		
Netherthorpe			123.275
Newcastle	119.7	124.375	
Newquay	123.4		
North Denes	123.4		
North Weald	123.525		
Norwich	124.25	119.35	
Old Warden	123.05		
Penzance	118.1		
Perth	119.8		
Plymouth	118.15	133.55	
Popham			129.8
Prestwick	118.15	120.55	
Redhill	120.275		
Rochester			122.25
Ronaldsway	118.9	120.85	
Sandown			123.5
Sandtoft			130.425
Scilly Isles			123.15
Seething			122.6
Sheffield City	128.525		
Sherburn			122.6
Shipdham			119.55
Shobdon			123.5
Shoreham	123.15		
Sibson			122.3
Sleap			122.45
Southampton	118.2	128.85	
Southend	127.725	128.95	
Stansted	123.8	120.625	
Stapleford			122.8
Sumburgh	118.25	123.15	
Swansea	119.7		
Swanton Morley			123.5
Sywell			122.7
Tatenhill	124.075		
Teesside	119.8	118.85	
Thruxton			130.45
Tollerton			122.8
Wellesbourne			124.02
Welshpool	123.25		
White Waltham			122.6
Wick	119.7		
Wickenby			122.45
Wolverhampton	123.0		
Woodford	120.7		
Woodvale	119.75	121.0	
Yeovil	125.4	130.8	

Airline Flight Codes

Those listed below identify both UK and overseas carriers appearing in the book.

Code	Airline	
AAF	Aeris	F
AAG	Atlantic A/L	G
AAL	American A/L	N
AAR	Asiana A/L	HL
ABD	Air Atlanta Iceland	TF
ABR	Air Contractors	EI
ACA	Air Canada	C
ADR	Adria A/W	S5
AEA	Air Europa	EC
AEF	Aero Lloyd	D
AEL	Air Europe Italy	I
AFG	Ariana	YA
AFL	Aeroflot	RA
AFM	Affretair	Z
AFX	Airfreight Express	G
AFR	Air France	F
AGX	Aviogenex	YU
AHK	Air Hong Kong	B
AIC	Air-India	VT
AIH	Airtours (European)	G
AIJ	Air Jet	F
AJM	Air Jamaica	6Y
AKL	Air Kilroe	G
ALK	SriLankan A/L	4R
AMC	Air Malta	9H
AMM	Air 2000	G
AMT	American Trans Air	N
ANA	All Nippon A/W	JA
ANS	Air Nostrum	EC
ANZ	Air New Zealand	ZK
APW	Arrow Air	N
ARF	Airlinair	F
ARG	Argentine A/W	LV
ATT	Aer Turas	EI
AUA	Austrian A/L	OE
AUB	Augsburg A/W	D
AUI	Ukraine Intl	UR
AUR	Aurigny A/S	G
AVA	Avianca	HK
AWC	Titan A/W	G
AWW	Air Wales	G
AXL	KLM exel	PH
AZA	Alitalia	I
AZW	Air Zimbabwe	Z
BAG	Deutsche BA	D
BAL	Britannia A/L	G
BAW	British Airways	G
BBC	Bangladesh Biman	S2
BCS	European A/T	OO
BCY	CityJet	EI
BER	Air Berlin	D
BIH	CHC Scotia	G
BMA	bmi british midland	G
BRA	Braathens	LN
BRT	British Regional	G
BRU	Belavia	EW
BTI	Air Baltic	YL
BWA	BWIA	9Y
BZH	Brit Air	F
CCA	Air China	B
CFE	CityFlyer	G
CFG	Condor	D
CIM	Cimber Air	OY
CLH	Lufthansa CityLine	D
CLX	Cargolux	LX
COA	Continental A/L	N
CPA	Cathay Pacific	B
CRL	Corsair	F
CRX	Crossair	HB
CSA	Czech A/L	OK
CTN	Croatia A/L	9A
CUB	Cubana	CU
CUS	Cronus A/L	SX
CYP	Cyprus A/W	5B
DAH	Air Algerie	7T
DAL	Delta A/L	N
DAN	Maersk Air	OY
DAT	Delta Air Transport	OO
DHL	DHL Express	N/OO
DLH	Lufthansa	D
DNM	Denim Air	PH
DSR	DAS Air Cargo	5X
DTR	Danish Air Transport	OY
EAE	European Air Xp	D
EAF	European A/Ch	G
ECY	Euroceltic A/W	G
EDW	Edelweiss Air	HB
EIA	Evergreen Intl	N
EIN	Aer Lingus	EI
ELY	El Al	4X
EPA	Express A/W	D
ETH	Ethiopian A/L	ET
EUL	Euralair	F
EWG	Eurowings	D
EXS	Channel Express	G
EZE	Eastern Airways	G
EZS	easyJet Switz	HB
EZY	easyJet	G
FDX	Federal Express	N
FIN	Finnair	OH
FLT	Flightline	G
FOB	Ford	G
FUA	Futura	EC
GBL	GB Airways	G
GCO	Gemini Air Cargo	N
GCR	Cougar A/L	G
GEC	Lufthansa Cargo	D
GFA	Gulf Air	A40
GHA	Ghana A/W	9G
GIA	Garuda	PK
GMI	Germania	D
GNT	British Midland Commuter	G
GOE	Go-Fly	G
GTI	Atlas Air	N
HCY	Helios A/L	5B
HHI	Hamburg Intl	D
HLA	HeavyLift	G
HLF	Hapag-Lloyd	D
HMS	Hemus Air	LZ
HWY	Highland A/W	G
IBE	Iberia	EC
ICE	Icelandair	TF
INS	Instone A/L	G
IOS	Skybus	G
ISS	Meridiana	I
IWD	Iberworld	EC
JAL	Japan A/L	JA
JAT	JAT	YU
JEM	Emerald A/W	G
JKK	Spanair	EC
JMC	jmc A/L	G
KAC	Kuwait A/W	9K
KAL	Korean Air	HL
KIS	Contactair	D
KLM	KLM	PH
KQA	Kenya A/W	5Y
KYV	Kibris Turkish	TC
LAJ	British Meditrn	G
LAZ	Bulgarian A/L	LZ
LDA	Lauda Air	OE
LFA	Air Alfa	TC
LGL	Luxair	LX
LIB	Air Lib	F
LIT	Air Littoral	F
LKA	Alkair	OY
LOG	Loganair	G
LOT	Polish A/L (LOT)	SP
LTE	LTE	EC
LTU	LTU	D
MAH	Malev	HA
MAS	Malaysian A/L	9M
MAU	Air Mauritius	3B
MEA	Middle East A/L	OD
MNX	Manx A/L	G
MON	Monarch A/L	G
MPD	Air Plus Comet	EC
MPH	Martinair	PH
MSK	Maersk Air Ltd	G
MSR	Egyptair	SU
NAW	Newair	OY
NCA	Nippon Cargo	JA
NEX	Northern Executive	G
NGA	Nigeria A/W	5N
NWA	Northwest A/L	N
OAL	Olympic A/L	SX
OHY	Onur Air	TC
PAL	Philippine A/L	RP
PGA	Portugalia	CS
PGT	Pegasus A/L	TC
PIA	Pakistan Intl	AP
QFA	Qantas	VH
QSC	African Safaris	5Y
RAM	Royal Air Maroc	CN
RBA	Royal Brunei	V8
REA	Aer Arran	EI
RJA	Royal Jordanian	JY
RLB	Highland A/W	G
RNA	Royal Nepal A/L	9N
ROT	Tarom	YR
RPX	BAC Express A/L	G
RWD	Air Rwanda	9XR
RYR	Ryanair	EI
RZO	SATA International	CS
SAA	South African A/W	ZS
SAS	SAS	SE OY LN
SAY	ScotAir	G
SCW	Malmo Aviation	SE
SCY	Air Scandic	G
SEU	Star Europe	F
SEY	Air Seychelles	S7
SIA	Singapore A/L	9V
SLR	Sobelair	OO
SNB	Sterling European	OY

AIRLINE FLIGHT CODES

SSW	Streamline Avn	G	TLE	Aeris	F	UPS	United Parcels	N
SUD	Sudan A/W	ST	TOW	Tower Air	N	UYC	Cameroon A/L	TJ
SVA	Saudia	HZ	TRA	Transavia	PH	UZB	Uzbekistan A/W	UK
SWE	Swedair	SE	TSC	Air Transat	C	VEX	Virgin Express	OO
SXS	Sun Express	TC	TWA	TWA	N	VIR	Virgin Atlantic	G
SYR	Syrian Arab	YK	TYR	Tyrolean	OE	VKG	Premiair	OY
TAP	Air Portugal	CS	UAE	Emirates A/L	A6	VLM	VLM	OO
TAR	Tunis Air	TS	UAL	United A/L	N	VRG	Varig	PP
TAY	TNT A/W	OO	UGA	Uganda A/L	5X	WDL	WDL	D
THA	Thai A/W Intl	HS	UKA	KLM uk/Euzz	G	WOA	World A/W	N
THY	Turkish A/L	TC	UKR	Air Ukraine	UR	XLA	Excel A/W	G
TIH	Airtours (US)	G	UPA	Air Foyle	G			

G-AMPY Douglas C-47B of Atlantic Airlines Pollution Control.

N18V Beech D17S Traveler (PB1).

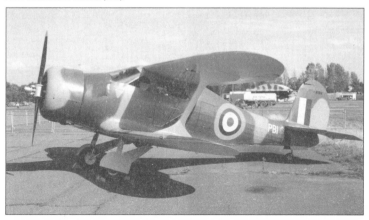

British Aircraft Preservation Council Register

The British Aircraft Preservation Council was formed in 1967 to co-ordinate the works of all bodies involved in the preservation, restoration and display of historical aircraft. Membership covers the whole spectrum of national, Service, commercial and voluntary groups, and meetings are held regularly at the bases of member organisations. The Council is able to provide a means of communication, helping to resolve any misunderstandings or duplication of effort. Every effort is taken to encourage the raising of standards of both organisation and technical capacity amongst the member groups to the benefit of everyone interested in aviation. To assist historians, the B.A.P.C. register has been set up and provides an identity for those aircraft which do not qualify for a Service serial or inclusion in the UK Civil Register.
  Aircraft on the current B.A.P.C. Register are as follows:

Notes	Reg.	Type	Owner or Operator
	6	Roe Triplane Type IV (replica)	Manchester Museum of Science & Industry
	7	Southampton University MPA	Southampton Hall of Aviation
	8	Dixon ornithopter	The Shuttleworth Collection
	9	Humber Monoplane (replica)	Midland Air Museum/Coventry
	10	Hafner R.II Revoplane	Museum of Army Flying/Middle Wallop
	12	Mignet HM.14	Museum of Flight/E. Fortune
	13	Mignet HM.14	Brimpex Metal Treatments
	14	Addyman Standard Training Glider	A. Lindsay & N. H. Ponsford
	15	Addyman Standard Training Glider	The Aeroplane Collection
	16	Addyman ultra-light aircraft	N. H. Ponsford
	17	Woodhams Sprite	The Aeroplane Collection
	18	Killick MP Gyroplane	A. Lindsay & N. H. Ponsford
	20	Lee-Richards annular biplane (replica)	Newark Air Musem
	21	Thruxton Jackaroo	M. J. Brett
	22	Mignet HM.14 (G-AEOF)	Aviodome/Schiphol
	25	Nyborg TGN-III glider	Midland Air Museum
	27	Mignet HM.14	M. J. Abbey
	28	Wright Flyer (replica)	Corn Exchange/Leeds
	29	Mignet HM.14 (replica) (G-ADRY)	Brooklands Museum of Aviation/ Weybridge
	32	Crossley Tom Thumb	Midland Air Museum
	33	DFS.108-49 Grunau Baby IIb	-
	34	DFS.108-49 Grunau Baby IIb	D. Elsdon
	35	EoN primary glider	-
	36	Fieseler Fi.103 (V-1) (replica)	Kent Battle of Britain Museum/Hawkinge
	37	Blake Bluetit (G-BXIY)	The Shuttleworth Collection/O. Warden
	38	Bristol Scout replica (A1742)	K. Williams & M. Thorn
	40	Bristol Boxkite (replica)	Bristol City Museum
	41	B.E.2C (replica) (6232)	Yorkshire Air Museum/Elvington
	42	Avro 504 (replica) (H1968)	Yorkshire Air Museum/Elvington
	43	Mignet HM.14	Newark Air Museum/Winthorpe
	44	Miles Magister (L6906)	Museum of Berkshire Aviation (G-AKKY)/ Woodley
	45	Pilcher Hawk (replica)	Stanford Hall Museum
	47	Watkins Monoplane	National Museum of Wales
	48	Pilcher Hawk (replica)	Glasgow Museum of Transport
	49	Pilcher Hawk	Royal Scottish Museum/East Fortune
	50	Roe Triplane Type 1	Science Museum/S. Kensington
	51	Vickers Vimy IV	Science Museum/S. Kensington
	52	Lilienthal glider	Science Museum Store/Hayes
	53	Wright Flyer (replica)	Science Museum/S. Kensington
	54	JAP-Harding monoplane	Science Museum/S. Kensington
	55	Levavasseur Antoinette VII	Science Museum/S. Kensington
	56	Fokker E.III (210/16)	Science Museum/S. Kensington
	57	Pilcher Hawk (replica)	Science Museum/S. Kensington
	58	Yokosuka MXY7 Ohka II (15-1585)	F.A.A. Museum/Yeovilton
	59	Sopwith Camel (replica) (D3419)	Aerospace Museum/Cosford
	60	Murray M.1 helicopter	The Aeroplane Collection Ltd
	61	Stewart man-powered ornithopter	Lincolnshire Aviation Museum
	62	Cody Biplane (304)	Science Museum/S. Kensington
	63	Hurricane (replica) (P3208)	Kent Battle of Britain Museum/Hawkinge
	64	Hurricane (replica) (P3059)	Kent Battle of Britain Museum/Hawkinge
	65	Spitfire (replica) (N3289)	Kent Battle of Britain Museum/Hawkinge
	66	Bf 109 (replica) (1480)	Kent Battle of Britain Museum/Hawkinge

Reg.	Type	Owner or Operator	Notes
67	Bf 109 (replica) (14)	Kent Battle of Britain Museum/Hawkinge	
68	Hurricane (replica) (H3426)	Midland Air Museum	
69	Spitfire (replica) (N3313)	Kent Battle of Britain Museum/Hawkinge	
70	Auster AOP.5 (TJ398)	Museum of Flight/E. Fortune	
71	Spitfire (replica) (P8140)	Norfolk & Suffolk Aviation Museum	
72	Hurricane (model) (V6779)	Gloucestershire Aviation Collection	
73	Hurricane (replica)	—	
74	Bf 109 (replica) (6357)	Kent Battle of Britain Museum/Hawkinge	
75	Mignet HM.14 (G-AEFG)	N. H. Ponsford	
76	Mignet HM.14 (G-AFFI)	Yorkshire Air Museum/Elvington	
77	Mignet HM.14 (replica) (G-ADRG)	Lower Stondon Transport Museum	
78	Hawker Hind (K5414) (G-AENP)	The Shuttleworth Collection/O. Warden	
79	Fiat G.46-4 (MM53211)	British Air Reserve/Lympne	
80	Airspeed Horsa (KJ351)	Museum of Army Flying/Middle Wallop	
81	Hawkridge Dagling	-	
82	Hawker Hind (Afghan)	RAF Museum/Hendon	
83	Kawasaki Ki-100-1b (24)	Aerospace Museum/Cosford	
84	Nakajima Ki-46 (Dinah III)(5439)	Aerospace Museum/Cosford	
85	Weir W-2 autogyro	Museum of Flight/E. Fortune	
86	de Havilland Tiger Moth (replica)	Yorkshire Aircraft Preservation Soc	
87	Bristol Babe (replica) (G-EASQ)	Bristol Aero Collection/Kemble	
88	Fokker Dr 1 (replica) (102/17)	F.A.A. Museum/Yeovilton	
89	Cayley glider (replica)	Manchester Museum of Science & Industry	
90	Colditz Cock (replica)	Imperial War Museum/Duxford	
91	Fieseler Fi 103 (V.1)	Lashenden Air Warfare Museum	
92	Fieseler Fi 103 (V.1)	RAF Museum/Hendon	
93	Fieseler Fi 103 (V.1)	Imperial War Museum/Duxford	
94	Fieseler Fi 103 (V.1)	Aerospace Museum/Cosford	
95	Gizmer autogyro	F. Fewsdale	
96	Brown helicopter	N.E. Aircraft Museum	
97	Luton L.A.4A Minor	N.E. Aircraft Museum	
98	Yokosuka MXY7 Ohka II (997)	Manchester Museum of Science & Industry	
99	Yokosuka MXY7 Ohka II (8486M)	Aerospace Museum/Cosford	
100	Clarke glider	RAF Museum/Hendon	
101	Mignet HM.14	Newark Air Museum/Winthorpe	
103	Pilcher glider (replica)	Personal Plane Services Ltd	
105	Blériot XI (replica)	Arango Collection/Los Angeles	
106	Blériot XI (164)	RAF Museum/Hendon	
107	Blériot XXVII	RAF Museum/Hendon	
108	Fairey Swordfish IV (HS503)	Cosford Aerospace Museum	
109	Slingsby Kirby Cadet TX.1	RAF Museum/Henlow store	
110	Fokker D.VII replica (static) (5125)	—	
111	Sopwith Triplane replica (static) (N5492)	F.A.A. Museum/Yeovilton	
112	D.H.2 replica (static) (5964)	Museum of Army Flying/Middle Wallop	
113	S.E.5A replica (static) (B4863)	—	
114	Vickers Type 60 Viking (static) (G-EBED)	Brooklands Museum of Aviation/Weybridge	
115	Mignet HM.14	Norfolk & Suffolk Aviation Museum/Flixton	
116	Santos-Dumont Demoiselle (replica)	Cornwall Aero Park/Helston	
117	B.E.2C (replica)(1701)	-	
118	Albatros D.V (replica) (C19/18)	North Weald Aircraft Restoration Flight	
119	Bensen B.7	N.E. Aircraft Museum	
120	Mignet HM.14 (G-AEJZ)	Bomber County Museum/Hemswell	
121	Mignet HM.14 (G-AEKR)	S. Yorks Aviation Soc	
122	Avro 504 (replica)	-	
123	Vickers FB.5 Gunbus (replica)	A. Topen *(stored)*/Cranfield	
124	Lilienthal Glider Type XI (replica)	Science Museum/S. Kensington	
126	D.31 Turbulent (static)	Midland Air Museum/Coventry	
127	Halton Jupiter MPA	The Shuttleworth Collection	
128	Watkinson Cyclogyroplane Mk IV	IHM/Weston-s-Mare	
129	Blackburn 1911 Monoplane (replica)	Cornwall Aero Park/Helston store	
130	Blackburn 1912 Monoplane (replica)		
131	Pilcher Hawk (replica)	C. Paton	
132	Blériot XI (G-BLXI)	Musée de L'Automobile/France	
133	Fokker Dr 1 (replica) (425/17)	Newark Air Museum/Winthorpe	
134	Pitts S-2A static (G-CARS)	Toyota Ltd/Sywell	
135	Bristol M.1C (replica) (C4912)	—	

Notes	Reg.	Type	Owner or Operator
	136	Deperdussin Seaplane (replica)	Reno/Nevada
	137	Sopwith Baby Floatplane (replica) (8151)	-
	138	Hansa Brandenburg W.29 Floatplane (replica) (2292)	-
	139	Fokker Dr 1 (replica) 150/17	-
	142	SE-5A (replica) (F5459)	-
	143	Paxton MPA	R. A. Paxton/Staverton
	144	Weybridge Mercury MPA	Cranwell Gliding Club
	146	Pedal Aeronauts Toucan MPA	The Shuttleworth Collection
	147	Bensen B.7	Norfolk & Suffolk Aviation Museum/Flixton
	148	Hawker Fury II (replica) (K7271)	Aerospace Museum/Cosford
	149	Short S.27 (replica)	F.A.A. Museum (stored)/Yeovilton
	150	SEPECAT Jaguar GR.1 (replica) (XX725)	RAF Exhibition Flight
	151	SEPECAT Jaguar GR.1 (replica) (XZ226)	RAF Exhibition Flight
	152	BAe Hawk T.1 (replica) (XX226)	RAF Exhibition Flight
	153	Westland WG.33	IHM/Weston-s-Mare
	154	D.31 Turbulent	Lincolnshire Aviation Museum/E. Kirkby
	155	Panavia Tornado GR.1 (model) (ZA556)	RAF Exhibition Flight
	157	Waco CG-4A(237123)	Yorkshire Air Museum/Elvington
	158	Fieseler Fi 103 (V.1)	Defence Ordnance Disposal School/ Chattenden
	159	Yokosuka MXY7 Ohka II	Defence Ordnance Disposal School/ Chattenden
	160	Chargus 108 hang glider	Museum of Flight/E. Fortune
	161	Stewart Ornithopter Coppelia	Bomber County Museum
	162	Goodhart Newbury Manflier MPA	Science Museum/Wroughton
	163	AFEE 10/42 Rotabuggy (replica)	Museum of Army Flying/Middle Wallop
	164	Wight Quadruplane Type 1 (replica)	Wessex Aviation Soc/Wimborne
	165	Bristol F.2b (E2466)	RAF Museum/Hendon
	167	S.E.5A replica	-
	168	D.H.60G Moth (static replica) (G-AAAH)	Yorkshire Air Museum/Elvington
	169	SEPECAT Jaguar GR.1 (static replica) (XX110)	No 1 S. of T.T. RAF Halton
	170	Pilcher Hawk (replica)	A. Gourlay/Strathallan
	171	BAe Hawk T.1 (model) (XX253)	RAF Exhibition Flight/Abingdon
	172	Chargus Midas Super 8 hang glider	Science Museum/Wroughton
	173	Birdman Promotions Grasshopper	Science Museum/Wroughton
	174	Bensen B.7	Science Museum/Wroughton
	175	Volmer VJ-23 Swingwing	Manchester Museum of Science & Industry
	176	SE-5A (replica) (A4850)	S. Yorks Aviation Soc/Firbeck
	177	Avro 504K (replica) (G-AACA)	Brooklands Museum of Aviation/ Weybridge
	178	Avro 504K (replica) (E373)	Bygone Times Antique Warehouse/ Eccleston, Lancs
	179	Sopwith Pup (replica) (A7317)	Midland Air Museum/Coventry
	181	RAF B.E.2b (replica) (687)	RAF Museum/Hendon
	182	Wood Ornithopter	Manchester Museum of Science & Industry
	183	Zurowski ZP.1	Newark Air Museum
	184	Spitfire IX (replica) (EN398)	Aces High Ltd/North Weald
	185	Waco CG-4A (243809)	Museum of Army Flying/Middle Wallop
	186	D.H.82B Queen Bee (LF789)	Mosquito Aircraft Museum
	187	Roe Type 1 biplane (replica)	Brooklands Museum of Aviation/ Weybridge
	188	McBroom Cobra 88	Science Museum/Wroughton
	190	Spitfire (replica) (K5054)	Barton Aviation Heritage
	191	BAe Harrier GR.7 (model) (ZD472)	RAF Exhibition Flight
	192	Weedhopper JC-24	The Aeroplane Collection
	193	Hovey WD-11 Whing Ding	The Aeroplane Collection
	194	Santos Dumont Demoiselle (replica)	Brooklands Museum of Aviation/ Weybridge
	195	Moonraker 77 hang glider	Museum of Flight/E. Fortune
	196	Sigma 2M hang glider	Museum of Flight/E. Fortune
	197	Cirrus III hang glider	Museum of Flight/E. Fortune
	198	Fieseler Fi.103 (V-1)	Imperial War Museum/Lambeth

BRITISH AIRCRAFT PRESERVATION

Reg.	Type	Owner or Operator	Notes
199	Fieseler Fi.103 (V-1)	Science Museum/S. Kensington	
200	Bensen B.7	K. Fern Collection/Stoke	
201	Mignet HM.14	Caernarfon Air Museum	
202	Spitfire V (model) (MAV467)	Maes Artro Craft Centre	
203	Chrislea LC.1 Airguard (G-AFIN)	The Aeroplane Collection	
204	McBroom hang glider	The Aeroplane Collection	
205	Hurricane (replica) (BE421)	RAF Museum/Hendon	
206	Spitfire (replica) (MH486)	RAF Museum/Hendon	
207	Austin Whippet (replica) (K.158)	N.E. Aircraft Museum/Usworth	
208	SE-5A (replica) (D276)	Prince's Mead Shopping Precinct/ Farnborough	
209	Spitfire IX (replica) (MJ751)	Museum of D-Day Aviation/Shoreham	
210	Avro 504J (replica) (C4451)	Southampton Hall of Aviation	
211	Mignet HM.14 (replica) (G-ADVU)	N.E. Aircraft Museum	
212	Bensen B.8	IHM/Weston-s-Mare	
213	Vertigo MPA	IHM/Weston-s-Mare	
214	Spitfire prototype (replica) (K5054)	The Spitfire Soc/Tangmere	
215	Airwave hang-glider	Southampton Hall of Aviation	
216	D.H.88 Comet (replica) (G-ACSS)	-/St Albans	
217	Spitfire (replica) (K9926)	RAF Museum/Bentley Priory	
218	Hurricane (replica) (P3386)	RAF Museum/Bentley Priory	
219	Hurricane (replica) (L1710)	RAF Memorial Chapel/Biggin Hill	
220	Spitfire 1 (replica) (N3194)	RAF Memorial Chapel/Biggin Hill	
221	Spitfire LF.IX (replica) (MH777)	RAF Museum/Northolt	
222	Spitfire IX (replica) (BR600)	RAF Museum/Uxbridge	
223	Hurricane 1 (replica) (V7467)	RAF Museum/Coltishall	
224	Spitfire V (replica) (BR600)	Ambassador Hotel/Norwich	
225	Spitfire IX (replica) (P8448)	RAF Museum/Swanton Morley	
226	Spitfire XI (replica) (EN343)	RAF Museum/Benson	
227	Spitfire 1A (replica) (L1070)	RAF Museum/Turnhouse	
228	Olympus hang-glider	N.E. Aircraft Museum/Usworth	
229	Spitfire IX (replica) (MJ832)	RAF Museum/Digby	
230	Spitfire (replica) (AA550)	Eden Camp/Malton	
231	Mignet HM.14 (G-ADRX)	South Copeland Aviation Group	
232	AS.58 Horsa I/II	De Havilland Heritage Museum	
233	Broburn Wanderlust sailplane	Museum of Berkshire Aviation/Woodley	
234	Vickers FB.5 Gunbus (replica)	Barton Aviation Heritage	
235	Fieseler Fi.103 (V-1) (replica)	Eden Camp Wartime Museum	
236	Hurricane (replica) (P2793)	Eden Camp Wartime Museum	
237	Fieseler Fi.103 (V-1)	RAF Museum/Cardington	
238	Waxflatter ornithopter	Personal Plane Services Ltd	
239	Fokker D.VIII 5/8 scale replica	Norfolk & Suffolk Aviation Museum	
240	Messerschmitt Bf.109G (replica)	Yorkshire Air Museum/Elvington	
241	Hurricane 1 (replica) (L1679)	Tangmere Military Aviation Museum	
242	Spitfire Vb (replica) (BL924)	Tangmere Military Aviation Museum	
243	Mignet HM.14 (replica) (G-ADYV)	P. Ward	
244	Solar Wings Typhoon	Museum of Flight/E. Fortune	
245	Electraflyer Floater	Museum of Flight/E. Fortune	
246	Hiway Cloudbase	Museum of Flight/E. Fortune	
247	Albatross ASG.21 hang glider	Museum of Flight/E. Fortune	
248	McBroom hang glider	Museum of Berkshire Aviation/Woodley	
249	Hawker Fury 1 (replica) (K5673)	Brooklands Museum of Aviation/Weybridge	
250	RAF SE-5A (replica) (F5475)	Brooklands Museum of Aviation/Weybridge	
251	Hiway Spectrum (replica)	Manchester Museum of Science & Industry	
252	Flexiform Wing	Manchester Museum of Science & Industry	
253	Mignet HM.14 (G-ADZW)	H. Shore/Sandown	
254	V.S.300 Spitfire I (R6690)	Yorkshire Air Museum/Elvington	
255	NA P-51D Mustang (replica) (463209)	American Air Museum/Duxford	
256	Santos Dumont Type 20 (replica)	Brooklands Museum of Aviation/ Weybridge	
257	D.H.88 Comet (G-ACSS)	The Galleria/Hatfield	
258	Adams balloon	British Balloon Museum	
261	GAL Hotspur (replica)	Museum of Army Flying/ Middle Wallop	
262	Catto CP-16	Museum of Flight/East Fortune	
263	Chargus Cyclone	Ulster Aviation Heritage/Langford Lodge	
264	Bensen B.8M	IHM/Weston-super-Mare	
265	Spitfire 1 (P3873)	Yorkshire Air Museum/Elvington	

Note: Registrations/Serials carried are mostly false identities.
MPA = Man Powered Aircraft, IHM = International Helicopter Museum.

Future Allocations Log (In-Sequence)

The grid provides the facility to record future in-sequence registrations as they are issued or seen. To trace a particular code, refer to the left hand column which contains the three letters following the G prefix. The final letter can be found by reading across the columns headed A to Z. For example, the box for G-CBMD is located five rows down (CBM) and then four across to the D column.

G-	A	B	C	D	E	F	G	H	I	J	K	L	M	N	O	P	R	S	T	U	V	W	X	Y	Z
CBI																									
CBJ																									
CBK																									
CBL																									
CBM																									
CBN																									
CBO																									
CBP																									
CBR																									
CBS																									
CBT																									
CBU																									
CBV																									
CBW																									
CBX																									
CBY																									
CBZ																									
CCA																									
CCB																									
CCC																									
CCD																									
CCE																									
CCF																									
CCG																									
CCH																									
CCI																									
CCJ																									
CCK																									
CCL																									
CCM																									
CCN																									
CCO																									
CCP																									
CCR																									
	A	B	C	D	E	F	G	H	I	J	K	L	M	N	O	P	R	S	T	U	V	W	X	Y	Z

Credit: *Wal Gandy*

Future Allocations Log (Out-of-Sequence)

This grid can be used to record out-of-sequence registrations as they are issued or seen. The first column is provided for the ranges prefixed with G-C, ie from G-CYxx to G-CZxx. The remaining columns cover the sequences from G-Dxxx to G-Zxxx and in this case it is necessary to insert the last three letters in the appropriate section.

G-C	G-D	G-F	G-H	G-J	G-L	G-N	G-O	G-P	G-S	G-U
										G-V
	G-E	G-G			G-M	G-O				
			G-K							
										G-W
		G-I								
							G-R			
									G-T	
										G-X
G-D	G-F			G-L	G-N					
										G-Y
										G-Z

Overseas Airliners Registration Log

This grid may be used to record airliner registrations not included in the main section.

Reg.	Type	Operator

ADDENDA

Reg.	Type	Owner or Operator	Notes
G-AAEG	D.H.60G Gipsy Moth	I. B. Grace	
G-ARHU	PA-22-Tri-Pacer 160	M. S. Bird	
G-BBDS	PA-31 Turbo Navajo	Elham Valley Aviation Ltd	
G-BDXC	Boeing 747-236B	European Aviation Ltd/Bournemouth	
G-BDXE	Boeing 747-236B	European Aviation Ltd/Bournemouth	
G-BDXF	Boeing 747-236B	European Aviation Ltd/Bournemouth	
G-BDXG	Boeing 747-236B	European Aviation Ltd/Bournemouth	
G-BDXH	Boeing 747-236B	European Aviation Ltd/Bournemouth	
G-BGBK	PA-38-112 Tomahawk	R. H. Cooper	
G-BIKB	Boeing 757-236F	DHL Air Ltd	
G-BIKC	Boeing 757-236F	DHL Air Ltd	
G-BIKD	Boeing 757-236F	DHL Air Ltd	
G-BIKG	Boeing 757-236F	DHL Air Ltd	
G-BIKH	Boeing 757-236F	DHL Air Ltd	
G-BIKI	Boeing 757-236F	DHL Air Ltd	
G-BIKJ	Boeing 757-236F	DHL Air Ltd	
G-BIKO	Boeing 757-236F	DHL Air Ltd	
G-BIKP	Boeing 757-236F	DHL Air Ltd	
G-BIKU	Boeing 757-236F	DHL Air Ltd	
G-BIKV	Boeing 757-236F	DHL Air Ltd	
G-BIKZ	Boeing 757-236F	DHL Air Ltd	
G-BLEB	Colt 69A balloon	I. R. M. Jacobs	
G-BPND	Boeing 727-2D3	Cougar Airlines Ltd	
G-BSXZ	BAe 146-300	Flightline Ltd (G-NJIB)/Southend	
G-BTPA	BAe ATP	Capital Bank Leasing 12 Ltd	
G-BTPC	BAe ATP	Capital Bank Leasing 1 Ltd	
G-BTPD	BAe ATP	Seaforth Maritime Ltd	
G-BTPF	BAe ATP	Capital Bank Leasing 5 Ltd	
G-BTPG	BAe ATP	Capital Bank Leasing 5 Ltd	
G-BTPH	BAe ATP	Capital Bank Leasing 6 Ltd	
G-BTPJ	BAe ATP	Capital Bank Leasing 7 Ltd	
G-BTVO	BAe 146-300	Flightline Ltd (G-NJID)/Southend	
G-CBHJ	Mainair Blade 912S	B. C. Jones	
G-CBHL	AS.350B-2 Ecureuil	Bishop Avionics Ltd	
G-CBIB	Flight Design CT.2K	J. A. Moss	
G-CBIM	Lindstrand LBL-90A balloon	R. K. Parsons	
G-CBIV	Skyranger 912 (1)	P. M. Dewhurst	
G-CBIW	Lindstrand LBL-310A balloon	C. E. Wood	
G-CBIY	Aerotechnik EV-97 Eurostar	E. M. Middleton	
G-CBJD	Stoddard-Hamilton Glastar	K. F. Farey	
G-CBJE	RAF 2000 GTX-SE gyroplane	K. F. Farey	
G-CBJF	Eurocopter EC.120B	McAlpine Helicopters Ltd/Kidlington	
G-CBJH	Aeroprakt A.22 Foxbat	H. Smith	
G-CBJN	RAF 2000 GTX-SE gyroplane	R. Hall	
G-CBJP	Zenair CH.601UL	R. E. Peirse	
G-CBJR	Aerotechnik EV-97 Eurostar	B. J. Crockett	
G-CBJU	Van's RV-7A	T. W. Waltham	
G-CBKB	Bücker Bu.181C Bestmann	W. R. Snadden	
G-CBKF	Easy Raider J2.2 (1)	R. J. Creasey	
G-CBKM	Mainair Blade 912	N. Purdy	
G-CBKS	Kiss 400-582 (1)	S. Kilpin	

G-ECAS	Boeing 737-36N	bmiBaby	
G-GNTZ	BAe 146-200	bmi Regional (G-CLHB)	
G-GSSA	Boeing 747-47UF	Global Supply Systems Ltd	
G-GSSB	Boeing 747-47UF	Global Supply Systems Ltd	
G-HTEL	Robinson R-44	Forestdale Hotels Ltd	
G-MLGL	Colt 21A balloon	H. C. J. Williams	
G-MANS	BAe 146-200	bmi Regional (G-CLHC)	
G-OGEO	SA.341G Gazelle 1	MW Helicopters Ltd (G-BXJK)	
G-OJTW	Boeing 737-36N	bmiBaby (G-JTWF)	
G-OKJN	Boeing 727-225RE	Cougar Airlines Ltd	
G-OPMN	Boeing 727-225RE	Cougar Airlines Ltd	

Notes	Reg.	Type	Owner or Operator
	G-UDOG	SA Bulldog Srs 120/121	Gamit Ltd
	G-YACB	Robinson R-22B	A. C. Barker (G-VOSL)
	G-YEWS	Rotorway Executive	R. Turrell

CANCELLATIONS

G-AVMI, G-AVMK, G-AVMW, G-BEEW, G-BKWE, G-BLXY, G-BLZT, G-BOAK, G-BPMV, G-BRVV, G-BUYM, G-BXAX, G-BXJK, G-BXKK, G-BXSB, G-BXYV, G-BYZB, G-BZYF, G-BZYH, G-CLHB, G-CLHC, G-FUND, G-IMAG, G-MVXH, G-MYJH, G-OHDC, G-SEAB, G-SEUK, G-UNIP, G-VOSL, G-VSSS, G-YSFT, G-ZOOI